Survey of Math

Custom Edition for Math 103 at Bryant and Stratton College

Excerpts taken from:

Thinking Mathematically, Fourth Edition
by Robert Blitzer

A Survey of Mathematics with Applications, Eighth Edition
by Allen R. Angel, Christine D. Abbott, and Dennis C. Runde

Using and Understanding Mathematics: A Quantitative Reasoning Approach, Fourth Edition
by Jeffrey Bennett and William Briggs

and

Math Basics for the Health Care Professional, Third Edition
by Michele Benjamin Lesmeister

D1455850

Custom Publishing

New York   Boston   San Francisco
London   Toronto   Sydney   Tokyo   Singapore   Madrid
Mexico City   Munich   Paris   Cape Town   Hong Kong   Montreal

Cover Art: *Courtesy of Bracha Rauch*

Taken from:

Thinking Mathematically, Fourth Edition
by Robert Blitzer
Copyright © 2008, 2005, 2003, 2000 by Pearson Education, Inc.
Published by Prentice Hall
Upper Saddle River, New Jersey 07458

A Survey of Mathematics with Applications, Eighth Edition
by Allen R. Angel, Christine D. Abbott, and Dennis C. Runde
Copyright © 2009 by Pearson Education, Inc.
Published by Addison Wesley
Boston, Massachusetts 02116

Using and Understanding Mathematics: A Quantitative Reasoning Approach, Fourth Edition
by Jeffrey Bennett and William Briggs
Copyright © 2008 by Pearson Education, Inc.
Published by Addison Wesley

Math Basics for the Health Care Professional, Third Edition
by Michele Benjamin Lesmeister
Copyright © 2009 by Pearson Education, Inc.
Published by Prentice Hall

This special edition published in cooperation with Pearson Custom Publishing.

All trademarks, service marks, registered trademarks, and registered service marks are the property of their respective owners and are used herein for identification purposes only.

The information, illustrations, and/or software contained in this book, and regarding the above-mentioned programs, are provided "As Is," without warranty of any kind, express or implied, including without limitation any warranty concerning the accuracy, adequacy, or completeness of such information. Neither the publisher, the authors, nor the copyright holders shall be responsible for any claims attributable to errors, omissions, or other inaccuracies contained in this book. Nor shall they be liable for direct, indirect, special, incidental, or consequential damages arising out of the use of such information or material.

Printed in the United States of America

7 8 9 10 11 12 V303 16 15 14 13 12 11

2008360915

SB

**Pearson
Custom Publishing**
is a division of

www.pearsonhighered.com

ISBN 10: 0-555-01364-2
ISBN 13: 978-0-555-01364-9

Welcome to MATH 103!

We are so excited to announce a textbook customized specifically to meet your needs! We have selected chapters and sections from some of the best selling math products available on the market today. We have added appendices based on our experience with B&S learners and hope you find them useful. The chapters are arranged in a logical fashion so that the basics are covered early. Instructors can place higher emphasis on certain topics based in the interests and pace of the class. Other usable features include an index and answers to selected problems.

The MATH 103 course was designed to meet the needs of the entire student population of Bryant & Stratton College. All the topics and skills covered in this text were carefully chosen to be applied in your future studies, your career and throughout your life. Each topic supports the outcomes of the course and the college. While some topics might seem unrelated to your particular major they were chosen to meet the needs of a vast array of majors over 14 campuses. For example, students in Ohio pursuing a degree related to electrical technology would need to learn different numeration systems before taking an analytical mathematics course and students in the medical field will find it necessary to perform dosage calculations.

This textbook is an excellent resource for you as you take the Survey of Mathematics course, however it does not stand alone. Your instructor brings a wealth of knowledge and experiences that no single textbook could ever cover. Other resources may also be necessary for you to get the most out of your learning experience. By applying yourself in this course you will gather the skills and knowledge that is highly valued in the corporate and business world regardless of your major of study.

We wish you well on your journey through Bryant & Stratton College. May you all strive toward greatness in everything you pursue.

Kathy Dilmore
Manzoor Syed
Daniel H. Moloney
Donald Emmett

Substitute each letter with a word that will solve the equation.

Example: 26 = L of the A

26 = Letters of the Alphabet

1. 7 = D of the W

2. 50 = S in the US

3. 52 = C in a D

4. 7 = W of the W

5. 365 = D in a Y

6. 24 = H in a D

7. 4 = W on a C

8. 60 = S in a M

9. 13 = S on a F

How much do you know about Bryant and Stratton?

10. 1 = N of I D # of instructional Dean

11. Over 155 = Y of E years of experience

12. 18 = N of L number of locations

13. 26 = D P Degree Programs

14. 10 = C P Certification programs

Contents ••••••

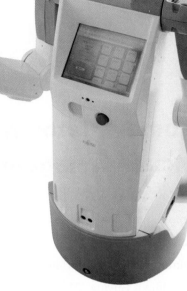

4

Consumer Mathematics and Financial Management   181

5

The Metric System   245

6

Geometry   287

7

Set Theory   375

8

Counting Methods and Probability Theory   437

9

Statistics   509

10

Number Representation and Calculation   577

1
Critical Thinking Skills

Life constantly presents new problems. The more sophisticated our society becomes, the more complex the problems. We as individuals are constantly solving problems. For example, when we consider ways to reduce our expenses or when we plan a trip, we make problem-solving decisions. Businesses are constantly trying to solve problems that involve making a profit for the company and keeping customers satisfied.

The goal of this chapter is to help you master the skills of reasoning, estimating, and problem solving. These skills will aid you in solving problems in the remainder of this book as well as problems you will encounter in everyday life.

●●●●●●
When creating a monthly budget, we may need to make problem-solving decisions to reduce our expenses.

SECTION 1.1 • INDUCTIVE REASONING

OBJECTIVES

1. Inductive and deductive reasoning processes

2. Estimation

3. Problem-solving techniques

A machine like this is used at Disney World to identify seasonal ticket holders.

Thus far, no two people have been found to have the same fingerprints or DNA, so fingerprints and DNA have become forms of identification. As technology improves, so do identification techniques. Today, when you purchase a seasonal pass at Disney World, you place your forefinger and middle finger in a device that measures and records your fingers' size, shape, and density. Then you are given a seasonal pass. Each time you enter Disney World, you put those two fingers in the device and it indicates whether you are or are not allowed entry under the seasonal pass that you show. The belief that no two people have the same finger size, shape, and density is based on a type of reasoning we will discuss in this section.

Inductive Reasoning

Before looking at some examples of inductive reasoning and problem solving, let us first review a few facts about certain numbers. The *natural numbers* or *counting numbers* are the numbers 1, 2, 3, 4, 5, 6, 7, 8, ... The three dots, called an *ellipsis*, mean that 8 is not the last number but that the numbers continue in the same manner. A word that we sometimes use is "divisible." If $a \div b$ has a remainder of zero, then *a is divisible by b*. The counting numbers that are divisible by 2 are 2, 4, 6, 8, ... These numbers are called the *even counting numbers*. The numbers that are not divisible by 2 are 1, 3, 5, 7, 9, ... These numbers are the *odd counting numbers*. When we refer to *odd numbers* or *even numbers*, we mean odd or even counting numbers.

Recognizing patterns is sometimes helpful in solving problems, as Examples 1 and 2 illustrate.

EXAMPLE 1   THE PRODUCT OF TWO EVEN NUMBERS

If two even numbers are multiplied together, will the product always be an even number?

SOLUTION To answer this question, we will examine the products of several pairs of even numbers to see if there is a pattern.

$2 \times 2 = 4$	$4 \times 6 = 24$	$6 \times 8 = 48$
$2 \times 4 = 8$	$4 \times 8 = 32$	$6 \times 10 = 60$
$2 \times 6 = 12$	$4 \times 10 = 40$	$6 \times 12 = 72$
$2 \times 8 = 16$	$4 \times 12 = 48$	$6 \times 14 = 84$

All the products are even numbers. Thus, we might predict from these examples that the product of any two even numbers is an even number.

Automated teller machines (ATMs) are now experimenting with determining identity by scanning the iris of a person's eye. When you open a bank account, your iris is scanned and the image is entered into a computer. When you use an ATM, a powerful camera automatically (without you even knowing it) checks the veins in your iris against the computer's files. Shortly, we will no longer need personal identification numbers (PINs) to withdraw money from our bank accounts. Iris scanning is also used now by law enforcement to locate missing children. The Children's Identification and Location Database (CHILD) Project, begun in 2004, is a voluntary program that uses iris-scanning machines. As of August 2005, 1200 sheriff's departments in 46 states had signed up with the CHILD Project. By 2010, the project hopes to have 3 million to 5 million participants in its registry. In the future, iris scanning may also be used to track down Alzheimer's and mentally disabled patients. Because iris scanning can be done in a matter of seconds, it can be a much quicker procedure than fingerprinting and just as accurate. Because the iris-scanning method of identification relies on the observation of specific cases to form a general conclusion, it is based on inductive reasoning.

EXAMPLE 2   THE SUM OF AN ODD NUMBER AND AN EVEN NUMBER

If an odd number and an even number are added, will the sum be an odd or an even number?

SOLUTION Let's look at a few examples in which one number is odd and the other number is even.

$$3 + 4 = 7 \qquad 9 + 6 = 15 \qquad 23 + 18 = 41$$
$$5 + 12 = 17 \qquad 5 + 14 = 19 \qquad 81 + 32 = 113$$

All these sums are odd numbers. Therefore, we might predict that the sum of an odd number and an even number is an odd number.

In Examples 1 and 2, we cannot conclude that the results are true for all counting numbers. From the patterns developed, however, we can make predictions. This type of reasoning process, arriving at a general conclusion from specific observations or examples, is called *inductive reasoning*, or *induction*.

> **Inductive reasoning** is the process of reasoning to a general conclusion through observations of specific cases.

Induction often involves observing a pattern and from that pattern predicting a conclusion. Imagine an endless row of dominoes. You knock down the first, which knocks down the second, which knocks down the third, and so on. Assuming the pattern will continue uninterrupted, you conclude that any one domino that you select in the row will eventually fall, even though you may not witness the event.

Inductive reasoning is often used by mathematicians and scientists to predict answers to complicated problems. For this reason, inductive reasoning is part of the *scientific method*. When a scientist or mathematician makes a prediction based on specific observations, it is called a *hypothesis* or *conjecture*. After looking at the products in Example 1, we might conjecture that the product of two even numbers will be an even number. After looking at the sums in Example 2, we might conjecture that the sum of an odd number and an even number is an odd number.

Examples 3 and 4 illustrate how we arrive at a conclusion using inductive reasoning.

EXAMPLE 3   FINGERPRINTS AND DNA

What reasoning process has led to the conclusion that no two people have the same fingerprints or DNA? This conclusion has resulted in fingerprints and DNA being used in courts of law as evidence to convict persons of crimes.

SOLUTION In millions of tests, no two people have been found to have the same fingerprints or DNA. By induction, then, we believe that fingerprints and DNA provide a unique identification and can therefore be used in a court of law as evidence. Is it possible that sometime in the future two people will be found who do have exactly the same fingerprints or DNA?

EXAMPLE 4   DIVISIBILITY BY 9

Consider the conjecture "If the sum of the digits of a number is divisible by 9, then the number itself is divisible by 9." We will test several numbers to see if the conjecture appears to be true or false.

AN EXPERIMENT REVISITED

Apollo 15 astronaut David Scott used the moon as his laboratory to show that a heavy object (a hammer) does indeed fall at the same rate as a light object (a feather). Had Galileo dropped a hammer and feather from the Tower of Pisa, the hammer would have fallen more quickly to the ground and he still would have concluded that a heavy object falls faster than a lighter one. If it is not the object's mass that is affecting the outcome, then what is it? The answer is air resistance or friction: Earth has an atmosphere that creates friction on falling objects. The moon does not have an atmosphere; therefore, no friction is created.

SOLUTION Let's look at some numbers whose sum of the digits is divisible by 9.

Number	Sum of the Digits	Is the Sum of the Digits Divisible by 9?	Is the Number Divisible by 9?
576	$5 + 7 + 6 = 18$	yes; $18 \div 9 = 2$	yes; $576 \div 9 = 64$
2115	$2 + 1 + 1 + 5 = 9$	yes; $9 \div 9 = 1$	yes; $2115 \div 9 = 235$
6777	$6 + 7 + 7 + 7 = 27$	yes; $27 \div 9 = 3$	yes; $6777 \div 9 = 753$
49,302	$4 + 9 + 3 + 0 + 2 = 18$	yes; $18 \div 9 = 2$	yes; $49{,}032 \div 9 = 5448$

In each case, we find that if the sum of the digits of a number is divisible by 9, then the number itself is divisible by 9. From these examples, we might be tempted to generalize that the conjecture "If the sum of the digits of a number is divisible by 9, then the number itself is divisible by 9" is true.

EXAMPLE 5   PICK A NUMBER, ANY NUMBER

Pick any number, multiply the number by 6, add 9 to the product, divide the sum by 3, and subtract 3 from the quotient. Repeat this procedure for several different numbers and then make a conjecture about the relationship between the original number and the final number.

SOLUTION Let's go through this one together.

Pick a number:	say, 5
Multiply the number by 6:	$6 \times 5 = 30$
Add 9 to the product:	$30 + 9 = 39$
Divide the sum by 3:	$39 \div 3 = 13$
Subtract 3 from the quotient:	$13 - 3 = 10$

Note that we started with the number 5 and finished with the number 10. If you start with the number 2, you will end with the number 4. Starting with 3 would result in a final number of 6, 4 would result in 8, and so on. On the basis of these few examples, we may conjecture that when you follow the given procedure, the number you end with will always be twice the original number.

The result reached by inductive reasoning is often correct for the specific cases studied but not correct for all cases. History has shown that not all conclusions arrived at by inductive reasoning are correct. For example, Aristotle (384–322 B.C.) reasoned inductively that heavy objects fall at a faster rate than light objects. About 2000 years later, Galileo (1564–1642) dropped two pieces of metal—one 10 times heavier than the other—from the Leaning Tower of Pisa in Italy. He found that both hit the ground at exactly the same moment, so they must have traveled at the same rate.

When forming a general conclusion using inductive reasoning, you should test it with several special cases to see whether the conclusion appears correct. If a special case is found that satisfies the conditions of the conjecture but produces a different result, such a case is called a *counterexample*. A counterexample proves that the conjecture is false because only one exception is needed to show that a conjecture is not valid. Galileo's counterexample disproved Aristotle's conjecture. If a counterexample cannot be found, the conjecture is neither proven nor disproven.

Deductive Reasoning

A second type of reasoning process is called *deductive reasoning*, or *deduction*. Mathematicians use deductive reasoning to *prove* conjectures true or false.

> **Deductive reasoning** is the process of reasoning to a specific conclusion from a general statement.

EXAMPLE 6   PICK A NUMBER, N

Prove, using deductive reasoning, that the procedure in Example 5 will always result in twice the original number selected.

SOLUTION To use deductive reasoning, we begin with the *general* case rather than specific examples. In Example 5, specific cases were used. Let's select the letter n to represent *any number*.

Pick any number:	n
Multiply the number by 6:	$6n$ *6n means 6 times n*
Add 9 to the product:	$6n + 9$
Divide the sum by 3:	$\dfrac{6n + 9}{3} = \dfrac{\overset{2}{6n}}{\underset{1}{3}} + \dfrac{\overset{3}{9}}{\underset{1}{3}} = 2n + 3$
Subtract 3 from the quotient:	$2n + 3 - 3 = 2n$

Note that for any number n selected, the result is $2n$, or twice the original number selected.

In Example 5, you may have *conjectured*, using specific examples and inductive reasoning, that the result would be twice the original number selected. In Example 6, we *proved*, using deductive reasoning, that the result will always be twice the original number selected.

EXERCISE SET 1.1 ●●●●●●●*

• Concept/Writing Exercises

1. a) List the natural numbers.

   b) What is another name for the natural numbers?

2. a) What does it mean to say, "*a* is divisible by *b*," where *a* and *b* represent natural numbers?

   b) List three natural numbers that are divisible by 4.

   c) List three natural numbers that are divisible by 9.

In Exercises 3–6, explain your answer in one or two sentences.

3. What is inductive reasoning?

4. What is deductive reasoning?

5. What is a counterexample?

6. What is a conjecture?

7. Which type of reasoning is generally used to arrive at a conjecture?

8. Which type of reasoning is used to prove a conjecture?

9. For many years, doctors noticed that many of their patients with heart disease also had high blood pressure. Doctors reasoned that high blood pressure increases a person's chance of developing heart disease. What type of reasoning did the doctors use? Explain.

10. You have purchased one lottery ticket each week for many months and have not won more than $5.00. You decide, based on your past experience, that you are not going to win the grand prize and so you stop playing the lottery. What type of reasoning did you use? Explain.

---

*Exercise numbers set in color indicate writing exercises.

• Practice the Skills

In Exercises 11–14, use inductive reasoning to predict the next line in the pattern.

11. $1 \times 7 = 7$
$2 \times 7 = 14$
$3 \times 7 = 21$
$4 \times 7 = 28$

12. $13 \times 10 = 130$
$13 \times 11 = 143$
$13 \times 12 = 156$
$13 \times 13 = 169$

13.
```
          1
        1   1
      1   2   1
    1   3   3   1
     ↘ ↙ ↘ ↙ ↘ ↙
   1   4   6   4   1
```

14. $10 = 10^1$
$100 = 10^2$
$1000 = 10^3$
$10,000 = 10^4$

In Exercises 15–18, draw the next figure in the pattern (or sequence).

15.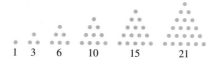

16. ...   **17.** 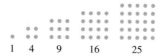 ...

18. , ...

In Exercises 19–28, use inductive reasoning to predict the next three numbers in the pattern (or sequence).

19. 5, 10, 15, 20, ...

20. 19, 16, 13, 10, ...

21. 1, −1, 1, −1, 1, ...

22. 5, 3, 1, −1, ...

23. 16, 4, 1, $\frac{1}{4}$, ...

24. 4, −20, 100, −500, ...

25. 1, 4, 9, 16, 25, ...

26. 0, 1, 3, 6, 10, 15, ...

27. 1, 1, 2, 3, 5, 8, 13, 21, ...

28. 3, $-\frac{9}{4}$, $\frac{27}{16}$, $-\frac{81}{64}$, ...

• Problem Solving

29. Find the letter that is the 118th entry in the following sequence. Explain how you determined your answer.

Y, R, R, Y, R, R, Y, R, R, Y, R, R, Y, R, R, ...

30. a) Select a variety of one- and two-digit numbers between 1 and 99 and multiply each by 9. Record your results.

b) Find the sum of the digits in each of your products in part (a). If the sum is not a one-digit number, find the sum of the digits again until you obtain a one-digit number.

c) Make a conjecture about the sum of the digits when a one- or two-digit number is multiplied by 9.

31. *A Square Pattern* The ancient Greeks labeled certain numbers as **square numbers**. The numbers 1, 4, 9, 16, 25, and so on are square numbers.

a) Determine the next three square numbers.

b) Describe a procedure to determine the next five square numbers without drawing the figures.

c) Is 72 a square number? Explain how you determined your answer.

32. *A Triangular Pattern* The ancient Greeks labeled certain numbers as **triangular numbers**. The numbers 1, 3, 6, 10, 15, 21, and so on are triangular numbers.

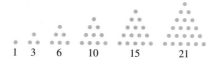

a) Can you determine the next two triangular numbers?

b) Describe a procedure to determine the next five triangular numbers without drawing the figures.

c) Is 72 a triangular number? Explain how you determined your answer.

33. *Quilt Design* The pattern shown is taken from a quilt design known as a triple Irish chain. Complete the color pattern by indicating the color assigned to each square.

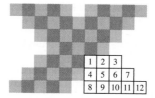

34. *Triangles in a Triangle* Four rows of a triangular figure are shown.

a) If you added six additional rows to the bottom of this triangle, using the same pattern displayed, how many triangles would appear in the 10th row?

b) If the triangles in all 10 rows were added, how many triangles would appear in the entire figure?

35. *Television Advertising* The graph shows the amount of money, in billions of dollars, advertisers spent or plan to spend on placing their products into television programs from 2000 to 2008.

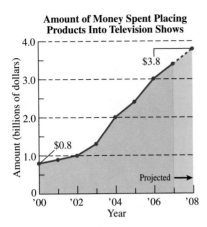

Amount of Money Spent Placing Products Into Television Shows

a) Assuming this trend continues, use the graph to predict the amount of money advertisers will spend on placing their products into television programs in 2012. Round your answer to the nearest billion dollars.

b) Explain how you are using inductive reasoning to determine your answer.

36. *Cable TV Cost* The graph above and to the right shows the average monthly cost for basic cable television for each year from 1994 through 2005.

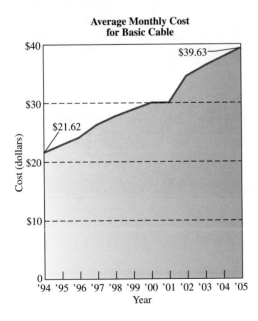

Average Monthly Cost for Basic Cable

a) Assuming this trend continues, use the graph to predict the average monthly cost for basic cable TV in 2008. Round your answer to the nearest dollar.

b) Using the graph, predict the average monthly cost for basic cable TV in 2012. Round your answer to the nearest dollar.

c) Explain how you are using inductive reasoning to determine your answer.

In Exercises 37 and 38, draw the next diagram in the pattern (or sequence).

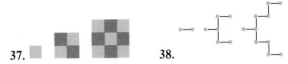

37.   38.

39. Pick any number, multiply the number by 8, add 16 to the product, divide the sum by 8, and subtract 2 from the quotient. See Example 5.

   a) What is the relationship between the number you started with and the final number?

   b) Arbitrarily select some different numbers and repeat the process, recording the original number and the result.

   c) Can you make a conjecture about the relationship between the original number and the final number?

   d) Try to prove, using deductive reasoning, the conjecture you made in part (c). See Example 6.

40. Pick any number and multiply the number by 4. Add 6 to the product. Divide the sum by 2 and subtract 3 from the quotient.

   a) What is the relationship between the number you started with and the final answer?

   b) Arbitrarily select some different numbers and repeat the process, recording the original number and the results.

   c) Can you make a conjecture about the relationship between the original number and the final number?

   d) Try to prove, using deductive reasoning, the conjecture you made in part (c).

41. Pick any number and add 1 to it. Find the sum of the new number and the original number. Add 9 to the sum. Divide the sum by 2 and subtract the original number from the quotient.

   a) What is the final number?

   b) Arbitrarily select some different numbers and repeat the process. Record the results.

   c) Can you make a conjecture about the final number?

   d) Try to prove, using deductive reasoning, the conjecture you made in part (c).

42. Pick any number and add 10 to the number. Divide the sum by 5. Multiply the quotient by 5. Subtract 10 from the product. Then subtract your original number.

   a) What is the result?

   b) Arbitrarily select some different numbers and repeat the process, recording the original number and the result.

c) Can you make a conjecture regarding the result when this process is followed?

d) Try to prove, using deductive reasoning, the conjecture you made in part (c).

In Exercises 43–48, find a counterexample to show that each statement is incorrect.

43. The sum of two odd numbers is an odd number.

44. The quotient of any two counting numbers is a counting number.

45. When a counting number is added to 3 and the sum is divided by 2, the quotient will be an even number.

46. The product of any two counting numbers is divisible by 2.

47. The difference of any two counting numbers will be a counting number.

48. The sum of any two odd numbers is divisible by 4.

49. *Interior Angles of a Triangle*

a) Construct a triangle and measure the three interior angles with a protractor. What is the sum of the measures?

b) Construct three other triangles, measure the angles, and record the sums. Are your answers the same?

c) Make a conjecture about the sum of the measures of the three interior angles of a triangle.

50. *Interior Angles of a Quadrilateral*

a) Construct a quadrilateral (a four-sided figure) and measure the four interior angles with a protractor. What is the sum of the measures?

b) Construct three other quadrilaterals, measure the angles, and record the sums. Are your answers the same?

c) Make a conjecture about the sum of the measures of the four interior angles of a quadrilateral.

• Challenge Problems/Group Activities

51. Complete the following square of numbers. Explain how you determined your answer.

1	2	3	4
2	5	10	17
3	10	25	52
4	17	52	?

52. Find the next three numbers in the sequence.

1, 8, 11, 88, 101, 111, 181, 1001, 1111, . . .

• Recreational Mathematics

53.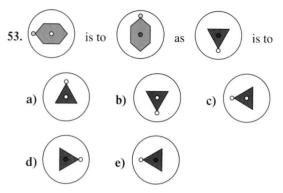

• Internet/Research Activities

54. a) Using newspapers, the Internet, magazines, and other sources, find examples of conclusions arrived at by inductive reasoning.

b) Explain how inductive reasoning was used in arriving at the conclusion.

55. When a jury decides whether or not a defendant is guilty, do the jurors collectively use primarily inductive reasoning, deductive reasoning, or an equal amount of each? Write a brief report supporting your answer.

SECTION 1.2 • ESTIMATION

Estimate the cost of the seventeen thirty-nine cent stamps shown in this photo.

What is the approximate sales tax on an $18,000 car if the sales tax is 8%? What is the approximate cost to purchase 52 forty-one cent stamps? In this section, we will introduce a technique for arriving at an approximate answer to a question.

An important step in solving mathematical problems—or, in fact, *any* problem—is to make sure that the answer you've arrived at makes sense. One technique for determining whether an answer is reasonable is to estimate. *Estimation* is the process of arriving at an approximate answer to a question. This section demonstrates several estimation methods.

To estimate, or approximate, an answer, we often round numbers as illustrated in the following examples. The symbol ≈ means *is approximately equal to*.

EXAMPLE 1   ESTIMATING THE COST OF LIBRARY BOOKS

Jean Boehm decides to purchase new books for the Sherman Elementary School Library. Estimate her cost if she purchases 19 books at $3.99 each.

SOLUTION We may round the amounts as follows to obtain an estimate.

Number		Number Rounded
19	$\rightarrow$	20
$\times\ \$3.99$	$\rightarrow$	$\times\ \$4.00$
		$\$80.00$

Thus, the 19 books would cost approximately $80.00 written ≈ $80.

In Example 1, the true cost is $3.99 × 19, or $75.81. *Estimates are not meant to give exact values for answers but are a means of determining whether your answer is reasonable.* If you calculated an answer of $75.81 and then did a quick estimate to check it, you would know that the answer is reasonable because it is close to your estimated answer.

EXAMPLE 2   TWO WAYS TO ESTIMATE

At a local supermarket, Kaitlyn purchased a cheesecake for $5.89, lettuce for $1.09, bread for $1.98, laundry detergent for $4.79, ground beef for $4.26, steaks for $15.37, and a green onion for $0.92. The cashier said the total bill was $44.08. Use estimation to determine whether this amount is reasonable.

SOLUTION The most expensive item is $15.37, and the least expensive is $0.92. How should we estimate? We will estimate two different ways. First, we will round the cost of each item to the nearest 10 cents. For the second method, we will round the cost of each item to the nearest dollar. Rounding to the nearest 10 cents is more accurate. To determine whether the total bill is reasonable, however, we may need to round only to the nearest dollar.

	Round to the Nearest 10 Cents		Round to the Nearest Dollar	
Cheesecake	$5.89 →	$5.90	$5.89 →	$6.00
Lettuce	1.09 →	1.10	1.09 →	1.00
Bread	1.98 →	2.00	1.98 →	2.00
Laundry detergent	4.79 →	4.80	4.79 →	5.00
Ground beef	4.26 →	4.30	4.26 →	4.00
Steaks	15.37 →	15.40	15.37 →	15.00
Onion	0.92 →	0.90	0.92 →	1.00
		$34.40		$34.00

Using either estimate, we find that the bill of $44.08 is quite high. Therefore, Kaitlyn should check the bill carefully before paying it. Adding the prices of all seven items gives the true cost of $34.30.

EXAMPLE 3   SELECT THE BEST ESTIMATE

The number of bushels of grapes produced at a vineyard are 71,309 Cabernet Sauvignon, 123,879 French Colombard, 106,490 Chenin Blanc, 5960 Charbono, and 12,104 Chardonnay. Select the best estimate of the total number of bushels produced by the vineyard.

a) 500,000   b) 30,000   c) 300,000   d) 5,000,000

SOLUTION   Following are suggested roundings. On the left, the numbers are rounded to thousands. For a less accurate estimate, round to ten thousands, as illustrated on the right.

Round to the Nearest Thousand		Round to the Nearest Ten Thousand	
71,309 →	71,000	71,309 →	70,000
123,879 →	124,000	123,879 →	120,000
106,490 →	106,000	106,490 →	110,000
5960 →	6000	5960 →	10,000
12,104 →	12,000	12,104 →	10,000
	319,000		320,000

Either rounding procedure indicates that the best estimate is (c), or 300,000.

EXAMPLE 4   USING ESTIMATION IN CALCULATIONS

The odometer of an automobile reads 58,289.6 miles.

a) If the automobile averaged 22.1 miles per gallon for that mileage, estimate the number of gallons of gasoline used.

b) If the cost of the gasoline averaged $2.39 per gallon, estimate the total cost of the gasoline.

SOLUTION

a) To estimate the number of gallons, divide the mileage by the number of miles per gallon.

$$\frac{58,289.6}{22.1}$$

Round these numbers to obtain an estimate.

$$\frac{60,000}{20} = 3000$$

Therefore, the car used approximately 3000 gallons of gasoline.

b) Rounding the price of the gasoline to $2.40 per gallon gives the cost of the gasoline as 3000 × $2.40, or $7200.

Now let's look at some different types of estimation problems.

EXAMPLE 5 ESTIMATING DISTANCES ON TRAILS TO THE WEST

In the mid-1800s, thousands of settlers followed trails to the West to gain cheap, fertile land and a chance to make a fortune. One of the main trails to the West was the Oregon Trail, which ran from Independence, Missouri, to the Oregon Territory. Another trail, the California Trail, ran from Fort Hall on the Oregon Trail to Sacramento, California. A map of the Oregon Trail and the California Trail is shown below.

Trails West, 1850

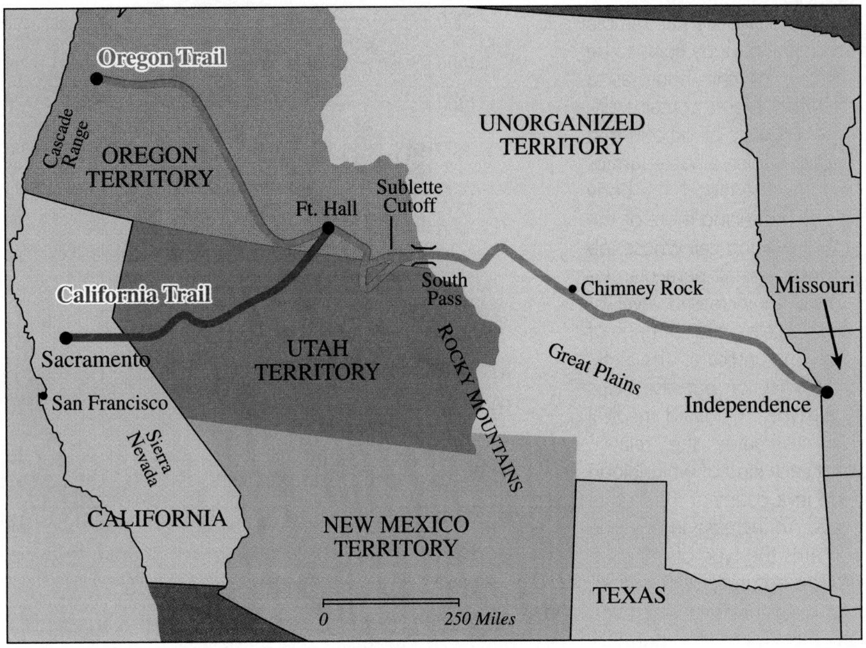

a) Using the Oregon Trail, estimate the distance from Independence, Missouri, to Ft. Hall in the Oregon Territory.

b) Using the California Trail, estimate the distance from Fort Hall in the Oregon Territory to Sacramento, California.

SOLUTION

a) Using a ruler and the scale given on the map, we can determine that approximately $\frac{3}{4}$ inch represents 250 miles (mi). One way to determine the distance from Independence, Missouri, to Ft. Hall in the Oregon Territory is to mark off $\frac{3}{4}$-inch intervals along the Oregon Trail. If you do so, you should obtain approximately 4 intervals. Thus, the distance is about 4 × 250 mi, or about 1000 mi.

   Sometimes on a map like this one, it may be difficult to get an accurate estimate because of the curves on the map. To get a more accurate estimate, you may want to use a piece of string. Place the beginning of the string at Independence, Missouri, and, using tape or pins, align the string with the road. Indicate on the string the point repre-

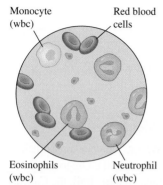
sented by Ft. Hall. Then remove the string and make $\frac{3}{4}$-inch interval markings on the string (or measure the length of string you marked off). If, for example, your string from Independence, Missouri, to Ft. Hall measures $3\frac{1}{4}$ inch, then the distance is about 1083 mi.

b) Using the procedure discussed in part (a), we estimate that the distance from Fort Hall in the Oregon Territory to Sacramento, California, is about $1\frac{5}{8}$ inch, or about 2.2 three-quarter-inch intervals. Thus, the distance from Fort Hall in the Oregon Territory to Sacramento, California, is about 2.2×250 mi, or about 550 mi.

EXAMPLE 6   ESTIMATED ENERGY USE

Some utility bills contain graphs illustrating the amount of electricity and natural gas used. The following graphs show gas and electric use at a specific residence for a period of 13 months, starting in November 2006 and going through November 2007 (the month of the current bill). Also shown, in red, is the bill for the average residential customer for November 2007. Using these graphs, answer the following questions.

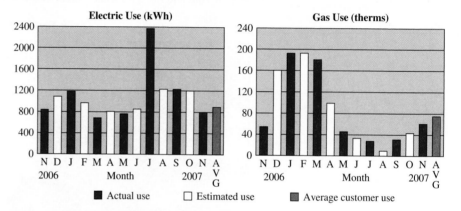

a) How often were actual gas and electric readings made?

b) Estimate the number of therms of gas used by the average residential customer in November 2007.

c) Estimate the amount of gas used by the resident in November 2007.

d) If the cost of gas is $1.71295 per therm, estimate the gas bill in March 2007.

e) In which month was the most electricity used? How many kilowatt hours (kWh) of electricity were used in this month?

f) If the cost of electricity is 8.1716 cents per kWh, estimate the cost of the electricity in January 2007.

SOLUTION

a) Actual readings were made every other month, in November 2006, January 2007, March 2007, May 2007, July 2007, September 2007, and November 2007. Thus, actual readings were made 7 times.

b) In November 2007, approximately 75 therms were used by the average residential customer, as shown by the height of the red bar.

c) In November 2007, approximately 60 therms were used by the resident.

d) In March 2007, about 180 therms were used. The rate is $1.71295 per therm. To get a rough approximation, round the rate to $1.70 per therm.

$$1.70 \times 180 = \$306$$

Thus, the cost of gas used was about $306.

e) The most electricity was used in July 2007. Approximately 2400 kWh of electricity were used.

f) In January 2007, about 1200 kWh were used. Write 8.1716 cents as $0.081716. Rounding the rate to $0.08 per kWh and multiplying by 1200 yields an estimate of $96.

$$0.08 \times 1200 = \$96$$

Thus, the cost of electricity in January 2007 was about $96.

EXAMPLE 7 ESTIMATING THE NUMBER OF BIRDS IN A PHOTO

Scientists who are concerned about dwindling animal populations often use aerial photography to make estimates. Estimate the number of birds in the accompanying photograph.

SOLUTION To estimate the number of birds, we can divide the photograph into rectangles with equal areas and then select one area that appears to be representative of all the areas. Estimate (or count) the number of birds in this single area and then multiply this number by the number of equal areas.

Let's divide the photo into 20 approximately equal areas. We will select the middle region in the bottom row as the representative region. We enlarge this region and count the birds in it. If half a bird is in the region, we count it (see enlargement). There are 13 birds in this region. Multiplying by 20 gives $13 \times 20 = 260$. Thus, there are about 260 birds in the photo.

In problems similar to that in Example 7, the number of regions or areas into which you choose to divide the total area is arbitrary. Generally, the more regions, the better the approximation, as long as the region selected is representative of the other regions in the map, diagram, or photo.

When you estimate an answer, the amount that your approximation differs from the actual answer will depend on how you round the numbers. Thus, in estimating

EARLY ESTIMATION

The ancient Egyptians and Greeks used sticks to estimate heights. To measure height, a person held a stick in his or her outstretched arm until it just covered the height of the object. The person then turned the stick through a right angle. Measuring the distance the stick appeared to cover on the ground provided an estimate of the object's height.

the product of 196,000 × 0.02520, using the rounded values 195,000 × 0.025 would yield an estimate much closer to the true answer than using the rounded values 200,000 × 0.03. Without a calculator, however, the product of 195,000 × 0.025 might be more difficult to find than 200,000 × 0.03. When estimating, you need to determine the accuracy desired in your estimate and round the numbers accordingly.

EXERCISE SET 1.2 ●●●●●●

• Practice the Skills

In Exercises 1–57, your answers may vary from the answers given in the back of the text, depending on how you round your answers.

In Exercises 1–12, estimate the answer. There is no one correct estimate. Your answer, however, should be something near the answer given.

1. 523 + 47.8 + 821.6 + 733 + 92.7

2. 3.76 + 76 + 821.7 + 654.93 + 321 + 0.89

3. 297,700 × 4087   4. 1854 × 0.0096

5. $\dfrac{405}{0.049}$ 6. 297.521 − 85.964

7. 0.63 × 1523   8. 51,608 × 6981

9. 9% of 2164   10. 18% of 1576

11. 592 × 2070 × 992.62   12. 296.3 ÷ 0.0096

• Problem Solving

In Exercises 13–24, estimate the answer.

13. The income earned for 27 hours at $8.25 an hour

14. The cost of copying 13 pages at $0.15 a page

15. The cost of 6 grocery items if the items cost $4.23, $2.79, $0.79, $7.62, $12.38, and $4.99

16. A 7% sales tax on a refrigerator that sells for $599

17. The distance traveled when driving 57 miles per hour for 3.2 hours

18. One fourth of an annual salary of $47,600

19. The weight of the load of an 18-wheel truck if the weight of the truck when empty is 14,292 pounds and the weight of the truck when loaded is 27,453 pounds

20. The weight of one pork chop in a package of six pork chops if the weight of the package is 3.25 lb

21. A 15% tip on a meal that costs $26.32

22. The average daily distance traveled if Paul Simon traveled 173 miles in one week

23. The number of months needed to save $400 if you save $23 each month

24. The average monthly gasoline expense for the Stappenbacks if their annual gasoline expense is $2900

25. *Utility Bill* Joe Martinez pays $139.99 per month for the Time Warner All-n-One package. This package includes local telephone service, unlimited long-distance telephone service, cable TV, and Road Runner Internet service. His previous monthly costs were local telephone service $29.99, long-distance telephone service $36.99, cable TV $59.99 and Road Runner Internet service $49.99. Estimate the amount Joe saves per month with the All-n-One package.

26. *Estimating Weights* In a tug of war, the weight of the members of the two three-person teams is given below. Estimate the difference in the weights of the teams.

Team A	Team B
189	183
172	229
191	167

27. *Picking Strawberries* Chuck Chase hires 11 people to pick strawberries from his field. He agrees to pay them $1.50 for each quart they pick. Estimate the total amount of money he will have to pay if each person picks 8 quarts.

28. *Estimating Area* Mrs. Sanchez determines that her lawn contains an average of 3.8 grubs per square foot. If her rectangular lawn measures 60 ft by 80.2 ft, estimate the total number of grubs in her lawn.

29. *Currency* Estimate the difference in the value of 100 Mexican pesos and 50 U.S. dollars. Assume that one Mexican peso is about 0.089 U.S. dollar.

30. *The Cost of a Vacation* The Kleins are planning a vacation in the Great Smoky Mountains National Park. Their round-trip airfare from Houston, Texas, to Knoxville, Tennessee, totals $973. Car rental is $61 per day and lodging is a total of $97 per day, and they estimate a total of $150 per day for food, gas, and other miscellaneous items. If they are planning to stay six full days and nights, estimate their total expenses.

31. *A Hike in Yellowstone National Park* Below is a map of a trail in Yellowstone National Park. Using the scale on the map, estimate the distance of the route shown in red starting at Fishing Bridge and ending at West Thumb.

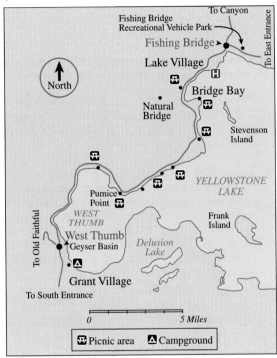

Source: National Park Service

32. *A Trolley Ride in San Diego* Below is a map of the trolley route in San Diego, California. Using the scale on the map, estimate the distance of the trolley route shown in red starting at Hazard Shopping Center and ending at Old Town.

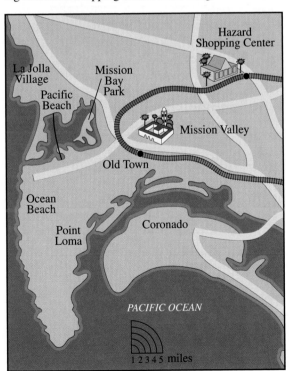

33. *Dream Jobs* The circle graph shows the kind of job parents of children ages 5 to 17 hope their children will grow up to have. The survey involved 504 parents.

a) Estimate the number of parents who hope their child will become a doctor.

b) Estimate the number of parents who hope their child will become a professional athlete.

c) Estimate the number of parents who hope their child will start a successful new business.

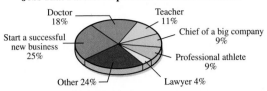

Source: Office Depot Back-to-School survey by Harris Interactive

34. *Latino Population* The circle graph shows the Latino population in the United States in 2005 by country of origin. Approximately 40 million Latinos were living in the United States in 2005.

a) Estimate the number of Latinos whose country of origin is Mexico.

b) Estimate the number of Latinos whose country of origin is El Savador.

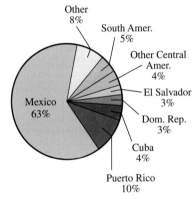

Source: U.S. Census Bureau

35. *An Aging Population* The bar graph shows population figures for 1900 and 2000 and estimated population figures for 2050.

a) Estimate the number of people 65 and over in 1900.

b) Estimate the number of people 65 and older in 2050.

c) Estimate the increase in the number of people 65 and older from 2000 to 2050.

d) Estimate the total U.S. population in 2000 by adding the five categories.

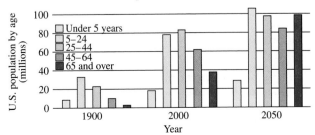

Source: U.S. Census Bureau

36. *Gaining Weight* As the graph shows, as a society we tend to get heavier as we get older. Also, with age, the amount of muscle tends to drop, and fat accounts for a greater percentage of weight.

a) Estimate the average percent of body fat for a woman, age 18 to 25.

b) Estimate the average percent of body fat for a man, age 56+.

c) Greg, an average 40-year-old man, weighs 179 lb. Estimate the number of pounds of body fat he has.

Getting Older Usually Means Getting Fatter

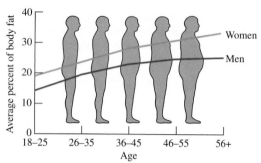

Source: Mayo Clinic Newsletter

37. *Land Ownership by the Federal Government* The federal government owns a great deal of land in the United States. The following graph shows the percent of land owned by the federal government in the 12 states in which the federal government owns the greatest percentage of a state's land.

Percent of Land Owned by the Federal Government

Source: Office of Governmentwide Policy, General Services Administration

a) Estimate the percent of land owned by the federal government in Nevada.

b) Estimate the difference in the percent of land owned by the federal government between Alaska and Oregon.

c) Nevada has a total area of 70,264,320 acres. Estimate the number of acres owned by the federal government in Nevada.

d) By just looking at the graph, is it possible to determine whether the federal government owns more land in Nevada or Utah? Explain.

38. *Calories and Exercise* The chart shows the calories burned per hour for an average person who weighs 150 lb.

a) Estimate the number of calories Phyllis Nye, who weighs 150 lb, burns in a week if she stair-climbs for 2 hours each week and jogs at 5 miles per hour for 4 hours each week.

b) Estimate the difference in the calories Phyllis will burn each week if she runs for 4 hours at 8 miles per hour rather than does casual bike riding for 4 hours.

c) Assume Phyllis jogs at 5 miles per hour for 3 hours and bicycles at 13 miles per hour for 3 hours each week. Estimate the number of calories she will burn in a year from these exercises.

Activity	Calories* per Hour
Running, 8 mph	920
Bicycling, 13 mph	545
Jogging, 5 mph	545
Air-walking	480
Stair-climbing	410
Weight-lifting	410
Walking, 4 mph	330
Casual bike riding	300

*For a 150 lb person.

In Exercises 39 and 40, estimate the maximum number of smaller figures (at left) that can be placed in the larger figure (at right) without the small figures overlapping.

39.

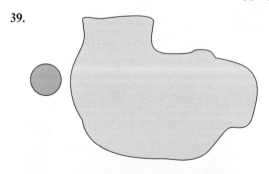

40.

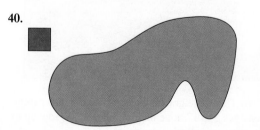

41. Estimate the number of bananas shown in the photo.

42. Estimate the number of berries shown in the photo.

In Exercises 43 and 44, estimate, in degrees, the measure of the angles depicted. For comparison purposes a right angle, ∟ *, measures 90°.*

43. **44.**

In Exercises 45 and 46, estimate the percent of area that is shaded in the following figures.

45. **46.**

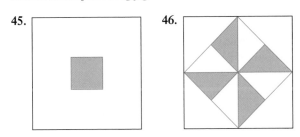

In Exercises 47 and 48, if each square represents one square unit, estimate the area of the shaded figure in square units.

47. **48.**

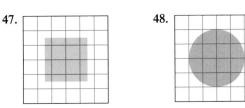

49. *Statue of Liberty* The length of the torch of the Statue of Liberty, from the tip of the flame to the bottom of the torch's baton, is 29 feet. Estimate the height of the Statue of Liberty from the top of the base to the top of the torch (the statue itself).

50. *Estimating Heights* If the height of the middle person in the photo is 62 in. tall, estimate the height of the tree.

51. *Distance* Estimate, without a ruler, a distance of 12 in. Measure the distance. How good was your estimate?

52. *Weight* In a bag, place objects that you believe have a total weight of 10 lb. Weigh the bag to determine the accuracy of your estimate.

53. *Phone Call* Estimate the number of times the phone will ring in 1 minute if unanswered. Have a classmate phone you so that you can count the rings and thus test your estimate.

54. *Temperature* Fill a glass with water and estimate the water's temperature. Then use a thermometer to measure the temperature and check your estimate.

55. *Pennies* Estimate the number of pennies that will fill a 3-ounce (oz) paper cup. Then actually fill a 3 oz paper cup with pennies, counting them to determine the accuracy of your estimate.

56. *Height* Estimate the ratio of your height to your waist size. Then have a friend measure your height and waist size. Determine the stated ratio and check the accuracy of your estimate.

57. *Walking Speed* Estimate how fast you can walk 60 ft. Then mark off a distance of 60 ft and use a watch with a second hand to time yourself walking it. Determine the accuracy of your estimate.

• Challenge Problems/Group Activities

58. *Shopping* Make a shopping list of 20 items you use regularly that can be purchased at a supermarket. Beside each item write down what you estimate to be its price. Add these price guesses to estimate the total cost of the 20 items. Next, make a trip to your local supermarket and record the actual price of each item. Add these prices to determine the actual total cost. How close was your estimate? (Don't forget to add tax on the taxable items.)

59. *A Ski Vacation* Two friends, Tiffany Connolly and Ana Pott, are planning a skiing vacation in the Rockies. They plan to purchase round-trip airline tickets from Atlanta, Georgia, to Denver, Colorado. They will fly into Denver on a Friday morning, rent a midsize car, and drive to Aspen that same day. They will stay at the Holiday Inn in Aspen. They will begin skiing at the Buttermilk Ski Area on Saturday, ski up to and including Wednesday, drive back to Denver on Thursday, and fly out of Denver Thursday evening.

a) Estimate the total cost of the vacation for the two friends. Do not forget items such as food, tips, gas, and other incidentals.

b) Using informational sources, including the Internet, determine the airfare cost, hotel cost, cost of ski tickets, cost of a car rental, and so forth. You will need to make an estimate for food and other incidentals.

c) How close was your estimate in part (a) to the amount you found in part (b)? Was your estimate in part (a) lower or higher than the amount obtained in part (b)?

• Recreational Mathematics

60. *A Dime* Look at a dime. Around the edge of a dime are many lines. Estimate the number of lines there are around the edge of a dime.

61. *Golf Ball* Look at a golf ball. Estimate the number of dimples (depressed areas) on a golf ball.

62. *A Million Dollars*

a) Estimate the time it would take, in days, to spend $1 million if you spent $1 a second until the $1 million is used up.

b) Calculate the actual time it would take, in days, to spend $1 million if you spent $1 a second. How close was your estimate?

• Internet/Research Activities

63. *Water Usage*

a) About how much water does your household use per day? Use the following data to estimate your household's daily water usage.

How much water do you use?

Activity	Typical Use
Running clothes washer	40 gal
Bath	35 gal
5-minute shower	25 gal
Doing dishes in sink, water running	20 gal
Running dishwasher	11 gal
Flushing toilet	4 gal
Brushing teeth, water running	2 gal

Source: U.S. Environmental Protection Agency

b) Determine from your water department (or company) your household's average daily usage by obtaining the total number of gallons used per year and dividing that amount by 365. How close was your estimate in part (a)?

c) Current records indicate that the average household uses about 300 gal of water per day (the average daily usage is 110 gal per person). Based on the number of people in your household, do you believe your household uses more or less than the average amount of water? Explain your answer.

64. Develop a monthly budget by estimating your monthly income and your monthly expenditures. Your monthly income should equal your monthly expenditures.

65. Identify three ways that you use estimation in your daily life. Discuss each of them briefly and give examples.

SECTION 1.3 • PROBLEM SOLVING

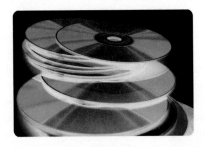

Getting the best deal for office supplies, such as CDs, can help businesses maximize their profits.

To maximize their profits, businesses try to keep their expenses down. We, as individuals, also try to keep our expenses down, and we often look for "bargains" or the "best deal." For example, suppose we need to purchase a large number of CD-RW discs and only have $250 to spend. How can we determine the maximum number of CDs that we can purchase if CDs are sold in packs of 50 for $38 and in packs of 25 for $20? We'll answer this question in Example 1.

Solving mathematical puzzles and real-life mathematical problems can be enjoyable. You should work as many exercises in this section as possible. By doing so, you will sample a variety of problem-solving techniques.

You can approach any problem by using a general procedure developed by George Polya. Before learning Polya's problem-solving procedure, let's consider an example that illustrates the procedure.

EXAMPLE 1   SAVING MONEY WHEN PURCHASING CDS

A law firm owned by Karen Morris plans to purchase a large number of CD-RW discs. One supplier, Staples, is selling packs of 50 CDs for $38 and packs of 25 CDs for $20. Only complete packs of CDs are sold.

a) Find the maximum number of CDs that can be purchased for $250 or less. Indicate how many packs of 50 CDs and how many packs of 25 CDs will be purchased.

b) If the maximum number of CDs determined in part (a) is purchased in the most economical way, how much will the CDs cost?

SOLUTION

a) The first thing to do is to read the problem carefully. Read it at least twice. Be sure you understand the facts given and what you are being asked to find. Next, make a list of the given facts and determine which facts are relevant to answering the question or questions asked.

GIVEN INFORMATION

   Law firm owner: Karen Morris

   Supplier: Staples

   A pack of 50 CDs costs $38.

   A pack of 25 CDs costs $20.

   Only complete packs of CDs can be purchased.

We need to determine the maximum number of CDs the law firm can purchase for $250 or less. To determine this number, we need to know the number of CDs in each of the packs and the cost of each pack. We also need to know that only complete packs of CDs can be purchased.

George Polya

George Polya (1887–1985) was educated in Europe and taught at Stanford University. In his book *How to Solve It,* Polya outlines four steps in problem solving. We will use Polya's four steps as guidelines for problem solving.

RELEVANT INFORMATION

A pack of 50 CDs costs $38.

A pack of 25 CDs costs $20.

Only complete packs of CDs can be purchased.

The next step is to determine the answer to the question. That is, we need to determine the maximum number of CDs that can be purchased for $250 or less.

We now need a plan for solving the problem. One method is to set up a table or chart to compare costs of different combinations of packs of CDs. Start by using the maximum number of packs of 50 CDs. Then reduce the number of packs of 50 CDs and add more packs of 25 CDs. In each case, we need to keep the cost at $250 or less.

Because 1 pack of 50 CDs costs $38, we can determine the number of packs of 50 CDs that can be purchased by dividing 250 by 38. Because the quotient is about 6.58 and because only whole packs of CDs may be purchased, only 6 packs of 50 CDs may be purchased. Six packs would cost $6 \times 38 = \$228$. The remaining $22 from the $250 could be used to purchase packs of 25 CDs. Because each pack of 25 CDs costs $20, only 1 pack of 25 CDs could be purchased. Thus, for $250 or less, one option is 6 packs of 50 CDs and 1 pack of 25 CDs. This option is indicated in the first row of the table below. Also given in the table is the cost of this option, which is $248. We complete the other rows of the table in a similar manner.

Packs of 50 and Packs of 25 CDs	Number of CDs	Cost
6 packs of 50 and 1 pack of 25	$(6 \times 50) + (1 \times 25) = 325$	$248
5 packs of 50 and 3 packs of 25	$(5 \times 50) + (3 \times 25) = 325$	$250
4 packs of 50 and 4 packs of 25	$(4 \times 50) + (4 \times 25) = 300$	$232
3 packs of 50 and 6 packs of 25	$(3 \times 50) + (6 \times 25) = 300$	$234
2 packs of 50 and 8 packs of 25	$(2 \times 50) + (8 \times 25) = 300$	$236
1 pack of 50 and 10 packs of 25	$(1 \times 50) + (10 \times 25) = 300$	$238
0 packs of 50 and 12 packs of 25	$(0 \times 50) + (12 \times 25) = 300$	$240

The question asks us to find the maximum number of CDs that can be purchased for $250 or less. From the second column of the table, we see that the answer is 325 CDs. This result can be done in two different ways: either 6 packs of 50 and 1 pack of 25 or 5 packs of 50 and 3 packs of 25.

b) When comparing the two possibilities for purchasing the 325 CDs discussed in part (a), we see that the most economical way to purchase the CDs is to purchase 6 packs of 50 CDs and 1 pack of 25 CDs. The cost is $248.

Following is a general procedure for problem solving as given by George Polya. Note that Example 1 demonstrates many of these guidelines.

GUIDELINES FOR PROBLEM SOLVING

1. *Understand the problem.*
   • Read the problem *carefully* at least twice. In the first reading, get a general overview of the problem. In the second reading, determine (a) exactly what you are being asked to find and (b) what information the problem provides.
   • Try to make a sketch to illustrate the problem. Label the information given.
   • Make a list of the given facts that are pertinent to the problem.
   • Determine if the information you are given is sufficient to solve the problem.

2. *Devise a plan to solve the problem.*
   • Have you seen the problem or a similar problem before? Are the procedures you used to solve the similar problem applicable to the new problem?

Scientists are using problem-solving techniques and modern technology to unlock ancient secrets. In May 2005, scientists at the Stanford Linear Accelerator Center used x-rays to decipher pages of the only known copy of a 2300-year-old Greek text by the mathematician Archimedes. Scholars believe that the 174-page treatise, *On Floating Bodies*, was copied by a scribe in the 10th century from Archimedes' original Greek scrolls, written in the 3rd century B.C. The treatise was erased 200 years later by a monk who reused the parchment for a prayer book, creating a twice-used parchment.

To reveal much of the hidden text, the scientists used digital cameras and processing techniques as well as ultraviolet and infrared filters developed for medicine and space research. Through the use of x-rays, scientists are now able to read the remaining pages of the treatise. The team, consisting of researchers from R. B. Toth Associates, Rochester Institute of Technology, Johns Hopkins University, Rutgers University, and ConocoPhillips, plan to create an interactive DVD once they've deciphered the entire text. The text and diagrams contain the roots of modern calculus and gravitational theory.

- Can you express the problem in terms of an algebraic equation?
- Look for patterns or relationships in the problem that may help in solving it.
- Can you express the problem more simply?
- Can you substitute smaller or simpler numbers to make the problem more understandable?
- Will listing the information in a table help in solving the problem?
- Can you make an educated guess at the solution? Sometimes if you know an approximate solution, you can work backward and eventually determine the correct procedure to solve the problem.

3. *Carry out the plan.*
   Use the plan you devised in step 2 to solve the problem.

4. *Check the results.*
   - Ask yourself, "Does the answer make sense?" and "Is the answer reasonable?" If the answer is not reasonable, recheck your method for solving the problem and your calculations.
   - Can you check the solution using the original statement?
   - Is there an alternative method to arrive at the same conclusion?
   - Can the results of this problem be used to solve other problems?

The following examples show how to apply the guidelines for problem solving.

EXAMPLE 2   HOTEL COST

At the Courtyard by Marriot Hotel in Irving, Texas (near the Dallas/Fort Worth airport), the room rate is $159 per day on weekdays and $89 per day on weekends (Saturday and Sunday). In addition, a 13% sales tax is added to the cost of a room. In-room movies cost $10.95 plus the 13% sales tax. Robin Ayers stays on the third floor of the Courtyard for four nights (Wednesday, Thursday, Friday, and Saturday) and watches three movies. Determine her hotel bill when she checks out.

SOLUTION   We need to find the total cost of the hotel bill. Let's make a list of the information given and mark with an asterisk (*) the information that is pertinent to solving the problem.

*Cost of room per day on Wednesday, Thursday, and Friday = $159 + sales tax

*Cost of room on Saturday = $89 + sales tax

*Days at hotel: one Wednesday, one Thursday, one Friday, one Saturday

*Sales tax is 13%

*Cost per movie = $10.95 + sales tax

*Movies watched: 3

Room on third floor

All the information is needed to solve the problem except for the floor on which Robin stayed.

Let's first determine the cost of the room, before tax, for the four days.

Day	Cost (before tax)
Wednesday	$159
Thursday	$159
Friday	$159
Saturday	$89
	$566

The cost of three movies before tax is $3 \times \$10.95 = \$32.85$. Thus, the total amount of the bill before tax is $\$566 + \$32.85 = \$598.85$. Let's determine the sales tax to be added. We could find the sales tax for each individual item and add it to the items separately. Be-

cause the same tax rate applies to each item, however, it is easier to just determine 13% of the total amount.

$$\text{Sales tax} = 13\% \text{ of } \$598.85$$
$$= 0.13(598.85) = \$77.85$$

The total hotel bill is determined by adding the tax to the pretax amount. Thus, the total hotel bill is $598.85 + $77.85 = $676.70.

In Example 2, the total cost could have been determined in other ways. We presented the method we believe you would understand best.

EXAMPLE 3   RETIREMENT

It is never too early to start planning for retirement. U.S. Census Bureau data indicate that at age 65 the average woman will live another 19.8 years and the average man will live another 16.8 years. The data also indicate that about 39% of the average person's retirement income will come from Social Security.

When discussing retirement planning, many investment firms and financial planners use the graph in Fig. 1.1,* which shows how long a typical retiree's assets (or "nest egg") will last based on the percentage of the assets withdrawn each year.

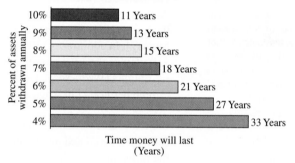

**How Much You Withdraw Annually Affects
How Long Your Money Will Last**

Percent of assets withdrawn annually

10%	11 Years
9%	13 Years
8%	15 Years
7%	18 Years
6%	21 Years
5%	27 Years
4%	33 Years

Time money will last
(Years)

Source: Ned Davis Research

FIGURE 1.1

a) If a typical retiree has retirement assets of $500,000, how much can he or she withdraw annually if he or she wishes the assets to last 21 years?

b) How much should a retiree have in assets if he or she wishes to withdraw $25,000 annually and wishes his or her assets to last 18 years?

SOLUTION

a) Quite a bit of information is provided in the example. We will first need to determine what information is needed to answer the question. To answer the question, we only need to use the information provided in the graph. From the graph, we can see that for assets to last 21 years, about 6% of the assets can be withdrawn annually. The amount that can be withdrawn annually is found as follows.

$$\text{Amount} = 6\% \text{ of assets}$$
$$\text{Amount} = 0.06 (500,000) = 30,000$$

Thus, about $30,000 can be withdrawn annually.

b) Again, to solve this part of the example, we only need the information provided in the graph. From the graph, we can determine that if a retiree wishes for his or her assets to

*The information in this graph is based on past performance of the stock market, with 50% invested in large company stocks and 50% invested in intermediate-term bonds. Past performance is not indicative of future results.

last 18 years, then 7% of the assets can be withdrawn annually. We need to determine the total assets such that 7% of the total assets is $25,000.

$$7\% \text{ of assets} = \$25,000 \quad \text{or} \quad 0.07 \times \text{assets} = \$25,000$$

Because 0.07 is multiplied by the assets to obtain $25,000, we can determine the assets by dividing the $25,000 by 0.07 as follows.

$$\text{Assets} = \frac{25,000}{0.07} = 357,142.85$$

Therefore, if the retiree has assets of about $357,142.85, he or she will be able to withdraw $25,000 annually and the assets will last 18 years.

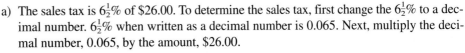

EXAMPLE 4   DETERMINING A TIP

The cost of Sarah Decker's meal before tax is $26.00.

a) If a $6\frac{1}{2}\%$ sales tax is added to her bill, determine the total cost of the meal including tax.

b) If Sarah wants to leave a 10% tip on the *pretax* cost of the meal, how much should she leave?

c) If she wants to leave a 15% tip on the *pretax* cost of the meal, how much should she leave?

SOLUTION

a) The sales tax is $6\frac{1}{2}\%$ of $26.00. To determine the sales tax, first change the $6\frac{1}{2}\%$ to a decimal number. $6\frac{1}{2}\%$ when written as a decimal number is 0.065. Next, multiply the decimal number, 0.065, by the amount, $26.00.

$$\text{Sales tax} = 6\tfrac{1}{2}\% \text{ of } 26.00$$
$$= 0.065(26.00) = 1.69$$

The sales tax is $1.69. The total bill is the cost of the meal plus the sales tax.

$$\text{Total bill} = \text{cost of meal} + \text{sales tax}$$
$$= 26.00 + 1.69 = 27.69$$

Thus, the bill, including sales tax, is $27.69.

b) To find 10% of any number, we can multiply the number by 0.10.

$$10\% \text{ of pretax cost} = 0.10(26.00)$$
$$= 2.60$$

A simple way to find 10% of any number is to simply move the decimal point in the number one place to the left. Moving the decimal point in $26.00 one place to the left gives $2.60, the same answer we obtained by our calculations.

c) To find 15% of $26.00, multiply as follows.

$$15\% \text{ of } 26.00 = 0.15(26.00) = 3.90$$

Thus, 15% of $26.00 is $3.90. A second method to find a 15% tip is to find 10% of the cost, as in part (b), then add to it half that amount. Following this procedure, we get

$$\$2.60 + \frac{\$2.60}{2} = \$2.60 + \$1.30 = \$3.90$$

In most cases, tips are rounded. If the service is excellent, some people leave a 20% tip. Can you give two methods to determine a 20% tip on $26.00? Determine the 20% tip now.

EXAMPLE 5   A RECIPE FOR 6

The chart below shows the amount of each ingredient recommended to make 2, 4, and 8 servings of Potato Buds. Determine the amount of each ingredient necessary to make 6 servings of Potato Buds by using the following procedures.

a) Multiply the amount for 2 servings by 3.

b) Add the amounts for 2 servings to the amounts for 4 servings.

c) Find the average of the amounts for 4 servings and for 8 servings.

d) Subtract the amounts for 2 servings from the amounts for 8 servings.

e) Compare the answers for parts (a) through (d). Are they the same? If not, explain why not.

f) Which is the correct procedure for obtaining 6 servings?

Servings	2	4	8
Water	$\frac{2}{3}$ cup	$1\frac{1}{3}$ cups	$2\frac{2}{3}$ cups
Milk	2 tbsp	$\frac{1}{3}$ cup	$\frac{2}{3}$ cup
Butter or margarine	1 tbsp	2 tbsp	4 tbsp
Salt*	$\frac{1}{4}$ tsp	$\frac{1}{2}$ tsp	1 tsp
Potato Buds	$\frac{2}{3}$ cup	$1\frac{1}{3}$ cups	$2\frac{2}{3}$ cups

*Less salt can be used if desired.

SOLUTION

a) We multiply the amounts for 2 servings by 3.

Water: $3\left(\frac{2}{3}\right) = 2$ cups

Milk: $3(2) = 6$ tablespoons (tbsp)

Butter or margarine: $3(1) = 3$ tbsp

Salt: $3\left(\frac{1}{4}\right) = \frac{3}{4}$ teaspoon (tsp)

Potato Buds: $3\left(\frac{2}{3}\right) = 2$ cups

b) We find the amount of each ingredient by adding the amount for 2 and 4 servings.

Water: $\frac{2}{3}$ cup $+ 1\frac{1}{3}$ cup $= 2$ cups

Milk: 2 tbsp $+ \frac{1}{3}$ cup

To add these two amounts, we must convert one of them so that both ingredients have the same units. By looking in a cookbook or a book of conversion factors, we see that 16 tbsp = 1 cup. The milk in part (a) was given in tablespoons, so we convert $\frac{1}{3}$ cup to tablespoons to compare answers. One-third cup equals $\frac{1}{3}(16) = \frac{16}{3}$ or $5\frac{1}{3}$ tbsp. Therefore,

Milk: 2 tbsp $+ 5\frac{1}{3}$ tbsp $= 7\frac{1}{3}$ tbsp

Let's continue with the rest of the ingredients:

Butter: 1 tbsp $+ 2$ tbsp $= 3$ tbsp

Salt: $\frac{1}{4}$ tsp $+ \frac{1}{2}$ tsp $= \frac{3}{4}$ tsp

Potato Buds: $\frac{2}{3}$ cup $+ 1\frac{1}{3}$ cups $= 2$ cups

c) We compute the amounts of the ingredients by finding the average of the amounts for 4 and 8 servings. We do so by adding the amounts for each ingredient and dividing the sum by 2.

Water: $\dfrac{1\frac{1}{3} \text{ cups} + 2\frac{2}{3} \text{ cups}}{2} = \dfrac{4 \text{ cups}}{2} = 2$ cups

Milk: $\dfrac{\frac{1}{3} \text{ cup} + \frac{2}{3} \text{ cup}}{2} = \dfrac{1 \text{ cup}}{2} = \frac{1}{2}$ cup (or 8 tbsp)

Butter: $\dfrac{2 \text{ tbsp} + 4 \text{ tbsp}}{2} = \dfrac{6 \text{ tbsp}}{2} = 3$ tbsp

Salt: $\dfrac{\frac{1}{2}\text{ tsp} + 1\text{ tsp}}{2} = \dfrac{\frac{3}{2}\text{ tsp}}{2} = \frac{3}{4}\text{ tsp}$

Potato Buds: $\dfrac{1\frac{1}{3}\text{ cups} + 2\frac{2}{3}\text{ cups}}{2} = \dfrac{4\text{ cups}}{2} = 2\text{ cups}$

d) We obtain the amounts of ingredients by subtracting the amounts for 2 servings from the amounts for 8 servings.

Water: $2\frac{2}{3}\text{ cups} - \frac{2}{3}\text{ cup} = 2\text{ cups}$

Milk: $\frac{2}{3}\text{ cup} - 2\text{ tbsp} = \frac{2}{3}(16)\text{ tbsp} - 2\text{ tbsp}$
$= \frac{32}{3}\text{ tbsp} - \frac{6}{3}\text{ tbsp}$
$= \frac{26}{3}\text{ tbsp, or } 8\frac{2}{3}\text{ tbsp}$

Butter: $4\text{ tbsp} - 1\text{ tbsp} = 3\text{ tbsp}$

Salt: $1\text{ tsp} - \frac{1}{4}\text{ tsp} = \frac{3}{4}\text{ tsp}$

Potato Buds: $2\frac{2}{3}\text{ cups} - \frac{2}{3}\text{ cup} = 2\text{ cups}$

e) Comparing the answers in parts (a) through (d), we find that the amounts of all ingredients, except milk, are the same. For milk, we get the following results.

Part (a): Milk = 6 tbsp   Part (c): Milk = 8 tbsp

Part (b): Milk = $7\frac{1}{3}$ tbsp   Part (d): Milk = $8\frac{2}{3}$ tbsp

Why are all these answers different? After rechecking, we find that all our calculations are correct, so we must look deeper. Note that milk is the only ingredient that has different units for 2 servings and 4 servings. Let's check the relationship between 2 tbsp and $\frac{1}{3}$ cup. In going from 2 servings to 4 servings, we would expect that $\frac{1}{3}$ cup should be twice 2 tbsp. We know that 1 cup = 16 tbsp, so

$$\tfrac{1}{3}\text{ cup} = \tfrac{1}{3}(16) = \tfrac{16}{3} = 5\tfrac{1}{3}\text{ tbsp}$$

Therefore, instead of the 4 tbsp of milk we expected for 4 servings, we get $5\frac{1}{3}$ tbsp. This change causes all our calculations for milk to be different.

f) Which is the correct answer? Because all our calculations for milk are correct, there is no single correct answer. All our answers are correct. Using 8 tbsp instead of $5\frac{1}{3}$ tbsp might make the Potato Buds a little thinner. When we cook, we generally do not add the *exact* amount recommended. We rely on experience to alter the recommended amounts according to individual taste.

Many real-life problems, such as the one in Example 6, can be solved by using proportions. A proportion is a statement of equality between two ratios (or fractions).

EXAMPLE 6   SPRAYING WEED KILLER

The instructions on the Ortho Weed-B-Gon lawn weed killer indicate that to cover 1000 square feet (ft²) of lawn, 20 teaspoons (tsp) of the weed killer should be mixed in 5 gallons (gal) of water. Ron Haines wishes to spray his lawn with the weed killer using his pressurized sprayer.

a) How much weed killer should be mixed with 8 gal of water to get a solution of the proper strength?

b) How much weed killer is needed to cover an area of 2820 ft² of lawn?

SOLUTION

a) Use the information that 20 teaspoons of weed killer is to be mixed with 5 gal of water.

Given ratio $\left\{ \dfrac{20\text{ tsp}}{5\text{ gal water}} = \dfrac{?\text{ tsp}}{8\text{ gal}} \right.$ ← Item to be found
← Other information given

TECHNOLOGY

EAST MEETS WEST:
MAGIC SQUARES

A Chinese myth says that in about 2200 B.C., a divine tortoise emerged from the Yellow River. On his back was a special diagram of numbers from which all mathematics was derived. The Chinese called this diagram Lo Shu. The Lo Shu diagram is the first known magic square.

Arab traders brought the Chinese magic square to Europe during the Middle Ages, when the plague was killing millions of people. Magic squares were considered strong talismans against evil, and possession of a magic square was thought to ensure health and wealth.

Notice in the proportion that teaspoons and gallons are placed in the same relative positions. Often, the unknown quantity is replaced with an x. The proportion may be written as follows and solved using cross multiplication.

$$\frac{20}{5} = \frac{x}{8}$$
$$20(8) = 5x$$
$$160 = 5x$$
$$\frac{160}{5} = \frac{5x}{5} \qquad \text{Divide both sides of the equation by 5 to solve for x.}$$
$$32 = x$$

Thus, Ron must mix 32 tsp [or $10\frac{2}{3}$ tablespoons (tbsp) or $\frac{2}{3}$ cup] of the weed killer with 8 gal of water. This answer seems reasonable because we would expect to get an answer greater than 20 tsp.

b) To answer this question, we use the same procedure discussed in part (a). This time, we will use the information that 1000 ft^2 requires 20 tsp of weed killer. The areas may be placed either on the top or the bottom of the fraction, as long as they are placed in the same relative position.

$$\text{Given ratio} \left\{ \frac{1000 \text{ sq ft}}{20 \text{ tsp}} = \frac{2820 \text{ sq ft}}{? \text{ tsp}} \begin{array}{l} \leftarrow \text{Other information given} \\ \leftarrow \text{Item to be found} \end{array} \right.$$

Now replace the question mark with an x and solve the proportion.

$$\frac{1000}{20} = \frac{2820}{x}$$
$$1000(x) = 20(2820)$$
$$1000x = 56{,}400$$
$$\frac{1000x}{1000} = \frac{56{,}400}{1000} \qquad \text{Divide both sides of the equation by 1000 to solve for x.}$$
$$x = 56.4$$

Thus, about 56.4 tsp are needed. This answer is reasonable because we would expect the answer to be more than twice the 20 tsp required for 1000 ft^2.

Most of the problems solved so far have been practical ones. Many people, however, enjoy solving brainteasers. One example of such a puzzle follows.

EXAMPLE 7   MAGIC SQUARES

A magic square is a square array of numbers such that the numbers in all rows, columns, and diagonals have the same sum. Use the digits 1, 2, 3, 4, 5, 6, 7, 8, and 9 to construct a magic square.

SOLUTION   The first step is to create a figure with nine cells as in Fig. 1.2(a). We must place the nine numbers in the cells so that the same sum is obtained in each row, column, and diagonal. Common sense tells us that 7, 8, and 9 cannot be in the same row, column, or diagonal. We need some small and large numbers in the same row, column, and diagonal. To see a relationship, we list the numbers in order:

1, 2, 3, 4, 5, 6, 7, 8, 9

Note that the middle number is 5 and the smallest and largest numbers are 1 and 9, respectively. The sum of 1, 5, and 9 is 15. If the sum of 2 and 8 is added to 5, the sum is 15. Likewise 3, 5, 7, and 4, 5, 6 have sums of 15. We see that in each group of three numbers the sum is 15 and 5 is a member of the group.

FIGURE 1.2

Because 5 is the middle number in the list of numbers, place 5 in the center square. Place 9 and 1 to the left and right of 5 as in Fig. 1.2(a). Now we place the 2 and the 8. The 8 cannot be placed next to 9 because $8 + 9 = 17$, which is greater than 15. Place the smaller number 2 next to the larger number 9. We elected to place the 2 in the lower left-hand cell and the 8 in the upper right-hand cell as in Fig. 1.2(b). The sum of 8 and 1 is 9. To arrive at a sum of 15, we place 6 in the lower right-hand cell as in Fig. 1.2(c). The sum of 9 and 2 is 11. To arrive at a sum of 15, we place 4 in the upper left-hand cell as in Fig. 1.2(c). Now the diagonals 2, 5, 8 and 4, 5, 6 have sums of 15. The numbers that remain to be placed in the empty cells are 3 and 7. Using arithmetic, we can see that 3 goes in the top middle cell and 7 goes in the bottom middle cell as in Fig. 1.2(d). A check shows that the sum in all the rows, columns, and diagonals is 15.

The solution to Example 7 is not unique. Other arrangements of the nine numbers in the cells will produce a magic square. Also, other techniques of arriving at a solution for a magic square may be used. In fact, the process described will not work if the number of squares is even, for example, 16 instead of 9. Magic squares are not limited to the operation of addition or to the set of counting numbers.

EXERCISE SET 1.3 ●●●●●●

• Practice the Skills/Problem Solving

1. *Reading a Map* The scale on a map is 1 inch = 18 miles. How long a distance is a route on the map if it measures 4.25 in.?

2. *Blueprints* Chalon Bridges, an architect, is designing a shopping mall. The scale of her plan is 1 in. = 12 ft. If one store in the mall is to have a frontage of 82 ft, how long will the line representing that store's frontage be on the blueprint?

3. *Height of a Tree* At a given time of day, the ratio of the height of an object to the length of its shadow is the same for all objects. If a 3-ft stick in the ground casts a shadow of 1.2 ft, find the length of the shadow of a 48.4 ft tree. See the diagram at right.

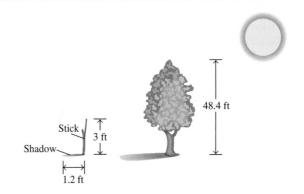

4. *Use of Fertilizer* A bag of fertilizer covers 6000 ft². How many bags are needed to cover an area of 32,000 ft²?

5. *College Tuition Cost* According to the College Board, the average tuition at a private four-year college increased by 5.7% from 2004 to 2005. The average tuition at a private four-year college in 2004 was $27,461. Determine the average tuition at a private four-year college in 2005. Round your answer to the nearest dollar.

6. *Fishing Charter* Sam Stevens and four other friends want to schedule a 6-hour fishing trip on Lake Ontario with Reel Easy Sport Fishing. The cost for five people is $445. The cost for six people is $510. How much money per person will Sam and each of his friends save if they can find one more friend to go on their fishing trip? Assume that they will split the total cost equally.

7. *Housing Market* The following table shows where U.S. house prices have increased the most and the least, on average, for the 5-year period 2000–2005. The table also shows the increase from 2004–2005 for those areas.

   a) If a house in Nevada cost $150,000 in 2004, how much did a similar house cost in 2005?

   b) From 2004 to 2005, how much more did a $200,000 house in California increase in price than a $200,000 house in New Hampshire?

   c) If a house in Tennessee cost $180,000 in 2000, how much did a similar house cost in 2005?

Where house prices have gone up most		
	% change 2000–2005	% change 2004–2005
District of Columbia	108.1%	22.2%
California	103.0%	25.4%
Rhode Island	97.6%	17.1%
Nevada	84.7%	31.2%
Hawaii	82.9%	24.4%
Florida	80.5%	21.4%
Maryland	77.9%	21.0%
New Jersey	76.5%	15.8%
New Hampshire	72.3%	12.1%
Massachusetts	71.8%	11.6%
U.S.	**50.5%**	**12.5%**

Where prices have lagged		
Utah	17.5%	6.3%
Indiana	19.9%	4.1%
Nebraska	21.8%	5.4%
Mississippi	21.8%	4.9%
Tennessee	22.4%	5.5%

Source: Office of Federal Housing Enterprise Oversight

8. *Who Receives Social Security?* The circle graph below shows that Social Security benefits are not just for retirees. In 2005, about 48 million Americans received Social Security benefits. Use the circle graph below to answer the following questions.

   a) How many more retirees than disabled workers received Social Security benefits?

   b) How many fewer spouses and children of retired and disabled workers than survivors of deceased workers received Social Security benefits?

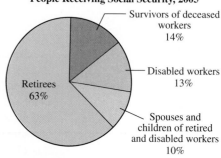

People Receiving Social Security, 2005

Survivors of deceased workers 14%

Disabled workers 13%

Retirees 63%

Spouses and children of retired and disabled workers 10%

Source: Social Security Administration

9. *Parking Costs* The Main Street Garage charges $2.50 for the first hour of parking and $1.00 for each additional hour or part thereof. Denise Tomey parks her car in the garage from 9 A.M. to 5 P.M., 5 days a week. How much money does she save by paying a weekly parking rate of $35.00?

10. *School Pictures* Luann Alexander has two packages from which to choose to purchase her son's school picture. Package 1 costs $27 and includes 23 pictures. Package 2 costs $17 and includes 10 pictures. If the pictures are all the same size, which package offers the better price per picture?

11. *Buying a Computer* Emily Putnam wants to purchase a computer that sells for $1250. She can either pay the total amount at the time of purchase or she can agree to pay the store $120 down and $80 a month for 15 months. How much money can she save by paying the total amount at the time of purchase?

12. *Flu Shots* The price of a flu shot at Maxim Health Systems increased by 25% from 2005 to 2006. In 2005, Maxim Health Systems charged $20 for a flu shot. If Maxim Health sold flu shots to 2 million people in 2005 and to 2 million people in 2006, how much more money did they earn from selling flu shots in 2006 than in 2005?

13. *Buying a House* The Browns want to purchase a house that costs $140,000. They plan to take out a $100,000 mortgage on the house and put $40,000 as a down payment. The bank informs them that with a 15-year mortgage their monthly payment would be $840.62 and with a 30-year mortgage their monthly payment would be $620.28. Determine the amount they would save on the cost of the house if they selected the 15-year mortgage rather than the 30-year mortgage.

14. *Getting an 80 Average* On four exams, Wallace Memmer's grades were 79, 93, 91, and 68. What grade must he obtain on his fifth exam to have an 80 average?

15. *Japanese Sizes* The following chart shows men's jacket sizes as would be given in the United States and in Japan.

    a) Justin Smith is in Japan and finds a sports jacket he wishes to buy. He is a size 48 in the United States. Determine the size of the jacket he should try on.

    b) Determine a procedure (or a formula) for converting a jacket from a U.S. size to a size in Japan.

U.S. chest	34	36	38	40	42	44	46	48
Japan	86.5	91.5	96.5	101.5	106.5	112	117	?

16. *Playing a Lottery* In one state lottery game, you must select a four-digit number (digits may be repeated). If your number matches exactly the four-digit number selected by the lottery commission, you win.

    a) How many different numbers may be chosen?

    b) If you purchase one lottery ticket, what is your chance of winning?

17. *Energy Value and Energy Consumption* The table gives the approximate energy values of some foods, in kilojoules (kJ) and the energy requirements of some activities.

    a) How soon would you use up the energy from a fried egg by swimming?

    b) How soon would you use up the energy from a hamburger by walking?

    c) How soon would you use up the energy from a piece of strawberry shortcake by cycling?

    d) How soon would you use up the energy from a hamburger and a chocolate milkshake by running?

Food	Energy Value (kJ)	Activity	Energy Consumption (kJ/min)
Chocolate milkshake	2200	Walking	25
Fried egg	460	Cycling	35
Hamburger	1550	Swimming	50
Strawberry shortcake	1400	Running	80
Glass of skim milk	350		

18. *Gas Mileage* Wendy Weisner fills her gas tank completely and makes a note that the odometer reads 38,451.4 miles. The next time she put gas in her car, filling the tank took 12.6 gal and the odometer read 38,687.0 miles. Determine the number of miles per gallon that Wendy's car got on this tank of gas.

19. *Household Credit Debt* The following graph shows the U.S. household credit debt, not including mortgages, from 1980 to 2005. Total debt includes revolving debt (the red area of the graph), such as credit card debt, and nonrevolving debt (the green area of the graph), such as auto and other installment loans.

    a) Use the green area of the graph to estimate the U.S. household nonrevolving debt in 2005.

    b) In 2005, there were 108,819,000 U.S. households. Estimate the average household total credit debt in 2005.

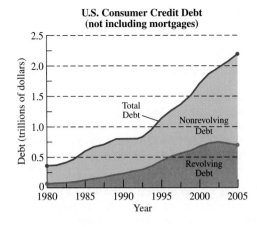

20. *Saving for a Stereo* Fernando Diez works 40 hours per week and makes $8.50 per hour.

    a) How much money can he expect to earn in 1 year (52 weeks)?

    b) If he saves all the money he earns, how long will he have to work to save for a stereo receiver that costs $1275?

21. *Mail-Order Purchase* Mary Liotta purchased 4 tires by mail order. She paid $52.80 per tire plus $5.60 per tire for shipping and handling. There is no sales tax on this purchase because the tires were purchased out of state. She also had to pay $8.56 per tire for mounting and balancing. At a local tire store, her total for the 4 tires with mounting and balancing would be $324 plus an 8% sales tax. How much did Mary save by purchasing the tires through the mail?

22. *Sealing a Gym Floor* A gymnasium floor has an area of 2400 square yards. Each gallon of floor sealant covers an area of 350 square feet. How many gallons of sealant are needed to cover the gymnasium floor?

23. *Profit Margins* The following chart shows retail stores' average percent profit margin on certain items.

Product Category	Average Profit Margin (%)
Video equipment	12
Audio components	14
Stereo speakers	20–25
Extended warranties	50–60

Source: *Consumer Reports*

    a) Determine the average profit of a store that has the list price on a camcorder of $620.

    b) Determine the average profit of a store that has a list price on a pair of speakers for $1200 (use a 22% profit margin).

    c) If you negotiate with the salesperson and get him or her to sell the speakers for $1000, find the store's profit (use a 22% profit margin).

24. *Income Taxes* The federal income tax rate schedule for a joint return in 2006 is illustrated in the table on the next page.

If Steve and Maureen Tomlin paid $13,365 in federal taxes, find the family's adjusted gross income.

Adjusted Gross Income	Taxes
$0–$15,100	10% of income
$15,100–$61,300	$1510 + 15% of amount over $15,100
$61,300–$123,700	$8440 + 25% of amount over $61,300
$123,700–$188,450	$24,040 + 28% of amount over $123,700
$188,450–$336,550	$42,170 + 33% of amount over $188,450
$336,550 and above	$91,043 + 35% of amount over $336,550

25. *Leaking Faucet* A faucet is leaking at a rate of one drop of water per second. Assume that the volume of one drop of water is 0.1 cubic centimeter (0.1 cm^3).

 a) Determine the volume of water in cubic centimeters lost in 1 year.

 b) How many days would it take to fill a rectangular basin 30 cm by 20 cm by 20 cm?

26. *Wasted Water* A faucet leaks 1 oz of water per minute.

 a) How many gallons of water are wasted in a year? (A gallon contains 128 oz.)

 b) If water costs $11.20 per 1000 gal, how much additional money is being spent on the water bill?

27. *Airport Parking* The chart shows parking rates at John F. Kennedy (JFK) Airport in New York, NY, as of August 1, 2006.

JFK Airport Parking Rates

SHORT-TERM RATES			
First half hour	$\frac{1}{2}$ hour–1 hour	Each Additional Hour After the First	Daily Maximum
$3	$6	$3	$30

LONG-TERM RATES	
Daily	Additional Day 0–8 Hours
$15	$5

 a) Jeff Grace is going out of town for 5 full days. How much will he save by parking in the long-term lot rather than the short-term lot?

 b) What is the cost of parking in the short-term lot for 4 hours?

 c) If Jeff plans to park at the airport for 5 hours, is it cheaper to park in short-term or long-term parking? How much is the difference?

28. *Tire Pressure* When a car's tire pressure is 30 pounds per square inch (psi), it averages 20.8 mpg of gasoline. If the tire pressure is increased to 35 psi, the car averages 21.6 mpg of gasoline.

 a) If Mr. Levy drives an average of 20,000 mi per year, how many gallons of gasoline will he save in a year by increasing his tire pressure from 30 to 35 psi?

 b) If gasoline costs $3.00 per gallon, how much will he save in a year?

 c) If we assume that there are about 140 million cars in the United States and that these changes are typical of each car, how many gallons of gasoline would be saved if all drivers increased their cars' tire pressure?

29. *Air Pollution* The table illustrates the 10 countries that produced the most carbon dioxide emissions in 2004. The table also illustrates the emissions per capita for each country listed. (The term *per capita* means per person.)

Producers of Carbon Dioxide

	Total Emissions (in millions of metric tons)	Emissions per Capita (in metric tons)
United States	5912.2	19.8
China	4707.3	3.6
Russia	1684.8	11.9
Japan	1262.1	9.9
India	1112.8	1.0
Germany	862.2	10.5
Canada	588.0	17.8
United Kingdom	579.7	9.6
South Korea	496.8	10.2
Italy	485.0	8.3

Source: U.S. Department of Energy

 a) By looking at the data provided, is it possible to determine the population of each country? If so, explain how to do so.

 b) Using the procedure you gave in part (a), determine the population of the United States.

 c) Using the procedure you gave in part (a), determine the population of China.

30. *Adjusting for Inflation* Assume that the rate of inflation is 6% per year for the next 2 years. What will the price of a dishwasher be 2 years from now if the dishwasher costs $799 today?

31. *Investing* You place $1000 in a mutual fund. The first year, the value of the fund increases by 10%. The second year, the value of the fund decreases by 10%. Determine the value of the fund at the end of the second year. Is it greater than, less than, or equal to your initial investment?

32. *X-rays* With a certain medical insurance policy, the customer must first pay an annual $100 deductible, then the policy covers 80% of the cost of x-rays. The first insurance claims for a specific year submitted by Yungchen Cheng are for two x-rays. The first x-ray cost $640, and the second x-ray cost $920. How much, in total, will Yungchen need to pay for these x-rays?

33. *A Photo Safari* Kelli Hammer is planning a trip to Africa where she will participate in a photo safari. She is planning to bring a great deal of film. A photography store is selling 4 packs of film for $17 and 10 packs of the same film for $41.

a) If she wishes to purchase only the 4 packs and 10 packs and wishes to spend a maximum of $200 on film, what is the maximum number of rolls of film she can purchase?

b) What will be the cost of the film?

34. ***Buying Film*** Erika Gutierrez is planning a vacation to Australia and wishes to bring a large supply of film. At Wal-Mart, 4 packs of 24-exposure film costs $4.08 and 4 packs of the same film with 36 exposures costs $5.76.

a) If she wishes to spend a maximum of $50 on film and get the most exposures, how many 4 packs of 24 exposures and how many 4 packs of 36 exposures should she purchase?

b) How many exposures will she get?

c) What will be the cost of the film? If there is more than one choice in part (a), give the minimum cost.

35. ***Making Cream of Wheat*** The following amounts of ingredients are recommended to make various servings of Nabisco Instant Cream of Wheat. *Note:* 16 tbsp = 1 cup.

Ingredient	1 Serving	2 Servings	4 Servings
Mix water or milk	1 cup	2 cups	$3\frac{3}{4}$ cups
With salt (optional)	$\frac{1}{8}$ tsp	$\frac{1}{4}$ tsp	$\frac{1}{2}$ tsp
Add Cream of Wheat	3 tbsp	$\frac{1}{2}$ cup	$\frac{3}{4}$ cup

Determine the amount of each ingredient needed to make 3 servings using the following procedures.

a) Multiply the amounts for 1 serving by 3.

b) Find the average of the amounts for 2 and 4 servings.

c) Subtract the amounts for 1 serving from the amounts for 4 servings.

d) Compare the answers obtained in parts (a) through (c) and explain any differences.

36. ***Making Rice*** Following are the amounts of ingredients recommended to make various servings of Uncle Ben's Original Converted Rice. *Note:* 1 tbsp = 3 tsp.

Ingredient	2 Servings	4 Servings	6 Servings	12 Servings
Rice (cups)	$\frac{1}{2}$	1	$1\frac{1}{2}$	3
Water (cups)	$1\frac{1}{3}$	$2\frac{1}{4}$	$3\frac{1}{3}$	6
Salt (teaspoons)	$\frac{1}{4}$	$\frac{1}{2}$	$\frac{3}{4}$	$1\frac{1}{2}$
Butter	1 tsp	2 tsp	1 tbsp	2 tbsp

Determine the amount of each ingredient needed to make 8 servings using the following procedures.

a) Multiply the amount for 2 servings by 4.

b) Multiply the amount for 4 servings by 2.

c) Add the amounts for 2 and 6 servings.

d) Subtract the amount for 4 servings from the amount for 12 servings.

e) Compare the answers obtained in parts (a) through (d) and explain any differences.

Solve the following problems.

37. ***One Square Foot*** How many square inches, 1 in. by 1 in., fit in an area of 1 square foot, 1 ft by 1 ft?

38. ***Cubic Inches*** How many cubic inches fit in 1 cubic foot?

39. ***Rectangle*** If the length and width of a rectangle each double, what happens to the area of the rectangle?

40. ***Cube*** If the length, width, and height of a cube all double, what happens to the volume of the cube?

41. ***Pole in a Lake*** A pole is in the middle of a small lake. One half of the pole is in the ground. One third of the pole is covered by water. Eleven feet, or one-sixth, of the pole are out of water. What is the length of the pole?

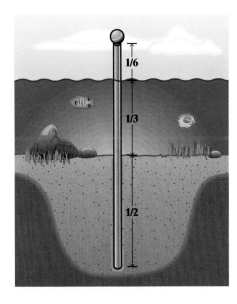

42. ***Buying Candy*** How much do 10 pieces of candy cost if 1000 pieces cost $10?

43. *A Balance* On the balance below, where should the one missing block ■ be placed so that the balance would balance on the triangle (the fulcrum). Assume that each block has the same weight.

44. *Ties, Ties, Ties* All my ties are red except two. All my ties are blue except two. All my ties are brown except two. How many ties do I have?

45. *Buying a Yacht* Four partners decide to share the cost of a yacht equally. By bringing in an additional partner, they can reduce the cost to each of the five partners by $3000. What is the total cost of the yacht?

46. *Palindromes* A *palindrome* is a number (or word) that reads the same forward and backward. The numbers 1991 and 43234 are examples of palindromes. How many palindromes are there between the numbers 2000 and 3000? List them.

47. *Supermarket Display* The figure shows grapefruits in a supermarket display stacked in a *square pyramid* (the base is a square).

a) How many grapefruits are in the pyramid shown if the base has 4 grapefruits by 4 grapefruits?

b) How many grapefruits would be in a square pyramid if the base has 7 grapefruits by 7 grapefruits?

48. *Balancing a Scale* If you have a balance scale and only the four weights 1 gram (g), 3 g, 9 g, and 27 g, explain how you could show that an object had the following weights. (*Hint:* Weights must be added to both sides of the balance scale.)

a) 5 g   b) 16 g

49. *Numbers in Circles* Place the numbers 1 through 6 in the circles below so that the sum along each of the three straight lines is the same. Each number must be used exactly once. (*Note:* There is more than one correct answer.)

50. *Cuts in Cheese* If you make the three complete cuts in the cheese as shown, how many pieces of cheese will you have?

51. *Magic Square* Create a magic square by using the numbers 2, 4, 6, 8, 10, 12, 14, 16, and 18. The sum of the numbers in every column, row, and diagonal must be 30.

52. *Magic Square* Create a magic square by using the numbers 1, 3, 5, 7, 9, 11, 13, 15, and 17. The sum of the numbers in every column, row, and diagonal must be 27.

In Exercises 53–55, use the three magic squares illustrated to obtain the answers.

6	5	10
11	7	3
4	9	8

3	2	7
8	4	0
1	6	5

10	9	14
15	11	7
8	13	12

53. *Magic Square* Examine the 3 by 3 magic squares and find the sum of the four corner entries of each magic square. How can you determine the sum by using a key number in the magic square?

54. *Magic Square* For a 3 by 3 magic square, how can you determine the sum of the numbers in any particular row, column, or diagonal by using a key value in the magic square?

55. *Magic Square* For a 3 by 3 magic square, how can you determine the sum of all the numbers in the square by using a key value in the magic square?

56. *Stack of Cubes* Identical cubes are stacked in the corner of a room as shown. How many of the cubes are not visible?

57. *Dominos* Consider a domino with six dots as shown. Two ways of connecting the three dots on the left with the three dots on the right are illustrated. Using three lines, in how many ways can the three dots on the left be connected with the three dots on the right?

58. *Handshakes All Around* Five salespeople gather for a sales meeting. How many handshakes will each person make if each must shake hands with each of the four others?

59. *Consecutive Digits* Place the digits 1 through 8 in the eight boxes so that each digit is used exactly once and no two consecutive digits touch horizontally, vertically, or diagonally.

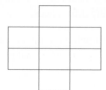

60. *A Digital Clock* Digital clocks display numerals by lighting all or some of the seven parts of the pattern shown. If each digit 0 through 9 is displayed once, which of the seven parts is used least often? Which part is used most often?

61. *A Grid* Place five 1's, five 2's, five 3's, five 4's, and five 5's in a 5 × 5 grid so that each digit—that is, 1, 2, 3, 4, 5—appears exactly once in each row and exactly once in each column.

• Challenge Problems/Group Activities

62. *Insurance Policies* Ray Kelley owns two cars (a Ford Mustang and a Ford Focus), a house, and a rental apartment. He has auto insurance for both cars, a homeowner's policy, and a policy for the rental property. The costs of the policies are

Mustang: $1648 per year
Focus: $1530 per year
Homeowner's: $640 per year
Rental property: $750 per year

Ray is considering taking out a $1 million personal umbrella liability policy. The annual cost of the umbrella policy would be $450. If he has the umbrella policy, he can lower the limits on parts of his auto policies and still have equal or better protection. If Ray purchases the umbrella policy, he can reduce his premium on the Mustang by $90 per year and his premium on the Focus by 12%. If he purchases the umbrella policy and reduces the amount he pays for auto insurance, what is the net amount he is actually paying for the umbrella policy?

63. *A Sports Puzzle* Peter, Paul, and Mary are three sports professionals. One is a tennis player, one is a golfer, and one is a skier. They live in three adjacent houses on City View Drive. From the following information determine which is the professional skier. (*Hint:* A table may be helpful.)

Mary does not play tennis.
Peter skis and plays tennis, but does not golf.
The golfer and the skier live next to each other.
Three years ago, Paul broke his leg skiing and has not tried it since.
Mary lives in the last house.
The golfer and the tennis player share a common backyard swimming pool.

64. *Counting Triangles* How many triangles are in the figure?

65. *Finding the Area* Rectangle ABCD is made up entirely of squares. The black square has a side of 1 unit. Find the area of ABCD.

• Recreational Math

66. *Ostriches* How many ostriches must replace the question mark to balance the fourth scale? Assume that all animals of the same kind have the same weight. That is, all giraffes weigh the same and so forth.

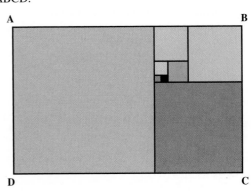

67. *Spending Money* Samantha Smith went into a store and spent half her money and then spent $20 more. Samantha then went into a second store and spent half her remaining money and then spent $20 more. After spending money in the second store, Samantha had no money left. How much money did she have when she went into the first store?

68. *Boxes of Fruit* There are three boxes on a table, each with a label. Thomas Abernathy knows that one box contains grapes, one box contains cherries, and the third box contains both grapes and cherries. He also knows that the three labels used—grapes, cherries, and grapes and cherries—

were mixed up and that none of the boxes received the correct label. He opens just one box and, without looking into the box, takes out one piece of fruit. He looks at the fruit and immediately labels all the boxes correctly. Which box did Thomas open? How did he know how to correctly label the boxes?

• Internet/Research Activity

69. *Puzzles* Many fun and interesting puzzle books and magazines are available. Using this chapter and puzzle books as a guide, construct five of your own puzzles and present them to your instructor.

●●●●●● CHAPTER SUMMARY, REVIEW, AND TEST

● S U M M A R Y   DEFINITIONS AND CONCEPTS

Important Facts

The **natural numbers** or **counting numbers** are 1, 2, 3, 4, ...

A **conjecture** is a prediction based on specific observations.

A **counterexample** is a special case that satisfies all the conditions of a conjecture, but proves the conjecture false.

Inductive reasoning is the process of reasoning to a general conclusion through observations of specific cases.

Deductive reasoning is the process of reasoning to a specific conclusion from a general statement.

Guidelines for Problem Solving

1. Understand the problem.
2. Devise a plan to solve the problem.
3. Carry out the plan.
4. Check the results.

R E V I E W   E X E R C I S E S

1.1

In Exercises 1–8, use inductive reasoning to predict the next three numbers or figures in the pattern.

1. 11, 16, 21, 26, . . .

2. 1, 4, 9, 16, . . .

3. −3, 6, −12, 24, . . .

4. 5, 7, 10, 14, 19, . . .

5. 25, 24, 22, 19, 15, . . .

6. 6, 3, $\frac{3}{2}$, $\frac{3}{4}$, . . .

7. ◷, ⊟, ◔, ⊟, . . .

8.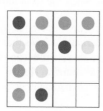

9. *Pattern* Examine the following grid for a pattern and then select the answer which completes the pattern. (*Hint:* Think about rotating groups of four squares at a time.)

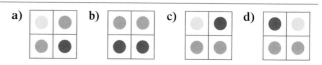

10. Pick any number and multiply the number by 10. Add 5 to the product. Divide the sum by 5. Subtract 1 from the quotient.

   a) What is the relationship between the number you started with and the final number?

   b) Arbitrarily select some different numbers and repeat the process, recording the original number and the results.

   c) Make a conjecture about the original number and the final number.

   d) Prove, using deductive reasoning, the conjecture you made in part (c).

11. Pick any number between 1 and 20. Add 5 to the number. Multiply the sum by 6. Subtract 12 from the product. Divide the difference by 2. Divide the quotient by 3. Subtract the number you started with from the quotient. What is your answer? Try this process with a different number. Make a conjecture as to what your final answer will always be.

12. *Counterexample* Find a counterexample to the statement "The sum of two squares is an even number."

1.2

In Exercises 13–25, estimate the answer. Your answers may vary from those given in the back of the book, depending on how you round to arrive at the answer, but your answers should be something near the answers given.

13. $210{,}302 \times 1992$

14. $215.9 + 128.752 + 3.6 + 861 + 792$

15. 21% of 1012

16. *Distance* Estimate the distance from your wrist to your elbow and estimate the length of your foot. Which do you think is greater? With the help of a friend, measure both lengths to determine which is longer.

17. *Cost* Estimate the cost of 74 brick pavers if the cost is 3.99 per paver.

18. *Sales Tax* Estimate the amount of a 6% sales tax on a chair that costs $589.

19. *Walking Speed* Estimate your average walking speed in miles per hour if you walked 1.1 mi in 22 min.

20. *Groceries* Estimate the total cost of six grocery items that cost $2.49, $0.79, $1.89, $0.10, $2.19, and $6.75.

21. *A Walking Path* The scale of the map is $\frac{1}{4}$ in. = 0.1 mi. Estimate the distance of the walking path indicated in red.

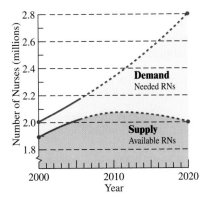
HISTORIC PHILADELPHIA

In Exercises 22 and 23, refer to the following graph, which illustrates the number of registered nurses (RNs) needed (demand) and the number of RNs available (supply) from 2000 to 2005. The graph also illustrates the projected number of RNs needed and the projected number of RNs available from 2006 to 2020.

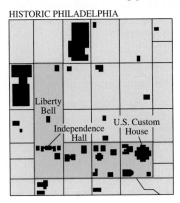
Source: Bureau of Health Professions

22. Estimate the difference in the number of RNs needed and the number of RNs available in 2005.

23. Estimate the difference in the projected number of RNs needed and the projected number of RNs available in 2020.

24. *Estimating an Area* If each square represents one square unit, estimate the size of the shaded area.

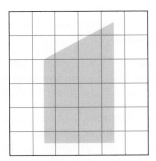

25. *Railroad Car Estimation* The scale of a model railroad is 1 in. = 12.5 ft. Estimate the size of an actual box car if this drawing is the same size as the model box car.

1.3

Solve the following problems.

26. *Change from a Twenty* Jeff Howard parked his car in a lot that charged $2.00 for the first hour and $1.50 for each additional hour. He left the car in the lot for 8 hr. How much change did he receive from a $20 bill?

27. *Buying in Quantity* A six-pack of cola costs $2.69. A carton of 4 six-packs costs $9.60. How much will be saved by purchasing the carton rather than 4 individual six-packs?

28. *Jet Ski Rental* The rental cost of a jet ski from Nola Akala's Ski Rental is $15 per 15 min, and the cost from Jill Berkman's Ski Rental is $25 per half hour. If you plan to rent the jet ski for 2 hr, which is the better deal, and by how much?

29. *Oscars* In 2001, shortly before the Academy Awards show, many Oscars were lost by the shipping company. Fifty-two of the 55 Oscars were found, before the awards ceremony, in a dumpster by an Illinois man. The man was awarded $50,000 (and two tickets to the ceremony). The actual cost to have each Oscar produced was $327. How much more had the man been awarded than the actual cost to produce the 52 Oscars he found (disregarding the cost of the tickets)?

30. *Applying Fertilizer* Ron Williams needs to apply fertilizer to his lawn on his farm. A 30-pound bag of fertilizer will cover an area of 2500 square feet.

a) How many pounds are needed to cover an area of 24,000 square feet?

b) If Ron only has 150 pounds of fertilizer, how many square feet can he fertilize?

31. *Auto Insurance* Most insurance companies reduce premiums by 10% until age 25 for people who successfully pass a driver's education course. A particular driver's education course costs $60. Patrick Flanigan, who just turned 18, has auto insurance that costs $530 per year. By taking the driver's education course, how much would he save in auto insurance, including the cost of the course, from the age of 18 until the age of 25?

32. *Pediatric Dosage* If 1.5 milligrams of a medicine is to be given for 10 lb of body weight, how many milligrams should be given to a child who weighs 47 lb?

33. *Qualifying for a Mortgage* Banks will usually grant an applicant a mortgage if the monthly payments are not greater than 28% of the person's take-home pay. What is the maximum monthly mortgage payment you can make if your gross salary is $4500 a month and your payroll deductions are 30% of your gross salary?

34. *Flying West* New York City is on eastern standard time, St. Louis is on central standard time (1 hr earlier than eastern standard time), and Las Vegas is on Pacific standard time (3 hr earlier than eastern standard time). A flight leaves New York City at 9 A.M. eastern standard time, stops for 50 min in St. Louis, and arrives in Las Vegas at 1:35 P.M. Pacific time. How long is the plane actually flying?

35. *Crossing Time Zones* The international date line is an imaginary line of longitude (from the North Pole to the South Pole) on Earth's surface between Japan and Hawaii in the Pacific Ocean. Crossing the line east to west adds a day to the present date. Crossing the line west to east subtracts a day. At 3:00 P.M. on July 25 in Hawaii, what is the time and date in Tokyo, Japan, which is four time zones to the west?

36. *Conversions* 1 in. = 2.54 cm.

a) How many square centimeters are in a square inch?

b) How many cubic centimeters are in a cubic inch?

c) How long is a centimeter in terms of inches?

37. *Dot Pattern* If the following pattern is continued, how many dots will be in the hundredth figure?

38. *Magic Square* The following magic square uses each number from 6 to 21 exactly once. Complete the magic square by using the unused numbers from 6 through 21 exactly once.

21	7		18
10		15	
14	12	11	17
9	19		

39. *Magic Square* Create a magic square by using the numbers 13, 15, 17, 19, 21, 23, 25, 27, and 29. The sum of the numbers in every row, column, and diagonal must be 63.

40. *Microbes in a Jar* A colony of microbes doubles in number every second. A single microbe is placed in a jar, and in an hour the jar is full. When was the jar half full?

41. *Brothers and Sisters* Jim Carraway has four more brothers than sisters. How many more brothers than sisters does his sister Mary have?

42. *A Missing Dollar* Three friends check into a single room in a motel and pay $10 apiece. The room costs $25 instead of $30, so a clerk is sent to the room to give $5 back. The friends each take back $1, and the clerk is given $2 for his trouble. Now each of the friends paid $9, a total of $27, and the clerk received $2. What happened to the missing dollar?

43. *The Average Weight* Four women in a room have an average weight of 130 lb. A fifth woman who weighs 180 lb enters the room. Find the average weight of all five women.

44. *Change for a Dollar* Could a person have $1.15 worth of change in his pocket and still not be able to give someone change for a dollar bill? If so, what coins might he have?

45. *Volume of a Cube* Here is a flat pattern for a cube to be formed by folding. The sides of each square are 6 cm. Find the volume of the cube.

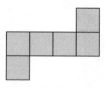

46. *The Heavier Coin* You have 13 coins, which all look alike. Twelve coins weigh exactly the same, but the other one is heavier. You have a pan balance. Tell how to find the heavier coin in just three weighings.

47. *The Sum of Numbers* Find the sum of the first 500 counting numbers. (*Hint:* Group in pairs.)

48. *Balancing a Scale* On a balance scale, three green balls balance six blue balls, two yellow balls balance five blue balls, and six blue balls balance four white balls. How many blue balls are needed to balance four green, two yellow, and two white balls?

49. *Palindromes* How many three-digit numbers greater than 100 are palindromes?

50. *Figures* Describe the fifth figure.

51. *Patterns* How many orange tiles will be required to build the sixth figure in this pattern?

52. *Sum of Numbers* Place the numbers 1 through 12 in the 12 circles so that the sum of the numbers in each of the six rows is 26. Use each number from 1 through 12 exactly once.

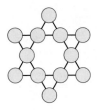

53. *People in a Line* People stand in a line at movies, the grocery store, and many other places.

a) In how many ways can two people stand in a line?

b) In how many ways can three people stand in a line?

c) In how many ways can four people stand in a line?

d) In how many ways can five people stand in a line?

e) Using the results from parts (a) through (d), make a conjecture about the number of ways in which *n* people can stand in a line.

●●●●●● CHAPTER 1 TEST

In Exercises 1 and 2, use inductive reasoning to determine the next three numbers in the pattern.

1. 3, 7, 11, 15, . . .

2. $1, \frac{1}{2}, \frac{1}{4}, \frac{1}{8}, \ldots$

3. Pick any number, multiply the number by 5, and add 10 to the number. Divide the sum by 5. Subtract 1 from the quotient.

a) What is the relationship between the number you started with and the final answer?

b) Arbitrarily select some different numbers and repeat the process. Record the original number and the results.

c) Make a conjecture about the relationship between the original number and the final answer.

d) Prove, using deductive reasoning, the conjecture made in part (c).

In Exercises 4 and 5, estimate the answers.

4. $0.18 \times 58{,}000$

5. $\dfrac{210{,}000}{0.12}$

6. *Estimating Area* If each square represents one square unit, estimate the area of the shaded figure.

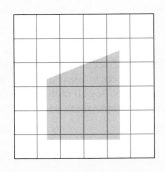

7. *Body Mass Index* The federal government gives a procedure to determine if a child is overweight. To make this decision, first determine the child's body mass index (BMI). Then compare the BMI with one of the two charts, one for boys and one for girls, provided by the government. On the right, we give the chart for boys up to age 20. To determine a child's BMI:

1) Divide the child's weight (in pounds) by the child's height (in inches).
2) Divide the results from part 1 by the child's height again.
3) Multiply the result from part 2 by 703.

Richard is a 14-year-old boy who weighs 130 lb and is 63 in. tall.

a) Determine his BMI.

b) Does he appear to be at risk for being overweight, or is he overweight? Explain.

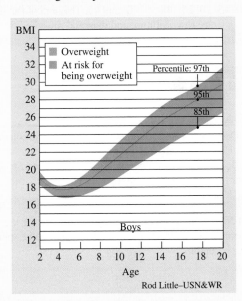

8. *Cell Phone Cost* AT & T charges $59.99 for its Nation 900 with Rollover Plan for cell phones, which includes 900 minutes of call time. The company charges $0.40 for each additional minute. If the Smiths' cell phone bill for December was $74.39, how many additional minutes did they use during that month?

9. *Cans of Soda* At a local store a six-pack of soda costs $2.59 and individual cans cost $0.80. What is the maximum number of cans of soda that can be purchased for $15?

10. *Cutting Wood* How much time does it take Carla Knab, a carpenter, to cut a 10 ft length of wood into four equal pieces, if each cut takes $2\frac{1}{2}$ min?

11. *Determining Size* In this photo of *Sunflowers*, a 1889 painting by Vincent van Gogh, 1 in. equals 15.8 in. on the actual painting. Find the dimensions of the actual painting.

12. *Payment Shortfall* Monica Wilson gets $12.75 per hour with time and a half for any time over 40 hours per week. If she works a 50 hr week and gets paid $652.25, by how much was she underpaid?

13. *Magic Square* Create a magic square by using the numbers 5, 10, 15, 20, 25, 30, 35, 40, and 45. The sum of the numbers in every row, column, and diagonal must be 75.

14. *A Drive to the Beach* Mary Chin drove from her home to the beach that is 30 mi from her house. The first 15 mi she drove at 60 mph, and the next 15 mi she drove at 30 mph. Would the trip take more, less, or the same time if she traveled the entire 30 mi at a steady 45 mph?

15. *Pick Five Numbers* From the six numbers 2, 6, 8, 9, 11, and 13, pick five that, when multiplied, give 11,232.

16. *Jelly Bean Guess* One guess is off by 9, another guess is off by 17, and yet another guess is off by 31. How many jelly beans are in the jar?

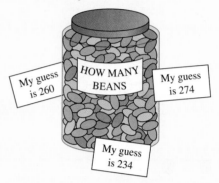

17. *Buying Plants* David Mackin wants to purchase nine herb plants. Countryside Nursery has herbs that are on sale at three for $3.99. David has a coupon for 25% off an unlimited number of herb plants at the original price of $1.75 per plant.

   a) Determine the cost of purchasing nine plants at the sale price.

   b) Determine the cost of purchasing nine plants if the coupon is used.

   c) Which is the least expensive way to purchase the nine plants, and by how much?

18. *Arranging Letters* In how many different ways can four letters, A, B, C, D, be arranged?

●●●●●● GROUP PROJECTS

HOLIDAY SHOPPING

1. It is December 1 and John needs to begin his holiday shopping. He intends to purchase gifts for three people: his girlfriend, Melissa; his mother, Ruth; and his father, Don. He doesn't want to spend more than a total of $325, including the 7% sales tax.

   a) If John were to spend the $325 equally among the three people, approximate the amount that would be spent on each person.

   b) If John were to spend the $325 equally among the three people, determine the maximum amount, *before tax*, that he could spend on each person and not exceed the maximum of $325, including tax.

   c) John decides to get a new set of wrenches for his father. He sees the specific set he wants on sale at Sears. He calls four Sears stores to see if they have the set of wrenches in stock. They all reply that the set is out of stock. He decides that calling additional Sears stores is useless because he believes that they will also tell him that the set of wrenches is out of stock. What type of reasoning did John use in arriving at his conclusion? Explain.

d) John finds an equivalent set of wrenches at a True Value hardware store. The set he is considering is a combination set that contains both standard U.S. size and metric size wrenches. The store's regular price before tax is $62 for the set, but it is selling them for 10% off the regular price. He can also purchase the same wrenches by purchasing two separate sets, one for standard U.S. size wrenches and the other for metric sizes. Each of these sets has a regular price, before tax, of $36, but both are on sale for 20% off their regular prices. Can John purchase the combination set or the two individual sets less expensively?

e) How much will John save, *after tax*, by using the less expensive method?

GOING ON VACATION

2. Bob and Kristen Williams decide to go on a vacation. They live in San Francisco, California, and plan to drive to New Orleans, Louisiana.

a) Obtain a map that shows routes that they may take from San Francisco to New Orleans. Write directions for them from San Francisco to New Orleans via the shortest distance. Use major highways whenever possible.

b) Use the scale on the map to estimate the one-way distance to New Orleans.

c) If the Williamses estimate that they will average 50 mph (including comfort stops), estimate the travel time, in hours, to New Orleans.

d) If the Williamses want to travel about 400 miles per day, locate a town in the vicinity of where they will stop each evening.

e) If they begin each segment of the trip each day at 9 A.M., at about what time will they look for a hotel each evening?

f) Use the information provided in parts (a) through (e) to estimate the time of day they will arrive in New Orleans.

g) Estimate the mileage of a typical midsized car and the cost per gallon of a gallon of regular unleaded gasoline. Then estimate the cost of gasoline for the Williams' trip.

h) Estimate the cost of a typical breakfast, a typical lunch, and a typical dinner for two adults, and the cost of a typical motel room. Then estimate the total cost, including meals, gas, and lodging, for the Williams' trip from San Francisco to New Orleans (one way).

PROBLEM SOLVING

3. Four acrobats who bill themselves as the "Tumbling Tumbleweeds" finish up their act with the amazing "Human Pillar," in which the acrobats form a tower, each one standing on the shoulders of the one below. Each acrobat (Ernie, Jed, Tex, and Zeke Tumbleweed) wears a different distinctive item of western garb (chaps, holster, Stetson hat, or leather vest) in the act. Can you identify the members of the "Human Pillar," from top to bottom, by name and apparel?

a) Jed Tumbleweed is not on top, but he is somewhere above the man in the Stetson.

b) Zeke Tumbleweed does not wear the holster.

c) The man in the vest is not on top.

d) The man in the chaps is somewhere above Tex but somewhere below Zeke.

ORDER	NAME	APPAREL
_____	_____	_____
_____	_____	_____
_____	_____	_____
_____	_____	_____

Number Theory and the Real Number System

While listening to the radio, you hear politicians discussing the problem of the $8.6 trillion national debt. They state that it's more than the gross domestic product of China, the world's second-richest nation, and four times greater than the combined net worth of America's 691 billionaires. They make it seem like the national debt is a real problem, but later you realize that you don't really know what a number like 8.6 trillion means. If the national debt were evenly divided among all citizens of the country, how much would every man, woman, and child have to pay?

• • • • • •
Literacy with numbers, called *numeracy*, is a prerequisite for functioning in a meaningful way personally, professionally, and as a citizen. In this chapter, our focus is on understanding numbers, their properties, and their applications. The problem of placing the $8.6 trillion national debt in perspective appears as Example 9 in Section 2.6.

SECTION 2.1 • NUMBER THEORY: PRIME AND COMPOSITE NUMBERS

OBJECTIVES

1. Determine divisibility.

2. Write the prime factorization of a composite number.

3. Find the greatest common divisor of two numbers.

4. Solve problems using the greatest common divisor.

5. Find the least common multiple of two numbers.

6. Solve problems using the least common multiple.

Number Theory and Divisibility

You are organizing an intramural league at your school. You need to divide 40 men and 24 women into all-male and all-female teams so that each team has the same number of people. The men's teams should have the same number of players as the women's teams. What is the largest number of people that can be placed on a team?

This problem can be solved using a branch of mathematics called **number theory**. Number theory is primarily concerned with the properties of numbers used for counting, namely 1, 2, 3, 4, 5, and so on. The set of counting numbers is also called the set of **natural numbers**. We represent this set by the letter **N**.

THE SET OF NATURAL NUMBERS

$$\mathbf{N} = \{1, 2, 3, 4, 5, 6, 7, 8, 9, 10, 11, \dots\}$$

We can solve the intramural league problem. However, to do so we must understand the concept of divisibility. For example, there are a number of different ways to divide the 24 women into teams, including

1 team with all 24 women:	$1 \times 24 = 24$
2 teams with 12 women per team:	$2 \times 12 = 24$
3 teams with 8 women per team:	$3 \times 8 = 24$
4 teams with 6 women per team:	$4 \times 6 = 24$
6 teams with 4 women per team:	$6 \times 4 = 24$
8 teams with 3 women per team:	$8 \times 3 = 24$
12 teams with 2 women per team:	$12 \times 2 = 24$
24 teams with 1 woman per team:	$24 \times 1 = 24.$

The natural numbers that are multiplied together resulting in a product of 24 are called *factors* of 24. Any natural number can be expressed as a product of two or more natural numbers. The natural numbers that are multiplied are called the **factors** of the product. Notice that a natural number may have many factors.

$$2 \times 12 = 24 \qquad 3 \times 8 = 24 \qquad 6 \times 4 = 24$$

Factors of 24   Factors of 24   Factors of 24

The numbers 1, 2, 3, 4, 6, 8, 12, and 24 are all factors of 24. Each of these numbers divides 24 without a remainder.

1 | Determine divisibility.

In general, let a and b represent natural numbers. We say that a is **divisible** by b if the operation of dividing a by b leaves a remainder of 0.

A natural number is divisible by all of its factors. Thus, 24 is divisible by 1, 2, 3, 4, 6, 8, 12, and 24. Using the factor 8, we can express this divisibility in a number of ways:

24 is **divisible** by 8.

8 is a **divisor** of 24.

8 **divides** 24.

Mathematicians use a special notation to indicate divisibility.

> **DIVISIBILITY**
>
> If a and b are natural numbers, a is **divisible** by b if the operation of dividing a by b leaves a remainder of 0. This is the same as saying that b is a **divisor** of a, or b **divides** a. All three statements are symbolized by writing
>
> $$b|a.$$

Using this new notation, we can write

$$12|24.$$

Twelve divides 24 because 24 divided by 12 leaves a remainder of 0. By contrast, 13 does not divide 24 because 24 divided by 13 does not leave a remainder of 0. The notation

$$13\!\!\!\not|\,24$$

means that 13 does not divide 24.

Table 2.1 shows some common rules for divisibility. Divisibility rules for 7 and 11 are difficult to remember and are not included in the table.

TABLE 2.1 RULES OF DIVISIBILITY		
Divisible By	**Test**	**Example**
2	The last digit is 0, 2, 4, 6, or 8.	5,892,796 is divisible by 2 because the last digit is 6.
3	The sum of the digits is divisible by 3.	52,341 is divisible by 3 because the sum of the digits is $5 + 2 + 3 + 4 + 1 = 15$, and 15 is divisible by 3.
4	The last two digits form a number divisible by 4.	3,947,136 is divisible by 4 because 36 is divisible by 4.
5	The number ends in 0 or 5.	28,160 and 72,805 end in 0 and 5, respectively. Both are divisible by 5.
6	The number is divisible by both 2 and 3. (In other words, the number is even and the sum of its digits is divisible by 3.)	954 is divisible by 2 because it ends in 4. 954 is also divisible by 3 because the digit sum is 18, which is divisible by 3. Because 954 is divisible by both 2 and 3, it is divisible by 6.
8	The last three digits form a number that is divisible by 8.	593,777,832 is divisible by 8 because 832 is divisible by 8.
9	The sum of the digits is divisible by 9.	5346 is divisible by 9 because the sum of the digits, 18, is divisible by 9.
10	The last digit is 0.	998,746,250 is divisible by 10 because the number ends in 0.
12	The number is divisible by both 3 and 4. (In other words, the sum of the digits is divisible by 3 and the last two digits form a number divisible by 4.)	614,608,176 is divisible by 3 because the digit sum is 39, which is divisible by 3. It is also divisible by 4 because the last two digits form 76, which is divisible by 4. Because 614,608,176 is divisible by both 3 and 4, it is divisible by 12.

EXAMPLE 1 USING THE RULES OF DIVISIBILITY

Which one of the following statements is true?

a. $4 \mid 3,754,086$ **b.** $9 \nmid 4,119,706,413$ **c.** $8 \mid 677,840$

SOLUTION

a. $4 \mid 3,754,086$ states that 4 divides 3,754,086. Table 2.1 indicates that for 4 to divide a number, the last two digits must form a number that is divisible by 4. Because 86 is not divisible by 4, the given statement is false.

b. $9 \nmid 4,119,706,413$ states that 9 does *not* divide 4,119,706,413. Based on Table 2.1, if the sum of the digits is divisible by 9, then 9 does indeed divide this number. The sum of the digits is $4 + 1 + 1 + 9 + 7 + 0 + 6 + 4 + 1 + 3 = 36$, which is divisible by 9. Because 4,119,706,413 is divisible by 9, the given statement is false.

c. $8 \mid 667,840$ states that 8 divides 677,840. Table 2.1 indicates that for 8 to divide a number, the last three digits must form a number that is divisible by 8. Because 840 is divisible by 8, then 8 divides 677,840, and the given statement is true.

The statement given in part (c) is the only true statement.

Which one of the following statements is true?

a. $8 \mid 48,324$ **b.** $6 \mid 48,324$ **c.** $4 \nmid 48,324$

Prime Factorization

By developing some other ideas of number theory, we will be able to solve the intramural league problem. We begin with the definition of a prime number.

> **PRIME NUMBERS**
> A **prime number** is a natural number greater than 1 that has only itself and 1 as factors.

Using this definition, we see that the number 7 is a prime number because it has only 1 and 7 as factors. Said in another way, 7 is prime because it is divisible by only 1 and 7. The first ten prime numbers are 2, 3, 5, 7, 11, 13, 17, 19, 23, and 29. Each number in this list has exactly two divisors, itself and 1. By contrast, 9 is not a prime number; in addition to being divisible by 1 and 9, it is also divisible by 3. The number 9 is an example of a *composite number*.

> **COMPOSITE NUMBERS**
> A **composite number** is a natural number greater than 1 that is divisible by a number other than itself and 1.

Using this definition, the first ten composite numbers are 4, 6, 8, 9, 10, 12, 14, 15, 16, and 18. Each number in this list has at least three divisors.

Every composite number can be expressed as the product of prime numbers. For example, the composite number 45 can be expressed as

$$45 = 3 \times 3 \times 5.$$

Note that 3 and 5 are prime numbers. Expressing a composite number as the product of prime numbers is called **prime factorization**. The prime factorization of 45 is $3 \times 3 \times 5$. The order in which we write these factors does not matter. This means that

$$45 = 3 \times 3 \times 5$$
$$\text{or } 45 = 5 \times 3 \times 3$$
$$\text{or } 45 = 3 \times 5 \times 3.$$

2 | Write the prime factorization of a composite number.

A **theorem** is a statement that can be proved using deductive reasoning. The ancient Greeks proved that if the order of the factors is disregarded, there is only one prime factorization possible for any given composite number. This statement is called the **Fundamental Theorem of Arithmetic**.

> **THE FUNDAMENTAL THEOREM OF ARITHMETIC**
> Every composite number can be expressed as a product of prime numbers in one and only one way (if the order of the factors is disregarded).

One method used to find the prime factorization of a composite number is called a **factor tree**. To use this method, begin by selecting any two numbers whose product is the number to be factored. If one or both of the factors are not prime numbers, continue to factor each composite number. Stop when all numbers are prime.

EXAMPLE 2   PRIME FACTORIZATION USING A FACTOR TREE

Find the prime factorization of 700.

SOLUTION Start with any two numbers whose product is 700, such as 7 and 100. This forms the first branch of the tree. Continue factoring the composite number or numbers that result (in this case 100), branching until the end of each branch contains a prime number.

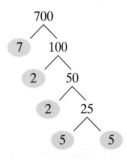

The prime factors are circled. Thus, the prime factorization of 700 is

$$700 = 7 \times 2 \times 2 \times 5 \times 5.$$

We can use exponents to show the repeated prime factors:

$$700 = 7 \times 2^2 \times 5^2.$$

Using a dot to indicate multiplication and arranging the factors from least to greatest, we can write

$$700 = 2^2 \cdot 5^2 \cdot 7.$$

 Find the prime factorization of 120.

STUDY TIP

It does not matter how you begin a factor tree. For example, in Example 2 you can factor 700 by starting with 5 and 140.
$(5 \times 140 = 700)$

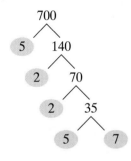

The prime factorization of 700 is

$$700 = 5 \times 2 \times 2 \times 5 \times 7$$
$$= 2^2 \times 5^2 \times 7.$$

This is the same prime factorization we obtained in Example 2.

---

3 Find the greatest common divisor of two numbers.

Greatest Common Divisor

The greatest common divisor of two or more natural numbers is the largest number that is a divisor (or factor) of all the numbers. For example, 8 is the greatest common divisor of 32 and 40 because it is the largest natural number that divides both 32 and 40. Some pairs of numbers have 1 as their greatest common divisor. Such number pairs are said to be **relatively prime**. For example, the greatest common divisor of 5 and 26 is 1. Thus, 5 and 26 are relatively prime.

BLITZER BONUS

Simple Questions with No Answers

In number theory, a good problem is one that can be stated quite simply, but whose solution turns out to be particularly difficult, if not impossible.

In 1742, the mathematician Christian Goldbach (1690–1764) wrote a letter to Leonhard Euler (1707–1783) in which he proposed, without a proof, that every even number greater than 2 is the sum of two primes. For example,

Even number	Sum of two primes

$$4 = 2 + 2$$
$$6 = 3 + 3$$
$$8 = 3 + 5$$
$$10 = 5 + 5$$
$$12 = 7 + 5$$

and so on.

Two and a half centuries later, it is still not known if this conjecture is true or false. Inductively, it appears to be true; computer searches have written even numbers as large as 400 trillion as the sum of two primes. Deductively, no mathematician has been able to prove that the conjecture is true. Even a reward of one million dollars for a proof offered by the publishing house Farber and Farber in 2000 to help publicize the novel *Uncle Petros and Goldbach's Conjecture* went unclaimed.

The greatest common divisor can be found using prime factorizations.

> ## FINDING THE GREATEST COMMON DIVISOR OF TWO OR MORE NUMBERS USING PRIME FACTORIZATIONS
>
> To find the greatest common divisor of two or more numbers,
>
> 1. Write the prime factorization of each number.
> 2. Select each prime factor with the smallest exponent that is common to each of the prime factorizations.
> 3. Form the product of the numbers from step 2. The greatest common divisor is the product of these factors.

EXAMPLE 3   FINDING THE GREATEST COMMON DIVISOR

Find the greatest common divisor of 216 and 234.

SOLUTION

Step 1. Write the prime factorization of each number. Begin by writing the prime factorizations of 216 and 234.

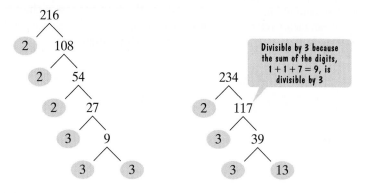

The factor tree at the left indicates that

$$216 = 2^3 \times 3^3.$$

The factor tree at the right indicates that

$$234 = 2 \times 3^2 \times 13.$$

Step 2. Select each prime factor with the smallest exponent that is common to each of the prime factorizations. Look at the factorizations of 216 and 234 from step 1. Can you see that 2 is a prime number common to the factorizations of 216 and 234? Likewise, 3 is also a prime number common to the two factorizations. By contrast, 13 is a prime number that is not common to both factorizations.

$$216 = 2^3 \times 3^3$$
$$234 = 2 \times 3^2 \times 13$$

2 is a prime number common to both factorizations.   3 is a prime number common to both factorizations.

$$216 = 2^3 \times 3^3$$

Smallest exponent on 2 is 1.   Smallest exponent on 3 is 2.

$$234 = 2^1 \times 3^2 \times 13$$

Now we need to use these prime factorizations to determine which exponent is appropriate for 2 and which exponent is appropriate for 3. The appropriate exponent is the smallest exponent associated with the prime number in the factorizations. The exponents associated with 2 in the factorizations are 1 and 3, so we select 1. Therefore, one factor for the greatest common divisor is 2^1, or 2. The exponents associated with 3 in the factorizations are 2 and 3, so we select 2. Therefore, another factor for the greatest common divisor is 3^2.

Step 3. Form the product of the numbers from step 2. The greatest common divisor is the product of these factors.

$$\text{Greatest common divisor} = 2 \times 3^2 = 2 \times 9 = 18$$

The greatest common divisor of 216 and 234 is 18.

CHECK POINT 3 Find the greatest common divisor of 225 and 825.

BLITZER BONUS

GIMPS

A prime number of the form $2^p - 1$, where p is prime, is called a **Mersenne prime**, named for the seventeenth-century monk Marin Mersenne (1588–1648), who stated that $2^p - 1$ is prime for $p = 2, 3, 5, 7, 13, 17, 19, 31, 67, 127,$ and 257. Without calculators and computers, it is not known how Mersenne arrived at these assertions, although it is now known that $2^p - 1$ is *not* prime for $p = 67$ and 257; it *is* prime for $p = 61, 89,$ and 107. In 2006, there were 43 known Mersenne primes: $2^p - 1$ is prime for $p = 2; 3; 5; 7; 13; 17; 19; 31; 61; 89; 107; 127; 521; 607; 1279; 2203; 2281; 3217; 4253; 4423; 9689; 9941; 11,213; 19,937; 21,701; 23,209; 44,497; 86,243; 110,503; 132,049; 216,091; 756,839; 859,433; 1,257,787; 1,398,269; 2,976,221; 3,021,377; 6,972,593; 13,466,917; 20,996,011; 24,036,583; 25,964,951;$ and $30,402,457$.

In 1995, the American computer scientist George Woltman began the *Great Internet Mersenne Prime Search* (*GIMPS*). By pooling the combined efforts of thousands of people interested in finding new Mersenne primes, GIMPS's participants have yielded several important results, including the record prime $2^{30,402,457} - 1$, a number with 9,152,052 digits that was discovered in 2006. As of December 2006, there was a $100,000 award to the first person to find a prime number with at least ten million digits.

5 | Find the least common multiple of two numbers.

EXAMPLE 4   SOLVING A PROBLEM USING THE GREATEST COMMON DIVISOR

For an intramural league, you need to divide 40 men and 24 women into all-male and all-female teams so that each team has the same number of people. What is the largest number of people that can be placed on a team?

SOLUTION Because 40 men are to be divided into teams, the number of men on each team must be a divisor of 40. Because 24 women are to be divided into teams, the number of women placed on a team must be a divisor of 24. Although the teams are all-male and all-female, the same number of people must be placed on each team. The largest number of people that can be placed on a team is the largest number that will divide into 40 and 24 without a remainder. This is the greatest common divisor of 40 and 24.

To find the greatest common divisor of 40 and 24, begin with their prime factorizations.

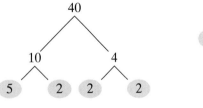 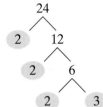

The factor trees indicate that

$$40 = 2^3 \times 5 \qquad \text{and} \qquad 24 = 2^3 \times 3.$$

We see that 2 is a prime number common to both factorizations. The exponents associated with 2 in the factorizations are 3 and 3, so we select 3.

$$\text{Greatest common divisor} = 2^3 = 2 \times 2 \times 2 = 8$$

The largest number of people that can be placed on a team is 8. Thus, the 40 men can form five teams with 8 men per team. The 24 women can form three teams with 8 women per team.

CHECK POINT 4 A choral director needs to divide 192 men and 288 women into all-male and all-female singing groups so that each group has the same number of people. What is the largest number of people that can be placed in each singing group?

Least Common Multiple

The **least common multiple** of two or more natural numbers is the smallest natural number that is divisible by all of the numbers. One way to find the least common multiple is to make a list of the numbers that are divisible by each number. This list represents the **multiples** of each number. For example, if we wish to find the least common multiple of 15 and 20, we can list the sets of multiples of 15 and multiples of 20.

$\begin{cases} \text{Numbers Divisible by 15:} \\ \quad \text{Multiples of 15:} \qquad \{15, 30, 45, 60, 75, 90, 105, 120, \dots \} \end{cases}$

$\begin{cases} \text{Numbers Divisible by 20:} \\ \quad \text{Multiples of 20:} \qquad \{20, 40, 60, 80, 100, 120, 140, 160, \dots \} \end{cases}$

Some common multiples of 15 and 20 are 60 and 120. The least common multiple is 60. Equivalently, 60 is the smallest number that is divisible by both 15 and 20.

Sometimes a partial list of the multiples for each of two numbers does not reveal the smallest number that is divisible by both given numbers. A more efficient method for finding the least common multiple is to use prime factorizations.

FINDING THE LEAST COMMON MULTIPLE USING PRIME FACTORIZATIONS

To find the least common multiple of two or more numbers,

1. Write the prime factorization of each number.
2. Select every prime factor that occurs, raised to the greatest power to which it occurs, in these factorizations.
3. Form the product of the numbers from step 2. The least common multiple is the product of these factors.

EXAMPLE 5   FINDING THE LEAST COMMON MULTIPLE

Find the least common multiple of 144 and 300.

SOLUTION

Step 1. Write the prime factorization of each number. Write the prime factorizations of 144 and 300.

$$144 = 2^4 \times 3^2$$
$$300 = 2^2 \times 3 \times 5^2$$

Step 2. Select every prime factor that occurs, raised to the greatest power to which it occurs, in these factorizations. The prime factors that occur are 2, 3, and 5. The greatest exponent that appears on 2 is 4, so we select 2^4. The greatest exponent that appears on 3 is 2, so we select 3^2. The greatest exponent that occurs on 5 is 2, so we select 5^2. Thus, we have selected 2^4, 3^2, and 5^2.

Step 3. Form the product of the numbers from step 2. The least common multiple is the product of these factors.

$$\text{Least common multiple} = 2^4 \times 3^2 \times 5^2 = 16 \times 9 \times 25 = 3600$$

The least common multiple of 144 and 300 is 3600. The smallest natural number divisible by 144 and 300 is 3600.

 CHECK POINT 5   Find the least common multiple of 18 and 30.

---

6 | Solve problems using the least common multiple.

EXAMPLE 6   SOLVING A PROBLEM USING THE LEAST COMMON MULTIPLE

A movie theater runs its films continuously. One movie runs for 80 minutes and a second runs for 120 minutes. Both movies begin at 4:00 P.M. When will the movies begin again at the same time?

SOLUTION The shorter movie lasts 80 minutes, or 1 hour, 20 minutes. It begins at 4:00, so it will be shown again at 5:20. The longer movie lasts 120 minutes, or 2 hours. It begins at 4:00, so it will be shown again at 6:00. We are asked to find when the movies will begin again at the same time. Therefore, we are looking for the least common multiple of 80 and 120. Find the least common multiple and then add this number of minutes to 4:00 P.M.

Begin with the prime factorizations of 80 and 120:

$$80 = 2^4 \times 5$$
$$120 = 2^3 \times 3 \times 5.$$

Now select each prime factor, with the greatest exponent from each factorization.

Least common multiple $= 2^4 \times 3 \times 5 = 16 \times 3 \times 5 = 240$

Therefore, it will take 240 minutes, or 4 hours, for the movies to begin again at the same time. By adding 4 hours to 4:00 P.M., they will start together again at 8:00 P.M.

○

STUDY TIP

Example 6 can also be solved by making a partial list of starting times for each movie.

Shorter Movie (Runs 1 hour, 20 minutes):

4:00,   5:20,   6:40,   8:00, . . .

Longer Movie (Runs 2 hours):

4:00,   6:00,   8:00, . . .

The list reveals that both movies start together again at 8:00 P.M.

CHECK POINT 6 A movie theater runs two documentary films continuously. One documentary runs for 40 minutes and a second documentary runs for 60 minutes. Both movies begin at 3:00 P.M. When will the movies begin again at the same time?

EXERCISE SET 2.1 ●●●●●●

• Practice Exercises

Use rules of divisibility to determine whether each number given in Exercises 1–10 is divisible by

   a. 2   **b.** 3   **c.** 4   **d.** 5   **e.** 6

   f. 8   **g.** 9   **h.** 10   **i.** 12.

1. 6944   **2.** 7245   **3.** 21,408   **4.** 25,025

5. 26,428   **6.** 89,001   **7.** 374,832   **8.** 347,712

9. 6,126,120   **10.** 5,941,221

In Exercises 11–24, use a calculator to determine whether each statement is true or false. If the statement is true, explain why this is so using one of the rules of divisibility in Table 2.1 on page 43.

11. 3|5958   **12.** 3|8142   **13.** 4|10,612

14. 4|15,984   **15.** 5|38,814   **16.** 5|48,659

17. 6|104,538   **18.** 6|163,944   **19.** 8|20,104

20. 8|28,096   **21.** 9|11,378   **22.** 9|23,772

23. 12|517,872   **24.** 12|785,172

In Exercises 25–44, find the prime factorization of each composite number.

25. 75   **26.** 45   **27.** 56   **28.** 48

29. 105   **30.** 180   **31.** 500   **32.** 360

33. 663   **34.** 510   **35.** 885   **36.** 999

37. 1440 **38.** 1280 **39.** 1996 **40.** 1575

41. 3675 **42.** 8316 **43.** 85,800 **44.** 30,600

In Exercises 45–56, find the greatest common divisor of the numbers.

45. 42 and 56   **46.** 25 and 70   **47.** 16 and 42

48. 66 and 90   **49.** 60 and 108   **50.** 96 and 212

51. 72 and 120   **52.** 220 and 400   **53.** 342 and 380

54. 224 and 430   **55.** 240 and 285   **56.** 150 and 480

In Exercises 57–68, find the least common multiple of the numbers.

57. 42 and 56   **58.** 25 and 70   **59.** 16 and 42

60. 66 and 90   **61.** 60 and 108   **62.** 96 and 212

63. 72 and 120   **64.** 220 and 400   **65.** 342 and 380

66. 224 and 430   **67.** 240 and 285   **68.** 150 and 480

• Practice Plus

In Exercises 69–74, determine all values of d that make each statement true.

69. 9|12,34d   **70.** 9|23,42d   **71.** 8|76,523,45d

72. 8|88,888,82d **73.** 4|963,23d   **74.** 4|752,67d

*A **perfect number** is a natural number that is equal to the sum of its factors, excluding the number itself. In Exercises 75–78, determine whether or not each number is perfect.*

75. 28   **76.** 6   **77.** 20   **78.** 50

*A prime number is an **emirp** ("prime" spelled backward) if it becomes a different prime number when its digits are reversed. In Exercises 79–82, determine whether or not each prime number is an emirp.*

79. 41   **80.** 43   **81.** 107   **82.** 113

A prime number p such that 2p + 1 is also a prime number is called a **Germain prime**, *named after the German mathematician Sophie Germain (1776–1831), who made major contributions to number theory. In Exercises 83–86, determine whether or not each prime number is a Germain prime.*

83. 13   **84.** 11   **85.** 241   **86.** 97

87. Find the product of the greatest common divisor of 24 and 27 and the least common multiple of 24 and 27. Compare this result to the product of 24 and 27. Write a conjecture based on your observation.

88. Find the product of the greatest common divisor of 48 and 72 and the least common multiple of 48 and 72. Compare this result to the product of 48 and 72. Write a conjecture based on your observation.

• Application Exercises

89. In Carl Sagan's novel *Contact*, Ellie Arroway, the book's heroine, has been working at SETI, the Search for Extraterrestrial Intelligence, listening to the crackle of the cosmos. One night, as the radio telescopes are turned toward Vega, they suddenly pick up strange pulses through the background noise. Two pulses are followed by a pause, then three pulses, five, seven,

$$11, \quad 13, \quad 17, \quad 19, \quad 23, \quad 29, \quad 31, \ldots$$

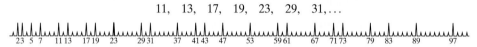

continuing through 97. Then it starts all over again. Ellie is convinced that only intelligent life could generate the structure in the sequence of pulses. "It's hard to imagine some radiating plasma sending out a regular set of mathematical signals like this." What is it about the structure of the pulses that the book's heroine recognizes as the sign of intelligent life? Asked in another way, what is significant about the number of pulses?

90. There are two species of insects, *Magicicada septendecim* and *Magicicada tredecim*, that live in the same environment. They have a life cycle of exactly 17 and 13 years, respectively. For all but their last year, they remain in the ground feeding on the sap of tree roots. Then, in their last year, they emerge en masse from the ground as fully formed cricketlike insects, taking over the forest in a single night. They chirp loudly, mate, eat, lay eggs, then die six weeks later.

(Source: Marcus du Sautoy, The Music of the Primes, HarperCollins, 2003)

a. Suppose that the two species have life cycles that are not prime, say 18 and 12 years, respectively. List the set of multiples of 18 that are less than or equal to 216. List the set of multiples of 12 that are less than or equal to 216. Over a 216-year period, how many times will the two species emerge in the same year and compete to share the forest?

b. Recall that both species have evolved prime-number life cycles, 17 and 13 years, respectively. Find the least common multiple of 17 and 13. How often will the two species have to share the forest?

c. Compare your answers to parts (a) and (b). What explanation can you offer for each species having a prime number of years as the length of its life cycle?

91. A relief worker needs to divide 300 bottles of water and 144 cans of food into groups that each contain the same number of items. Also, each group must have the same type of item (bottled water or canned food). What is the largest number of relief supplies that can be put in each group?

92. A choral director needs to divide 180 men and 144 women into all-male and all-female singing groups so that each group has the same number of people. What is the largest number of people that can be placed in each singing group?

93. You have in front of you 310 five-dollar bills and 460 ten-dollar bills. Your problem: Place the five-dollar bills and the ten-dollar bills in stacks so that each stack has the same number of bills, and each stack contains only one kind of bill (five-dollar or ten-dollar). What is the largest number of bills that you can place in each stack?

94. Harley collects sports cards. He has 360 football cards and 432 baseball cards. Harley plans to arrange his cards in stacks so that each stack has the same number of cards. Also, each stack must have the same type of card (football or baseball). Every card in Harley's collection is to be placed in one of the stacks. What is the largest number of cards that can be placed in each stack?

95. You and your brother both work the 4:00 P.M. to midnight shift. You have every sixth night off. Your brother has every tenth night off. Both of you were off on June 1. Your brother would like to see a movie with you. When will the two of you have the same night off again?

96. A movie theater runs its films continuously. One movie is a short documentary that runs for 40 minutes. The other movie is a full-length feature that runs for 100 minutes. Each film is shown in a separate theater. Both movies begin at noon. When will the movies begin again at the same time?

97. Two people are jogging around a circular track in the same direction. One person can run completely around the track in 15 minutes. The second person takes 18 minutes. If they both start running in the same place at the same time, how long will it take them to be together at this place if they continue to run?

98. Two people are in a bicycle race around a circular track. One rider can race completely around the track in 40 seconds. The other rider takes 45 seconds. If they both begin the race at a designated starting point, how long will it take them to be together at this starting point again if they continue to race around the track?

• Writing in Mathematics

99. If *a* is a factor of *c*, what does this mean?

100. Why is 45 divisible by 5?

101. What does "*a* is divisible by *b*" mean?

102. Describe the difference between a prime number and a composite number.

103. What does the Fundamental Theorem of Arithmetic state?

104. What is the greatest common divisor of two or more natural numbers?

105. Describe how to find the greatest common divisor of two numbers.

106. What is the least common multiple of two or more natural numbers?

107. Describe how to find the least common multiple of two natural numbers.

108. The process of finding the greatest common divisor of two natural numbers is similar to finding the least common multiple of the numbers. Describe how the two processes differ.

109. What does the Blitzer Bonus on page 46 have to do with Gödel's discovery about mathematics and logic?

• Critical Thinking Exercises

110. Write a four-digit natural number that is divisible by 4 and not by 8.

111. Find the greatest common divisor and the least common multiple of $2^{17} \cdot 3^{25} \cdot 5^{31}$ and $2^{14} \cdot 3^{37} \cdot 5^{30}$. Express answers in the same form as the numbers given.

112. A middle-age man observed that his present age was a prime number. He also noticed that the number of years in which his age would again be prime was equal to the number of years ago in which his age was prime. How old is the man?

113. A movie theater runs its films continuously. One movie runs for 85 minutes and a second runs for 100 minutes. The theater has a 15-minute intermission after each movie, at which point the movie is shown again. If both movies start at noon, when will the two movies start again at the same time?

114. The difference between consecutive prime numbers is always an even number, except for two particular prime numbers. What are those numbers?

• Technology Exercises

Use the divisibility rules listed in Table 2.1 on page 43 to answer the questions in Exercises 115–117. Then, using a calculator, perform the actual division to determine whether your answer is correct.

115. Is 67,234,096 divisible by 4?

116. Is 12,541,750 divisible by 3?

117. Is 48,201,651 divisible by 9?

• Group Exercises

The following topics from number theory are appropriate for either individual or group research projects. A report should be given to the class on the researched topic. Useful references include liberal arts mathematics textbooks, books about numbers and number theory, books whose purpose is to excite the reader about mathematics, history of mathematics books, encyclopedias, and the World Wide Web.

118. Euclid and Number Theory

119. An Unsolved Problem from Number Theory

120. Perfect Numbers

121. Deficient and Abundant Numbers

122. Formulas that Yield Primes

123. The Sieve of Eratosthenes

SECTION 2.2 • THE INTEGERS; ORDER OF OPERATIONS

OBJECTIVES

1. Define the integers.
2. Graph integers on a number line.
3. Use the symbols $<$ and $>$.
4. Find the absolute value of an integer.
5. Perform operations with integers.
6. Use the order of operations agreement.

From the political left and right, watchdogs of the federal budget are warning of fiscal trouble. David Walker, Comptroller General of the United States and the nation's top auditor, admits to being "terrified" about the budget deficit in coming decades. To hear him tell it, the United States can be likened to Rome before the fall of the empire. America's financial condition is "worse than advertised," he says. It has a "broken business model. It faces deficits in its budget, its balance of payments, and its savings." In this section, we use operations on a set of numbers called the *integers* to describe numerically the sad state of the nation's finances.

1 Define the integers.

Defining the Integers

In Section 2.1, we applied some ideas of number theory to the set of natural, or counting, numbers:

$$\text{Natural numbers} = \{1, 2, 3, 4, 5, \ldots\}.$$

When we combine the number 0 with the natural numbers, we obtain the set of **whole numbers**:

$$\text{Whole numbers} = \{0, 1, 2, 3, 4, 5, \ldots\}.$$

The whole numbers do not allow us to describe certain everyday situations. For example, if the balance in your checking account is $30 and you write a check for $35, your checking account is overdrawn by $5. We can write this as -5, read *negative* 5. The set consisting of the natural numbers, 0, and the negatives of the natural numbers is called the set of **integers**.

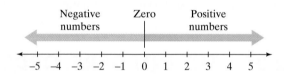

Notice that the term *positive integers* is another name for the natural numbers. The positive integers can be written in two ways:

1. Use a "+" sign. For example, +4 is "positive four."
2. Do not write any sign. For example, 4 is assumed to be "positive four."

The Number Line; The Symbols < and >

The **number line** is a graph we use to visualize the set of integers, as well as sets of other numbers. The number line is shown in Figure 2.1.

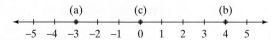

FIGURE 2.1 The number line

The number line extends indefinitely in both directions, shown by the arrows on the left and right. Zero separates the positive numbers from the negative numbers on the number line. The positive integers are located to the right of 0 and the negative integers are located to the left of 0. **Zero is neither positive nor negative.** For every positive integer on a number line, there is a corresponding negative integer on the opposite side of 0.

Integers are graphed on a number line by placing a dot at the correct location for each number.

2 Graph integers on a number line.

EXAMPLE 1   GRAPHING INTEGERS ON A NUMBER LINE

Graph: **a.** -3 **b.** 4   **c.** 0.

SOLUTION Place a dot at the correct location for each integer.

CHECK POINT **1**   Graph:

       a. -4 **b.** 0   **c.** 3.

3 | Use the symbols < and >.

We will use the following symbols for comparing two integers:

< means "is less than."

> means "is greater than."

On the number line, the integers increase from left to right. The *lesser* of two integers is the one farther to the *left* on a number line. The *greater* of two integers is the one farther to the *right* on a number line.

Look at the number line in Figure 2.2. The integers -4 and -1 are graphed.

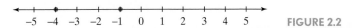

FIGURE 2.2

Observe that -4 is to the left of -1 on the number line. This means that -4 is less than -1.

$$-4 < -1$$ ⟵ −4 is less than −1 because −4 is to the **left** of −1 on the number line.

In Figure 2.2, we can also observe that -1 is to the right of -4 on the number line. This means that -1 is greater than -4.

$$-1 > -4$$ ⟵ −1 is greater than −4 because −1 is to the **right** of −4 on the number line.

The symbols < and > are called **inequality symbols**. These symbols always point to the lesser of the two real numbers when the inequality statement is true.

−4 is less than −1. ⟶ $-4 < -1$ The symbol points to -4, the lesser number.

−1 is greater than −4. ⟶ $-1 > -4$ The symbol still points to -4, the lesser number.

EXAMPLE 2   USING THE SYMBOLS < AND >

Insert either < or > in the shaded area between the integers to make each statement true:

a. $-4 \blacksquare 3$ **b.** $-1 \blacksquare -5$ **c.** $-5 \blacksquare -2$ **d.** $0 \blacksquare -3$.

SOLUTION The solution is illustrated by the number line in Figure 2.3.

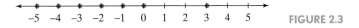

FIGURE 2.3

a. $-4 < 3$ (negative 4 is less than 3) because -4 is to the left of 3 on the number line.

b. $-1 > -5$ (negative 1 is greater than negative 5) because -1 is to the right of -5 on the number line.

c. $-5 < -2$ (negative 5 is less than negative 2) because -5 is to the left of -2 on the number line.

d. $0 > -3$ (zero is greater than negative 3) because 0 is to the right of -3 on the number line.

 Insert either < or > in the shaded area between the integers to make each statement true:

a. $6 \blacksquare -7$ **b.** $-8 \blacksquare -1$ **c.** $-25 \blacksquare -2$ **d.** $-14 \blacksquare 0$.

The symbols $<$ and $>$ may be combined with an equal sign, as shown in the following table:

	Symbols	Meaning	Examples	Explanation
This inequality is true if either the $<$ part or the $=$ part is true.	$a \leq b$	a is less than or equal to b.	$2 \leq 9$ $9 \leq 9$	Because $2 < 9$ Because $9 = 9$
This inequality is true if either the $>$ part or the $=$ part is true.	$b \geq a$	b is greater than or equal to a.	$9 \geq 2$ $2 \geq 2$	Because $9 > 2$ Because $2 = 2$

4 | Find the absolute value of an integer.

Absolute Value

Absolute value describes distance from 0 on a number line. If a represents an integer, the symbol $|a|$, represents its absolute value, read "the absolute value of a." For example,

$$|-5| = 5.$$

The absolute value of -5 is 5 because -5 is 5 units from 0 on a number line.

> **ABSOLUTE VALUE**
> The **absolute value** of an integer a, denoted by $|a|$, is the distance from 0 to a on the number line. Because absolute value describes a distance, it is never negative.

EXAMPLE 3   FINDING ABSOLUTE VALUE

Find the absolute value:

a. $|-3|$ **b.** $|5|$ **c.** $|0|$.

SOLUTION

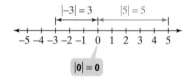

a. $|-3| = 3$ The absolute value of -3 is 3 because -3 is 3 units from 0.

b. $|5| = 5$ 5 is 5 units from 0.

c. $|0| = 0$ 0 is 0 units from itself.

Example 3 illustrates that the absolute value of a positive integer or 0 is the number itself. The absolute value of a negative integer, such as -3, is the number without the negative sign. Zero is the only real number whose absolute value is 0: $|0| = 0$. **The absolute value of any integer other than 0 is always positive.**

 Find the absolute value:

a. $|-8|$ **b.** $|6|$.

5 | Perform operations with integers.

Addition of Integers

It has not been a good day! First, you lost your wallet with $30 in it. Then, you borrowed $10 to get through the day, which you somehow misplaced. Your loss of $30 followed by a loss of $10 is an overall loss of $40. This can be written

$$-30 + (-10) = -40.$$

The result of adding two or more numbers is called the **sum** of the numbers. The sum of -30 and -10 is -40.

You can think of gains and losses of money to find sums. For example, to find $17 + (-13)$, think of a gain of $17 followed by a loss of $13. There is an overall gain of $4. Thus, $17 + (-13) = 4$. In the same way, to find $-17 + 13$, think of a loss of $17 followed by a gain of $13. There is an overall loss of $4, so $-17 + 13 = -4$.

Using gains and losses, we can develop the following rules for adding integers:

RULES FOR ADDITION OF INTEGERS

Rule   **Examples**

If the integers have the same sign,

1. Add their absolute values. $-11 + (-15) = -26$ > Add absolute values:
2. The sign of the sum is the   11 + 15 = 26.
   same as the sign of the two   > Use the common sign.
   numbers.

If the integers have different $-13 + 4 = -9$ > Subtract absolute values:
signs,   13 − 4 = 9.
1. Subtract the smaller   > Use the sign of the number with
   absolute value from the   the greater absolute value.
   larger absolute value.
2. The sign of the sum is the $13 + (-6) = 7$ > Subtract absolute values:
   same as the sign of the   13 − 6 = 7.
   number with the larger
   absolute value.   > Use the sign of the number with
                                    the greater absolute value.

TECHNOLOGY

CALCULATORS AND ADDING INTEGERS

You can use a calculator to add integers. Here are the keystrokes for finding $-11 + (-15)$:

SCIENTIFIC CALCULATOR

11 $+/-$ $+$ 15 $+/-$ $=$

GRAPHING CALCULATOR

$(-)$ 11 $+$ $(-)$ 15 ENTER .

Here are the keystrokes for finding $-13 + 4$:

SCIENTIFIC CALCULATOR

13 $+/-$ $+$ 4 $=$

GRAPHING CALCULATOR

$(-)$ 13 $+$ 4 ENTER .

STUDY TIP

In addition to gains and losses of money, another good analogy for adding integers is temperatures above and below zero on a thermometer. Think of the thermometer as a number line standing straight up. For example,

$$-11 + (-15) = -26$$

> If it's 11 below zero and the temperature falls 15 degrees, it will then be 26 below zero.

$$-13 + 4 = -9$$

> If it's 13 below zero and the temperature rises 4 degrees, the new temperature will be 9 below zero.

$$13 + (-6) = 7.$$

> If it's 13 above zero and the temperature falls 6 degrees, it will then be 7 above zero.

Using the analogies of gains and losses of money or temperatures can make the formal rules for addition of integers easy to use.

Can you guess what number is displayed if you use a calculator to find a sum such as $18 + (-18)$? If you gain 18 and then lose 18, there is neither an overall gain or loss. Thus,

$$18 + (-18) = 0.$$

We call 18 and -18 **additive inverses**. Additive inverses have the same absolute value, but lie on opposite sides of zero on the number line. Thus, -7 is the additive inverse of 7, and 5 is the additive inverse of -5. In general, the sum of any integer and its additive inverse is 0:

$$a + (-a) = 0.$$

Subtraction of Integers

Suppose that a computer that normally sells for $1500 has a price reduction of $600. The computer's reduced price, $900, can be expressed in two ways:

$$1500 - 600 = 900 \quad \text{or} \quad 1500 + (-600) = 900.$$

This means that

$$1500 - 600 = 1500 + (-600).$$

To subtract 600 from 1500, we add 1500 and the additive inverse of 600. Generalizing from this situation, we define subtraction as follows:

> **DEFINITION OF SUBTRACTION**
> For all integers a and b,
> $$a - b = a + (-b).$$
> In words, to subtract b from a, add the additive inverse of b to a. The result of subtraction is called the **difference**.

TECHNOLOGY

CALCULATORS AND SUBTRACTING INTEGERS

You can use a calculator to subtract integers. Here are the keystrokes for finding $17 - (-11)$:

SCIENTIFIC CALCULATOR

17 − 11 +/− =

GRAPHING CALCULATOR

17 − (−) 11 ENTER .

Here are the keystrokes for finding $-18 - (-5)$:

SCIENTIFIC CALCULATOR

18 +/− − 5 +/− =

GRAPHING CALCULATOR

(−) 18 − (−) 5 ENTER .

Don't confuse the subtraction key on a graphing calculator, − , with the sign change or additive inverse key, (−) . What happens if you do?

EXAMPLE 4   SUBTRACTING INTEGERS

Subtract:

a. $17 - (-11)$ **b.** $-18 - (-5)$ **c.** $-18 - 5$.

SOLUTION

a. $17 - (-11) = 17 + 11 = 28$

> Change the subtraction to addition.   Replace −11 with its additive inverse.

b. $-18 - (-5) = -18 + 5 = -13$

> Change the subtraction to addition.   Replace −5 with its additive inverse.

c. $-18 - 5 = -18 + (-5) = -23$

> Change the subtraction to addition.   Replace 5 with its additive inverse.

CHECK POINT 4   Subtract:

a. $30 - (-7)$ **b.** $-14 - (-10)$ **c.** $-14 - 10$.

STUDY TIP

You can think of subtracting a negative integer as taking away a debt. Let's apply this analogy to $17 - (-11)$. Your checking account balance is $17 after an erroneous $11 charge was made against your account. When you bring this error to the bank's attention, they will take away the $11 debit and your balance will go up to $28:

$$17 - (-11) = 28.$$

Subtraction is used to solve problems in which the word *difference* appears. The difference between integers a and b is expressed as $a - b$.

EXAMPLE 5	AN APPLICATION OF SUBTRACTION USING THE WORD *DIFFERENCE*

The bar graph in Figure 2.4 shows the budget surplus or deficit for the United States government from 2000 through 2005. What is the difference between the 2000 surplus and the 2005 deficit?

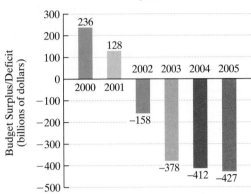

U.S. Government Budget Surplus/Deficit

FIGURE 2.4
Source: Budget of the U.S. Government

SOLUTION

The difference	is	the 2000 surplus	minus	the 2005 deficit.

$$= 236 \quad - \quad (-427)$$
$$= 236 + 427 = 663$$

The difference between the 2000 surplus and the 2005 deficit is $663 billion.

 Use Figure 2.4 to find the difference between the 2004 deficit and the 2005 deficit.

Multiplication of Integers

The result of multiplying two or more numbers is called the **product** of the numbers. You can think of multiplication as repeated addition or subtraction that starts at 0. For example,

$$3(-4) = 0 + (-4) + (-4) + (-4) = -12$$

The numbers have different signs and the product is negative.

and

$$(-3)(-4) = 0 - (-4) - (-4) - (-4) = 0 + 4 + 4 + 4 = 12.$$

The numbers have the same sign and the product is positive.

These observations give us the following rules for multiplying integers:

RULES FOR MULTIPLYING INTEGERS

Rule   **Examples**

1. The product of two integers with different signs is found by multiplying their absolute values. The product is negative.

- $7(-5) = -35$

2. The product of two integers with the same sign is found by multiplying their absolute values. The product is positive.

- $(-6)(-11) = 66$

3. The product of 0 and any integer is 0:

$a \cdot 0 = 0$ and $0 \cdot a = 0.$

- $-17(0) = 0$

4. If no number is 0, a product with an odd number of negative factors is found by multiplying absolute values. The product is negative.

- $-2(-3)(-5) = -30$

    Three (odd) negative factors

5. If no number is 0, a product with an even number of negative factors is found by multiplying absolute values. The product is positive.

- $-2(3)(-5) = 30$

    Two (even) negative factors

Exponential Notation

Because exponents indicate repeated multiplication, rules for multiplying real numbers can be used to evaluate exponential expressions.

EXAMPLE 6   EVALUATING EXPONENTIAL EXPRESSIONS

Evaluate: **a.** $(-6)^2$ **b.** -6^2 **c.** $(-5)^3$ **d.** $(-2)^4.$

SOLUTION

a. $(-6)^2 = (-6)(-6) = 36$

Base is −6.   Same signs give positive product.

b. $-6^2 = -(6 \cdot 6) = -36$

Base is 6. The negative is not inside parentheses and is not taken to the second power.

c. $(-5)^3 = (-5)(-5)(-5) = -125$

An odd number of negative factors gives a negative product.

d. $(-2)^4 = (-2)(-2)(-2)(-2) = 16$

An even number of negative factors gives a positive product.

 Evaluate:

a. $(-5)^2$ **b.** -5^2 **c.** $(-4)^3$ **d.** $(-3)^4.$

BLITZER BONUS

Exponential Representations of the Beast

The New Testament book of Revelation designates 666 as the Number of the Beast (the Antichrist):

"Here is wisdom. Let him that hath understanding count the number of the beast: for it is the number of a man; and his number is six hundred threescore and six." (Revelation 13:18)

Although your author has no idea of what this actually means, he is intrigued by the beast's curious exponential representations:

$$666 = 6 + 6 + 6 + 6^3 + 6^3 + 6^3$$

$$666 = 1^3 + 2^3 + 3^3 + 4^3 + 5^3 + 6^3 + 5^3 + 4^3 + 3^3 + 2^3 + 1^3$$

$$666 = 2^2 + 3^2 + 5^2 + 7^2 + 11^2 + 13^2 + 17^2$$

> Sum of the squares of the first seven prime numbers

$$666 = 1^6 - 2^6 + 3^6.$$

The beast is even interesting in Roman numerals:

$$666 = \text{DCLXVI.}$$

> Contains all Roman numerals from D(500) to I (1) in decending order

Division of Integers

The result of dividing the integer a by the nonzero integer b is called the **quotient** of the numbers. We can write this quotient as $a \div b$ or $\frac{a}{b}$.

A relationship exists between multiplication and division. For example,

$$\frac{-12}{4} = -3 \text{ means that } 4(-3) = -12.$$

$$\frac{-12}{-4} = 3 \text{ means that } -4(3) = -12.$$

Because of the relationship between multiplication and division, the rules for obtaining the sign of a quotient are the same as those for obtaining the sign of a product.

TECHNOLOGY

MULTIPLYING AND DIVIDING ON A CALCULATOR

Example: $(-173)(-256)$

SCIENTIFIC CALCULATOR

173 [+/-] [×] 256 [+/-] [=]

GRAPHING CALCULATOR

[(−)] 173 [×] [(−)] 256 [ENTER]

The number 44288 should be displayed.
Division is performed in the same manner, using [÷] instead of [×]. What happens when you divide by 0? Try entering

8 [÷] 0

and pressing [=] or [ENTER].

RULES FOR DIVIDING INTEGERS

Rule	Examples
1. The quotient of two integers with different signs is found by dividing their absolute values. The quotient is negative.	• $\frac{80}{-4} = -20$ • $\frac{-15}{5} = -3$
2. The quotient of two integers with the same sign is found by dividing their absolute values. The quotient is positive.	• $\frac{27}{9} = 3$ • $\frac{-45}{-3} = 15$
3. Zero divided by any nonzero integer is zero.	• $\frac{0}{-5} = 0$ (because $-5(0) = 0$)
4. Division by 0 is undefined.	• $\frac{-8}{0}$ is undefined (because 0 cannot be multiplied by an integer to obtain -8).

6 Use the order of operations agreement.

Order of Operations

Suppose that you want to find the value of $3 + 7 \cdot 5$. Which procedure shown below is correct?

$$3 + 7 \cdot 5 = 3 + 35 = 38 \quad \text{or} \quad 3 + 7 \cdot 5 = 10 \cdot 5 = 50$$

If you know the answer, you probably know certain rules, called the **order of operations**, to make sure that there is only one correct answer. One of these rules states that if a problem contains no parentheses, perform multiplication before addition. Thus, the procedure on the left is correct because the multiplication of 7 and 5 is done first. Then the addition is performed. The correct answer is 38.

Here are the rules for determining the order in which operations should be performed:

STUDY TIP

Here's a sentence to help remember the order of operations: "Please excuse my dear Aunt Sally."

Please	**P**arentheses
Excuse	**E**xponents
{ **M**y	{ **M**ultiplication
{ **D**ear	{ **D**ivision
{ **A**unt	{ **A**ddition
{ **S**ally	{ **S**ubtraction

ORDER OF OPERATIONS

1. Perform all operations within grouping symbols.
2. Evaluate all exponential expressions.
3. Do all multiplications and divisions in the order in which they occur, working from left to right.
4. Finally, do all additions and subtractions in the order in which they occur, working from left to right.

In the third step, be sure to do all multiplications and divisions *as they occur* from left to right. For example,

$$8 \div 4 \cdot 2 = 2 \cdot 2 = 4$$

Do the division first because it occurs first.

$$8 \cdot 4 \div 2 = 32 \div 2 = 16.$$

Do the multiplication first because it occurs first.

EXAMPLE 7   USING THE ORDER OF OPERATIONS

Simplify: $6^2 - 24 \div 2^2 \cdot 3 + 1$.

SOLUTION There are no grouping symbols. Thus, we begin by evaluating exponential expressions. Then we multiply or divide. Finally, we add or subtract.

$$6^2 - 24 \div 2^2 \cdot 3 + 1$$

$$= 36 - 24 \div 4 \cdot 3 + 1$$ Evaluate exponential expressions: $6^2 = 6 \cdot 6 = 36$ and $2^2 = 2 \cdot 2 = 4$.

$$= 36 - 6 \cdot 3 + 1$$ Perform the multiplications and divisions from left to right. Start with $24 \div 4 = 6$.

$$= 36 - 18 + 1$$ Now do the multiplication: $6 \cdot 3 = 18$.

$$= 18 + 1$$ Finally, perform the additions and subtractions from left to right. Subtract: $36 - 18 = 18$.

$$= 19$$ Add: $18 + 1 = 19$.

 7 Simplify: $7^2 - 48 \div 4^2 \cdot 5 + 2$.

EXAMPLE 8   USING THE ORDER OF OPERATIONS

Simplify: $(-6)^2 - (5 - 7)^2(-3)$.

SOLUTION   Because grouping symbols appear, we perform the operation within parentheses first.

$$(-6)^2 - (5 - 7)^2(-3)$$

$$= (-6)^2 - (-2)^2(-3)$$ Work inside parentheses first:
$5 - 7 = 5 + (-7) = -2$.

$$= 36 - 4(-3)$$ Evaluate exponential expressions:
$(-6)^2 = (-6)(-6) = 36$ and
$(-2)^2 = (-2)(-2) = 4$.

$$= 36 - (-12)$$ Multiply: $4(-3) = -12$.

$$= 48$$ Subtract: $36 - (-12) = 36 + 12 = 48$.

 Simplify $(-8)^2 - (10 - 13)^2(-2)$.

EXERCISE SET 2.2 ●●●●●●

• Practice Exercises

In Exercises 1–4, start by drawing a number line that shows integers from −5 to 5. Then graph each of the following integers on your number line.

1. 3   **2.** 5   **3.** −4   **4.** −2

In Exercises 5–12, insert either < or > in the shaded area between the integers to make the statement true.

5. −2 ■ 7   **6.** −1 ■ 13   **7.** −13 ■ −2   **8.** −1 ■ −13
9. 8 ■ −50   **10.** 7 ■ −9   **11.** −100 ■ 0   **12.** 0 ■ −300

In Exercises 13–18, find the absolute value.

13. $|-14|$ **14.** $|-16|$ **15.** $|14|$
16. $|16|$ **17.** $|-300,000|$ **18.** $|-1,000,000|$

In Exercises 19–30, find each sum.

19. $-7 + (-5)$ **20.** $-3 + (-4)$ **21.** $12 + (-8)$
22. $13 + (-5)$ **23.** $6 + (-9)$ **24.** $3 + (-11)$
25. $-9 + (+4)$ **26.** $-7 + (+3)$ **27.** $-9 + (-9)$
28. $-13 + (-13)$ **29.** $9 + (-9)$ **30.** $13 + (-13)$

In Exercises 31–42, perform the indicated subtraction.

31. $13 - 8$ **32.** $14 - 3$ **33.** $8 - 15$
34. $9 - 20$ **35.** $4 - (-10)$ **36.** $3 - (-17)$
37. $-6 - (-17)$ **38.** $-4 - (-19)$ **39.** $-12 - (-3)$
40. $-19 - (-2)$ **41.** $-11 - 17$ **42.** $-19 - 21$

In Exercises 43–52, find each product.

43. $6(-9)$ **44.** $5(-7)$ **45.** $(-7)(-3)$
46. $(-8)(-5)$ **47.** $(-2)(6)$ **48.** $(-3)(10)$
49. $(-13)(-1)$ **50.** $(-17)(-1)$ **51.** $0(-5)$
52. $0(-8)$

In Exercises 53–66, evaluate each exponential expression.

53. 5^2 **54.** 6^2 **55.** $(-5)^2$ **56.** $(-6)^2$
57. 4^3 **58.** 2^3 **59.** $(-5)^3$ **60.** $(-4)^3$
61. $(-5)^4$ **62.** $(-4)^4$ **63.** -3^4 **64.** -1^4
65. $(-3)^4$ **66.** $(-1)^4$

In Exercises 67–80, find each quotient, or, if applicable, state that the expression is undefined.

67. $\frac{-12}{4}$ **68.** $\frac{-40}{5}$ **69.** $\frac{21}{-3}$ **70.** $\frac{60}{-6}$
71. $\frac{-90}{-3}$ **72.** $\frac{-66}{-6}$ **73.** $\frac{0}{-7}$ **74.** $\frac{0}{-8}$
75. $\frac{-7}{0}$ **76.** $\frac{0}{0}$
77. $(-480) \div 24$ **78.** $(-300) \div 12$
79. $(465) \div (-15)$ **80.** $(-594) \div (-18)$

In Exercises 81–98, use the order of operations to find the value of each expression.

81. $7 + 6 \cdot 3$ **82.** $-5 + (-3) \cdot 8$
83. $(-5) - 6(-3)$ **84.** $-8(-3) - 5(-6)$
85. $6 - 4(-3) - 5$ **86.** $3 - 7(-1) - 6$
87. $3 - 5(-4 - 2)$ **88.** $3 - 9(-1 - 6)$
89. $(2 - 6)(-3 - 5)$ **90.** $9 - 5(6 - 4) - 10$
91. $3(-2)^2 - 4(-3)^2$ **92.** $5(-3)^2 - 2(-2)^3$
93. $(2 - 6)^2 - (3 - 7)^2$ **94.** $(4 - 6)^2 - (5 - 9)^3$
95. $6(3 - 5)^3 - 2(1 - 3)^3$
96. $-3(-6 + 8)^3 - 5(-3 + 5)^3$
97. $8^2 - 16 \div 2^2 \cdot 4 - 3$
98. $10^2 - 100 \div 5^2 \cdot 2 - (-3)$

• Practice Plus

In Exercises 99–104, use the order of operations to find the value of each expression.

99. $8 - 3[-2(2 - 5) - 4(8 - 6)]$

100. $8 - 3[-2(5 - 7) - 5(4 - 2)]$

101. $-2^2 + 4[16 \div (3 - 5)]$

102. $-3^2 + 2[20 \div (7 - 11)]$

103. $4|10 - (8 - 20)|$

104. $-5|7 - (20 - 8)|$

In Exercises 105–108, express each sentence as a single numerical expression. Then use the order of operations to simplify the expression.

105. Cube -2. Subtract this exponential expression from -10.

106. Cube -5. Subtract this exponential expression from -100.

107. Subtract 10 from 7. Multiply this difference by 2. Square this product.

108. Subtract 11 from 9. Multiply this difference by 2. Raise this product to the fourth power.

• Application Exercises

The bar graph shows the U.S. trade balance in goods and services, in billions of dollars, from 2000 through 2005. The most complete scorecard of the U.S. international trade performance deteriorated to a record $805 billion deficit in 2005. Use the information shown by the graph to solve Exercises 109–112. Express answers in billions of dollars.

U.S. Trade Deficit

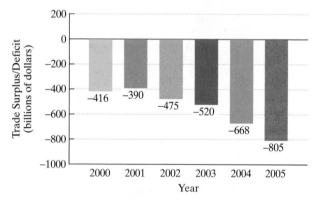

Source: Bureau of Economic Analysis

109. Find the difference between the 2000 trade deficit and the 2005 trade deficit.

110. Find the difference between the 2001 trade deficit and the 2005 trade deficit.

111. By how much did the 2005 deficit exceed twice the 2001 deficit?

112. Find the average trade deficit for 2003 and 2004 combined. By how much did the 2005 deficit exceed this average?

113. The peak of Mount Kilimanjaro, the highest point in Africa, is 19,321 feet above sea level. Qattara Depression, Egypt, the lowest point in Africa, is 436 feet below sea level. What is the difference in elevation between the peak of Mount Kilimanjaro and the Qattara Depression?

114. The peak of Mount Everest is 8848 meters above sea level. The Marianas Trench, on the floor of the Pacific Ocean, is 10,915 meters below sea level. What is the difference in elevation between the peak of Mount Everest and the Marianas Trench?

The following table shows the amount of money, in billions of dollars, collected and spent by the U.S. government from 2001 through 2005. Use the information from the table to solve Exercises 115–118. Express answers in billions of dollars.

Year	Money Collected (billions of dollars)	Money Spent (billions of dollars)
2001	$1991	$1863
2002	$1853	$2011
2003	$1782	$2160
2004	$1880	$2292
2005	$2053	$2479

Source: Budget of the U.S. Government

115. In 2002, what was the difference between the amount of money collected and the amount spent? Was there a budget surplus or deficit in 2002?

116. In 2003, what was the difference between the amount of money collected and the amount spent? Was there a budget surplus or deficit in 2003?

117. What is the difference between the 2001 surplus and the 2005 deficit?

118. What is the difference between the 2001 surplus and the 2004 deficit?

The way that we perceive the temperature on a cold day depends on both air temperature and wind speed. The windchill is what the air temperature would have to be with no wind to achieve the same chilling effect on the skin. In 2002, the National Weather Service issued new windchill temperatures, shown in the table below. Use the information from the table to solve Exercises 119–122.

New Windchill Temperature Index

	\multicolumn{11}{c}{Air Temperature (°F)}

Wind Speed (miles per hour)	30	25	20	15	10	5	0	−5	−10	−15	−20	−25
5	25	19	13	7	1	−5	−11	−16	−22	−28	−34	−40
10	21	15	9	3	−4	−10	−16	−22	−28	−35	−41	−47
15	19	13	6	0	−7	−13	−19	−26	−32	−39	−45	−51
20	17	11	4	−2	−9	−15	−22	−29	−35	−42	−48	−55
25	16	9	3	−4	−11	−17	−24	−31	−37	−44	−51	−58
30	15	8	1	−5	−12	−19	−26	−33	−39	−46	−53	−60
35	14	7	0	−7	−14	−21	−27	−34	−41	−48	−55	−62
40	13	6	−1	−8	−15	−22	−29	−36	−43	−50	−57	−64
45	12	5	−2	−9	−16	−23	−30	−37	−44	−51	−58	−65
50	12	4	−3	−10	−17	−24	−31	−38	−45	−52	−60	−67
55	11	4	−3	−11	−18	−25	−32	−39	−46	−54	−61	−68
60	10	3	−4	−11	−19	−26	−33	−40	−48	−55	−62	−69

Frostbite occurs in 15 minutes or less.

Source: National Weather Service

119. What is the difference between how cold the temperature feels with winds at 10 miles per hour and 25 miles per hour when the air temperature is 15°F?

120. What is the difference between how cold the temperature feels with winds at 5 miles per hour and 30 miles per hour when the air temperature is 10°F?

121. What is the difference in the windchill temperature between an air temperature of 5°F with winds at 50 miles per hour and an air temperature of −10°F with winds at 5 miles per hour?

122. What is the difference in the windchill temperature between an air temperature of 5°F with winds at 55 miles per hour and an air temperature of −5°F with winds at 10 miles per hour?

• Writing in Mathematics

123. How does the set of integers differ from the set of whole numbers?

124. Explain how to graph an integer on a number line.

125. If you are given two integers, explain how to determine which one is smaller.

126. Explain how to add integers.

127. Explain how to subtract integers.

128. Explain how to multiply integers.

129. Explain how to divide integers.

130. Describe what it means to raise a number to a power. In your description, include a discussion of the difference between -5^2 and $(-5)^2$.

131. Why is $\frac{0}{4}$ equal to 0, but $\frac{4}{0}$ undefined?

• Critical Thinking Exercises

In Exercises 132–133, insert one pair of parentheses to make each calculation correct.

132. $8 - 2 \cdot 3 - 4 = 10$

133. $8 - 2 \cdot 3 - 4 = 14$

• Technology Exercises

Scientific calculators that have parentheses keys allow for the entry and computation of relatively complicated expressions in a single step. For example, the expression $15 + (10 - 7)^2$ can be evaluated by entering the following keystrokes:

$$15 \;\boxed{+}\; \boxed{(} \; 10 \; \boxed{-} \; 7 \; \boxed{)} \; \boxed{y^x} \; 2 \; \boxed{=}.$$

Find the value of each expression in Exercises 134–136 in a single step on your scientific calculator.

134. $8 - 2 \cdot 3 - 9$

135. $(8 - 2) \cdot (3 - 9)$

136. $5^3 + 4 \cdot 9 - (8 + 9 \div 3)$

SECTION 2.3 • THE RATIONAL NUMBERS

OBJECTIVES

1. Define the rational numbers.

2. Reduce rational numbers.

3. Convert between mixed numbers and improper fractions.

4. Express rational numbers as decimals.

5. Express decimals in the form $\frac{a}{b}$.

6. Multiply and divide rational numbers.

7. Add and subtract rational numbers.

8. Apply the density property of rational numbers.

9. Solve problems involving rational numbers.

You are making eight dozen chocolate chip cookies for a large neighborhood block party. The recipe lists the ingredients needed to prepare five dozen cookies, such as $\frac{3}{4}$ cup sugar. How do you adjust the amount of sugar, as well as each of the other ingredients, given in the recipe?

Adapting a recipe to suit a different number of portions usually involves working with numbers that are not integers. For example, the number describing the amount of sugar, $\frac{3}{4}$ (cup), is not an integer, although it consists of the quotient of two integers, 3 and 4. Before returning to the problem of changing the size of a recipe, we study a new set of numbers consisting of the quotient of integers.

1 | Define the rational numbers.

Defining the Rational Numbers

If two integers are added, subtracted, or multiplied, the result is always another integer. This, however, is not always the case with division. For example, 10 divided by 5 is the integer 2. By contrast, 5 divided by 10 is $\frac{1}{2}$, and $\frac{1}{2}$ is not an integer. To permit divisions such as $\frac{5}{10}$, we enlarge the set of integers, calling the new collection the *rational numbers*. The set of **rational numbers** consists of all the numbers that can be expressed as a quotient of two integers, with the denominator not 0.

> **THE RATIONAL NUMBERS**
> The set of **rational numbers** is the set of all numbers which can be expressed in the form $\frac{a}{b}$, where a and b are integers and b is not equal to 0. The integer a is called the **numerator** and the integer b is called the **denominator**.

STUDY TIP

We know that the quotient of two numbers with different signs is a negative number. Thus,

$$\frac{-3}{4} = -\frac{3}{4} \quad \text{and} \quad \frac{3}{-4} = -\frac{3}{4}.$$

2 | Reduce rational numbers.

The following numbers are examples of rational numbers:

$$\frac{1}{2}, \frac{-3}{4}, 5, 0.$$

The integer 5 is a rational number because it can be expressed as the quotient of integers: $5 = \frac{5}{1}$. Similarly, 0 can be written as $\frac{0}{1}$.

In general, every integer a is a rational number because it can be expressed in the form $\frac{a}{1}$.

Reducing Rational Numbers

A rational number is **reduced to its lowest terms**, or **simplified**, when the numerator and denominator have no common divisors other than 1. Reducing rational numbers to lowest terms is done using the **Fundamental Principle of Rational Numbers**.

> **THE FUNDAMENTAL PRINCIPLE OF RATIONAL NUMBERS**
> If $\frac{a}{b}$ is a rational number and c is any number other than 0,
> $$\frac{a \cdot c}{b \cdot c} = \frac{a}{b}.$$
> The rational numbers $\frac{a}{b}$ and $\frac{a \cdot c}{b \cdot c}$ are called **equivalent fractions**.

When using the Fundamental Principle to reduce a rational number, the simplification can be done in one step by finding the greatest common divisor of the numerator and the denominator, and using it for c. Thus, **to reduce a rational number to its lowest terms, divide both the numerator and the denominator by their greatest common divisor.**

For example, consider the rational number $\frac{12}{100}$. The greatest common divisor of 12 and 100 is 4. We reduce to lowest terms as follows:

$$\frac{12}{100} = \frac{3 \cdot 4}{25 \cdot 4} = \frac{3}{25} \quad \text{or} \quad \frac{12}{100} = \frac{12 \div 4}{100 \div 4} = \frac{3}{25}.$$

EXAMPLE 1   REDUCING A RATIONAL NUMBER

Reduce $\frac{130}{455}$ to lowest terms.

SOLUTION Begin by finding the greatest common divisor of 130 and 455.

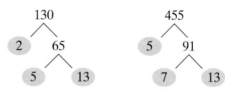

Thus, $130 = 2 \cdot 5 \cdot 13$ and $455 = 5 \cdot 7 \cdot 13$. The greatest common divisor is $5 \cdot 13$, or 65. Divide the numerator and the denominator of the given rational number by $5 \cdot 13$ or by 65.

$$\frac{130}{455} = \frac{2 \cdot 5 \cdot 13}{5 \cdot 7 \cdot 13} = \frac{2}{7} \quad \text{or} \quad \frac{130}{455} = \frac{130 \div 65}{455 \div 65} = \frac{2}{7}$$

There are no common divisors of 2 and 7 other than 1. Thus, the rational number $\frac{2}{7}$ is in its lowest terms.

 Reduce $\frac{72}{90}$ to lowest terms.

3 | Convert between mixed numbers and improper fractions.

Mixed Numbers and Improper Fractions

A **mixed number** consists of the sum of an integer and a rational number, expressed without the use of an addition sign. Here is an example of a mixed number:

$$3\frac{4}{5}.$$

The integer is 3 and the rational number is $\frac{4}{5}$. $3\frac{4}{5}$ means $3 + \frac{4}{5}$.

An **improper fraction** is a rational number whose numerator is greater than its denominator. An example of an improper fraction is $\frac{19}{5}$.

The mixed number $3\frac{4}{5}$ can be converted to the improper fraction $\frac{19}{5}$ using the following procedure:

> **CONVERTING A POSITIVE MIXED NUMBER TO AN IMPROPER FRACTION**
>
> **1.** Multiply the denominator of the rational number by the integer and add the numerator to this product.
> **2.** Place the sum in step 1 over the denominator in the mixed number.

EXAMPLE 2   CONVERTING FROM A MIXED NUMBER TO AN IMPROPER FRACTION

Convert $3\frac{4}{5}$ to an improper fraction.

SOLUTION

$$3\frac{4}{5} = \frac{5 \cdot 3 + 4}{5}$$

Multiply the denominator by the integer and add the numerator.

Place the sum over the mixed number's denominator.

$$= \frac{15 + 4}{5} = \frac{19}{5}$$

 CHECK POINT 2 Convert $2\frac{5}{8}$ to an improper fraction.

When converting a negative mixed number to an improper fraction, copy the negative sign and then follow the previous procedure. For example,

$$-2\frac{3}{4} = -\frac{4 \cdot 2 + 3}{4} = -\frac{8 + 3}{4} = -\frac{11}{4}.$$

Copy the negative sign from step to step and convert $2\frac{3}{4}$ to an improper fraction.

A positive improper fraction can be converted to a mixed number using the following procedure:

> **CONVERTING A POSITIVE IMPROPER FRACTION TO A MIXED NUMBER**
>
> **1.** Divide the denominator into the numerator. Record the quotient and the remainder.
> **2.** Write the mixed number using the following form:
>
> $$\text{quotient } \frac{\text{remainder}}{\text{original denominator}}.$$
>
> integer part   rational number part

| EXAMPLE 3 | CONVERTING FROM AN IMPROPER FRACTION TO A MIXED NUMBER |

Convert $\frac{42}{5}$ to a mixed number.

SOLUTION

Step 1. Divide the denominator into the numerator.

$$\begin{array}{r} 8 \leftarrow \text{quotient} \\ 5\overline{)42} \\ \underline{40} \\ 2 \leftarrow \text{remainder} \end{array}$$

Step 2. Write the mixed number using quotient $\dfrac{\text{remainder}}{\text{original denominator}}$. Thus,

$$\frac{42}{5} = 8\frac{2}{5}.$$

with labels: remainder (numerator 2), original denominator (denominator 5), quotient (8)

CHECK POINT 3 Convert $\frac{5}{3}$ to a mixed number.

When converting a negative improper fraction to a mixed number, copy the negative sign and then follow the previous procedure. For example,

$$-\frac{29}{8} = -3\frac{5}{8}.$$

Copy the negative sign.

Convert $\frac{29}{8}$ to a mixed number.

$$\begin{array}{r} 3 \leftarrow \text{quotient} \\ 8\overline{)29} \\ \underline{24} \\ 5 \leftarrow \text{remainder} \end{array}$$

4 | Express rational numbers as decimals.

Rational Numbers and Decimals

We have seen that a rational number is the quotient of integers. Rational numbers can also be expressed as decimals. As shown in the place-value chart in the margin, it is convenient to represent rational numbers with denominators of 10, 100, 1000, and so on as decimals. For example,

$$\frac{7}{10} = 0.7, \quad \frac{3}{100} = 0.03, \quad \text{and} \quad \frac{8}{1000} = 0.008.$$

Any rational number $\frac{a}{b}$ can be expressed as a decimal by dividing the denominator, b, into the numerator, a.

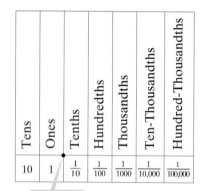

decimal point

Tens	Ones	Tenths	Hundredths	Thousandths	Ten-Thousandths	Hundred-Thousandths
10	1	$\frac{1}{10}$	$\frac{1}{100}$	$\frac{1}{1000}$	$\frac{1}{10,000}$	$\frac{1}{100,000}$

| EXAMPLE 4 | EXPRESSING RATIONAL NUMBERS AS DECIMALS |

Express each rational number as a decimal:

a. $\frac{5}{8}$ **b.** $\frac{7}{11}$.

SOLUTION In each case, divide the denominator into the numerator.

a.
$$\begin{array}{r} 0.625 \\ 8\overline{)5.000} \\ \underline{4\,8} \\ 20 \\ \underline{16} \\ 40 \\ \underline{40} \\ 0 \end{array}$$

b.
$$\begin{array}{r} 0.6363\ldots \\ 11\overline{)7.0000\ldots} \\ \underline{6\,6} \\ 40 \\ \underline{33} \\ 70 \\ \underline{66} \\ 40 \\ \underline{33} \\ 70 \\ \vdots \end{array}$$

In Example 4, the decimal for $\frac{5}{8}$, namely 0.625, stops and is called a **terminating decimal**. Other examples of terminating decimals are

$$\frac{1}{4} = 0.25, \qquad \frac{2}{5} = 0.4, \qquad \text{and} \qquad \frac{7}{8} = 0.875.$$

By contrast, the division process for $\frac{7}{11}$ results in 0.6363..., with the digits 63 repeating over and over indefinitely. To indicate this, write a bar over the digits that repeat. Thus,

$$\frac{7}{11} = 0.\overline{63}.$$

The decimal for $\frac{7}{11}$, $0.\overline{63}$, is called a **repeating decimal**. Other examples of repeating decimals are

$$\frac{1}{3} = 0.333\ldots = 0.\overline{3} \qquad \text{and} \qquad \frac{2}{3} = 0.666\ldots = 0.\overline{6}.$$

RATIONAL NUMBERS AND DECIMALS

Any rational number can be expressed as a decimal. The resulting decimal will either terminate (stop), or it will have a digit that repeats or a block of digits that repeat.

CHECK POINT 4 Express each rational number as a decimal:

a. $\frac{3}{8}$ **b.** $\frac{5}{11}$.

---

5 Express decimals in the form $\frac{a}{b}$.

Reversing Directions: Expressing Decimals as a Quotient of Two Integers

Terminating decimals can be expressed with denominators of 10, 100, 1000, 10,000, and so on. Use the place-value chart shown in the margin. The digits to the right of the decimal point are the numerator of the rational number. To find the denominator, observe the last digit to the right of the decimal point. The place-value of this digit will indicate the denominator.

Tens	Ones	Tenths	Hundredths	Thousandths	Ten-Thousandths	Hundred-Thousandths
10	1	$\frac{1}{10}$	$\frac{1}{100}$	$\frac{1}{1000}$	$\frac{1}{10,000}$	$\frac{1}{100,000}$

decimal point

EXAMPLE 5 EXPRESSING TERMINATING DECIMALS IN $\frac{a}{b}$ FORM

Express each terminating decimal as a quotient of integers:

a. 0.7 **b.** 0.49 **c.** 0.048.

SOLUTION

a. $0.7 = \frac{7}{10}$ because the 7 is in the tenths position.

b. $0.49 = \frac{49}{100}$ because the digit on the right, 9, is in the hundredths position.

c. $0.048 = \frac{48}{1000}$ because the digit on the right, 8, is in the thousandths position. Reducing to lowest terms, $\frac{48}{1000} = \frac{48 \div 8}{1000 \div 8} = \frac{6}{125}$.

CHECK POINT 5 Express each terminating decimal as a quotient of integers, reduced to lowest terms:

a. 0.9 **b.** 0.86 **c.** 0.053.

If you are given a rational number as a repeating decimal, there is a technique for expressing the number as a quotient of integers. Although we will not be discussing algebra until Chapter 3, the basic algebra used in this technique should be familiar to you. We begin by illustrating the technique with an example. Then we will summarize the steps in the procedure and apply them to another example.

EXAMPLE 6 EXPRESSING A REPEATING DECIMAL IN $\frac{a}{b}$ FORM

Express $0.\overline{6}$ as a quotient of integers.

SOLUTION

Step 1. Let n equal the repeating decimal. Let $n = 0.\overline{6}$, so that $n = 0.66666\ldots$.

Step 2. If there is one repeating digit, multiply both sides of the equation in step 1 by 10.

$n = 0.66666\ldots$	This is the equation from step 1.
$10n = 10(0.66666\ldots)$	Multiply both sides by 10.
$10n = 6.66666\ldots$	Multiplying by 10 moves the decimal point one place to the right.

Step 3. Subtract the equation in step 1 from the equation in step 2.

Remember from algebra that n means $1n$. Thus, $10n - 1n = 9n$.

$10n = 6.66666\ldots$	This is the equation from step 2.
$-\ \ n = 0.66666\ldots$	This is the equation from step 1.
$9n = 6$	

Step 4. Divide both sides of the equation in step 3 by the number in front of n and solve for n. We solve $9n = 6$ for n by dividing both sides by 9.

$9n = 6$	This is the equation from step 3.
$\dfrac{9n}{9} = \dfrac{6}{9}$	Divide both sides by 9.
$n = \dfrac{6}{9} = \dfrac{2}{3}$	Reduce $\frac{6}{9}$ to lowest terms: $\dfrac{6}{9} = \dfrac{2 \cdot \cancel{3}}{3 \cdot \cancel{3}} = \dfrac{2}{3}.$

We began the solution process with $n = 0.\overline{6}$, and now we have $n = \frac{2}{3}$. Therefore,

$$0.\overline{6} = \frac{2}{3}.$$

Here are the steps for expressing a repeating decimal as a quotient of integers. Assume that the repeating digit or digits begin directly to the right of the decimal point.

EXPRESSING A REPEATING DECIMAL AS A QUOTIENT OF INTEGERS

Step 1. Let n equal the repeating decimal.

Step 2. Multiply both sides of the equation in step 1 by 10 if one digit repeats, by 100 if two digits repeat, by 1000 if three digits repeat, and so on.

Step 3. Subtract the equation in step 1 from the equation in step 2.

Step 4. Divide both sides of the equation in step 3 by the number in front of n and solve for n.

 Express $0.\overline{2}$ as a quotient of integers.

EXAMPLE 7	EXPRESSING A REPEATING DECIMAL IN $\frac{a}{b}$ FORM

Express $0.\overline{53}$ as a quotient of integers.

SOLUTION

Step 1. Let n equal the repeating decimal. Let $n = 0.\overline{53}$, so that $n = 0.535353\ldots$.

Step 2. If there are two repeating digits, multiply both sides of the equation in step 2 by 100.

$n = 0.535353\ldots$	This is the equation from step 1.
$100n = 100(0.535353\ldots)$	Multiply both sides by 100.
$100n = 53.535353\ldots$	Multiplying by 100 moves the decimal point two places to the right.

Step 3. Subtract the equation in step 1 from the equation in step 2.

$100n = 53.535353\ldots$	This is the equation from step 2.
$-\quad n = \quad 0.535353\ldots$	This is the equation from step 1.
$99n = 53$	

Step 4. Divide both sides of the equation in step 3 by the number in front of n and solve for n. We solve $99n = 53$ for n by dividing both sides by 99.

$99n = 53$	This is the equation from step 3.
$\dfrac{99n}{99} = \dfrac{53}{99}$	Divide both sides by 99.
$n = \dfrac{53}{99}$	

Because n equals $0.\overline{53}$ and n equals $\frac{53}{99}$,

$$0.\overline{53} = \frac{53}{99}.$$

 7 Express $0.\overline{79}$ as a quotient of integers.

Multiplying and Dividing Rational Numbers

6 | Multiply and divide rational numbers.

The product of two rational numbers is found as follows:

> **MULTIPLYING RATIONAL NUMBERS**
> The product of two rational numbers is the product of their numerators divided by the product of their denominators.
> If $\frac{a}{b}$ and $\frac{c}{d}$ are rational numbers, then $\frac{a}{b} \cdot \frac{c}{d} = \frac{a \cdot c}{b \cdot d}$.

EXAMPLE 8	MULTIPLYING RATIONAL NUMBERS

Multiply. If possible, reduce the product to its lowest terms:

a. $\frac{3}{8} \cdot \frac{5}{11}$ **b.** $\left(-\frac{2}{3}\right)\left(-\frac{9}{4}\right)$ **c.** $\left(3\frac{2}{3}\right)\left(1\frac{1}{4}\right)$.

SOLUTION

a. $\frac{3}{8} \cdot \frac{5}{11} = \frac{3 \cdot 5}{8 \cdot 11} = \frac{15}{88}$

b. $\left(-\frac{2}{3}\right)\left(-\frac{9}{4}\right) = \frac{(-2)(-9)}{3 \cdot 4} = \frac{18}{12} = \frac{3 \cdot \cancel{6}}{2 \cdot \cancel{6}} = \frac{3}{2}$ or $1\frac{1}{2}$

c. $\left(3\frac{2}{3}\right)\left(1\frac{1}{4}\right) = \frac{11}{3} \cdot \frac{5}{4} = \frac{11 \cdot 5}{3 \cdot 4} = \frac{55}{12}$ or $4\frac{7}{12}$

8 Multiply. If possible, reduce the product to its lowest terms:

  a. $\frac{4}{11} \cdot \frac{2}{3}$ **b.** $\left(-\frac{3}{7}\right)\left(-\frac{14}{4}\right)$ **c.** $\left(3\frac{2}{5}\right)\left(1\frac{1}{2}\right)$.

STUDY TIP

You can divide numerators and denominators by common factors *before* performing multiplication. Then multiply the remaining factors in the numerators and multiply the remaining factors in the denominators. For example,

$$\frac{7}{15} \cdot \frac{20}{21} = \frac{\overset{1}{\cancel{7}}}{\underset{3}{\cancel{15}}} \cdot \frac{\overset{4}{\cancel{20}}}{\underset{3}{\cancel{21}}} = \frac{1 \cdot 4}{3 \cdot 3} = \frac{4}{9}.$$

Two numbers whose product is 1 are called **reciprocals**, or **multiplicative inverses**, of each other. Thus, the reciprocal of 2 is $\frac{1}{2}$ and the reciprocal of $\frac{1}{2}$ is 2 because $2 \cdot \frac{1}{2} = 1$. In general, if $\frac{c}{d}$ is a nonzero rational number, its reciprocal is $\frac{d}{c}$ because $\frac{c}{d} \cdot \frac{d}{c} = 1$.

Reciprocals are used to find the quotient of two rational numbers.

> #### DIVIDING RATIONAL NUMBERS
> The quotient of two rational numbers is the product of the first number and the reciprocal of the second number.
>   If $\frac{a}{b}$ and $\frac{c}{d}$ are rational numbers and $\frac{c}{d}$ is not 0, then $\frac{a}{b} \div \frac{c}{d} = \frac{a}{b} \cdot \frac{d}{c} = \frac{a \cdot d}{b \cdot c}$.

EXAMPLE 9   DIVIDING RATIONAL NUMBERS

Divide. If possible, reduce the quotient to its lowest terms:

  a. $\frac{4}{5} \div \frac{1}{10}$ **b.** $-\frac{3}{5} \div \frac{7}{11}$ **c.** $4\frac{3}{4} \div 1\frac{1}{2}$.

SOLUTION

a. $\frac{4}{5} \div \frac{1}{10} = \frac{4}{5} \cdot \frac{10}{1} = \frac{4 \cdot 10}{5 \cdot 1} = \frac{40}{5} = 8$

b. $-\frac{3}{5} \div \frac{7}{11} = -\frac{3}{5} \cdot \frac{11}{7} = \frac{-3(11)}{5 \cdot 7} = -\frac{33}{35}$

c. $4\frac{3}{4} \div 1\frac{1}{2} = \frac{19}{4} \div \frac{3}{2} = \frac{19}{4} \cdot \frac{2}{3} = \frac{19 \cdot 2}{4 \cdot 3} = \frac{38}{12} = \frac{19 \cdot \cancel{2}}{6 \cdot \cancel{2}} = \frac{19}{6}$ or $3\frac{1}{6}$

9 Divide. If possible, reduce the quotient to its lowest terms:

  a. $\frac{9}{11} \div \frac{5}{4}$ **b.** $-\frac{8}{15} \div \frac{2}{5}$ **c.** $3\frac{3}{8} \div 2\frac{1}{4}$.

---

7 | Add and subtract rational numbers.

Adding and Subtracting Rational Numbers

Rational expressions with identical denominators are added and subtracted using the following rules:

> #### ADDING AND SUBTRACTING RATIONAL NUMBERS WITH IDENTICAL DENOMINATORS
> The sum or difference of two rational numbers with identical denominators is the sum or difference of their numerators over the common denominator.
>   If $\frac{a}{b}$ and $\frac{c}{b}$ are rational numbers, then $\frac{a}{b} + \frac{c}{b} = \frac{a + c}{b}$ and $\frac{a}{b} - \frac{c}{b} = \frac{a - c}{b}$.

EXAMPLE 10	ADDING AND SUBTRACTING RATIONAL NUMBERS WITH IDENTICAL DENOMINATORS

Perform the indicated operations:

a. $\frac{3}{7} + \frac{2}{7}$ **b.** $\frac{11}{12} - \frac{5}{12}$ **c.** $-5\frac{1}{4} - \left(-2\frac{3}{4}\right).$

SOLUTION

a. $\frac{3}{7} + \frac{2}{7} = \frac{3+2}{7} = \frac{5}{7}$

b. $\frac{11}{12} - \frac{5}{12} = \frac{11-5}{12} = \frac{6}{12} = \frac{1\cdot6}{2\cdot6} = \frac{1}{2}$

c. $-5\frac{1}{4} - \left(-2\frac{3}{4}\right) = -\frac{21}{4} - \left(-\frac{11}{4}\right) = -\frac{21}{4} + \frac{11}{4} = \frac{-21+11}{4} = \frac{-10}{4} = -\frac{5}{2}$ or $-2\frac{1}{2}$

 Perform the indicated operations:

a. $\frac{5}{12} + \frac{3}{12}$ **b.** $\frac{7}{4} - \frac{1}{4}$ **c.** $-3\frac{3}{8} - \left(-1\frac{1}{8}\right).$

If the rational numbers to be added or subtracted have different denominators, we use the least common multiple of their denominators to rewrite the rational numbers. The least common multiple of the denominators is called the **least common denominator**.

Rewriting rational numbers with a least common denominator is done using the Fundamental Principle of Rational Numbers, discussed at the beginning of this section. Recall that if $\frac{a}{b}$ is a rational number and c is a nonzero number, then

$$\frac{a}{b} = \frac{a}{b}\cdot\frac{c}{c} = \frac{a\cdot c}{b\cdot c}.$$

Multiplying the numerator and the denominator of a rational number by the same nonzero number is equivalent to multiplying by 1, resulting in an equivalent fraction.

EXAMPLE 11	ADDING RATIONAL NUMBERS WITH UNLIKE DENOMINATORS

Find the sum: $\frac{3}{4} + \frac{1}{6}.$

SOLUTION The smallest number divisible by both 4 and 6 is 12. Therefore, 12 is the least common multiple of 4 and 6, and will serve as the least common denominator. To obtain a denominator of 12, multiply the denominator and the numerator of the first rational number, $\frac{3}{4}$, by 3. To obtain a denominator of 12, multiply the denominator and the numerator of the second rational number, $\frac{1}{6}$, by 2.

$$\frac{3}{4} + \frac{1}{6} = \frac{3}{4}\cdot\frac{3}{3} + \frac{1}{6}\cdot\frac{2}{2}$$

Rewrite each rational number as an equivalent fraction with a denominator of 12. $\frac{3}{3} = 1$ and $\frac{2}{2} = 1$, and multiplying by 1 does not change a number's value.

$$= \frac{9}{12} + \frac{2}{12}$$

Multiply.

$$= \frac{11}{12}$$

Add numerators and put this sum over the least common denominator.

 Find the sum: $\frac{1}{5} + \frac{3}{4}.$

If the least common denominator cannot be found by inspection, use prime factorizations of the denominators and the method for finding their least common multiple, discussed in Section 2.1.

| EXAMPLE 12 | SUBTRACTING RATIONAL NUMBERS WITH UNLIKE DENOMINATORS |

Perform the indicated operation: $\frac{1}{15} - \frac{7}{24}$.

SOLUTION We need to first find the least common denominator, which is the least common multiple of 15 and 24. What is the smallest number divisible by both 15 and 24? The answer is not obvious, so we begin with the prime factorization of each number.

$$15 = 5 \cdot 3$$
$$24 = 8 \cdot 3 = 2^3 \cdot 3$$

The different factors are 5, 3, and 2. Using the greatest number of times each factor appears in any factorization, the least common multiple is $5 \cdot 3 \cdot 2^3 = 5 \cdot 3 \cdot 8 = 120$. We will now express each rational number with a denominator of 120, which is the least common denominator. For the first rational number, $\frac{1}{15}$, 120 divided by 15 is 8. Thus, we will multiply the numerator and denominator by 8. For the second rational number, $\frac{7}{24}$, 120 divided by 24 is 5. Thus, we will multiply the numerator and denominator by 5.

$$\frac{1}{15} - \frac{7}{24} = \frac{1}{15} \cdot \frac{8}{8} - \frac{7}{24} \cdot \frac{5}{5}$$ Rewrite each rational number as an equivalent fraction with a denominator of 120.

$$= \frac{8}{120} - \frac{35}{120}$$ Multiply.

$$= \frac{8 - 35}{120}$$ Subtract the numerators and put this difference over the least common denominator.

$$= \frac{-27}{120}$$ Perform the subtraction.

$$= \frac{-9 \cdot \cancel{3}}{40 \cdot \cancel{3}}$$ Reduce to lowest terms.

$$= -\frac{9}{40}$$

 Perform the indicated operation: $\frac{3}{10} - \frac{7}{12}$.

TECHNOLOGY

Here is a possible keystroke sequence on a graphing calculator for the subtraction problem in Example 12:

1 ÷ 15 − 7 ÷ 24

▶Frac   ENTER .

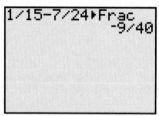

The calculator display reads −9/40, serving as a check for our answer in Example 12.

8 | Apply the density property of rational numbers.

Density of Rational Numbers

It is always possible to find a rational number between any two given rational numbers. Mathematicians express this idea by saying that the set of rational numbers is **dense**.

DENSITY OF THE RATIONAL NUMBERS

If r and t represent rational numbers, with $r < t$, then there is a rational number s such that s is between r and t:

$$r < s < t.$$

One way to find a rational number between two given rational numbers is to find the rational number halfway between them. Add the given rational numbers and divide their sum by 2, thereby finding the average of the numbers.

EXAMPLE 13   ILLUSTRATING THE DENSITY PROPERTY

Find a rational number halfway between $\frac{1}{2}$ and $\frac{3}{4}$.

SOLUTION First, add $\frac{1}{2}$ and $\frac{3}{4}$.

$$\frac{1}{2} + \frac{3}{4} = \frac{2}{4} + \frac{3}{4} = \frac{5}{4}$$

Next, divide this sum by 2.

$$\frac{5}{4} \div \frac{2}{1} = \frac{5}{4} \cdot \frac{1}{2} = \frac{5}{8}$$

The number $\frac{5}{8}$ is halfway between $\frac{1}{2}$ and $\frac{3}{4}$. Thus,

$$\frac{1}{2} < \frac{5}{8} < \frac{3}{4}.$$

STUDY TIP

The inequality $\frac{1}{2} < \frac{5}{8} < \frac{3}{4}$ is more obvious if all denominators are changed to 8:

$$\frac{4}{8} < \frac{5}{8} < \frac{6}{8}.$$

We can repeat the procedure of Example 13 and find a rational number halfway between $\frac{1}{2}$ and $\frac{5}{8}$. Repeated application of this procedure implies the following surprising result:

Between any two given rational numbers are *infinitely many* rational numbers.

 Find a rational number halfway between $\frac{1}{3}$ and $\frac{1}{2}$.

---

9 | Solve problems involving rational numbers.

Problem Solving with Rational Numbers

A common application of rational numbers involves preparing food for a different number of servings than what the recipe gives. The amount of each ingredient can be found as follows:

Amount of ingredient needed

$$= \frac{\text{desired serving size}}{\text{recipe serving size}} \times \text{ingredient amount in the recipe.}$$

EXAMPLE 14   CHANGING THE SIZE OF A RECIPE

A chocolate-chip cookie recipe for five dozen cookies requires $\frac{3}{4}$ cup sugar. If you want to make eight dozen cookies, how much sugar is needed?

SOLUTION Amount of sugar needed

$$= \frac{\text{desired serving size}}{\text{recipe serving size}} \times \text{sugar amount in recipe}$$

$$= \frac{8 \ \text{dozen}}{5 \ \text{dozen}} \times \frac{3}{4} \ \text{cup}$$

The amount of sugar, in cups, needed is determined by multiplying the rational numbers:

$$\frac{8}{5} \times \frac{3}{4} = \frac{8 \cdot 3}{5 \cdot 4} = \frac{24}{20} = \frac{6 \cdot 4}{5 \cdot 4} = 1\frac{1}{5}.$$

Thus, $1\frac{1}{5}$ cups of sugar is needed. (Depending on the measuring cup you are using, you may need to round the sugar amount to $1\frac{1}{4}$ cups.)

14 A chocolate-chip cookie recipe for five dozen cookies requires two eggs. If you want to make seven dozen cookies, exactly how many eggs are needed? Now round your answer to a realistic number that does not involve a fractional part of an egg.

EXERCISE SET 2.3 ●●●●●○

• Practice Exercises

In Exercises 1–12, reduce each rational number to its lowest terms.

1. $\frac{10}{15}$ **2.** $\frac{18}{45}$ **3.** $\frac{15}{18}$ **4.** $\frac{16}{64}$

5. $\frac{24}{42}$ **6.** $\frac{32}{80}$ **7.** $\frac{60}{108}$ **8.** $\frac{112}{128}$

9. $\frac{342}{380}$ **10.** $\frac{210}{252}$ **11.** $\frac{308}{418}$ **12.** $\frac{144}{300}$

In Exercises 13–18, convert each mixed number to an improper fraction.

13. $2\frac{3}{8}$ **14.** $2\frac{7}{9}$ **15.** $-7\frac{3}{5}$

16. $-6\frac{2}{5}$ **17.** $12\frac{7}{16}$ **18.** $11\frac{5}{16}$

In Exercises 19–24, convert each improper fraction to a mixed number.

19. $\frac{23}{5}$ **20.** $\frac{47}{8}$ **21.** $-\frac{76}{9}$

22. $-\frac{59}{9}$ **23.** $\frac{711}{20}$ **24.** $\frac{788}{25}$

In Exercises 25–36, express each rational number as a decimal.

25. $\frac{3}{4}$ **26.** $\frac{3}{5}$ **27.** $\frac{7}{20}$ **28.** $\frac{3}{20}$

29. $\frac{7}{8}$ **30.** $\frac{5}{16}$ **31.** $\frac{9}{11}$ **32.** $\frac{3}{11}$

33. $\frac{22}{7}$ **34.** $\frac{20}{3}$ **35.** $\frac{2}{7}$ **36.** $\frac{5}{7}$

In Exercises 37–48, express each terminating decimal as a quotient of integers. If possible, reduce to lowest terms.

37. 0.3   **38.** 0.9   **39.** 0.4   **40.** 0.6

41. 0.39   **42.** 0.59   **43.** 0.82   **44.** 0.64

45. 0.725   **46.** 0.625   **47.** 0.5399   **48.** 0.7006

In Exercises 49–56, express each repeating decimal as a quotient of integers. If possible, reduce to lowest terms.

49. $0.\overline{7}$ **50.** $0.\overline{1}$ **51.** $0.\overline{9}$ **52.** $0.\overline{3}$

53. $0.\overline{36}$ **54.** $0.\overline{81}$ **55.** $0.\overline{257}$ **56.** $0.\overline{529}$

In Exercises 57–92, perform the indicated operations. If possible, reduce the answer to its lowest terms.

57. $\frac{3}{8} \cdot \frac{7}{11}$ **58.** $\frac{5}{8} \cdot \frac{3}{11}$ **59.** $\left(-\frac{1}{10}\right)\left(\frac{7}{12}\right)$

60. $\left(-\frac{1}{8}\right)\left(\frac{5}{9}\right)$ **61.** $\left(-\frac{2}{3}\right)\left(-\frac{9}{4}\right)$ **62.** $\left(-\frac{5}{4}\right)\left(-\frac{6}{7}\right)$

63. $\left(3\frac{3}{4}\right)\left(1\frac{3}{5}\right)$ **64.** $\left(2\frac{4}{5}\right)\left(1\frac{1}{4}\right)$ **65.** $\frac{5}{4} \div \frac{3}{8}$

66. $\frac{5}{8} \div \frac{4}{3}$ **67.** $-\frac{7}{8} \div \frac{15}{16}$ **68.** $-\frac{13}{20} \div \frac{4}{5}$

69. $6\frac{3}{5} \div 1\frac{1}{10}$ **70.** $1\frac{3}{4} \div 2\frac{5}{8}$ **71.** $\frac{2}{11} + \frac{3}{11}$

72. $\frac{5}{13} + \frac{2}{13}$ **73.** $\frac{5}{6} - \frac{1}{6}$ **74.** $\frac{7}{12} - \frac{5}{12}$

75. $\frac{7}{12} - \left(-\frac{1}{12}\right)$ **76.** $\frac{5}{16} - \left(-\frac{5}{16}\right)$ **77.** $\frac{1}{2} + \frac{1}{5}$

78. $\frac{1}{3} + \frac{1}{5}$ **79.** $\frac{3}{4} + \frac{3}{20}$ **80.** $\frac{2}{5} + \frac{2}{15}$

81. $\frac{5}{24} + \frac{7}{30}$ **82.** $\frac{7}{108} + \frac{55}{144}$ **83.** $\frac{13}{18} - \frac{2}{9}$

84. $\frac{13}{15} - \frac{2}{45}$ **85.** $\frac{4}{3} - \frac{3}{4}$ **86.** $\frac{3}{2} - \frac{2}{3}$

87. $\frac{1}{15} - \frac{27}{50}$ **88.** $\frac{4}{15} - \frac{1}{6}$ **89.** $3\frac{3}{4} - 2\frac{1}{3}$

90. $3\frac{2}{3} - 2\frac{1}{2}$ **91.** $\left(\frac{1}{2} - \frac{1}{3}\right) \div \frac{5}{8}$ **92.** $\left(\frac{1}{2} + \frac{1}{4}\right) \div \left(\frac{1}{2} + \frac{1}{3}\right)$

In Exercises 93–98, find a rational number halfway between the two numbers in each pair.

93. $\frac{1}{4}$ and $\frac{1}{3}$ **94.** $\frac{2}{3}$ and $\frac{5}{6}$ **95.** $\frac{1}{2}$ and $\frac{2}{3}$

96. $\frac{3}{5}$ and $\frac{2}{3}$ **97.** $-\frac{2}{3}$ and $-\frac{5}{6}$ **98.** -4 and $-\frac{7}{2}$

Different operations with the same rational numbers usually result in different answers. Exercises 99–100 illustrate some curious exceptions.

99. Show that $\frac{13}{4} + \frac{13}{9}$ and $\frac{13}{4} \times \frac{13}{9}$ give the same answer.

100. Show that $\frac{169}{30} + \frac{13}{15}$ and $\frac{169}{30} \div \frac{13}{15}$ give the same answer.

• Practice Plus

In Exercises 101–106, perform the indicated operations. If possible, reduce the answer to its lowest terms.

101. $-\frac{9}{4}\left(\frac{1}{2}\right) + \frac{3}{4} \div \frac{5}{6}$

102. $\left[-\frac{4}{7} - \left(-\frac{2}{5}\right)\right]\left[-\frac{3}{8} + \left(-\frac{1}{9}\right)\right]$

103. $\dfrac{\frac{7}{9} - 3}{\frac{5}{6}} \div \frac{3}{2} + \frac{3}{4}$

104. $\dfrac{\frac{17}{25}}{\frac{3}{5} - 4} \div \frac{1}{5} + \frac{1}{2}$

105. $\frac{1}{4} - 6(2 + 8) \div \left(-\frac{1}{3}\right)\left(-\frac{1}{9}\right)$

106. $\frac{3}{4} - 4(2 + 7) \div \left(-\frac{1}{2}\right)\left(-\frac{1}{6}\right)$

In Exercises 107–110, perform the indicated operations. Leave denominators in prime factorization form.

107. $\frac{5}{2^2 \cdot 3^2} - \frac{1}{2 \cdot 3^2}$ **108.** $\frac{7}{3^2 \cdot 5^2} - \frac{1}{3 \cdot 5^3}$

109. $\frac{1}{2^4 \cdot 5^3 \cdot 7} + \frac{1}{2 \cdot 5^4} - \frac{1}{2^3 \cdot 5^2}$

110. $\frac{1}{2^3 \cdot 17^8} + \frac{1}{2 \cdot 17^9} - \frac{1}{2^2 \cdot 3 \cdot 17^8}$

In Exercises 111–114, express each rational number as a decimal. Then insert either < or > in the shaded area between the rational numbers to make the statement true.

111. $\frac{6}{11}$ ▦ $\frac{7}{12}$ **112.** $\frac{29}{36}$ ▦ $\frac{28}{35}$

113. $-\frac{5}{6}$ ▦ $-\frac{8}{9}$ **114.** $-\frac{1}{125}$ ▦ $-\frac{3}{500}$

• Application Exercises

The circle graph shows the breakdown of the number of countries in the world that are free, partly free, or not free. Use the information in the graph to solve Exercises 115–116.

World's Countries by Status of Freedom

Source: Larry Berman and Bruce Murphy, *Approaching Democracy,* 4th Edition, Prentice Hall, 2003

115. What fractional part of the world's countries is free? Reduce the answer to its lowest terms.

116. What fractional part of the world's countries is not free? Reduce the answer to its lowest terms.

Use the following list of ingredients for chocolate brownies to solve Exercises 117–122.

Ingredients for 16 Brownies

$\frac{2}{3}$ cup butter, 5 ounces unsweetened chocolate, $1\frac{1}{2}$ cups sugar, 2 teaspoons vanilla, 2 eggs, 1 cup flour

117. How much of each ingredient is needed to make 8 brownies?

118. How much of each ingredient is needed to make 12 brownies?

119. How much of each ingredient is needed to make 20 brownies?

120. How much of each ingredient is needed to make 24 brownies?

121. With only one cup of butter, what is the greatest number of brownies that you can make? (Ignore part of a brownie.)

122. With only one cup of sugar, what is the greatest number of brownies that you can make? (Ignore part of a brownie.)

A mix for eight servings of instant potatoes requires $2\frac{2}{3}$ cups of water. Use this information to solve Exercises 123–124.

123. If you want to make 11 servings, how much water is needed?

124. If you want to make six servings, how much water is needed?

In most societies, women say they prefer to marry men who are older than themselves, whereas men say they prefer women who are younger. Evolutionary psychologists attribute these preferences to female concern with a partner's material resources and male concern with a partner's fertility (Source: David M. Buss, Psychological Inquiry, 6, 1–30). The graph shows the preferred age in a mate in five selected countries. Use the information in

the graph to solve Exercises 125–128. Express each answer as a mixed number.

Preferred Age in a Mate

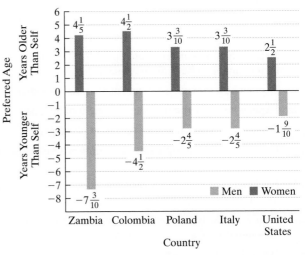

Source: Carole Wade and Carol Tavris, *Psychology,* 6th Edition, Prentice Hall, 2000

125. What is the difference between the preferred age in a mate for women in Italy and women in the United States?

126. What is the difference between the preferred age in a mate for women in Zambia and women in the United States?

127. What is the difference between the preferred age in a mate for men in Italy and men in the United States?

128. What is the difference between the preferred age in a mate for men in Colombia and men in the United States?

129. A franchise is owned by three people. The first owns $\frac{5}{12}$ of the business and the second owns $\frac{1}{4}$ of the business. What fractional part of the business is owned by the third person?

130. At a workshop on enhancing creativity, $\frac{1}{4}$ of the participants are musicians, $\frac{2}{5}$ are artists, $\frac{1}{10}$ are actors, and the remaining participants are writers. What fraction of the people attending the workshop are writers?

131. If you walk $\frac{3}{4}$ mile and then jog $\frac{2}{5}$ mile, what is the total distance covered? How much farther did you walk than jog?

132. Some companies pay people extra when they work more than a regular 40-hour work week. The overtime pay is often $1\frac{1}{2}$ times the regular hourly rate. This is called time and a half. A summer job for students pays $12 an hour and offers time and a half for the hours worked over 40. If a student works 46 hours during one week, what is the student's total pay before taxes?

133. A will states that $\frac{3}{5}$ of the estate is to be divided among relatives. Of the remaining estate, $\frac{1}{4}$ goes to the National Foundation for AIDS Research. What fraction of the estate goes to the National Foundation for AIDS Research?

134. The legend of a map indicates that 1 inch = 16 miles. If the distance on the map between two cities is $2\frac{3}{8}$ inches, how far apart are the cities?

• Writing in Mathematics

135. What is a rational number?

136. Explain how to reduce a rational number to its lowest terms.

137. Explain how to convert from a mixed number to an improper fraction. Use $7\frac{2}{3}$ as an example.

138. Explain how to convert from an improper fraction to a mixed number. Use $\frac{47}{5}$ as an example.

139. Explain how to write a rational number as a decimal.

140. Explain how to write 0.083 as a quotient of integers.

141. Explain how to write $0.\overline{9}$ as a quotient of integers.

142. Explain how to multiply rational numbers. Use $\frac{5}{6} \cdot \frac{1}{2}$ as an example.

143. Explain how to divide rational numbers. Use $\frac{5}{6} \div \frac{1}{2}$ as an example.

144. Explain how to add rational numbers with different denominators. Use $\frac{5}{6} + \frac{1}{2}$ as an example.

145. What does it mean when we say that the set of rational numbers is dense?

146. Explain what is wrong with this statement. "If you'd like to save some money, I'll be happy to sell you my computer system for only $\frac{3}{2}$ of the price I originally paid for it."

• Critical Thinking Exercises

147. Shown in the next column is a short excerpt from "The Star-Spangled Banner." The time is $\frac{3}{4}$, which means that each measure must contain notes that add up to $\frac{3}{4}$. The values of the different notes tell musicians how long to hold each note.

$$\circ = 1 \qquad \downarrow = \frac{1}{2} \qquad \downarrow = \frac{1}{4} \qquad \downarrow = \frac{1}{8}$$

Use vertical lines to divide this line of "The Star-Spangled Banner" into measures.

say does that Star-span-gled Ban-ner yet wave O'er the

148. Use inductive reasoning to predict the addition problem and the sum that will appear in the fourth row. Then perform the arithmetic to verify your conjecture.

$$\frac{1}{1 \cdot 2} + \frac{1}{2 \cdot 3} = \frac{2}{3}$$

$$\frac{1}{1 \cdot 2} + \frac{1}{2 \cdot 3} + \frac{1}{3 \cdot 4} = \frac{3}{4}$$

$$\frac{1}{1 \cdot 2} + \frac{1}{2 \cdot 3} + \frac{1}{3 \cdot 4} + \frac{1}{4 \cdot 5} = \frac{4}{5}$$

• Technology Exercises

149. Use a calculator to express the following rational numbers as decimals.

a. $\frac{197}{800}$ **b.** $\frac{4539}{3125}$ **c.** $\frac{7}{6250}$

150. Some calculators have a fraction feature. This feature allows you to perform operations with fractions and displays the answer as a fraction reduced to its lowest terms. If your calculator has this feature, use it to verify any five of the answers that you obtained in Exercises 57–92.

• Group Exercise

151. Each member of the group should present an application of rational numbers. The application can be based on research or on how the group member uses rational numbers in his or her life. If you are not sure where to begin, ask yourself how your life would be different if fractions and decimals were concepts unknown to our civilization.

SECTION 2.4 • THE IRRATIONAL NUMBERS

OBJECTIVES

1. Define the irrational numbers.
2. Simplify square roots.
3. Perform operations with square roots.
4. Rationalize the denominator.

Pythagoras

Shown here is Renaissance artist Raphael Sanzio's (1483–1520) image of Pythagoras from *The School of Athens* mural. Detail of left side.
Stanza della Segnatura, Vatican Palace, Vatican State. Scala/Art Resource, NY.

For the followers of the Greek mathematician Pythagoras in the sixth century B.C., numbers took on a life-and-death importance. The "Pythagorean Brotherhood" was a secret group whose members were convinced that properties of whole numbers were the key to understanding the universe. Members of the Brotherhood (which admitted women) thought that all numbers that were not whole numbers could be

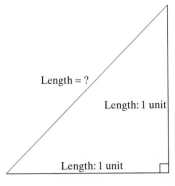

FIGURE 2.5

represented as the ratio of whole numbers. A crisis occurred for the Pythagoreans when they discovered the existence of a number that was not rational. Because the Pythagoreans viewed numbers with reverence and awe, the punishment for speaking about this number was death. However, a member of the Brotherhood revealed the secret of the number's existence. When he later died in a shipwreck, his death was viewed as punishment from the gods.

The triangle in Figure 2.5 led the Pythagoreans to the discovery of a number that could not be expressed as the quotient of integers. Based on their understanding of the relationship among the sides of this triangle, they knew that the length of the side shown in red had to be a number that, when squared, is equal to 2. The Pythagoreans discovered that this number seemed to be close to the rational numbers

$$\frac{14}{10}, \frac{141}{100}, \frac{1414}{1000}, \frac{14{,}141}{10{,}000}, \text{ and so on.}$$

However, they were shocked to find that there is no quotient of integers whose square is equal to 2.

The positive number whose square is equal to 2 is written $\sqrt{2}$. We read this "the square root of 2," or "radical 2." The symbol $\sqrt{}$ is called the **radical sign**. The number under the radical sign, in this case 2, is called the **radicand**. The entire symbol $\sqrt{2}$ is called a **radical**.

Using deductive reasoning, mathematicians have proved that $\sqrt{2}$ cannot be represented as a quotient of integers. This means that there is no terminating or repeating decimal that can be multiplied by itself to give 2. We can, however, give a decimal approximation for $\sqrt{2}$. We use the symbol $\approx$, which means "is approximately equal to." Thus,

$$\sqrt{2} \approx 1.414214.$$

We can verify that this is only an approximation by multiplying 1.414214 by itself. The product is not exactly 2:

$$1.414214 \times 1.414214 = 2.000001237796.$$

A number like $\sqrt{2}$, whose decimal representation does not come to an end and does not have a block of repeating digits, is an example of an **irrational number**.

1 | Define the irrational numbers.

> ### THE IRRATIONAL NUMBERS
> The set of **irrational numbers** is the set of numbers whose decimal representations are neither terminating nor repeating.

Perhaps the best known of all the irrational numbers is π (pi). This irrational number represents the distance around a circle (its circumference) divided by the diameter of the circle. In the *Star Trek* episode "Wolf in the Fold," Spock foils an evil computer by telling it to "compute the last digit in the value of π." Because π is an irrational number, there is no last digit in its decimal representation:

$$\pi = 3.1415926535897932384626433832795\ldots.$$

The nature of the irrational number π has fascinated mathematicians for centuries. Amateur and professional mathematicians have taken up the challenge of calculating π to more and more decimal places. Although such an exercise may seem pointless, it serves as the ultimate stress test for new high-speed computers and also as a test for the long-standing, but still unproven, conjecture that the distribution of digits in π is completely random.

TECHNOLOGY

You can obtain decimal approximations for irrational numbers using a calculator. For example, to approximate $\sqrt{2}$, use the following keystrokes:

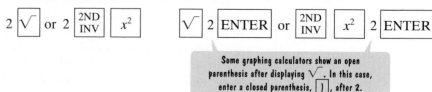

Scientific Calculator

$2\ \boxed{\sqrt{\ }}$ or $2\ \boxed{\begin{array}{c}2ND\\INV\end{array}}\ \boxed{x^2}$

Graphing Calculator

$\boxed{\sqrt{\ }}\ 2\ \boxed{ENTER}$ or $\boxed{\begin{array}{c}2ND\\INV\end{array}}\ \boxed{x^2}\ 2\ \boxed{ENTER}$

> Some graphing calculators show an open parenthesis after displaying $\sqrt{\ }$. In this case, enter a closed parenthesis, $\boxed{\ )\ }$, after 2.

The display may read 1.41421356237, although your calculator may show more or fewer digits. Between which two integers would you graph $\sqrt{2}$ on a number line?

Square Roots

The U.N. building is designed with three golden rectangles.

The United Nations Building in New York was designed to represent its mission of promoting world harmony. Viewed from the front, the building looks like three rectangles stacked upon each other. In each rectangle, the width divided by the height is $\sqrt{5} + 1$ to 2, approximately 1.618 to 1. The ancient Greeks believed that such a rectangle, called a **golden rectangle**, was the most pleasing of all rectangles. The comparison 1.618 to 1 is approximate because $\sqrt{5}$ is an irrational number.

The **principal square root** of a nonnegative number n, written $\sqrt{n}$, is the positive number that when multiplied by itself gives n. Thus,

$$\sqrt{36} = 6 \text{ because } 6 \cdot 6 = 36$$

and

$$\sqrt{81} = 9 \text{ because } 9 \cdot 9 = 81.$$

Notice that both $\sqrt{36}$ and $\sqrt{81}$ are rational numbers because 6 and 9 are terminating decimals. Thus, **not all square roots are irrational**.

Numbers such as 36 and 81 are called *perfect squares*. A **perfect square** is a number that is the square of a whole number. The first few perfect squares are listed below.

0 = 0^2	**16** = 4^2	**64** = 8^2	**144** = 12^2
1 = 1^2	**25** = 5^2	**81** = 9^2	**169** = 13^2
4 = 2^2	**36** = 6^2	**100** = 10^2	**196** = 14^2
9 = 3^2	**49** = 7^2	**121** = 11^2	**225** = 15^2

The principal square root of a perfect square is a whole number. For example,

$$\sqrt{0} = 0, \sqrt{1} = 1, \sqrt{4} = 2, \sqrt{9} = 3, \sqrt{16} = 4, \sqrt{25} = 5, \sqrt{36} = 6,$$

and so on.

Simplifying Square Roots

2 | Simplify square roots.

A rule for simplifying square roots can be generalized by comparing $\sqrt{25 \cdot 4}$ and $\sqrt{25} \cdot \sqrt{4}$. Notice that

$$\sqrt{25 \cdot 4} = \sqrt{100} = 10 \quad \text{and} \quad \sqrt{25} \cdot \sqrt{4} = 5 \cdot 2 = 10.$$

Because we obtain 10 in both situations, the original radicals must be equal. That is,

$$\sqrt{25 \cdot 4} = \sqrt{25} \cdot \sqrt{4}.$$

There are no addition or subtraction rules for square roots:

$$\sqrt{a+b} \neq \sqrt{a} + \sqrt{b}$$
$$\sqrt{a-b} \neq \sqrt{a} - \sqrt{b}.$$

For example, if $a = 9$ and $b = 16$,

$$\sqrt{9+16} = \sqrt{25} = 5$$

and

$$\sqrt{9} + \sqrt{16} = 3 + 4 = 7.$$

Thus,

$$\sqrt{9+16} \neq \sqrt{9} + \sqrt{16}.$$

This result is a particular case of the **product rule for square roots** that can be generalized as follows:

> **THE PRODUCT RULE FOR SQUARE ROOTS**
> If a and b represent nonnegative numbers, then
> $$\sqrt{ab} = \sqrt{a} \cdot \sqrt{b} \quad \text{and} \quad \sqrt{a} \cdot \sqrt{b} = \sqrt{ab}.$$
> The square root of a product is the product of the square roots.

Example 1 shows how the product rule is used to remove from the square root any perfect squares that occur as factors.

EXAMPLE 1   SIMPLIFYING SQUARE ROOTS

Simplify, if possible:

a. $\sqrt{75}$ **b.** $\sqrt{500}$ **c.** $\sqrt{17}$.

SOLUTION

a. $\sqrt{75} = \sqrt{25 \cdot 3}$ 25 is the greatest perfect square that is a factor of 75.
$\phantom{\sqrt{75}} = \sqrt{25} \cdot \sqrt{3}$ $\sqrt{ab} = \sqrt{a} \cdot \sqrt{b}$
$\phantom{\sqrt{75}} = 5\sqrt{3}$ Write $\sqrt{25}$ as 5.

b. $\sqrt{500} = \sqrt{100 \cdot 5}$ 100 is the greatest perfect square factor of 500.
$\phantom{\sqrt{500}} = \sqrt{100} \cdot \sqrt{5}$ $\sqrt{ab} = \sqrt{a} \cdot \sqrt{b}$
$\phantom{\sqrt{500}} = 10\sqrt{5}$ Write $\sqrt{100}$ as 10.

c. Because 17 has no perfect square factors (other than 1), $\sqrt{17}$ cannot be simplified.

 Simplify, if possible:

a. $\sqrt{12}$ **b.** $\sqrt{60}$ **c.** $\sqrt{55}$.

---

3 | Perform operations with square roots.

Multiplying Square Roots

If a and b are nonnegative, then we can use the product rule

$$\sqrt{a} \cdot \sqrt{b} = \sqrt{a \cdot b}$$

to multiply square roots. The product of the square roots is the square root of the product. Once the square roots are multiplied, simplify the square root of the product when possible.

EXAMPLE 2   MULTIPLYING SQUARE ROOTS

Multiply:

a. $\sqrt{2} \cdot \sqrt{5}$ **b.** $\sqrt{7} \cdot \sqrt{7}$ **c.** $\sqrt{6} \cdot \sqrt{12}$.

SOLUTION

It is possible to multiply irrational numbers and obtain a rational number for the product.

a. $\sqrt{2} \cdot \sqrt{5} = \sqrt{2 \cdot 5} = \sqrt{10}$

b. $\sqrt{7} \cdot \sqrt{7} = \sqrt{7 \cdot 7} = \sqrt{49} = 7$

c. $\sqrt{6} \cdot \sqrt{12} = \sqrt{6 \cdot 12} = \sqrt{72} = \sqrt{36 \cdot 2} = \sqrt{36} \cdot \sqrt{2} = 6\sqrt{2}$

 Multiply:

a. $\sqrt{3} \cdot \sqrt{10}$ **b.** $\sqrt{10} \cdot \sqrt{10}$ **c.** $\sqrt{6} \cdot \sqrt{2}$.

A Radical Idea: Time Is Relative

What does travel in space have to do with square roots? Imagine that in the future we will be able to travel at velocities approaching the speed of light (approximately 186,000 miles per second). According to Einstein's theory of relativity, time would pass more quickly on Earth than it would in the moving spaceship. The square root expression

$$R_f\sqrt{1 - \left(\frac{v}{c}\right)^2}$$

gives the aging rate of an astronaut relative to the aging rate of a friend on Earth, R_f. In the expression, v is the astronaut's speed and c is the speed of light. As the astronaut's speed approaches the speed of light, we can substitute c for v:

$$R_f\sqrt{1 - \left(\frac{v}{c}\right)^2} \quad \text{Let } v = c.$$

$$= R_f\sqrt{1 - \left(\frac{c}{c}\right)^2}$$

$$= R_f\sqrt{1 - 1^2}$$

$$= R_f\sqrt{0} = 0.$$

Close to the speed of light, the astronaut's aging rate relative to a friend on Earth is nearly 0. What does this mean? As we age here on Earth, the space traveler would barely get older. The space traveler would return to a futuristic world in which friends and loved ones would be long dead.

Dividing Square Roots

Another property for square roots involves division.

> ### THE QUOTIENT RULE FOR SQUARE ROOTS
> If a and b represent nonnegative numbers and $b \neq 0$, then
> $$\frac{\sqrt{a}}{\sqrt{b}} = \sqrt{\frac{a}{b}} \quad \text{and} \quad \sqrt{\frac{a}{b}} = \frac{\sqrt{a}}{\sqrt{b}}.$$
> The quotient of two square roots is the square root of the quotient.

Once the square roots are divided, simplify the square root of the quotient when possible.

EXAMPLE 3   DIVIDING SQUARE ROOTS

Find the quotient:

a. $\dfrac{\sqrt{75}}{\sqrt{3}}$ **b.** $\dfrac{\sqrt{90}}{\sqrt{2}}$.

SOLUTION

a. $\dfrac{\sqrt{75}}{\sqrt{3}} = \sqrt{\dfrac{75}{3}} = \sqrt{25} = 5$

b. $\dfrac{\sqrt{90}}{\sqrt{2}} = \sqrt{\dfrac{90}{2}} = \sqrt{45} = \sqrt{9 \cdot 5} = \sqrt{9} \cdot \sqrt{5} = 3\sqrt{5}$

 CHECK POINT 3 Find the quotient:

a. $\dfrac{\sqrt{80}}{\sqrt{5}}$ **b.** $\dfrac{\sqrt{48}}{\sqrt{6}}$.

Adding and Subtracting Square Roots

The number that multiplies a square root is called the square root's **coefficient**. For example, in $3\sqrt{5}$, 3 is the coefficient of the square root.

Square roots with the same radicand can be added or subtracted by adding or subtracting their coefficients:

$$a\sqrt{c} + b\sqrt{c} = (a + b)\sqrt{c} \qquad a\sqrt{c} - b\sqrt{c} = (a - b)\sqrt{c}.$$

Sum of coefficients times the common square root

Difference of coefficients times the common square root

EXAMPLE 4   ADDING AND SUBTRACTING SQUARE ROOTS

Add or subtract as indicated:

a. $7\sqrt{2} + 5\sqrt{2}$ **b.** $2\sqrt{5} - 6\sqrt{5}$ **c.** $3\sqrt{7} + 9\sqrt{7} - \sqrt{7}$.

SOLUTION

a. $7\sqrt{2} + 5\sqrt{2} = (7 + 5)\sqrt{2}$
$$= 12\sqrt{2}$$

b. $2\sqrt{5} - 6\sqrt{5} = (2 - 6)\sqrt{5}$
$$= -4\sqrt{5}$$

c. $3\sqrt{7} + 9\sqrt{7} - \sqrt{7} = 3\sqrt{7} + 9\sqrt{7} - 1\sqrt{7}$ Write $\sqrt{7}$ as $1\sqrt{7}$.

$$= (3 + 9 - 1)\sqrt{7}$$
$$= 11\sqrt{7}$$

 Add or subtract as indicated:

     a. $8\sqrt{3} + 10\sqrt{3}$ **b.** $4\sqrt{13} - 9\sqrt{13}$ **c.** $7\sqrt{10} + 2\sqrt{10} - \sqrt{10}$.

In some situations, it is possible to add and subtract square roots that do not contain a common square root by first simplifying.

EXAMPLE 5   ADDING AND SUBTRACTING SQUARE ROOTS BY FIRST SIMPLIFYING

STUDY TIP

Sums or differences of square roots that cannot be simplified and that do not contain a common square root cannot be combined into one term by adding or subtracting coefficients. Some examples:

- $5\sqrt{3} + 3\sqrt{5}$ cannot be combined by adding coefficients. The square roots, $\sqrt{3}$ and $\sqrt{5}$, are different.

- $28 + 7\sqrt{3}$, or $28\sqrt{1} + 7\sqrt{3}$, cannot be combined by adding coefficients. The square roots, $\sqrt{1}$ and $\sqrt{3}$, are different.

Add or subtract as indicated:

   a. $\sqrt{2} + \sqrt{8}$ **b.** $4\sqrt{50} - 6\sqrt{32}$.

SOLUTION

   a. $\sqrt{2} + \sqrt{8}$

      $= \sqrt{2} + \sqrt{4 \cdot 2}$ Split 8 into two factors such that one is a perfect square.

      $= 1\sqrt{2} + 2\sqrt{2}$ $\sqrt{4 \cdot 2} = \sqrt{4} \cdot \sqrt{2} = 2\sqrt{2}$

      $= (1 + 2)\sqrt{2}$ Add coefficients and retain the common square root.

      $= 3\sqrt{2}$ Simplify.

   b. $4\sqrt{50} - 6\sqrt{32}$

      $= 4\sqrt{25 \cdot 2} - 6\sqrt{16 \cdot 2}$ 25 is the greatest perfect square factor of 50 and 16 is the greatest perfect square factor of 32.

      $= 4 \cdot 5\sqrt{2} - 6 \cdot 4\sqrt{2}$ $\sqrt{25 \cdot 2} = \sqrt{25}\sqrt{2} = 5\sqrt{2}$ and $\sqrt{16 \cdot 2} = \sqrt{16}\sqrt{2} = 4\sqrt{2}$.

      $= 20\sqrt{2} - 24\sqrt{2}$ Multiply.

      $= (20 - 24)\sqrt{2}$ Subtract coefficients and retain the common square root.

      $= -4\sqrt{2}$ Simplify.

 Add or subtract as indicated:

     a. $\sqrt{3} + \sqrt{12}$ **b.** $4\sqrt{8} - 7\sqrt{18}$.

4   Rationalize the denominator.

Rationalizing the Denominator

You can use a calculator to compare the approximate values for $\dfrac{1}{\sqrt{3}}$ and $\dfrac{\sqrt{3}}{3}$. The two approximations are the same. This is not a coincidence:

$$\frac{1}{\sqrt{3}} = \frac{1}{\sqrt{3}} \cdot \boxed{\frac{\sqrt{3}}{\sqrt{3}}} = \frac{\sqrt{3}}{\sqrt{9}} = \frac{\sqrt{3}}{3}$$

Any number divided by itself is 1. Multiplication by 1 does not change the value of $\dfrac{1}{\sqrt{3}}$.

This process involves rewriting a radical expression as an equivalent expression in which the denominator no longer contains any radicals. The process is called

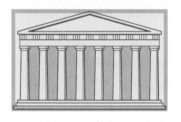

STUDY TIP

You can rationalize the denominator of $\frac{12}{\sqrt{8}}$ by multiplying by $\frac{\sqrt{8}}{\sqrt{8}}$. However, it takes more work to simplify the result.

rationalizing the denominator. If the denominator contains the square root of a natural number that is not a perfect square, **multiply the numerator and the denominator by the smallest number that produces the square root of a perfect square in the denominator**.

EXAMPLE 6   RATIONALIZING DENOMINATORS

Rationalize the denominator:

a. $\dfrac{15}{\sqrt{6}}$ **b.** $\sqrt{\dfrac{3}{5}}$ **c.** $\dfrac{12}{\sqrt{8}}$.

SOLUTION

a. If we multiply numerator and denominator of $\dfrac{15}{\sqrt{6}}$ by $\sqrt{6}$, the denominator becomes $\sqrt{6} \cdot \sqrt{6} = \sqrt{36} = 6$. Therefore, we multiply by 1, choosing $\dfrac{\sqrt{6}}{\sqrt{6}}$ for 1.

$$\frac{15}{\sqrt{6}} = \frac{15}{\sqrt{6}} \cdot \frac{\sqrt{6}}{\sqrt{6}} = \frac{15\sqrt{6}}{\sqrt{36}} = \frac{15\sqrt{6}}{6} = \frac{5\sqrt{6}}{2}$$

Multiply by 1.

Simplify: $\dfrac{15}{6} = \dfrac{5 \cdot 3}{2 \cdot 3} = \dfrac{5}{2}$.

b. $\sqrt{\dfrac{3}{5}} = \dfrac{\sqrt{3}}{\sqrt{5}} = \dfrac{\sqrt{3}}{\sqrt{5}} \cdot \dfrac{\sqrt{5}}{\sqrt{5}} = \dfrac{\sqrt{15}}{\sqrt{25}} = \dfrac{\sqrt{15}}{5}$

Multiply by 1.

c. The *smallest* number that will produce a perfect square in the denominator of $\dfrac{12}{\sqrt{8}}$ is $\sqrt{2}$, because $\sqrt{8} \cdot \sqrt{2} = \sqrt{16} = 4$. We multiply by 1, choosing $\dfrac{\sqrt{2}}{\sqrt{2}}$ for 1.

$$\frac{12}{\sqrt{8}} = \frac{12}{\sqrt{8}} \cdot \frac{\sqrt{2}}{\sqrt{2}} = \frac{12\sqrt{2}}{\sqrt{16}} = \frac{12\sqrt{2}}{4} = 3\sqrt{2}$$

 CHECK POINT 6 Rationalize the denominator:

a. $\dfrac{25}{\sqrt{10}}$ **b.** $\sqrt{\dfrac{2}{7}}$ **c.** $\dfrac{5}{\sqrt{18}}$.

Irrational Numbers and Other Kinds of Roots

Irrational numbers appear in roots other than square roots. The symbol $\sqrt[3]{}$ represents the **cube root** of a number. For example,

$$\sqrt[3]{8} = 2 \text{ because } 2 \cdot 2 \cdot 2 = 8 \quad \text{and} \quad \sqrt[3]{64} = 4 \text{ because } 4 \cdot 4 \cdot 4 = 64.$$

Although these cube roots are rational numbers, most cube roots are not. For example,

$$\sqrt[3]{217} \approx 6.0092 \text{ because } (6.0092)^3 \approx 216.995, \text{ not exactly } 217.$$

There is no end to the kinds of roots for numbers. For example, $\sqrt[4]{}$ represents the **fourth root** of a number. Thus, $\sqrt[4]{81} = 3$ because $3 \cdot 3 \cdot 3 \cdot 3 = 81$. Although the fourth root of 81 is rational, most fourth roots, fifth roots, and so on tend to be irrational.

EXERCISE SET 2.4 ●●●●●○

• Practice Exercises

Evaluate each expression in Exercises 1–10.

1. $\sqrt{9}$ **2.** $\sqrt{16}$ **3.** $\sqrt{25}$ **4.** $\sqrt{49}$

5. $\sqrt{64}$ **6.** $\sqrt{100}$ **7.** $\sqrt{121}$ **8.** $\sqrt{144}$

9. $\sqrt{169}$ **10.** $\sqrt{225}$

*In Exercises 11–16, use a calculator with a square root key to find a decimal approximation for each square root. Round the number displayed to the nearest **a**. tenth, **b**. hundredth, **c**. thousandth.*

11. $\sqrt{173}$ **12.** $\sqrt{3176}$ **13.** $\sqrt{17{,}761}$

14. $\sqrt{779{,}264}$ **15.** $\sqrt{\pi}$ **16.** $\sqrt{2\pi}$

In Exercises 17–24, simplify the square root.

17. $\sqrt{20}$ **18.** $\sqrt{50}$ **19.** $\sqrt{80}$ **20.** $\sqrt{12}$

21. $\sqrt{250}$ **22.** $\sqrt{192}$ **23.** $7\sqrt{28}$ **24.** $3\sqrt{52}$

In Exercises 25–56, perform the indicated operation. Simplify the answer when possible.

25. $\sqrt{7}\cdot\sqrt{6}$ **26.** $\sqrt{19}\cdot\sqrt{3}$ **27.** $\sqrt{6}\cdot\sqrt{6}$

28. $\sqrt{5}\cdot\sqrt{5}$ **29.** $\sqrt{3}\cdot\sqrt{6}$ **30.** $\sqrt{12}\cdot\sqrt{2}$

31. $\sqrt{2}\cdot\sqrt{26}$ **32.** $\sqrt{5}\cdot\sqrt{50}$ **33.** $\dfrac{\sqrt{54}}{\sqrt{6}}$

34. $\dfrac{\sqrt{75}}{\sqrt{3}}$ **35.** $\dfrac{\sqrt{90}}{\sqrt{2}}$ **36.** $\dfrac{\sqrt{60}}{\sqrt{3}}$

37. $\dfrac{-\sqrt{96}}{\sqrt{2}}$ **38.** $\dfrac{-\sqrt{150}}{\sqrt{3}}$ **39.** $7\sqrt{3}+6\sqrt{3}$

40. $8\sqrt{5}+11\sqrt{5}$ **41.** $4\sqrt{13}-6\sqrt{13}$

42. $6\sqrt{17}-8\sqrt{17}$ **43.** $\sqrt{5}+\sqrt{5}$

44. $\sqrt{3}+\sqrt{3}$ **45.** $4\sqrt{2}-5\sqrt{2}+8\sqrt{2}$

46. $6\sqrt{3}+8\sqrt{3}-16\sqrt{3}$ **47.** $\sqrt{5}+\sqrt{20}$

48. $\sqrt{3}+\sqrt{27}$ **49.** $\sqrt{50}-\sqrt{18}$

50. $\sqrt{63}-\sqrt{28}$ **51.** $3\sqrt{18}+5\sqrt{50}$

52. $4\sqrt{12}+2\sqrt{75}$ **53.** $\dfrac{1}{4}\sqrt{12}-\dfrac{1}{2}\sqrt{48}$

54. $\dfrac{1}{5}\sqrt{300}-\dfrac{2}{3}\sqrt{27}$ **55.** $3\sqrt{75}+2\sqrt{12}-2\sqrt{48}$

56. $2\sqrt{72}+3\sqrt{50}-\sqrt{128}$

In Exercises 57–66, rationalize the denominator.

57. $\dfrac{5}{\sqrt{3}}$ **58.** $\dfrac{12}{\sqrt{5}}$ **59.** $\dfrac{21}{\sqrt{7}}$

60. $\dfrac{30}{\sqrt{5}}$ **61.** $\dfrac{12}{\sqrt{30}}$ **62.** $\dfrac{15}{\sqrt{50}}$

63. $\dfrac{15}{\sqrt{12}}$ **64.** $\dfrac{13}{\sqrt{40}}$ **65.** $\sqrt{\dfrac{2}{5}}$ **66.** $\sqrt{\dfrac{5}{7}}$

• Practice Plus

In Exercises 67–74, perform the indicated operations. Simplify the answer when possible.

67. $3\sqrt{8}-\sqrt{32}+3\sqrt{72}-\sqrt{75}$

68. $3\sqrt{54}-2\sqrt{24}-\sqrt{96}+4\sqrt{63}$

69. $3\sqrt{7}-5\sqrt{14}\cdot\sqrt{2}$

70. $4\sqrt{2}-8\sqrt{10}\cdot\sqrt{5}$

71. $\dfrac{\sqrt{32}}{5}+\dfrac{\sqrt{18}}{7}$ **72.** $\dfrac{\sqrt{27}}{2}+\dfrac{\sqrt{75}}{7}$

73. $\dfrac{\sqrt{2}}{\sqrt{3}}+\dfrac{\sqrt{3}}{\sqrt{2}}$ **74.** $\dfrac{\sqrt{2}}{\sqrt{7}}+\dfrac{\sqrt{7}}{\sqrt{2}}$

• Application Exercises

The formula

$$d=\sqrt{\dfrac{3h}{2}}$$

models the distance, d, in miles, that a person h feet high can see to the horizon. Use this formula to solve Exercises 75–76.

75. The pool deck on a cruise ship is 72 feet above the water. How far can passengers on the pool deck see? Write the answer in simplified radical form. Then use the simplified radical form and a calculator to express the answer to the nearest tenth of a mile.

76. The captain of a cruise ship is on the star deck, which is 120 feet above the water. How far can the captain see? Write the answer in simplified radical form. Then use the simplified radical form and a calculator to express the answer to the nearest tenth of a mile.

Police use the formula $v=2\sqrt{5L}$ to estimate the speed of a car, v, in miles per hour, based on the length, L, in feet, of its skid marks upon sudden braking on a dry asphalt road. Use the formula to solve Exercises 77–78.

77. A motorist is involved in an accident. A police officer measures the car's skid marks to be 245 feet long. Estimate the speed at which the motorist was traveling before braking. If the posted speed limit is 50 miles per hour and the motorist tells the officer he was not speeding, should the officer believe him? Explain.

78. A motorist is involved in an accident. A police officer measures the car's skid marks to be 45 feet long. Estimate the speed at which the motorist was traveling before braking. If the posted speed limit is 35 miles per hour and the motorist tells the officer she was not speeding, should the officer believe her? Explain.

79. The graph shows the median heights for boys of various ages in the United States from birth through 60 months, or five years old.

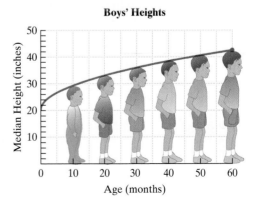

Boys' Heights

Source: Laura Walther Nathanson, *The Portable Pediatrician for Parents*

a. Use the graph at the bottom of the previous page to estimate the median height, to the nearest inch, of boys who are 50 months old.

b. The formula $h = 2.9\sqrt{x} + 20.1$ models the median height, h, in inches, of boys who are x months of age. According to the formula, what is the median height of boys who are 50 months old? Use a calculator and round to the nearest tenth of an inch. How well does your estimate from part (a) describe the median height obtained from the formula?

80. The graph shows the median heights for girls of various ages in the United States from birth through 60 months, or five years old.

Girls' Heights

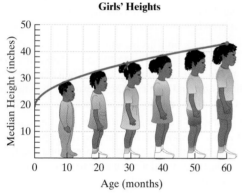

Source: Laura Walther Nathanson, *The Portable Pediatrician for Parents*

a. Use the graph to estimate the median height, to the nearest inch, of girls who are 50 months old.

b. The formula $h = 3.1\sqrt{x} + 19$ models the median height, h, in inches, of girls who are x months of age. According to the formula, what is the median height of girls who are 50 months old? Use a calculator and round to the nearest tenth of an inch. How well does your estimate from part (a) describe the median height obtained from the formula?

Autism is a neurological disorder that impedes language and derails social and emotional development. New findings suggest that the condition is not a sudden calamity that strikes children at the age of 2 or 3, but a developmental problem linked to abnormally rapid brain growth during infancy. The graphs show that the heads of severely autistic children start out smaller than average and then go through a period of explosive growth. Exercises 81–82 involve mathematical models for the data shown by the graphs.

Developmental Differences between Healthy Children and Severe Autistics

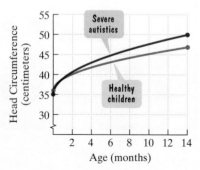

Source: The Journal of the American Medical Association

81. The data for one of the two groups shown by the graphs in the previous column can be modeled by

$$H = 2.9\sqrt{x} + 36,$$

where H is the head circumference, in centimeters, at age x months, $0 \le x \le 14$.

a. According to the model, what is the head circumference at birth?

b. According to the model, what is the head circumference at 9 months?

c. According to the model, what is the head circumference at 14 months? Use a calculator and round to the nearest tenth of a centimeter.

d. Use the values that you obtained in parts (a) through (c) and the graphs shown at the bottom of the previous column to determine if the given model describes healthy children or severe autistics.

82. The data for one of the two groups shown by the graphs in the previous column can be modeled by

$$H = 4\sqrt{x} + 35,$$

where H is the head circumference, in centimeters, at age x months, $0 \le x \le 14$.

a. According to the model, what is the head circumference at birth?

b. According to the model, what is the head circumference at 9 months?

c. According to the model, what is the head circumference at 14 months? Use a calculator and round to the nearest centimeter.

d. Use the values that you obtained in parts (a) through (c) and the graphs shown at the bottom of the previous column to determine if the given model describes healthy children or severe autistics.

The Blitzer Bonus on page 80 gives the square root expression

$$R_f\sqrt{1 - \left(\frac{v}{c}\right)^2}$$

for the aging rate of an astronaut relative to the aging rate of a friend on Earth, R_f, where v is the astronaut's speed and c is the speed of light. Take a few minutes to read the essay and then solve Exercises 83–84.

83. You are moving at 80% of the speed of light. Substitute $0.8c$ in the expression shown above. What is your aging rate relative to a friend on Earth? If 100 weeks have passed for your friend, how long were you gone?

84. You are moving at 90% of the speed of light. Substitute $0.9c$ in the expression shown above. What is your aging rate, correct to two decimal places, relative to a friend on Earth? If 100 weeks have passed for your friend, how long, to the nearest week, were you gone?

• **Writing in Mathematics**

85. Describe the difference between a rational number and an irrational number.

86. Describe what is wrong with this statement: $\pi = \frac{22}{7}$.

87. Using $\sqrt{50}$, explain how to simplify a square root.

88. Describe how to multiply square roots.

89. Explain how to add square roots with the same radicand.

90. Explain how to add $\sqrt{3} + \sqrt{12}$.

91. Describe what it means to rationalize a denominator. Use $\dfrac{2}{\sqrt{5}}$ in your explanation.

• **Critical Thinking Exercises**

92. Which one of the following is true?

a. The product of any two irrational numbers is always an irrational number.

b. $\sqrt{9} + \sqrt{16} = \sqrt{25}$

c. $\sqrt{\sqrt{16}} = 2$

d. $\dfrac{\sqrt{64}}{2} = \sqrt{32}$

In Exercises 93–95, insert either $<$ or $>$ in the shaded area between the numbers to make each statement true.

93. $\sqrt{2}$ ▪ 1.5 **94.** $-\pi$ ▪ -3.5 **95.** $-\dfrac{3.14}{2}$ ▪ $-\dfrac{\pi}{2}$

96. How does doubling a number affect its square root?

97. Between which two consecutive integers is $-\sqrt{47}$?

98. Simplify: $\sqrt{2} + \sqrt{\dfrac{1}{2}}$.

99. Create a counterexample to show that the following statement is false: The difference between two irrational numbers is always an irrational number.

• **Group Exercises**

The following topics related to irrational numbers are appropriate for either individual or group research projects. A report should be given to the class on the researched topic.

100. A History of How Irrational Numbers Developed

101. Pi: Its History, Applications, and Curiosities

102. Proving That $\sqrt{2}$ Is Irrational

103. Imaginary Numbers: Their History, Applications, and Curiosities

104. The Golden Rectangle in Art and Architecture

SECTION 2.5 • REAL NUMBERS AND THEIR PROPERTIES

O B J E C T I V E S

1. Recognize subsets of the real numbers.

2. Recognize properties of real numbers.

Horror films offer the pleasure of vicarious terror, of being safely scared.

1 | Recognize subsets of the real numbers.

The Set of Real Numbers

The vampire legend is death as seducer; he/she sucks our blood to take us to a perverse immortality. The vampire resembles us, but appears only at night, hidden among mortals. In this section, you will find vampires in the world of numbers. Mathematicians even use the labels *vampire* and *weird* to describe sets of numbers. However, the label that appears most frequently is *real*. The union of the rational numbers and the irrational numbers is the set of **real numbers**.

The sets that make up the real numbers are summarized in Table 2.2 on the next page. We refer to these sets as **subsets** of the real numbers, meaning that all elements in each subset are also elements in the set of real numbers.

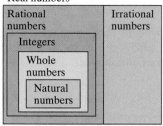

Real numbers

Rational numbers	Irrational numbers
Integers	
Whole numbers	
Natural numbers	

This diagram shows that every real number is rational or irrational.

TABLE 2.2 IMPORTANT SUBSETS OF THE REAL NUMBERS

Name	Description	Examples
Natural numbers	$\{1, 2, 3, 4, 5, \dots\}$ These are the numbers that we use for counting.	$2, 3, 5, 17$
Whole numbers	$\{0, 1, 2, 3, 4, 5, \dots\}$ The set of whole numbers includes 0 and the natural numbers.	$0, 2, 3, 5, 17$
Integers	$\{\dots, -5, -4, -3, -2, -1, 0, 1, 2, 3, 4, 5, \dots\}$ The set of integers includes the negatives of the natural numbers and the whole numbers.	$-17, -5, -3, -2, 0, 2, 3, 5, 17$
Rational numbers	$\left\{\dfrac{a}{b} \,\middle|\, a \text{ and } b \text{ are integers and } b \neq 0\right\}$ The set of rational numbers is the set of all numbers that can be expressed as a quotient of two integers, with the denominator not 0. Rational numbers can be expressed as terminating or repeating decimals.	$-17 = \frac{-17}{1}, -5 = \frac{-5}{1}, -3, -2,$ $0, 2, 3, 5, 17,$ $\frac{2}{5} = 0.4,$ $\frac{-2}{3} = -0.6666\dots = -0.\overline{6}$
Irrational numbers	The set of irrational numbers is the set of all numbers whose decimal representations are neither terminating nor repeating. Irrational numbers cannot be expressed as a quotient of integers.	$\sqrt{2} \approx 1.414214$ $-\sqrt{3} \approx -1.73205$ $\pi \approx 3.142$ $-\frac{\pi}{2} \approx -1.571$

EXAMPLE 1   CLASSIFYING REAL NUMBERS

Consider the following set of numbers:

$$\left\{-7, -\frac{3}{4}, 0, 0.\overline{6}, \sqrt{5}, \pi, 7.3, \sqrt{81}\right\}.$$

List the numbers in the set that are

a. natural numbers. **b.** whole numbers. **c.** integers.

d. rational numbers. **e.** irrational numbers. **f.** real numbers.

SOLUTION

a. Natural numbers: The natural numbers are the numbers used for counting. The only natural number in the set is $\sqrt{81}$ because $\sqrt{81} = 9$. (9 multiplied by itself, or 9^2, is 81.)

b. Whole numbers: The whole numbers consist of the natural numbers and 0. The elements of the set that are whole numbers are 0 and $\sqrt{81}$.

c. Integers: The integers consist of the natural numbers, 0, and the negatives of the natural numbers. The elements of the set that are integers are $\sqrt{81}$, 0, and -7.

d. Rational numbers: All numbers in the set that can be expressed as the quotient of integers are rational numbers. These include $-7\left(-7 = \frac{-7}{1}\right), -\frac{3}{4}, 0\left(0 = \frac{0}{1}\right)$, and $\sqrt{81}\left(\sqrt{81} = \frac{9}{1}\right)$. Furthermore, all numbers in the set that are terminating or repeating decimals are also rational numbers. These include $0.\overline{6}$ and 7.3.

e. Irrational numbers: The irrational numbers in the set are $\sqrt{5}\,(\sqrt{5} \approx 2.236)$ and $\pi\,(\pi \approx 3.14)$. Both $\sqrt{5}$ and π are only approximately equal to 2.236 and 3.14, respectively. In decimal form, $\sqrt{5}$ and π neither terminate nor have blocks of repeating digits.

f. Real numbers: All the numbers in the given set are real numbers.   ○

 CHECK POINT 1 Consider the following set of numbers:

$$\left\{-9, -1.3, 0, 0.\overline{3}, \frac{\pi}{2}, \sqrt{9}, \sqrt{10}\right\}.$$

List the numbers in the set that are

a. natural numbers.   **b.** whole numbers.   **c.** integers.

d. rational numbers.   **e.** irrational numbers.   **f.** real numbers.

Vampire Numbers

Like legendary vampires that lie concealed among humans, vampire numbers lie hidden within the set of real numbers, mostly undetected. By definition, vampire numbers have an even number of digits. Furthermore, they are the product of two numbers whose digits all survive, in scrambled form, in the vampire. For example, 1260, 1435, and 2187 are vampire numbers.

$$21 \times 60 = 1260 \qquad 35 \times 41 = 1435 \qquad 27 \times 81 = 2187$$

> The digits 2, 1, 6, and 0 lie scrambled in the vampire number.

> The digits 3, 5, 4, and 1 lurk within the vampire number.

> The digits 2, 7, 8, and 1 survive in the vampire number.

As the real numbers grow increasingly larger, is it necessary to pull out a wooden stake with greater frequency? How often can you expect to find vampires hidden among the giants? And is it possible to find a weird vampire?

On the right of the equal sign is a 40-digit vampire number that was discovered using a Pascal program on a personal computer:

$$98{,}765{,}432{,}198{,}765{,}432{,}198 \times 98{,}765{,}432{,}198{,}830{,}604{,}534 = 9{,}754{,}610{,}597{,}415{,}368{,}368{,}844{,}499{,}268{,}390{,}128{,}385{,}732.$$

Source: Clifford Pickover, *Wonders of Numbers*, Oxford University Press, 2001

---

2 | Recognize properties of real numbers.

Properties of the Real Numbers

When you use your calculator to add two real numbers, you can enter them in either order. The fact that two real numbers can be added in either order is called the **commutative property of addition.** You probably use this property, as well as other properties of real numbers listed in Table 2.3, without giving it much thought. The properties of the real numbers are especially useful in algebra, as we shall see in Chapter 3.

The Associative Property and the English Language

In the English language, phrases can take on different meanings depending on the way the words are associated with commas. Here are three examples.

- Woman, without her man, is nothing.
  Woman, without her, man is nothing.
- What's the latest dope?
  What's the latest, dope?
- Population of Amsterdam broken down by age and sex
  Population of Amsterdam, broken down by age and sex

TABLE 2.3 PROPERTIES OF THE REAL NUMBERS

Name	Meaning	Examples
Closure Property of Addition	The sum of any two real numbers is a real number.	$4\sqrt{2}$ is a real number and $5\sqrt{2}$ is a real number, so $4\sqrt{2} + 5\sqrt{2}$, or $9\sqrt{2}$, is a real number.
Closure Property of Multiplication	The product of any two real numbers is a real number.	10 is a real number and $\frac{1}{2}$ is a real number, so $10 \cdot \frac{1}{2}$, or 5, is a real number.
Commutative Property of Addition	Changing order when adding does not affect the sum. $a + b = b + a$	$13 + 7 = 7 + 13$
Commutative Property of Multiplication	Changing order when multiplying does not affect the product. $ab = ba$	$13 \cdot 7 = 7 \cdot 13$ $\sqrt{2} \cdot \sqrt{5} = \sqrt{5} \cdot \sqrt{2}$
Associative Property of Addition	Changing grouping when adding does not affect the sum. $(a + b) + c = a + (b + c)$	$(7 + 2) + 5 = 7 + (2 + 5)$ $9 + 5 = 7 + 7$ $14 = 14$
Associative Property of Multiplication	Changing grouping when multiplying does not affect the product. $(ab)c = a(bc)$	$(7 \cdot 2) \cdot 5 = 7 \cdot (2 \cdot 5)$ $14 \cdot 5 = 7 \cdot 10$ $70 = 70$
Distributive Property of Multiplication over Addition	Multiplication distributes over addition. $a \cdot (b + c) = a \cdot b + a \cdot c$	$7(4 + \sqrt{3}) = 7 \cdot 4 + 7 \cdot \sqrt{3}$ $= 28 + 7\sqrt{3}$

STUDY TIP

Commutative: Changes *order*.
Associative: Changes *grouping*.

EXAMPLE 2   IDENTIFYING PROPERTIES OF THE REAL NUMBERS

Name the property illustrated:

a. $\sqrt{3} \cdot 7 = 7 \cdot \sqrt{3}$

b. $(4 + 7) + 6 = 4 + (7 + 6)$

c. $2(3 + \sqrt{5}) = 6 + 2\sqrt{5}$

d. $\sqrt{2} + (\sqrt{3} + \sqrt{7}) = \sqrt{2} + (\sqrt{7} + \sqrt{3}).$

SOLUTION

a. $\sqrt{3} \cdot 7 = 7 \cdot \sqrt{3}$ Commutative property of multiplication

b. $(4 + 7) + 6 = 4 + (7 + 6)$ Associative property of addition

c. $2(3 + \sqrt{5}) = 6 + 2\sqrt{5}$ Distributive property of multiplication over addition

d. $\sqrt{2} + (\sqrt{3} + \sqrt{7}) = \sqrt{2} + (\sqrt{7} + \sqrt{3})$ The only change between the left and the right sides is in the order that $\sqrt{3}$ and $\sqrt{7}$ are added. The order is changed from $\sqrt{3} + \sqrt{7}$ to $\sqrt{7} + \sqrt{3}$ using the commutative property of addition.

2 Name the property illustrated:

a. $(4 \cdot 7) \cdot 3 = 4 \cdot (7 \cdot 3)$

b. $3(\sqrt{5} + 4) = 3(4 + \sqrt{5})$

c. $3(\sqrt{5} + 4) = 3\sqrt{5} + 12$

d. $2(\sqrt{3} + \sqrt{7}) = (\sqrt{3} + \sqrt{7})2.$

Although the entire set of real numbers is closed with respect to addition and multiplication, some of the subsets of the real numbers do not satisfy the closure property for a given operation. If an operation on a set results in just one number that is not in that set, then the set is not closed for that operation.

EXAMPLE 3   VERIFYING CLOSURE

a. Are the integers closed with respect to multiplication?

b. Are the irrational numbers closed with respect to multiplication?

c. Are the natural numbers closed with respect to division?

SOLUTION

a. Consider some examples of the multiplication of integers:

$$3 \cdot 2 = 6 \qquad 3(-2) = -6 \qquad -3(-2) = 6 \qquad -3 \cdot 0 = 0.$$

The product of any two integers is always a positive integer, a negative integer, or zero, which is an integer. Thus, the integers are closed under the operation of multiplication.

b. If we multiply two irrational numbers, must the product always be an irrational number? The answer is no. Here is an example:

$$\sqrt{7} \cdot \sqrt{7} = \sqrt{49} = 7.$$

Both irrational   Not an irrational number

This means that the irrational numbers are not closed under the operation of multiplication.

c. If we divide any two natural numbers, must the quotient always be a natural number? The answer is no. Here is an example:

$$4 \div 8 = \frac{1}{2}.$$

Both natural numbers   Not a natural number

Thus, the natural numbers are not closed under the operation of division.

a. Are the natural numbers closed with respect to multiplication?

b. Are the integers closed with respect to division?

The commutative property involves a change in order with no change in the final result. However, changing the order in which we subtract and divide real numbers can produce different answers. For example,

$$7 - 4 \neq 4 - 7 \quad \text{and} \quad 6 \div 2 \neq 2 \div 6.$$

Because the real numbers are not commutative with respect to subtraction and division, it is important that you enter numbers in the correct order when using a calculator to perform these operations.

The associative property does not hold for the operations of subtraction and division. The examples below show that if we change groupings when subtracting or dividing three numbers, the answer may change.

$$(6 - 1) - 3 \neq 6 - (1 - 3) \qquad (8 \div 4) \div 2 \neq 8 \div (4 \div 2)$$
$$5 - 3 \neq 6 - (-2) \qquad\qquad 2 \div 2 \neq 8 \div 2$$
$$2 \neq 8 \qquad\qquad\qquad 1 \neq 4$$

BLITZER BONUS

Beyond the Real Numbers

THE KID WHO LEARNED ABOUT MATH ON THE STREET

If you divide 6,973 by 0, you die.

Once, this guy tried to find the square root of -9, and his eyeballs turned black.

This girl my brother knows found out exactly what π equals, but she went nuts.

R. Chast

Only real numbers greater than or equal to zero have real number square roots. The square root of -1, $\sqrt{-1}$, is not a real number. This is because there is no real number that can be multiplied by itself that results in -1. Multiplying any real number by itself can never give a negative product. In the sixteenth century, mathematician Girolamo Cardano wrote that square roots of negative numbers would cause "mental tortures." In spite of these "tortures," mathematicians invented a new number, called i, to represent $\sqrt{-1}$. The number i is not a real number; it is called an **imaginary number**. Thus, $\sqrt{9} = 3$, $-\sqrt{9} = -3$, but $\sqrt{-9}$ is not a real number. However, $\sqrt{-9}$ is an imaginary number, represented by $3i$. The adjective *real* as a way of describing what we now call the real numbers was first used by the French mathematician and philosopher René Descartes (1596–1650) in response to the concept of imaginary numbers.

EXERCISE SET 2.5 ●●●●●●

• Practice Exercises

In Exercises 1–4, list all numbers from the given set that are

a. *natural numbers.* **b.** *whole numbers.* **c.** *integers.*

d. *rational numbers.* **e.** *irrational numbers.* **f.** *real numbers.*

1. $\left\{-9, -\frac{4}{5}, 0, 0.25, \sqrt{3}, 9.2, \sqrt{100}\right\}$
2. $\left\{-7, -0.\overline{6}, 0, \sqrt{49}, \sqrt{50}\right\}$
3. $\left\{-11, -\frac{5}{6}, 0, 0.75, \sqrt{5}, \pi, \sqrt{64}\right\}$
4. $\left\{-5, -0.\overline{3}, 0, \sqrt{2}, \sqrt{4}\right\}$

5. Give an example of a whole number that is not a natural number.

6. Give an example of an integer that is not a whole number.

7. Give an example of a rational number that is not an integer.

8. Give an example of a rational number that is not a natural number.

9. Give an example of a number that is an integer, a whole number, and a natural number.

10. Give an example of a number that is a rational number, an integer, and a real number.

11. Give an example of a number that is an irrational number and a real number.

12. Give an example of a number that is a real number, but not an irrational number.

Complete each statement in Exercises 13–15 to illustrate the commutative property.

13. $3 + (4 + 5) = 3 + (5 + \underline{\quad})$
14. $\sqrt{5} \cdot 4 = 4 \cdot \underline{\quad}$
15. $9 \cdot (6 + 2) = 9 \cdot (2 + \underline{\quad})$

Complete each statement in Exercises 16–17 to illustrate the associative property.

16. $(3 + 7) + 9 = \underline{\quad} + (7 + \underline{\quad})$
17. $(4 \cdot 5) \cdot 3 = \underline{\quad} \cdot (5 \cdot \underline{\quad})$

Complete each statement in Exercises 18–20 to illustrate the distributive property.

18. $3 \cdot (6 + 4) = 3 \cdot 6 + 3 \cdot \underline{\quad}$
19. $\underline{\quad} \cdot (4 + 5) = 7 \cdot 4 + 7 \cdot 5$
20. $2 \cdot (\underline{\quad} + 3) = 2 \cdot 7 + 2 \cdot 3$

Use the distributive property to simplify the radical expressions in Exercises 21–28.

21. $5\left(6 + \sqrt{2}\right)$ 22. $4\left(3 + \sqrt{5}\right)$
23. $\sqrt{7}\left(3 + \sqrt{2}\right)$ 24. $\sqrt{6}\left(7 + \sqrt{5}\right)$
25. $\sqrt{3}\left(5 + \sqrt{3}\right)$ 26. $\sqrt{7}\left(9 + \sqrt{7}\right)$
27. $\sqrt{6}\left(\sqrt{2} + \sqrt{6}\right)$ 28. $\sqrt{10}\left(\sqrt{2} + \sqrt{10}\right)$

In Exercises 29–38, state the name of the property illustrated.

29. $6 + (-4) = (-4) + 6$
30. $11 \cdot (7 + 4) = 11 \cdot 7 + 11 \cdot 4$
31. $6 + (2 + 7) = (6 + 2) + 7$
32. $6 \cdot (2 \cdot 3) = 6 \cdot (3 \cdot 2)$

33. $(2 + 3) + (4 + 5) = (4 + 5) + (2 + 3)$
34. $7 \cdot (11 \cdot 8) = (11 \cdot 8) \cdot 7$
35. $2(-8 + 6) = -16 + 12$
36. $-8(3 + 11) = -24 + (-88)$
37. $\left(2\sqrt{3}\right) \cdot \sqrt{5} = 2\left(\sqrt{3} \cdot \sqrt{5}\right)$
38. $\sqrt{2}\pi = \pi\sqrt{2}$

In Exercises 39–43, use two numbers to show that

39. the natural numbers are not closed with respect to subtraction.

40. the natural numbers are not closed with respect to division.

41. the integers are not closed with respect to division.

42. the irrational numbers are not closed with respect to subtraction.

43. the irrational numbers are not closed with respect to multiplication.

• Practice Plus

In Exercises 44–47, determine if each statement is true or false. Do not use a calculator.

44. $468(787 + 289) = 787 + 289(468)$

45. $468(787 + 289) = 787(468) + 289(468)$

46. $58 \cdot 9 + 32 \cdot 9 = (58 + 32) \cdot 9$

47. $58 \cdot 9 \cdot 32 \cdot 9 = (58 \cdot 32) \cdot 9$

In Exercises 48–49, name the property used to go from step to step each time that (why?) *occurs.*

48. $7 + 2(x + 9)$
   $= 7 + (2x + 18)$ (why?)
   $= 7 + (18 + 2x)$ (why?)
   $= (7 + 18) + 2x$ (why?)
   $= 25 + 2x$
   $= 2x + 25$ (why?)

49. $5(x + 4) + 3x$
   $= (5x + 20) + 3x$ (why?)
   $= (20 + 5x) + 3x$ (why?)
   $= 20 + (5x + 3x)$ (why?)
   $= 20 + (5 + 3)x$ (why?)
   $= 20 + 8x$
   $= 8x + 20$ (why?)

• Application Exercises

In Exercises 50–53, use the definition of vampire numbers from the Blitzer Bonus on page 87 to determine which products are vampires.

50. $15 \times 93 = 1395$

51. $80 \times 86 = 6880$

52. $20 \times 51 = 1020$

53. $146 \times 938 = 136{,}948$

A **narcissistic number** *is an n-digit number equal to the sum of each of its digits raised to the nth power. Here's an example:*

$$153 = 1^3 + 5^3 + 3^3.$$

Three digits, so exponents are 3

In Exercises 54–57, determine which real numbers are narcissistic.

54. 370   **55.** 371   **56.** 372   **57.** 9474

58. Closure illustrates that a characteristic of a set is not necessarily a characteristic of all of its subsets. The real numbers are closed with respect to multiplication, but the irrational numbers, a subset of the real numbers, are not. Give an example of a set that is not mathematical that has a particular characteristic, but which has a subset without this characteristic.

59. The algebraic expressions

$$\frac{D(A + 1)}{24} \quad \text{and} \quad \frac{DA + D}{24}$$

describe the drug dosage for children between the ages of 2 and 13. In each algebraic expression, D stands for an adult dose and A represents the child's age.

a. Name the property that explains why these expressions are equal for all values of D and A.

b. If an adult dose of ibuprofen is 200 milligrams, what is the proper dose for a 12-year-old child? Use both forms of the algebraic expressions to answer the question. Which form is easier to use?

• Writing in Mathematics

60. What does it mean when we say that the rational numbers are a subset of the real numbers?

61. What does it mean if we say that a set is closed under a given operation?

62. State the commutative property of addition and give an example.

63. State the commutative property of multiplication and give an example.

64. State the associative property of addition and give an example.

65. State the associative property of multiplication and give an example.

66. State the distributive property of multiplication over addition and give an example.

67. Does $7 \cdot (4 \cdot 3) = 7 \cdot (3 \cdot 4)$ illustrate the commutative property or the associative property? Explain your answer.

• Critical Thinking Exercises

68. Which one of the following statements is true?

a. Every rational number is an integer.

b. Some whole numbers are not integers.

c. Some rational numbers are not positive.

d. Irrational numbers cannot be negative.

69. Which one of the following statements is true?

a. Subtraction is a commutative operation.

b. $(24 \div 6) \div 2 = 24 \div (6 \div 2)$

c. $7 \cdot a + 3 \cdot a = a \cdot (7 + 3)$

d. $2 \cdot a + 5 = 5 \cdot a + 2$

SECTION 2.6 • EXPONENTS AND SCIENTIFIC NOTATION

O B J E C T I V E S

1. Use properties of exponents.

2. Convert from scientific notation to decimal notation.

3. Convert from decimal notation to scientific notation.

4. Perform computations using scientific notation.

5. Solve applied problems using scientific notation.

We frequently encounter very large and very small numbers. Governments throughout the world are concerned about the billions of tons of carbon dioxide that the global population of 6.5 billion people release into the atmosphere each year. In the photo shown above, the national debt of the United States was about $8.2 trillion. A typical atom has a diameter of about one-ten-billionth of a meter. Exponents provide a way of putting these large and small numbers in perspective.

1 | Use properties of exponents.

Properties of Exponents

We have seen that exponents are used to indicate repeated multiplication. Now consider the multiplication of two exponential expressions, such as $b^4 \cdot b^3$. We are multiplying 4 factors of b and 3 factors of b. We have a total of 7 factors of b:

4 factors of b 3 factors of b

$$b^4 \cdot b^3 = (b \cdot b \cdot b \cdot b)(b \cdot b \cdot b) = b^7.$$

Total: 7 factors of b

The product is exactly the same if we add the exponents:

$$b^4 \cdot b^3 = b^{4+3} = b^7.$$

Properties of exponents allow us to perform operations with exponential expressions without having to write out long strings of factors. Three such properties are given in Table 2.4.

TABLE 2.4 PROPERTIES OF EXPONENTS		
Property	**Meaning**	**Examples**
The Product Rule $b^m \cdot b^n = b^{m+n}$	When multiplying exponential expressions with the same base, add the exponents. Use this sum as the exponent of the common base.	$9^6 \cdot 9^{12} = 9^{6+12} = 9^{18}$
The Power Rule $(b^m)^n = b^{m \cdot n}$	When an exponential expression is raised to a power, multiply the exponents. Place the product of the exponents on the base and remove the parentheses.	$(3^4)^5 = 3^{4 \cdot 5} = 3^{20}$ $(5^3)^8 = 5^{3 \cdot 8} = 5^{24}$
The Quotient Rule $\dfrac{b^m}{b^n} = b^{m-n}$	When dividing exponential expressions with the same base, subtract the exponent in the denominator from the exponent in the numerator. Use this difference as the exponent of the common base.	$\dfrac{5^{12}}{5^4} = 5^{12-4} = 5^8$ $\dfrac{9^{40}}{9^5} = 9^{40-5} = 9^{35}$

The third property in Table 2.4, the quotient rule, can lead to a zero exponent when subtracting exponents. Here is an example:

$$\frac{4^3}{4^3} = 4^{3-3} = 4^0.$$

We can see what this zero exponent means by evaluating 4^3 in the numerator and the denominator:

$$\frac{4^3}{4^3} = \frac{4 \cdot 4 \cdot 4}{4 \cdot 4 \cdot 4} = \frac{64}{64} = 1.$$

This means that 4^0 must equal 1. This example illustrates the zero exponent rule.

THE ZERO EXPONENT RULE

If b is any real number other than 0,

$$b^0 = 1.$$

EXAMPLE 1   USING THE ZERO EXPONENT RULE

Use the zero exponent rule to simplify:

a. 7^0 **b.** π^0 **c.** $(-5)^0$ **d.** -5^0.

SOLUTION

a. $7^0 = 1$ **b.** $\pi^0 = 1$ **c.** $(-5)^0 = 1$ **d.** $-5^0 = -1$

> Only 5 is raised to the 0 power.

1 Use the zero exponent rule to simplify:

     a. 19^0 **b.** $(3\pi)^0$ **c.** $(-14)^0$ **d.** -14^0.

The quotient rule can result in a negative exponent. Consider, for example, $4^3 \div 4^5$:

$$\frac{4^3}{4^5} = 4^{3-5} = 4^{-2}.$$

STUDY TIP

$\frac{4^3}{4^5}$ and $\frac{4^5}{4^3}$ represent different numbers:

$$\frac{4^3}{4^5} = 4^{3-5} = 4^{-2} = \frac{1}{4^2} = \frac{1}{16}$$

$$\frac{4^5}{4^3} = 4^{5-3} = 4^2 = 16.$$

We can see what this negative exponent means by evaluating the numerator and the denominator:

$$\frac{4^3}{4^5} = \frac{\cancel{4} \cdot \cancel{4} \cdot \cancel{4}}{\cancel{4} \cdot \cancel{4} \cdot \cancel{4} \cdot 4 \cdot 4} = \frac{1}{4^2}.$$

Notice that $\frac{4^3}{4^5}$ equals both 4^{-2} and $\frac{1}{4^2}$. This means that 4^{-2} must equal $\frac{1}{4^2}$. This example is a particular case of the negative exponent rule.

THE NEGATIVE EXPONENT RULE
If b is any real number other than 0 and m is a natural number,

$$b^{-m} = \frac{1}{b^m}.$$

EXAMPLE 2   USING THE NEGATIVE EXPONENT RULE

Use the negative exponent rule to simplify:

a. 8^{-2} **b.** 5^{-3} **c.** 7^{-1}.

SOLUTION

a. $8^{-2} = \dfrac{1}{8^2} = \dfrac{1}{8 \cdot 8} = \dfrac{1}{64}$

b. $5^{-3} = \dfrac{1}{5^3} = \dfrac{1}{5 \cdot 5 \cdot 5} = \dfrac{1}{125}$

c. $7^{-1} = \dfrac{1}{7^1} = \dfrac{1}{7}$

2 Use the negative exponent rule to simplify:

     a. 9^{-2} **b.** 6^{-3} **c.** 12^{-1}.

John Scott "*Invoking the Googolplex*" 1981, water-colour on paper, 24 × 18 in. *Source*: Photo courtesy of The Gallery, Stratford, Ontario.

Powers of Ten

Exponents and their properties allow us to represent and compute with numbers that are large or small. For example, one billion, or 1,000,000,000 can be written as 10^9. In terms of exponents, 10^9 might not look very large, but consider this: If you can count to 200 in one minute and decide to count for 12 hours a day at this rate, it would take you in the region of 19 years, 9 days, 5 hours, and 20 minutes to count to 10^9!

Powers of ten follow two basic rules:

1. **A positive exponent tells how many 0s follow the 1.** For example, 10^9 (one billion) is a 1 followed by nine zeros: 1,000,000,000. A googol, 10^{100}, is a 1 followed by one hundred zeros. (A googol far exceeds the number of protons, neutrons, and electrons in the universe.) A googol is a veritable pipsqueak compared to the googolplex, 10 raised to the googol power, or $10^{10^{100}}$; that's a 1 followed by a googol zeros. (If each zero in a googolplex were no larger than a grain of sand, there would not be enough room in the universe to represent the number.)

2. **A negative exponent tells how many places there are to the right of the decimal point.** For example, 10^{-9} (one billionth) has nine places to the right of the decimal point. The nine places contain eight 0s and the 1.

$$10^{-9} = 0.\underbrace{000000001}_{\text{nine places}}$$

Earthquakes and Powers of Ten

The earthquake that ripped through northern California on October 17, 1989, measured 7.1 on the Richter scale, killed more than 60 people, and injured more than 2400. Shown here is San Francisco's Marina district, where shock waves tossed houses off their foundations and into the street.

The Richter scale is misleading because it is not actually a 1 to 8, but rather a 1 to 10 million scale. Each level indicates a tenfold increase in magnitude from the previous level, making a 7.0 earthquake a million times greater than a 1.0 quake.

The following is a translation of the Richter scale:

Richter number (R)	Magnitude (10^{R-1})
1	$10^{1-1} = 10^0 = 1$
2	$10^{2-1} = 10^1 = 10$
3	$10^{3-1} = 10^2 = 100$
4	$10^{4-1} = 10^3 = 1000$
5	$10^{5-1} = 10^4 = 10{,}000$
6	$10^{6-1} = 10^5 = 100{,}000$
7	$10^{7-1} = 10^6 = 1{,}000{,}000$
8	$10^{8-1} = 10^7 = 10{,}000{,}000$

TABLE 2.5 NAMES OF LARGE NUMBERS

10^2	hundred
10^3	thousand
10^6	million
10^9	billion
10^{12}	trillion
10^{15}	quadrillion
10^{18}	quintillion
10^{21}	sextillion
10^{24}	septillion
10^{27}	octillion
10^{30}	nonillion
10^{100}	googol
10^{googol}	googolplex

Scientific Notation

As of December 2006, the national debt of the United States was about $8.6 trillion. This is the amount of money the government has had to borrow over the years, most-ly by selling bonds, because it has spent more than it has collected in taxes. A stack of $1 bills equaling the national debt would rise to twice the distance from Earth to the moon. Because a trillion is 10^{12} (see Table 2.5), the national debt can be expressed as

$$8.6 \times 10^{12}.$$

The number 8.6×10^{12} is written in a form called *scientific notation*.

> ### SCIENTIFIC NOTATION
>
> A positive number is written in **scientific notation** when it is expressed in the form
>
> $$a \times 10^n,$$
>
> where a is a number greater than or equal to 1 and less than 10 ($1 \le a < 10$) and n is an integer.

It is customary to use the multiplication symbol, $\times$, rather than a dot, when writing a number in scientific notation.

Here are two examples of numbers in scientific notation:

- Each day, 2.6×10^7 pounds of dust from the atmosphere settle on Earth.
- The length of the AIDS virus is 1.1×10^{-4} millimeter.

2 | Convert from scientific notation to decimal notation.

We can use n, the exponent on the 10 in $a \times 10^n$, to change a number in scientific notation to decimal notation. If n is **positive**, move the decimal point in a to the **right** n places. If n is **negative**, move the decimal point in a to the **left** $|n|$ places.

EXAMPLE 3   CONVERTING FROM SCIENTIFIC TO DECIMAL NOTATION

Write each number in decimal notation:

a. 2.6×10^7 **b.** 1.1×10^{-4}.

SOLUTION   In each case, we use the exponent on the 10 to move the decimal point. In part (a), the exponent is positive, so we move the decimal point to the right. In part (b), the exponent is negative, so we move the decimal point to the left.

a. $2.6 \times 10^7 = 26,000,000$

$n = 7$

Move the decimal point 7 places to the right.

b. $1.1 \times 10^{-4} = 0.00011$

$n = -4$

Move the decimal point $|-4|$ places, or 4 places, to the left.

Write each number in decimal notation:

a. 7.4×10^9 **b.** 3.017×10^{-6}.

---

3 | Convert from decimal notation to scientific notation.

To convert a positive number from decimal notation to scientific notation, we reverse the procedure of Example 3.

CONVERTING FROM DECIMAL TO SCIENTIFIC NOTATION

Write the number in the form $a \times 10^n$.

- Determine a, the numerical factor. Move the decimal point in the given number to obtain a number greater than or equal to 1 and less than 10.
- Determine n, the exponent on 10^n. The absolute value of n is the number of places the decimal point was moved. The exponent n is positive if the given number is greater than 10 and negative if the given number is between 0 and 1.

EXAMPLE 4   CONVERTING FROM DECIMAL NOTATION TO SCIENTIFIC NOTATION

Write each number in scientific notation:

a. 4,600,000   **b.** 0.000023.

You can use your calculator's
EE (enter exponent) or

EXP key to convert from
decimal to scientific notation.
Here is how it's done for 0.000023:

MANY SCIENTIFIC CALCULATORS

Keystrokes	Display
.000023 EE =	2.3 − 05

MANY GRAPHING CALCULATORS
Use the mode setting for scientific
notation.

Keystrokes	Display
.000023 ENTER	2.3ᴇ − 5

SOLUTION

a. $4{,}600{,}000 \;=\; 4.6 \;\times\; 10^6$

| This number is greater than 10, so n is positive in $a \times 10^n$. | Move the decimal point in 4,600,000 to get $1 \le a < 10$. | The decimal point moved 6 places from 4,600,000 to 4.6. |

b. $0.000023 \;=\; 2.3 \;\times\; 10^{-5}$

| This number is less than 1, so n is negative in $a \times 10^n$. | Move the decimal point in 0.000023 to get $1 \le a < 10$. | The decimal point moved 5 places from 0.000023 to 2.3. |

 4 Write each number in scientific notation:

    a. 7,410,000,000   **b.** 0.000000092.

EXAMPLE 5   EXPRESSING THE NUMBER OF CELLPHONE SPAM MESSAGES IN SCIENTIFIC NOTATION

As feature-rich cellphones function more like PCs, digital intruders are targeting them with viruses, spam, and phishing scams. The bar graph in Figure 2.6 shows the number of cellphone spam messages, in millions, from 2002 through 2005. Express the number of spam messages in 2005 in scientific notation.

SOLUTION Because a million is 10^6, the number of cellphone spam messages in 2005 can be expressed as

$$500 \times 10^6.$$

| This factor is not between 1 and 10, so the number is not in scientific notation. |

The voice balloon indicates that we need to convert 500 to scientific notation.

$$500 \times 10^6 = (5 \times 10^2) \times 10^6 = 5 \times (10^2 \times 10^6) = 5 \times 10^{2+6} = 5 \times 10^8$$

There were 5×10^8 cellphone spam messages in 2005.

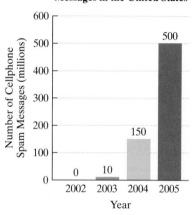

Number of Cellphone Spam Messages in the United States

FIGURE 2.6
Source: Ferris Research

STUDY TIP

Many of the large numbers we encounter in newspapers, magazines, and almanacs are expressed in millions (10^6), billions (10^9), and trillions (10^{12}). We can use exponential properties to describe the number of cellphone spam messages in 2005 using millions or billions.

$$500 \times 10^6 \;=\; 5 \times 10^8 \;=\; 0.5 \times 10^9$$

| There were 500 million messages. | This expresses the number of messages in scientific notation. | There were half a billion messages. |

 5 In 2005, the federal cost of social security was \$519 billion. Express this amount in scientific notation.

4 Perform computations using scientific notation.

Computations with Scientific Notation

We use the product rule for exponents to multiply numbers in scientific notation:

$$(a \times 10^n) \times (b \times 10^m) = (a \times b) \times 10^{n+m}.$$

Add the exponents on 10 and multiply the other parts of the numbers separately.

EXAMPLE 6	MULTIPLYING NUMBERS IN SCIENTIFIC NOTATION

Multiply: $(3.4 \times 10^9)(2 \times 10^{-5})$. Write the product in decimal notation.

SOLUTION

$$
\begin{aligned}
(3.4 \times 10^9)(2 \times 10^{-5}) &= (3.4 \times 2) \times (10^9 \times 10^{-5}) && \text{Regroup factors.}\\
&= 6.8 \times 10^{9+(-5)} && \text{Add the exponents on 10 and multiply the other parts.}\\
&= 6.8 \times 10^4 && \text{Simplify.}\\
&= 68{,}000 && \text{Write the product in decimal notation.}
\end{aligned}
$$

 6 Multiply: $(1.3 \times 10^7)(4 \times 10^{-2})$. Write the product in decimal notation.

We use the quotient rule for exponents to divide numbers in scientific notation:

$$\frac{a \times 10^n}{b \times 10^m} = \left(\frac{a}{b}\right) \times 10^{n-m}.$$

Subtract the exponents on 10 and divide the other parts of the numbers separately.

EXAMPLE 7	DIVIDING NUMBERS IN SCIENTIFIC NOTATION

Divide: $\dfrac{8.4 \times 10^{-7}}{4 \times 10^{-4}}$. Write the quotient in decimal notation.

SOLUTION

$$
\begin{aligned}
\frac{8.4 \times 10^{-7}}{4 \times 10^{-4}} &= \left(\frac{8.4}{4}\right) \times \left(\frac{10^{-7}}{10^{-4}}\right) && \text{Regroup factors.}\\
&= 2.1 \times 10^{-7-(-4)} && \text{Subtract the exponents on 10 and divide the other parts.}\\
&= 2.1 \times 10^{-3} && \text{Simplify: } -7 - (-4) = -7 + 4 = -3.\\
&= 0.0021 && \text{Write the quotient in decimal notation.}
\end{aligned}
$$

 7 Divide: $\dfrac{6.9 \times 10^{-8}}{3 \times 10^{-2}}$. Write the quotient in decimal notation.

Multiplication and division involving very large or very small numbers can be performed by first converting each number to scientific notation.

EXAMPLE 8   USING SCIENTIFIC NOTATION TO MULTIPLY

Multiply: $0.00064 \times 9,400,000,000$. Express the product in **a.** scientific notation and **b.** decimal notation.

SOLUTION

a. $0.00064 \times 9,400,000,000$

$$= 6.4 \times 10^{-4} \times 9.4 \times 10^{9} \qquad \text{Write each number in scientific notation.}$$

$$= (6.4 \times 9.4) \times (10^{-4} \times 10^{9}) \qquad \text{Regroup factors.}$$

$$= 60.16 \times 10^{-4+9} \qquad \text{Add the exponents on 10 and multiply the other parts.}$$

$$= 60.16 \times 10^{5} \qquad \text{Simplify.}$$

$$= (6.016 \times 10) \times 10^{5} \qquad \text{Express 60.16 in scientific notation.}$$

$$= 6.016 \times 10^{6} \qquad \text{Add exponents on 10: } 10^{1} \times 10^{5} = 10^{1+5} = 10^{6}.$$

b. The answer in decimal notation is obtained by moving the decimal point in 6.016 six places to the right. The product is 6,016,000. ○

8 Multiply: $0.0036 \times 5,200,000$. Express the product in **a.** scientific notation and **b.** decimal notation.

5 | Solve applied problems using scientific notation.

Applications: Putting Numbers in Perspective

Due to tax cuts and spending increases, the United States began accumulating large deficits in the 1980s. To finance the deficit, the government had borrowed $8.6 trillion as of December 2006. The graph in Figure 2.7 shows the national debt increasing over time.

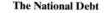

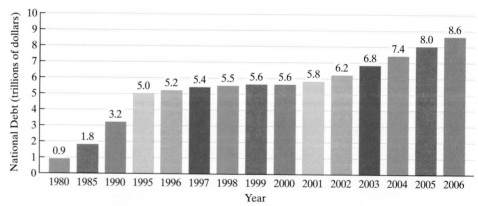

The National Debt

FIGURE 2.7

Source: Office of Management and Budget

Example 9 shows how we can use scientific notation to comprehend the meaning of a number such as 8.6 trillion.

TECHNOLOGY

Here is the keystroke sequence for solving Example 9 using a calculator:

8.4 $\boxed{\text{EE}}$ 12 $\boxed{\div}$ 3 $\boxed{\text{EE}}$ 8.

The quotient is displayed by pressing $\boxed{=}$ on a scientific calculator or $\boxed{\text{ENTER}}$ on a graphing calculator. The answer can be displayed in scientific or decimal notation. Consult your manual.

EXAMPLE 9   THE NATIONAL DEBT

As of December 2006, the national debt was \$8.6 trillion, or 8.6×10^{12} dollars. At that time, the U.S. population was approximately 300,000,000 (300 million), or 3×10^8. If the national debt was evenly divided among every individual in the United States, how much would each citizen have to pay?

SOLUTION The amount each citizen must pay is the total debt, 8.6×10^{12} dollars, divided by the number of citizens, 3×10^8.

$$\frac{8.6 \times 10^{12}}{3 \times 10^8} = \left(\frac{8.6}{3}\right) \times \left(\frac{10^{12}}{10^8}\right)$$
$$\approx 2.87 \times 10^{12-8}$$
$$= 2.87 \times 10^4$$
$$= 28{,}700$$

Every U.S. citizen would have to pay approximately \$28,700 to the federal government to pay off the national debt.

CHECK POINT 9 Pell Grants help low-income undergraduate students pay for college. In 2006, the federal cost of this program was \$13 billion (\$13 $\times$ 10^9) and there were 5.1 million (5.1×10^6) grant recipients. How much, to the nearest hundred dollars, was the average grant?

BLITZER BONUS

Fermat's Last Theorem

Pierre de Fermat (1601–1665) was a lawyer who enjoyed studying mathematics. In a margin of one of his books, he claimed that no natural numbers satisfy

$$a^n + b^n = c^n$$

if n is an integer greater than or equal to 3.

If $n = 2$, we can find numbers satisfying $a^n + b^n = c^n$, or $a^2 + b^2 = c^2$. For example,

$$3^2 + 4^2 = 5^2.$$

However, Fermat claimed that no natural numbers satisfy

$$a^3 + b^3 = c^3, \qquad a^4 + b^4 = c^4, \qquad a^5 + b^5 = c^5,$$

and so on.

Fermat claimed to have a proof of his conjecture, but added, "The margin of my book is too narrow to write it down." Some believe that he never had a proof and intended to frustrate his colleagues.

In June 1993, 40-year-old Princeton math professor Andrew Wiles claimed that he discovered a proof of the theorem. Subsequent study revealed flaws, but Wiles corrected them. In 1995, his final proof served as a classic example of how great mathematicians accomplish great things: a combination of genius, hard work, frustration, and trial and error.

(Andrew Wiles 1953–)

EXERCISE SET 2.6 ●●●●●●

• Practice Exercises

In Exercises 1–12, use properties of exponents to simplify each expression. First express the answer in exponential form. Then evaluate the expression.

1. $2^2 \cdot 2^3$ **2.** $3^3 \cdot 3^2$ **3.** $4 \cdot 4^2$ **4.** $5 \cdot 5^2$

5. $(2^2)^3$ **6.** $(3^3)^2$ **7.** $(1^4)^5$ **8.** $(1^3)^7$

9. $\dfrac{4^7}{4^5}$ **10.** $\dfrac{6^7}{6^5}$ **11.** $\dfrac{2^8}{2^4}$ **12.** $\dfrac{3^8}{3^4}$

In Exercises 13–24, use the zero and negative exponent rules to simplify each expression.

13. 3^0 **14.** 9^0 **15.** $(-3)^0$ **16.** $(-9)^0$

17. -3^0 **18.** -9^0 **19.** 2^{-2} **20.** 3^{-2}

21. 4^{-3} **22.** 2^{-3} **23.** 2^{-5} **24.** 2^{-6}

In Exercises 25–30, use properties of exponents to simplify each expression. First express the answer in exponential form. Then evaluate the expression.

25. $3^4 \cdot 3^{-2}$ **26.** $2^5 \cdot 2^{-2}$ **27.** $3^{-3} \cdot 3$

28. $2^{-3} \cdot 2$ **29.** $\dfrac{2^3}{2^7}$ **30.** $\dfrac{3^4}{3^7}$

In Exercises 31–46, express each number in decimal notation.

31. 2.7×10^2 **32.** 4.7×10^3 **33.** 9.12×10^5
34. 8.14×10^4 **35.** 8×10^7 **36.** 7×10^6
37. 1×10^5 **38.** 1×10^8 **39.** 7.9×10^{-1}
40. 8.6×10^{-1} **41.** 2.15×10^{-2} **42.** 3.14×10^{-2}
43. 7.86×10^{-4} **44.** 4.63×10^{-5} **45.** 3.18×10^{-6}
46. 5.84×10^{-7}

In Exercises 47–66, express each number in scientific notation.

47. 370 **48.** 530 **49.** 3600 **50.** 2700
51. 32,000 **52.** 64,000 **53.** 220,000,000
54. 370,000,000,000 **55.** 0.027 **56.** 0.014
57. 0.0037 **58.** 0.00083 **59.** 0.00000293
60. 0.000000647 **61.** 820×10^5 **62.** 630×10^8
63. 0.41×10^6 **64.** 0.57×10^9 **65.** 2100×10^{-9}
66. $97,000 \times 10^{-11}$

In Exercises 67–80, perform the indicated operation and express each answer in decimal notation.

67. $(2 \times 10^3)(3 \times 10^2)$ **68.** $(5 \times 10^2)(4 \times 10^4)$
69. $(2 \times 10^9)(3 \times 10^{-5})$ **70.** $(4 \times 10^8)(2 \times 10^{-4})$
71. $(4.1 \times 10^2)(3 \times 10^{-4})$ **72.** $(1.2 \times 10^3)(2 \times 10^{-5})$
73. $\dfrac{12 \times 10^6}{4 \times 10^2}$ **74.** $\dfrac{20 \times 10^{20}}{10 \times 10^{15}}$
75. $\dfrac{15 \times 10^4}{5 \times 10^{-2}}$ **76.** $\dfrac{18 \times 10^2}{9 \times 10^{-3}}$
77. $\dfrac{6 \times 10^3}{2 \times 10^5}$ **78.** $\dfrac{8 \times 10^4}{2 \times 10^7}$
79. $\dfrac{6.3 \times 10^{-6}}{3 \times 10^{-3}}$ **80.** $\dfrac{9.6 \times 10^{-7}}{3 \times 10^{-3}}$

In Exercises 81–90, perform the indicated operation by first expressing each number in scientific notation. Write the answer in scientific notation.

81. $(82,000,000)(3,000,000,000)$
82. $(94,000,000)(6,000,000,000)$
83. $(0.0005)(6,000,000)$ **84.** $(0.000015)(0.004)$
85. $\dfrac{9,500,000}{500}$ **86.** $\dfrac{30,000}{0.0005}$
87. $\dfrac{0.00008}{200}$ **88.** $\dfrac{0.0018}{0.0000006}$
89. $\dfrac{480,000,000,000}{0.00012}$ **90.** $\dfrac{0.000000096}{16,000}$

• Practice Plus

In Exercises 91–94, perform the indicated operations. Express each answer as a fraction reduced to its lowest terms.

91. $\dfrac{2^4}{2^5} + \dfrac{3^3}{3^5}$ **92.** $\dfrac{3^5}{3^6} + \dfrac{2^3}{2^6}$

93. $\dfrac{2^6}{2^4} - \dfrac{5^4}{5^6}$ **94.** $\dfrac{5^6}{5^4} - \dfrac{2^4}{2^6}$

In Exercises 95–98, perform the indicated computations. Express answers in scientific notation.

95. $(5 \times 10^3)(1.2 \times 10^{-4}) \div (2.4 \times 10^2)$
96. $(2 \times 10^2)(2.6 \times 10^{-3}) \div (4 \times 10^3)$
97. $\dfrac{(1.6 \times 10^4)(7.2 \times 10^{-3})}{(3.6 \times 10^8)(4 \times 10^{-3})}$
98. $\dfrac{(1.2 \times 10^6)(8.7 \times 10^{-2})}{(2.9 \times 10^6)(3 \times 10^{-3})}$

• Application Exercises

The graph shows the net worth, in billions of dollars, of the five richest Americans. Use 10^9 for one billion and the figures shown to solve Exercises 99–102. Express all answers in scientific notation.

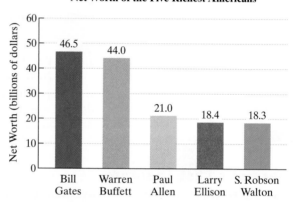

Net Worth of the Five Richest Americans

Source: Forbes Billionaires List, 2005

99. How much is Bill Gates worth?

100. How much is Warren Buffett worth?

101. By how much does Larry Ellison's worth exceed that of S. Robson Walton?

102. If each person doubled his net worth, by how much would Larry Ellison's worth exceed that of S. Robson Walton?

Our ancient ancestors hunted for their meat and expended a great deal of energy chasing it down. Today, our animal protein is raised in cages and on feedlots, delivered in great abundance nearly to our door. Use the numbers shown below to solve Exercises 103–106. Use 10^6 for one million and 10^9 for one billion.

Overproteined

600 million	8 billion	127	20 billion
Big Macs consumed by Americans at McDonald's each year	Chickens raised for food each year in the U.S.	Chickens eaten per second in America	Hot dogs consumed by Americans each year

Source: Time, October 20, 2003

In Exercises 103–104, use 300 million, or 3×10^8, for the U.S. population. Express answers in decimal notation, rounded to the nearest whole number.

103. Find the number of hot dogs consumed by each American in a year.

104. If the consumption of Big Macs was divided evenly among all Americans, how many Big Macs would we each consume in a year?

In Exercises 105–106, use the Overproteined table and the fact that there are approximately 3.2×10^7 seconds in a year.

105. How many chickens are raised for food each second in the United States? Express the answer in scientific and decimal notations.

106. How many chickens are eaten per year in the United States? Express the answer in scientific notation.

The graph shows the cost, in billions of dollars, and the enrollment, in millions of people, for various federal social programs in 2005. Use the numbers shown to solve Exercises 107–109.

Cost and Enrollment for Federal Social Programs

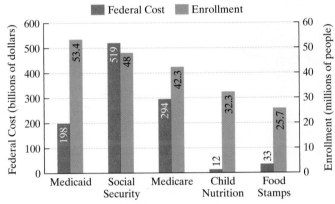

Source: Office of Management and Budget

107. a. What was the average per person benefit for Social Security? Express the answer in scientific notation and in decimal notation, rounded to the nearest dollar.

b. What was the average monthly per person benefit, rounded to the nearest dollar, for Social Security?

108. a. What was the average per person benefit for the food stamps program? Express the answer in scientific notation and in decimal notation, rounded to the nearest dollar.

b. What was the average monthly per person benefit, rounded to the nearest dollar, for the food stamps program?

109. Medicaid provides health insurance for the poor. Medicare provides health insurance for people 65 and older, as well as younger people who are disabled. Which program provides the greater per person benefit? By how much, rounded to the nearest dollar?

110. The area of Alaska is approximately 3.66×10^8 acres. The state was purchased in 1867 from Russia for $7.2 million. What price per acre, to the nearest cent, did the United States pay Russia?

111. The mass of one oxygen molecule is 5.3×10^{-23} gram. Find the mass of 20,000 molecules of oxygen. Express the answer in scientific notation.

112. The mass of one hydrogen atom is 1.67×10^{-24} gram. Find the mass of 80,000 hydrogen atoms. Express the answer in scientific notation.

113. In Exercises 105–106, we used 3.2×10^7 as an approximation for the number of seconds in a year. Convert 365 days (one year) to hours, to minutes, and, finally, to seconds, to determine precisely how many seconds there are in a year. Express the answer in scientific notation.

• Writing in Mathematics

114. Explain the product rule for exponents. Use $2^3 \cdot 2^5$ in your explanation.

115. Explain the power rule for exponents. Use $(3^2)^4$ in your explanation.

116. Explain the quotient rule for exponents. Use $\dfrac{5^8}{5^2}$ in your explanation.

117. Explain the zero exponent rule and give an example.

118. Explain the negative exponent rule and give an example.

119. How do you know if a number is written in scientific notation?

120. Explain how to convert from scientific to decimal notation and give an example.

121. Explain how to convert from decimal to scientific notation and give an example.

122. Suppose you are looking at a number in scientific notation. Describe the size of the number you are looking at if the exponent on ten is **a.** positive, **b.** negative, **c.** zero.

123. Describe one advantage of expressing a number in scientific notation over decimal notation.

• Critical Thinking Exercises

124. Which one of the following is true?
  a. $4^{-2} < 4^{-3}$
  b. $5^{-2} > 2^{-5}$
  c. $(-2)^4 = 2^{-4}$
  d. $5^2 \cdot 5^{-2} > 2^5 \cdot 2^{-5}$

125. Which one of the following is true?
  a. $534.7 = 5.347 \times 10^3$
  b. $\dfrac{8 \times 10^{30}}{4 \times 10^{-5}} = 2 \times 10^{25}$
  c. $(7 \times 10^5) + (2 \times 10^{-3}) = 9 \times 10^2$
  d. $(4 \times 10^3) + (3 \times 10^2) = 43 \times 10^2$

126. Give an example of a number for which there is no advantage to using scientific notation instead of decimal notation. Explain why this is the case.

127. The mad Dr. Frankenstein has gathered enough bits and pieces (so to speak) for $2^{-1} + 2^{-2}$ of his creature-to-be. Write a fraction that represents the amount of his creature that must still be obtained.

• Technology Exercises

128. Use a calculator in a fraction mode to check your answers in Exercises 19–24.

129. Use a calculator to check any three of your answers in Exercises 31–46.

130. Use a calculator to check any three of your answers in Exercises 47–66.

131. Use a calculator with an $\boxed{\text{EE}}$ or $\boxed{\text{EXP}}$ key to check any four of your computations in Exercises 67–90. Display the result of the computation in scientific notation and in decimal notation.

• Group Exercises

132. Putting Numbers into Perspective. A large number can be put into perspective by comparing it with another number. For example, we put the $8.6 trillion national debt into perspective by comparing it to the number of U.S. citizens and computing the debt per person. For this project, each group member should consult an almanac, a newspaper, or the World Wide Web to find a number greater than one million. Explain to other members of the group the con-

text in which the large number is used. Express the number in scientific notation. Then put the number into perspective by comparing it with another number.

133. Fermat's most notorious theorem baffled the greatest minds for more than three centuries. In 1994, after ten years of work, Princeton University's Andrew Wiles proved Fermat's Last Theorem. *People* magazine put him on its list of "the 25 most intriguing people of the year," the Gap asked him to model jeans, and Barbara Walters chased him for an interview. "Who's Barbara Walters?" asked the bookish Wiles, who had somehow gone through life without a television.

Using the 1993 PBS documentary "Solving Fermat: Andrew Wiles" or information about Andrew Wiles on the Internet, research and present a group seminar on what Wiles did to prove Fermat's Last Theorem, problems along the way, and how Wiles overcame them.

SECTION 2.7 • ARITHMETIC AND GEOMETRIC SEQUENCES

OBJECTIVES

1. Write terms of an arithmetic sequence.

2. Use the formula for the general term of an arithmetic sequence.

3. Write terms of a geometric sequence.

4. Use the formula for the general term of a geometric sequence.

Sequences

Many creations in nature involve intricate mathematical designs, including a variety of spirals. For example, the arrangement of the individual florets in the head of a sunflower forms spirals. In some species, there are 21 spirals in the clockwise direction and 34 in the counterclockwise direction. The precise numbers depend on the species of sunflower: 21 and 34, or 34 and 55, or 55 and 89, or even 89 and 144.

This observation becomes even more interesting when we consider a sequence of numbers investigated by Leonardo of Pisa, also known as Fibonacci, an Italian mathematician of the thirteenth century. The **Fibonacci sequence** of numbers is an infinite sequence that begins as follows:

$$1, 1, 2, 3, 5, 8, 13, 21, 34, 55, 89, 144, 233, \ldots.$$

The first two terms are 1. Every term thereafter is the sum of the two preceding terms. For example, the third term, 2, is the sum of the first and second terms: $1 + 1 = 2$. The fourth term, 3, is the sum of the second and third terms: $1 + 2 = 3$, and so on. Did you know that the number of spirals in a daisy or a sunflower, 21 and 34, are two Fibonacci numbers? The number of spirals in a pinecone, 8 and 13, and a pineapple, 8 and 13, are also Fibonacci numbers.

We can think of a **sequence** as a list of numbers that are related to each other by a rule. The numbers in a sequence are called its **terms**. The letter a with a subscript is used to represent the terms of a sequence. Thus, a_1 represents the first term of the sequence, a_2 represents the second term, a_3 the third term, and so on. This notation is shown for the first six terms of the Fibonacci sequence:

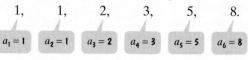

1,   1,   2,   3,   5,   8.

$a_1 = 1$ $a_2 = 1$ $a_3 = 2$ $a_4 = 3$ $a_5 = 5$ $a_6 = 8$

Fibonacci Numbers on the Piano Keyboard

One Octave

Numbers in the Fibonacci sequence can be found in an octave on the piano keyboard. The octave contains 2 black keys in one cluster, 3 black keys in another cluster, a total of 5 black keys, 8 white keys, and a total of 13 keys altogether. The numbers 2, 3, 5, 8, and 13 are the third through seventh terms of the Fibonacci sequence.

Arithmetic Sequences

The bar graph in Figure 2.8 shows annual salaries, rounded to the nearest thousand dollars, of U.S. senators from 2000 to 2005. The graph illustrates that each year salaries increased by $4 thousand. The sequence of annual salaries

142, 146, 150, 154, 158, 162, . . .

shows that each term after the first, 142, differs from the preceding term by a constant amount, namely 4. This sequence is an example of an *arithmetic sequence*.

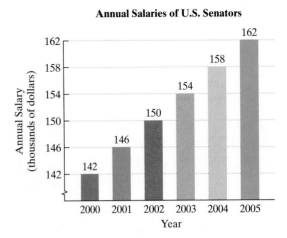

Annual Salaries of U.S. Senators

FIGURE 2.8
Source: U.S. Senate

DEFINITION OF AN ARITHMETIC SEQUENCE

An **arithmetic sequence** is a sequence in which each term after the first differs from the preceding term by a constant amount. The difference between consecutive terms is called the **common difference** of the sequence.

The common difference, d, is found by subtracting any term from the term that directly follows it. In the following examples, the common difference is found by subtracting the first term from the second term: $a_2 - a_1$.

Arithmetic Sequence	Common Difference
142, 146, 150, 154, 158, . . .	$d = 146 - 142 = 4$
$-5, -2, 1, 4, 7, . . .$	$d = -2 - (-5) = -2 + 5 = 3$
$8, 3, -2, -7, -12, . . .$	$d = 3 - 8 = -5$

If the first term of an arithmetic sequence is a_1, each term after the first is obtained by adding d, the common difference, to the previous term.

---

1 | Write terms of an arithmetic sequence.

EXAMPLE 1   WRITING THE TERMS OF AN ARITHMETIC SEQUENCE

Write the first six terms of the arithmetic sequence with first term 6 and common difference 4.

SOLUTION   The first term is 6. The second term is 6 + 4, or 10. The third term is 10 + 4, or 14, and so on. The first six terms are

6, 10, 14, 18, 22, and 26.

 Write the first six terms of the arithmetic sequence with first term 100 and common difference 20.

EXAMPLE 2   WRITING THE TERMS OF AN ARITHMETIC SEQUENCE

Write the first six terms of the arithmetic sequence with $a_1 = 5$ and $d = -2$.

SOLUTION   The first term, a_1, is 5. The common difference, d, is -2. To find the second term, we add -2 to 5, giving 3. For the next term, we add -2 to 3, and so on. The first six terms are

$5, 3, 1, -1, -3$, and -5.

CHECK POINT 2 Write the first six terms of the arithmetic sequence with first term 8 and common difference -3.

2 Use the formula for the general term of an arithmetic sequence.

The General Term of an Arithmetic Sequence

Consider an arithmetic sequence whose first term is a_1 and whose common difference is d. We are looking for a formula for the general term, a_n. Let's begin by writing the first six terms. The first term is a_1. The second term is $a_1 + d$. The third term is $a_1 + d + d$, or $a_1 + 2d$. Thus, we start with a_1 and add d to each successive term. The first six terms are

$$a_1, \quad a_1 + d, \quad a_1 + 2d, \quad a_1 + 3d, \quad a_1 + 4d, \quad a_1 + 5d.$$

a_1, first term a_2, second term a_3, third term a_4, fourth term a_5, fifth term a_6, sixth term

Applying inductive reasoning to the pattern of the terms results in the following formula for the general term, or the nth term, of an arithmetic sequence:

> **GENERAL TERM OF AN ARITHMETIC SEQUENCE**
> The nth term (the general term) of an arithmetic sequence with first term a_1 and common difference d is
> $$a_n = a_1 + (n - 1)d.$$

EXAMPLE 3   USING THE FORMULA FOR THE GENERAL TERM OF AN ARITHMETIC SEQUENCE

Find the eighth term of the arithmetic sequence whose first term is 4 and whose common difference is -7.

SOLUTION To find the eighth term, a_8, we replace n in the formula with 8, a_1 with 4, and d with -7.

$$a_n = a_1 + (n - 1)d$$
$$a_8 = 4 + (8 - 1)(-7) = 4 + 7(-7) = 4 + (-49) = -45$$

The eighth term is -45. We can check this result by writing the first eight terms of the sequence:

$$4, -3, -10, -17, -24, -31, -38, -45.$$

CHECK POINT 3 Find the ninth term of the arithmetic sequence whose first term is 6 and whose common difference is -5.

The process of finding formulas to describe real-world phenomena is called mathematical modeling. Such formulas, together with the meaning assigned to the variables, are called mathematical models. Example 4 illustrates how the formula for the general term of an arithmetic sequence can be used to develop a mathematical model.

Changing Times in the U.S.

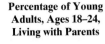

Percentage of Young Adults, Ages 18–24, Living with Parents

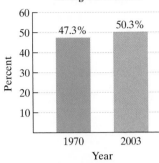

Number (in millions) Completing Four or More Years of College

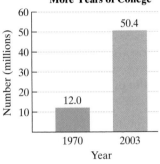

FIGURE 2.9
Source: U.S. Census Bureau

EXAMPLE 4   USING AN ARITHMETIC SEQUENCE TO MODEL CHANGING TIMES

The top graph in Figure 2.9 shows that in 1970, 47.3% of young adults, ages 18–24, lived at home with their parents. On average, this has increased by approximately 0.09% per year.

a. Write a formula for the nth term of the arithmetic sequence that models the percentage of young adults living at home with their parents n years after 1969.

b. According to the model in part (a), what percentage of young adults will be living at home with their parents in 2009?

SOLUTION

a. We can express the percentage of young adults living with their parents by the following arithmetic sequence:

$$47.3, \qquad 47.39, \qquad 47.48, \ldots$$

a_1: 47.3% lived with parents in 1970, 1 year after 1969.

a_2: 47.39% lived with parents in 1971, 2 years after 1969.

a_3: 47.48% lived with parents in 1972, 3 years after 1969.

In this sequence, a_1, the first term, represents the percentage of young adults who lived at home in 1970. Each subsequent year this increased by 0.09%, so $d = 0.09$. We use the formula for the general term of an arithmetic sequence to write the nth term of the sequence that describes the percentage of young adults living at home with their parents n years after 1969.

$a_n = a_1 + (n - 1)d$ This is the formula for the general term of an arithmetic sequence.

$a_n = 47.3 + (n - 1)0.09$ $a_1 = 47.3$ and $d = 0.09$.

$a_n = 47.3 + 0.09n - 0.09$ Distribute 0.09 to each term in parentheses.

$a_n = 0.09n + 47.21$ Simplify: $47.3 - 0.09 = 47.21$.

Thus, the percentage of young adults living at home with their parents n years after 1969 can be described by $a_n = 0.09n + 47.21$.

b. Now we need to find the percentage who will be living with their parents in 2009. The year 2009 is 40 years after 1969: That is, $2009 - 1969 = 40$. We substitute 40 for n in $a_n = 0.09n + 47.21$.

$$a_{40} = 0.09(40) + 47.21 = 50.81$$

The 40th term of the sequence is 50.81. Therefore, the model indicates that 50.81% of young adults will be living at home with their parents by the year 2009.

CHECK POINT 4   The bottom graph in Figure 2.9 shows that in 1970, 12.0 million Americans had completed four or more years of college. On average, this has increased by approximately 1.16 million people per year.

a. Write a formula for the nth term of the arithmetic sequence that models the number of Americans, in millions, completing four or more years of college n years after 1969.

b. According to the model in part (a), how many Americans, to the nearest tenth of a million, will have completed four or more years of college in 2019?

Geometric Sequences

Figure 2.10 shows a sequence in which the number of squares is increasing. From left to right, the number of squares is 1, 5, 25, 125, and 625. In this sequence, each term after the first, 1, is obtained by multiplying the preceding term by a constant amount, namely 5. This sequence of increasing numbers of squares is an example of a *geometric sequence*.

FIGURE 2.10 A geometric sequence of squares

> ### DEFINITION OF A GEOMETRIC SEQUENCE
> A **geometric sequence** is a sequence in which each term after the first is obtained by multiplying the preceding term by a fixed nonzero constant. The amount by which we multiply each time is called the **common ratio** of the sequence.

The common ratio, r, is found by dividing any term after the first term by the term that directly precedes it. In the examples below, the common ratio is found by dividing the second term by the first term: $\dfrac{a_2}{a_1}$.

Geometric sequence	Common ratio
$1, 5, 25, 125, 625, \ldots$	$r = \frac{5}{1} = 5$
$4, 8, 16, 32, 64, \ldots$	$r = \frac{8}{4} = 2$
$6, -12, 24, -48, 96, \ldots$	$r = \frac{-12}{6} = -2$
$9, -3, 1, -\frac{1}{3}, \frac{1}{9}, \ldots$	$r = \frac{-3}{9} = -\frac{1}{3}$

STUDY TIP

When the common ratio of a geometric sequence is negative, the signs of the terms alternate.

3 | Write terms of a geometric sequence.

How do we write out the terms of a geometric sequence when the first term and the common ratio are known? We multiply the first term by the common ratio to get the second term, multiply the second term by the common ratio to get the third term, and so on.

EXAMPLE 5 WRITING THE TERMS OF A GEOMETRIC SEQUENCE

Write the first six terms of the geometric sequence with first term 6 and common ratio $\frac{1}{3}$.

SOLUTION The first term is 6. The second term is $6 \cdot \frac{1}{3}$, or 2. The third term is $2 \cdot \frac{1}{3}$, or $\frac{2}{3}$. The fourth term is $\frac{2}{3} \cdot \frac{1}{3}$, or $\frac{2}{9}$, and so on. The first six terms are

$$6, 2, \frac{2}{3}, \frac{2}{9}, \frac{2}{27}, \text{ and } \frac{2}{81}.$$

CHECK POINT 5 Write the first six terms of the geometric sequence with first term 12 and common ratio $-\frac{1}{2}$.

4 | Use the formula for the general term of a geometric sequence.

The General Term of a Geometric Sequence

Consider a geometric sequence whose first term is a_1 and whose common ratio is r. We are looking for a formula for the general term, a_n. Let's begin by writing the first six terms. The first term is a_1. The second term is $a_1 r$. The third term is $a_1 r \cdot r$, or $a_1 r^2$. The fourth term is $a_1 r^2 \cdot r$, or $a_1 r^3$, and so on. Starting with a_1 and multiplying each successive term by r, the first six terms are

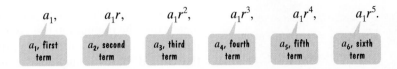

$$a_1, \quad a_1 r, \quad a_1 r^2, \quad a_1 r^3, \quad a_1 r^4, \quad a_1 r^5.$$

| a_1, first term | a_2, second term | a_3, third term | a_4, fourth term | a_5, fifth term | a_6, sixth term |

Applying inductive reasoning to the pattern of the terms results in the following formula for the general term, or the nth term, of a geometric sequence:

> **GENERAL TERM OF A GEOMETRIC SEQUENCE**
> The nth term (the general term) of a geometric sequence with first term a_1 and common ratio r is
> $$a_n = a_1 r^{n-1}.$$

EXAMPLE 6 | USING THE FORMULA FOR THE GENERAL TERM OF A GEOMETRIC SEQUENCE

Find the eighth term of the geometric sequence whose first term is -4 and whose common ratio is -2.

STUDY TIP

Be careful with the order of operations when evaluating
$$a_1 r^{n-1}.$$
First find r^{n-1}. Then multiply the result by a_1.

SOLUTION To find the eighth term, a_8, we replace n in the formula with 8, a_1 with -4, and r with -2.

$$a_n = a_1 r^{n-1}$$
$$a_8 = -4(-2)^{8-1} = -4(-2)^7 = -4(-128) = 512$$

The eighth term is 512. We can check this result by writing the first eight terms of the sequence:

$$-4, 8, -16, 32, -64, 128, -256, 512.$$

CHECK POINT 6 Find the seventh term of the geometric sequence whose first term is 5 and whose common ratio is -3.

EXAMPLE 7 | GEOMETRIC POPULATION GROWTH

The table shows the population of the United States in 2000, with estimates given by the Census Bureau for 2001 through 2006.

Year	2000	2001	2002	2003	2004	2005	2006
Population (millions)	281.4	284.5	287.6	290.8	294.0	297.2	300.5

a. Show that the population is increasing geometrically.

b. Write the general term for the geometric sequence describing population growth for the United States n years after 1999.

c. Project the U.S. population, in millions, for the year 2009.

Geometric Population Growth

Economist Thomas Malthus (1766–1834) predicted that population growth would increase as a geometric sequence and food production would increase as an arithmetic sequence. He concluded that eventually population would exceed food production. If two sequences, one geometric and one arithmetic, are increasing, the geometric sequence will eventually overtake the arithmetic sequence, regardless of any head start that the arithmetic sequence might initially have.

SOLUTION

a. First, we use the sequence of population growth, 281.4, 284.5, 287.6, 290.8, and so on, to divide the population for each year by the population in the preceding year.

$$\frac{284.5}{281.4} \approx 1.011, \quad \frac{287.6}{284.5} \approx 1.011, \quad \frac{290.8}{287.6} \approx 1.011$$

Continuing in this manner, we will keep getting approximately 1.011. This means that the population is increasing geometrically with $r \approx 1.011$. In this situation, the common ratio is the growth rate, indicating that the population of the United States in any year shown in the sequence is approximately 1.011 times the population the year before.

b. The sequence of the U.S. population growth is

$$281.4, 284.5, 287.6, 290.8, 294.0, 297.2, 300.5, \ldots.$$

Because the population is increasing geometrically, we can find the general term of this sequence using

$$a_n = a_1 r^{n-1}.$$

In this sequence, $a_1 = 281.4$ and [from part (a)] $r \approx 1.011$. We substitute these values into the formula for the general term. This gives the general term for the geometric sequence describing the U.S. population n years after 1999.

$$a_n = 281.4(1.011)^{n-1}$$

c. We can use the formula for the general term, a_n, in part (b) to project the U.S. population for the year 2009. The year 2009 is 10 years after 1999—that is, $2009 - 1999 = 10$. Thus, $n = 10$. We substitute 10 for n in $a_n = 281.4(1.011)^{n-1}$.

$$a_{10} = 281.4(1.011)^{10-1} = 281.4(1.011)^9 \approx 310.5$$

The model projects that the United States will have a population of approximately 310.5 million in the year 2009.

  Write the general term for the geometric sequence

$$3, 6, 12, 24, 48, \ldots.$$

Then use the formula for the general term to find the eighth term.

EXERCISE SET 2.7 ●●●●●●

• Practice Exercises

In Exercises 1–20, write the first six terms of the arithmetic sequence with the first term, a_1, and common difference, d.

1. $a_1 = 8, d = 2$

2. $a_1 = 5, d = 3$

3. $a_1 = 200, d = 20$

4. $a_1 = 300, d = 50$

5. $a_1 = -7, d = 4$

6. $a_1 = -8, d = 5$

7. $a_1 = -400, d = 300$

8. $a_1 = -500, d = 400$

9. $a_1 = 7, d = -3$

10. $a_1 = 9, d = -5$

11. $a_1 = 200, d = -60$

12. $a_1 = 300, d = -90$

13. $a_1 = \frac{5}{2}, d = \frac{1}{2}$

14. $a_1 = \frac{3}{4}, d = \frac{1}{4}$

15. $a_1 = \frac{3}{2}, d = \frac{1}{4}$

16. $a_1 = \frac{3}{2}, d = -\frac{1}{4}$

17. $a_1 = 4.25, d = 0.3$

18. $a_1 = 6.3, d = 0.25$

19. $a_1 = 4.5, d = -0.75$

20. $a_1 = 3.5, d = -1.75$

In Exercises 21–40, find the indicated term for the arithmetic sequence with first term, a_1, and common difference, d.

21. Find a_6, when $a_1 = 13, d = 4$.

22. Find a_{16}, when $a_1 = 9, d = 2$.

23. Find a_{50}, when $a_1 = 7, d = 5$.

24. Find a_{60}, when $a_1 = 8, d = 6$.

25. Find a_9, when $a_1 = -5, d = 9$.

26. Find a_{10}, when $a_1 = -8, d = 10$.

27. Find a_{200}, when $a_1 = -40, d = 5$.

28. Find a_{150}, when $a_1 = -60, d = 5$.

29. Find a_{10}, when $a_1 = -8, d = 10$.

30. Find a_{11}, when $a_1 = 10, d = -6$.

31. Find a_{60}, when $a_1 = 35, d = -3$.

32. Find a_{70}, when $a_1 = -32, d = 4$.

33. Find a_{12}, when $a_1 = 12, d = -5$.

34. Find a_{20}, when $a_1 = -20, d = -4$.

35. Find a_{90}, when $a_1 = -70, d = -2$.

36. Find a_{80}, when $a_1 = 106, d = -12$.

37. Find a_{12}, when $a_1 = 6, d = \frac{1}{2}$.

38. Find a_{14}, when $a_1 = 8, d = \frac{1}{4}$.

39. Find a_{50}, when $a_1 = 14, d = -0.25$.

40. Find a_{110}, when $a_1 = -12, d = -0.5$.

In Exercises 41–48, write a formula for the general term (the nth term) of each arithmetic sequence. Then use the formula for a_n to find a_{20}, the 20th term of the sequence.

41. $1, 5, 9, 13, \ldots$

42. $2, 7, 12, 17, \ldots$

43. $7, 3, -1, -5, \ldots$

44. $6, 1, -4, -9, \ldots$

45. $a_1 = 9, d = 2$

46. $a_1 = 6, d = 3$

47. $a_1 = -20, d = -4$

48. $a_1 = -70, d = -5$

In Exercises 49–70, write the first six terms of the geometric sequence with the first term, a_1, and common ratio, r.

49. $a_1 = 4, r = 2$

50. $a_1 = 2, r = 3$

51. $a_1 = 1000, r = 1$

52. $a_1 = 5000, r = 1$

53. $a_1 = 3, r = -2$

54. $a_1 = 2, r = -3$

55. $a_1 = 10, r = -4$

56. $a_1 = 20, r = -4$

57. $a_1 = 2000, r = -1$

58. $a_1 = 3000, r = -1$

59. $a_1 = -2, r = -3$

60. $a_1 = -4, r = -2$

61. $a_1 = -6, r = -5$

62. $a_1 = -8, r = -5$

63. $a_1 = \frac{1}{4}, r = 2$

64. $a_1 = \frac{1}{2}, r = 2$

65. $a_1 = \frac{1}{4}, r = \frac{1}{2}$

66. $a_1 = \frac{1}{5}, r = \frac{1}{2}$

67. $a_1 = -\frac{1}{16}, r = -4$

68. $a_1 = -\frac{1}{8}, r = -2$

69. $a_1 = 2, r = 0.1$

70. $a_1 = -1000, r = 0.1$

In Exercises 71–90, find the indicated term for the geometric sequence with first term, a_1, and common ratio, r.

71. Find a_7, when $a_1 = 4, r = 2$.

72. Find a_5, when $a_1 = 4, r = 3$.

73. Find a_{20}, when $a_1 = 2, r = 3$.

74. Find a_{20}, when $a_1 = 2, r = 2$.

75. Find a_{100}, when $a_1 = 50, r = 1$.

76. Find a_{200}, when $a_1 = 60, r = 1$.

77. Find a_7, when $a_1 = 5, r = -2$.

78. Find a_4, when $a_1 = 4, r = -3$.

79. Find a_{30}, when $a_1 = 2, r = -1$.

80. Find a_{40}, when $a_1 = 6, r = -1$.

81. Find a_6, when $a_1 = -2, r = -3$.

82. Find a_5, when $a_1 = -5, r = -2$.

83. Find a_8, when $a_1 = 6, r = \frac{1}{2}$.

84. Find a_8, when $a_1 = 12, r = \frac{1}{2}$.

85. Find a_6, when $a_1 = 18, r = -\frac{1}{3}$.

86. Find a_4, when $a_1 = 9, r = -\frac{1}{3}$.

87. Find a_{40}, when $a_1 = 1000, r = -\frac{1}{2}$.

88. Find a_{30}, when $a_1 = 8000, r = -\frac{1}{2}$.

89. Find a_8, when $a_1 = 1{,}000{,}000, r = 0.1$.

90. Find a_8, when $a_1 = 40{,}000, r = 0.1$.

In Exercises 91–98, write a formula for the general term (the nth term) of each geometric sequence. Then use the formula for a_n to find a_7, the seventh term of the sequence.

91. $3, 12, 48, 192, \ldots$

92. $3, 15, 75, 375, \ldots$

93. $18, 6, 2, \frac{2}{3}, \ldots$

94. $12, 6, 3, \frac{3}{2}, \ldots$

95. $1.5, -3, 6, -12, \ldots$

96. $5, -1, \frac{1}{5}, -\frac{1}{25}, \ldots$

97. $0.0004, -0.004, 0.04, -0.4, \ldots$

98. $0.0007, -0.007, 0.07, -0.7, \ldots$

Determine whether each sequence in Exercises 99–114 is arithmetic or geometric. Then find the next two terms.

99. $2, 6, 10, 14, \ldots$

100. $3, 8, 13, 18, \ldots$

101. $5, 15, 45, 135, \ldots$

102. $15, 30, 60, 120, \ldots$

103. $-7, -2, 3, 8, \ldots$

104. $-9, -5, -1, 3, \ldots$

105. $3, \frac{3}{2}, \frac{3}{4}, \frac{3}{8}, \ldots$

106. $6, 3, \frac{3}{2}, \frac{3}{4}, \ldots$

107. $\frac{1}{2}, 1, \frac{3}{2}, 2, \ldots$

108. $\frac{2}{3}, 1, \frac{4}{3}, \frac{5}{3}, \ldots$

109. $7, -7, 7, -7, \ldots$

110. $6, -6, 6, -6, \ldots$

111. $7, -7, -21, -35, \ldots$

112. $6, -6, -18, -30, \ldots$

113. $\sqrt{5}, 5, 5\sqrt{5}, 25, \ldots$

114. $\sqrt{3}, 3, 3\sqrt{3}, 9, \ldots$

• Practice Plus

The sum, S_n, of the first n terms of an arithmetic sequence is given by

$$S_n = \frac{n}{2}(a_1 + a_n),$$

in which a_1 is the first term and a_n is the nth term. The sum, S_n, of the first n terms of a geometric series is given by

$$S_n = \frac{a_1(1 - r^n)}{1 - r},$$

in which a_1 is the first term and r is the common ratio ($r \neq 1$). In Exercises 115–122, determine whether each sequence is arithmetic or geometric. Then use the appropriate formula to find S_{10}, the sum of the first ten terms.

115. $4, 10, 16, 22, \ldots$

116. $7, 19, 31, 43, \ldots$

117. $2, 6, 18, 54, \ldots$

118. $3, 6, 12, 24, \ldots$

119. $3, -6, 12, -24, \ldots$

120. $4, -12, 36, -108, \ldots$

121. $-10, -6, -2, 2, \ldots$

122. $-15, -9, -3, 3, \ldots$

123. Use the appropriate formula shown above to find $1 + 2 + 3 + 4 + \cdots + 100$, the sum of the first 100 natural numbers.

124. Use the appropriate formula shown above to find $2 + 4 + 6 + 8 + \cdots + 200$, the sum of the first 100 positive even integers.

• Application Exercises

Use the formula for the nth term of an arithmetic sequence to solve Exercises 125–128.

The bar graphs show changes that have taken place in the United States from 1970 to 2002 or 2003. Exercises 125–126 involve developing arithmetic sequences that model the data.

Changing Times in the United States

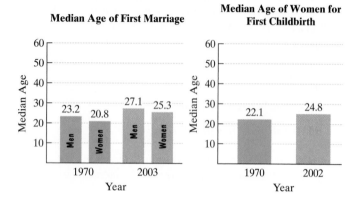

Source: U.S. Census Bureau

125. In 1970, the median age of first marriage for U.S. men was 23.2. On average, this age has increased by approximately 0.12 per year.

  a. Write a formula for the nth term of the arithmetic sequence that describes the median age of first marriage for U.S. men n years after 1969.

  b. According to the model in part (a), what will be the median age of first marriage for U.S. men in 2009?

126. In 1970, the median age of women for first childbirth was 22.1. On average, this age has increased by approximately 0.08 per year.

  a. Write a formula for the nth term of the arithmetic sequence that describes the median age for first childbirth for U.S. women n years after 1969.

  b. According to the model in part (a), what will be the median age for first childbirth for U.S. women in 2009?

127. Company A pays $24,000 yearly with raises of $1600 per year. Company B pays $28,000 yearly with raises of $1000 per year. Which company will pay more in year 10? How much more?

128. Company A pays $23,000 yearly with raises of $1200 per year. Company B pays $26,000 yearly with raises of $800 per year. Which company will pay more in year 10? How much more?

Use the formula for the nth term of a geometric sequence to solve Exercises 129–134.

In Exercises 129–130, suppose you save $1 the first day of a month, $2 the second day, $4 the third day, and so on. That is, each day you save twice as much as you did the day before.

129. What will you put aside for savings on the fifteenth day of the month?

130. What will you put aside for savings on the thirtieth day of the month?

131. A professional baseball player signs a contract with a beginning salary of $3,000,000 for the first year with an annual increase of 4% per year beginning in the second year. That is, beginning in year 2, the athlete's salary will be 1.04 times what it was in the previous year. What is the athlete's salary for year 7 of the contract? Round to the nearest dollar.

132. You are offered a job that pays $30,000 for the first year with an annual increase of 5% per year beginning in the second year. That is, beginning in year 2, your salary will be 1.05 times what it was in the previous year. What can you expect to earn in your sixth year on the job? Round to the nearest dollar.

133. The population of California from 1990 through 1997 is shown in the following table.

Year	1990	1991	1992	1993
Population in millions	29.76	30.15	30.54	30.94

Year	1994	1995	1996	1997
Population in millions	31.34	31.75	32.16	32.58

  a. Divide the population for each year by the population in the preceding year. Round to three decimal places and show that the population of California is increasing geometrically.

  b. Write the general term of the geometric sequence describing population growth for California n years after 1989.

  c. Estimate California's population, in millions, for the year 2000. According to the U.S. Census Bureau, California's population in 2000 was 33.87 million. How well does your geometric sequence describe the actual population?

134. The population of Texas from 1990 through 1997 is shown in the following table.

Year	1990	1991	1992	1993
Population in millions	16.99	17.35	17.71	18.08

Year	1994	1995	1996	1997
Population in millions	18.46	18.85	19.25	19.65

  a. Divide the population for each year by the population in the preceding year. Round to three decimal places and show that the population of Texas is increasing geometrically.

  b. Write the general term of the geometric sequence describing population growth for Texas n years after 1989.

  c. Estimate Texas's population, in millions, for the year 2000. According to the U.S. Census Bureau, Texas's population in 2000 was 20.85 million. How well does your geometric sequence describe the actual population?

• Writing in Mathematics

135. What is a sequence? Give an example with your description.

136. What is an arithmetic sequence? Give an example with your description.

137. What is the common difference in an arithmetic sequence?

138. What is a geometric sequence? Give an example with your description.

139. What is the common ratio in a geometric sequence?

140. If you are given a sequence that is arithmetic or geometric, how can you determine which type of sequence it is?

141. For the first 30 days of a flu outbreak, the number of students on your campus who become ill is increasing. Which is worse: The number of students with the flu is increasing arithmetically or is increasing geometrically? Explain your answer.

• **Critical Thinking Exercises**

142. Which one of the following is true?

a. The common difference for the arithmetic sequence given by $1, -1, -3, -5, \ldots$ is 2.

b. The sequence $1, 4, 8, 13, 19, 26, \ldots$ is an arithmetic sequence.

c. The nth term of an arithmetic sequence whose first term is a_1 and whose common difference is d is $a_n = a_1 + nd$.

d. If the first term of an arithmetic sequence is 5 and the third term is -3, then the fourth term is -7.

143. Which one of the following is true?

a. The sequence $2, 6, 24, 120, \ldots$ is an example of a geometric sequence.

b. Adjacent terms in a geometric sequence have a common difference.

c. A sequence that is not arithmetic must be geometric.

d. If a sequence is geometric, we can write as many terms as we want by repeatedly multiplying by the common ratio.

144. A person is investigating two employment opportunities. They both have a beginning salary of $20,000 per year. Company A offers an increase of $1000 per year. Company B offers 5% more than during the preceding year. Which company will pay more in the sixth year?

• **Group Exercise**

145. Enough curiosities involving the Fibonacci sequence exist to warrant a flourishing Fibonacci Association. It publishes a quarterly journal. Do some research on the Fibonacci sequence by consulting the research department of your library or the Internet, and find one property that interests you. After doing this research, get together with your group to share these intriguing properties.

●●●●●● CHAPTER SUMMARY, REVIEW, AND TEST

● S U M M A R Y   DEFINITIONS AND CONCEPTS   EXAMPLES

2.1   Number Theory: Prime and Composite Numbers

a. The set of natural numbers is $\{1, 2, 3, 4, 5, \ldots\}$. $b \mid a$ (b divides a: a is divisible by b) for natural numbers a and b if the operation of dividing a by b leaves a remainder of 0. Rules of divisibility are given in Table 2.1 on page 43.

Ex. 1, p. 44

b. A prime number is a natural number greater than 1 that has only itself and 1 as factors. A composite number is a natural number greater than 1 that is divisible by a number other than itself and 1. The Fundamental Theorem of Arithmetic: Every composite number can be expressed as a product of prime numbers in one and only one way (if the order of the factors is disregarded).

Ex. 2, p. 45

c. The greatest common divisor of two or more natural numbers is the largest number that is a divisor (or factor) of all the numbers. The procedure for finding the greatest common divisor is given in the box on page 46.

Ex. 3, p. 46;
Ex. 4, p. 47

d. The least common multiple of two or more natural numbers is the smallest natural number that is divisible by all of the numbers. The procedure for finding the least common multiple is given in the box on page 48.

Ex. 5, p. 48;
Ex. 6, p. 48

2.2   The Integers; Order of Operations

a. The set of whole numbers is $\{0, 1, 2, 3, 4, 5, \ldots\}$. The set of integers is $\{\ldots, -3, -2, -1, 0, 1, 2, 3, \ldots\}$. Integers are graphed on a number line by placing a dot at the correct location for each number.

Ex. 1, p. 52

b. $a < b$ (a is less than b) means a is to the left of b on a number line.

$a > b$ (a is greater than b) means a is to the right of b on a number line.

Ex. 2, p. 53

c. $|a|$, the absolute value of a, is the distance of a from 0 on a number line. The absolute value of a positive number is the number itself. The absolute value of 0 is 0: $|0| = 0$. The absolute value of a negative number is the number without the negative sign. For example, $|-8| = 8$.

Ex. 3, p. 54

5   **d.** Rules for performing operations with integers are given in the boxes on pages 55, 56, 58, and 59.

Ex. 4, p. 56;
Ex. 5, p. 57;
Ex. 6, p. 58

e. Order of Operations

Ex. 7, p. 60;
Ex. 8, p. 61

   1. Perform all operations within grouping symbols.

   2. Evaluate all exponential expressions.

   3. Do all multiplications and divisions from left to right.

   4. Do all additions and subtractions from left to right.

2.3 The Rational Numbers

a. The set of rational numbers is the set of all numbers which can be expressed in the form $\frac{a}{b}$, where a and b are integers and b is not equal to 0.

b. A rational number is reduced to its lowest terms, or simplified, by dividing both the numerator and the denominator by their greatest common divisor.

Ex. 1, p. 64

c. A mixed number consists of the sum of an integer and a rational number, expressed without the use of an addition sign. An improper fraction is a rational number whose numerator is greater than its denominator. Procedures for converting between these forms are given in the boxes on page 65.

Ex. 2, p. 65;
Ex. 3, p. 66

d. Any rational number can be expressed as a decimal. The resulting decimal will either terminate (stop), or it will have a digit that repeats or a block of digits that repeat. The rational number $\frac{a}{b}$ is expressed as a decimal by dividing b into a.

Ex. 4, p. 66

e. To express a terminating decimal as a quotient of integers, the digits to the right of the decimal point are the numerator. The place-value of the last digit to the right of the decimal point is the denominator.

Ex. 5, p. 67

f. To express a repeating decimal as a quotient of integers, use the boxed procedure on page 68.

Ex. 6, p. 68;
Ex. 7, p. 69

g. The product of two rational numbers is the product of their numerators divided by the product of their denominators.

Ex. 8, p. 69

h. Two numbers whose product is 1 are called reciprocals, or multiplicative inverses, of each other. The quotient of two rational numbers is the product of the first number and the reciprocal of the second number.

Ex. 9, p. 70

i. The sum or difference of two rational numbers with identical denominators is the sum or difference of their numerators over the common denominator.

Ex. 10, p. 71

j. Add or subtract rational numbers with unlike denominators by first expressing each rational number with the least common denominator and then following part (i) above.

Ex. 11, p. 71;
Ex. 12, p. 72

k. Density of the Rational Numbers
Given any two rational numbers, there is always a rational number between them. To find the rational number halfway between two rational numbers, add the rational numbers and divide their sum by 2.

Ex. 13, p. 73

2.4 The Irrational Numbers

a. The set of irrational numbers is the set of numbers whose decimal representations are neither terminating nor repeating. Examples of irrational numbers are $\sqrt{2} \approx 1.414$ and $\pi \approx 3.142$.

b. Simplifying square roots: Use the product rule, $\sqrt{ab} = \sqrt{a} \cdot \sqrt{b}$, to remove from the square root any perfect squares that occur as factors.

Ex. 1, p. 79

c. Multiplying square roots: $\sqrt{a} \cdot \sqrt{b} = \sqrt{ab}$. The product of square roots is the square root of the product.

Ex. 2, p. 79

d. Dividing square roots: $\dfrac{\sqrt{a}}{\sqrt{b}} = \sqrt{\dfrac{a}{b}}$. The quotient of the square roots is the square root of the quotient. Ex. 3, p. 80

e. Adding and subtracting square roots: If the radicals have the same radicand, add or subtract their coefficients. The answer is the sum or difference of the coefficients times the common square root. Addition or subtraction is sometimes possible by first simplifying the square roots. Ex. 4, p. 80; Ex. 5, p. 81

f. Rationalizing denominators: Multiply the numerator and denominator by the smallest number that produces a perfect square radicand in the denominator. Ex. 6, p. 82

2.5 Real Numbers and Their Properties

a. The set of real numbers is obtained by combining the rational numbers with the irrational numbers. The important subsets of the real numbers are summarized in Table 2.2 on page 86. A diagram representing the relationships among the subsets of the real numbers is given to the left of Table 2.2. Ex. 1, p. 86

b. Properties of real numbers, including closure properties ($a + b$ and ab are real numbers), commutative properties ($a + b = b + a$; $ab = ba$), associative properties [$(a + b) + c = a + (b + c)$; $(ab)c = a(bc)$], and the distributive property [$a(b + c) = ab + ac$], are summarized in Table 2.3 on page 87. Ex. 2, p. 88; Ex. 3, p. 88

2.6 Exponents and Scientific Notation

a. Properties of Exponents Table 2.4, p. 92; Ex. 1, p. 93; Ex. 2, p. 93

- Product rule: $b^m \cdot b^n = b^{m+n}$
- Zero exponent rule: $b^0 = 1, b \neq 0$
- Power rule: $(b^m)^n = b^{m \cdot n}$
- Negative exponent rule: $b^{-m} = \dfrac{1}{b^m}, b \neq 0$
- Quotient rule: $\dfrac{b^m}{b^n} = b^{m-n}, b \neq 0$

b. A positive number in scientific notation is expressed as $a \times 10^n$, where $1 \leq a < 10$ and n is an integer.

c. Changing from Scientific to Decimal Notation: If n is positive, move the decimal point in a to the right n places. If n is negative, move the decimal point in a to the left $|n|$ places. Ex. 3, p. 95

d. Changing from Decimal to Scientific Notation: Move the decimal point in the given number to obtain a, where $1 \leq a < 10$. The number of places the decimal point moves gives the absolute value of n in $a \times 10^n$; n is positive if the number is greater than 10 and negative if the number is less than 1. Ex. 4, p. 95

e. The product and quotient rules for exponents are used to multiply and divide numbers in scientific notation. Ex. 6, p. 97; Ex. 7, p. 97; Ex. 8, p. 98; Ex. 9, p. 99

2.7 Arithmetic and Geometric Sequences

a. In an arithmetic sequence, each term after the first differs from the preceding term by a constant, the common difference. Subtract any term from the term that directly follows to find the common difference. Ex. 1, p. 103; Ex. 2, p. 103

b. The general term or the nth term of an arithmetic sequence is Ex. 3, p. 104; Ex. 4, p. 105

$$a_n = a_1 + (n - 1)d,$$

where a_1 is the first term and d is the common difference.

c. In a geometric sequence, each term after the first is obtained by multiplying the preceding term by a nonzero constant, the common ratio. Divide any term after the first by the term that directly precedes it to find the common ratio. Ex. 5, p. 106

d. The general term or the nth term of a geometric sequence is Ex. 6, p. 107; Ex. 7, p. 107

$$a_n = a_1 r^{n-1},$$

where a_1 is the first term and r is the common ratio.

REVIEW EXERCISES

2.1

In Exercises 1 and 2, determine whether the number is divisible by each of the following numbers: 2, 3, 4, 5, 6, 8, 9, 10, and 12. If you are using a calculator, explain the divisibility shown by your calculator using one of the rules of divisibility.

1. 238,632

2. 421,153,470

In Exercises 3–5, find the prime factorization of each composite number.

3. 705

4. 960

5. 6825

In Exercises 6–8, find the greatest common divisor and the least common multiple of the numbers.

6. 30 and 48

7. 36 and 150

8. 216 and 254

9. For an intramural league, you need to divide 24 men and 60 women into all-male and all-female teams so that each team has the same number of people. What is the largest number of people that can be placed on a team?

10. The media center at a college runs videotapes of two lectures continuously. One videotape runs for 42 minutes and a second runs for 56 minutes. Both videotapes begin at 9:00 A.M. When will the videos of the two lectures begin again at the same time?

2.2

In Exercises 11–12, insert either $<$ or $>$ in the shaded area between the integers to make the statement true.

11. $-93 \blacksquare 17$

12. $-2 \blacksquare -200$

In Exercise 13–15, find the absolute value.

13. $|-860|$

14. $|53|$

15. $|0|$

Perform the indicated operations in Exercises 16–28.

16. $8 + (-11)$

17. $-6 + (-5)$

18. $-7 - 8$

19. $-7 - (-8)$

20. $(-9)(-11)$

21. $5(-3)$

22. $\dfrac{-36}{-4}$

23. $\dfrac{20}{-5}$

24. $-40 \div 5 \cdot 2$

25. $-6 + (-2) \cdot 5$

26. $6 - 4(-3 + 2)$

27. $28 \div (2 - 4^2)$

28. $36 - 24 \div 4 \cdot 3 - 1$

29. For the year 2015, the Congressional Budget Office projects a budget deficit of $-\$57$ billion. For the same year, the Brookings Institution forecasts a budget deficit of $-\$715$ billion. What is the difference between the CBO projection and the Brookings projection?

2.3

In Exercises 30–32, reduce each rational number to its lowest terms.

30. $\dfrac{40}{75}$

31. $\dfrac{36}{150}$

32. $\dfrac{165}{180}$

In Exercises 33–34, convert each mixed number to an improper fraction.

33. $5\dfrac{9}{11}$

34. $-3\dfrac{2}{7}$

In Exercises 35–36, convert each improper fraction to a mixed number.

35. $\dfrac{27}{5}$

36. $-\dfrac{17}{9}$

In Exercises 37–40, express each rational number as a decimal.

37. $\dfrac{4}{5}$

38. $\dfrac{3}{7}$

39. $\dfrac{5}{8}$

40. $\dfrac{9}{16}$

In Exercises 41–44, express each terminating decimal as a quotient of integers in lowest terms.

41. 0.6

42. 0.68

43. 0.588

44. 0.0084

In Exercises 45–47, express each repeating decimal as a quotient of integers in lowest terms.

45. $0.\overline{5}$

46. $0.\overline{34}$

47. $0.\overline{113}$

In Exercises 48–56, perform the indicated operations. Where possible, reduce the answer to lowest terms.

48. $\dfrac{3}{5} \cdot \dfrac{7}{10}$

49. $\left(3\dfrac{1}{3}\right)\left(1\dfrac{3}{4}\right)$

50. $\dfrac{4}{5} \div \dfrac{3}{10}$

51. $-1\dfrac{2}{3} \div 6\dfrac{2}{3}$

52. $\dfrac{2}{9} + \dfrac{4}{9}$

53. $\dfrac{7}{9} + \dfrac{5}{12}$

54. $\dfrac{3}{4} - \dfrac{2}{15}$

55. $\dfrac{1}{3} + \dfrac{1}{2} \cdot \dfrac{4}{5}$

56. $\dfrac{3}{8}\left(\dfrac{1}{2} + \dfrac{1}{3}\right)$

In Exercises 57–58, find a rational number halfway between the two numbers in each pair.

57. $\dfrac{1}{7}$ and $\dfrac{1}{8}$

58. $\dfrac{3}{4}$ and $\dfrac{3}{5}$

59. A recipe for coq au vin is meant for six people and requires $4\dfrac{1}{2}$ pounds of chicken. If you want to serve 15 people, how much chicken is needed?

60. The gas tank of a car is filled to its capacity. The first day, $\dfrac{1}{4}$ of the tank's gas is used for travel. The second day, $\dfrac{1}{3}$ of the tank's original amount of gas is used for travel. What fraction of the tank is filled with gas at the end of the second day?

2.4

In Exercises 61–64, simplify the square root.

61. $\sqrt{28}$

62. $\sqrt{72}$

63. $\sqrt{150}$

64. $\sqrt{300}$

In Exercises 65–73, perform the indicated operation. Simplify the answer when possible.

65. $\sqrt{6} \cdot \sqrt{8}$

66. $\sqrt{10} \cdot \sqrt{5}$

67. $\dfrac{\sqrt{24}}{\sqrt{2}}$

68. $\dfrac{\sqrt{27}}{\sqrt{3}}$

69. $\sqrt{5} + 4\sqrt{5}$

70. $7\sqrt{11} - 13\sqrt{11}$

71. $\sqrt{50} + \sqrt{8}$

72. $\sqrt{3} - 6\sqrt{27}$

73. $2\sqrt{18} + 3\sqrt{8}$

In Exercises 74–75, rationalize the denominator.

74. $\dfrac{30}{\sqrt{5}}$

75. $\sqrt{\dfrac{2}{3}}$

76. Paleontologists use the mathematical model $W = 4\sqrt{2x}$ to estimate the walking speed of a dinosaur, W, in feet per second, where x is the length, in feet, of the dinosaur's leg. What is the walking speed of a dinosaur whose leg length is 6 feet? Express the answer in simplified radical form. Then use your calculator to estimate the walking speed to the nearest tenth of a foot per second.

2.5

77. Consider the set

$$\left\{-17, -\dfrac{9}{13}, 0, 0.75, \sqrt{2}, \pi, \sqrt{81}\right\}.$$

List all numbers from the set that are **a.** natural numbers, **b.** whole numbers, **c.** integers, **d.** rational numbers, **e.** irrational numbers, **f.** real numbers.

78. Give an example of an integer that is not a natural number.

79. Give an example of a rational number that is not an integer.

80. Give an example of a real number that is not a rational number.

In Exercises 81–86, state the name of the property illustrated.

81. $3 + 17 = 17 + 3$

82. $(6 \cdot 3) \cdot 9 = 6 \cdot (3 \cdot 9)$

83. $\sqrt{3}(\sqrt{5} + \sqrt{3}) = \sqrt{15} + 3$

84. $(6 \cdot 9) \cdot 2 = 2 \cdot (6 \cdot 9)$

85. $\sqrt{3}(\sqrt{5} + \sqrt{3}) = (\sqrt{5} + \sqrt{3})\sqrt{3}$

86. $(3 \cdot 7) + (4 \cdot 7) = (4 \cdot 7) + (3 \cdot 7)$

In Exercises 87–88, give on example to show that

87. The natural numbers are not closed with respect to division.

88. The whole numbers are not closed with respect to subtraction.

2.6

In Exercises 89–99, evaluate each expression.

89. $6 \cdot 6^2$ **90.** $2^3 \cdot 2^3$ **91.** $(2^2)^2$ **92.** $(3^3)^2$

93. $\dfrac{5^6}{5^4}$ **94.** 7^0 **95.** $(-7)^0$ **96.** 6^{-3}

97. 2^{-4} **98.** $\dfrac{7^4}{7^6}$ **99.** $3^5 \cdot 3^{-2}$

In Exercises 100–103, express each number in decimal notation.

100. 4.6×10^2 **101.** 3.74×10^4

102. 2.55×10^{-3} **103.** 7.45×10^{-5}

In Exercises 104–109, express each number in scientific notation.

104. 7520 **105.** $3{,}590{,}000$ **106.** 0.00725

107. 0.000000409 **108.** 420×10^{11} **109.** 0.97×10^{-4}

In Exercises 110–117, perform the indicated operation and express each answer in decimal notation.

110. $(3 \times 10^7)(1.3 \times 10^{-5})$ **111.** $(5 \times 10^3)(2.3 \times 10^2)$

112. $\dfrac{6.9 \times 10^3}{3 \times 10^5}$ **113.** $\dfrac{2.4 \times 10^{-4}}{6 \times 10^{-6}}$

In Exercises 114–117, perform the indicated operation by first expressing each number in scientific notation. Write the answer in scientific notation.

114. $(60{,}000)(540{,}000)$ **115.** $(91{,}000)(0.0004)$

116. $\dfrac{8{,}400{,}000}{4000}$ **117.** $\dfrac{0.000003}{0.00000006}$

118. If you earned $1 million per year ($10^6$), how long would it take to accumulate $1 billion dollars ($10^9$)?

119. If the population of the United States is 3×10^8 and each person spends about $150 per year going to the movies (or renting movies), express the total annual spending on movies in scientific notation.

120. The world's population is approximately 6.5×10^9 people. Current projections double this population in 40 years. Write the population 40 years from now in scientific notation.

2.7

In Exercises 121–123, write the first six terms of the arithmetic sequence with the first term, a_1, and common difference, d.

121. $a_1 = 7, d = 4$

122. $a_1 = -4, d = -5$

123. $a_1 = \frac{3}{2}, d = -\frac{1}{2}$

In Exercises 124–126, find the indicated term for the arithmetic sequence with first term, a_1, and common difference, d.

124. Find a_6, when $a_1 = 5, d = 3$.

125. Find a_{12}, when $a_1 = -8, d = -2$.

126. Find a_{14}, when $a_1 = 14, d = -4$.

In Exercises 127–128, write a formula for the general term (the nth term) of each arithmetic sequence. Then use the formula for a_n to find a_{20}, the 20th term of the sequence.

127. $-7, -3, 1, 5, \ldots$ **128.** $a_1 = 200, d = -20$

In Exercises 129–131, write the first six terms of the geometric sequence with the first term, a_1, and common ratio, r.

129. $a_1 = 3, r = 2$ **130.** $a_1 = \frac{1}{2}, r = \frac{1}{2}$ **131.** $a_1 = 16, r = -\frac{1}{2}$

In Exercises 132–134, find the indicated term for the geometric sequence with first term, a_1, and common ratio, r.

132. Find a_4, when $a_1 = 2, r = 3$.

133. Find a_6, when $a_1 = 16, r = \frac{1}{2}$.

134. Find a_5, when $a_1 = -3, r = 2$.

In Exercises 135–136, write a formula for the general term (the nth term) of each geometric sequence. Then use the formula for a_n to find a_8, the eighth term of the sequence.

135. $1, 2, 4, 8, \ldots$ **136.** $100, 10, 1, \frac{1}{10}, \ldots$

Determine whether each sequence in Exercises 137–140 is arithmetic or geometric. Then find the next two terms.

137. $4, 9, 14, 19, \ldots$ **138.** $2, 6, 18, 54, \ldots$

139. $1, \frac{1}{4}, \frac{1}{16}, \frac{1}{64}, \ldots$ **140.** $0, -7, -14, -21, \ldots$

141. The graph shows the percentage of in-home dinners in the United States having various items as a side dish from 1993 through 2004.

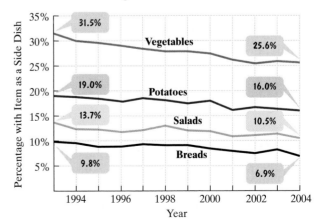

Percentage of U.S. In-Home Dinners Having Various Items as a Side Dish

Source: The NPD Group

In 1993, 31.5% of home dinners had vegetables as a side dish. On average, this decreased by approximately 0.54% per year since then.

a. Write a formula for the nth term of the arithmetic sequence that describes the percentage of dinners that included vegetables n years after 1992.

b. Use the model to predict the percentage of dinners that will include vegetables by the year 2010.

c. Repeat parts (a) and (b) for the change in another one of the items shown in the graph at the bottom of the previous page from 1993 to 2004.

142. Projections for the U.S. population, ages 85 and older, are shown in the following table.

Year	2000	2010	2020	2030	2040	2050
Projected Population in millions	4.2	5.9	8.3	11.6	16.2	22.7

Actual 2000 population

Source: U.S. Census Bureau

a. Show that the U.S. population, ages 85 and older, is projected to increase geometrically.

b. Write the general term of the geometric sequence describing the U.S. population, ages 85 and older, in millions, n decades after 1990.

c. Use the model in part (b) to project the U.S. population, ages 85 and older, in 2080.

●●●●●●● CHAPTER 2 TEST

1. Which of the numbers 2, 3, 4, 5, 6, 8, 9, 10, and 12 divide 391,248?

2. Find the prime factorization of 252.

3. Find the greatest common divisor and the least common multiple of 48 and 72.

Perform the indicated operations in Exercises 4–6.

4. $-6 - (5 - 12)$ **5.** $(-3)(-4) \div (7 - 10)$

6. $(6 - 8)^2(5 - 7)^3$

7. Express $\frac{7}{12}$ as a decimal.

8. Express $0.\overline{64}$ as a quotient of integers in lowest terms.

In Exercises 9–11, perform the indicated operations. Where possible, reduce the answer to its lowest terms.

9. $\left(-\frac{3}{7}\right) \div \left(-2\frac{1}{7}\right)$ **10.** $\frac{19}{24} - \frac{7}{40}$ **11.** $\frac{1}{2} - 8\left(\frac{1}{4} + 1\right)$

12. Find a rational number halfway between $\frac{1}{2}$ and $\frac{2}{3}$.

13. Multiply and simplify: $\sqrt{10} \cdot \sqrt{5}$.

14. Add: $\sqrt{50} + \sqrt{32}$.

15. Rationalize the denominator: $\dfrac{6}{\sqrt{2}}$.

16. List all the rational numbers in this set:

$$\left\{-7, -\frac{4}{5}, 0, 0.25, \sqrt{3}, \sqrt{4}, \frac{22}{7}, \pi\right\}.$$

In Exercises 17–18, state the name of the property illustrated.

17. $3(2 + 5) = 3(5 + 2)$

18. $6(7 + 4) = 6 \cdot 7 + 6 \cdot 4$

In Exercises 19–21, evaluate each expression.

19. $3^3 \cdot 3^2$ **20.** $\dfrac{4^6}{4^3}$ **21.** 8^{-2}

22. Multiply and express the answer in decimal notation.

$$(3 \times 10^8)(2.5 \times 10^{-5})$$

23. Divide by first expressing each number in scientific notation. Write the answer in scientific notation.

$$\frac{49,000}{0.007}$$

24. In 2006, the U.S. government collected 2.18×10^{12} dollars in taxes. At that time, the U.S. population was approximately 300 million, or 3×10^8. If the total tax collections were evenly divided among all Americans, how much would each citizen pay? Express the answer in decimal notation, rounded to the nearest dollar.

25. Write the first six terms of the arithmetic sequence with first term, a_1, and common difference, d.

$$a_1 = 1, d = -5$$

26. Find a_9, the ninth term of the arithmetic sequence with the first term, a_1, and common difference, d.

$$a_1 = -2, d = 3$$

27. Write the first six terms of the geometric sequence with first term, a_1, and common ratio, r.

$$a_1 = 16, r = \frac{1}{2}$$

28. Find a_7, the seventh term of the geometric sequence with the first term, a_1, and common ratio, r.

$$a_1 = 5, r = 2$$

Algebra: Equations and Inequalities

America is a nation of immigrants. Since 1820, over 40 million people have immigrated to the United States from all over the world. They chose to come for various reasons, such as to live in freedom, to practice religion without persecution, to escape poverty or oppression, and to make better lives for themselves and their children. As a result, in 2003, 11.7% of the U.S. population was foreign-born. How can we use mathematical models to project when this percentage might grow to one in every five Americans, or even more?

In this chapter, you will learn to use formulas and mathematical models in new ways. With these skills, you will gain insights into a variety of issues, ranging from the growing diversity of the U.S. population to concerns about Social Security, and even the positive benefits that humor and laughter can have on our lives.

The foreign-born U.S. population model appears as Exercises 85–88 in Exercise Set 3.3. You will develop and use models for Social Security's income and outflow in Exercises 27–29 in the Chapter 3 Test. Humor opens Section 3.2, and the advantage of having a sense of humor becomes laughingly evident in the models in Example 6 on page 131.

SECTION 3.1 • ALGEBRAIC EXPRESSIONS AND FORMULAS

OBJECTIVES

1. Evaluate algebraic expressions.
2. Use mathematical models.
3. Understand the vocabulary of algebraic expressions.
4. Simplify algebraic expressions.

Algebraic Expressions

Feeling attractive with a suntan that gives you a "healthy glow"? Think again. Direct sunlight is known to promote skin cancer. Although sunscreens protect you from burning, dermatologists are concerned with the long-term damage that results from the sun even without sunburn.

Algebra uses letters, such as x and y, to represent numbers. If a letter is used to represent various numbers, it is called a **variable**. For example, we can let x represent the number of minutes that a person can stay in the sun without burning with no sunscreen. With a number 6 sunscreen, exposure time without burning is six times as long, or 6 times x. This can be written $6 \cdot x$, but it is usually expressed as $6x$. Placing a number and a letter next to one another indicates multiplication.

Notice that $6x$ combines the number 6 and the variable x using the operation of multiplication. A combination of variables and numbers using the operations of addition, subtraction, multiplication, or division, as well as powers or roots, is called an **algebraic expression**. Here are some examples of algebraic expressions:

$$x + 6, \quad x^2 - 6, \quad 6x, \quad \frac{x}{6}, \quad 3x + 5, \quad \sqrt{x} + 7.$$

| 1 | Evaluate algebraic expressions. |

Evaluating Algebraic Expressions

Evaluating an algebraic expression means finding the value of the expression for a given value of the variable. For example, we can evaluate $6x$ (from the sunscreen example) when $x = 15$. We substitute 15 for x. We obtain $6 \cdot 15$, or 90. This means that if you can stay in the sun for 15 minutes without burning when you don't put on any lotion, then with a number 6 lotion, you can "cook" for 90 minutes without burning.

Many algebraic expressions contain more than one operation. Evaluating an algebraic expression correctly involves carefully applying the order of operations agreement that we studied in Chapter 2.

THE ORDER OF OPERATIONS AGREEMENT

1. Perform operations within the innermost parentheses and work outward. If the algebraic expression involves a fraction, treat the numerator and the denominator as if they were each enclosed in parentheses.
2. Evaluate all exponential expressions.
3. Perform multiplications and divisions as they occur, working from left to right.
4. Perform additions and subtractions as they occur, working from left to right.

EXAMPLE 1 EVALUATING AN ALGEBRAIC EXPRESSION

Evaluate $7 + 5(x - 4)^3$ for $x = 6$.

SOLUTION

$$
\begin{aligned}
7 + 5(x - 4)^3 &= 7 + 5(6 - 4)^3 && \text{Replace } x \text{ with 6.} \\
&= 7 + 5(2)^3 && \text{First work inside parentheses: } 6 - 4 = 2. \\
&= 7 + 5(8) && \text{Evaluate the exponential expression:} \\
& && 2^3 = 2 \cdot 2 \cdot 2 = 8. \\
&= 7 + 40 && \text{Multiply: } 5(8) = 40. \\
&= 47 && \text{Add.}
\end{aligned}
$$

 Evaluate $8 + 6(x - 3)^2$ for $x = 13$.

STUDY TIP

Notice the difference between the following evaluations:

- x^2 for $x = -6$

  $x^2 = (-6)^2$

  $= (-6)(-6) = 36$

- $-x^2$ for $x = 6$

  $-x^2 = -6^2 = -6 \cdot 6 = -36$

  The negative is not inside parentheses and is not taken to the second power.

Work carefully when evaluating algebraic expressions with exponents and negatives.

EXAMPLE 2 EVALUATING AN ALGEBRAIC EXPRESSION

Evaluate $x^2 + 5x - 3$ for $x = -6$.

SOLUTION We substitute -6 for each of the two occurrences of x. Then we use the order of operations to evaluate the algebraic expression.

$$
\begin{aligned}
x^2 + 5x - 3 \quad && \text{This is the given algebraic expression.} \\
= (-6)^2 + 5(-6) - 3 && \text{Substitute } -6 \text{ for each } x. \\
= 36 + 5(-6) - 3 && \text{Evaluate the exponential expression:} \\
& && (-6)^2 = (-6)(-6) = 36. \\
= 36 + (-30) - 3 && \text{Multiply: } 5(-6) = -30. \\
= 6 - 3 && \text{Add and subtract from left to right.} \\
& && \text{First add: } 36 + (-30) = 6. \\
= 3 && \text{Subtract.}
\end{aligned}
$$

 Evaluate $x^2 + 4x - 7$ for $x = -5$.

EXAMPLE 3 EVALUATING AN ALGEBRAIC EXPRESSION

Evaluate $-2x^2 + 5xy - y^3$ for $x = 4$ and $y = -2$.

SOLUTION We substitute 4 for each x and -2 for each y. Then we use the order of operations to evaluate the algebraic expression.

$$
\begin{aligned}
-2x^2 + 5xy - y^3 \quad && \text{This is the given algebraic expression.} \\
= -2 \cdot 4^2 + 5 \cdot 4(-2) - (-2)^3 && \text{Substitute 4 for } x \text{ and } -2 \text{ for } y. \\
= -2 \cdot 16 + 5(4)(-2) - (-8) && \text{Evaluate the exponential expressions:} \\
& && 4^2 = 4 \cdot 4 = 16 \text{ and} \\
& && (-2)^3 = (-2)(-2)(-2) = -8. \\
= -32 + (-40) - (-8) && \text{Multiply: } -2 \cdot 16 = -32 \text{ and} \\
& && 5(4)(-2) = 20(-2) = -40. \\
= -72 - (-8) && \text{Add and subtract from left to right. First add:} \\
& && -32 + (-40) = -72. \\
= -64 && \text{Subtract: } -72 - (-8) = -72 + 8 = -64.
\end{aligned}
$$

 Evaluate $-3x^2 + 4xy - y^3$ for $x = 5$ and $y = -1$.

2 | Use mathematical models.

Formulas and Mathematical Models

An **equation** is formed when an equal sign is placed between two algebraic expressions. One aim of algebra is to provide a compact, symbolic description of the world. These descriptions involve the use of *formulas*. A **formula** is an equation that uses letters to express a relationship between two or more variables. Here is an example of a formula:

$$C = \frac{5}{9}(F - 32).$$

| Celsius temperature | is | $\frac{5}{9}$ of | the difference between Fahrenheit temperature and 32°. |

The process of finding formulas to describe real-world phenomena is called **mathematical modeling**. Such formulas, together with the meaning assigned to the variables, are called **mathematical models**. We often say that these formulas model, or describe, the relationships among the variables.

> These important definitions are repeated from earlier chapters in case your course did not cover this material.

EXAMPLE 4   MODELING THE AMOUNT SPENT ON ONLINE DATING

In 2003, 28.5 million U.S. adults browsed Internet personals and 17.4 million posted online personal ads. The bar graph in Figure 3.1 shows the amount spent in the United States, in millions of dollars, on online dating. Here are three mathematical models for the data shown in the graph. In each formula, D represents the amount spent on online dating, in millions of dollars, x years after 2002.

Model 1 — $D = 236(1.5)^x$

Model 2 — $D = 127x + 239$

Model 3 — $D = -54x^2 + 234x + 220$

Which model best describes the data for 2004?

SOLUTION Because 2004 is 2 years after 2002, we substitute 2 for x in each formula. Then we use the order of operations to find D, the amount spent, in millions of dollars, on online dating. The best model is the one that comes closest to giving the actual amount spent in 2004, namely $473 million.

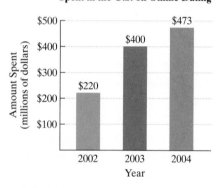

Shopping for a Date: Millions of Dollars Spent in the U.S. on Online Dating

FIGURE 3.1
Source: Jupiter Research

Model 1	Model 2	Model 3
$D = 236(1.5)^x$	$D = 127x + 239$	$D = -54x^2 + 234x + 220$
$D = 236(1.5)^2$	$D = 127(2) + 239$	$D = -54 \cdot 2^2 + 234 \cdot 2 + 220$
$= 236(2.25)$	$= 254 + 239$	$= -54 \cdot 4 + 234 \cdot 2 + 220$
$= 531$	$= 493$	$= -216 + 468 + 220$
		$= 472$

> Figure 6.1 shows that $473 million was spent in 2004.

The formula for model 3 indicates that in 2004, $472 million was spent on online dating. The number given in Figure 3.1 is $473 million, so model 3 best describes the data for that year.

In Example 4, model 1 does not provide a very good approximation for the 2004 data. If a mathematical model gives an estimate that is a poor approximation or is extended to include values of the variable that do not make sense, we say that **model breakdown** has occurred.

 Use the three models in Example 4 to determine which model best describes the data for 2003.

3 | Understand the vocabulary of algebraic expressions.

The Vocabulary of Algebraic Expressions

We have seen that an algebraic expression combines numbers and variables. Here is another example of an algebraic expression:

$$7x - 9y - 3.$$

The **terms** of an algebraic expression are those parts that are separated by addition. For example, we can rewrite $7x - 9y - 3$ as

$$7x + (-9y) + (-3).$$

This expression contains three terms, namely $7x$, $-9y$, and -3.

The numerical part of a term is called its **coefficient**. In the term $7x$, the 7 is the coefficient. In the term $-9y$, the -9 is the coefficient.

Coefficients of 1 and -1 are not written. Thus, the coefficient of x, meaning $1x$, is 1. Similarly, the coefficient of $-y$, meaning $-1y$, is -1.

A term that consists of just a number is called a **numerical term** or a **constant**. The numerical term of $7x - 9y - 3$ is -3.

The parts of each term that are multiplied are called the **factors** of the term. The factors of the term $7x$ are 7 and x.

Like terms are terms that have the same variable factors. For example, $3x$ and $7x$ are like terms.

4 | Simplify algebraic expressions.

Simplifying Algebraic Expressions

The properties of real numbers that we discussed in Chapter 2 can be applied to algebraic expressions.

PROPERTIES OF REAL NUMBERS

Property	**Example**
Commutative Property of Addition $a + b = b + a$	$13x^2 + 7x = 7x + 13x^2$
Commutative Property of Multiplication $ab = ba$	$x \cdot 6 = 6x$
Associative Property of Addition $(a + b) + c = a + (b + c)$	$3 + (8 + x) = (3 + 8) + x = 11 + x$
Associative Property of Multiplication $(ab)c = a(bc)$	$-2(3x) = (-2 \cdot 3)x = -6x$
Distributive Property $a(b + c) = ab + ac$	$5(3x + 7) = 5 \cdot 3x + 5 \cdot 7 = 15x + 35$
$a(b - c) = ab - ac$	$4(2x - 5) = 4 \cdot 2x - 4 \cdot 5 = 8x - 20$

The distributive property in the form

$$ba + ca = (b + c)a$$

enables us to add or subtract like terms. For example,

$$3x + 7x = (3 + 7)x = 10x$$

$$7y^2 - y^2 = 7y^2 - 1y^2 = (7 - 1)y^2 = 6y^2.$$

This process is called **combining like terms.**

An algebraic expression is **simplified** when parentheses have been removed and like terms have been combined.

EXAMPLE 5 SIMPLIFYING AN ALGEBRAIC EXPRESSION

Simplify: $5(3x - 7) - 6x$.

SOLUTION

$$5(3x - 7) - 6x$$

$$= 5 \cdot 3x - 5 \cdot 7 - 6x \quad \text{Use the distributive property to remove the parentheses.}$$

$$= 15x - 35 - 6x \quad \text{Multiply.}$$

$$= (15x - 6x) - 35 \quad \text{Group like terms.}$$

$$= 9x - 35 \quad \text{Combine like terms: } 15x - 6x = (15 - 6)x = 9x.$$

○

CHECK POINT 5 Simplify: $7(2x - 3) - 11x$.

- ●

EXAMPLE 6 SIMPLIFYING AN ALGEBRAIC EXPRESSION

Simplify: $6(2x^2 + 4x) + 10(4x^2 + 3x)$.

SOLUTION

$$6(2x^2 + 4x) + 10(4x^2 + 3x)$$
$$= 6 \cdot 2x^2 + 6 \cdot 4x + 10 \cdot 4x^2 + 10 \cdot 3x$$

> $52x^2$ and $54x$ are not like terms. They contain different variable factors, x^2 and x, and cannot be combined.

$$= 12x^2 + 24x + 40x^2 + 30x \quad \text{Use the distributive property to remove the parentheses.}$$
$$= (12x^2 + 40x^2) + (24x + 30x) \quad \text{Multiply.}$$
$$= 52x^2 + 54x$$

Group like terms.

Combine like terms:
$12x^2 + 40x^2 = (12 + 40)x^2 = 52x^2$
and $24x + 30x = (24 + 30)x = 54x$.

○

CHECK POINT 6 Simplify: $7(4x^2 + 3x) + 2(5x^2 + x)$.

- ●

It is not uncommon to see algebraic expressions with parentheses preceded by a negative sign or subtraction. An expression of the form $-(a + b)$ can be simplified as follows:

$$-(a + b) = -1(a + b) = (-1)a + (-1)b = -a + (-b) = -a - b.$$

Do you see a fast way to obtain the simplified expression on the right? **If a negative sign or a subtraction symbol appears outside parentheses, drop the parentheses and change the sign of every term within the parentheses.** For example,

$$-(3x^2 - 7x - 4) = -3x^2 + 7x + 4.$$

EXAMPLE 7	SIMPLIFYING AN ALGEBRAIC EXPRESSION

Simplify: $8x + 2[5 - (x - 3)]$.

SOLUTION

$$8x + 2[5 - (x - 3)]$$

$$= 8x + 2[5 - x + 3]$$ Drop parentheses and change the sign of each term in parentheses: $-(x - 3) = -x + 3$.

$$= 8x + 2[8 - x]$$ Simplify inside brackets: $5 + 3 = 8$.

$$= 8x + 16 - 2x$$ Apply the distributive property:

$$2[8 - x] = 2 \cdot 8 - 2x = 16 - 2x.$$

$$= (8x - 2x) + 16$$ Group like terms.

$$= 6x + 16$$ Combine like terms: $8x - 2x = (8 - 2)x = 6x.$

 Simplify: $6x + 4[7 - (x - 2)]$.

EXERCISE SET 3.1 ●●●●●●

• Practice Exercises

In Exercises 1–30, evaluate the algebraic expression for the given value or values of the variables.

1. $5x + 7$; $x = 4$
2. $9x + 6$; $x = 5$
3. $-7x - 5$; $x = -4$
4. $-6x - 13$; $x = -3$
5. $x^2 + 4$; $x = 5$
6. $x^2 + 9$; $x = 3$
7. $x^2 - 6$; $x = -2$
8. $x^2 - 11$; $x = -3$
9. $x^2 + 4x$; $x = 10$
10. $x^2 + 6x$; $x = 9$
11. $8x^2 + 17$; $x = 5$
12. $7x^2 + 25$; $x = 3$
13. $x^2 - 5x$; $x = -11$
14. $x^2 - 8x$; $x = -5$
15. $x^2 + 5x - 6$; $x = 4$
16. $x^2 + 7x - 4$; $x = 6$
17. $4 + 5(x - 7)^3$; $x = 9$
18. $6 + 5(x - 6)^3$; $x = 8$
19. $x^2 - 3(x - y)$; $x = 2, y = 8$
20. $x^2 - 4(x - y)$; $x = 3, y = 8$
21. $2x^2 - 5x - 6$; $x = -3$
22. $3x^2 - 4x - 9$; $x = -5$
23. $-5x^2 - 4x - 11$; $x = -1$
24. $-6x^2 - 11x - 17$; $x = -2$
25. $3x^2 + 2xy + 5y^2$; $x = 2, y = 3$
26. $4x^2 + 3xy + 2y^2$; $x = 3, y = 2$
27. $-x^2 - 4xy + 3y^3$; $x = -1, y = -2$
28. $-x^2 - 3xy + 4y^3$; $x = -3, y = -1$
29. $\dfrac{2x + 3y}{x + 1}$; $x = -2, y = 4$
30. $\dfrac{2x + y}{xy - 2x}$; $x = -2, y = 4$

The formula

$$C = \frac{5}{9}(F - 32)$$

expresses the relationship between Fahrenheit temperature, F, and Celsius temperature, C. In Exercises 31–32, use the formula to convert the given Fahrenheit temperature to its equivalent temperature on the Celsius scale.

31. $50°F$
32. $86°F$

A football was kicked vertically upward from a height of 4 feet with an initial speed of 60 feet per second. The formula

$$h = 4 + 60t - 16t^2$$

describes the ball's height above the ground, h, in feet, t seconds after it was kicked. Use this formula to solve Exercises 33–34.

33. What was the ball's height 2 seconds after it was kicked?
34. What was the ball's height 3 seconds after it was kicked?

In Exercises 35–52, simplify each algebraic expression.

35. $7x + 10x$
36. $5x + 13x$
37. $5x^2 - 8x^2$
38. $7x^2 - 10x^2$
39. $3(x + 5)$
40. $4(x + 6)$
41. $4(2x - 3)$
42. $3(4x - 5)$
43. $5(3x + 4) - 4$
44. $2(5x + 4) - 3$
45. $5(3x - 2) + 12x$
46. $2(5x - 1) + 14x$
47. $7(3y - 5) + 2(4y + 3)$
48. $4(2y - 6) + 3(5y + 10)$
49. $5(3y - 2) - (7y + 2)$
50. $4(5y - 3) - (6y + 3)$
51. $7 - 4[3 - (4y - 5)]$
52. $6 - 5[8 - (2y - 4)]$

• Practice Plus

In Exercises 53–56, simplify each algebraic expression.

53. $18x^2 + 4 - [6(x^2 - 2) + 5]$
54. $14x^2 + 5 - [7(x^2 - 2) + 4]$
55. $2(3x^2 - 5) - [4(2x^2 - 1) + 3]$
56. $4(6x^2 - 3) - [2(5x^2 - 1) + 1]$

In Exercises 57–64, write each English phrase as an algebraic expression. Then simplify the expression. Let x represent the number.

57. A number decreased by the sum of the number and four

58. A number decreased by the difference between eight and the number

59. Six times the product of negative five and a number

60. Ten times the product of negative four and a number

61. The difference between the product of five and a number and twice the number

62. The difference between the product of six and a number and negative two times the number

63. The difference between eight times a number and six more than three times the number

64. Eight decreased by three times the sum of a number and six

• Application Exercises

The bar graph shows the number of billionaires in the United States from 2000 through 2004.

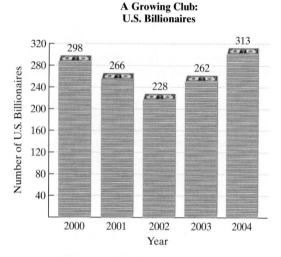

A Growing Club:
U.S. Billionaires

Source: Forbes magazine

The formula

$$N = 17x^2 - 65.4x + 302.2$$

models the number of billionaires, N, in the United States, x years after 2000. Use the formula to solve Exercises 65–68.

65. According to the formula, how many U.S. billionaires, to the nearest whole number, were there in 2004? How well does the formula model the actual data shown in the bar graph?

66. According to the formula, how many U.S. billionaires, to the nearest whole number, were there in 2003? How well does the formula model the actual data shown in the bar graph?

67. According to the formula, how many U.S. billionaires, to the nearest whole number, will there be in 2010?

68. According to the formula, how many U.S. billionaires, to the nearest whole number, will there be in 2008?

The bar graph shows the number of people in the United States, in millions, who do yoga.

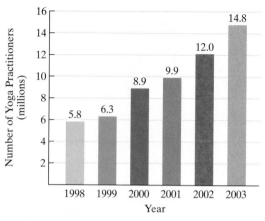

Yoga Stretch:
Number of U.S. Yoga Practitioners

Source: Yoga Journal

Here are four mathematical models for the data shown in the graph. In each formula, N represents the number of U.S. yoga practitioners, in millions, x years after 1998.

Model 1 $N = 1.8x + 5.1$

Model 2 $N = 5.6(1.2)^x$

Model 3 $N = 0.17x^2 + 0.95x + 5.68$

Model 4 $N = 0.01x^3 + 0.09x^2 + 1.1x + 5.64$

Use these models to solve Exercises 69–72.

69. Which model best describes the data for 2000?

70. Which model best describes the data for 1998?

71. How well does model 3 describe the data for 2003?

72. How well does model 4 describe the data for 2002?

The line graph shows the cost of inflation. What cost $10,000 in 1975 would cost the amount shown by the graph in subsequent years.

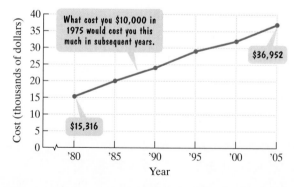

The Cost of Inflation

Source: Bureau of Labor Statistics

Here are two mathematical models for the data shown in the graph. In each formula, C represents the cost x years after 1980 of what cost $10,000 in 1975.

Model 1 $C = 865x + 15,316$

Model 2 $C = -2x^2 + 900x + 15,397$

Use these models to solve Exercises 73–75.

73. a. Use the graph to estimate the cost in 2000, to the nearest thousand dollars, of what cost $10,000 in 1975.
   b. Use model 1 to determine the cost in 2000. How well does this describe your estimate from part (a)?
   c. Use model 2 to determine the cost in 2000. How well does this describe your estimate from part (a)?

74. a. Use the graph to estimate the cost in 1990, to the nearest thousand dollars, of what cost $10,000 in 1975.
   b. Use model 1 to determine the cost in 1990. How well does this describe your estimate from part (a)?
   c. Use model 2 to determine the cost in 1990. How well does this describe your estimate from part (a)?

75. Which model is a better description for the cost in 2005 of what cost $10,000 in 1975?

• Writing in Mathematics

76. What is an algebraic expression? Provide an example with your description.

77. What does it mean to evaluate an algebraic expression? Provide an example with your description.

78. What is a term? Provide an example with your description.

79. What are like terms? Provide an example with your description.

80. Explain how to add like terms. Give an example.

81. What does it mean to simplify an algebraic expression?

82. An algebra student incorrectly used the distributive property and wrote $3(5x + 7) = 15x + 7$. If you were that student's teacher, what would you say to help the student avoid this kind of error?

• Critical Thinking Exercises

83. Which one of the following is true?
   a. The term x has no coefficient.
   b. $5 + 3(x - 4) = 8(x - 4) = 8x - 32$
   c. $-x - x = -x + (-x) = 0$
   d. $x - 0.02(x + 200) = 0.98x - 4$

84. Which one of the following is true?
   a. $3 + 7x = 10x$
   b. $b \cdot b = 2b$
   c. $(3y - 4) - (8y - 1) = -5y - 3$
   d. $-4y + 4 = -4(y + 4)$

85. A business that manufactures small alarm clocks has weekly fixed costs of $5000. The average cost per clock for the business to manufacture x clocks is described by

$$\frac{0.5x + 5000}{x}.$$

   a Find the average cost when $x = 100, 1000,$ and $10,000.$
   b. Like all other businesses, the alarm clock manufacturer must make a profit. To do this, each clock must be sold for at least 50¢ more than what it costs to manufacture. Due to competition from a larger company, the clocks can be sold for $1.50 each and no more. Our small manufacturer can only produce 2000 clocks weekly. Does this business have much of a future? Explain.

SECTION 3.2 • LINEAR EQUATIONS IN ONE VARIABLE

OBJECTIVES

1. Solve linear equations.
2. Solve linear equations containing fractions.
3. Solve a formula for a variable.
4. Identify equations with no solution or infinitely many solutions.

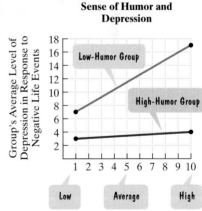

FIGURE 3.2
Source: Steven Davis and Joseph Palladino, *Psychology,* 3rd Edition. Prentice Hall, 2003.

The belief that humor and laughter can have positive benefits on our lives is not new. The graphs in Figure 3.2 indicate that persons with a low sense of humor have higher levels of depression in response to negative life events than those with a high sense of humor. These graphs can be modeled by the following formulas:

Low-Humor Group   High-Humor Group

$$D = \frac{10}{9}x + \frac{53}{9} \qquad D = \frac{1}{9}x + \frac{26}{9}.$$

In each formula, x represents the intensity of a negative life event (from 1, low, to 10, high) and D is the level of depression in response to that event.

Suppose that the low-humor group averages a level of depression of 10 in response to a negative life event. We can determine the intensity of that event by substituting 10 for D in the low-humor model, $D = \dfrac{10}{9}x + \dfrac{53}{9}$:

$$10 = \frac{10}{9}x + \frac{53}{9}.$$

The two sides of an equation can be reversed. So, we can also express this equation as

$$\frac{10}{9}x + \frac{53}{9} = 10.$$

Notice that the highest exponent on the variable is 1. Such an equation is called a *linear equation in one variable*. In this section, we will study how to solve linear equations.

1 | Solve linear equations.

Solving Linear Equations in One Variable

We begin with a general definition of a linear equation in one variable.

> **DEFINITION OF A LINEAR EQUATION**
>
> A **linear equation in one variable** x is an equation that can be written in the form
> $$ax + b = 0,$$
> where a and b are real numbers, and $a \neq 0$.

An example of a linear equation in one variable is

$$4x + 12 = 0.$$

Solving an equation in x involves determining all values of x that result in a true statement when substituted into the equation. Such values are **solutions**, or **roots**, of the equation. For example, substitute -3 for x in $4x + 12 = 0$. We obtain

$$4(-3) + 12 = 0, \quad \text{or} \quad -12 + 12 = 0.$$

This simplifies to the true statement $0 = 0$. Thus, -3 is a solution of the equation $4x + 12 = 0$. We also say that -3 **satisfies** the equation $4x + 12 = 0$, because when we substitute -3 for x, a true statement results. The set of all such solutions is called the equation's **solution set**. For example, the solution set of the equation $4x + 12 = 0$ is $\{-3\}$.

Two or more equations that have the same solution set are called **equivalent equations**. For example, the equations

$$4x + 12 = 0 \quad \text{and} \quad 4x = -12 \quad \text{and} \quad x = -3$$

are equivalent equations because the solution set for each is $\{-3\}$. To solve a linear equation in x, we transform the equation into an equivalent equation one or more times. Our final equivalent equation should be of the form

$$x = \text{a number}.$$

The solution set of this equation is the set consisting of the number.

To generate equivalent equations, we will use the following properties:

> **THE ADDITION AND MULTIPLICATION PROPERTIES OF EQUALITY**
>
> THE ADDITION PROPERTY OF EQUALITY
>
> The same real number or algebraic expression may be added to both sides of an equation without changing the equation's solution set.
>
> $a = b$ and $a + c = b + c$ are equivalent equations.
>
> THE MULTIPLICATION PROPERTY OF EQUALITY
>
> The same nonzero real number may multiply both sides of an equation without changing the equation's solution set.
>
> $a = b$ and $ac = bc$ are equivalent equations as long as $c \neq 0$.

Because subtraction is defined in terms of addition, the addition property also lets us subtract the same number from both sides of an equation without changing the equation's solution set. Similarly, because division is defined in terms of multiplication, the multiplication property of equality can be used to divide both sides of an equation by the same nonzero number to obtain an equivalent equation.

Table 3.1 illustrates how these properties are used to isolate x to obtain an equation of the form $x =$ a number.

TABLE 3.1 USING PROPERTIES OF EQUALITY TO SOLVE EQUATIONS

Equation	How to Isolate x	Solving the Equation	The Equation's Solution Set
$x - 3 = 8$	Add 3 to both sides.	$x - 3 + 3 = 8 + 3$ $x = 11$	$\{11\}$
$x + 7 = -15$	Subtract 7 from both sides.	$x + 7 - 7 = -15 - 7$ $x = -22$	$\{-22\}$
$6x = 30$	Divide both sides by 6 (or multiply both sides by $\frac{1}{6}$).	$\dfrac{6x}{6} = \dfrac{30}{6}$ $x = 5$	$\{5\}$
$\dfrac{x}{5} = 9$	Multiply both sides by 5.	$5 \cdot \dfrac{x}{5} = 5 \cdot 9$ $x = 45$	$\{45\}$

These equations are solved using the **Addition Property of Equality.**

These equations are solved using the **Multiplication Property of Equality.**

EXAMPLE 1   USING PROPERTIES OF EQUALITY TO SOLVE AN EQUATION

Solve and check: $2x + 3 = 17$.

SOLUTION Our goal is to obtain an equivalent equation with x isolated on one side and a number on the other side.

$$2x + 3 = 17 \qquad \text{This is the given equation.}$$
$$2x + 3 - 3 = 17 - 3 \qquad \text{Subtract 3 from both sides.}$$
$$2x = 14 \qquad \text{Simplify.}$$
$$\frac{2x}{2} = \frac{14}{2} \qquad \text{Divide both sides by 2.}$$
$$x = 7 \qquad \text{Simplify: } \frac{2x}{2} = 1x = x \text{ and } \frac{14}{2} = 7.$$

Now we check the proposed solution, 7, by replacing x with 7 in the original equation.

$$2x + 3 = 17 \qquad \text{This is the original equation.}$$
$$2 \cdot 7 + 3 \stackrel{?}{=} 17 \qquad \text{Substitute 7 for x. The question mark indicates that we do not yet know if the two sides are equal.}$$
$$14 + 3 \stackrel{?}{=} 17 \qquad \text{Multiply: } 2 \cdot 7 = 14.$$
$$17 = 17 \qquad \text{Add: } 14 + 3 = 17.$$

This statement is true.

Because the check results in a true statement, we conclude that the solution set of the given equation is $\{7\}$.

 Solve and check: $4x + 5 = 29$.

Here is a step-by-step procedure for solving a linear equation in one variable. Not all of these steps are necessary to solve every equation.

> ### SOLVING A LINEAR EQUATION
> 1. Simplify the algebraic expression on each side by removing grouping symbols and combining like terms.
> 2. Collect all the variable terms on one side and all the constants, or numerical terms, on the other side.
> 3. Isolate the variable and solve.
> 4. Check the proposed solution in the original equation.

EXAMPLE 2   SOLVING A LINEAR EQUATION

Solve and check: $2(x - 4) - 5x = -5$.

SOLUTION

Step 1. Simplify the algebraic expression on each side.

$$2(x - 4) - 5x = -5 \qquad \text{This is the given equation.}$$
$$2x - 8 - 5x = -5 \qquad \text{Use the distributive property.}$$
$$-3x - 8 = -5 \qquad \text{Combine like terms: } 2x - 5x = -3x.$$

Step 2. Collect variable terms on one side and constants on the other side. The only variable term, $-3x$, is already on the left side. We will collect constants on the right side by adding 8 to both sides.

$$-3x - 8 + 8 = -5 + 8 \qquad \text{Add 8 to both sides.}$$
$$-3x = 3 \qquad \text{Simplify.}$$

Step 3. Isolate the variable and solve. We isolate the variable, x, by dividing both sides of $-3x = 3$ by -3.

$$\frac{-3x}{-3} = \frac{3}{-3} \qquad \text{Divide both sides by } -3.$$

$$x = -1 \qquad \text{Simplify: } \frac{-3x}{-3} = 1x = x \text{ and } \frac{3}{-3} = -1.$$

Step 4. Check the proposed solution in the original equation. Substitute -1 for x in the original equation.

$$2(x - 4) - 5x = -5 \qquad \text{This is the original equation.}$$
$$2(-1 - 4) - 5(-1) \overset{?}{=} -5 \qquad \text{Substitute } -1 \text{ for } x.$$
$$2(-5) - 5(-1) \overset{?}{=} -5 \qquad \begin{array}{l}\text{Simplify inside parentheses:}\\ -1 - 4 = -1 + (-4) = -5.\end{array}$$
$$-10 - (-5) \overset{?}{=} -5 \qquad \begin{array}{l}\text{Multiply: } 2(-5) = -10 \text{ and}\\ 5(-1) = -5.\end{array}$$

$$\boxed{\text{This statement is true.}} \quad -5 = -5 \qquad -10 - (-5) = -10 + 5 = -5$$

Because the check results in a true statement, we conclude that the solution set of the given equation is $\{-1\}$.

 Solve and check: $6(x - 3) - 10x = -10$.

STUDY TIP

We simplify algebraic expressions. We solve algebraic equations. Although basic rules of algebra are used in both procedures, notice the differences between the procedures:

Simplifying an Algebraic Expression	**Solving an Algebraic Equation**
Simplify: $3(x - 7) - (5x - 11)$.	Solve: $3(x - 7) - (5x - 11) = 14$.

> This is not an equation. There is no equal sign.

> This is an equation. There is an equal sign.

Solution
$$3(x - 7) - (5x - 11)$$
$$= 3x - 21 - 5x + 11$$
$$= (3x - 5x) + (-21 + 11)$$
$$= -2x + (-10)$$
$$= -2x - 10$$

> Stop! Further simplification is not possible. Avoid the common error of setting $-2x - 10$ equal to 0.

Solution $3(x - 7) - (5x - 11) = 14$
$$3x - 21 - 5x + 11 = 14$$
$$-2x - 10 = 14$$

> Add 10 to both sides.

$$-2x - 10 + 10 = 14 + 10$$
$$-2x = 24$$

> Divide both sides by -2.

$$\frac{-2x}{-2} = \frac{24}{-2}$$
$$x = -12$$

The solution set is $\{-12\}$.

EXAMPLE 3   SOLVING A LINEAR EQUATION

Solve and check: $5x - 12 = 8x + 24$.

SOLUTION

Step 1. Simplify the algebraic expression on each side. Neither side contains grouping symbols or like terms that can be combined. Therefore, we can skip this step.

Step 2. Collect variable terms on one side and constants on the other side. One way to do this is to collect variable terms on the left and constants on the right. This is accomplished by subtracting $8x$ from both sides and adding 12 to both sides.

$5x - 12 = 8x + 24$	This is the given equation.
$5x - 12 - 8x = 8x + 24 - 8x$	Subtract $8x$ from both sides.
$-3x - 12 = 24$	Simplify: $5x - 8x = -3x$.
$-3x - 12 + 12 = 24 + 12$	Add 12 to both sides and collect constants on the right side.
$-3x = 36$	Simplify.

Step 3. Isolate the variable and solve. We isolate the variable, x, by dividing both sides of $-3x = 36$ by -3.

$\dfrac{-3x}{-3} = \dfrac{36}{-3}$	Divide both sides by -3.
$x = -12$	Simplify.

Step 4. Check the proposed solution in the original equation. Substitute -12 for x in the original equation.

$5x - 12 = 8x + 24$	This is the original equation.
$5(-12) - 12 \overset{?}{=} 8(-12) + 24$	Substitute -12 for x.
$-60 - 12 \overset{?}{=} -96 + 24$	Multiply: $5(-12) = -60$ and $8(-12) = -96$.
$-72 = -72$	Add: $-60 + (-12) = -72$ and $-96 + 24 = -72$.

> This statement is true.

Because the check results in a true statement, we conclude that the solution set of the given equation is $\{-12\}$.

STUDY TIP

You can solve
$$5x - 12 = 8x + 24$$

by collecting x-terms on the right and numbers on the left. To collect x-terms on the right, subtract $5x$ from both sides:

$$5x - 12 - 5x = 8x + 24 - 5x$$
$$-12 = 3x + 24.$$

To collect numbers on the left, subtract 24 from both sides:

$$-12 - 24 = 3x + 24 - 24$$
$$-36 = 3x.$$

Now isolate x by dividing both sides by 3:

$$\frac{-36}{3} = \frac{3x}{3}$$
$$-12 = x.$$

This is the same solution that we obtained in Example 3.

Solve the equation: $2x + 9 = 8x - 3$.

EXAMPLE 4   SOLVING A LINEAR EQUATION

Solve and check: $2(x - 3) - 17 = 13 - 3(x + 2)$.

SOLUTION

Step 1. Simplify the algebraic expression on each side.

> Do not begin with 13 − 3. Multiplication (the distributive property) is applied before subtraction.

$$2(x - 3) - 17 = 13 - 3(x + 2)$$ This is the given equation.
$$2x - 6 - 17 = 13 - 3x - 6$$ Use the distributive property.
$$2x - 23 = -3x + 7$$ Combine like terms.

Step 2. Collect variable terms on one side and constants on the other side. We will collect variable terms on the left by adding $3x$ to both sides. We will collect the numbers on the right by adding 23 to both sides.

$$2x - 23 + 3x = -3x + 7 + 3x$$ Add 3x to both sides.
$$5x - 23 = 7$$ Simplify: $2x + 3x = 5x$.
$$5x - 23 + 23 = 7 + 23$$ Add 23 to both sides.
$$5x = 30$$ Simplify.

Step 3. Isolate the variable and solve. We isolate the variable, x, by dividing both sides of $5x = 30$ by 5.

$$\frac{5x}{5} = \frac{30}{5}$$ Divide both sides by 5.
$$x = 6$$ Simplify.

Step 4. Check the proposed solution in the original equation. Substitute 6 for x in the original equation.

$$2(x - 3) - 17 = 13 - 3(x + 2)$$ This is the original equation.
$$2(6 - 3) - 17 \stackrel{?}{=} 13 - 3(6 + 2)$$ Substitute 6 for x.
$$2(3) - 17 \stackrel{?}{=} 13 - 3(8)$$ Simplify inside parentheses.
$$6 - 17 \stackrel{?}{=} 13 - 24$$ Multiply.
$$-11 = -11$$ Subtract.

The true statement $-11 = -11$ verifies that the solution set is $\{6\}$.

 Solve and check: $4(2x + 1) = 29 + 3(2x - 5)$.

---

2 Solve linear equations containing fractions.

Linear Equations with Fractions

Equations are easier to solve when they do not contain fractions. How do we remove fractions from an equation? We begin by multiplying both sides of the equation by the least common denominator of the fractions in the equation. The least common denominator is the smallest number that all denominators will divide into. Multiplying every term on both sides of the equation by the least common denominator will eliminate the fractions in the equation. Example 5 shows how we "clear an equation of fractions."

EXAMPLE 5   SOLVING A LINEAR EQUATION INVOLVING FRACTIONS

Solve the equation: $\dfrac{3x}{2} = \dfrac{8x}{5} - \dfrac{39}{5}$.

SOLUTION The denominators are 2, 5, and 5. The smallest number that is divisible by 2, 5, and 5 is 10. We begin by multiplying both sides of the equation by 10, the least common denominator.

$$\dfrac{3x}{2} = \dfrac{8x}{5} - \dfrac{39}{5}$$
This is the given equation.

$$10 \cdot \dfrac{3x}{2} = 10\left(\dfrac{8x}{5} - \dfrac{39}{5}\right)$$
Multiply both sides by 10.

$$10 \cdot \dfrac{3x}{2} = 10 \cdot \dfrac{8x}{5} - 10 \cdot \dfrac{39}{5}$$
Use the distributive property. Be sure to multiply all terms by 10.

$$\overset{5}{\cancel{10}} \cdot \dfrac{3x}{\underset{1}{\cancel{2}}} = \overset{2}{\cancel{10}} \cdot \dfrac{8x}{\underset{1}{\cancel{5}}} - \overset{2}{\cancel{10}} \cdot \dfrac{39}{\underset{1}{\cancel{5}}}$$
Divide out common factors in the multiplications.

$$15x = 16x - 78$$
Complete the multiplications. The fractions are now cleared.

At this point, we have an equation similar to those we have previously solved. Collect the variable terms on one side and the constants on the other side.

$$15x - 16x = 16x - 16x - 78$$
Subtract 16x from both sides to get the variable terms on the left.

$$-x = -78$$
Simplify.

> We're not finished. A negative sign should not precede x.

Isolate x by multiplying or dividing both sides of this equation by -1.

$$\dfrac{-x}{-1} = \dfrac{-78}{-1}$$
Divide both sides by -1.

$$x = 78$$
Simplify.

Check the proposed solution. Substitute 78 for x in the original equation. You should obtain $117 = 117$. This true statement verifies that the solution set is $\{78\}$.

CHECK POINT 5 Solve the equation: $\dfrac{x}{4} = \dfrac{2x}{3} + \dfrac{5}{6}$.

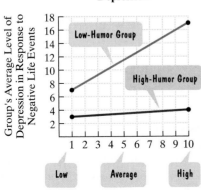

Sense of Humor and Depression

FIGURE 3.2 (repeated)

EXAMPLE 6   AN APPLICATION: RESPONDING TO NEGATIVE LIFE EVENTS

In the section opener, we used two formulas to model the level of depression, D, in response to the intensity of a negative life event, x, from 1, low, to 10, high:

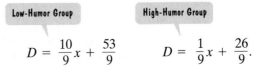

Low-Humor Group   High-Humor Group

$$D = \dfrac{10}{9}x + \dfrac{53}{9} \qquad D = \dfrac{1}{9}x + \dfrac{26}{9}.$$

If the high-humor group averages a level of depression of 3.5, or $\dfrac{7}{2}$, in response to a negative life event, what is the intensity of that event? How is the solution shown on the red line graph in Figure 3.2?

SOLUTION We are interested in the intensity of a negative life event with an average level of depression of $\frac{7}{2}$ for the high-humor group. We substitute $\frac{7}{2}$ for D in the high-humor model and solve for x, the intensity of the negative life event.

$$D = \frac{1}{9}x + \frac{26}{9}$$

This is the given formula for the high-humor group.

$$\frac{7}{2} = \frac{1}{9}x + \frac{26}{9}$$

Replace D with $\frac{7}{2}$.

$$18 \cdot \frac{7}{2} = 18\left(\frac{1}{9}x + \frac{26}{9}\right)$$

Multiply both sides by 18, the least common denominator.

$$18 \cdot \frac{7}{2} = 18 \cdot \frac{1}{9}x + 18 \cdot \frac{26}{9}$$

Use the distributive property.

$$\overset{9}{\cancel{18}} \cdot \frac{7}{\underset{1}{\cancel{2}}} = \overset{2}{\cancel{18}} \cdot \frac{1}{\underset{1}{\cancel{9}}}x + \overset{2}{\cancel{18}} \cdot \frac{26}{\underset{1}{\cancel{9}}}$$

Divide out common factors in the multiplications.

$$63 = 2x + 52$$

Complete the multiplications. The fractions are now cleared.

$$63 - 52 = 2x + 52 - 52$$

Subtract 52 from both sides to get constants on the left.

$$11 = 2x$$

Simplify.

$$\frac{11}{2} = \frac{2x}{2}$$

Divide both sides by 2.

$$\frac{11}{2} = x$$

Simplify.

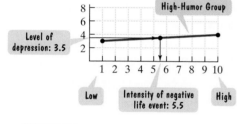

8
6
4
2

High-Humor Group

Level of depression: 3.5

1 2 3 4 5 6 7 8 9 10

Low   Intensity of negative life event: 5.5   High

FIGURE 3.3

The formula indicates that if the high-humor group averages a level of depression of 3.5 in response to a negative life event, the intensity of that event is $\frac{11}{2}$, or 5.5. This is illustrated on the line graph for the high-humor group in Figure 3.3.

CHECK POINT 6 Use the model for the low-humor group given in Example 6 on the previous page to solve this problem. If the low-humor group averages a level of depression of 10 in response to a negative life event, what is the intensity of that event? How is the solution shown on the blue line graph in Figure 3.2?

3 | Solve a formula for a variable.

Solving a Formula for One of Its Variables

We know that solving an equation is the process of finding the number (or numbers) that make the equation a true statement. All of the equations we have solved contained only one letter, x.

By contrast, formulas contain two or more letters, representing two or more variables. An example is the formula for the perimeter of a rectangle:

$$2l + 2w = P.$$

A rectangle's perimeter is the sum of twice its length and twice its width.

We say that this formula is solved for the variable P because P is alone on one side of the equation and the other side does not contain a P.

Solving a formula for a variable means rewriting the formula so that the variable is isolated on one side of the equation. It does not mean obtaining a numerical value for that variable.

To solve a formula for one of its variables, treat that variable as if it were the only variable in the equation. Think of the other variables as if they were numbers. Isolate all terms with the specified variable on one side of the equation and all terms without the specified variable on the other side. Then divide both sides by the same nonzero quantity to get the specified variable alone. The next example shows how to do this.

EXAMPLE 7   SOLVING A FORMULA FOR A VARIABLE

Solve the formula $2l + 2w = P$ for l.

SOLUTION First, isolate $2l$ on the left by subtracting $2w$ from both sides. Then solve for l by dividing both sides by 2.

> We need to isolate l.

$$2l + 2w = P \qquad \text{This is the given formula.}$$

$$2l + 2w - 2w = P - 2w \qquad \text{Isolate } 2l \text{ by subtracting } 2w \text{ from both sides.}$$

$$2l = P - 2w \qquad \text{Simplify.}$$

$$\frac{2l}{2} = \frac{P - 2w}{2} \qquad \text{Solve for } l \text{ by dividing both sides by 2.}$$

$$l = \frac{P - 2w}{2} \qquad \text{Simplify.}$$

 7 Solve the formula $2l + 2w = P$ for w.

EXAMPLE 8   SOLVING A FORMULA FOR A VARIABLE

The total price of an article purchased on a monthly deferred payment plan is described by the following formula:

$$T = D + pm.$$

In this formula, T is the total price, D is the down payment, p is the monthly payment, and m is the number of months one pays. Solve the formula for p.

SOLUTION First, isolate pm on the right by subtracting D from both sides. Then, isolate p from pm by dividing both sides of the formula by m.

> We need to isolate p.

$$T = D + pm \qquad \text{This is the given formula. We want } p \text{ alone.}$$

$$T - D = D - D + pm \qquad \text{Isolate } pm \text{ by subtracting } D \text{ from both sides.}$$

$$T - D = pm \qquad \text{Simplify.}$$

$$\frac{T - D}{m} = \frac{pm}{m} \qquad \text{Now isolate } p \text{ by dividing both sides by } m.$$

$$\frac{T - D}{m} = p \qquad \text{Simplify: } \frac{pm}{m} = \frac{p\cancel{m}}{\cancel{m}} = \frac{p}{1} = p.$$

 8 Solve the formula $T = D + pm$ for m.

4 | Identify equations with no solution or infinitely many solutions.

Linear Equations with No Solution or Infinitely Many Solutions

Thus far, each equation that we have solved has had a single solution. However, some equations are not true for even one real number. By contrast, other equations are true for all real numbers.

If you attempt to solve an equation with no solution, you will eliminate the variable and obtain a false statement, such as $2 = 5$. If you attempt to solve an equation that is true for every real number, you will eliminate the variable and obtain a true statement, such as $4 = 4$.

EXAMPLE 9   SOLVING A LINEAR EQUATION

Solve: $2x + 6 = 2(x + 4)$.

SOLUTION

$2x + 6 = 2(x + 4)$	This is the given equation.
$2x + 6 = 2x + 8$	Use the distributive property.
$2x + 6 - 2x = 2x + 8 - 2x$	Subtract 2x from both sides.

Keep reading. 6 = 8 is not the solution. $6 = 8$ Simplify.

The original equation, $2x + 6 = 2(x + 4)$, is equivalent to the statement $6 = 8$, which is false for every value of x. The equation has no solution. The solution set is $\varnothing$, the empty set.

 Solve: $3x + 7 = 3(x + 1)$.

EXAMPLE 10   SOLVING A LINEAR EQUATION

Solve: $4x + 6 = 6(x + 1) - 2x$.

SOLUTION

$4x + 6 = 6(x + 1) - 2x$	This is the given equation.
$4x + 6 = 6x + 6 - 2x$	Apply the distributive property on the right side.
$4x + 6 = 4x + 6$	Combine like terms on the right side: $6x - 2x = 4x$.

Can you see that the equation $4x + 6 = 4x + 6$ is true for every value of x? Let's continue solving the equation by subtracting $4x$ from both sides.

$$4x - 4x + 6 = 4x - 4x + 6$$

Keep reading. 6 = 6 is not the solution. $6 = 6$

The original equation is equivalent to the statement $6 = 6$, which is true for every value of x. Thus, the solution set consists of the set of all real numbers, expressed in set-builder notation as $\{x \mid x \text{ is a real number}\}$. Try substituting any real number of your choice for x in the original equation. You will obtain a true statement.

STUDY TIP

Because of the fundamental role that sets play in mathematics, it's a good idea to use set notation to express an equation's solution set. If a linear equation has no solution, its solution set is $\varnothing$, the empty set. If a linear equation with variable x has infinitely many solutions, its solution set is $\{x \mid x \text{ is a real number}\}$.

 Solve: $7x + 9 = 9(x + 1) - 2x$.

EXERCISE SET 3.2 ●●●●●○

• Practice Exercises

In Exercises 1–42, solve each equation. Be sure to check your proposed solution by substituting it for the variable in the given equation.

1. $x - 7 = 3$

2. $x - 3 = -17$

3. $x + 5 = -12$

4. $x + 12 = -14$

5. $\dfrac{x}{3} = 4$

6. $\dfrac{x}{5} = 3$

7. $5x = 45$

8. $6x = 18$

9. $8x = -24$

10. $5x = -25$

11. $-8x = 2$

12. $-6x = 3$

13. $5x + 3 = 18$

14. $3x + 8 = 50$

15. $6x - 3 = 63$

16. $5x - 8 = 72$

17. $4x - 14 = -82$

18. $9x - 14 = -77$

19. $14 - 5x = -41$

20. $25 - 6x = -83$

21. $9(5x - 2) = 45$

22. $10(3x + 2) = 70$

23. $5x - (2x - 10) = 35$

24. $11x - (6x - 5) = 40$

25. $3x + 5 = 2x + 13$

26. $2x - 7 = 6 + x$

27. $8x - 2 = 7x - 5$

28. $13x + 14 = -5 + 12x$

29. $7x + 4 = x + 16$

30. $8x + 1 = x + 43$

31. $8y - 3 = 11y + 9$

32. $5y - 2 = 9y + 2$

33. $2(4 - 3x) = 2(2x + 5)$

34. $3(5 - x) = 4(2x + 1)$

35. $8(y + 2) = 2(3y + 4)$

36. $3(3y - 1) = 4(3 + 3y)$

37. $3(x + 1) = 7(x - 2) - 3$

38. $5x - 4(x + 9) = 2x - 3$

39. $5(2x - 8) - 2 = 5(x - 3) + 3$

40. $7(3x - 2) + 5 = 6(2x - 1) + 24$

41. $5(x - 2) - 2(2x + 1) = 2 + 5x$

42. $2(5x + 4) + 3(2x + 11) = 4x - 19$

Solve and check each equation in Exercises 43–50. Begin your work by rewriting each equation without fractions.

43. $\dfrac{x}{3} + \dfrac{x}{2} = \dfrac{5}{6}$

44. $\dfrac{x}{4} - 1 = \dfrac{x}{5}$

45. $\dfrac{x}{2} = 20 - \dfrac{x}{3}$

46. $\dfrac{x}{5} - \dfrac{1}{2} = \dfrac{x}{6}$

47. $\dfrac{3y}{4} - 3 = \dfrac{y}{2} + 2$

48. $y + \dfrac{1}{2} = 1 - \dfrac{y}{3}$

49. $\dfrac{3x}{5} - x = \dfrac{x}{10} - \dfrac{5}{2}$

50. $2x - \dfrac{2x}{7} = \dfrac{x}{2} + \dfrac{17}{2}$

In Exercises 51–68, solve each formula for the specified variable. Do you recognize the formula? If so, what does it describe?

51. $A = LW$ for L

52. $D = RT$ for R

53. $A = \frac{1}{2}bh$ for b

54. $V = \frac{1}{3}Bh$ for B

55. $I = Prt$ for P

56. $C = 2\pi r$ for r

57. $E = mc^2$ for m

58. $V = \pi r^2 h$ for h

59. $y = mx + b$ for m

60. $P = C + MC$ for M

61. $A = \frac{1}{2}(a + b)$ for a

62. $A = \frac{1}{2}(a + b)$ for b

63. $S = P + Prt$ for r

64. $S = P + Prt$ for t

65. $Ax + By = C$ for x

66. $Ax + By = C$ for y

67. $a_n = a_1 + (n - 1)d$ for n

68. $a_n = a_1 + (n - 1)d$ for d

In Exercises 69–84, solve each equation. Use set notation to express solution sets for equations with no solution or equations that are true for all real numbers.

69. $3x - 7 = 3(x + 1)$

70. $2(x - 5) = 2x + 10$

71. $2(x + 4) = 4x + 5 - 2x + 3$

72. $3(x - 1) = 8x + 6 - 5x - 9$

73. $7 + 2(3x - 5) = 8 - 3(2x + 1)$

74. $2 + 3(2x - 7) = 9 - 4(3x + 1)$

75. $4x + 1 - 5x = 5 - (x + 4)$

76. $5x - 5 = 3x - 7 + 2(x + 1)$

77. $4(x + 2) + 1 = 7x - 3(x - 2)$

78. $5x - 3(x + 1) = 2(x + 3) - 5$

79. $3 - x = 2x + 3$

80. $5 - x = 4x + 5$

81. $\dfrac{x}{3} + 2 = \dfrac{x}{3}$

82. $\dfrac{x}{4} + 3 = \dfrac{x}{4}$

83. $\dfrac{x}{2} - \dfrac{x}{4} + 4 = x + 4$

84. $\dfrac{x}{2} + \dfrac{2x}{3} + 3 = x + 3$

• Practice Plus

85. Evaluate $x^2 - x$ for the value of x satisfying $4(x - 2) + 2 = 4x - 2(2 - x)$.

86. Evaluate $x^2 - x$ for the value of x satisfying $2(x - 6) = 3x + 2(2x - 1)$.

87. Evaluate $x^2 - (xy - y)$ for x satisfying $\dfrac{x}{5} - 2 = \dfrac{x}{3}$ and y satisfying $-2y - 10 = 5y + 18$.

88. Evaluate $x^2 - (xy - y)$ for x satisfying $\dfrac{3x}{2} + \dfrac{3x}{4} = \dfrac{x}{4} - 4$ and y satisfying $5 - y = 7(y + 4) + 1$.

In Exercises 89–96, solve each equation.

89. $[(3 + 6)^2 \div 3] \cdot 4 = -54x$

90. $2^3 - [4(5 - 3)^3] = -8x$

91. $5 - 12x = 8 - 7x - [6 \div 3(2 + 5^3) + 5x]$

92. $2(5x + 58) = 10x + 4(21 \div 3.5 - 11)$

93. $0.7x + 0.4(20) = 0.5(x + 20)$

94. $0.5(x + 2) = 0.1 + 3(0.1x + 0.3)$

95. $4x + 13 - \{2x - [4(x - 3) - 5]\} = 2(x - 6)$

96. $-2\{7 - [4 - 2(1 - x) + 3]\} = 10 - [4x - 2(x - 3)]$

• Application Exercises

The bar graph shows the average amount of time, in hours, that each American aged 12 or older spent playing video games from 2001 through 2006.

Hours Spent per Person Playing Video Games

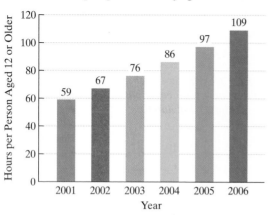

Source: U.S. Census Bureau

The data can be modeled by

$$H = 10x + 59,$$

where H is the annual hours spent playing video games per person x years after 2001. Use this formula to solve Exercises 97–98.

97. If trends continue, in which year will Americans average 179 hours per person playing video games?

98. If trends continue, in which year will Americans average 199 hours per person playing video games?

The formula

$$\frac{n}{2} + 80 = 2T$$

models the relationship between temperature, T, in degrees Fahrenheit, and the number of cricket chirps per minute, n, for the snow tree cricket. Use this mathematical model to solve Exercises 99–100.

99. Find the number of chirps per minute at a temperature of 70°F.

100. Find the number of chirps per minute at a temperature of 80°F.

The formula

$$p = 15 + \frac{5d}{11}$$

describes the pressure of sea water, p, in pounds per square foot, at a depth of d feet below the surface. Use the formula to solve Exercises 101–102.

101. The record depth for breath-held diving, by Francisco Ferreras (Cuba) off Grand Bahama Island, on November 14, 1993, involved pressure of 201 pounds per square foot. To what depth did Ferreras descend on this ill-advised venture? (He was underwater for 2 minutes and 9 seconds!)

102. At what depth is the pressure 20 pounds per square foot?

The line graphs show the average writing test scores for U.S. high school seniors. The graphs reflect general trends in which boys continue to fall behind girls in reading and writing proficiency, with fewer boys than girls going to college.

Average Writing Test Scores for High School Seniors

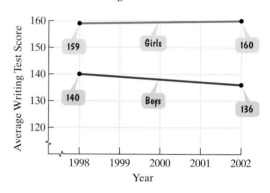

Source: Newsweek, January 30, 2006

The data can be modeled by the following formulas:

Girls $\quad W = \dfrac{1}{4}x + 159$ **Boys** $\quad W = -x + 140.$

In each formula, W is the average writing test score x years after 1998. Use the formulas to solve Exercises 103–108.

103. If current trends continue, when will the average test score for boys be 127?

104. If current trends continue, when will the average test score for boys be 126?

105. If current trends continue, when will the average test score for girls be 163?

106. If current trends continue, when will the average test score for girls be 164?

107. If current trends continue, when will the average test score for girls be 49 points higher than for boys?

108. If current trends continue, when will the average test score for girls be 54 points higher than for boys?

• Writing in Mathematics

109. What is the solution set of an equation?

110. State the addition property of equality and give an example.

111. State the multiplication property of equality and give an example.

112. How do you know if a linear equation has one solution, no solution, or infinitely many solutions?

113. What is the difference between solving an equation such as $2(x - 4) + 5x = 34$ and simplifying an algebraic expression such as $2(x - 4) + 5x$? If there is a difference, which topic should be taught first? Why?

114. Suppose that you solve $\dfrac{x}{5} - \dfrac{x}{2} = 1$ by multiplying both sides by 20, rather than the least common denominator of 5 and 2 (namely, 10). Describe what happens. If you get the correct solution, why do you think we clear the equation of fractions by multiplying by the *least* common denominator?

115. Suppose you are an algebra teacher grading the following solution on an examination:

$$\text{Solve:} \quad -3(x - 6) = 2 - x.$$
$$\text{Solution:} \quad -3x - 18 = 2 - x$$
$$-2x - 18 = 2$$
$$-2x = -16$$
$$x = 8.$$

You should note that 8 checks, and the solution set is {8}. The student who worked the problem therefore wants full credit. Can you find any errors in the solution? If full credit is 10 points, how many points should you give the student? Justify your position.

116. Although the formulas in Example 6 on page 131 are correct, some people object to representing the variables with numbers, such as a 1-to-10 scale for the intensity of a negative life event. What might be their objection to quantifying the variables in this situation?

• **Critical Thinking Exercises**

117. Which one of the following is true?

a. If $3x + 7 = 0$, then $x = \dfrac{7}{3}$.

b. Solving $A = LW$ for W gives $W = \dfrac{L}{A}$.

c. The equation $6x = 0$ has exactly one solution.

d. The final step in solving $x - b = 6x - c$ for x is $x = 6x - c + b$.

118. Write three equations whose solution set is {5}.

119. If x represents a number, write an English sentence about the number that results in an equation with no solution.

120. A woman's height, h, is related to the length of the femur, f (the bone from the knee to the hip socket), by the formula $f = 0.432h - 10.44$. Both h and f are measured in inches. A partial skeleton is found of a woman in which the femur is 16 inches long. Police find the skeleton in an area where a woman slightly over 5 feet tall has been missing for over a year. Can the partial skeleton be that of the missing woman? Explain.

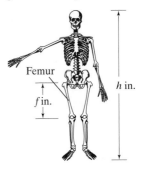

Femur

f in.

h in.

SECTION 3.3 • APPLICATIONS OF LINEAR EQUATIONS

O B J E C T I V E

1. Use linear equations to solve problems.

The human race is undeniably becoming a faster race. Since the beginning of the past century, track-and-field records have fallen in everything from sprints to miles to marathons. The performance arc is clearly rising, but no one knows how much higher it can climb. At some point, even the best-trained body simply has to up and quit. The question is, just where is that point, and is it possible for athletes, trainers, and genetic engineers to push it higher? In this section, you will learn a problem-solving strategy that uses linear equations to determine if anyone will ever run a 3-minute mile.

1 | Use linear equations to solve problems.

Problem Solving with Linear Equations

We have seen that a model is a mathematical representation of a real-world situation. In this section, we will be solving problems that are presented in English. This means that we must obtain models by translating from the ordinary language of English into the language of algebraic equations. To translate, however, we must understand the English prose and be familiar with the forms of algebraic language. Here are some general steps we will follow in solving word problems:

STRATEGY FOR SOLVING WORD PROBLEMS

Step 1. Read the problem carefully at least twice. Attempt to state the problem in your own words and state what the problem is looking for. Let x (or any variable) represent one of the quantities in the problem.

Step 2. If necessary, write expressions for any other unknown quantities in the problem in terms of x.

Step 3. Write an equation in x that models the verbal conditions of the problem.

Step 4. Solve the equation and answer the problem's question.

Step 5. Check the solution *in the original wording* of the problem, not in the equation obtained from the words.

The most difficult step in this process is step 3 because it involves translating verbal conditions into an algebraic equation. Translations of some commonly used English phrases are listed in Table 3.2. We choose to use x to represent the variable, but we can use any letter.

STUDY TIP

Cover the right column in Table 3.2 with a sheet of paper and attempt to formulate the algebraic expression in the column on your own. Then slide the paper down and check your answer. Work through the entire table in this manner.

TABLE 3.2 ALGEBRAIC TRANSLATIONS OF ENGLISH PHRASES

English Phrase	Algebraic Expression
Addition	
The sum of a number and 7	$x + 7$
Five more than a number; a number plus 5	$x + 5$
A number increased by 6; 6 added to a number	$x + 6$
Subtraction	
A number minus 4	$x - 4$
A number decreased by 5	$x - 5$
A number subtracted from 8	$8 - x$
The difference between a number and 6	$x - 6$
The difference between 6 and a number	$6 - x$
Seven less than a number	$x - 7$
Seven minus a number	$7 - x$
Nine fewer than a number	$x - 9$
Multiplication	
Five times a number	$5x$
The product of 3 and a number	$3x$
Two-thirds of a number (used with fractions)	$\dfrac{2}{3}x$
Seventy-five percent of a number (used with decimals)	$0.75x$
Thirteen multiplied by a number	$13x$
A number multiplied by 13	$13x$
Twice a number	$2x$
Division	
A number divided by 3	$\dfrac{x}{3}$
The quotient of 7 and a number	$\dfrac{7}{x}$
The quotient of a number and 7	$\dfrac{x}{7}$
The reciprocal of a number	$\dfrac{1}{x}$
More than one operation	
The sum of twice a number and 7	$2x + 7$
Twice the sum of a number and 7	$2(x + 7)$
Three times the sum of 1 and twice a number	$3(1 + 2x)$
Nine subtracted from 8 times a number	$8x - 9$
Twenty-five percent of the sum of 3 times a number and 14	$0.25(3x + 14)$
Seven times a number, increased by 24	$7x + 24$
Seven times the sum of a number and 24	$7(x + 24)$

STUDY TIP

Here are three similar English phrases that have very different translations:

7 minus 10: $7 - 10$

7 less than 10: $10 - 7$

7 is less than 10: $7 < 10$.

Think carefully about what is expressed in English before you translate into the language of algebra.

EXAMPLE 1   SOLVING A WORD PROBLEM

Nine subtracted from eight times a number is 39. Find the number.

SOLUTION

Step 1. Let x represent one of the quantities. Because we are asked to find a number, let

$$x = \text{the number.}$$

Step 2. Represent other quantities in terms of x. There are no other unknown quantities to find, so we can skip this step.

Step 3. Write an equation in x that models the conditions.

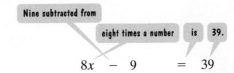

$$8x \quad - \quad 9 \quad = \quad 39$$

Step 4. Solve the equation and answer the question.

$$8x - 9 = 39 \qquad \text{This is the equation that models the problem's conditions.}$$
$$8x - 9 + 9 = 39 + 9 \qquad \text{Add 9 to both sides.}$$
$$8x = 48 \qquad \text{Simplify.}$$
$$\frac{8x}{8} = \frac{48}{8} \qquad \text{Divide both sides by 8.}$$
$$x = 6 \qquad \text{Simplify.}$$

The number is 6.

Step 5. Check the proposed solution in the original wording of the problem. "Nine subtracted from eight times a number is 39." The proposed number is 6. Eight times 6 is $8 \cdot 6$, or 48. Nine subtracted from 48 is $48 - 9$, or 39. The proposed solution checks in the problem's wording, verifying that the number is 6.

 Four subtracted from six times a number is 68. Find the number.

EXAMPLE 2   WILL ANYONE EVER RUN A THREE-MINUTE MILE?

One yardstick for measuring how steadily—if slowly—athletic performance has improved is the mile run. In 1923, the record for the mile was a comparatively sleepy 4 minutes, 10.4 seconds. In 1954, Roger Bannister of Britain cracked the 4-minute mark, coming in at 3 minutes, 59.4 seconds. In the half-century since, about 0.3 second per year has been shaved off Bannister's record. If this trend continues, by which year will someone run a 3-minute mile?

SOLUTION In solving this problem, we will express time for the mile run in seconds. Our interest is in a time of 3 minutes, or 180 seconds.

Step 1. Let x represent one of the quantities. Here is the critical information in the problem:

- In 1954, the record was 3 minutes, 59.4 seconds, or 239.4 seconds.
- The record has decreased by 0.3 second per year since then.

We are interested in when the record will be 180 seconds. Let

$$x = \text{the number of years after 1954 when someone will run a 3-minute mile.}$$

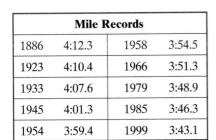

Mile Records			
1886	4:12.3	1958	3:54.5
1923	4:10.4	1966	3:51.3
1933	4:07.6	1979	3:48.9
1945	4:01.3	1985	3:46.3
1954	3:59.4	1999	3:43.1

Source: U.S.A. Track and Field

A Poky Species

For a species that prides itself on its athletic prowess, human beings are a pretty poky group. Lions can sprint at up to 50 miles per hour; cheetahs move even faster, flooring it to a sizzling 70 miles per hour. But most humans—with our willowy spines and awkward, upright gait—would have trouble cracking 20 miles per hour with a tail wind, a flat track, and a good pair of running shoes.

Step 2. Represent other quantities in terms of x. There are no other unknown quantities to find, so we can skip this step.

Step 3. Write an equation in x that models the conditions.

The 1954 record time	decreased by	0.3 second per year for x years	equals	the 3-minute, or 180-second, mile.
239.4	−	0.3x	=	180

Step 4. Solve the equation and answer the question.

$$239.4 - 0.3x = 180 \qquad \text{This is the equation that models the problem's conditions.}$$

$$239.4 - 239.4 - 0.3x = 180 - 239.4 \qquad \text{Subtract 239.4 from both sides.}$$

$$-0.3x = -59.4 \qquad \text{Simplify.}$$

$$\frac{-0.3x}{-0.3} = \frac{-59.4}{-0.3} \qquad \text{Divide both sides by } -0.3.$$

$$x = 198 \qquad \text{Simplify.}$$

Using current trends, 198 years (gasp!) after 1954, or in 2152, someone will run a 3-minute mile.

Step 5. Check the proposed solution in the original wording of the problem. The problem states that the record time should be 180 seconds. Do we obtain 180 seconds if we decrease the 1954 record time, 239.4 seconds, by 0.3 second per year for 198 years, our proposed solution?

$$239.4 - 0.3(198) = 239.4 - 59.4 = 180$$

This verifies that, using current trends, the 3-minute mile will be run 198 years after 1954.

CHECK POINT 2 Got organic milk? Although organic milk accounts for only 1.2% of the market, consumption is increasing. In 2004, Americans purchased 40.7 million gallons of organic milk, increasing at a rate of 5.6 million gallons per year. If this trend continues, when will Americans purchase 79.9 million gallons of organic milk? (*Source:* National Dairy Council)

EXAMPLE 3   WALK IT OFF

Experts concerned with fitness and health suggest that we should walk 10,000 steps per day, about 5 miles. Depending on stride length, each mile ranges between 2000 and 2500 steps. The graph in Figure 3.4 shows the number of steps it takes to burn off various foods. (The data are based on a body weight of 150 to 165 pounds.)

The number of steps needed to burn off a cheeseburger exceeds the number needed to burn off a 12-ounce soda by 4140. The number needed to burn off a doughnut exceeds the number needed to burn off a 12-ounce soda by 2300. If you chow down a cheeseburger, doughnut, and 12-ounce soda, a 16,790-step walk is needed to burn off the calories (and perhaps alleviate the guilt). Determine the number of steps it takes to burn off a cheeseburger, a doughnut, and a 12-ounce soda.

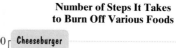

Number of Steps It Takes to Burn Off Various Foods

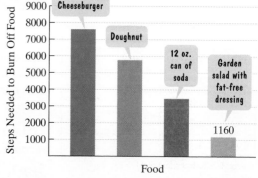

FIGURE 3.4
Source: The Step Diet Book

SOLUTION

Step 1. Let x represent one of the quantities. We know something about the number of steps needed to burn off a cheeseburger and a doughnut: The numbers exceed that of a 12-ounce soda by 4140 and 2300, respectively. We will let

x = the number of steps needed to burn off a 12-ounce soda.

Step 2. Represent other quantities in terms of x. Because the number of steps needed to burn off a cheeseburger exceeds the number needed to burn off a 12-ounce soda by 4140, let

$x + 4140$ = the number of steps needed to burn off a cheeseburger.

Because the number of steps needed to burn off a doughnut exceeds the number needed to burn off a 12-ounce soda by 2300, let

$x + 2300$ = the number of steps needed to burn off a doughnut.

Step 3. Write an equation in x that models the conditions. A 16,790-step walk is needed to burn off a "meal" consisting of a cheeseburger, a doughnut, and a 12-ounce soda.

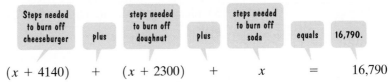

$$(x + 4140)\quad +\quad (x + 2300)\quad +\quad x\quad =\quad 16{,}790$$

Step 4. Solve the equation and answer the question.

$(x + 4140) + (x + 2300) + x = 16{,}790$ This is the equation that models the problem's conditions.

$3x + 6440 = 16{,}790$ Remove parentheses, regroup, and combine like terms.

$3x = 10{,}350$ Subtract 6440 from both sides.

$x = 3450$ Divide both sides by 3.

Thus,

the number of steps needed to burn off a 12-ounce soda = x = 3450.

the number of steps needed to burn off a cheeseburger

= $x + 4140 = 3450 + 4140 = 7590$.

the number of steps needed to burn off a doughnut

= $x + 2300 = 3450 + 2300 = 5750$.

It takes 7590 steps to burn off a cheeseburger, 5750 steps to burn off a doughnut, and 3450 steps to burn off a 12-ounce soda.

Step 5. Check the proposed solution in the original wording of the problem. The problem states that a 16,790-step walk is needed to burn off the calories in the three foods combined. By adding 7590, 5750, and 3450, the numbers that we found for each of the foods, we obtain

$$7590 + 5750 + 3450 = 16{,}790,$$

as specified by the problem's conditions.

STUDY TIP

Modeling with the word *exceeds* can be a bit tricky. It's helpful to identify the smaller quantity. Then add to this quantity to represent the larger quantity. For example, suppose that Tim's height exceeds Tom's height by a inches. Tom is the shorter person. If Tom's height is represented by x, then Tim's height is represented by $x + a$.

CHECK POINT 3 Basketball, bicycle riding, and football are the three sports and recreational activities in the United States with the greatest number of medically treated injuries. In 2004, the number of injuries from basketball exceeded those from football by 0.6 million. The number of injuries from bicycling exceeded those from football by 0.3 million. Combined, basketball, bicycling, and football accounted for 3.9 million injuries. Determine the number of medically treated injuries from each of these recreational activities in 2004.

(*Source:* U.S. Consumer Product Safety Commission)

EXAMPLE 4   SELECTING A LONG-DISTANCE CARRIER

You are choosing between two long-distance telephone plans. Plan A has a monthly fee of $20 with a charge of $0.05 per minute for all long-distance calls. Plan B has a monthly fee of $5 with a charge of $0.10 per minute for all long-distance calls. For how many minutes of long-distance calls will the costs for the two plans be the same?

SOLUTION

Step 1. Let x represent one of the quantities. Let

$$x = \text{the number of minutes of long-distance calls}$$
for which the two plans cost the same.

Step 2. Represent other unknown quantities in terms of x. There are no other unknown quantities, so we can skip this step.

Step 3. Write an equation in x that models the conditions. The monthly cost for plan A is the monthly fee, $20, plus the per minute charge, $0.05, times the number of minutes of long-distance calls, x. The monthly cost for plan B is the monthly fee, $5, plus the per-minute charge, $0.10, times the number of minutes of long-distance calls, x.

The monthly cost for plan A	must equal	the monthly cost for plan B.

$$20 + 0.05x = 5 + 0.10x$$

Step 4. Solve the equation and answer the question.

$20 + 0.05x = 5 + 0.10x$	This is the equation that models the problem's conditions.
$20 = 5 + 0.05x$	Subtract 0.05x from both sides.
$15 = 0.05x$	Subtract 5 from both sides.
$\dfrac{15}{0.05} = \dfrac{0.05x}{0.05}$	Divide both sides by 0.05.
$300 = x$	Simplify.

Because x represents the number of minutes of long-distance calls for which the two plans cost the same, the costs will be the same with 300 minutes of long-distance calls.

Step 5. Check the proposed solution in the original wording of the problem. The problem states that the costs for the two plans should be the same. Let's see if they are with 300 minutes of long-distance calls.

$$\text{Cost for plan A} = \$20 + \$0.05(300) = \$20 + \$15 = \$35$$

Monthly fee	Per-minute charge

$$\text{Cost for plan B} = \$5 + \$0.10(300) = \$5 + \$30 = \$35$$

With 300 minutes, or 5 hours, of long-distance calls, both plans cost $35 for the month. Thus, the proposed solution, 300 minutes, satisfies the problem's conditions.

CHECK POINT 4   You are choosing between two long-distance telephone plans. Plan A has a monthly fee of $15 with a charge of $0.08 per minute for all long-distance calls. Plan B has a monthly fee of $3 with a charge of $0.12 per minute for all long-distance calls. For how many minutes of long-distance calls will the costs for the two plans be the same?

EXERCISE SET 3.3 ●●●●●○

• Practice and Application Exercises

In Exercises 1–24, use the five-step strategy to solve each problem.

1. When five times a number is decreased by 4, the result is 26. What is the number?

2. When two times a number is decreased by 3, the result is 11. What is the number?

3. One number exceeds another by 26. The sum of the numbers is 64. What are the numbers?

4. One number exceeds another by 24. The sum of the numbers is 58. What are the numbers?

According to one mathematical model, the average life expectancy for American men born in 1900 was 55 years. Life expectancy has increased by about 0.2 year for each birth year after 1900. Use this information to solve Exercises 5–6.

5. If this trend continues, for which birth year will the average life expectancy be 85 years?

6. If this trend continues, for which birth year will the average life expectancy be 91 years?

The graph shows the number of Americans without health insurance from 2000 through 2003.

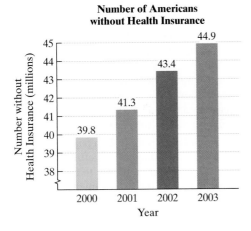

Number of Americans without Health Insurance

Source: U.S. Census Bureau

In 2000, there were 39.8 million Americans without health insurance. This number has increased at an average rate of 1.7 million people per year. Use this description to solve Exercises 7–8.

7. Determine when the number of Americans without health insurance will exceed the number in 2003 by 8.5 million.

8. Determine when the number of Americans without health insurance will exceed the number in 2003 by 10.2 million.

9. In 2000, the population of Greece was 10,600,000, with projections of a population decrease of 28,000 people per year. In the same year, the population of Belgium was 10,200,000, with projections of a population decrease of 12,000 people per year. (*Source:* United Nations) According to these projections, when will the two countries have the same population? What will be the population at that time?

10. In 2007, there were 13,300 students at college A, with a projected enrollment increase of 1000 students per year. In the same year, there were 26,800 students at college B, with a projected enrollment decline of 500 students per year. According to these projections, when will the colleges have the same enrollment? What will be the enrollment in each college at that time?

11. Each day, the number of births in the world exceeds the number of deaths by 229 thousand. The combined number of births and deaths is 521 thousand. Determine the number of births and the number of deaths per day.

Daily Growth of World Population

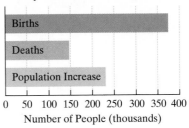

Source: "Population Update" 2000

12. The number of pages in the U.S. tax code exceeds the number of pages in the King James Bible by 18,528. The combined number of pages in the U.S. tax code and the King James Bible is 21,472. Determine the number of pages in each. (*Sources:* Amazon.com and Internal Revenue Service)

13. The bar graph shows the breakdown of the 7485 hate crimes reported in the United States in 2004. The number of hate crimes based on race exceeded three times the number based on sexual orientation by 127. Find the number of hate crimes reported in the United States in 2004 based on race and based on sexual orientation.

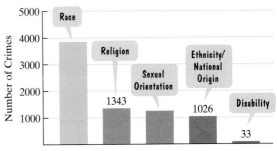

Hate Crimes in the U.S.

Source: FBI.

14. The bar graph on the next page shows the percentage of global energy used by the countries consuming the most energy. The percentage of global energy used by China exceeds Russia by 6% and the percentage of global energy used by the United States exceeds Russia by 16.4%.

Combined, the United States, China, and Russia consume 40.4% of the world's energy. Determine the percentage of global energy used by each country.

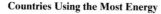

Countries Using the Most Energy

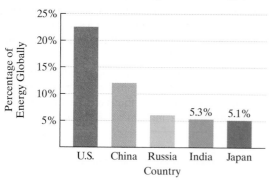

Source: World Bank Group

15. You are choosing between two health club plans. Plan A offers membership for a fee of $40 plus a monthly fee of $25. Plan B offers membership for a fee of $15 plus a monthly fee of $30. After how many months will the total cost for each plan be the same? What will be the total cost for each plan?

16. Video Store A charges $9 to rent a video game for one week. Although only members can rent from the store, membership is free. Video Store B charges only $4 to rent a video game for one week. Only members can rent from the store and membership is $50 per year. After how many video-game rentals will the total amount spent at each store be the same? What will be the total amount spent at each store?

17. The bus fare in a city is $1.25. People who use the bus have the option of purchasing a monthly coupon book for $15.00. With the coupon book, the fare is reduced to $0.75. Determine the number of times in a month the bus must be used so that the total monthly cost without the coupon book is the same as the total monthly cost with the coupon book.

18. A coupon book for a bridge costs $30 per month. The toll for the bridge is normally $5.00, but it is reduced to $3.50 for people who have purchased the coupon book. Determine the number of times in a month the bridge must be crossed so that the total monthly cost without the coupon book is the same as the total monthly cost with the coupon book.

19. You are choosing between two plans at a discount warehouse. Plan A offers an annual membership fee of $100 and you pay 80% of the manufacturer's recommended list price. Plan B offers an annual membership fee of $40 and you pay 90% of the manufacturer's recommended list price. How many dollars of merchandise would you have to purchase in a year to pay the same amount under both plans? What will be the cost for each plan?

20. You are choosing between two plans at a discount warehouse. Plan A offers an annual membership fee of $300 and you pay 70% of the manufacturer's recommended list price. Plan B offers an annual membership fee of $40 and you pay 90% of the manufacturer's recommended list

price. How many dollars of merchandise would you have to purchase in a year to pay the same amount under both plans? What will be the cost for each plan?

21. An automobile repair shop charged a customer $448, listing $63 for parts and the remainder for labor. If the cost of labor is $35 per hour, how many hours of labor did it take to repair the car?

22. A repair bill on a sailboat came to $1603, including $532 for parts and the remainder for labor. If the cost of labor is $63 per hour, how many hours of labor did it take to repair the sailboat?

23. A job pays an annual salary of $33,150, which includes a holiday bonus of $750. If paychecks are issued twice a month, what is the gross amount for each paycheck?

24. A bookcase is to be constructed as shown in the figure. The length is to be 3 times the height. If 60 feet of lumber is available for the entire unit, find the length and height of the bookcase.

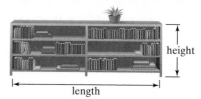

• Writing in Mathematics

25. In your own words, describe a step-by-step approach for solving algebraic word problems.

26. Many students find solving linear equations much easier than solving algebraic word problems. Discuss some of the reasons why this is the case.

27. Did you have difficulties solving some of the problems that were assigned in this exercise set? Discuss what you did if this happened to you. Did your course of action enhance your ability to solve algebraic word problems?

28. The mile records in Example 2 on page 139 are a yardstick for measuring how athletes are getting better and better. Do you think that there is a limit to human performance? Explain your answer. If so, when might we reach it?

• Critical Thinking Exercises

29. An HMO pamphlet contains the following recommended weight for women: "Give yourself 100 pounds for the first 5 feet plus 5 pounds for every inch over 5 feet tall." Using this description, which height corresponds to an ideal weight of 135 pounds?

30. The rate for a particular international long distance telephone call is $0.55 for the first minute and $0.40 for each additional minute. Determine the length of a call that cost $6.95.

31. In a film, the actor Charles Coburn plays an elderly "uncle" character criticized for marrying a woman when he is 3 times her age. He wittily replies, "Ah, but in 20 years time I shall only be twice her age." How old are the "uncle" and the woman?

32. Suppose that we agree to pay you 8¢ for every problem in this chapter that you solve correctly and fine you 5¢ for every problem done incorrectly. If at the end of 26 problems we do not owe each other any money, how many problems did you solve correctly?

33. It was wartime when the Ricardos found out Mrs. Ricardo was pregnant. Ricky Ricardo was drafted and made out a will, deciding that $14,000 in a savings account was to be divided between his wife and his child-to-be. Rather strangely, and certainly with gender bias, Ricky stipulated that if the child were a boy, he would get twice the amount of the mother's portion. If it were a girl, the mother would get twice the amount the girl was to receive. We'll never know what Ricky was thinking of, for (as fate would have it) he did not return from war. Mrs. Ricardo gave birth to twins—a boy and a girl. How was the money divided?

34. A thief steals a number of rare plants from a nursery. On the way out, the thief meets three security guards, one after another. To each security guard, the thief is forced to give one-half the plants that he still has, plus 2 more. Finally, the thief leaves the nursery with 1 lone palm. How many plants were originally stolen?

• Group Exercise

35. One of the best ways to learn how to *solve* a word problem in algebra is to *design* word problems of your own. Creating a word problem makes you very aware of precisely how much information is needed to solve the problem. You must also focus on the best way to present information to a reader and on how much information to give. As you write your problem, you gain skills that will help you solve problems created by others.

The group should design five different word problems that can be solved using algebraic equations. All of the problems should be on different topics. For example, the group should not have more than one problem on finding a number. The group should turn in both the problems and their algebraic solutions.

SECTION 3.4 • RATIO, PROPORTION, AND VARIATION

O B J E C T I V E S

1. Solve proportions.

2. Solve problems using proportions.

3. Solve direct variation problems.

4. Solve inverse variation problems.

The possibility of seeing a blue whale, the largest mammal ever to grace the Earth, increases the excitement of gazing out over the ocean's swell of waves. Blue whales were hunted to near extinction in the last half of the nineteenth and the first half of the twentieth centuries. Using a method for estimating wildlife populations that we discuss in this section, by the mid-1960s it was determined that the world population of blue whales was less than 1000. This led the International Whaling Commission to ban the killing of blue whales to prevent their extinction. A dramatic increase in blue whale sightings indicates an ongoing increase in their population and the success of the killing ban.

1 | Solve proportions.

Proportions

A **ratio** compares quantities by division. For example, a group contains 60 women and 30 men. The ratio of women to men is $\frac{60}{30}$. We can express this ratio as a fraction reduced to lowest terms:

$$\frac{60}{30} = \frac{2 \cdot \cancel{30}}{1 \cdot \cancel{30}} = \frac{2}{1}.$$

This ratio can be expressed as 2:1, or 2 to 1.

A **proportion** is a statement that says that two ratios are equal. If the ratios are $\frac{a}{b}$ and $\frac{c}{d}$, then the proportion is

$$\frac{a}{b} = \frac{c}{d}.$$

We can clear this equation of fractions by multiplying both sides by bd, the least common denominator:

$$\frac{a}{b} = \frac{c}{d} \qquad \text{This is the given proportion.}$$

$$bd \cdot \frac{a}{b} = bd \cdot \frac{c}{d} \qquad \text{Multiply both sides by } bd(b \neq 0 \text{ and } d \neq 0). \text{ Then simplify.}$$

On the left, $\dfrac{\cancel{b}d}{1} \cdot \dfrac{a}{\cancel{b}} = da = ad$. On the right, $\dfrac{b\cancel{d}}{1} \cdot \dfrac{c}{\cancel{d}} = bc$.

$$ad = bc$$

We see that the following principle is true for any proportion:

The cross-products principle: $ad = bc$

> ### THE CROSS-PRODUCTS PRINCIPLE FOR PROPORTIONS
>
> If $\dfrac{a}{b} = \dfrac{c}{d}$, then $ad = bc$. $(b \neq 0 \text{ and } d \neq 0.)$
>
> The cross products ad and bc are equal.

For example, if $\frac{2}{3} = \frac{6}{9}$, we see that $2 \cdot 9 = 3 \cdot 6$, or $18 = 18$.

If three of the numbers in a proportion are known, the value of the missing quantity can be found by using the cross-products principle. This idea is illustrated in Example 1.

EXAMPLE 1   SOLVING PROPORTIONS

Solve each proportion for x:

a. $\dfrac{63}{x} = \dfrac{7}{5}$ **b.** $\dfrac{20}{x-10} = \dfrac{30}{x}$.

SOLUTION

Cross products

a.

$$\frac{63}{x} = \frac{7}{5} \qquad \text{This is the given proportion.}$$

$$63 \cdot 5 = 7x \qquad \text{Apply the cross-products principle.}$$

$$315 = 7x \qquad \text{Simplify.}$$

$$\frac{315}{7} = \frac{7x}{7} \qquad \text{Divide both sides by 7.}$$

$$45 = x \qquad \text{Simplify.}$$

The solution set is $\{45\}$.

Check

$$\frac{63}{45} \overset{?}{=} \frac{7}{5} \qquad \text{Substitute 45 for } x \text{ in } \frac{63}{x} = \frac{7}{5}.$$

$$\frac{7 \cdot \cancel{9}}{5 \cdot \cancel{9}} \overset{?}{=} \frac{7}{5} \qquad \text{Reduce } \frac{63}{45} \text{ to lowest terms.}$$

$$\frac{7}{5} = \frac{7}{5} \qquad \text{This true statement verifies that the solution set is } \{45\}.$$

b.

$$\frac{20}{x-10} = \frac{30}{x} \qquad \text{This is the given proportion.}$$

$$20x = 30(x-10) \qquad \text{Apply the cross-products principle.}$$

$$20x = 30x - 30 \cdot 10 \qquad \text{Use the distributive property.}$$

$$20x = 30x - 300 \qquad \text{Simplify.}$$

$$20x - 30x = 30x - 300 - 30x \qquad \text{Subtract 30x from both sides.}$$
$$-10x = -300 \qquad \text{Simplify.}$$
$$\frac{-10x}{-10} = \frac{-300}{-10} \qquad \text{Divide both sides by } -10.$$
$$x = 30 \qquad \text{Simplify.}$$

Check

$$\frac{20}{30 - 10} \overset{?}{=} \frac{30}{30} \qquad \text{Substitute 30 for x in } \frac{20}{x - 10} = \frac{30}{x}.$$

$$\frac{20}{20} \overset{?}{=} \frac{30}{30} \qquad \text{Subtract: } 30 - 10 = 20.$$

$$1 = 1 \qquad \text{This true statement verifies that the solution is 30.}$$

The solution set is $\{30\}$.

 Solve each proportion for x:

$$\textbf{a. } \frac{10}{x} = \frac{2}{3} \qquad\qquad \textbf{b. } \frac{11}{910 - x} = \frac{2}{x}.$$

2 | Solve problems using proportions.

Applications of Proportions

We now turn to practical application problems that can be solved using proportions. Here is a procedure for solving these problems:

> **SOLVING APPLIED PROBLEMS USING PROPORTIONS**
>
> 1. Read the problem and represent the unknown quantity by x (or any letter).
> 2. Set up a proportion by listing the given ratio on one side and the ratio with the unknown quantity on the other side. Each respective quantity should occupy the same corresponding position on each side of the proportion.
> 3. Drop units and apply the cross-products principle.
> 4. Solve for x and answer the question.

EXAMPLE 2 — APPLYING PROPORTIONS: CALCULATING TAXES

The property tax on a house whose assessed value is $65,000 is $825. Determine the property tax on a house with an assessed value of $180,000, assuming the same tax rate.

STUDY TIP

Here are three other correct proportions you can use in step 2:

- $\dfrac{\$65{,}000 \text{ value}}{\$825 \text{ tax}} = \dfrac{\$180{,}000 \text{ value}}{\$x \text{ tax}}$

- $\dfrac{\$65{,}000 \text{ value}}{\$180{,}000 \text{ value}} = \dfrac{\$825 \text{ tax}}{\$x \text{ tax}}$

- $\dfrac{\$180{,}000 \text{ value}}{\$65{,}000 \text{ value}} = \dfrac{\$x \text{ tax}}{\$825 \text{ tax}}$.

Each proportion gives the same cross product obtained in step 3.

SOLUTION

Step 1. Represent the unknown by x. Let x = the tax on a $180,000 house.

Step 2. Set up a proportion. We will set up a proportion comparing taxes to assessed value.

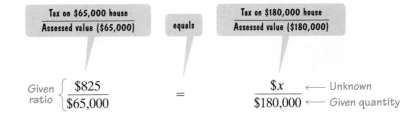

Step 3. Drop the units and apply the cross-products principle. We drop the dollar signs and begin to solve for x.

$$\frac{825}{65,000} = \frac{x}{180,000}$$ This is the proportion that models the problem's conditions.

$$65,000x = (825)(180,000)$$ Apply the cross-products principle.

$$65,000x = 148,500,000$$ Multiply.

Step 4. Solve for x and answer the question.

$$\frac{65,000x}{65,000} = \frac{148,500,000}{65,000}$$ Divide both sides by 65,000.

$$x \approx 2284.62$$ Round the value of x to the nearest cent.

The property tax on the $180,000 house is approximately $2284.62.

CHECK POINT 2 The property tax on a house with an assessed value of $45,000 is $600. Determine the property tax on a house with an assessed value of $112,500, assuming the same tax rate.

Sampling in Nature

The method that was used to estimate the blue whale population described in the section opener is called the **capture-recapture method**. Because it is impossible to count each individual animal within a population, wildlife biologists randomly catch and tag a given number of animals. Sometime later they recapture a second sample of animals and count the number of recaptured tagged animals. The total size of the wildlife population is then estimated using the following proportion:

Initially unknown $(x) \longrightarrow$ $$\frac{\text{Original number of tagged animals}}{\text{Total number of animals in the population}} = \frac{\text{Number of recaptured tagged animals}}{\text{Number of animals in second sample}}.$$ Known ratio

Although this is called the capture-recapture method, it is not necessary to recapture animals in order to observe whether or not they are tagged. This could be done from a distance, with binoculars for instance.

EXAMPLE 3   APPLYING PROPORTIONS: ESTIMATING WILDLIFE POPULATION

Wildlife biologists catch, tag, and then release 135 deer back into a wildlife refuge. Two weeks later they observe a sample of 140 deer, 30 of which are tagged. Assuming the ratio of tagged deer in the sample holds for all deer in the refuge, approximately how many deer are in the refuge?

SOLUTION

Step 1. Represent the unknown by x. Let x = the total number of deer in the refuge.

Step 2. Set up a proportion.

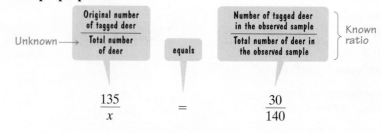

Unknown $\longrightarrow$ $\dfrac{\text{Original number of tagged deer}}{\text{Total number of deer}}$ equals $\dfrac{\text{Number of tagged deer in the observed sample}}{\text{Total number of deer in the observed sample}}$ Known ratio

$$\frac{135}{x} = \frac{30}{140}$$

Steps 3 and 4. Apply the cross-products principle, solve, and answer the question.

$$\frac{135}{x} = \frac{30}{140}$$ This is the proportion that models the problem's conditions.

$$(135)(140) = 30x$$ Apply the cross-products principle.

$$18,900 = 30x$$ Multiply.

$$\frac{18,900}{30} = \frac{30x}{30}$$ Divide both sides by 30.

$$630 = x$$ Simplify.

There are approximately 630 deer in the refuge.

③ Wildlife biologists catch, tag, and then release 120 deer back into the wildlife refuge. Two weeks later they observe a sample of 150 deer, 25 of which are tagged. Assuming the ratio of tagged deer in the sample holds for all deer in the refuge, approximately how many deer are in the refuge?

3 | Solve direct variation problems.

Direct Variation

In Example 2, we saw that as the assessed value on a house goes up, so do the taxes. When the assessed value is doubled, the taxes are doubled; when the assessed value is tripled, the taxes are tripled. Because of this, the tax on a house is said to **vary directly** as its assessed value. Direct variation situations can be solved using a proportion.

EXAMPLE 4   SOLVING A DIRECT VARIATION PROBLEM

An alligator's tail length varies directly as its body length. An alligator with a body length of 4 feet has a tail length of 3.6 feet. What is the tail length of an alligator whose body length is 6 feet?

|← ——— Body length ——— →|← ——— Tail length ——— →|

SOLUTION

Step 1. Represent the unknown by *x*. Let x = the tail length of an alligator whose body length is 6 feet.

Step 2. Set up a proportion. We will set up a proportion comparing body length to tail length.

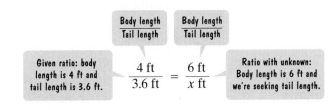

Steps 3 and 4. Apply the cross-products principle, solve, and answer the question.

$$\frac{4}{3.6} = \frac{6}{x}$$ This is the proportion that models the problem's conditions.

$$4x = (3.6)(6)$$ Apply the cross-products principle.

$$4x = 21.6$$ Multiply.

$$\frac{4x}{4} = \frac{21.6}{4}$$ Divide both sides by 4.

$$x = 5.4$$ Simplify.

An alligator whose body length is 6 feet has a tail length measuring 5.4 feet.

CHECK POINT 4   The number of gallons of water used when taking a shower varies directly as the time, in minutes, in the shower. A shower lasting 5 minutes uses 30 gallons of water. How much water is used in a shower lasting 11 minutes?

EXAMPLE 5   SOLVING A DIRECT VARIATION PROBLEM

The distance that the sky divers shown in the photograph fall varies directly as the square of the time in which they fall. The sky divers fall 64 feet in 2 seconds. How far will they fall in 5 seconds?

SOLUTION

Step 1. Represent the unknown by _x_. Let x = the distance the sky divers fall in 5 seconds.

Step 2. Set up a proportion. We will set up a proportion comparing the distance that the sky divers fall to the square of the time in which they fall.

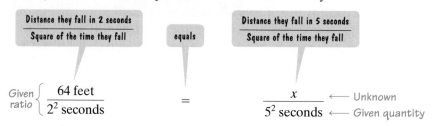

$$\text{Given ratio} \left\{ \frac{64 \text{ feet}}{2^2 \text{ seconds}} \right. = \frac{x}{5^2 \text{ seconds}} \begin{array}{l} \leftarrow \text{Unknown} \\ \leftarrow \text{Given quantity} \end{array}$$

Steps 3 and 4. Apply the cross-products principle, solve, and answer the question.

$$\frac{64}{2^2} = \frac{x}{5^2}$$ This is the proportion that models the problem's conditions.

$$\frac{64}{4} = \frac{x}{25}$$ Square 2 and 5: $2^2 = 2 \cdot 2 = 4$ and $5^2 = 5 \cdot 5 = 25$.

$$4x = (64)(25)$$ Apply the cross-products principle.

$$4x = 1600$$ Multiply.

$$\frac{4x}{4} = \frac{1600}{4}$$ Divide both sides by 4.

$$x = 400$$ Simplify.

The sky divers will fall 400 feet in 5 seconds.

CHECK POINT 5   The distance required to stop a car varies directly as the square of its speed. If 200 feet are required to stop a car traveling 60 miles per hour, how many feet are required to stop a car traveling 100 miles per hour? Round to the nearest foot.

4 | Solve inverse variation problems.

Inverse Variation

So far, we have created models for situations in which an increase in one quantity is accompanied by an increase in a second quantity. However, there are other situations in which one quantity increases as the other decreases, or vice versa. For example, if you drive to campus, consider the rate at which you drive and the time it takes you to get there. As your driving rate increases, the time it takes you to get to campus decreases. This is an example of *inverse variation*. When two quantities **vary inversely**, as one quantity increases, the other decreases, and vice versa.

The distance from Atlanta, Georgia, to Orlando, Florida, is 450 miles. If you average 45 miles per hour, the time for the drive is 10 hours. If you average 75 miles per hour, the time for the drive is 6 hours. The following proportion represents this situation in which time varies inversely as driving rate:

$$\frac{\text{time at the slower rate}}{\text{the faster rate}} = \frac{\text{time at the faster rate}}{\text{the slower rate}}$$

$$\frac{10 \text{ hours}}{75 \text{ miles per hour}} = \frac{6 \text{ hours}}{45 \text{ miles per hour}}.$$

The cross products are equal:

$$\frac{10 \text{ hours}}{1} \cdot \frac{45 \text{ miles}}{\text{hour}} = 10 \cdot 45 \text{ miles} = 450 \text{ miles}$$

$$\frac{75 \text{ miles}}{\text{hour}} \cdot \frac{6 \text{ hours}}{1} = 75 \cdot 6 \text{ miles} = 450 \text{ miles}.$$

Because the product of rate and time is distance, each cross product gives the distance from Atlanta to Orlando.

There is something unusual about the placement of quantities in a proportion in an inverse variation situation:

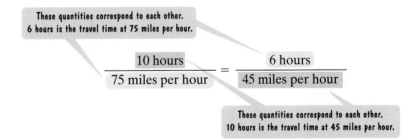

These quantities correspond to each other. 6 hours is the travel time at 75 miles per hour.

$$\frac{10 \text{ hours}}{75 \text{ miles per hour}} = \frac{6 \text{ hours}}{45 \text{ miles per hour}}$$

These quantities correspond to each other. 10 hours is the travel time at 45 miles per hour.

In an inverse variation situation, corresponding values are not placed in the same ratio. *Placing corresponding values in opposite ratios* allows one quantity to increase while the other decreases, or vice versa.

STUDY TIP

When you apply the cross-products principle in an inverse variation proportion, you multiply corresponding quantities.

SETTING UP A PROPORTION WHEN y VARIES INVERSELY AS x

$$\frac{\text{The first value for } y}{\text{The value for } x \text{ corresponding to the second value for } y} = \frac{\text{The second value for } y}{\text{The value for } x \text{ corresponding to the first value for } y}$$

FIGURE 3.5

EXAMPLE 6   SOLVING AN INVERSE VARIATION PROBLEM

Figure 3.5 shows that a bicyclist tips the cycle when making a turn. The angle B, formed by the vertical direction and the bicycle, is called the banking angle. The banking angle varies inversely as the cycle's turning radius. When the turning radius is 4 feet, the banking angle is 28°. What is the banking angle when the turning radius is 3.5 feet?

SOLUTION

Step 1. Represent the unknown by x. Let

$$x = \text{the banking angle when the turning}$$
$$\text{radius is 3.5 feet.}$$

Step 2. Set up a proportion. We will set up a proportion comparing the banking angle to the turning radius. Because this is an inverse variation situation, we place corresponding values in opposite ratios.

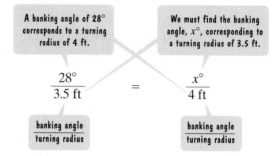

A banking angle of 28° corresponds to a turning radius of 4 ft.

We must find the banking angle, $x°$, corresponding to a turning radius of 3.5 ft.

$$\frac{28°}{3.5 \text{ ft}} = \frac{x°}{4 \text{ ft}}$$

$\dfrac{\text{banking angle}}{\text{turning radius}}$ $\dfrac{\text{banking angle}}{\text{turning radius}}$

Steps 3 and 4. Apply the cross-products principle, solve, and answer the question.

$$\frac{28}{3.5} = \frac{x}{4} \qquad \text{This is the proportion that models the problem's conditions.}$$

$$3.5x = 28 \cdot 4 \qquad \text{Apply the cross-products principle.}$$

$$3.5x = 112 \qquad \text{Multiply.}$$

$$\frac{3.5x}{3.5} = \frac{112}{3.5} \qquad \text{Divide both sides by 3.5.}$$

$$x = 32 \qquad \text{Simplify.}$$

When the turning radius is 3.5 feet, the banking angle is 32°.

$2P$

P

$2V$

V

Doubling the pressure halves the volume.

CHECK POINT 6 When you use a spray can and press the value at the top, you decrease the pressure of the gas in the can. This decrease of pressure causes the volume of the gas in the can to increase. Because the gas needs more room than is provided in the can, it expands in spray form through the small hole near the valve. In general, if the temperature is constant, the pressure of a gas in a container varies inversely as the volume of the container. The pressure of a gas sample in a container whose volume is 8 cubic inches is 12 pounds per square inch. If the sample expands to a volume of 22 cubic inches, what is the new pressure of the gas?

EXERCISE SET 3.4 ●●●●●●

• Practice Exercises

In Exercises 1–12, solve each proportion.

1. $\dfrac{24}{x} = \dfrac{12}{7}$

2. $\dfrac{56}{x} = \dfrac{8}{7}$

3. $\dfrac{x}{6} = \dfrac{18}{4}$

4. $\dfrac{x}{32} = \dfrac{3}{24}$

5. $\dfrac{x}{3} = -\dfrac{3}{4}$

6. $\dfrac{x}{2} = -\dfrac{1}{5}$

7. $\dfrac{-3}{8} = \dfrac{x}{40}$

8. $\dfrac{-3}{8} = \dfrac{6}{x}$

9. $\dfrac{x-2}{5} = \dfrac{3}{10}$

10. $\dfrac{x+4}{8} = \dfrac{3}{16}$

11. $\dfrac{y+10}{10} = \dfrac{y-2}{4}$

12. $\dfrac{2}{y-5} = \dfrac{3}{y+6}$

In Exercises 13–16, use a proportion to solve each variation problem.

13. y varies directly as x. $y = 65$ when $x = 5$. Find y when $x = 12$.

14. y varies directly as x. $y = 45$ when $x = 5$. Find y when $x = 13$.

15. y varies inversely as x. $y = 12$ when $x = 5$. Find y when $x = 2$.

16. y varies inversely as x. $y = 6$ when $x = 3$. Find y when $x = 9$.

• Practice Plus

In Exercises 17–22, solve each proportion for x.

17. $\dfrac{x}{a} = \dfrac{b}{c}$

18. $\dfrac{a}{x} = \dfrac{b}{c}$

19. $\dfrac{a+b}{c} = \dfrac{x}{d}$

20. $\dfrac{a-b}{c} = \dfrac{x}{d}$

21. $\dfrac{x+a}{a} = \dfrac{b+c}{c}$

22. $\dfrac{ax-b}{b} = \dfrac{c-d}{d}$

• Application Exercises

Use a proportion to solve Exercises 23–28.

23. The tax on a property with an assessed value of $65,000 is $725. Find the tax on a property with an assessed value of $100,000.

24. The maintenance bill for a shopping center containing 180,000 square feet is $45,000. What is the bill for a store in the center that is 4800 square feet?

25. St. Paul Island in Alaska has 12 fur seal rookeries (breeding places). In 1961, to estimate the fur seal pup population in the Gorbath rookery, 4963 fur seal pups were tagged in early August. In late August, a sample of 900 pups was observed and 218 of these were found to have been previously tagged. Estimate the total number of fur seal pups in this rookery.

26. To estimate the number of bass in a lake, wildlife biologists tagged 50 bass and released them in the lake. Later they netted 108 bass and found that 27 of them were tagged. Approximately how many bass are in the lake?

27. The ratio of monthly child support to a father's yearly income is 1:40. How much should a father earning $38,000 annually pay in monthly child support?

28. Many areas of Northern California depend on the snowpack of the Sierra Nevada mountain range for their water supply. Meteorologists have determined that 250 cubic centimeters of snow will melt to 28 cubic centimeters of water. How much water does 1200 cubic centimeters of melting snow produce?

Exercises 29–42 involve direct and inverse variation. Use a proportion to solve each exercise.

29. An object's weight on the moon varies directly as its weight on Earth. Neil Armstrong, the first person to step on the moon on July 20, 1969, weighed 360 pounds on Earth (with all of his equipment on) and 60 pounds on the moon. What is the moon weight of a person who weighs 186 pounds on Earth?

30. The height that a ball bounces varies directly as the height from which it was dropped. A tennis ball dropped from 12 inches bounces 8.4 inches. From what height was the tennis ball dropped if it bounces 56 inches?

31. Height varies directly as foot length. A person whose foot length is 10 inches is 67 inches tall. In 1951, photos of large footprints were published. Some believed that these footprints were made by the "Abominable Snowman." Each footprint was 23 inches long. If indeed they belonged to the Abominable Snowman, how tall is the critter?

32. A person's hair length varies directly as the number of years it has been growing. After 2 years, a person's hair length is 8 inches. The longest moustache on record was grown by Kalyan Sain of India. Sain grew his moustache for 17 years. How long was it?

33. If all men had identical body types, their weights would vary directly as the cube of their heights. Shown is Robert Wadlow, who reached a record height of 8 feet 11 inches (107 inches) before his death at age 22. If a man who is 5 feet 10 inches tall (70 inches) with the same body type as Mr. Wadlow weighs 170 pounds, what was Robert Wadlow's weight shortly before his death?

34. The Mach number is a measurement of speed named after the man who suggested it, Ernst Mach (1838–1916). The speed of an aircraft varies directly as its Mach number. Shown here are two aircraft. Use the figures for the Concorde to determine the Blackbird's speed.

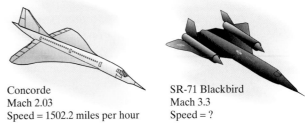

Concorde
Mach 2.03
Speed = 1502.2 miles per hour

SR-71 Blackbird
Mach 3.3
Speed = ?

35. On a dry asphalt road, a car's stopping distance varies directly as the square of its speed. A car traveling at 45 miles per hour can stop in 67.5 feet. What is the stopping distance for a car traveling at 60 miles per hour?

36. The distance that an object falls varies directly as the square of the time it has been falling. An object falls 144 feet in 3 seconds. Find how far it will fall in 7 seconds.

37. The water temperature of the Pacific Ocean varies inversely as the water's depth. At a depth of 1000 meters, the water temperature is 4.4° Celsius. What is the water temperature at a depth of 5000 meters?

38. The time that it takes you to get to campus varies inversely as your driving rate. Averaging 20 miles per hour in terrible traffic, it takes you 1.5 hours to get to campus. How long would the trip take averaging 60 miles per hour?

39. The volume of a gas in a container at a constant temperature varies inversely as the pressure. If the volume is 32 cubic centimeters at a pressure of 8 pounds, find the pressure when the volume is 40 cubic centimeters.

40. The current in a circuit varies inversely as the resistance. The current is 20 amperes when the resistance is 5 ohms. Find the current for a resistance of 16 ohms.

41. The loudness of a stereo speaker, measured in decibels, varies inversely as the square of your distance from the speaker. When you are 8 feet from the speaker, the loudness is 28 decibels. What is the loudness when you are 4 feet from the speaker?

42. Radiation machines, used to treat tumors, produce an intensity of radiation that varies inversely as the square of the distance from the machine. At 3 meters, the radiation intensity is 62.5 milliroentgens per hour. What is the intensity at a distance of 2.5 meters?

• Writing in Mathematics

43. What is a ratio? Give an example with your description.

44. What is a proportion? Give an example with your description.

45. Explain how to solve a proportion. Illustrate your explanation with an example.

46. Explain the meaning of this statement: A company's monthly sales vary directly as its advertising budget.

47. Explain the meaning of this statement: A company's monthly sales vary inversely as the price of its product.

48. Explain the difference between setting up proportions for direct and inverse variation problems.

• Critical Thinking Exercises

49. The front sprocket on a bicycle has 60 teeth and the rear sprocket has 20 teeth. For mountain biking, an owner needs a 5:1 front: rear ratio. If only one of the sprockets is to be replaced, describe the two ways in which this can be done.

50. My friend is 44 years old. My dog Phideaux is 7 years old. If Phideaux were human, he would be 56. Phideaux thinks my friend is another dog, which makes me wonder: If my friend were a dog, how old would my friend be?

51. In a hurricane, the wind pressure varies directly as the square of the wind velocity. If wind pressure is a measure of a hurricane's destructive capacity, what happens to this destructive power when the wind velocity doubles?

52. The illumination from a light source varies inversely as the square of the distance from the light source. If you raise a lamp from 15 inches to 30 inches over your desk, what happens to the illumination?

SECTION 3.5 • LINEAR INEQUALITIES IN ONE VARIABLE

OBJECTIVES

1. Graph subsets of real numbers on a number line.

2. Solve linear inequalities.

3. Solve applied problems using linear inequalities.

Rent-a-Heap, a car rental company, charges $125 per week plus $0.20 per mile to rent one of their cars. Suppose you are limited by how much money you can spend for the week: You can spend at most $335. If we let x represent the number of miles you drive the heap in a week, we can write an inequality that models the given conditions:

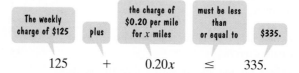

The weekly charge of $125	plus	the charge of $0.20 per mile for x miles	must be less than or equal to	$335.
125	+	0.20x	≤	335.

Notice that the highest exponent on the variable is 1. Such an inequality is called a *linear inequality in one variable*. The symbol between the two sides of an inequality can be ≤ (is less than or equal to), < (is less than), ≥ (is greater than or equal to), or > (is greater than).

In this section, we will study how to solve linear inequalities such as $125 + 0.20x \leq 335$. **Solving an inequality** is the process of finding the set of numbers that make the inequality a true statement. These numbers are called the **solutions** of the inequality and we say that they **satisfy** the inequality. The set of all solutions is called the **solution set** of the inequality. We begin by discussing how to represent these solution sets, which are subsets of real numbers, on a number line.

1 Graph subsets of real numbers on a number line.

Graphing Subsets of Real Numbers on a Number Line

Table 3.3 shows how to represent various subsets of real numbers on a number line. Open dots ($\circ$) indicate that a number is not included in a set. Closed dots ($\bullet$) indicate that a number is included in a set.

TABLE 3.3 GRAPHS OF SUBSETS OF REAL NUMBERS

Let a and b be real numbers such that $a < b$.

Set-Builder Notation		Graph
$\{x \mid x < a\}$	x is a real number less than a.	
$\{x \mid x \leq a\}$	x is a real number less than or equal to a.	
$\{x \mid x > b\}$	x is a real number greater than b.	
$\{x \mid x \geq b\}$	x is a real number greater than or equal to b.	
$\{x \mid a < x < b\}$	x is a real number greater than a and less than b.	
$\{x \mid a \leq x \leq b\}$	x is a real number greater than or equal to a and less than or equal to b.	
$\{x \mid a \leq x < b\}$	x is a real number greater than or equal to a and less than b.	
$\{x \mid a < x \leq b\}$	x is a real number greater than a and less than or equal to b.	

EXAMPLE 1   GRAPHING SUBSETS OF REAL NUMBERS

Graph each set:
a. $\{x \mid x < 3\}$ **b.** $\{x \mid x \geq -1\}$ **c.** $\{x \mid -1 < x \leq 3\}$.

SOLUTION

a. $\{x \mid x < 3\}$ x is a real number less than 3.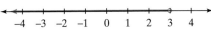

b. $\{x \mid x \geq -1\}$ x is a real number greater than or equal to -1.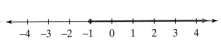

c. $\{x \mid -1 < x \leq 3\}$ x is a real number greater than -1 and less than or equal to 3.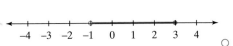

 Graph each set:

a. $\{x \mid x < 4\}$ **b.** $\{x \mid x \geq -2\}$ **c.** $\{x \mid -4 \leq x < 1\}$.

2 | Solve linear inequalities.

Solving Linear Inequalities in One Variable

We know that a linear equation in x can be expressed as $ax + b = 0$. A **linear inequality in** x can be written in one of the following forms: $ax + b < 0$, $ax + b \leq 0$, $ax + b > 0$, $ax + b \geq 0$. In each form, $a \neq 0$. Back to our question that opened this section: How many miles can you drive your Rent-a-Heap car if you can spend at most \$335 per week? We answer the question by solving

$$0.20x + 125 \leq 335$$

for x. The solution procedure is nearly identical to that for solving

$$0.20x + 125 = 335.$$

Our goal is to get x by itself on the left side. We do this by subtracting 125 from both sides to isolate $0.20x$:

$0.20x + 125 \leq 335$	This is the given inequality.
$0.20x + 125 - 125 \leq 335 - 125$	Subtract 125 from both sides.
$0.20x \leq 210.$	Simplify.

STUDY TIP

English phrases such as "at least" and "at most" can be represented by inequalities.

English Sentence	Inequality
x is at least 5.	$x \geq 5$
x is at most 5.	$x \leq 5$
x is between 5 and 7.	$5 < x < 7$
x is no more than 5.	$x \leq 5$
x is no less than 5.	$x \geq 5$

Finally, we isolate x from $0.20x$ by dividing both sides of the inequality by 0.20:

$\dfrac{0.20x}{0.20} \leq \dfrac{210}{0.20}$	Divide both sides by 0.20
$x \leq 1050.$	Simplify.

With at most \$335 per week to spend, you can travel at most 1050 miles.

We started with the inequality $0.20x + 125 \leq 335$ and obtained the inequality $x \leq 1050$ in the final step. Both of these inequalities have the same solution set, namely $\{x \mid x \leq 1050\}$. Inequalities such as these, with the same solution set, are said to be **equivalent**.

We isolated x from $0.20x$ by dividing both sides of $0.20x \leq 210$ by 0.20, a positive number. Let's see what happens if we divide both sides of an inequality by a negative number. Consider the inequality $10 < 14$. Divide 10 and 14 by -2:

$$\frac{10}{-2} = -5 \quad \text{and} \quad \frac{14}{-2} = -7.$$

Because -5 lies to the right of -7 on the number line, -5 is greater than -7:

$$-5 > -7.$$

Notice that the direction of the inequality symbol is reversed:

$$10 < 14$$

Dividing by -2 changes the direction of the inequality symbol.

$$-5 > -7.$$

In general, **when we multiply or divide both sides of an inequality by a negative number, the direction of the inequality symbol is reversed**. When we reverse the direction of the inequality symbol, we say that we change the *sense* of the inequality.

We can summarize this discussion with the following statement:

SOLVING LINEAR INEQUALITIES

The procedure for solving linear inequalities is the same as the procedure for solving linear equations, with one important exception: When multiplying or dividing both sides of the inequality by a negative number, reverse the direction of the inequality symbol, changing the sense of the inequality.

EXAMPLE 2   SOLVING A LINEAR INEQUALITY

Solve and graph the solution set: $4x - 7 \geq 5$.

SOLUTION   Our goal is to get x by itself on the left side. We do this by getting $4x$ by itself, adding 7 to both sides.

$$4x - 7 \geq 5 \qquad \text{This is the given inequality.}$$

$$4x - 7 + 7 \geq 5 + 7 \qquad \text{Add 7 to both sides.}$$

$$4x \geq 12 \qquad \text{Simplify.}$$

Next, we isolate x from $4x$ by dividing both sides by 4. The inequality symbol stays the same because we are dividing by a positive number.

$$\frac{4x}{4} \geq \frac{12}{4} \qquad \text{Divide both sides by 4.}$$

$$x \geq 3 \qquad \text{Simplify.}$$

The solution set consists of all real numbers that are greater than or equal to 3, expressed in set-builder notation as $\{x | x \geq 3\}$. The graph of the solution set is shown as follows:

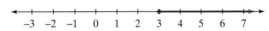

We cannot check all members of an inequality's solution set, but we can take a few values to get an indication of whether or not it is correct. In Example 2, we found that the solution set of $4x - 7 \geq 5$ is $\{x | x \geq 3\}$. Show that 3 and 4 satisfy the inequality, whereas 2 does not.

  Solve and graph the solution set: $5x - 3 \leq 17$.

EXAMPLE 3   SOLVING LINEAR INEQUALITIES

Solve and graph the solution set:

a. $\dfrac{1}{3}x < 5$ **b.** $-3x < 21$.

SOLUTION   In each case, our goal is to isolate x. In the first inequality, this is accomplished by multiplying both sides by 3. In the second inequality, we can do this by dividing both sides by -3.

a. $\dfrac{1}{3}x < 5 \qquad \text{This is the given inequality.}$

$3 \cdot \dfrac{1}{3}x < 3 \cdot 5 \qquad \text{Isolate x by multiplying by 3 on both sides.}$

$\qquad\qquad\qquad\qquad \text{The symbol } < \text{ stays the same because we are multiplying both sides by a positive number.}$

$x < 15 \qquad \text{Simplify.}$

The solution set is $\{x | x < 15\}$. The graph of the solution set is shown as follows:

b. $-3x < 21$ This is the given inequality.

$$\frac{-3x}{-3} \underset{\uparrow}{>} \frac{21}{-3}$$ Isolate x by dividing by -3 on both sides.
The symbol $<$ must be reversed because we are dividing both sides by a negative number.

$x > -7$ Simplify.

The solution set is $\{x \mid x > -7\}$. The graph of the solution set is shown as follows:

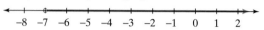

 Solve and graph the solution set:

     a. $\frac{1}{4}x < 2$ **b.** $-6x < 18.$

EXAMPLE 4   SOLVING A LINEAR INEQUALITY

Solve and graph the solution set: $6x - 12 > 8x + 2.$

SOLUTION We will get x by itself on the left side. We begin by subtracting $8x$ from both sides so that the x-term appears on the left.

$6x - 12 > 8x + 2$ This is the given inequality.

$6x - 8x - 12 > 8x - 8x + 2$ Subtract 8x on both sides with the goal of isolating x on the left.

$-2x - 12 > 2$ Simplify.

Next, we get $-2x$ by itself, adding 12 to both sides.

$-2x - 12 + 12 > 2 + 12$ Add 12 to both sides.

$-2x > 14$ Simplify.

In the last step, we isolate x from $-2x$ by dividing both sides by -2. The direction of the inequality symbol must be reversed because we are dividing by a negative number.

$$\frac{-2x}{-2} < \frac{14}{-2}$$ Divide both sides by -2 and change the sense of the inequality.

$x < -7$ Simplify.

The solution set is $\{x \mid x < -7\}$. The graph of the solution set is shown as follows:

 Solve and graph the solution set: $7x - 3 > 13x + 33.$

EXAMPLE 5   SOLVING A LINEAR INEQUALITY

Solve and graph the solution set:

$$2(x - 3) + 5x \le 8(x - 1).$$

SOLUTION Begin by simplifying the algebraic expression on each side.

$2(x - 3) + 5x \le 8(x - 1)$ This is the given inequality.

$2x - 6 + 5x \le 8x - 8$ Use the distributive property.

$7x - 6 \le 8x - 8$ Add like terms on the left: $2x + 5x = 7x.$

You can solve

$$7x - 6 \leq 8x - 8$$

by isolating x on the right side. Subtract $7x$ from both sides and add 8 to both sides:

$$7x - 6 - 7x \leq 8x - 8 - 7x$$
$$-6 \leq x - 8$$
$$-6 + 8 \leq x - 8 + 8$$
$$2 \leq x.$$

This last inequality means the same thing as

$$x \geq 2.$$

We will get x by itself on the left side. Subtract $8x$ from both sides.

$$7x - 8x - 6 \leq 8x - 8x - 8$$
$$-x - 6 \leq -8$$

Next, we get $-x$ by itself, adding 6 to both sides.

$$-x - 6 + 6 \leq -8 + 6$$
$$-x \leq -2$$

To isolate x, we must eliminate the negative sign in front of the x. Because $-x$ means $-1x$, we can do this by dividing both sides of the inequality by -1. This reverses the direction of the inequality symbol.

$$\frac{-x}{-1} \geq \frac{-2}{-1} \qquad \text{Divide both sides by } -1 \text{ and change the sense of the inequality.}$$

$$x \geq 2 \qquad \text{Simplify.}$$

The solution set is $\{x \mid x \geq 2\}$. The graph of the solution set is shown as follows:

 Solve and graph the solution set:

$$2(x - 3) - 1 \leq 3(x + 2) - 14.$$

In our next example, the inequality has three parts:

$$-3 < 2x + 1 \leq 3.$$

> 2x + 1 is greater than −3 and less than or equal to 3.

By performing the same operation on all three parts of the inequality, our goal is to **isolate x in the middle**.

EXAMPLE 6   SOLVING A THREE-PART INEQUALITY

Solve and graph the solution set:

$$-3 < 2x + 1 \leq 3.$$

SOLUTION We would like to isolate x in the middle. We can do this by first subtracting 1 from all three parts of the inequality. Then we isolate x from $2x$ by dividing all three parts of the inequality by 2.

$$-3 < 2x + 1 \leq 3 \qquad \text{This is the given inequality.}$$
$$-3 - 1 < 2x + 1 - 1 \leq 3 - 1 \qquad \text{Subtract 1 from all three parts.}$$
$$-4 < 2x \leq 2 \qquad \text{Simplify.}$$
$$\frac{-4}{2} < \frac{2x}{2} \leq \frac{2}{2} \qquad \text{Divide each part by 2.}$$
$$-2 < x \leq 1 \qquad \text{Simplify.}$$

The solution set consists of all real numbers greater than -2 and less than or equal to 1, represented by $\{x \mid -2 < x \leq 1\}$. The graph is shown as follows:

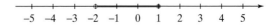

 Solve and graph the solution set on a number line: $1 \leq 2x + 3 < 11.$

As you know, different professors may use different grading systems to determine your final course grade. Some professors require a final examination; others do not. In our next example, a final exam is required *and* it counts as two grades.

3 | Solve applied problems using linear inequalities.

EXAMPLE 7　AN APPLICATION: FINAL COURSE GRADE

To earn an A in a course, you must have a final average of at least 90%. On the first four examinations, you have grades of 86%, 88%, 92%, and 84%. If the final examination counts as two grades, what must you get on the final to earn an A in the course?

SOLUTION　We will use our five-step strategy for solving algebraic word problems.

Steps 1 and 2. Represent unknown quantities in terms of x. Let $x =$ your grade on the final examination.

Step 3. Write an inequality in x that models the conditions. The average of the six grades is found by adding the grades and dividing the sum by 6.

$$\text{Average} = \frac{86 + 88 + 92 + 84 + x + x}{6}$$

Because the final counts as two grades, the x (your grade on the final examination) is added twice. This is also why the sum is divided by 6.

　　To get an A, your average must be at least 90. This means that your average must be greater than or equal to 90.

| Your average | must be greater than or equal to | 90. |

$$\frac{86 + 88 + 92 + 84 + x + x}{6} \qquad \geq \qquad 90$$

Step 4. Solve the inequality and answer the problem's question.

$$\frac{86 + 88 + 92 + 84 + x + x}{6} \geq 90 \qquad \text{This is the inequality that models the given conditions.}$$

$$\frac{350 + 2x}{6} \geq 90 \qquad \text{Combine like terms in the numerator.}$$

$$6\left(\frac{350 + 2x}{6}\right) \geq 6(90) \qquad \text{Multiply both sides by 6, clearing the fraction.}$$

$$350 + 2x \geq 540 \qquad \text{Multiply.}$$

$$350 + 2x - 350 \geq 540 - 350 \qquad \text{Subtract 350 from both sides.}$$

$$2x \geq 190 \qquad \text{Simplify.}$$

$$\frac{2x}{2} \geq \frac{190}{2} \qquad \text{Divide both sides by 2.}$$

$$x \geq 95 \qquad \text{Simplify.}$$

You must get at least 95% on the final examination to earn an A in the course.

Step 5. Check. We can perform a partial check by computing the average with any grade that is at least 95. We will use 96. If you get 96% on the final examination, your average is

$$\frac{86 + 88 + 92 + 84 + 96 + 96}{6} = \frac{542}{6} = 90\frac{1}{3}.$$

Because $90\frac{1}{3} > 90$, you earn an A in the course.

○

CHECK POINT 7　To earn a B in a course, you must have a final average of at least 80%. On the first three examinations, you have grades of 82%, 74%, and 78%. If the final examination counts as two grades, what must you get on the final to earn a B in the course?

EXERCISE SET 3.5 ●●●●●●

• Practice Exercises

In Exercises 1–12, graph each set of real numbers on a number line.

1. $\{x|x > 6\}$ **2.** $\{x|x > -2\}$

3. $\{x|x < -4\}$ **4.** $\{x|x < 0\}$

5. $\{x|x \geq -3\}$ **6.** $\{x|x \geq -5\}$

7. $\{x|x \leq 4\}$ **8.** $\{x|x \leq 7\}$

9. $\{x|-2 < x \leq 5\}$ **10.** $\{x|-3 \leq x < 7\}$

11. $\{x|-1 < x < 4\}$ **12.** $\{x|-7 \leq x \leq 0\}$

In Exercises 13–66, solve each inequality and graph the solution set on a number line.

13. $x - 3 > 2$ **14.** $x + 1 < 5$

15. $x + 4 \leq 9$ **16.** $x - 5 \geq 1$

17. $x - 3 < 0$ **18.** $x + 4 \geq 0$

19. $4x < 20$ **20.** $6x \geq 18$

21. $3x \geq -15$ **22.** $7x < -21$

23. $2x - 3 > 7$ **24.** $3x + 2 \leq 14$

25. $3x + 3 < 18$ **26.** $8x - 4 > 12$

27. $\frac{1}{2}x < 4$ **28.** $\frac{1}{2}x > 3$

29. $\frac{x}{3} > -2$ **30.** $\frac{x}{4} < -1$

31. $-3x < 15$ **32.** $-7x > 21$

33. $-3x \geq -15$ **34.** $-7x \leq -21$

35. $3x + 4 \leq 2x + 7$ **36.** $2x + 9 \leq x + 2$

37. $5x - 9 < 4x + 7$ **38.** $3x - 8 < 2x + 11$

39. $-2x - 3 < 3$ **40.** $14 - 3x > 5$

41. $3 - 7x \leq 17$ **42.** $5 - 3x \geq 20$

43. $-x < 4$ **44.** $-x > -3$

45. $5 - x \leq 1$ **46.** $3 - x \geq -3$

47. $2x - 5 > -x + 6$ **48.** $6x - 2 \geq 4x + 6$

49. $2x - 5 < 5x - 11$ **50.** $4x - 7 > 9x - 2$

51. $3(x + 1) - 5 < 2x + 1$ **52.** $4(x + 1) + 2 \geq 3x + 6$

53. $8x + 3 > 3(2x + 1) - x + 5$

54. $7 - 2(x - 4) < 5(1 - 2x)$

55. $\frac{x}{4} - \frac{3}{2} \leq \frac{x}{2} + 1$ **56.** $\frac{3x}{10} + 1 \geq \frac{1}{5} - \frac{x}{10}$

57. $1 - \frac{x}{2} > 4$ **58.** $7 - \frac{4}{5}x < \frac{3}{5}$

59. $6 < x + 3 < 8$ **60.** $7 < x + 5 < 11$

61. $-3 \leq x - 2 < 1$ **62.** $-6 < x - 4 \leq 1$

63. $-11 < 2x - 1 \leq -5$ **64.** $3 \leq 4x - 3 < 19$

65. $-3 \leq \frac{2}{3}x - 5 < -1$ **66.** $-6 \leq \frac{1}{2}x - 4 < -3$

• Practice Plus

In Exercises 67–70, write an inequality with x isolated on the left side that is equivalent to the given inequality.

67. $Ax + By > C$; Assume $A > 0$.

68. $Ax + By \leq C$; Assume $A > 0$.

69. $Ax + By > C$; Assume $A < 0$.

70. $Ax + By \leq C$; Assume $A < 0$.

In Exercises 71–76, use set-builder notation to describe all real numbers satisfying the given conditions.

71. A number increased by 5 is at least two times the number.

72. A number increased by 12 is at least four times the number.

73. Twice the sum of four and a number is at most 36.

74. Three times the sum of five and a number is at most 48.

75. If the quotient of three times a number and five is increased by four, the result is no more than 34.

76. If the quotient of three times a number and four is decreased by three, the result is no less than 9.

• Application Exercises

The graphs show that the three components of love, namely passion, intimacy, and commitment, progress differently over time. Passion peaks early in a relationship and then declines. By contrast, intimacy and commitment build gradually. Use the graphs to solve Exercises 77–84. Assume that x represents years in a relationship.

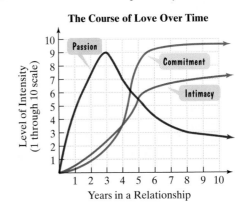

The Course of Love Over Time

Source: R. J. Sternberg, A Triangular Theory of Love, *Psychological Review*, 93, 119–135.

77. Use set-builder notation to write an inequality that expresses for which years in a relationship intimacy is greater that commitment.

78. Use set-builder notation to write an inequality that expresses for which years in a relationship passion is greater than or equal to intimacy.

79. What is the relationship between passion and intimacy for $\{x|5 \leq x < 7\}$?

80. What is the relationship between intimacy and commitment for $\{x|4 \leq x < 7\}$?

81. What is the relationship between passion and commitment for $\{x|6 < x < 8\}$?

82. What is the relationship between passion and commitment for $\{x|7 < x < 9\}$?

83. What is the maximum level of intensity for passion? After how many years in a relationship does this occur?

84. After approximately how many years do levels of intensity for commitment exceed the maximum level of intensity for passion?

The bar graph shows the percentage of U.S. college freshmen with no religious preference for selected years from 1984 through 2004.

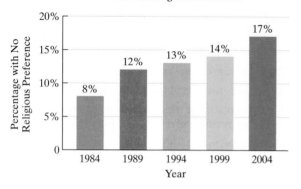

Percentage of U.S. College Freshmen with No Religious Preference

Source: UCLA Higher Education Research Institute

The data can be modeled by the formula

$$P = 0.4x + 8.8,$$

where P is the percentage of freshmen with no religious preference x years after 1984. Use this formula to solve Exercises 85–86.

85. If trends modeled by the formula continue, describe how many years after 1984 more than 20% of college freshmen will have no religious preference. What years are included in your description?

86. If trends modeled by the formula continue, describe how many years after 1984 more than 22% of college freshmen will have no religious preference. What years are included in your description?

87. On three examinations, you have grades of 88, 78, and 86. There is still a final examination, which counts as one grade.

a. In order to get an A, your average must be at least 90. If you get 100 on the final, compute your average and determine if an A in the course is possible.

b. To earn a B in the course, you must have a final average of at least 80. What must you get on the final to earn a B in the course?

88. On two examinations, you have grades of 86 and 88. There is an optional final examination, which counts as one grade. You decide to take the final in order to get a course grade of A, meaning a final average of at least 90.

a. What must you get on the final to earn an A in the course?

b. By taking the final, if you do poorly, you might risk the B that you have in the course based on the first two exam grades. If your final average is less than 80, you will lose your B in the course. Describe the grades on the final that will cause this to happen.

89. A car can be rented from Continental Rental for $80 per week plus 25 cents for each mile driven. How many miles can you travel if you can spend at most $400 for the week?

90. A car can be rented from Basic Rental for $60 per week plus 50 cents for each mile driven. How many miles can you travel if you can spend at most $600 for the week?

91. An elevator at a construction site has a maximum capacity of 3000 pounds. If the elevator operator weighs 245 pounds and each cement bag weighs 95 pounds, up to how many bags of cement can be safely lifted on the elevator in one trip?

92. An elevator at a construction site has a maximum capacity of 2800 pounds. If the elevator operator weighs 265 pounds and each cement bag weighs 65 pounds, up to how many bags of cement can be safely lifted on the elevator in one trip?

93. A basic cellular phone plan costs $20 per month for 60 calling minutes. Additional time costs $0.40 per minute. The formula

$$C = 20 + 0.40(x - 60)$$

gives the monthly cost for this plan, *C*, for *x* calling minutes, where *x* > 60. How many calling minutes are possible for a monthly cost of at least $28 and at most $40?

• Writing in Mathematics

94. When graphing the solutions of an inequality, what is the difference between an open dot and a closed dot?

95. When solving an inequality, when is it necessary to change the direction of the inequality symbol? Give an example.

96. Describe ways in which solving a linear inequality is similar to solving a linear equation.

97. Describe ways in which solving a linear inequality is different than solving a linear equation.

• Critical Thinking Exercises

98. A car can be rented from Basic Rental for $260 per week with no extra charge for mileage. Continental charges $80 per week plus 25 cents for each mile driven to rent the same car. How many miles must be driven in a week to make the rental cost for Basic Rental a better deal than Continental's?

99. A company manufactures and sells personalized stationery. The weekly fixed cost is $3000 and it cost $3.00 to produce each package of stationery. The selling price is $5.50 per package. How many packages of stationery must be produced and sold each week for the company to generate a profit?

SECTION 3.6 • QUADRATIC EQUATIONS

OBJECTIVES

1. Multiply binomials using the FOIL method.

2. Factor trinomials.

3. Solve quadratic equations by factoring.

4. Solve quadratic equations using the quadratic formula.

5. Solve problems modeled by quadratic equations.

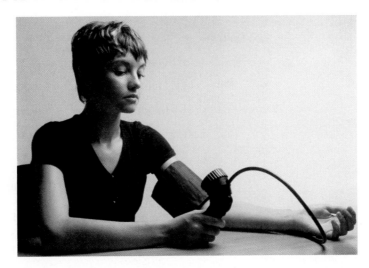

Until fairly recently, many doctors believed that your blood pressure was theirs to know and yours to worry about. Today, however, people are encouraged to find out their blood pressure. That pumped-up cuff that squeezes against your upper arm measures blood pressure in millimeters (mm) of mercury (Hg). Blood pressure is given in two numbers: systolic pressure over diastolic pressure, such as 120 over 80. Systolic pressure is the pressure of blood against the artery walls when the heart contracts. Diastolic pressure is the pressure of blood against the artery walls when the heart is at rest.

There is a tendency for systolic pressure to increase with age as the arteries become less elastic. In this section, we will use equations to model normal systolic pressure based on age and gender. Unlike linear equations, these equations have a term in which the greatest exponent on the variable is 2. We focus on two methods for solving such equations: factoring and using a formula.

1 | Multiply binomials using the FOIL method.

Multiplying Two Binomials Using the FOIL Method

Before we learn about the first method, factoring, we need to consider the FOIL method for multiplying two binomials. A **binomial** is a simplified algebraic expression that contains two terms in which each exponent that appears on a variable is a whole number.

Examples of Binomials

$$x + 3, \quad x + 4, \quad 3x + 4, \quad 5x - 3$$

Two binomials can be quickly multiplied by using the FOIL method, in which **F** represents the product of the **first** terms in each binomial, **O** represents the product of the **outside** terms, **I** represents the product of the two **inside** terms, and **L** represents the product of the **last,** or second, terms in each binomial.

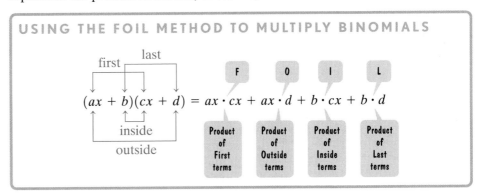

USING THE FOIL METHOD TO MULTIPLY BINOMIALS

$$(ax + b)(cx + d) = ax \cdot cx + ax \cdot d + b \cdot cx + b \cdot d$$

Product of First terms Product of Outside terms Product of Inside terms Product of Last terms

Once you have multiplied first, outside, inside, and last terms, combine all like terms.

EXAMPLE 1   USING THE FOIL METHOD

Multiply: $(x + 3)(x + 4)$.

SOLUTION

F : First terms $= x \cdot x = x^2$ $(x + 3)(x + 4)$

O: Outside terms $= x \cdot 4 = 4x$ $(x + 3)(x + 4)$

I : Inside terms $= 3 \cdot x = 3x$ $(x + 3)(x + 4)$

L : Last terms $= 3 \cdot 4 = 12$ $(x + 3)(x + 4)$

$$(x + 3)(x + 4) = x \cdot x + x \cdot 4 + 3 \cdot x + 3 \cdot 4$$
$$= x^2 + 4x + 3x + 12$$
$$= x^2 + 7x + 12 \quad \text{Combine like terms.}$$

 Multiply: $(x + 5)(x + 6)$.

EXAMPLE 2   USING THE FOIL METHOD

Multiply: $(3x + 4)(5x - 3)$.

SOLUTION

$$(3x + 4)(5x - 3) = 3x \cdot 5x + 3x(-3) + 4 \cdot 5x + 4(-3)$$
$$= 15x^2 - 9x + 20x - 12$$
$$= 15x^2 + 11x - 12 \quad \text{Combine like terms.}$$

 Multiply: $(7x + 5)(4x - 3)$.

2 | Factor trinomials.

Factoring a Trinomial Where the Coefficient of the Squared Term Is 1

The algebraic expression $x^2 + 7x + 12$ is called a trinomial. A **trinomial** is a simplified algebraic expression that contains three terms in which all variables have whole number exponents.

We can use the FOIL method to multiply two binomials to obtain the trinomial $x^2 + 7x + 12$:

Factored Form   F   O   I   L   Trinomial Form
$$(x + 3)(x + 4) = x^2 + 4x + 3x + 12 = x^2 + 7x + 12$$

Because the product of $x + 3$ and $x + 4$ is $x^2 + 7x + 12$, we call $x + 3$ and $x + 4$ the **factors** of $x^2 + 7x + 12$. **Factoring** an algebraic expression containing the sum or difference of terms means finding an equivalent expression that is a product. Thus, to factor $x^2 + 7x + 12$, we write

$$x^2 + 7x + 12 = (x + 3)(x + 4).$$

We can make several important observations about the factors on the right side.

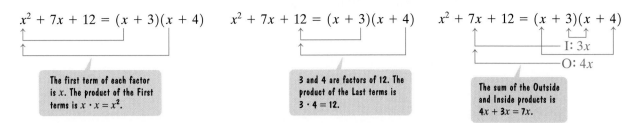

$$x^2 + 7x + 12 = (x + 3)(x + 4) \qquad x^2 + 7x + 12 = (x + 3)(x + 4) \qquad x^2 + 7x + 12 = (x + 3)(x + 4)$$

I: 3x
O: 4x

The first term of each factor is x. The product of the First terms is $x \cdot x = x^2$.

3 and 4 are factors of 12. The product of the Last terms is $3 \cdot 4 = 12$.

The sum of the Outside and Inside products is $4x + 3x = 7x$.

These observations provide us with a procedure for factoring $x^2 + bx + c$.

A STRATEGY FOR FACTORING $x^2 + bx + c$

1. Enter x as the first term of each factor.
$$(x \quad)(x \quad) = x^2 + bx + c$$

2. List pairs of factors of the constant c.

3. Try various combinations of these factors. Select the combination in which the sum of the Outside and Inside products is equal to bx.
$$(x + \square)(x + \square) = x^2 + bx + c$$

I
O
Sum of O + I

4. Check your work by multiplying the factors using the FOIL method. You should obtain the original trinomial.

If none of the possible combinations yield an Outside product and an Inside product whose sum is equal to bx, the trinomial cannot be factored using integers and is called **prime**.

EXAMPLE 3   FACTORING A TRINOMIAL IN $x^2 + bx + c$ FORM

Factor: $x^2 + 6x + 8$.

SOLUTION

Step 1. Enter x as the first term of each factor.
$$x^2 + 6x + 8 = (x \quad)(x \quad)$$

To find the second term of each factor, we must find two integers whose product is 8 and whose sum is 6.

Step 2. List all pairs of factors of the constant, 8.

Factors of 8	8, 1	4, 2	−8, −1	−4, −2

Step 3. Try various combinations of these factors. The correct factorization of $x^2 + 6x + 8$ is the one in which the sum of the Outside and Inside products is equal to $6x$. Here is a list of the possible factorizations:

Possible Factorizations of $x^2 + 6x + 8$	Sum of Outside and Inside Products (Should Equal $6x$)
$(x + 8)(x + 1)$	$x + 8x = 9x$
$(x + 4)(x + 2)$	$2x + 4x = 6x$
$(x - 8)(x - 1)$	$-x - 8x = -9x$
$(x - 4)(x - 2)$	$-2x - 4x = -6x$

This is the required middle term.

Thus, $x^2 + 6x + 8 = (x + 4)(x + 2)$.

STUDY TIP

To factor $x^2 + bx + c$ when c is positive, find two numbers with the same sign as the middle term.

$$x^2 + 6x + 8 = (x + 2)(x + 4)$$

Same signs

$$x^2 - 5x + 6 = (x - 3)(x - 2)$$

Same signs

Using this observation, it is not necessary to list the last two factorizations in step 3 on the right.

We can check that $x^2 + 6x + 8 = (x + 4)(x + 2)$ by multiplying the right side using the FOIL method. You should obtain the original trinomial. Because of the commutative property, we can also say that

$$x^2 + 6x + 8 = (x + 2)(x + 4).$$

 Factor: $x^2 + 5x + 6.$

| EXAMPLE 4 | FACTORING A TRINOMIAL IN $x^2 + bx + c$ FORM |

Factor: $x^2 + 2x - 35.$

SOLUTION

Step 1. Enter x as the first term of each factor.

$$x^2 + 2x - 35 = (x \quad)(x \quad)$$

To find the second term of each factor, we must find two integers whose product is -35 and whose sum is 2.

Step 2. List pairs of factors of the constant, -35.

| Factors of -35 | $35, -1$ | $-35, 1$ | $-7, 5$ | $7, -5$ |

Step 3. Try various combinations of these factors. The correct factorization of $x^2 + 2x - 35$ is the one in which the sum of the Outside and Inside products is equal to $2x$. Here is a list of the possible factorizations:

Possible Factorizations of $x^2 + 2x - 35$	Sum of Outside and Inside Products (Should Equal $2x$)
$(x - 1)(x + 35)$	$35x - x = 34x$
$(x + 1)(x - 35)$	$-35x + x = -34x$
$(x - 7)(x + 5)$	$5x - 7x = -2x$
$(x + 7)(x - 5)$	$-5x + 7x = 2x$

This is the required middle term.

Thus, $x^2 + 2x - 35 = (x + 7)(x - 5)$ or $(x - 5)(x + 7)$.

Step 4. Verify the factorization using the FOIL method.

F   O   I   L

$$(x + 7)(x - 5) = x^2 - 5x + 7x - 35 = x^2 + 2x - 35$$

Because the product of the factors is the original trinomial, the factorization is correct.

 Factor: $x^2 + 3x - 10.$

STUDY TIP

To factor $x^2 + bx + c$ when c is negative, find two numbers with opposite signs whose sum is the coefficient of the middle term.

$$x^2 + 2x - 35 = (x + 7)(x - 5)$$

Negative   Opposite signs

Factoring a Trinomial Where the Coefficient of the Squared Term Is Not 1

How do we factor a trinomial such as $3x^2 - 20x + 28$? Notice that the coefficient of the squared term is 3. We must find two binomials whose product is $3x^2 - 20x + 28$. The product of the First terms must be $3x^2$:

$$(3x \quad)(x \quad).$$

From this point on, the factoring strategy is exactly the same as the one we use to factor trinomials whose coefficient of the squared term is 1.

EXAMPLE 5   FACTORING A TRINOMIAL

Factor: $3x^2 - 20x + 28$.

SOLUTION

Step 1. Find two First terms whose product is $3x^2$.

$$3x^2 - 20x + 28 = (3x \qquad)(x \qquad)$$

Step 2. List all pairs of factors of the constant, 28. The number 28 has pairs of factors that are either both positive or both negative. Because the middle term, $-20x$, is negative, both factors must be negative. The negative factorizations of 28 are $-1(-28)$, $-2(-14)$, and $-4(-7)$.

Step 3. Try various combinations of these factors. The correct factorization of $3x^2 - 20x + 28$ is the one in which the sum of the Outside and Inside products is equal to $-20x$. Here is a list of the possible factorizations:

STUDY TIP

With practice, you will find that it is not necessary to list every possible factorization of the trinomial. As you practice factoring, you will be able to narrow down the list of possible factorizations to just a few. When it comes to factoring, practice makes perfect. (Sorry about the cliché!)

Possible Factorizations of $3x^2 - 20x + 28$	Sum of Outside and Inside Products (Should Equal $-20x$)
$(3x - 1)(x - 28)$	$-84x - x = -85x$
$(3x - 28)(x - 1)$	$-3x - 28x = -31x$
$(3x - 2)(x - 14)$	$-42x - 2x = -44x$
$(3x - 14)(x - 2)$	$-6x - 14x = -20x$
$(3x - 4)(x - 7)$	$-21x - 4x = -25x$
$(3x - 7)(x - 4)$	$-12x - 7x = -19x$

This is the required middle term.

Thus,

$$3x^2 - 20x + 28 = (3x - 14)(x - 2) \quad \text{or} \quad (x - 2)(3x - 14).$$

Step 4. Verify the factorization using the FOIL method.

F   O   I   L

$$(3x - 14)(x - 2) = 3x \cdot x + 3x(-2) + (-14) \cdot x + (-14)(-2)$$
$$= 3x^2 - 6x - 14x + 28$$
$$= 3x^2 - 20x + 28$$

Because this is the trinomial we started with, the factorization is correct.

Factor: $5x^2 - 14x + 8$.

EXAMPLE 6   FACTORING A TRINOMIAL

Factor: $8y^2 - 10y - 3$.

SOLUTION

Step 1. Find two first terms whose product is $8y^2$.

$$8y^2 - 10y - 3 \stackrel{?}{=} (8y \qquad)(y \qquad)$$
$$8y^2 - 10y - 3 \stackrel{?}{=} (4y \qquad)(2y \qquad)$$

Step 2. List all pairs of factors of the constant, -3. The possible factorizations are $1(-3)$ and $-1(3)$.

Step 3. Try various combinations of these factors. The correct factorization of $8y^2 - 10y - 3$ is the one in which the sum of the Outside and Inside products is equal to $-10y$. Here is a list of the possible factorizations:

Possible Factorizations of $8y^2 - 10y - 3$	Sum of Outside and Inside Products (Should Equal $-10y$)
$(8y + 1)(y - 3)$	$-24y + y = -23y$
$(8y - 3)(y + 1)$	$8y - 3y = 5y$
$(8y - 1)(y + 3)$	$24y - y = 23y$
$(8y + 3)(y - 1)$	$-8y + 3y = -5y$
$(4y + 1)(2y - 3)$	$-12y + 2y = -10y$
$(4y - 3)(2y + 1)$	$4y - 6y = -2y$
$(4y - 1)(2y + 3)$	$12y - 2y = 10y$
$(4y + 3)(2y - 1)$	$-4y + 6y = 2y$

This is the required middle term.

Thus,

$$8y^2 - 10y - 3 = (4y + 1)(2y - 3) \quad \text{or} \quad (2y - 3)(4y + 1).$$

Show that this factorization is correct by multiplying the factors using the FOIL method. You should obtain the original trinomial.

 CHECK POINT 6 Factor: $6y^2 + 19y - 7$.

---

3 | Solve quadratic equations by factoring.

Solving Quadratic Equations by Factoring

We have seen that in a linear equation, the highest exponent on the variable is 1. We now define a quadratic equation, in which the greatest exponent on the variable is 2.

> **DEFINITION OF A QUADRATIC EQUATION**
> A **quadratic equation** in x is an equation that can be written in the form
> $$ax^2 + bx + c = 0,$$
> where a, b, and c are real numbers, with $a \neq 0$.

Here is an example of a quadratic equation:

$$x^2 - 7x + 10 = 0.$$

$a = 1$ $b = -7$ $c = 10$

Notice that we can factor the left side of this equation.

$$x^2 - 7x + 10 = 0$$
$$(x - 5)(x - 2) = 0$$

If a quadratic equation has zero on one side and a factored trinomial on the other side, it can be solved using the **zero-product principle**:

> **THE ZERO-PRODUCT PRINCIPLE**
> If the product of two factors is zero, then one (or both) of the factors must have a value of zero.
>
> If $AB = 0$, then $A = 0$ or $B = 0$.

EXAMPLE 7   SOLVING A QUADRATIC EQUATION USING THE ZERO-PRODUCT PRINCIPLE

Solve: $(x - 5)(x - 2) = 0$.

SOLUTION The product $(x - 5)(x - 2)$ is equal to zero. By the zero-product principle, the only way that this product can be zero is if at least one of the factors is zero. We set each individual factor equal to zero and solve each resulting equation for x.

$$(x - 5)(x - 2) = 0$$
$$x - 5 = 0 \quad \text{or} \quad x - 2 = 0$$
$$x = 5 \qquad\qquad x = 2$$

Check the proposed solutions by substituting each one separately for x in the original equation.

Check 5:	**Check** 2:
$(x - 5)(x - 2) = 0$	$(x - 5)(x - 2) = 0$
$(5 - 5)(5 - 2) \stackrel{?}{=} 0$	$(2 - 5)(2 - 2) \stackrel{?}{=} 0$
$0(3) \stackrel{?}{=} 0$	$-3(0) \stackrel{?}{=} 0$
$0 = 0, \quad$ true	$0 = 0, \quad$ true

The resulting true statements indicate that the solutions are 5 and 2. The solution set is $\{2, 5\}$.

 Solve: $(x + 6)(x - 3) = 0$.

SOLVING A QUADRATIC EQUATION BY FACTORING

1. If necessary, rewrite the equation in the form $ax^2 + bx + c = 0$, moving all terms to one side, thereby obtaining zero on the other side.
2. Factor.
3. Apply the zero-product principle, setting each factor equal to zero.
4. Solve the equations in step 3.
5. Check the solutions in the original equation.

EXAMPLE 8   SOLVING A QUADRATIC EQUATION BY FACTORING

Solve: $x^2 - 2x = 35$.

SOLUTION

Step 1. Move all terms to one side and obtain zero on the other side. Subtract 35 from both sides and write the equation in $ax^2 + bx + c = 0$ form.

$$x^2 - 2x = 35$$
$$x^2 - 2x - 35 = 35 - 35$$
$$x^2 - 2x - 35 = 0$$

Step 2. Factor. $(x - 7)(x + 5) = 0$

Steps 3 and 4. Set each factor equal to zero and solve each resulting equation.

$$x - 7 = 0 \quad \text{or} \quad x + 5 = 0$$
$$x = 7 \qquad\qquad x = -5$$

Step 5. Check the solutions in the original equation.

Check 7:	Check -5:
$x^2 - 2x = 35$	$x^2 - 2x = 35$
$7^2 - 2 \cdot 7 \overset{?}{=} 35$	$(-5)^2 - 2(-5) \overset{?}{=} 35$
$49 - 14 \overset{?}{=} 35$	$25 + 10 \overset{?}{=} 35$
$35 = 35$, true	$35 = 35$, true

The resulting true statements indicate that the solutions are 7 and -5. The solution set is $\{-5, 7\}$.

 Solve: $x^2 - 6x = 16.$

EXAMPLE 9   SOLVING A QUADRATIC EQUATION BY FACTORING

Solve: $5x^2 - 33x + 40 = 0.$

SOLUTION All terms are already on the left and zero is on the other side. Thus, we can factor the trinomial on the left side. $5x^2 - 33x + 40$ factors as $(5x - 8)(x - 5)$.

$5x^2 - 33x + 40 = 0$	This is the given quadratic equation.
$(5x - 8)(x - 5) = 0$	Factor.
$5x - 8 = 0$ or $x - 5 = 0$	Set each factor equal to zero.
$5x = 8$ $x = 5$	Solve the resulting equations.
$x = \dfrac{8}{5}$	

Check these values in the original equation to confirm that the solution set is $\left\{\frac{8}{5}, 5\right\}$.

 Solve: $2x^2 + 7x - 4 = 0.$

---

4 | Solve quadratic equations using the quadratic formula.

Solving Quadratic Equations Using the Quadratic Formula

The solutions of a quadratic equation cannot always be found by factoring. Some trinomials are difficult to factor, and others cannot be factored (that is, they are prime). However, there is a formula that can be used to solve all quadratic equations, whether or not they contain factorable trinomials. The formula is called the *quadratic formula*.

STUDY TIP

The entire numerator of the quadratic formula must be divided by $2a$. Always write the fraction bar all the way across the numerator.

$$x = \frac{-b \pm \sqrt{b^2 - 4ac}}{2a}$$

THE QUADRATIC FORMULA
The solutions of a quadratic equation in the form $ax^2 + bx + c = 0$, with $a \neq 0$, are given by the **quadratic formula**

$$x = \frac{-b \pm \sqrt{b^2 - 4ac}}{2a}.$$

x equals negative *b* plus or minus the square root of $b^2 - 4ac$, all divided by 2*a*.

To use the quadratic formula, be sure that the quadratic equation is expressed with all terms on one side and zero on the other side. It may be necessary to begin by rewriting the equation in this form. Then determine the numerical values for a (the coefficient of the x^2-term), b (the coefficient of the x-term), and c (the constant term). Substitute the values of a, b, and c into the quadratic formula and evaluate the expression. The $\pm$ sign indicates that there are two solutions of the equation.

EXAMPLE 10   SOLVING A QUADRATIC EQUATION USING THE QUADRATIC FORMULA

Solve using the quadratic formula: $2x^2 + 9x - 5 = 0$.

SOLUTION The given equation is in the desired form, with all terms on one side and zero on the other side. Begin by identifying the values for a, b, and c.

$$2x^2 + 9x - 5 = 0.$$

$a = 2$ $b = 9$ $c = -5$

Substituting these values into the quadratic formula and simplifying gives the equation's solutions.

$$x = \frac{-b \pm \sqrt{b^2 - 4ac}}{2a}$$ Use the quadratic formula.

$$x = \frac{-9 \pm \sqrt{9^2 - 4(2)(-5)}}{2(2)}$$ Substitute the values for a, b, and c: $a = 2$, $b = 9$, and $c = -5$.

$$= \frac{-9 \pm \sqrt{81 + 40}}{4}$$ $9^2 - 4(2)(-5) = 81 - (-40) = 81 + 40$

$$= \frac{-9 \pm \sqrt{121}}{4}$$ Add under the radical sign.

$$= \frac{-9 \pm 11}{4}$$ $\sqrt{121} = 11$

Now we will evaluate this expression in two different ways to obtain the two solutions. At the left, we will *add* 11 to -9. At the right, we will *subtract* 11 from -9.

$$x = \frac{-9 + 11}{4} \quad \text{or} \quad x = \frac{-9 - 11}{4}$$

$$= \frac{2}{4} = \frac{1}{2} \qquad\qquad = \frac{-20}{4} = -5$$

The solution set is $\left\{-5, \frac{1}{2}\right\}$.

 Solve using the quadratic formula: $8x^2 + 2x - 1 = 0$.

The quadratic equation in Example 10 has rational solutions, namely -5 and $\frac{1}{2}$. The equation can also be solved by factoring. Take a few minutes to do this now and convince yourself that you will arrive at the same two solutions.

Any quadratic equation that has rational solutions can be solved by factoring or using the quadratic formula. However, quadratic equations with irrational solutions cannot be solved by factoring. These equations can be readily solved using the quadratic formula.

EXAMPLE 11   SOLVING A QUADRATIC EQUATION USING THE QUADRATIC FORMULA

Solve using the quadratic formula: $2x^2 = 4x + 1$.

SOLUTION The quadratic equation must have zero on one side to identify the values for a, b, and c. To move all terms to one side and obtain zero on the right, we subtract $4x + 1$ from both sides. Then we can identify the values for a, b, and c.

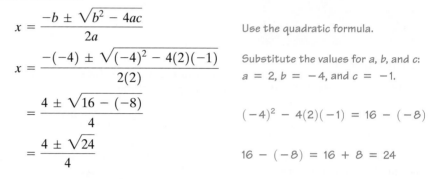

$2x^2 = 4x + 1$ This is the given equation.

$2x^2 - 4x - 1 = 0$.   Subtract 4x + 1 from both sides.

$a = 2$ $b = -4$ $c = -1$

Substituting these values into the quadratic formula and simplifying gives the equation's solutions.

$$x = \frac{-b \pm \sqrt{b^2 - 4ac}}{2a}$$ Use the quadratic formula.

$$x = \frac{-(-4) \pm \sqrt{(-4)^2 - 4(2)(-1)}}{2(2)}$$ Substitute the values for a, b, and c: $a = 2$, $b = -4$, and $c = -1$.

$$= \frac{4 \pm \sqrt{16 - (-8)}}{4}$$ $(-4)^2 - 4(2)(-1) = 16 - (-8)$

$$= \frac{4 \pm \sqrt{24}}{4}$$ $16 - (-8) = 16 + 8 = 24$

The solutions are $\dfrac{4 + \sqrt{24}}{4}$ and $\dfrac{4 - \sqrt{24}}{4}$. These solutions are irrational numbers. You can use a calculator to obtain a decimal approximation for each solution. However, in situations such as this that do not involve applications, it is best to leave the irrational solutions in radical form as exact answers. In some cases, we can simplify this radical form. Using methods for simplifying square roots discussed in Section 2.4, we can simplify $\sqrt{24}$:

$$\sqrt{24} = \sqrt{4 \cdot 6} = \sqrt{4}\sqrt{6} = 2\sqrt{6}.$$

Now we can use this result to simplify the two solutions. First, use the distributive property to factor out 2 from both terms in the numerator. Then, divide the numerator and the denominator by 2.

$$x = \frac{4 \pm \sqrt{24}}{4} = \frac{4 \pm 2\sqrt{6}}{4} = \frac{\overset{1}{2}(2 \pm \sqrt{6})}{\underset{2}{4}} = \frac{2 \pm \sqrt{6}}{2}$$

In simplified radical form, the equation's solution set is

$$\left\{ \frac{2 + \sqrt{6}}{2}, \frac{2 - \sqrt{6}}{2} \right\}.$$

Examples 10 and 11 illustrate that the solutions of quadratic equations can be rational or irrational numbers. In Example 10, the expression under the square root was 121, a perfect square ($\sqrt{121} = 11$), and we obtained rational solutions. In Example 11, this expression was 24, which is not a perfect square (although we simplified $\sqrt{24}$ to $2\sqrt{6}$), and we obtained irrational solutions. If the expression under the square root simplifies to a negative number, then the quadratic equation has **no real solution**. The solution set consists of *imaginary numbers*, discussed in the Blitzer Bonus on page 89.

 Solve using the quadratic formula: $2x^2 = 6x - 1$.

TECHNOLOGY

Using a Calculator to Approximate $\dfrac{4 + \sqrt{24}}{4}$:

MANY SCIENTIFIC CALCULATORS

(4 + 24 √)) ÷ 4 =

MANY GRAPHING CALCULATORS

(4 + √ 24)) ÷ 4 ENTER

Correct to the nearest tenth,

$$\frac{4 + \sqrt{24}}{4} \approx 2.2.$$

STUDY TIP

Avoid these common errors by factoring the numerator *before* you divide.

INCORRECT:

$$\frac{\overset{1}{4} \pm \sqrt{24}}{\underset{1}{4}} = 1 \pm \sqrt{24}$$

INCORRECT:

$$\frac{4 \pm \overset{1}{2}\sqrt{6}}{\underset{2}{4}} = \frac{4 \pm \sqrt{6}}{2}$$

You cannot divide just one term in the numerator and the denominator by their greatest common divisor.

5 | Solve problems modeled by quadratic equations.

Applications

EXAMPLE 12   BLOOD PRESSURE AND AGE

The graphs in Figure 3.6 illustrate that a person's normal systolic blood pressure, measured in millimeters of mercury (mm Hg), depends on his or her age. The formula

$$P = 0.006A^2 - 0.02A + 120$$

models a man's normal systolic pressure, P, at age A.

a. Find the age, to the nearest year, of a man whose normal systolic blood pressure is 125 mm Hg.

b. Use the graphs in Figure 3.6 to describe the differences between the normal systolic blood pressures of men and women as they age.

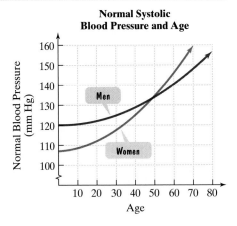

FIGURE 3.6

SOLUTION

a. We are interested in the age of a man with a normal systolic blood pressure of 125 millimeters of mercury. Thus, we substitute 125 for P in the given formula for men. Then we solve for A, the man's age.

$$P = 0.006A^2 - 0.02A + 120$$ This is the given formula for men.

$$125 = 0.006A^2 - 0.02A + 120$$ Substitute 125 for P.

$$0 = 0.006A^2 - 0.02A - 5$$ Subtract 125 from both sides and obtain zero on one side.

$a = 0.006$ $b = -0.02$ $c = -5$

Because the trinomial on the right side of the equation is prime, we solve using the quadratic formula.

Notice that the variable is A, rather than the usual x.

$$A = \frac{-b \pm \sqrt{b^2 - 4ac}}{2a}$$ Use the quadratic formula.

$$= \frac{-(-0.02) \pm \sqrt{(-0.02)^2 - 4(0.006)(-5)}}{2(0.006)}$$ Substitute the values for a, b, and c: $a = 0.006$, $b = -0.02$, and $c = -5$.

$$= \frac{0.02 \pm \sqrt{0.1204}}{0.012}$$ Use a calculator to simplify the expression under the square root.

$$\approx \frac{0.02 \pm 0.347}{0.012}$$ Use a calculator: $\sqrt{0.1204} \approx 0.347$.

$$A \approx \frac{0.02 + 0.347}{0.012} \quad \text{or} \quad A \approx \frac{0.02 - 0.347}{0.012}$$

$$A \approx 31 \qquad\qquad\qquad A \approx -27$$ Use a calculator and round to the nearest integer.

Reject this solution. Age cannot be negative.

The positive solution, $A \approx 31$, indicates that 31 is the approximate age of a man whose normal systolic blood pressure is 125 mm Hg. This is illustrated by the black lines with the arrows on the red graph representing men in Figure 3.7.

b. Take a second look at the graphs in Figure 3.7. Before approximately age 50, the blue graph representing women's normal systolic blood pressure lies below the red graph representing men's normal systolic blood pressure. Thus, up to age 50, women's normal systolic blood pressure is lower than men's, although it is increasing at a faster rate. After age 50, women's normal systolic blood pressure is higher than men's.

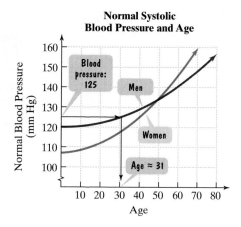

Normal Systolic Blood Pressure and Age

FIGURE 3.7

CHECK POINT 12 The formula $P = 0.01A^2 + 0.05A + 107$ models a woman's normal systolic blood pressure, P, at age A. Use this formula to find the age, to the nearest year, of a woman whose normal systolic blood pressure is 115 mm Hg. Use the blue graph in Figure 3.7 to verify your solution.

EXERCISE SET 3.6 ●●●●●●

Practice Exercises

Use FOIL to find the products in Exercises 1–8.

1. $(x + 3)(x + 5)$ **2.** $(x + 7)(x + 2)$

3. $(x - 5)(x + 3)$ **4.** $(x - 1)(x + 2)$

5. $(2x - 1)(x + 2)$ **6.** $(2x - 5)(x + 3)$

7. $(3x - 7)(4x - 5)$ **8.** $(2x - 9)(7x - 4)$

Factor the trinomials in Exercises 9–20, or state that the trinomial is prime. Check your factorization using FOIL multiplication.

9. $x^2 + 5x + 6$ **10.** $x^2 + 8x + 15$

11. $x^2 - 2x - 15$ **12.** $x^2 - 4x - 5$

13. $x^2 - 8x + 15$ **14.** $x^2 - 14x + 45$

15. $x^2 - 9x - 36$ **16.** $x^2 - x - 90$

17. $x^2 - 8x + 32$ **18.** $x^2 - 9x + 81$

19. $x^2 + 17x + 16$ **20.** $x^2 - 7x - 44$

Factor the trinomials in Exercises 21–32, or state that the trinomial is prime. Check your factorization using FOIL multiplication. Unlike the trinomials you factored in Exercises 9–20, the trinomials that follow have coefficients of squared terms that are not equal to 1.

21. $2x^2 + 7x + 3$ **22.** $3x^2 + 7x + 2$

23. $2x^2 - 17x + 30$ **24.** $5x^2 - 13x + 6$

25. $3x^2 - x - 2$ **26.** $2x^2 + 5x - 3$

27. $3x^2 - 25x - 28$ **28.** $3x^2 - 2x - 5$

29. $6x^2 - 11x + 4$ **30.** $6x^2 - 17x + 12$

31. $4x^2 + 16x + 15$ **32.** $8x^2 + 33x + 4$

In Exercises 33–36, solve each equation using the zero-product principle.

33. $(x - 8)(x + 3) = 0$ **34.** $(x + 11)(x - 5) = 0$

35. $(4x + 5)(x - 2) = 0$ **36.** $(x + 9)(3x - 1) = 0$

Solve the quadratic equations in Exercises 37–52 by factoring.

37. $x^2 + 8x + 15 = 0$ **38.** $x^2 + 5x + 6 = 0$

39. $x^2 - 2x - 15 = 0$ **40.** $x^2 + x - 42 = 0$

41. $x^2 - 4x = 21$ **42.** $x^2 + 7x = 18$

43. $x^2 + 9x = -8$ **44.** $x^2 - 11x = -10$

45. $x^2 - 12x = -36$ **46.** $x^2 - 14x = -49$

47. $2x^2 = 7x + 4$ **48.** $3x^2 = x + 4$

49. $5x^2 + x = 18$ **50.** $3x^2 - 4x = 15$

51. $x(6x + 23) + 7 = 0$ **52.** $x(6x + 13) + 6 = 0$

Solve the equations in Exercises 53–72 using the quadratic formula.

53. $x^2 + 8x + 15 = 0$ **54.** $x^2 + 8x + 12 = 0$

55. $x^2 + 5x + 3 = 0$ **56.** $x^2 + 5x + 2 = 0$

57. $x^2 + 4x = 6$ **58.** $x^2 + 2x = 4$

59. $x^2 + 4x - 7 = 0$ **60.** $x^2 + 4x + 1 = 0$

61. $x^2 - 3x = 18$ **62.** $x^2 - 3x = 10$

63. $6x^2 - 5x - 6 = 0$ **64.** $9x^2 - 12x - 5 = 0$

65. $x^2 - 2x - 10 = 0$ **66.** $x^2 + 6x - 10 = 0$

67. $x^2 - x = 14$ **68.** $x^2 - 5x = 10$

69. $6x^2 + 6x + 1 = 0$ **70.** $3x^2 = 5x - 1$

71. $4x^2 = 12x - 9$ **72.** $9x^2 + 6x + 1 = 0$

Practice Plus

In Exercises 73–80, solve each equation by the method of your choice.

73. $\dfrac{3x^2}{4} - \dfrac{5x}{2} - 2 = 0$ **74.** $\dfrac{x^2}{3} - \dfrac{x}{2} - \dfrac{3}{2} = 0$

75. $(x - 1)(3x + 2) = -7(x - 1)$

76. $x(x + 1) = 4 - (x + 2)(x + 2)$

77. $(2x - 6)(x + 2) = 5(x - 1) - 12$

78. $7x(x - 2) = 3 - 2(x + 4)$

79. $2x^2 - 9x - 3 = 9 - 9x$

80. $3x^2 - 6x - 3 = 12 - 6x$

81. When the sum of 6 and twice a positive number is subtracted from the square of the number, 0 results. Find the number.

82. When the sum of 1 and twice a negative number is subtracted from twice the square of the number, 0 results. Find the number.

Application Exercises

The formula

$$N = \frac{t^2 - t}{2}$$

describes the number of football games, N, that must be played in a league with t teams if each team is to play every other team once. Use this information to solve Exercises 83–84.

83. If a league has 36 games scheduled, how many teams belong to the league, assuming that each team plays every other team once?

84. If a league has 45 games scheduled, how many teams belong to the league, assuming that each team plays every other team once?

The bar graph shows the percentage of foreign-born Americans from 1930 through 2003. The percentage, P, of the U.S. population that was foreign-born x years after 1930 can be modeled by the formula

$$P = 0.005x^2 - 0.37x + 11.8.$$

Use the formula to solve Exercises 85–88.

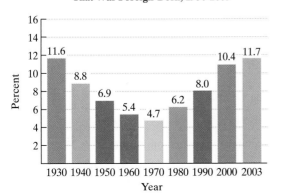

Percentage of U.S. Population That Was Foreign-Born, 1930-2003

Source: U.S. Census Bureau

85. How well does the formula model the data for 2000?

86. How well does the formula model the data for 1940?

87. In which future year does the model project that 16% of the U.S. population will be foreign-born?

88. In which future year does the model project that 19% of the U.S. population will be foreign-born?

A driver's age has something to do with his or her chance of getting into a fatal car crash. The bar graph shows the number of fatal vehicle crashes per 100 million miles driven for drivers of various age groups. For example, 25-year-old drivers are involved in 4.1 fatal crashes per 100 million miles driven. Thus, when a group of 25-year-old Americans has driven a total of 100 million miles, approximately 4 have been in accidents in which someone died.

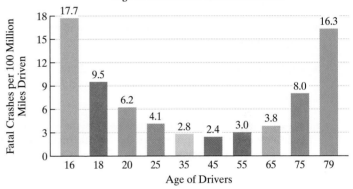

Age of U.S. Drivers and Fatal Crashes

Source: Insurance Institute for Highway Safety

The number of fatal vehicle crashes per 100 million miles, N, for drivers of age x can be modeled by the formula

$$N = 0.013x^2 - 1.19x + 28.24.$$

Use the formula to solve Exercises 89–90. Use a calculator and round answers to the nearest year.

89. What age groups are expected to be involved in 3 fatal crashes per 100 million miles driven? How well does the formula model the trend in the actual data shown in the bar graph?

90. What age groups are expected to be involved in 10 fatal crashes per 100 million miles driven? How well does the formula model the trend in the actual data shown in the bar graph?

• Writing in Mathematics

91. Explain how to multiply two binomials using the FOIL method. Give an example with your explanation.

92. Explain how to factor $x^2 - 5x + 6$.

93. Explain how to solve a quadratic equation by factoring. Use the equation $x^2 + 6x + 8 = 0$ in your explanation.

94. Explain how to solve a quadratic equation using the quadratic formula. Use the equation $x^2 + 6x + 8 = 0$ in your explanation.

95. Describe the trend shown by the data for the percentage of foreign-born Americans in the graph for Exercises 85–88. Do you believe that this trend is likely to continue or might something occur that would make it impossible to extend the model into the future? Explain your answer.

• Critical Thinking Exercises

96. The radicand of the quadratic formula, $b^2 - 4ac$, can be used to determine whether $ax^2 + bx + c = 0$ has solutions that are rational, irrational, or not real numbers. Explain how this works. Is it possible to determine the kinds of answers that one will obtain to a quadratic equation without actually solving the equation? Explain.

In Exercises 97–98, find all positive integers b so that the trinomial can be factored.

97. $x^2 + bx + 15$

98. $x^2 + 4x + b$

99. Factor: $x^{2n} + 20x^n + 99$.

100. Solve: $x^2 + 2\sqrt{3}x - 9 = 0$.

●●●●●● CHAPTER SUMMARY, REVIEW, AND TEST

● S U M M A R Y	DEFINITIONS AND CONCEPTS	EXAMPLES

3.1 Algebraic Expressions and Formulas

a. An algebraic expression combines variables and numbers using addition, subtraction, multiplication, division, powers, or roots.

b. Evaluating an algebraic expression means finding its value for a given value of the variable or for given values of the variables. Once these values are substituted, follow the order of operations agreement in the box on page 118. — Ex. 1, p. 119; Ex. 2, p. 119; Ex. 3, p. 119

c. An equation is a statement that two expressions are equal. Formulas are equations that express relationships among two or more variables. Mathematical modeling is the process of finding formulas to describe real-world phenomena. Such formulas, together with the meaning assigned to the variables, are called mathematical models. The formulas are said to model, or describe, the relationships among the variables. — Ex. 4, p. 120

d. Terms of an algebraic expression are separated by addition. Like terms have the same variables with the same exponents on the variables. To add or subtract like terms, add or subtract the coefficients and copy the common variable

e. An algebraic expression is simplified when parentheses have been removed (using the distributive property) and like terms have been combined. — Ex. 5, p. 122; Ex. 6, p. 122; Ex. 7, p. 123

3.2 Linear Equations in One Variable

a. A linear equation in one variable can be written in the form $ax + b = 0$, where a and b are real numbers, and $a \neq 0$.

b. Solving a linear equation is the process of finding the set of numbers that make the equation a true statement. These numbers are the solutions. The set of all such solutions is the solution set.

c. Equivalent equations have the same solution set. Properties for generating equivalent equations are given in the box on page 126. — Ex. 1, p. 127

d. A step-by-step procedure for solving a linear equation is given in the box on page 128. — Ex. 2, p. 128; Ex. 3, p. 129; Ex. 4, p. 130

e. If an equation contains fractions, begin by multiplying both sides of the equation by the least common denominator of the fractions in the equation, thereby clearing fractions. — Ex. 5, p. 131; Ex. 6, p. 131

f. Solving a formula for a variable means rewriting the formula so that the variable is isolated on one side of the equation. — Ex. 7, p. 133; Ex. 8, p. 133

g. If a false statement (such as $-6 = 7$) is obtained in solving a linear equation, the equation has no solution. The solution set is $\varnothing$, the empty set. — Ex. 9, p. 134

h. If a true statement (such as $-6 = -6$) is obtained in solving a linear equation, the equation has infinitely many solutions. The solution set is the set of all real numbers, written $\{x \mid x \text{ is a real number}\}$. — Ex. 10, p. 134

3.3 Applications of Linear Equations

a. Algebraic translations of English phrases are given in Table 3.2 on page 138.

b. A step-by-step strategy for solving word problems using linear equations is given in the box on page 138.

3.4 Ratio, Proportion, and Variation

a. The ratio of a to b is written $\dfrac{a}{b}$, or $a:b$.

b. A proportion is a statement in the form $\dfrac{a}{b} = \dfrac{c}{d}$.

c. The cross-products principle states that if $\dfrac{a}{b} = \dfrac{c}{d}$, then $ad = bc$.

d. A step-by-step procedure for solving applied problems using proportions is given in the box on page 147.

e. If two quantities vary directly, as one increases, so does the other. As one decreases, so does the other. Proportions can be used to solve direct variation problems.

f. If two quantities vary inversely, as one increases, the other decreases. As one decreases, the other increases. Proportions, as explained in the box on page 151, can be used to solve inverse variation problems.

3.5 Linear Inequalities in One Variable

A procedure for solving a linear inequality is given in the box on page 156. Remember to reverse the direction of the inequality symbol when multiplying or dividing both sides of an inequality by a negative number.

3.6 Quadratic Equations

a. A quadratic equation can be written in the form $ax^2 + bx + c = 0, a \neq 0$.

b. Some quadratic equations can be solved using factoring and the zero-product principle. A step-by-step procedure is given in the box on page 169.

c. All quadratic equations in the form $ax^2 + bx + c = 0$ can be solved using the quadratic formula:

$$x = \frac{-b \pm \sqrt{b^2 - 4ac}}{2a}.$$

REVIEW EXERCISES

3.1

In Exercises 1–3, evaluate the algebraic expression for the given value of the variable.

1. $6x + 9$; $x = 4$
2. $7x^2 + 4x - 5$; $x = -2$

3. $6 + 2(x - 8)^3$; $x = 5$

4. The bar graph on the right shows the number of music CD sales, in millions, in the United States from 1998 through 2002. The data can be modeled by the formula

$$N = -26x^2 + 143x + 740,$$

where N represents the number of music CD sales, in millions, x years after 1997. According to the formula, how many millions of CDs were sold in 2002? How well does the formula describe sales for that year shown by the graph?

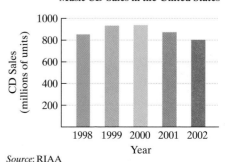

Music CD Sales in the United States

Source: RIAA

In Exercises 5–7, simplify each algebraic expression.

5. $5(2x - 3) + 7x$

6. $3(4y - 5) - (7y - 2)$

7. $2(x^2 + 5x) + 3(4x^2 - 3x)$

3.2

In Exercises 8–14, solve each equation.

8. $4x + 9 = 33$

9. $5x - 3 = x + 5$

10. $3(x + 4) = 5x - 12$

11. $2(x - 2) + 3(x + 5) = 2x - 2$

12. $\dfrac{2x}{3} = \dfrac{x}{6} + 1$

13. $7x + 5 = 5(x + 3) + 2x$

14. $7x + 13 = 2(2x - 5) + 3x + 23$

In Exercises 15–18, solve each formula for the specified variable.

15. $Ax - By = C$ for x

16. $A = \frac{1}{2}bh$ for h

17. $A = \dfrac{B + C}{2}$ for B

18. $vt + gt^2 = s$ for g

19. The bar graph shows the average prescription-drug price in the United States from 2000 through 2004. The data can be modeled by the formula

$$P = 4.6x + 45.8,$$

where P is the average price of a prescription drug, in dollars, x years after 2000. In which year does this model project that the average prescription-drug price will be $101?

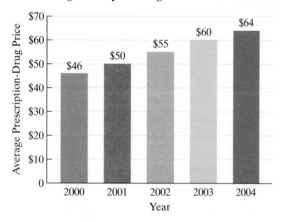

Average Prescription-Drug Price in the United States

Source: U.S. Census Bureau

3.3

In Exercises 20–24, use an equation to solve each problem.

20. When 7 times a number is decreased by 1, the result is 9 more than 5 times the number. Find the number.

21. The fast-food chains may be touting their "new and improved" salads, but how do they measure up in terms of calories?

| Burger King | Taco Bell | Wendy's |
| Chicken Caesar | Express Taco Salad | Mandarin Chicken Salad |

Number of calories exceeds the Chicken Caesar by 125.

Number of calories exceeds the Chicken Caesar by 95.

Source: Newsweek

Combined, the three salads contain 1705 calories. Determine the number of calories in each salad.

22. The bar graph shows the number of endangered plant species in the United States from 1998 through 2003. In 1998, there were 567 endangered species. For the period shown, the number of endangered plants increased at an average rate of 6.4 species per year. If this trend continues, in which year will there be 663 endangered plant species in the United States?

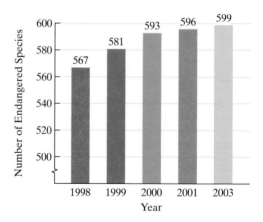

Endangered Plant Species in the United States

Source: U.S. Fish and Wildlife Service

23. You are choosing between two long-distance telephone plans. One plan has a monthly fee of $15 with a charge of $0.05 per minute. The other plan has a monthly fee of $5 with a charge of $0.07 per minute. For how many minutes of long-distance calls will the costs for the two plans be the same?

24. In 2004, the world's largest oil consumers were the United States and China. Oil consumption in the United States exceeded three times that of China by 1 million barrels per day. If the two countries combined consumed 27 million barrels of oil per day, determine the oil consumption, in millions of barrels per day, for each country.

(*Source*: Energy Information Administration)

3.4

In Exercises 25–28, solve each proportion.

25. $\dfrac{3}{x} = \dfrac{15}{25}$

26. $\dfrac{-7}{5} = \dfrac{91}{x}$

27. $\dfrac{x+2}{3} = \dfrac{4}{5}$

28. $\dfrac{5}{x+7} = \dfrac{3}{x+3}$

Use a proportion to solve Exercises 29–30.

29. If a school board determines that there should be 3 teachers for every 50 students, how many teachers are needed for an enrollment of 5400 students?

30. To determine the number of trout in a lake, a conservationist catches 112 trout, tags them, and returns them to the lake. Later, 82 trout are caught, and 32 of them are found to be tagged. How many trout are in the lake?

Exercises 31–33 involve direct and inverse variation. Use a proportion to solve each exercise.

31. An electric bill varies directly as the amount of electricity used. The bill for 1400 kilowatts of electricity is $98. What is the bill for 2200 kilowatts of electricity?

32. The distance that a body falls from rest varies directly as the square of the time of the fall. If skydivers fall 144 feet in 3 seconds, how far will they fall in 10 seconds?

33. The time it takes to drive a certain distance varies inversely as the rate of travel. If it takes 4 hours at 50 miles per hour to drive the distance, how long will it take at 40 miles per hour?

3.5

In Exercises 34–40, solve each inequality and graph the solution set on a number line.

34. $2x - 5 < 3$

35. $\dfrac{x}{2} > -4$

36. $3 - 5x \le 18$

37. $4x + 6 < 5x$

38. $6x - 10 \ge 2(x + 3)$

39. $4x + 3(2x - 7) \le x - 3$

40. $-1 < 4x + 2 \le 6$

41. To pass a course, a student must have an average on three examinations of at least 60. If a student scores 42 and 74 on the first two tests, what must be earned on the third test to pass the course?

3.6

Use FOIL to find the products in Exercises 42–43.

42. $(x + 9)(x - 5)$

43. $(4x - 7)(3x + 2)$

Factor the trinomials in Exercises 44–49, or state that the trinomial is prime.

44. $x^2 - x - 12$

45. $x^2 - 8x + 15$

46. $x^2 + 2x + 3$

47. $3x^2 - 17x + 10$

48. $6x^2 - 11x - 10$

49. $3x^2 - 6x - 5$

Solve the quadratic equations in Exercises 50–53 by factoring.

50. $x^2 + 5x - 14 = 0$

51. $x^2 - 4x = 32$

52. $2x^2 + 15x - 8 = 0$

53. $3x^2 = -21x - 30$

Solve the quadratic equations in Exercises 54–57 using the quadratic formula.

54. $x^2 - 4x + 3 = 0$

55. $x^2 - 5x = 4$

56. $2x^2 + 5x - 3 = 0$

57. $3x^2 - 6x = 5$

58. In 1945, 35.4% of taxes collected by the U.S. Treasury came from corporate income taxes. Since then, corporations have worked hard to convince lawmakers that they shouldn't pay taxes. The bar graph shows the percentage of federal taxes from corporate income taxes for selected years from 1985 through 2003. The data can be modeled by the formula

$$P = -0.035x^2 + 0.65x + 7.6,$$

where P represents the percentage of federal taxes from corporations x years after 1985. If these trends continue, by which year (to the nearest year) will corporations pay no taxes?

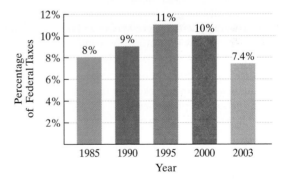

Percentage of Federal Taxes from Corporate Income Taxes

Source: White House Office of Management and Budget

●●●●●● CHAPTER 3 TEST

1. Evaluate $x^3 - 4(x - 1)^2$ when $x = -2$.

2. Simplify: $5(3x - 2) - (x - 6)$.

3. The formula

$$F = 24t^2 - 260t + 816$$

models the number of police officers in the United States, F, convicted of felonies t years after 1990. How many convictions of police officers were there in 2000?
(*Source:* FBI)

In Exercises 4–7, solve each equation.

4. $12x + 4 = 7x - 21$

5. $3(2x - 4) = 9 - 3(x + 1)$

6. $3(x - 4) + x = 2(6 + 2x)$

7. $\dfrac{x}{5} - 2 = \dfrac{x}{3}$

8. Solve for y: $By - Ax = A$.

9. The formula $D = 0.12x + 5.44$ models the number of children in the United States with physical disabilities, D, in millions, x years after 2000. According to this model, in which year will there be 6.4 million children in the United States with physical disabilities?

In Exercises 10–13, use an equation to solve each problem.

10. The product of 5 and a number, decreased by 9, is 310. What is the number?

11. In New York City, a fitness trainer earns $22,870 more per year than a preschool teacher. The yearly average salaries for fitness trainers and preschool teachers combined are $79,030. Determine the average yearly salary of a fitness trainer and a preschool teacher in New York City.

(*Source: Time*, April 14, 2003)

12. You bought a new car for $13,805. Its value is decreasing by $1820 per year. After how many years will its value be $4705?

13. Photo Shop A charges $1.60 to develop a roll of film plus $0.11 for each print. Photo Shop B charges $1.20 to develop a roll of film plus $0.13 per print. For how many prints will the amount spent at each photo shop be the same? What will be that amount?

In Exercises 14–15, solve each proportion.

14. $\dfrac{5}{8} = \dfrac{x}{12}$ **15.** $\dfrac{x + 5}{8} = \dfrac{x + 2}{5}$

16. Park rangers catch, tag, and release 200 tule elk back into a wildlife refuge. Two weeks later they observe a sample of 150 elk, of which 5 are tagged. Assuming that the ratio of tagged elk in the sample holds for all elk in the refuge, how many elk are there in the park?

17. The pressure of water on an object below the surface varies directly as its distance below the surface. If a submarine experiences a pressure of 25 pounds per square inch 60 feet below the surface, how much pressure will it experience 330 feet below the surface?

18. The time required to accomplish a task varies inversely as the number of people working on the task. It takes 6 hours for 20 people to put a new roof on a porch. How long would it take 30 people to do the job?

In Exercises 19–21, solve each inequality and graph the solution set on a number line.

19. $6 - 9x \geq 33$

20. $4x - 2 > 2(x + 6)$

21. $-3 \leq 2x + 1 < 6$

22. A student has grades on three examinations of 76, 80, and 72. What must the student earn on a fourth examination in order to have an average of at least 80?

23. Use FOIL to find this product: $(2x - 5)(3x + 4)$.

24. Factor: $2x^2 - 9x + 10$.

25. Solve by factoring: $x^2 + 5x = 36$.

26. Solve using the quadratic formula: $2x^2 + 4x = -1$.

Without changes, the graphs show projections for the amount being paid in Social Security benefits and the amount going into the system. All data are expressed in billions of dollars.

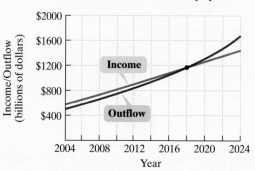

Social Insecurity: Projected Income and Outflow of the Social Security System

Source: 2004 Social Security Trustees Report

Exercises 27–29 are based on the data shown by the graphs.

27. In 2004, the system's income was $575 billion, projected to increase at an average rate of $43 billion per year. In which year will the system's income be $1177 billion?

28. The data for the system's outflow can be modeled by the formula

$$B = 0.07x^2 + 47.4x + 500,$$

where B represents the amount paid in benefits, in billions of dollars, x years after 2004. According to this model, when will the amount paid in benefits be $1177 billion? Round to the nearest year.

29. How well do your answers to Exercises 27 and 28 model the data shown by the graphs?

CHAPTER 4

Consumer Mathematics and Financial Management

"I realize, of course, that it's no shame to be poor, but it's no great honor either. So what would have been so terrible if I had a small fortune?"

—TEVYE, A POOR DAIRYMAN, IN THE MUSICAL *FIDDLER ON THE ROOF*

We all want a wonderful life with fulfilling work, good health, and loving relationships. And let's be honest: Financial security, or even a small fortune, wouldn't hurt! Achieving this goal depends on understanding basic ideas about savings, loans, and investments. A solid understanding of the topics in this chapter can pay, literally, by making your financial goals a reality.

A number of examples illustrate how to attain fortunes ranging from over a half-million dollars to $4 million through regular savings. See Example 3 in Section 4.4 and Exercises 35–36 in Exercise Set 4.4.

181

SECTION 4.1 • PERCENT, SALES TAX, AND INCOME TAX

OBJECTIVES

1. Express a fraction as a percent.

2. Express a decimal as a percent.

3. Express a percent as a decimal.

4. Solve applied problems involving sales tax and discounts.

5. Compute income tax.

6. Determine percent increase or decrease.

7. Investigate some of the ways percent can be abused.

"And if elected, it is my solemn pledge to cut your taxes by 10% for each of my first three years in office, for a total cut of 30%."

Did you know that one of the most common ways that you are given numerical information is with percents? This section will provide you with the tools to make sense of the politician's promise, as we present the uses, and abuses, of percent.

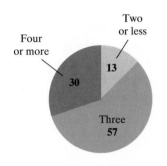

Source: U.S. Census Bureau and HUD

FIGURE 4.1 Number of bedrooms in privately owned single-family U.S. houses per 100 houses

Basics of Percent

Percents are the result of expressing numbers as a part of 100. The word *percent* means *per hundred*. For example, the circle graph in Figure 4.1 shows that 57 out of every 100 single-family homes have three bedrooms. Thus, $\frac{57}{100} = 57\%$, indicating that 57% of the houses have three bedrooms. The percent sign, %, is used to indicate the number of parts out of one hundred parts.

A fraction can be expressed as a percent using the following procedure:

> **EXPRESSING A FRACTION AS A PERCENT**
> 1. Divide the numerator by the denominator.
> 2. Multiply the quotient by 100. This is done by moving the decimal point in the quotient two places to the right.
> 3. Add a percent sign.

1 | Express a fraction as a percent.

EXAMPLE 1 EXPRESSING A FRACTION AS A PERCENT

Express $\frac{5}{8}$ as a percent.

SOLUTION

Step 1. Divide the numerator by the denominator.
$$5 \div 8 = 0.625$$

Step 2. Multiply the quotient by 100.
$$0.625 \times 100 = 62.5$$

Step 3. Add a percent sign.
$$62.5\%$$

Thus, $\frac{5}{8} = 62.5\%$.

Express $\frac{1}{8}$ as a percent.

2 | Express a decimal as a percent.

STUDY TIP

Dictionaries indicate that the word *percentage* has the same meaning as the word *percent*. Use the word that sounds best in the circumstance.

Our work in Example 1 shows that $0.625 = 62.5\%$. This illustrates the procedure for expressing a decimal number as a percent.

EXPRESSING A DECIMAL NUMBER AS A PERCENT

1. Move the decimal point two places to the right.
2. Attach a percent sign.

EXAMPLE 2   EXPRESSING A DECIMAL AS A PERCENT

Express 0.47 as a percent.

SOLUTION

Move decimal point two places right.

0.47   %   Add a percent sign.

Thus, $0.47 = 47\%$.

CHECK POINT 2   Express 0.023 as a percent.

3 | Express a percent as a decimal.

We reverse the procedure of Example 2 to express a percent as a decimal number.

EXPRESSING A PERCENT AS A DECIMAL NUMBER

1. Move the decimal point two places to the left.
2. Remove the percent sign.

EXAMPLE 3   EXPRESSING PERCENTS AS DECIMALS

Express each percent as a decimal:

a. 19%   **b.** 180%.

SOLUTION Use the two steps in the box.

a.

The percent sign is removed.

$$19\% = 19.\% = 0.19\%$$

The decimal point starts at the far right.

The decimal point is moved two places to the left.

Thus, $19\% = 0.19$.

b. $180\% = 1.80\% = 1.80$ or 1.8.

CHECK POINT 3   Express each percent as a decimal:

a. 67%   **b.** 250%.

If a fraction is part of a percent, as in $\frac{1}{4}\%$, begin by expressing the fraction as a decimal, retaining the percent sign. Then, use the two steps in the box to express the percent as a decimal number. For example,

$$\frac{1}{4}\% = 0.25\% = 00.25\% = 0.0025.$$

4 | Solve applied problems involving sales tax and discounts.

Percent, Sales Tax, and Discounts

Many applications involving percent are based on the following formula:

$$A \quad \text{is} \quad P \text{ percent} \quad \text{of} \quad B.$$
$$A \quad = \quad P \quad \cdot \quad B.$$

Note that the word *of* implies multiplication.

We can use this formula to determine the **sales tax** collected by states, counties, and cities on sales of items to customers. The sales tax is a percent of the cost of an item.

> Sales tax amount = tax rate × item's cost

EXAMPLE 4   PERCENT AND SALES TAX

Suppose that the local sales tax rate is 7.5% and you purchase a bicycle for $394.

a. How much tax is paid?

b. What is the bicycle's total cost?

SOLUTION

a.   Sales tax amount = tax rate × item's cost

= 7.5% × $394 = 0.075 × $394 = $29.55

> 7.5% of the item's cost, or 7.5% of $394

The tax paid is $29.55.

b. The bicycle's total cost is the purchase price, $394, plus the sales tax, $29.55.

Total cost = $394.00 + $29.55 = $423.55

The bicycle's total cost is $423.55.

 Suppose that the local sales tax rate is 6% and you purchase a computer for $1260.

a. How much tax is paid?

b. What is the computer's total cost?

None of us is thrilled about sales tax, but we do like buying things that are *on sale*. Businesses reduce prices, or **discount**, to attract customers and to reduce inventory. The discount rate is a percent of the original price.

Discount amount = discount rate × original price

EXAMPLE 5   PERCENT AND SALES PRICE

A computer with an original price of $1460 is on sale at 15% off.

a. What is the discount amount?

b. What is the computer's sale price?

SOLUTION

a.   Discount amount = discount rate × original price

= 15% × $1460 = 0.15 × $1460 = $219

> 15% of the original price, or 15% of $1460

The discount amount is $219.

A calculator is useful, and sometimes essential, in this chapter. The keystroke sequence that gives the sale price in Example 5 is

1460 $\boxed{-}$ .15 $\boxed{\times}$ 1460.

Press $\boxed{=}$ on a scientific calculator or $\boxed{\text{ENTER}}$ on a graphing calculator to display the answer, 1241.

b. The computer's sale price is the original price, $1460, minus the discount amount, $219.

$$\text{Sale price} = \$1460 - \$219 = \$1241$$

The computer's sale price is $1241.

 A CD player with an original price of $380 is on sale at 35% off.

    a. What is the discount amount?

    b. What is the CD player's sale price?

Percent and Income Tax

We have seen how tax rates determine the amount of sales tax on an item. They also determine the amount that we must each pay in income tax.

5 | Compute income tax.

CALCULATING INCOME TAX

1. Determine your adjusted gross income:

$$\text{Adjusted gross income} = \text{Gross income} - \text{Adjustments.}$$

> All income for the year, including wages, tips, earnings from investments, and unemployment compensation

> Includes payments to tax-deferred savings plans

2. Determine your taxable income:

$$\text{Taxable income} = \text{Adjusted gross income} - (\text{Exemptions} + \text{Deductions}).$$

> A fixed amount for yourself ($3200 in 2005) and the same amount for each dependent

> Choose the greater of a standard deduction or an itemized deduction, which includes interest on home mortgages, state income taxes, property taxes, charitable contributions, and medical expenses exceeding 7.5% of adjusted gross income.

3. Determine the income tax:

$$\text{Income tax} = \text{Tax computation} - \text{Tax credits.}$$

> Use your taxable income and tax rates for your filing status (single, married, etc.) to determine this amount.

> May include up to $1000 per child, the cost of child care so a parent can work, and adoption credits for qualified expenses.

Tax Rate	Single
10%	up to $7300
15%	$7301 to $29,700

A portion of Table 4.1. (The complete table appears on the next page.)

Table 4.1 on the next page shows 2005 tax rates, standard deductions, and exemptions for the four **filing status** categories described in the voice balloons. The tax rates in the left column, called **marginal tax rates**, are assigned to various income ranges, called **margins**. For example, suppose you are single and your taxable income is $25,000. The singles column of the table shows that you must pay 10% tax on the first $7300, which is

$$10\% \text{ of } \$7300 = 0.10 \times \$7300 = \$730.$$

You must also pay 15% tax on the remaining $17,700 ($25,000 − $7300 = $17,700), which is

$$15\% \text{ of } \$17,700 = 0.15 \times \$17,700 = \$2655.$$

Your total tax is $730 + $2655 = $3385. In this scenario, your *marginal rate* is 15% and you are in the 15% *tax bracket*.

TABLE 4.1 2005 MARGINAL TAX RATES, STANDARD DEDUCTIONS, AND EXEMPTIONS				
	Unmarried, divorced, or legally separated	*Married and each partner files a separate tax return*	*Married and both partners file a single tax return*	*Unmarried and paying more than half the cost of supporting a child or parent*
Tax Rate	**Single**	**Married Filing Separately**	**Married Filing Jointly**	**Head of Household**
10%	up to $7300	up to $7300	up to $14,600	up to $10,450
15%	$7301 to $29,700	$7301 to $29,700	$14,601 to $59,400	$10,451 to $39,800
25%	$29,701 to $71,950	$29,701 to $59,975	$59,401 to $119,950	$39,801 to $102,800
28%	$71,951 to $150,150	$59,976 to $91,400	$119,951 to $182,800	$102,801 to $166,450
33%	$150,151 to $326,450	$91,401 to $163,225	$182,801 to $326,450	$166,451 to $326,450
35%	more than $326,450	more than $163,225	more than $326,450	more than $326,450
Standard Deduction	$5000	$5000	$10,000	$7300
Exemptions (per person)	$3200	$3200	$3200	$3200

SINGLE WOMAN WITH NO DEPENDENTS

Gross income: $52,000

Adjustments: $4000 paid to a tax-deferred IRA (Individual Retirement Account)

Deductions:
- $7500: mortgage interest
- $2200: property taxes
- $2400: charitable contributions
- $1500: medical expenses not covered by insurance

Tax credit: $500

EXAMPLE 6   COMPUTING INCOME TAX

Calculate the income tax owed by a single woman with no dependents whose gross income, adjustments, deductions, and credits are given in the margin. Use the 2005 marginal tax rates in Table 4.1.

SOLUTION

Step 1. Determine the adjusted gross income.

$$\text{Adjusted gross income} = \text{Gross income} - \text{Adjustments}$$
$$= \$52,000 - \$4000$$
$$= \$48,000$$

Step 2. Determine the taxable income.

$$\text{Taxable income} = \text{Adjusted gross income} - (\text{Exemptions} + \text{Deductions})$$
$$= \$48,000 - (\$3200 + \text{Deductions})$$

The singles column in Table 8.1 shows a personal exemption of $3200.

The singles column in Table 8.1 shows a $5000 standard deduction. A greater deduction can be obtained by itemizing.

Itemized Deductions

$7500 : mortgage interest

$2200 : property taxes

$2400 : charitable contributions

Can only deduct amount in excess of 7.5% of gross income:
0.075 × $52,000 = $3900

$1500 : ~~medical expenses~~

$12,100 : total of deductible expenditures

We substitute $12,100 for deductions in the formula for taxable income.

$$\text{Taxable income} = \text{Adjusted gross income} - (\text{Exemptions} + \text{Deductions})$$
$$= \$48,000 - (\$3200 + \$12,100)$$
$$= \$48,000 - \$15,300$$
$$= \$32,700$$

Step 3. Determine the income tax.

$$\text{Income Tax} = \text{Tax computation} - \text{Tax credits}$$
$$= \text{Tax computation} - \$500$$

Tax Rate	Single
10%	up to $7300
15%	$7301 to $29,700
25%	$29,701 to $71,950

A portion of Table 4.1 (repeated)

We perform the tax computation using the singles rates in Table 4.1. Our taxpayer is in the 25% tax bracket because her taxable income, $32,700, is in the $29,701 to $71,950 income range. This means that she owes 10% on the first $7300 of her taxable income, 15% on her taxable income between $7301 and $29,700, inclusive, and 25% on her taxable income above $29,700.

> 10% marginal rate on first $7300 of taxable income

> 15% marginal rate on taxable income between $7301 and $29,700

> 25% marginal rate on taxable income above $29,700

$$\text{Tax computation} = 0.10 \times \$7300 + 0.15 \times (\$29,700 - \$7300) + 0.25 \times (\$32,700 - \$29,700)$$

$$= 0.10 \times \$7300 + 0.15 \times \$22,400 + 0.25 \times \$3000$$
$$= \$730 + \$3360 + \$750$$
$$= \$4840$$

STUDY TIP

A tax credit is not the same thing as a tax deduction. The *tax credit* of $500 in Example 6 *reduces the income tax owed by the full dollar-for-dollar amount*, namely, $500. The *tax deduction* of $12,100 *reduces the taxable income* by $12,100, thereby saving only a percentage of $12,100 in taxes.

We substitute $4840 for the tax computation in the formula for income tax.

$$\text{Income tax} = \text{Tax computation} - \text{Tax credits}$$
$$= \$4840 - \$500$$
$$= \$4340$$

The income tax owed is $4340.

CHECK POINT 6 Use the 2005 marginal tax rates in Table 4.1 to calculate the tax owed by a single man with no dependents whose gross income, adjustments, deductions, and credits are given as follows:

> Gross income: $40,000
>
> Adjustments: $1000
>
> Deductions: $3000: charitable contributions
>
> $1500: theft loss
>
> $300: cost of tax preparation
>
> Tax credit: none.

6 Determine percent increase or decrease.

Percent and Change

Percents are used for comparing changes, such as increases or decreases in sales, population, prices, and production. If a quantity changes, its **percent increase** or its **percent decrease** can be found as follows:

> **FINDING PERCENT INCREASE OR PERCENT DECREASE**
>
> **1.** Find the fraction for the percent increase or the percent decrease:
>
> $$\frac{\text{amount of increase}}{\text{original amount}} \quad \text{or} \quad \frac{\text{amount of decrease}}{\text{original amount}}.$$
>
> **2.** Find the percent increase or the percent decrease by expressing the fraction in step 1 as a percent.

EXAMPLE 7 FINDING PERCENT INCREASE AND DECREASE

In 2000, world population was approximately 6 billion. Figure 4.2 shows world population projections through the year 2150. The data are from the United Nations Family Planning Program and are based on optimistic or pessimistic expectations for successful control of human population growth.

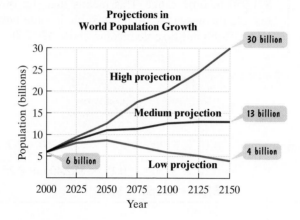

Projections in World Population Growth

FIGURE 4.2
Source: United Nations

a. Find the percent increase in world population from 2000 to 2150 using the high projection data.

b. Find the percent decrease in world population from 2000 to 2150 using the low projection data.

SOLUTION

a. Use the data shown on the blue, high-projection, graph.

$$\text{Percent increase} = \frac{\text{amount of increase}}{\text{original amount}}$$

$$= \frac{30 - 6}{6} = \frac{24}{6} = 4 = 400\%$$

The projected percent increase in world population is 400%.

b. Use the data shown on the green, low-projection, graph.

$$\text{Percent decrease} = \frac{\text{amount of decrease}}{\text{original amount}}$$

$$= \frac{6 - 4}{6} = \frac{2}{6} = \frac{1}{3} = 0.33\frac{1}{3} = 33\frac{1}{3}\%$$

The projected percent decrease in world population is $33\frac{1}{3}\%$.

In Example 7, we expressed the percent decrease as $33\frac{1}{3}\%$ because of the familiar conversion $\frac{1}{3} = 0.33\frac{1}{3}$. However, in many situations, rounding is needed. We suggest that you round to the nearest tenth of a percent. Carry the division in the fraction for percent increase or decrease to four places after the decimal point. Then round the decimal to three places, or to the nearest thousandth. Expressing this rounded decimal as a percent gives percent increase or decrease to the nearest tenth of a percent.

a. If 6 is increased to 10, find the percent increase.

b. If 10 is decreased to 6, find the percent decrease.

EXAMPLE 8   FINDING PERCENT DECREASE

A jacket regularly sells for $135.00. The sale price is $60.75. Find the percent decrease of the sale price from the regular price.

SOLUTION

$$\text{Percent decrease} = \frac{\text{amount of decrease}}{\text{original amount}}$$

$$= \frac{135.00 - 60.75}{135} = \frac{74.25}{135} = 0.55 = 55\%$$

The percent decrease of the sale price from the regular price is 55%. This means that the sale price of the jacket is 55% lower than the regular price.   ○

 A television regularly sells for $940. The sale price is $611. Find the percent decrease of the sale price from the regular price.

7   Investigate some of the ways percent can be abused.

Abuses of Percent

In our next examples, we look at a few of the many ways that percent can be used incorrectly. Confusion often arises when percent increase (or decrease) refers to a changing quantity that is itself a percent.

EXAMPLE 9   PERCENTS OF PERCENTS

John Tesh, while he was still coanchoring *Entertainment Tonight*, reported that the PBS series *The Civil War* had an audience of 13% versus the usual 4% PBS audience, "an increase of more than 300%." Did Tesh report the percent increase correctly?

SOLUTION We begin by finding the percent increase.

$$\text{Percent increase} = \frac{\text{amount of increase}}{\text{original amount}}$$

$$= \frac{13\% - 4\%}{4\%} = \frac{9\%}{4\%} = \frac{9}{4} = 2.25 = 225\%$$

The percent increase for PBS was 225%. This is not more than 300%, so Tesh did not report the percent increase correctly.   ○

 An episode of a television series had an audience of 12% versus its usual 10%. What was the percent increase for this episode?

EXAMPLE 10   PROMISES OF A POLITICIAN

A politician states, "If you elect me to office, I promise to cut your taxes for each of my first three years in office by 10% each year, for a total reduction of 30%." Evaluate the accuracy of the politician's statement.

SOLUTION To make things simple, let's assume that a taxpayer paid $100 in taxes in the year previous to the politician's election. A 10% reduction during year 1 is 10% of $100.

$$10\% \text{ of previous year tax} = 10\% \text{ of } \$100 = 0.10 \times \$100 = \$10$$

Percents and Tax Rates

In 1944 and 1945, the highest marginal tax rate in the United States was a staggering 94%. (Does a 94% tax bracket qualify as an abuse of percent?) The tax rate on the highest-income Americans remained at approximately 90% throughout the 1950s, decreased to 70% in the 1960s and 1970s, and to 50% in the early 1980s before reaching a post–World War II low of 28% in 1998. (*Source*: IRS) In 2006, Denmark had the world's highest tax rate, starting at 43.7% and climbing to 62.9% for its wealthiest taxpayers.

With a 10% reduction the first year, the taxpayer will pay only $100 − $10, or $90, in taxes during the politician's first year in office.

The following table shows how we calculate the new, reduced tax for each of the first three years in office:

Year	Tax Paid the Year Before	10% Reduction	Taxes Paid This Year
1	$100	0.10 × $100 = $10	$100 − $10 = $90
2	$90	0.10 × $90 = $9	$90 − $9 = $81
3	$81	0.10 × $81 = $8.10	$81 − $8.10 = $72.90

Now, we determine the percent decrease in taxes over the three years.

$$\text{Percent decrease} = \frac{\text{amount of decrease}}{\text{original amount}}$$

$$= \frac{\$100 - \$72.90}{\$100} = \frac{\$27.10}{\$100} = \frac{27.1}{100} = 0.271 = 27.1\%$$

The taxes decline by 27.1%, not by 30%. The politician is ill-informed in saying that three consecutive 10% cuts add up to a total tax cut of 30%. In our calculation, which serves as a counterexample to the promise, the total tax cut is only 27.1%.

CHECK POINT 10 Suppose you paid $1200 in taxes. During year 1, taxes decrease by 20%. During year 2, taxes increase by 20%.

a. What do you pay in taxes for year 2?

b. How do your taxes for year 2 compare with what you originally paid, namely $1200? If the taxes are not the same, find the percent increase or decrease.

EXERCISE SET 4.1 ●●●●●●

• Practice Exercises

In Exercises 1–10, express each fraction as a percent.

1. $\frac{2}{5}$ **2.** $\frac{3}{5}$ **3.** $\frac{1}{4}$ **4.** $\frac{3}{4}$

5. $\frac{3}{8}$ **6.** $\frac{7}{8}$ **7.** $\frac{1}{40}$ **8.** $\frac{3}{40}$

9. $\frac{9}{80}$ **10.** $\frac{13}{80}$

In Exercises 11–20, express each decimal as a percent.

11. 0.59   **12.** 0.96   **13.** 0.3844   **14.** 0.003

15. 2.87   **16.** 9.83   **17.** 14.87   **18.** 19.63

19. 100   **20.** 95

In Exercises 21–34, express each percent as a decimal.

21. 72%   **22.** 38%   **23.** 43.6%   **24.** 6.25%

25. 130%   **26.** 260%   **27.** 2%   **28.** 6%

29. $\frac{1}{2}$%   **30.** $\frac{3}{4}$%   **31.** $\frac{5}{8}$%   **32.** $\frac{1}{8}$%

33. $62\frac{1}{2}$%   **34.** $87\frac{1}{2}$%

Use the percent formula, $A = PB$: A is P percent of B, to solve Exercises 35–38.

35. What is 3% of 200?   **36.** What is 8% of 300?

37. What is 18% of 40?   **38.** What is 16% of 90?

• Practice Plus

There are three basic types of percent problems that can be solved using the percent formula $A = PB$.

Question	Given	Percent Formula
What is *P* percent of *B*?	*P* and *B*	Solve for *A*.
A is *P* percent of what?	*A* and *P*	Solve for *B*.
A is what percent of *B*?	*A* and *B*	Solve for *P*.

Exercises 35–38 involved using the formula to answer the first question. In Exercises 39–46, use the percent formula to answer the second or third question.

39. 3 is 60% of what?

40. 8 is 40% of what?

41. 24% of what number is 40.8?

42. 32% of what number is 51.2?

43. 3 is what percent of 15?

44. 18 is what percent of 90?

45. What percent of 2.5 is 0.3?

46. What percent of 7.5 is 0.6?

• Application Exercises

47. Suppose that the local sales tax rate is 6% and you purchase a car for $16,800.

   a. How much tax is paid?

   b. What is the car's total cost?

48. Suppose that the local sales tax rate is 7% and you purchase a graphing calculator for $96.

   a. How much tax is paid?

   b. What is the calculator's total cost?

49. An exercise machine with an original price of $860 is on sale at 12% off.

   a. What is the discount amount?

   b. What is the exercise machine's sale price?

50. A dictionary that normally sells for $16.50 is on sale at 40% off.

   a. What is the discount amount?

   b. What is the dictionary's sale price?

In Exercises 51–54, use the 2005 marginal tax rates in Table 4.1 on page 186 to calculate the income tax owed by each person.

51. Single male, no dependents

   Gross income: $75,000

   Adjustments: $4000

   Deductions:

      $28,000 mortgage interest

      $4200 property taxes

      $3000 charitable contributions

   Tax credit: none

52. Single female, no dependents

   Gross income: $70,000

   Adjustments: $2000

   Deductions:

      $10,000 mortgage interest

      $2500 property taxes

      $1200 charitable contributions

   Tax credit: none

53. Unmarried head of household with two dependent children

   Gross income: $50,000

   Adjustments: none

   Deductions:

      $4500 state taxes

      $2000 theft loss

   Tax credit: $2000

54. Unmarried head of household with one dependent child

   Gross income: $40,000

   Adjustments: $1500

   Deductions:

      $3600 state taxes

      $800 charitable contributions

   Tax credit: $2500

In addition to income tax, we are required to pay the federal government FICA (Federal Insurance Contribution Act) taxes that are used for Social Security and Medicare benefits. For people who are not self-employed, the 2005 FICA tax rates were as follows:

- *7.65% on the first $90,000 from wages and tips*
- *1.45% on income in excess of $90,000.*

The individual's employer must also pay matching amounts of FICA taxes. People who are self-employed pay double the rates shown above. Taxpayers are not permitted to subtract adjustments, exemptions, or deductions when determining FICA taxes. Use this information to solve Exercises 55–60.

55. If you are not self-employed and earn $100,000, what are your FICA taxes?

56. If you are not self-employed and earn $120,000, what are your FICA taxes?

57. If you are self-employed and earn $140,000, what are your FICA taxes?

58. If you are self-employed and earn $160,000, what are your FICA taxes?

59. In 2005, to help pay for college, you worked part-time at a local restaurant, earning $20,000 in wages and tips.

   a. Calculate your FICA taxes.

   b. Use Table 4.1 on page 186 to calculate your income tax. Assume you are single with no dependents, have no adjustments or tax credit, and you take the standard deduction.

   c. Including both FICA and income tax, what percent of your gross income are your federal taxes? Round to the nearest tenth of a percent.

60. In 2005, to help pay for college, you worked part-time at a local restaurant, earning $18,000 in wages and tips.

   a. Calculate your FICA taxes.

   b. Use Table 4.1 on page 186 to calculate your income tax. Assume you are single with no dependents, have no adjustments or tax credit, and take the standard deduction.

   c. Including both FICA and income tax, what percent of your gross income are your federal taxes? Round to the nearest tenth of a percent.

The table shows the fastest-growing U.S. jobs, by number of 2004 employees and expected employees in 2014.

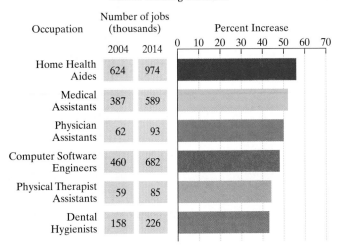

Fastest-Growing U.S. Jobs

Source: Bureau of Labor Statistics

In Exercises 61–64, use the number of jobs given at the bottom of the previous page to find the percent increase, to the nearest tenth of a percent, in the number of employees in the given occupation from 2004 to 2014.

61. home health aides   **62.** medical assistants

63. physician assistants   **64.** computer software engineers

65. A sofa regularly sells for $840. The sale price is $714. Find the percent decrease of the sale price from the regular price.

66. A FAX machine regularly sells for $380. The sale price is $266. Find the percent decrease of the sale price from the regular price.

67. Suppose that you have $10,000 in a rather risky investment recommended by your financial advisor. During the first year, your investment decreases by 30% of its original value. During the second year, your investment increases by 40% of its first-year value. Your advisor tells you that there must have been a 10% overall increase of your original $10,000 investment. Is your financial advisor using percentages properly? If not, what is your actual percent gain or loss of your original $10,000 investment?

68. The price of a color printer is reduced by 30% of its original price. When it still does not sell, its price is reduced by 20% of the reduced price. The salesperson informs you that there has been a total reduction of 50%. Is the salesperson using percentages properly? If not, what is the actual percent reduction from the original price?

• Writing in Mathematics

69. What is a percent?

70. Describe how to express a decimal number as a percent and give an example.

71. Describe how to express a percent as a decimal number and give an example.

72. Explain how to use the sales tax rate to determine an item's total cost.

73. A common complaint about income tax is "I can't afford to work more because it will put me in a higher tax bracket." Is it possible that being in a higher bracket means you actually lose money? Explain your answer.

74. Because of the mortgage interest tax deduction, is it possible to save money buying a house rather than renting, even though rent payments are lower than mortgage payments? Explain your answer.

75. Describe how to find percent increase and give an example.

• Critical Thinking Exercises

76. Which one of the following is true?
   a. If your weight increases by 5% this year and 5% next year, the increase in weight over two years is 10%.
   b. A grade point average that increases by 10% this semester and decreases by 10% next semester will be unchanged after two semesters.
   c. If $\frac{1}{10}$ of a person's salary is spent for clothing, $\frac{1}{3}$ for food, and $\frac{1}{5}$ for rent, the percent of the salary that is left is $36\frac{2}{3}\%$.
   d. If the amount that a person spends on rent increases from 20% to 30% of that person's income, the percent increase is 10%.

77. A condominium is taxed based on its $78,500 value. The tax rate is $3.40 for every $100 of value. If the tax is paid before March 1, 3% of the normal tax is given as a discount. How much tax is paid if the condominium owner takes advantage of the discount?

78. In January, each of 60 people purchased a $200 washing machine. In February, 10% fewer customers purchased the same washing machine that had increased in price by 20%. What was the change in sales from January to February?

• Group Exercise

79. Group members should research and present a report on the Alternative Minimum Tax (AMT). How do the AMT calculations differ from the income tax calculations that we discussed in this section? What are some of the hot political issues surrounding the AMT? On whom will it have the greatest financial impact?

SECTION 4.2 • SIMPLE INTEREST

OBJECTIVES

1. Calculate simple interest.
2. Use the future value formula.
3. Use the simple interest formula on discounted loans.

In 1626, Peter Minuit convinced the Wappinger Indians to sell him Manhattan Island for $24. If the native Americans had put the $24 into a bank account at a 5% interest rate compounded monthly, by the year 2006 there would be well over $4 billion in the account!

Although you may not yet understand terms such as *interest rate* and *compounded monthly*, one thing seems clear: Money in certain savings accounts grows in remarkable ways. You, too, can take advantage of such accounts with astonishing results. In the next two sections, we will show you how.

1 │ Calculate simple interest.

Simple Interest

Interest is the dollar amount that we get paid for lending money or pay for borrowing money. When we deposit money in a savings institution, the institution pays us interest for its use. When we borrow money, interest is the price we pay for the privilege of using the money until we repay it.

The amount of money that we deposit or borrow is called the **principal**. For example, if you deposit $2000 in a savings account, then $2000 is the principal. The amount of interest depends on the principal, the interest **rate**, which is given as a percent and varies from bank to bank, and the length of time for which the money is deposited. In this section, the rate is assumed to be per year.

Simple interest involves interest calculated only on the principal. The following formula is used to find simple interest:

> ### CALCULATING SIMPLE INTEREST
>
> Interest = principal × rate × time
>
> $$I = Prt$$
>
> The rate, r, is expressed as a decimal when calculating simple interest.

EXAMPLE 1   CALCULATING SIMPLE INTEREST FOR A YEAR

You deposit $2000 in a savings account at Hometown Bank, which has a rate of 6%. Find the interest at the end of the first year.

SOLUTION To find the interest at the end of the first year, we use the simple interest formula.

$$I = Prt = (2000)(0.06)(1) = 120$$

| Principal, or amount deposited, is $2000. | Rate is 6% = 0.06. | Time is 1 year. |

At the end of the first year, the interest is $120. You can withdraw the $120 interest and you still have $2000 in the savings account.   ○

 You deposit $3000 in a savings account at Yourtown Bank, which has a rate of 5%. Find the interest at the end of the first year.

EXAMPLE 2   CALCULATING SIMPLE INTEREST FOR MORE THAN A YEAR

A student took out a simple interest loan for $1800 for two years at a rate of 8% to purchase a used car. What is the interest on the loan?

SOLUTION To find the interest on the loan, we use the simple interest formula.

$$I = Prt = (1800)(0.08)(2) = 288$$

| Principal, or amount borrowed, is $1800. | Rate is 8% = 0.08. | Time is 2 years. |

The interest on the loan is $288.   ○

CHECK POINT 2 A student took out a simple interest loan for $2400 for two years at a rate of 7%. What is the interest on the loan?

2

Use the future value formula.

Future Value: Principal Plus Interest

When a loan is repaid, the interest is added to the original principal to find the total amount due. In Example 2, at the end of two years, the student will have to repay

$$\text{principal} + \text{interest} = \$1800 + \$288 = \$2088.$$

In general, if a principal P is borrowed at a simple interest rate r, then after t years the amount due, A, can be determined as follows:

$$A = P + I = P + Prt = P(1 + rt).$$

The amount due, A, is called the **future value** of the loan. The principal borrowed now, P, is also known as the loan's **present value**.

> ### CALCULATING FUTURE VALUE FOR SIMPLE INTEREST
> The future value, A, of P dollars at simple interest rate r (as a decimal) for t years is given by
> $$A = P(1 + rt).$$

EXAMPLE 3   CALCULATING FUTURE VALUE

A loan of $1060 has been made at 6.5% for three months. Find the loan's future value.

SOLUTION The amount borrowed, or principal, P, is $1060. The rate, r, is 6.5%, or 0.065. The time, t, is given as 3 months. We need to express the time in years because the rate is understood to be 6.5% per year. Because 3 months is $\frac{3}{12}$ of a year, $t = \frac{3}{12} = \frac{1}{4} = 0.25$.

The loan's future value, or the total amount due after three months, is

$$A = P(1 + rt) = 1060[1 + (0.065)(0.25)] \approx \$1077.23.$$

Rounded to the nearest cent, the loan's future value is $1077.23.

CHECK POINT 3 A loan of $2040 has been made at 7.5% for four months. Find the loan's future value.

Simple interest is used for many short-term loans, including automobile and consumer loans. Imagine that a short-term loan is taken for 125 days. The time of the loan is $\frac{125}{365}$ because there are 365 days in a year. However, the **Banker's rule** allows financial institutions to use 360 in the denominator of such a fraction, claiming that this simplifies the interest calculation. The time, t, for a 125-day short-term loan is

$$\frac{125 \text{ days}}{360 \text{ days}} = \frac{125}{360}.$$

Consumer groups question whether a year should be simplified to 360 days. Why? Compare the values for time, t, for a 125-day short-term loan using denominators of 360 and 365.

$$\frac{125}{360} \approx 0.347 \qquad \frac{125}{365} \approx 0.342$$

The denominator of 360 benefits the bank by resulting in a greater period of time for the loan, and consequently more interest.

The formula for future value, $A = P(1 + rt)$, has four variables. If we are given values for any three of these variables, we can solve for the fourth.

EXAMPLE 4   DETERMINING A SIMPLE INTEREST RATE

You borrow $2500 from a friend and promise to pay back $2655 in six months. What simple interest rate will you pay?

SOLUTION We use the formula for future value, $A = P(1 + rt)$. You borrow $2500: $P = 2500$. You will pay back $2655, so this is the future value: $A = 2655$. You will do this in six months, which must be expressed in years: $t = \frac{6}{12} = \frac{1}{2} = 0.5$. To determine the simple interest rate you will pay, we solve the future value formula for r.

$A = P(1 + rt)$	This is the formula for future value.
$2655 = 2500[1 + r(0.5)]$	Substitute the given values.
$2655 = 2500 + 1250r$	Use the distributive property.
$155 = 1250r$	Subtract 2500 from both sides.
$\dfrac{155}{1250} = \dfrac{1250r}{1250}$	Divide both sides by 1250.
$r = 0.124 = 12.4\%$	Express $\dfrac{155}{1250}$ as a percent.

You will pay a simple interest rate of 12.4%.

You borrow $5000 from a friend and promise to pay back $6800 in two years. What simple interest rate will you pay?

EXAMPLE 5   DETERMINING A PRESENT VALUE

You plan to save $2000 for a trip to Europe in two years. You decide to purchase a certificate of deposit (CD) from your bank that pays a simple interest rate of 4%. How much must you put in this CD now in order to have the $2000 in two years?

SOLUTION We use the formula for future value, $A = P(1 + rt)$. We are interested in finding the principal, P, or the present value.

$A = P(1 + rt)$	This is the formula for future value.
$2000 = P[1 + (0.04)(2)]$	A(future value) $= \$2000$, r(interest rate) $= 0.04$, and $t = 2$ (you want $2000 in two years).
$2000 = 1.08P$	Simplify: $1 + (0.04)(2) = 1.08$.
$\dfrac{2000}{1.08} = \dfrac{1.08P}{1.08}$	Divide both sides by 1.08.
$P \approx 1851.852$	Simplify.

To make sure you will have enough money for the vacation, let's round this principal *up* to $1851.86. Thus, you should put $1851.86 in the CD now to have $2000 in two years.

How much should you put in an investment paying a simple interest rate of 8% if you need $4000 in six months?

3 | Use the simple interest formula on discounted loans.

Discounted Loans

Some lenders collect the interest from the amount of the loan at the time that the loan is made. This type of loan is called a **discounted loan**. The interest that is deducted from the loan is the **discount**.

EXAMPLE 6   A DISCOUNTED LOAN

You borrow $10,000 on a 10% discounted loan for a period of 8 months.

a. What is the loan's discount?

b. Determine the net amount of money you receive.

c. What is the loan's actual interest rate?

SOLUTION

a. Because the loan's discount is the deducted interest, we use the simple interest formula.

$$I = Prt = (10,000)(0.10)\left(\tfrac{2}{3}\right) \approx 666.67$$

Principal is $10,000.   Rate is 10% = 0.10.   Time is 8 months $= \tfrac{8}{12} = \tfrac{2}{3}$ year.

The loan's discount is $666.67.

b. The net amount that you receive is the amount of the loan, $10,000, minus the discount, $666.67:

$$10,000 - 666.67 = 9333.33.$$

Thus, you receive $9333.33.

c. We can calculate the loan's actual interest rate, rather than the stated 10%, by using the simple interest formula.

$$I = Prt$$

This is the simple interest formula.

$$666.67 = (9333.33)r\left(\frac{2}{3}\right)$$

I(interest) $=$ $666.67, P (principal, or the net amount received) $=$ $9333.33, and $t = \dfrac{2}{3}$ year.

$$666.67 = 6222.22r$$

Simplify: $9333.33\left(\dfrac{2}{3}\right) = 6222.22$.

$$r = \frac{666.67}{6222.22} \approx 0.107 = 10.7\%$$

Solve for r and express r to the nearest tenth of a percent.

The actual rate of interest on the 10% discounted loan is approximately 10.7%.

CHECK POINT 6 You borrow $5000 on a 12% discounted loan for a period of two years. Determine: **a.** the loan's discount; **b.** the net amount you receive; **c.** the actual interest rate.

EXERCISE SET 4.2 ●●●●●●

• Practice Exercises

In Exercises 1–8, the principal P is borrowed at simple interest rate r for a period of time t. Find the simple interest owed for the use of the money. Assume 360 days in a year and round answers to the nearest cent.

1. $P = \$4000, r = 6\%, t = 1$ year

2. $P = \$7000, r = 5\%, t = 1$ year

3. $P = \$180, r = 3\%, t = 2$ years

4. $P = \$260, r = 4\%, t = 3$ years

5. $P = \$5000, r = 8.5\%, t = 9$ months

6. $P = \$18,000, r = 7.5\%, t = 18$ months

7. $P = \$15,500, r = 11\%, t = 90$ days

8. $P = \$12,600, r = 9\%, t = 60$ days

In Exercises 9–14, the principal P is borrowed at simple interest rate r for a period of time t. Find the loan's future value, A, or the total amount due at time t. Round answers to the nearest cent.

9. $P = \$3000, r = 7\%, t = 2$ years

10. $P = \$2000, r = 6\%, t = 3$ years

11. $P = \$26{,}000, r = 9.5\%, t = 5$ years

12. $P = \$24{,}000, r = 8.5\%, t = 6$ years

13. $P = \$9000, r = 6.5\%, t = 8$ months

14. $P = \$6000, r = 4.5\%, t = 9$ months

In Exercises 15–20, the principal P is borrowed and the loan's future value, A, at time t is given. Determine the loan's simple interest rate, r, to the nearest tenth of a percent.

15. $P = \$2000, A = \$2150, t = 1$ year

16. $P = \$3000, A = \$3180, t = 1$ year

17. $P = \$5000, A = \$5900, t = 2$ years

18. $P = \$10{,}000, A = \$14{,}060, t = 2$ years

19. $P = \$2300, A = \$2840, t = 9$ months

20. $P = \$1700, A = \$1820, t = 6$ months

In Exercises 21–26, determine the present value, P, you must invest to have the future value, A, at simple interest rate r after time t. Round answers up to the nearest cent.

21. $A = \$6000, r = 8\%, t = 2$ years

22. $A = \$8500, r = 7\%, t = 3$ years

23. $A = \$14{,}000, r = 9.5\%, t = 6$ years

24. $A = \$16{,}000, r = 11.5\%, t = 5$ years

25. $A = \$5000, r = 14.5\%, t = 9$ months

26. $A = \$2000, r = 12.6\%, t = 8$ months

Exercises 27–30 involve discounted loans. In each exercise, determine

    a. *the loan's discount.*

    b. *the net amount of money you receive.*

    c. *the loan's actual interest rate, to the nearest tenth of a percent.*

27. You borrow \$2000 on a 7% discounted loan for a period of 8 months.

28. You borrow \$3000 on an 8% discounted loan for a period of 9 months.

29. You borrow \$12,000 on a 6.5% discounted loan for a period of two years.

30. You borrow \$20,000 on an 8.5% discounted loan for a period of three years.

• Practice Plus

31. Solve for r: $A = P(1 + rt)$.

32. Solve for t: $A = P(1 + rt)$.

33. Solve for P: $A = P(1 + rt)$.

34. Solve for P: $A = P\left(1 + \frac{r}{n}\right)^{nt}$. (We will be using this formula in the next section.)

• Application Exercises

35. In order to start a small business, a student takes out a simple interest loan for \$4000 for 9 months at a rate of 8.25%.

    a. How much interest must the student pay?

    b. Find the future value of the loan.

36. In order to pay for baseball uniforms, a school takes out a simple interest loan for \$20,000 for 7 months at a rate of 12%.

    a. How much interest must the school pay?

    b. Find the future value of the loan.

37. You borrow \$1400 from a friend and promise to pay back \$2000 in two years. What simple interest rate, to the nearest tenth of a percent, will you pay?

38. Treasury bills (T-bills) can be purchased from the U.S. Treasury Department. You buy a T-bill for \$981.60 that pays \$1000 in 13 weeks. What simple interest rate, to the nearest tenth of a percent, does this T-bill earn?

39. A bank offers a CD that pays a simple interest rate of 6.5%. How much must you put in this CD now in order to have \$3000 for a home-entertainment center in two years? Round *up* to the nearest cent.

40. A bank offers a CD that pays a simple interest rate of 5.5%. How much must you put in this CD now in order to have \$8000 for a kitchen remodeling project in two years? Round *up* to the nearest cent.

• Writing in Mathematics

41. Explain how to calculate simple interest.

42. What is the future value of a loan and how is it determined?

43. What is a discounted loan? How is the net amount of money received from such a loan determined?

• Critical Thinking Exercises

44. Use the future value formula to show that the time required for an amount of money P to double in value to $2P$ is given by

$$t = \frac{1}{r}.$$

45. You deposit \$5000 in an account that earns 5.5% simple interest.

    a. Express the future value in the account as a linear function of time, t.

    b. Determine the slope of the function in part (a) and describe what this means. Use the phrase "rate of change" in your description.

SECTION 4.3 • COMPOUND INTEREST

So, how did the present value of Manhattan in 1626—that is, the $24 paid to the native Americans—attain a future value of over $4 billion in 2006, 380 years later, at a mere 5% interest rate? After all, the future value on $24 for 380 years at 5% simple interest is

$$A = P(1 + rt)$$
$$= 24[1 + (0.05)(380)] = 480,$$

or a paltry $480, compared to over $4 billion. To understand this dramatic difference in future value, we turn to the concept of *compound interest*.

1 | Use compound interest formulas.

Compound Interest

Compound interest is interest computed on the original principal as well as on any accumulated interest. Many savings accounts pay compound interest. For example, suppose you deposit $1000 in a savings account at a rate of 5%. Table 4.2 shows how the investment grows if the interest earned is automatically added on to the principal.

TABLE 4.2 CALCULATING THE AMOUNT IN AN ACCOUNT SUBJECT TO COMPOUND INTEREST

Use $A = P(1 + rt)$ with $r = 0.05$ and $t = 1$, or $A = P(1 + 0.05)$.

Year	Starting Balance	Amount in the Account at Year's End
1	$1000	$A = \$1000(1 + 0.05) = \$1050$
2	$1050 or $1000(1 + 0.05)$	$A = \$1050(1 + 0.05) = \$1102.50$ or $A = \$1000(1 + 0.05)(1 + 0.05) = \$1000(1 + 0.05)^2$
3	$1102.50 or $1000(1 + 0.05)^2$	$A = \$1102.50(1 + 0.05) \approx \$1157.63$ or $A = \$1000(1 + 0.05)^2(1 + 0.05) = \$1000(1 + 0.05)^3$

Using inductive reasoning, the amount, A, in the account after t years is the original principal, $1000, times $(1 + 0.05)^t$: $A = 1000(1 + 0.05)^t$.

If the original principal is P and the interest rate is r, we can use this same approach to determine the amount, A, in an account subject to compound interest.

> **CALCULATING THE AMOUNT IN AN ACCOUNT FOR COMPOUND INTEREST PAID ONCE A YEAR**
>
> If you deposit P dollars at rate r, in decimal form, subject to compound interest, then the amount, A, of money in the account after t years is given by
>
> $$A = P(1 + r)^t.$$
>
> The amount A is called the account's **future value** and the principal P is called its **present value**.

| EXAMPLE 1 | USING THE COMPOUND INTEREST FORMULA |

You deposit $2000 in a savings account at Hometown Bank, which has a rate of 6%.

a. Find the amount, A, of money in the account after 3 years subject to compound interest.

b. Find the interest.

SOLUTION

a. The amount deposited, or principal, P, is $2000. The rate, r, is 6%, or 0.06. The time of the deposit, t, is three years. The amount in the account after three years is

$$A = P(1 + r)^t = 2000(1 + 0.06)^3 = 2000(1.06)^3 \approx 2382.03.$$

Rounded to the nearest cent, the amount in the savings account after three years is $2382.03.

b. Because the amount in the account is $2382.03 and the original principal is $2000, the interest is $2382.03 − $2000, or $382.03.

 You deposit $1000 in a savings account at a bank that has a rate of 4%.

      a. Find the amount, A, of money in the account after 5 years subject to compound interest. Round to the nearest cent.

      b. Find the interest.

TECHNOLOGY

Here are the calculator keystrokes to compute $2000(1.06)^3$:

MANY SCIENTIFIC CALCULATORS

2000 $\boxed{\times}$ 1.06 $\boxed{y^x}$ 3 $\boxed{=}$

MANY GRAPHING CALCULATORS

2000 $\boxed{\times}$ 1.06 $\boxed{\wedge}$ 3 $\boxed{\text{ENTER}}$.

Compound Interest Paid More Than Once a Year

The period of time between two interest payments is called the **compounding period**. When compound interest is paid once per year, the compounding period is one year. We say that the interest is **compounded annually**.

Most savings institutions have plans in which interest is paid more than once per year. If compound interest is paid twice per year, the compounding period is six months. We say that the interest is **compounded semiannually**. When compound interest is paid four times per year, the compounding period is three months and the interest is said to be **compounded quarterly**. Some plans allow for monthly compounding or daily compounding.

In general, when compound interest is paid n times per year, we say that there are **n compounding periods per year**. The following formula is used to calculate the amount in an account subject to compound interest with n compounding periods per year:

> **CALCULATING THE AMOUNT IN AN ACCOUNT FOR COMPOUND INTEREST PAID n TIMES A YEAR**
>
> If you deposit P dollars at rate r, in decimal form, subject to compound interest paid n times per year, then the amount, A, of money in the account after t years is given by
>
> $$A = P\left(1 + \frac{r}{n}\right)^{nt}.$$
>
> A is the account's **future value** and the principal P is its **present value**.

| EXAMPLE 2 | USING THE COMPOUND INTEREST FORMULA |

You deposit $7500 in a savings account that has a rate of 6%. The interest is compounded monthly.

a. How much money will you have after five years?

b. Find the interest after five years.

TECHNOLOGY

Here are the calculator keystrokes to compute

$$7500\left(1 + \frac{0.06}{12}\right)^{12 \cdot 5}:$$

MANY SCIENTIFIC CALCULATORS

7500 $\boxed{\times}$ $\boxed{(}$ 1 $\boxed{+}$ .06 $\boxed{\div}$ 12 $\boxed{)}$

$\boxed{y^x}$ $\boxed{(}$ 12 $\boxed{\times}$ 5 $\boxed{)}$ $\boxed{=}$

MANY GRAPHING CALCULATORS

7500 $\boxed{(}$ 1 $\boxed{+}$ .06 $\boxed{\div}$ 12 $\boxed{)}$

$\boxed{\wedge}$ $\boxed{(}$ 12 $\boxed{\times}$ 5 $\boxed{)}$ $\boxed{\text{ENTER}}$.

SOLUTION

a. The amount deposited, or principal, P, is $7500. The rate, r, is 6%, or 0.06. Because interest is compounded monthly, there are 12 compounding periods per year, so $n = 12$. The time of the deposit, t, is five years. The amount in the account after five years is

$$A = P\left(1 + \frac{r}{n}\right)^{nt} = 7500\left(1 + \frac{0.06}{12}\right)^{12 \cdot 5} = 7500(1.005)^{60} \approx 10{,}116.38.$$

Rounded to the nearest cent, you will have $10,116.38 after five years.

b. Because the amount in the account is $10,116.38 and the original principal is $7500, the interest after five years is $10,116.38 − $7500, or $2616.38.

 CHECK POINT 2 You deposit $4200 in a savings account that has a rate of 4%. The interest is compounded quarterly.

    a. How much money will you have after ten years? Round to the nearest cent.

    b. Find the interest after ten years.

Continuous Compounding

Some banks use **continuous compounding**, where the compounding periods increase infinitely (compounding interest every trillionth of a second, every quadrillionth of a second, etc.). As n, the number of compounding periods in a year, increases without bound, the expression $\left(1 + \frac{1}{n}\right)^n$ approaches the irrational number e: $e \approx 2.71828$. This is illustrated in Table 4.3. As a result, the formula for the balance in an account with n compoundings per year, $A = P\left(1 + \frac{r}{n}\right)^{nt}$, becomes $A = Pe^{rt}$ with continuous compounding. Although continuous compounding sounds terrific, it yields only a fraction of a percent more interest over a year than daily compounding.

TABLE 4.3 AS n TAKES ON INCREASINGLY LARGE VALUES, THE EXPRESSION $\left(1 + \frac{1}{n}\right)^n$ APPROACHES THE IRRATIONAL NUMBER e.

n	$\left(1 + \dfrac{1}{n}\right)^n$
1	2
2	2.25
5	2.48832
10	2.59374246
100	2.704813829
1000	2.716923932
10,000	2.718145927
100,000	2.718268237
1,000,000	2.718280469
1,000,000,000	2.718281827

> **FORMULAS FOR COMPOUND INTEREST**
> After t years, the balance, A, in an account with principal P and annual interest rate r (in decimal form) is given by the following formulas:
>
> **1.** For n compoundings per year: $A = P\left(1 + \dfrac{r}{n}\right)^{nt}$
>
> **2.** For continuous compounding: $A = Pe^{rt}$.

TECHNOLOGY

You can compute e to a power using the $\boxed{e^x}$ key on your calculator. Use the key to enter e^1 and verify that e is approximately equal to 2.71828.

Scientific Calculators	**Graphing Calculators**
1 $\boxed{e^x}$	$\boxed{e^x}$ 1 $\boxed{\text{ENTER}}$

EXAMPLE 3   CHOOSING BETWEEN INVESTMENTS

You decide to invest $8000 for 6 years and you have a choice between two accounts. The first pays 7% per year, compounded monthly. The second pays 6.85% per year, compounded continuously. Which is the better investment?

SOLUTION The better investment is the one with the greater balance in the account after 6 years. Let's begin with the account with monthly compounding. We use the compound interest formula with $P = 8000$, $r = 7\% = 0.07$, $n = 12$ (monthly compounding means 12 compoundings per year), and $t = 6$.

$$A = P\left(1 + \frac{r}{n}\right)^{nt} = 8000\left(1 + \frac{0.07}{12}\right)^{12 \cdot 6} \approx 12{,}160.84$$

The balance in this account after 6 years would be $12,160.84.

For the second investment option, we use the formula for continuous compounding with $P = 8000$, $r = 6.85\% = 0.0685$, and $t = 6$.

$$A = Pe^{rt} = 8000e^{0.0685(6)} \approx 12{,}066.60$$

The balance in this account after 6 years would be $12,066.60, slightly less than the previous amount. Thus, the better investment is the 7% monthly compounding option.

TECHNOLOGY

Here are the calculator keystrokes to compute

$$8000e^{0.0685(6)}:$$

MANY SCIENTIFIC CALCULATORS

8000 × (.0685 × 6) e^x =

MANY GRAPHING CALCULATORS

8000 e^x (.0685 × 6) ENTER

CHECK POINT 3 A sum of $10,000 is invested at an annual rate of 8%. Find the balance in the account after 5 years subject to **a.** quarterly compounding and **b.** continuous compounding.

---

2 | Calculate present value.

Planning for the Future with Compound Interest

Just as we did in Section 4.2, we can determine P, the principal or present value, that should be deposited now in order to have a certain amount, A, in the future. If an account earns compound interest, the amount of money that should be invested today to obtain a future value of A dollars can be determined by solving the compound interest formula for P:

> **CALCULATING PRESENT VALUE**
> If A dollars are to be accumulated in t years in an account that pays rate r compounded n times per year, then the present value, P, that needs to be invested now is given by
> $$P = \frac{A}{\left(1 + \dfrac{r}{n}\right)^{nt}}.$$

TECHNOLOGY

Here are the keystrokes for Example 4:

MANY SCIENTIFIC CALCULATORS

20000 ÷ (1 + .08 ÷ 12)

y^x (12 × 5) =

MANY GRAPHING CALCULATORS

20000 ÷ (1 + .08 ÷ 12)

∧ (12 × 5) ENTER.

EXAMPLE 4   CALCULATING PRESENT VALUE

How much money should be deposited in an account today that earns 8% compounded monthly so that it will accumulate to $20,000 in five years?

SOLUTION The amount we need today, or the present value, is determined by the present value formula. Because the interest is compounded monthly, $n = 12$. Furthermore, A (the future value) = $20,000, r (the rate) = 8% = 0.08, and t (time in years) = 5.

$$P = \frac{A}{\left(1 + \dfrac{r}{n}\right)^{nt}} = \frac{20{,}000}{\left(1 + \dfrac{0.08}{12}\right)^{12 \cdot 5}} \approx 13{,}424.21$$

Approximately $13,424.21 should be invested today in order to accumulate to $20,000 in five years.

CHECK POINT 4 How much money should be deposited in an account today that earns 6% compounded weekly so that it will accumulate to $10,000 in eight years?

3 | Understand and compute effective annual yield.

Effective Annual Yield

As we've seen before, a common problem in financial planning is selecting the best investment from two or more investments. For example, is an investment that pays 8.25% interest compounded quarterly better than one that pays 8.3% interest compounded semiannually? Another way to answer the question is to compare their *effective rates*, also called their *effective annual yields*.

> ### EFFECTIVE ANNUAL YIELD
> The **effective annual yield**, or the **effective rate**, is the simple interest rate that produces the same amount of money in an account at the end of one year as when the account is subjected to compound interest at a stated rate.

EXAMPLE 5   UNDERSTANDING EFFECTIVE ANNUAL YIELD

You deposit $4000 in an account that pays 8% interest compounded monthly.

a. Find the future value after one year.

b. Use the future value formula for simple interest to determine the effective annual yield.

SOLUTION

a. We use the compound interest formula to find the account's future value after one year.

$$A = P\left(1 + \frac{r}{n}\right)^{nt} = 4000\left(1 + \frac{0.08}{12}\right)^{12 \cdot 1} \approx \$4332.00$$

Principal is $4000.   Stated rate is 8% = 0.08.   Monthly compounding: $n = 12$ Time is one year: $t = 1$.

Rounded to the nearest cent, the future value after one year is $4332.00.

b. **The effective annual yield**, or effective rate, **is a simple interest rate**. We use the future value formula for simple interest to determine the simple interest rate that produces a future value of $4332 for a $4000 deposit after one year.

$$A = P(1 + rt)$$ This is the future value formula for simple interest.

$$4332 = 4000(1 + r \cdot 1)$$ Substitute the given values.

$$4332 = 4000 + 4000r$$ Use the distributive property.

$$332 = 4000r$$ Subtract 4000 from both sides.

$$\frac{332}{4000} = \frac{4000r}{4000}$$ Divide both sides by 4000.

$$r = \frac{332}{4000} = 0.083 = 8.3\%$$ Express r as a percent.

The effective annual yield, or effective rate, is 8.3%. This means that money invested at 8.3% simple interest earns the same amount in one year as money invested at 8% interest compounded monthly.

In Example 5, the stated 8% rate is called the **nominal rate**. The 8.3% rate is the effective rate and is a simple interest rate.

5 You deposit $6000 in an account that pays 10% interest compounded monthly.

a. Find the future value after one year.

b. Determine the effective annual yield.

Generalizing the procedure of Example 5 and Check Point 5 gives a formula for effective annual yield:

> **CALCULATING EFFECTIVE ANNUAL YIELD**
>
> Suppose that an investment has a nominal interest rate, r, in decimal form, and pays compound interest n times per year. The investment's effective annual yield, Y, is given by
>
> $$Y = \left(1 + \frac{r}{n}\right)^n - 1.$$

TECHNOLOGY

Here are the keystrokes for Example 6:

 MANY SCIENTIFIC CALCULATORS

$\boxed{(}$ 1 $\boxed{+}$ .05 $\boxed{\div}$ 360 $\boxed{)}$ $\boxed{y^x}$ 360

$\boxed{-}$ 1 $\boxed{=}$

 MANY GRAPHING CALCULATORS

$\boxed{(}$ 1 $\boxed{+}$ .05 $\boxed{\div}$ 360 $\boxed{)}$ $\boxed{\wedge}$ 360

$\boxed{-}$ 1 $\boxed{ENTER}$.

Given the nominal rate and the number of compounding periods per year, some graphing calculators display the effective annual yield. The screen shows the calculation of the effective rate in Example 6 on the TI-83 Plus.

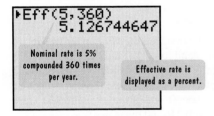

Nominal rate is 5% compounded 360 times per year.

Effective rate is displayed as a percent.

EXAMPLE 6   CALCULATING EFFECTIVE ANNUAL YIELD

A passbook savings account has a nominal rate of 5%. The interest is compounded daily. Find the account's effective annual yield. (Assume 360 days in a year.)

SOLUTION The rate, r, is 5%, or 0.05. Because interest is compounded daily and we assume 360 days in a year, $n = 360$. The account's effective annual yield is

$$Y = \left(1 + \frac{r}{n}\right)^n - 1 = \left(1 + \frac{0.05}{360}\right)^{360} - 1 \approx 0.0513 = 5.13\%.$$

The effective annual yield is 5.13%. Thus, money invested at 5.13% simple interest earns the same amount of interest in one year as money invested at 5% interest, the nominal rate, compounded daily.

 What is the effective annual yield of an account paying 8% compounded quarterly?

The effective annual yield is often included in the information about investments or loans. Because it's the true interest rate you're earning or paying, it's the number you should pay attention to. **If you are selecting the best investment from two or more investments, the best choice is the account with the greatest effective annual yield.** However, there are differences in the types of accounts that you need to take into consideration. Some pay interest from the day of deposit to the day of withdrawal. Other accounts start paying interest the first day of the month that follows the day of deposit. Some savings institutions stop paying interest if the balance in the account falls below a certain amount.

When borrowing money, the effective rate or effective annual yield is usually called the **annual percentage rate**. If all other factors are equal and you are borrowing money, select the option with the least annual percentage rate. In the section on installment buying, we will discuss annual percentage rates in more detail.

EXERCISE SET 4.3 ••••••

• Practice Exercises

In Exercises 1–12, the principal represents an amount of money deposited in a savings account subject to compound interest at the given rate.

    a. Use the formula $A = P(1 + r)^t$ for one compounding period per year or $A = P\left(1 + \frac{r}{n}\right)^{nt}$ for n compounding periods per year to find how much money there will be in the account after the given number of years. (Assume 360 days in a year.)

    b. Find the interest earned.

Round answers to the nearest cent.

	Principal	Rate	Compounded	Time
1.	$10,000	4%	annually	2 years
2.	$8000	6%	annually	3 years
3.	$3000	5%	semiannually	4 years
4.	$4000	4%	semiannually	5 years
5.	$9500	6%	quarterly	5 years
6.	$2500	8%	quarterly	6 years
7.	$4500	4.5%	monthly	3 years
8.	$2500	6.5%	monthly	4 years
9.	$1500	8.5%	daily	2.5 years
10.	$1200	8.5%	daily	3.5 years
11.	$20,000	4.5%	daily	20 years
12.	$25,000	5.5%	daily	20 years

Use the compound interest formulas $A = P\left(1 + \dfrac{r}{n}\right)^{nt}$ and $A = Pe^{rt}$ to solve Exercises 13–16. Round answers to the nearest cent.

13. Find the accumulated value of an investment of $10,000 for 5 years at an interest rate of 5.5% if the money is **a.** compounded semiannually; **b.** compounded quarterly; **c.** compounded monthly; **d.** compounded continuously.

14. Find the accumulated value of an investment of $5000 for 10 years at an interest rate of 6.5% if the money is **a.** compounded semiannually; **b.** compounded quarterly; **c.** compounded monthly; **d.** compounded continuously.

15. Suppose that you have $12,000 to invest. Which investment yields the greater return over 3 years: 7% compounded monthly or 6.85% compounded continuously?

16. Suppose that you have $6000 to invest. Which investment yields the greater return over 4 years: 8.25% compounded quarterly or 8.3% compounded semiannually?

Solve Exercises 17–20 using the present value formula:

$$P = \dfrac{A}{\left(1 + \dfrac{r}{n}\right)^{nt}}.$$

Round answers up to the nearest cent.

17. How much money should be deposited today in an account that earns 6% compounded semiannually so that it will accumulate to $10,000 in three years?

18. How much money should be deposited today in an account that earns 7% compounded semiannually so that it will accumulate to $12,000 in four years?

19. How much money should be deposited today in an account that earns 9.5% compounded monthly so that it will accumulate to $10,000 in three years?

20. How much money should be deposited today in an account that earns 10.5% compounded monthly so that it will accumulate to $22,000 in four years?

21. You deposit $10,000 in an account that pays 4.5% interest compounded quarterly.
    a. Find the future value after one year.
    b. Use the future value formula for simple interest to determine the effective annual yield.

22. You deposit $12,000 in an account that pays 6.5% interest compounded quarterly.
    a. Find the future value after one year.
    b. Use the future value formula for simple interest to determine the effective annual yield.

Solve Exercises 23–28 using the effective annual yield formula:

$$Y = \left(1 + \dfrac{r}{n}\right)^{n} - 1.$$

A passbook savings account has a rate of 6%. Find the effective annual yield, rounded to the nearest tenth of a percent, if the interest is compounded

23. semiannually.   24. quarterly.

25. monthly.

26. daily. (Assume 360 days in a year.)

27. 1000 times per year.

28. 100,000 times per year.

In Exercises 29–32, determine the effective annual yield, to the nearest tenth of a percent, for each investment. Then select the better investment. Assume 360 days in a year.

29. 8% compounded monthly; 8.25% compounded annually

30. 5% compounded monthly; 5.25% compounded quarterly

31. 5.5% compounded semiannually; 5.4% compounded daily

32. 7% compounded annually; 6.85% compounded daily

• Practice Plus

In Exercises 33–38, assume that you place money in an account subject to interest compounded annually. Use the formula $A = P(1 + r)^{t}$, a calculator, and trial and error to answer each question. Give answers to the nearest tenth of a year.

33. How long will it take for the investment to triple at an interest rate of 5%?

34. How long will it take for the investment to triple at an interest rate of 10%?

35. How long will it take for the investment to increase by 50% at an interest rate of 10%?

36. How long will it take for the investment to increase by 50% at an interest rate of 5%?

37. How long will it take for the investment to increase by 90% at an interest rate of 8%?

38. How long will it take for the investment to increase by 90% at an interest rate of 12%?

• Application Exercises

39. In 1626, Peter Minuit convinced the Wappinger Indians to sell him Manhattan Island for $24. If the Native Americans had put the $24 into a bank account paying compound interest at a 5% rate, how much would the investment be worth in the year 2006 ($t = 380$ years) if interest were compounded **a.** monthly? **b.** 360 times per year?

40. In 1777, Jacob DeHaven loaned George Washington's army $450,000 in gold and supplies. Due to a disagreement over the method of repayment (gold versus Continental money), DeHaven was never repaid, dying penniless. In 1989, his descendants sued the U.S. government over the 212-year-old debt. If the DeHavens used an interest rate of 6% and daily compounding (the rate offered by the Continental Congress in 1777), how much money did the DeHaven family demand in their suit? (*Hint:* Use the compound interest formula with $n = 360$ and $t = 212$ years.)

41. At the time of her grandson's birth, a grandmother deposits $10,000 in an account that pays 9% compounded monthly. What will be the value of the account at the child's twenty-first birthday, assuming that no other deposits or withdrawals are made during this period?

42. Parents wish to have $80,000 available for a child's education. If the child is now 5 years old, how much money must be set aside at 6% compounded semiannually to meet their financial goal when the child is 18?

43. A 30-year-old worker plans to retire at age 65. He believes that $500,000 is needed to retire comfortably. How much should be deposited now at 9% compounded monthly to meet the $500,000 retirement goal?

44. In 2001, First Internet Bank of Indiana offered a money market account paying 4.5% interest compounded monthly. NetBank offered a money market account paying 4.4% interest compounded daily. (*Source:* www.bankrate.com) Which account is the better investment?

• Writing in Mathematics

45. Describe the difference between simple and compound interest.

46. Give two examples that illustrate the difference between a compound interest problem involving future value and a compound interest problem involving present value.

47. What is effective annual yield?

48. Explain how to select the best investment from two or more investments.

49. Shown are figures in an actual advertisement for Great Western Bank. Explain the meaning of the given percents, as well as the statement below these percents.

9.21%	**8.85%**
Yield	*Rate*

Interest compounded monthly

• Critical Thinking Exercises

50. A depositor opens a new savings account with $6000 at 5% compounded semiannually. At the beginning of year 3, an additional $4000 is deposited. At the end of six years, what is the balance in the account?

51. A depositor opens a money market account with $5000 at 8% compounded monthly. After two years, $1500 is withdrawn from the account to buy a new computer. A year later, $2000 is put in the account. What will be the ending balance if the money is kept in the account for another three years?

52. Use the future value formulas for simple and compound interest in one year to derive the formula for effective annual yield.

• Group Exercise

53. This activity is a group research project intended for four or five people. Present your research in a seminar on the history of interest and banking. The seminar should last about 30 minutes. Address the following questions:

When was interest first charged on loans? How was lending money for a fee opposed historically? What is usury? What connection did banking and interest rates play in the historic European rivalries between Christians and Jews? When and where were some of the highest interest rates charged? What were the rates? Where does the word *interest* come from? What is the origin of the word *shylock*? What is the difference between usury and interest in modern times? What is the history of a national bank in the United States?

SECTION 4.4 • ANNUITIES, STOCKS, AND BONDS

OBJECTIVES

1. Determine the value of an annuity.

2. Determine regular annuity payments needed to achieve a financial goal.

3. Understand stocks and bonds as investments.

4. Read stock tables.

"Good Times Are Predicted in 1929"

—THE WASHINGTON POST, JAN. 1, 1929

"In a few months, I expect to see the stock market much higher than today."

—ESTEEMED ECONOMIST IRVING FISHER: OCT. 14, 1929

Date on which the stock market crashed and began the Depression: Oct. 29, 1929

According to the *Forbes Billionaires List*, in 2005 the two richest Americans were Bill Gates (net worth: $46.5 billion) and Warren Buffett (net worth: $44 billion). In May 1965, Buffett's new company, Berkshire Hathaway, was selling one share of stock for $18. By the end of 2004, the price of a share had increased to $86,300. If you purchased one share, your **return**, or percent increase, would be

$$\frac{\text{amount of increase}}{\text{original amount}} = \frac{\$86{,}300 - \$18}{\$18} \approx 4793.44 = 479{,}344\%.$$

What does a return of nearly 480,000% mean? If you invested $250 in Warren Buffett's company in May 1965, your shares would have been worth over $1.1 million by December 2004. (*Source*: *Pensions and Investments*)

Of course, investments that potentially offer outrageous returns come with great risk of losing part or all of the principal. The bottom line: Is there a safe way to save regularly and have an investment worth one million dollars or more? In this section, we consider such savings plans, some of which come with special tax treatment, as well as riskier investments in stocks and bonds.

1 | Determine the value of an annuity.

Annuities

The compound interest formula

$$A = P(1 + r)^t$$

gives the future value, A, after t years, when a fixed amount of money, P, the principal, is deposited in an account that pays an annual interest rate r (in decimal form) compounded once a year. However, money is often invested in small amounts at periodic intervals. For example, to save for retirement, you might decide to place $1000 into an Individual Retirement Account (IRA) at the end of each year until you retire. An **annuity** is a sequence of equal payments made at equal time periods. An IRA is an example of an annuity.

The **value of an annuity** is the sum of all deposits plus all interest paid. Our first example illustrates how to find this value.

EXAMPLE 1 DETERMINING THE VALUE OF AN ANNUITY

You deposit $1000 into a savings plan at the end of each year for three years. The interest rate is 8% per year compounded annually.

a. Find the value of the annuity after three years.

b. Find the interest.

SOLUTION

a. The value of the annuity after three years is the sum of all deposits made plus all interest paid over three years.

> This is the $1000 deposit at year's end.

Value at end of year 1 = $1000

> This is the first-year deposit with interest earned for a year.

> This is the $1000 deposit at year's end.

Value at end of year 2 = $1000(1 + 0.08) + $1000

> Use $A = P(1 + r)^t$ with $r = 0.08$ and $t = 1$, or $A = P(1 + 0.08)$.

> This is the second-year balance, $2080, with interest earned for a year.

> This is the $1000 deposit at year's end.

= $1080 + $1000 = $2080

Value at end of year 3 = $2080(1 + 0.08) + $1000

= $2246.40 + $1000 = $3246.40

The value of the annuity at the end of three years is $3246.40.

b. You made three payments of $1000 each, depositing a total of 3 × $1000, or $3000. Because the value of the annuity is $3246.40, the interest is $3246.40 − $3000, or $246.40.

○

You deposit $2000 into a savings plan at the end of each year for three years. The interest rate is 10% per year compounded annually.

    a. Find the value of the annuity after three years.

    b. Find the interest.

Suppose that you deposit P dollars into an account at the end of each year. The account pays an annual interest rate, r, compounded annually. At the end of the first year, the account contains P dollars. At the end of the second year, P dollars is deposited again. At the time of this deposit, the first deposit has received interest earned during the second year. Thus, the value of the annuity after two years is

$$P + P(1 + r).$$

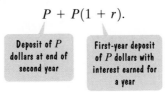

The value of the annuity after three years is

$$P \quad + \quad P(1 + r) \quad + \quad P(1 + r)^2.$$

The value of the annuity after t years is

$$P + P(1 + r) + P(1 + r)^2 + P(1 + r)^3 + \cdots + P(1 + r)^{t-1}.$$

Each term in this sum is obtained by multiplying the preceding term by $(1 + r)$. Thus, the terms form a geometric sequence. Using a formula for the sum of the terms of a geometric sequence, we can obtain the following formula that gives the value of this annuity:

> **VALUE OF AN ANNUITY: INTEREST COMPOUNDED ONCE A YEAR**
>
> If P is the deposit made at the end of each year for an annuity that pays an annual interest rate r (in decimal form) compounded once a year, the value, A, of the annuity after t years is
>
> $$A = \frac{P[(1 + r)^t - 1]}{r}.$$

EXAMPLE 2   DETERMINING THE VALUE OF AN ANNUITY

To save for retirement, you decide to deposit $1000 into an IRA at the end of each year for the next 30 years. If you can count on an interest rate of 10% per year compounded annually,

    a. How much will you have from the IRA after 30 years?

    b. Find the interest.

SOLUTION

a. The amount that you will have from the IRA is its value after 30 years.

$$A = \frac{P[(1 + r)^t - 1]}{r}$$ *Use the formula for the value of an annuity.*

$$A = \frac{1000[(1 + 0.10)^{30} - 1]}{0.10}$$ *The annuity involves year-end deposits of $1000: P = 1000. The interest rate is 10%: r = 0.10. The number of years is 30: t = 30.*

$$= \frac{1000[(1.10)^{30} - 1]}{0.10}$$ *Using parentheses keys on a graphing calculator, this calculation can be done in a single step.*

$$\approx \frac{1000(17.4494 - 1)}{0.10}$$ *Use a calculator to find $(1.10)^{30}$:*
1.1 $\boxed{y^x}$ 30 $\boxed{=}$.

$$= \frac{1000(16.4494)}{0.10}$$

$$= 164{,}494$$

After 30 years, you will have approximately $164,494 from the IRA.

b. You made 30 payments of $1000 each, depositing a total of 30 × $1000, or $30,000. Because the value of the annuity is approximately $164,494, the interest is approximately

$$\$164{,}494 - \$30{,}000, \text{ or } \$134{,}494.$$

The interest is nearly $4\frac{1}{2}$ times the amount of your payments, illustrating the power of compounding.

○

 You deposit $3000 into an IRA at the end of each year for the next 40 years. If you can count on an interest rate of 8% per year compounded annually,

    a. How much will you have from the IRA after 40 years?

    b. Find the interest.

We can adjust the formula for the value of an annuity if equal payments are made at the end of each of *n* yearly compounding periods.

VALUE OF AN ANNUITY: INTEREST COMPOUNDED *n* TIMES PER YEAR

If *P* is the deposit made at the end of each compounding period for an annuity that pays an annual interest rate *r* (in decimal form) compounded *n* times per year, the value, *A*, of the annuity after *t* years is

$$A = \frac{P\left[\left(1 + \dfrac{r}{n}\right)^{nt} - 1\right]}{\dfrac{r}{n}}.$$

EXAMPLE 3   DETERMINING THE VALUE OF AN ANNUITY

At age 25, to save for retirement, you decide to deposit $200 at the end of each month into an IRA that pays 7.5% compounded monthly.

    a. How much will you have from the IRA when you retire at age 65?

    b. Find the interest.

SOLUTION

a. Because you are 25, the amount that you will have from the IRA when you retire at 65 is its value after 40 years.

$$A = \frac{P\left[\left(1 + \dfrac{r}{n}\right)^{nt} - 1\right]}{\dfrac{r}{n}}$$ Use the formula for the value of an annuity.

$$A = \frac{200\left[\left(1 + \dfrac{0.075}{12}\right)^{12 \cdot 40} - 1\right]}{\dfrac{0.075}{12}}$$ The annuity involves month-end deposits of $200: $P = 200$. The interest rate is 7.5%: $r = 0.075$. The interest is compounded monthly: $n = 12$. The number of years is 40: $t = 40$.

$$= \frac{200[(1 + 0.00625)^{480} - 1]}{0.00625}$$ Using parentheses keys, this can be performed in a single step on a graphing calculator.

$$= \frac{200[(1.00625)^{480} - 1]}{0.00625}$$

$$\approx \frac{200(19.8989 - 1)}{0.00625}$$ Use a calculator to find $(1.00625)^{480}$:
1.00625 $\boxed{y^x}$ 480 $\boxed{=}$.

$$\approx 604{,}765$$

After 40 years, you will have approximately $604,765 when retiring at age 65.

b.   Interest = Value of the IRA − Total deposits
$$\approx \$604{,}765 - \$200 \cdot 12 \cdot 40$$

> $200 per month × 12 months per year × 40 years

$$= \$604{,}765 - \$96{,}000 = \$508{,}765$$

The interest is approximately $508,765, more than five times the amount of your contributions to the IRA.

At age 30, to save for retirement, you decide to deposit $100 at the end of each month into an IRA that pays 9.5% compounded monthly.

a. How much will you have from the IRA when you retire at age 65?

b. Find the interest.

2 Determine regular annuity payments needed to achieve a financial goal.

Planning for the Future with an Annuity

By solving the annuity formula for P, we can determine the amount of money that should be deposited at the end of each compounding period so that an annuity has a future value of A dollars. The following formula gives the regular payments, P, needed to reach a financial goal, A:

> **REGULAR PAYMENTS NEEDED TO ACHIEVE A FINANCIAL GOAL**
>
> The deposit, P, that must be made at the end of each compounding period into an annuity that pays an annual interest rate r (in decimal form) compounded n times per year in order to achieve a value of A dollars after t years is
>
> $$P = \frac{A\left(\dfrac{r}{n}\right)}{\left[\left(1 + \dfrac{r}{n}\right)^{nt} - 1\right]}.$$

EXAMPLE 4 ACHIEVING A FINANCIAL GOAL

You would like to have $20,000 to use as a down payment for a home in five years by making regular, end-of-month deposits in an annuity that pays 8% compounded monthly.

a. How much should you deposit each month?

b. How much of the $20,000 down payment comes from deposits and how much comes from interest?

SOLUTION

a. $$P = \frac{A\left(\dfrac{r}{n}\right)}{\left[\left(1 + \dfrac{r}{n}\right)^{nt} - 1\right]}$$

Use the formula for regular payments, P, needed to achieve a financial goal, A.

$$P = \frac{20{,}000\left(\dfrac{0.08}{12}\right)}{\left[\left(1 + \dfrac{0.08}{12}\right)^{12\cdot5} - 1\right]}$$

Your goal is to accumulate $20,000 ($A = 20{,}000$) over five years ($t = 5$). The interest rate is 8% ($r = 0.08$) compounded monthly ($n = 12$).

$$\approx 273$$

Use a calculator and round up to the nearest dollar to be certain you do not fall short of your goal.

You should deposit $273 each month to be certain of having $20,000 for a down payment on a home.

b. Total deposits = $273 · 12 · 5 = $16,380

> $273 per month × 12 months per year × 5 years

Interest = $20,000 − $16,380 = $3620

We see that $16,380 of the $20,000 comes from your deposits and the remainder, $3620, comes from interest.

STUDY TIP

In Example 4 of Section 4.3, we saw that a lump-sum deposit of approximately $13,424 at 8% compounded monthly would accumulate to $20,000 in five years. In Example 4 on the right, we see that total deposits of $16,380 are required to reach the same goal. With the same interest rate, compounding period, and time period, a lump-sum deposit will generate more interest than an annuity. If you don't have a large sum of money to open an account, an annuity is a realistic, although more expensive, option to a lump-sum deposit for achieving the same financial goal.

CHECK POINT 4 Parents of a baby girl are in a financial position to begin saving for her college education. They plan to have $100,000 in a college fund in 18 years by making regular, end-of-month deposits in an annuity that pays 9% compounded monthly.

a. How much should they deposit each month? Round up to the nearest dollar.

b. How much of the $100,000 college fund comes from deposits and how much comes from interest?

3 Understand stocks and bonds as investments.

Investments

When you deposit money into a bank account, you are making a **cash investment**. Bank accounts up to $100,000 are insured by the federal government, so there is no risk of losing the principal you've invested. The account's interest rate guarantees a certain percent increase in your investment, called its **return**. For example, if you deposit $7500 in a savings account that has a rate of 4% compounded annually, the annual return is 4%. There are other kinds of investments that are riskier, meaning that it is possible to lose all or part of your principal. These investments include **stocks** and **bonds**.

Risk

Danger   Opportunity

The Chinese define *risk* as a combination of danger and opportunity. Investments in which all or part of the principal is in danger frequently offer the opportunity of a greater return. Table 4.4 includes five types of investments, listed from no risk to high risk, and their average annual returns from 1926 through 2004. Although stocks offer the prospects of greater returns, large-company shareholders lost money for 22 of the 79 years shown in the table.

TABLE 4.4 INVESTMENTS FROM NO RISK TO HIGH RISK AND THEIR RETURNS: 1926-2004

Investment Type	Average Annual Return
U.S. Treasury Bills (Federally insured and risk free)	3.8%
Long-Term Government Bonds	5.8%
Long-Term Corporate Bonds	6.2%
Large-Company Stocks	12.4%
Small-Company Stocks	17.5%

Source: Summary Statistics of Annual Total Returns: 1926 to 2004 Yearbook, Ibbotson Associates, Chicago

Stocks

Investors purchase **stock**, shares of ownership in a company. The shares indicate the percent of ownership. For example, if a company has issued a total of one million shares and an investor owns 20,000 of these shares, that investor owns

$$\frac{20,000 \text{ shares}}{1,000,000 \text{ shares}} = 0.02$$

or 2% of the company. Any investor who owns some percentage of the company is called a **shareholder**.

Buying or selling stock is referred to as **trading**. Shares of stock need both a seller and a buyer to be traded. Stocks are traded on a **stock exchange**. The price of a share of stock is determined by the law of supply and demand. If a company is prospering, investors will be willing to pay a good price for its stock, and so the stock price goes up. If the company does not do well, investors may decide to sell, and the stock price goes down. Stock prices indicate the performance of the companies they represent, as well as the state of the national and global economies.

There are two ways to make money by investing in stock:

- You sell the shares for more money than what you paid for them, in which case you have a **capital gain** on the sale of stock. (There can also be a capital loss by selling for less than what you paid, or if the company goes bankrupt.)

- While you own the stock, the company distributes all or part of its profits to shareholders as **dividends**. Each share is paid the same dividend, so the amount you receive depends on the number of shares owned. (Some companies reinvest all profits and do not distribute dividends.)

When more and more average Americans began investing and making money in stocks in the 1990s, the federal government cut the capital-gains tax rate in 1997. Long-term capital gains (profits on items held for more than a year before being sold) and dividends are taxed at lower rates than wages and interest earnings.

Bonds

People who buy stock become part owners in a company. In order to raise money and not dilute the ownership of current stockholders, companies sell **bonds**. People who buy a bond are **lending money** to the company from which they buy the bond. Bonds are a commitment from a company to pay the price an investor pays for the bond at the time it was purchased, called the **face value**, along with interest payments at a given rate.

There are many reasons for issuing bonds. A company might need to raise money for research on a drug that has the potential for curing AIDS, so it issues bonds. The U.S. Treasury Department issues 30-year bonds at a fixed 7% annual rate to borrow money to cover possible federal deficits. Local governments often issue bonds to borrow money to build schools, parks, and libraries.

Bonds are traded like stock, and their price is a function of supply and demand. If a company goes bankrupt, bondholders are the first to claim the company's assets. They make their claims before the stockholders, even though (unlike stockholders) they do not own a share of the company. Buying and selling bonds is frequently done through online investing.

Generally speaking, investing in bonds is less risky than investing in stocks, although the return is lower. A listing of all the investments that a person holds is called a **financial portfolio**. Most financial advisors recommend a portfolio with a mixture of low-risk and high-risk investments, called a **diversified portfolio**.

4 | Read stock tables.

Reading Stock Tables

Daily newspapers and online services give current stock prices and other information about stocks. We will use Citigroup stock to learn how to read these daily stock tables. Look at the following newspaper listing of Citigroup stock.

52-Week High	Low	Stock	SYM	Div	Yld %	PE	Vol 100s	Hi	Lo	Close	Net Chg
77	28.50	Citigroup	C	.84	1.1	29	64981	76	74.44	74.56	−0.94

The headings indicate the meanings of the numbers across the row.

The heading **52-Week High** refers to the *highest price* at which Citigroup stock traded during the past 52 weeks. The highest price was $77.00 per share. This means that during the past 52 weeks an investor was willing to pay $77.00 for a share of stock. Notice that 77 represents a quantity in dollars, although the stock table does not show the dollar sign.

The heading **52-Week Low** refers to the *lowest price* that Citigroup stock reached during the past 52 weeks. This price is $28.50.

The heading **Stock** is the *company name*, Citigroup. The heading **SYM** is the *symbol* the company uses for trading. Citigroup uses the symbol C.

The heading **Div** refers to *dividends* paid per share to stockholders last year. Citigroup paid a dividend of $0.84 per share. Once again, the dollar symbol does not appear in the table. Thus, if you owned 100 shares, you received a dividend of $0.84 × 100, or $84.00.

The heading **Yld %** stands for *percent yield*. In this case, the percent yield is 1.1%. (The stock table does not show the percent sign.) This means that the dividends alone give investors an annual return of 1.1%. This is much lower than interest rates offered by most banks. However, this percent does not take into account the fact that Citigroup stock prices might rise. If an investor sells shares for more than what they were paid for, the gain will probably make Citigroup stock a much better investment than a bank account.

In order to understand the meaning of the heading PE, we need to understand some of the other numbers in the table. We will return to this column.

The heading **Vol 100s** stands for *sales volume in hundreds*. This is the number of shares traded yesterday, in hundreds. The number in the table is 64,981. This means that yesterday, a total of 64,981 × 100, or 6,498,100 shares of Citigroup were traded.

The heading **Hi** stands for the *highest price* at which Citigroup stock traded *yesterday*. This number is 76. Yesterday, Citigroup's highest trading price was $76 a share.

The heading **Lo** stands for the *lowest price* at which Citigroup stock traded *yesterday*. This number is 74.44. Yesterday, Citigroup's lowest trading price was $74.44 a share.

The heading **Close** stands for the *price* at which shares traded *when the stock exchange closed yesterday*. This number is 74.56. Thus, the the price at which shares of Citigroup traded when the stock exchange closed yesterday was $74.56 per share. This is called yesterday's **closing price**.

The heading **Net Chg** stands for *net change*. This is the change in price from the market close two days ago to yesterday's market close. This number is −0.94. Thus, the price of a share of Citigroup stock went down by $0.94. For some stock listings, the notation . . . appears under Net Chg. This means that there was *no change in price* for a share of stock from the market close two days ago to yesterday's market close.

Now, we are ready to return to the heading **PE**, standing for the *price-to-earnings ratio*.

52-Week High
77

52-Week Low
28.50

Stock	SYM
Citigroup	C

Div
.84

Yld %
1.1

Vol 100s
64981

Hi
76

Lo
74.44

Close
74.56

Net Chg
−0.94

PE
29

$$\text{PE ratio} = \frac{\text{Yesterday's closing price per share}}{\text{Annual earnings per share}}$$

This can be expressed as

$$\text{Annual earnings per share} = \frac{\text{Yesterday's closing price per share}}{\text{PE ratio}}.$$

Close
74.56

PE
29

The PE ratio for Citigroup is given to be 29. Yesterday's closing price per share was 74.56. We can substitute these numbers into the formula to find annual earnings per share:

$$\text{Annual earnings per share} = \frac{74.56}{29} \approx 2.57.$$

The annual earnings per share for Citigroup are $2.57. The PE ratio, 29, tells us that yesterday's closing price per share, $74.56, is 29 times greater than the earnings per share, $2.57.

EXAMPLE 5   READING STOCK TABLES

52-Week					Yld		Vol				Net
High	Low	Stock	SYM	Div	%	PE	100s	Hi	Lo	Close	Chg
42.38	22.50	Disney	DIS	.21	.6	43	115900	32.50	31.25	32.50	...

Use the stock table for Disney to answer the following questions.

a. What were the high and low prices for the past 52 weeks?

b. If you owned 3000 shares of Disney stock last year, what dividend did you receive?

c. What is the annual return for dividends alone? How does this compare to a bank account offering a 3.5% interest rate?

d. How many shares of Disney were traded yesterday?

e. What were the high and low prices for Disney shares yesterday?

f. What was the price at which Disney shares traded when the stock exchange closed yesterday?

g. What does . . . in the net change column mean?

h. Compute Disney's annual earnings per share using

$$\text{Annual earnings per share} = \frac{\text{Yesterday's closing price per share}}{\text{PE ratio}}.$$

SOLUTION

a. We find the high price for the past 52 weeks by looking under the heading **High**. The price is listed in dollars, given as 42.38. Thus, the high price for a share of stock for the past 52 weeks was $42.38. We find the low price for the past 52 weeks by looking under the heading **Low**. This price is also listed in dollars, given as 22.50. Thus, the low price for a share of Disney stock for the past 52 weeks was $22.50.

b. We find the dividend paid for a share of Disney stock last year by looking under the heading **Div**. The price is listed in dollars, given as .21. Thus, Disney paid a dividend of $0.21 per share to stockholders last year. If you owned 3000 shares, you received a dividend of $0.21 × 3000, or $630.

c. We find the annual return for dividends alone by looking under the heading **Yld %**, standing for percent yield. The number in the table, .6, is a percent. This means that the dividends alone give Disney investors an annual return of 0.6%. This is much lower than a bank account paying a 3.5% interest rate. However, if Disney shares increase in value, the gain might make Disney stock a better investment than the bank account.

| 52-Week | | | | | Yld | | Vol | | | | Net |
High	Low	Stock	SYM	Div	%	PE	100s	Hi	Lo	Close	Chg
42.38	22.50	Disney	DIS	.21	.6	43	115900	32.50	31.25	32.50	...

Disney stock table (repeated)

d. We find the number of shares of Disney traded yesterday by looking under the heading **Vol 100s**, standing for sales volume in hundreds. The number in the table is 115900. This means that yesterday, a total of 115,900 × 100, or 11,590,000 shares, were traded.

e. We find the high and low prices for Disney shares yesterday by looking under the headings **Hi** and **Lo**. Both prices are listed in dollars, given as 32.50 and 31.25. Thus, the high and low prices for Disney shares yesterday were $32.50 and $31.25, respectively.

f. We find the price at which Disney shares traded when the stock exchange closed yesterday by looking under the heading **Close**. The price is listed in dollars, given as 32.50. Thus, when the stock exchange closed yesterday, the price of a share of Disney stock was $32.50.

g. The ... under **Net Chg** means that there was no change in price in Disney stock from the market close two days ago to yesterday's market close. In part (f), we found that the price of a share of Disney stock at yesterday's close was $32.50, so the price at the market close two days ago was also $32.50.

h. We are now ready to use

$$\text{Annual earnings per share} = \frac{\text{Yesterday's closing price per share}}{\text{PE ratio}}$$

to compute Disney's annual earnings per share. We found that yesterday's closing price per share was $32.50. We find the PE ratio under the heading **PE**. The given number is 43. Thus,

$$\text{Annual earnings per share} = \frac{\$32.50}{43} \approx \$0.76.$$

The annual earnings per share for Disney are $0.76. The PE ratio, 43, tells us that yesterday's closing price per share, $32.50, is 43 times greater than the earnings per share, approximately $0.76.

 CHECK POINT 5 Use the stock table for Coca Cola to solve parts (a) through (h) in Example 5.

| 52-Week | | | | Yld | | Vol | | | | Net |
High	Low	Stock	Div	%	PE	100s	Hi	Lo	Close	Chg
63.38	42.37	CocaCl	.72	1.5	37	72032	49.94	48.33	49.50	+0.03

Ways to Invest in Annuities, Stocks, and Bonds

Investments in annuities, stocks, and bonds can be bought directly, which means making these investments on your own. You can open an IRA at a bank, purchase stock through stockbrokers, who charge a commission for their services, or buy bonds from the government.

It is not an easy job to determine which stocks and bonds to buy or sell, or when to do so. Even IRAs can be funded by mixing stocks and bonds. Many small investors have decided that they do not have the time to stay informed about the progress of corporations, even with the help of online industry research. Instead, they invest in a **mutual fund**. A mutual fund is a group of stocks and/or bonds managed by a professional investor. When you purchase shares in a mutual fund, you give your money to the **fund manager**. Your money is combined with the money of other investors in the mutual fund. The fund manager invests this pool of money, buying and selling shares of stocks and bonds to obtain the maximum possible returns.

Investors in mutual funds own a small portion of many different companies, which may protect them against the poor performance of a single company. When comparing mutual funds, consider both the fees charged for investing and how well the fund manager is doing with the fund's money. Newspapers publish ratings from 1 (worst) to 5 (best) of mutual fund performance based on whether the manager is doing a good job with its investors' money. Two numbers are given. The first number compares the performance of the mutual fund to a large group of similar funds. The second number compares the performance to funds that are nearly identical. The best rating a fund manager can receive is 5/5; the worst is 1/1.

E X E R C I S E   S E T   4 . 4 ●●●●●●

• Practice Exercises

In Exercises 1–10,

  a. *Use the formula*

$$A = \frac{P[(1 + r)^t - 1]}{r} \quad \text{or} \quad A = \frac{P\left[\left(1 + \dfrac{r}{n}\right)^{nt} - 1\right]}{\dfrac{r}{n}}$$

  to find the value of each annuity. Round to the nearest dollar.

  b. *Find the interest.*

Periodic Deposit	Rate	Time
1. $2000 at the end of each year	5% compounded annually	20 years
2. $3000 at the end of each year	4% compounded annually	20 years
3. $4000 at the end of each year	6.5% compounded annually	40 years
4. $4000 at the end of each year	5.5% compounded annually	40 years
5. $50 at the end of each month	6% compounded monthly	30 years
6. $60 at the end of each month	5% compounded monthly	30 years
7. $100 at the end of every six months	4.5% compounded semiannually	25 years
8. $150 at the end of every six months	6.5% compounded semiannually	25 years
9. $1000 at the end of every three months	6.25% compounded quarterly	6 years
10. $1200 at the end of every three months	3.25% compounded quarterly	6 years

In Exercises 11–18,

  a. *Use the formula*

$$P = \frac{A\left(\dfrac{r}{n}\right)}{\left[\left(1 + \dfrac{r}{n}\right)^{nt} - 1\right]}$$

  to determine the periodic deposit. Round up to the nearest dollar.

  b. *How much of the financial goal comes from deposits and how much comes from interest?*

Periodic Deposit	Rate	Time	Financial Goal
11. $? at the end of each year	6% compounded annually	18 years	$140,000
12. $? at the end of each year	5% compounded annually	18 years	$150,000
13. $? at the end of each month	4.5% compounded monthly	10 years	$200,000
14. $? at the end of each month	7.5% compounded monthly	10 years	$250,000
15. $? at the end of each month	7.25% compounded monthly	40 years	$1,000,000
16. $? at the end of each month	8.25% compounded monthly	40 years	$1,500,000
17. $? at the end of every three months	3.5% compounded quarterly	5 years	$20,000
18. $? at the end of every three months	4.5% compounded quarterly	5 years	$25,000

Exercises 19 and 20 refer to the stock tables for Goodyear (the tire company) and JC Penney (the department store) given below. In each exercise, use the stock table to answer the following questions. Where necessary, round dollar amounts to the nearest cent.

a. *What were the high and low prices for a share for the past 52 weeks?*

b. *If you owned 700 shares of this stock last year, what dividend did you receive?*

c. *What is the annual return for the dividends alone? How does this compare to a bank offering a 3% interest rate?*

d. *How many shares of this company's stock were traded yesterday?*

e. *What were the high and low prices for a share yesterday?*

f. *What was the price at which a share traded when the stock exchange closed yesterday?*

g. *What was the change in price for a share of stock from the market close two days ago to yesterday's market close?*

h. *Compute the company's annual earnings per share using*

$$\text{Annual earnings per share} = \frac{\text{Yesterday's closing price per share}}{\text{PE ratio}}.$$

19.	52-Week High	Low	Stock	SYM	Div	Yld %	PE	Vol 100s	Hi	Lo	Close	Net Chg
	73.25	45.44	Goodyear	GT	1.20	2.2	17	5915	56.38	54.38	55.50	+1.25

20.	52-Week High	Low	Stock	SYM	Div	Yld %	PE	Vol 100s	Hi	Lo	Close	Net Chg
	78.34	35.38	Penney JC	JCP	2.18	4.7	22	7473	48.19	46.63	46.88	−1.31

• Practice Plus

In Exercises 21–22, round all answers to the nearest dollar.

21. Here are two ways of investing $30,000 for 20 years.

Lump-Sum Deposit	Rate	Time
$30,000	5% compounded annually	20 years

Periodic Deposit	Rate	Time
$1500 at the end of each year	5% compounded annually	20 years

a. After 20 years, how much more will you have from the lump-sum investment than from the annuity?

b. After 20 years, how much more interest will be earned from the lump-sum investment than from the annuity?

22. Here are two ways of investing $40,000 for 25 years.

Lump-Sum Deposit	Rate	Time
$40,000	6.5% compounded annually	25 years

Periodic Deposit	Rate	Time
$1600 at the end of each year	6.5% compounded annually	25 years

a. After 25 years, how much more will you have from the lump-sum investment than from the annuity?

b. After 25 years, how much more interest will be earned from the lump-sum investment than from the annuity?

In Exercises 23–24,

a. *Determine the deposit at the end of each month. Round up to the nearest dollar.*

b. *Assume that the annuity in part (a) is a tax-deferred IRA belonging to a man whose gross income in 2005 was $50,000. Use Table 4.1 on page 448 to calculate his 2005 taxes first with and then without the IRA. Assume the man is single with no dependents, has no tax credits, and takes the standard deduction.*

c. *What percent of his gross income are the man's federal taxes with and without the IRA? Round to the nearest tenth of a percent.*

	Periodic Deposit	Rate	Time	Financial Goal
23.	$? at the end of each month	8% compounded monthly	40 years	$1,000,000
24.	$? at the end of each month	7% compounded monthly	40 years	$650,000

25. Solve for P:

$$A = \frac{P[(1 + r)^t - 1]}{r}.$$

What does the resulting formula describe?

26. Solve for P:

$$A = \frac{P\left[\left(1 + \dfrac{r}{n}\right)^{nt} - 1\right]}{\dfrac{r}{n}}.$$

What does the resulting formula describe?

Application Exercises

In Exercises 27–32, use the formula

$$A = \frac{P[(1 + r)^t - 1]}{r} \quad \text{or} \quad A = \frac{P\left[\left(1 + \dfrac{r}{n}\right)^{nt} - 1\right]}{\dfrac{r}{n}}.$$

Round to the nearest dollar.

27. To save money for a sabbatical to earn a master's degree, you deposit $2000 at the end of each year in an annuity that pays 7.5% compounded annually.
   a. How much will you have saved at the end of five years?
   b. Find the interest.

28. To save money for a sabbatical to earn a master's degree, you deposit $2500 at the end of each year in an annuity that pays 6.25% compounded annually.
   a. How much will you have saved at the end of five years?
   b. Find the interest.

29. At age 25, to save for retirement, you decide to deposit $50 at the end of each month in an IRA that pays 5.5% compounded monthly.
   a. How much will you have from the IRA when you retire at age 65?
   b. Find the interest.

30. At age 25, to save for retirement, you decide to deposit $75 at the end of each month in an IRA that pays 6.5% compounded monthly.
   a. How much will you have from the IRA when you retire at age 65?
   b. Find the interest.

31. To offer scholarship funds to children of employees, a company invests $10,000 at the end of every three months in an annuity that pays 10.5% compounded quarterly.
   a. How much will the company have in scholarship funds at the end of ten years?
   b. Find the interest.

32. To offer scholarship funds to children of employees, a company invests $15,000 at the end of every three months in an annuity that pays 9% compounded quarterly.
   a. How much will the company have in scholarship funds at the end of ten years?
   b. Find the interest.

In Exercises 33–36, use the formula

$$P = \frac{A\left(\dfrac{r}{n}\right)}{\left[\left(1 + \dfrac{r}{n}\right)^{nt} - 1\right]}.$$

Round up to the nearest dollar.

33. You would like to have $3500 in four years for a special vacation following graduation by making deposits at the end of every six months in an annuity that pays 5% compounded semiannually.
   a. How much should you deposit at the end of every six months?
   b. How much of the $3500 comes from deposits and how much comes from interest?

34. You would like to have $4000 in four years for a special vacation following graduation by making deposits at the end of every six months in an annuity that pays 7% compounded semiannually.
   a. How much should you deposit at the end of every six months?
   b. How much of the $4000 comes from deposits and how much comes from interest?

35. How much should you deposit at the end of each month into an IRA that pays 8.5% compounded monthly to have $4 million when you retire in 45 years? How much of the $4 million comes from interest?

36. How much should you deposit at the end of each month into an IRA that pays 6.5% compounded monthly to have $2 million when you retire in 45 years? How much of the $2 million comes from interest?

• Writing in Mathematics

37. What is an annuity?

38. What is meant by the value of an annuity?

39. Write a problem involving the formula for regular payments needed to achieve a financial goal. The problem should be similar to Example 4 on page 472. However, the problem should be unique to your situation. Include something for which you would like to save, how much you need to save, and how long it will take to achieve your goal. Then solve the problem.

40. What is stock?

41. Describe how to find the percent ownership that a shareholder has in a company.

42. Describe the two ways that investors make money with stock.

43. What is a bond? Describe the difference between a stock and a bond.

44. Using a recent newspaper, copy the stock table for a company of your choice. Then explain the meaning of the numbers in the columns.

45. If an investor sees that the dividends for a stock have a lower annual rate than those for a no-risk bank account, should the stock be sold and the money placed in the bank account? Explain your answer.

Use the following investments to answer Exercises 46–49.

Investment 1: 1000 shares of IBM stock
Investment 2: A 5-year bond with a 22% interest rate issued by a small company that is testing and planning to sell delicious, nearly zero-calorie desserts
Investment 3: A 30-year U.S. treasury bond at a fixed 7% annual rate

46. Which of these investments has the greatest risk? Explain why.

47. Which of these investments has the least risk? Explain why.

48. Which of these investments has the possibility of the greatest return? Explain why.

49. If you could be given one of these investments as a gift, which one would you choose? Explain why.

• Critical Thinking Exercise

50. How much should you deposit at the end of each month in an IRA that pays 8% compounded monthly to earn $60,000 per year from interest alone, while leaving the principal untouched, when you retire in 30 years?

• Group Exercises

51. Each group should have a newspaper with current stock quotations. Choose nine stocks that group members think would make good investments. Imagine that you invest $1000 in each of these nine investments. Check the value of your stock each day over the next five weeks and then sell the nine stocks after five weeks. What is the group's profit or loss over the five-week period? Compare this figure with the profit or loss of other groups in your class for this activity.

52. This activity is a group research project intended for four or five people. Use the research to present a seminar on investments. The seminar is intended to last about 30 minutes and should result in an interesting and informative presentation to the entire class. The seminar should include investment considerations, how to read the bond section of the newspaper, how to read the mutual fund section, and higher-risk investments.

53. Group members have inherited $1 million. However, the group cannot spend any of the money for ten years. As a group, determine how to invest this money in order to maximize the money you will make over ten years. The money can be invested in as many ways as the group decides. Explain each investment decision. What are the risks involved in each investment plan?

SECTION 4.5 • INSTALLMENT BUYING

OBJECTIVES

1. Determine the amount financed, the installment price, and the finance charge for a fixed loan.

2. Determine the APR.

3. Compute unearned interest and the payoff amount for a loan paid off early.

4. Find the interest, the balance due, and the minimum monthly payment for credit card loans.

5. Calculate interest on credit cards using three methods.

Do you buy products with a credit card? Although your card lets you use a product while paying for it, the costs associated with such cards, including their high interest rates, fees, and penalties, stack the odds in favor of your getting hurt by them. In 2004, the average credit-card debt per U.S. household was $9312. If you use a credit card, you are engaging in **installment buying**, in which you repay a loan for the cost of a product on a monthly basis. A loan that you pay off with weekly or monthly payments, or payments in some other time period, is called an **installment loan**. The advantage of an installment loan is that the consumer gets to use a product immediately. In this section, we will see that the disadvantage is that it can add a substantial amount to the cost of a purchase. When it comes to installment buying, consumer beware!

1 | Determine the amount financed, the installment price, and the finance charge for a fixed loan.

Fixed Installment Loans

You decide to purchase a used pick-up truck that costs $9345. You can finance the truck by paying $300 at the time of purchase, called the **down payment**, and $194.38 per month for 60 months. A loan like this that has a schedule for paying a fixed amount each period is called a **fixed installment loan**. We begin with three terms associated with such loans.

> ### THE VOCABULARY OF FIXED INSTALLMENT LOANS
>
> The **amount financed** is what the consumer borrows:
>
> $$\text{Amount financed} = \text{Cash price} - \text{Down payment}.$$
>
> The **total installment price** is the sum of all monthly payments plus the down payment:
>
> $$\text{Total installment price} = \text{Total of all monthly payments} + \text{Down payment}.$$
>
> The **finance charge** is the interest on the installment loan:
>
> $$\text{Finance charge} = \text{Total installment price} - \text{Cash price}.$$

EXAMPLE 1	BUYING A PICK-UP TRUCK USING A FIXED INSTALLMENT LOAN

The cost of a used pick-up truck is $9345. We can finance the truck by paying $300 down and $194.38 per month for 60 months.

a. Determine the amount financed.

b. Determine the total installment price.

c. Determine the finance charge.

SOLUTION

a. Amount financed = Cash price − Down payment
$$= \$9345 - \$300$$
$$= \$9045$$

The amount financed is $9045.

b. The total installment price is obtained by adding the total of all monthly payments and the down payment. Because we are paying $194.38 per month for 60 months, the total of all monthly payments is

$$\frac{\$194.38}{\text{month}} \times 60 \text{ months} = \$194.38 \times 60.$$

Total installment price = Total of all monthly payments + Down payment
$$= \$194.38 \times 60 + \$300$$
$$= \$11{,}662.80 + \$300$$
$$= \$11{,}962.80$$

The total installment price is $11,962.80.

c. Finance charge = Total installment price − Cash price
$$= \$11{,}962.80 - \$9345$$
$$= \$2617.80$$

The finance charge for the loan is $2617.80.

1 The cost of a new car is $14,000. You can finance the car by paying $280 down and $315 per month for 60 months.

a. Determine the amount financed.

b. Determine the total installment price.

c. Determine the finance charge.

You will be using these figures in Check Points 2, 3, and 4, so keep track of your answers.

2

Determine the APR.

STUDY TIP

Do not confuse effective annual yield with annual percentage rate. Effective annual yield applies to *interest earned* on invested money. By contrast, annual percentage rate applies to *interest owed* on loans.

In Example 1, the finance charge for the loan, $2617.80, is the **interest** paid to finance the truck. What interest rate are we paying when we pay $2617.80 interest over 60 months? The interest rate per year is called the **annual percentage rate**, abbreviated **APR**. In 1969, the Federal Reserve Board established the **Truth-in-Lending Act**. It requires lending institutions to inform borrowers in writing of a loan's APR. **When comparing two or more loans with different terms, the loan with the lowest APR is the one that charges the least interest.** For many people, an important factor in deciding on a fixed installment loan is the cash down payment that is required. If you do not have a lot of cash at the time of purchase, you might select a loan with a smaller down payment even though it has a not-so-desirable APR.

The APR for a fixed installment loan can be determined using a table similar to the abbreviated version shown in Table 4.5. Here are the steps involved in using an APR table. These steps are illustrated in Example 2.

STEPS IN USING AN APR TABLE

1. Compute the finance charge per $100 financed:
$$\frac{\text{Finance charge}}{\text{Amount financed}} \times \$100.$$

2. Look in the row corresponding to the number of payments to be made and find the entry closest to the value in step 1.

3. Find the APR at the top of the column in which the entry from step 2 is found. (This is the APR rounded to the nearest $\frac{1}{2}$%.)

TABLE 4.5 ANNUAL PERCENTAGE RATE (APR) FOR MONTHLY PAYMENT LOANS

Number of Monthly Payments	Annual Percentage Rate (APR)												
	10.0%	10.5%	11.0%	11.5%	12.0%	12.5%	13.0%	13.5%	14.0%	14.5%	15.0%	15.5%	16.0%
	(Finance charge per $100 of amount financed)												
6	$2.94	$3.08	$3.23	$3.38	$3.53	$3.68	$3.83	$3.97	$4.12	$4.27	$4.42	$4.57	$4.72
12	5.50	5.78	6.06	6.34	6.62	6.90	7.18	7.46	7.74	8.03	8.31	8.59	8.88
18	8.10	8.52	8.93	9.35	9.77	10.19	10.61	11.03	11.45	11.87	12.29	12.72	13.14
24	10.75	11.30	11.86	12.42	12.98	13.54	14.10	14.66	15.23	15.80	16.37	16.94	17.51
30	13.43	14.13	14.83	15.54	16.24	16.95	17.66	18.38	19.10	19.81	20.54	21.26	21.99
36	16.16	17.01	17.86	18.71	19.57	20.43	21.30	22.17	23.04	23.92	24.80	25.68	26.57
48	21.74	22.90	24.06	25.23	26.40	27.58	28.77	29.97	31.17	32.37	33.59	34.81	36.03
60	27.48	(28.96)	30.45	31.96	33.47	34.99	36.52	38.06	39.61	41.17	42.74	44.32	45.91

EXAMPLE 2   DETERMINING THE APR

In Example 1, we found that the amount financed for the truck was $9045 and the finance charge was $2617.80. The borrower financed the truck with 60 monthly payments. Use Table 4.5 to determine the APR.

SOLUTION

Step 1. Find the finance charge per $100 of the amount financed.

$$\text{Finance charge per \$100 financed} = \frac{\text{Finance charge}}{\text{Amount financed}} \times \$100$$

$$= \frac{\$2617.80}{\$9045.00} \times \$100$$

$$\approx \$28.94$$

This means that the borrower pays $28.94 interest for each $100 being financed.

STUDY TIP

Use Table 4.5 for this example as follows.

10.5%

60 → (28.96)

Step 2. Look in the row corresponding to the number of payments to be made (60) and find the entry closest to the value in step 1 ($28.94). Table 4.5 presents three types of information: the number of monthly payments, the APR, and the finance charge per $100 financed. There are 60 monthly payments, so look for 60 in the left column. Then move across to the right until you find the amount closest to the finance charge per $100 financed, namely $28.94. This amount, $28.96, is circled in the table.

Step 3. Find the APR at the top of the column in which the entry from step 2 is found. Take a second look at the circled entry, $28.96. At the top of this column is 10.5%. Thus, the APR for the fixed installment truck loan is approximately 10.5%.

○

CHECK POINT 2 Use Table 4.5 to determine the APR for the car loan described in Check Point 1.

3 | Compute unearned interest and the payoff amount for a loan paid off early.

A fixed installment loan can be paid off early so that a borrower need not pay the entire finance charge. The amount by which the finance charge is reduced is called the **unearned interest**. The interest saved by paying off the loan early can be calculated by one of two methods, the **actuarial method** or the **rule of 78**. The actuarial method uses the APR table and the rule of 78 does not. The Truth-in-Lending Act requires that the method for calculating the reduction of the finance charge be disclosed at the time the loan is signed.

Here are two formulas for computing unearned interest:

STUDY TIP

Keep in mind that a loan's finance charge is the same thing as the loan's interest.

METHODS FOR COMPUTING UNEARNED INTEREST

Unearned interest is the amount by which a loan's finance charge is reduced when the loan is paid off early.

Actuarial Method	**Rule of 78**
$u = \dfrac{kRV}{100 + V}$	$u = \dfrac{k(k + 1)}{n(n + 1)} \times F$
u = unearned interest	u = unearned interest
k = remaining number of scheduled payments (excluding current payment)	k = remaining number of scheduled payments (excluding current payment)
R = regular monthly payment	n = original number of payments
V = finance charge per $100 (from the APR table) for a loan with the same APR and k monthly payments	F = original finance charge

---

The total amount due on the day that a loan is paid off early is called the **payoff amount**. Unearned interest is subtracted in computing the payoff amount. Examples 3 and 4 illustrate how the payoff amount is computed using the actuarial method in Example 3 and the rule of 78 in Example 4. Both examples refer back to the pick-up truck in Example 1. Shown in the margin is a summary of given and computed amounts for the truck.

Pick-up truck
cost: $9345
Financing: $300 + $194.38 per month for 60 months
Amount financed: $9045
Total installment price: $11,962.80
Finance charge (interest): $2617.80
Finance charge per $100 financed: $28.94
APR: 10.5%

EXAMPLE 3 EARLY PAYOFF: THE ACTUARIAL METHOD

You got a big bonus at work—and a raise. Instead of making the thirty-sixth payment on your truck, you decide to pay the remaining balance and terminate the loan.

a. Use the actuarial method to determine how much interest will be saved (the unearned interest, u) by repaying the loan early.

b. Find the payoff amount.

Pick-up truck
cost: $9345
Financing: $300 + $194.38 per month for 60 months
Amount financed: $9045
Total installment price: $11,962.80
Finance charge (interest): $2617.80
Finance charge per $100 financed: $28.94
APR: 10.5%

Given and computed amounts for the truck (repeated)

SOLUTION

a. We will use the formula $u = \dfrac{kRV}{100 + V}$ to find u, the unearned interest. We need values for k, R, and V. The current payment is payment number 36. There are 60 payments total. We subtract the number of the current payment from the total number of payments to find the number of remaining payments, k: $k = 60 - 36 = 24$. The value of R, the regular monthly payment, is given: $R = \$194.38$. To find the value for the finance charge per $100, V, use the APR table (Table 4.5 on page 220). In the Number of Monthly Payments Column, find the number of remaining payments, 24, and then look to the right until you reach the column headed by 10.5%, the APR. This row and column intersect at 11.30. Thus, $V = 11.30$. This is the finance charge per $100 for a loan with the same APR and k ($k = 24$) monthly payments. We substitute these values into the actuarial method formula.

$$u = \frac{kRV}{100 + V} = \frac{24 \times 194.38 \times 11.30}{100 + 11.30} \approx 473.64$$

Approximately $473.64 will be saved in interest by terminating the loan early using the actuarial method.

b. The payoff amount, the amount due on the day of the loan's termination, is determined as follows:

Payoff amount	=	payment number 36	plus	total of remaining payments after payment 36	minus	interest saved (unearned interest).

$$= \$194.38 \quad + \quad 24 \times \$194.38 \quad - \quad \$473.64$$

$$= \$4385.86.$$

The payment needed to terminate the loan at the end of 36 months is $4385.86.

CHECK POINT 3 Instead of making the twenty-fourth payment on the car loan described in Check Points 1 and 2, you decide to pay the remaining balance and terminate the loan.

a. Use the actuarial method to determine how much interest will be saved (the unearned interest, u) by repaying the loan early.

b. Find the payoff amount.

EXAMPLE 4 EARLY PAYOFF: THE RULE OF 78

The loan in Example 3 is paid off at the time of the thirty-sixth monthly payment. Use the rule of 78 to find

a. the unearned interest.

b. the payoff amount.

SOLUTION

a. We will use the formula

$$u = \frac{k(k + 1)}{n(n + 1)} \times F$$

to find u, the unearned interest. We need values for k, n, and F. From Example 3, k, the number of remaining payments, is 24: $k = 24$. The original number of payments, n, is 60: $n = 60$. The summary of figures for the pick-up truck shown in the margin lists the finance charge: $F = \$2617.80$. We substitute these values into the rule of 78 formula.

$$u = \frac{k(k + 1)}{n(n + 1)} \times F = \frac{24(24 + 1)}{60(60 + 1)} \times \$2617.80 \approx \$429.15$$

By the rule of 78, the borrower will save \$429.15 in interest.

b. Next, we determine the payoff amount.

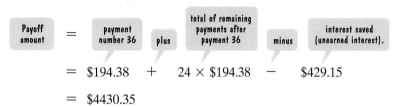

$$= \quad \$194.38 \quad + \quad 24 \times \$194.38 \quad - \quad \$429.15$$

$$= \$4430.35$$

The payoff amount is \$4430.35.

In Example 3, we found that \$473.64 is saved in interest using the actuarial method, while in Example 4, we found that \$429.15 is saved in interest using the rule of 78. These examples illustrate that the actuarial method is more beneficial to the borrower than the rule of 78 because it results in greater savings in interest at the loan's termination. For loans of 61 months or longer, only the actuarial method is allowed. Also, some states have shorter loan periods that do not allow the rule of 78.

The loan in Check Point 3 is paid off at the time of the twenty-fourth monthly payment. Use the rule of 78 to find

a. the unearned interest.

b. the payoff amount.

4 | Find the interest, the balance due, and the minimum monthly payment for credit card loans.

Open-End Installment Loans

Using a credit card is an example of an open-end installment loan, commonly called **revolving credit**. Open-end loans differ from fixed installment loans in that there is no schedule for paying a fixed amount each period. Credit card loans require users to make only a minimum monthly payment that depends on the unpaid balance and the interest rate. Credit cards have high interest rates compared to other kinds of loans. The interest on credit cards is computed using the simple interest formula $I = Prt$. However, r represents the *monthly* interest rate and t is time in months rather than in years. A typical interest rate is 1.57% monthly. This is equivalent to a yearly rate of $12 \times 1.57\%$, or 18.84%. With such a high APR, credit card balances should be paid off as quickly as possible.

Most credit card customers are billed every month. A typical billing period is May 1 through May 31, but it can also run from, say, May 5 through June 4. Customers receive a statement, called an **itemized billing**, that contains the unpaid balance on the first day of the billing period, the total balance owed on the last day of the billing period, a list of purchases and cash advances made during the billing period, the date of the last day of the billing period, the payment due date, and the minimum payment required.

Customers who make a purchase during the billing period and pay the entire amount of the purchase by the payment due date are not charged interest. By contrast, customers who make cash advances using their credit cards must pay interest from the day the money is advanced until the day it is repaid.

One method for calculating interest on credit cards is the **unpaid balance method**. Interest is calculated on the unpaid balance on the first day of the billing period less payments and credits.

EXAMPLE 5   BALANCE DUE ON A CREDIT CARD

A particular VISA card calculates interest using the unpaid balance method. The monthly interest rate is 1.3% on the unpaid balance on the first day of the billing period less payments and credits. Here are some of the details in the May 1–May 31 itemized billing:

May 1 Unpaid Balance: $1350

Payment Received May 8: $250

Purchases Charged to the VISA Account: Airline tickets: $375, Books: $57, Meals: $65

Last Day of the Billing Period: May 31

Payment Due Date: June 9

a. Find the interest due on the payment due date.

b. Find the total balance owed on the last day of the billing period.

c. This credit card requires a $10 minimum monthly payment if the total balance owed on the last day of the billing period is less than $360. Otherwise, the minimum monthly payment is $\frac{1}{36}$ of the balance owed on the last day of the billing period, rounded to the nearest whole dollar. What is the minimum monthly payment due by June 9?

SOLUTION

a. The monthly interest rate is 1.3% on the unpaid balance on the first day of the billing period, $1350, less payments and credits, $250. The interest due is computed using $I = Prt$.

$$I = Prt = (\$1350 - \$250) \times 0.013 \times 1 = \$1100 \times 0.013 \times 1 = \$14.30$$

Time, t, is measured in months, and $t = 1$ month.

The interest due on the payment due date is $14.30.

b. The total balance owed on the last day of the billing period is determined as follows:

Balance owed = (unpaid balance on the first day of the billing period minus payments) plus interest plus charges for three items during billing period.

$$= \$1100 \quad + \quad \$14.30 \quad + \quad \$375 + \$57 + \$65$$

$$= \$1611.30.$$

The total balance owed on the last day of the billing period is $1611.30.

c. Because the balance owed on the last day of the billing period, $1611.30, exceeds $360, the customer must pay a minimum of $\frac{1}{36}$ of the balance owed.

$$\text{Minimum monthly payment} = \frac{\text{balance owed}}{36} = \frac{\$1611.30}{36} \approx \$45$$

Rounded to the nearest whole dollar, the minimum monthly payment due by June 9 is $45.

○

CHECK POINT 5 A credit card calculates interest using the unpaid balance method. The monthly interest rate is 1.6% on the unpaid balance on the first day of the billing period less payments and credits. Here are some of the details in the May 1–May 31 itemized billing:

May 1 Unpaid Balance: $4720

Payment Received May 8: $1000

Purchases Charged to the Account: Computer: $1025, Meals: $45

Last Day of the Billing Period: May 31

Payment Due Date: June 9

Answer parts (a) through (c) in Example 5 using this information.

---

5 | Calculate interest on credit cards using three methods.

Methods for calculating interest on credit cards vary and the interest can differ on credit cards that show the same APR. The three methods for calculating interest are summarized in the following box:

> ## METHODS FOR CALCULATING INTEREST ON CREDIT CARDS
>
> For all three methods, $I = Prt$, where r is the monthly rate and t is one month.
>
> **Unpaid balance method:**
>
> The principal, P, is the balance on the first day of the billing period less payments and credits.
>
> **Previous balance method:**
>
> The principal, P, is the unpaid balance on the first day of the billing period.
>
> **Average daily balance method:**
>
> The principal, P, is the **average daily balance**. This is determined by adding the unpaid balances for each day in the billing period and dividing by the number of days in the billing period.

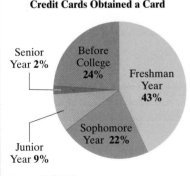
EXAMPLE 6   COMPARING METHODS FOR CALCULATING INTEREST

A credit card has a monthly rate of 1.75%. (The APR is 21%.) In the January 1–January 31 itemized billing, the January 1 unpaid balance is $2500. A payment of $1000 was received on January 8. There are no purchases or cash advances in this billing period. The payment due date is February 9. Find the interest due on this date using each of the three methods for calculating credit card interest.

SOLUTION Because the monthly rate is 1.75%, for all three methods $I = Prt = P \times 0.0175 \times 1$ month. The principal, P, is different for each method.

a. The Unpaid Balance Method

The principal, P, is the unpaid balance on the first day of the billing period, $2500, less payments and credits, $1000. The interest is

$$I = Prt = (\$2500 - \$1000) \times 0.0175 \times 1 = \$1500 \times 0.0175 \times 1 = \$26.25.$$

The interest due on the payment due date is $26.25.

b. The Previous Balance Method

The principal, P, is the unpaid balance on the first day of the billing period, $2500. The interest is

$$I = Prt = \$2500 \times 0.0175 \times 1 = \$43.75.$$

The interest due on the payment due date is $43.75.

c. The Average Daily Balance Method

The principal, P, is the average daily balance. Add the unpaid balances for each day in the billing period and divide by the number of days in the billing period, 31. The unpaid balance on the first day of the billing period is $2500 and a $1000 payment is recorded on January 8. The sum of the balances owed for each day of

Comparing Credit Cards

With features such as miles toward air travel, insurance on rental cars, and special introductory rates, shopping for a credit card can be a daunting task. You can search the Internet for the most current information regarding annual fees and interest rates. Compare credit cards at Web sites such as Bankrate.com and CardWeb.com. Also check *Consumer Reports'* site, www.consumerreports.org, for the "ten most consumer-friendly credit cards."

the billing period is $2500 added for each of the first 7 days, expressed as $2500 × 7, plus $1500 added for each of the remaining 24 days, expressed as $1500 × 24.

Average daily balance

$$= \frac{\text{Sum of the unpaid balances for each day in the billing period}}{\text{Number of days in the billing period}}$$

$$= \frac{\$2500(7) + \$1500(24)}{31} \approx \$1725.81$$

The average daily balance serves as the principal. The interest is

$$I = Prt = \$1725.81 \times 0.0175 \times 1 \approx \$30.20.$$

The interest due on the payment due date is $30.20.

Most credit cards use the average daily balance method to determine interest due. Calculating the average daily balance by hand can be quite tedious when there are numerous transactions during a billing period. Credit card customers who are charged interest by the average daily balance method will find the average daily balance provided on monthly statements.

CHECK POINT 6 A credit card has a monthly rate of 1.8%. In the January 1–January 31 itemized billing, the January 1 unpaid balance is $6800. A payment of $500 was received on January 8. There are no purchases or cash advances in this billing period. The payment due date is February 9. Find the interest due on this date using each of the three methods for calculating credit card interest.

EXERCISE SET 4.5 ●●●●●●

• Practice and Application Exercises

1. The cost of a sports utility vehicle is $27,000. We can finance this by paying $5000 down and $410 per month for 60 months. Determine **a.** the amount financed; **b.** the total installment price; **c.** the finance charge.

2. The cost of a computer is $2450. We can finance this by paying $550 down and $94.50 per month for 24 months. Determine **a.** the amount financed; **b.** the total installment price; **c.** the finance charge.

3. The cost of a washer-dryer is $1100. We can finance this by paying $100 down and $110 per month for 12 months. Determine **a.** the amount financed; **b.** the total installment price; **c.** the finance charge.

4. The cost of a used car is $5675. We can finance this by paying $1223 down and $125 per month for 48 months. Determine **a.** the amount financed; **b.** the total installment price; **c.** the finance charge.

5. You plan to pay for a computer in 12 equal monthly payments. The finance charge per $100 financed is $6.90. Use Table 4.5 on page 220 to find the APR for this loan.

6. You plan to pay for a refrigerator in 18 equal monthly payments. The finance charge per $100 financed is $12.72. Use Table 4.5 on page 220 to find the APR for this loan.

7. The finance charge per $100 financed for a computer that is paid off in 24 equal monthly payments is $15.80. Use Table 4.5 on page 220 to find the APR for this loan.

8. The finance charge per $100 financed for a refrigerator that is paid off in 12 monthly payments is $8.59. Use Table 8.5 on page 220 to find the APR for this loan.

9. A used car is financed for $4450 over 48 months. If the total finance charge is $1279, find the APR for this loan.

10. A desk is financed for $1200 over 30 months. If the total finance charge is $264, find the APR for this loan.

11. The cash price for furniture for all rooms of a three-bedroom house is $17,500. The furniture can be financed by paying $500 down and $360.55 per month for 60 months.
    a. Determine the amount financed.
    b. Determine the total installment price.
    c. Determine the finance charge.
    d. What is the APR for this loan?

12. The cost of a Blazer is $18,000, which can be financed by paying $600 down and $385 per month for 60 months.
  a. Determine the amount financed.
  b. Determine the total installment price.
  c. Determine the finance charge.
  d. What is the APR for this loan?

13. In Exercise 11, instead of making the twenty-fourth payment, the borrower decides to pay the remaining balance and terminate the loan for the furniture.
  a. Use the actuarial method to determine how much interest will be saved by repaying the loan early.
  b. By the actuarial method, what is the total amount due on the day of the loan's termination?
  c. Use the rule of 78 to determine how much interest will be saved by repaying the loan early.
  d. By the rule of 78, what is the total amount due on the day of the loan's termination?

14. In Exercise 12, instead of making the twenty-fourth payment, the borrower decides to pay the remaining balance and terminate the loan for the Blazer.
  a. Use the actuarial method to determine how much interest will be saved by repaying the loan early.
  b. By the actuarial method, what is the total amount due on the day of the loan's termination?
  c. Use the rule of 78 to determine how much interest will be saved by repaying the loan early.
  d. By the rule of 78, what is the total amount due on the day of the loan's termination?

15. A particular VISA card calculates interest using the unpaid balance method. The monthly interest rate is 1.3% on the unpaid balance on the first day of the billing period less payments and credits. Here are some of the details in the May 1–May 31 itemized billing:

May 1 Unpaid Balance: $950
Payment Received May 8: $100
Purchases Charged to the VISA Account: clothing, $85 and car repair, $67
Last Day of the Billing Period: May 31
Payment Due Date: June 9
  a. Find the interest due on the payment due date.
  b. Find the total balance owed on the last day of the billing period.
  c. This credit card requires a $10 minimum monthly payment if the total balance owed on the last day of the billing period is less than $360. Otherwise, the minimum monthly payment is $\frac{1}{36}$ of the balance owed on the last day of the billing period, rounded to the nearest whole dollar. What is the minimum monthly payment due by June 9?

16. A particular credit card calculates interest using the unpaid balance method. The monthly interest rate is 1.75% on the unpaid balance on the first day of the billing period less payments and credits. Here are some of the details in the September 1–September 30 itemized billing:

September 1 Unpaid Balance: $425
Payment Received September 6: $75
Purchases Charged to the Account: groceries, $45 and clothing, $77
Last Day of the Billing Period: September 30
Payment Due Date: October 9

  a. Find the interest due on the payment due date.
  b. Find the total balance owed on the last day of the billing period.
  c. Terms for this credit card are shown in the following table. What is the minimum monthly payment due by October 9?

New Balance	Minimum Payment
$0.01 to $10.00	No payment due
10.01 to 200.00	$10.00
200.01 to 250.00	15.00
250.01 to 300.00	20.00
300.01 to 350.00	25.00
350.01 to 400.00	30.00
400.01 to 450.00	35.00
450.01 to 500.00	40.00
Over $500.00	$\frac{1}{10}$ of new balance

17. A credit card has a monthly rate of 1.5% and uses the average daily balance method for calculating interest. Here are some of the details in the April 1–April 30 itemized billing:

April 1 Unpaid Balance: $445.59
Payment Received April 5: $110
Purchases Charged to the Account: $278.06
Average Daily Balance: $330.90
Last Day of the Billing Period: April 30
Payment Due Date: May 9
  a. Find the interest due on the payment due date.
  b. Find the total balance owed on the last day of the billing period.
  c. Terms for this credit card are given in Exercise 16. What is the minimum monthly payment due by May 9?

18. A credit card has a monthly rate of 1.8% and uses the average daily balance method for calculating interest. Here are some of the details in the December 1–December 31 itemized billing:

December 1 Unpaid Balance: $220
Payment Received December 7: $60
Purchases Charged to the Account: $90
Average Daily Balance: $205.60
Last Day of the Billing Period: December 31
Payment Due Date: January 9
  a. Find the interest due on the payment due date.
  b. Find the total balance owed on the last day of the billing period.
  c. Terms for this credit card are given in Exercise 16. What is the minimum monthly payment due on January 9?

19. A credit card has a monthly rate of 1.5%. In the September 1–September 30 itemized billing, the September 1 unpaid balance is $3000. A payment of $2500 was received on September 6. There are no purchases or cash advances in this billing period. The payment due date is October 9. Find the interest due on this date using
  a. the unpaid balance method.
  b. the previous balance method.
  c. the average daily balance method.

20. A credit card has a monthly rate of 2.2%. In the October 1–October 31 itemized billing, the October 1 unpaid balance is $2000. A payment of $400 was received on October 6. There are no purchases or cash advances in this billing period. The payment due date is November 9. Find the interest due on this date using

    a. the unpaid balance method.

    b. the previous balance method.

    c. the average daily balance method.

• Writing in Mathematics

21. Describe the difference between a fixed installment loan and an open-end installment loan.

22. For a fixed installment loan, what is the total installment price?

23. For a fixed installment loan, how is the total finance charge determined?

24. What is the APR?

25. What are the two methods for computing unearned interest when a loan is paid off early? Describe how the payoff amount is determined regardless of which method is used in the computation.

26. Name and describe each of the three methods for calculating interest on credit cards.

27. For a credit card billing period, describe how the average daily balance is determined. Why is this computation somewhat tedious when done by hand?

28. Which method for calculating interest on credit cards is most beneficial to the borrower and which is least benefical? Explain why this is so.

29. A Sears Revolving Charge Card has a monthly rate of 1.75%. The interest is a minimum of 50¢ if the average daily balance is $28.50 or less. Explain how this policy is beneficial to Sears.

• Critical Thinking Exercise

30. Which one of the following is true?

    a. The finance charge on a fixed installment loan is the cash price minus the total installment price.

    b. It is to a borrower's advantage to have unearned interest computed by the rule of 78 rather than by the actuarial method.

    c. It is not necessary to know the number of days in a credit card billing period to determine the average daily balance.

    d. If a credit card has a 2.2% monthly interest rate, the annual rate exceeds 25%.

Use estimation and not calculation to select the most reasonable value in Exercises 31–32.

31. If you purchase a $1400 item, put $200 down, and pay the balance in 30 monthly installments, what is a reasonable estimate of the monthly payment?

    a. $35   **b.** $47   **c.** $70   **d.** $100

32. A reasonable estimate of the monthly interest on an average daily balance of $359.58 at a 1.3% monthly rate is

    a. $50   **b.** $10   **c.** $5   **d.** $2

33. A bank bills its credit card holders on the first of each month for each itemized billing. The card provides a 20-day period in which to pay the bill before charging interest. If the card holder wants to buy an expensive gift for a September 30 wedding but can't pay for it until November 5, explain how this can be done without adding an interest charge.

34. A $1500 computer can be purchased using a credit card that charges a monthly rate of 1.5% using the unpaid balance method. The borrower is considering one of the following options:

Option A: Make a credit card payment of $300 at the end of each month for five months and pay off the balance at the end of the sixth month.

Option B: Make a credit card payment of $300 plus the month's interest at the end of each month for five months.

How much is saved in interest using option B?

• Technology Exercises

35. Set up a spreadsheet with one column each for the balance, number of days at that balance, payments, charges, and the product of each balance and the number of days at that balance. The balance on John and Jane Doe's credit card on July 5, their billing date, was $375.80. For the period ending August 4, they had the following transactions:

July 13, Payment: $150.00
July 15, Charge: Computer Store, $74.35
July 23, Charge: Clothing, $123.50
July 29, Charge: Restaurant, $42.50

    a. Use the summation capabilities of the spreadsheet to determine the number of days in the billing period and the average daily balance.

    b. Find the finance charge (the interest) that is owed on August 4. Assume the monthly rate is 1.3%.

    c. Find the balance that is owed on August 4.

36. Set up a spreadsheet with one column each for the balance, number of days at that balance, payments, charges, and the product of each balance and the number of days at that balance. The balance on the Does' credit card on May 12, their billing date, was $378.50. For the period ending June 11, they had the following transactions:

May 13, Charge: Toys, $129.79

May 15, Payment: $50.00

May 18, Charge: Clothing, $135.85

May 29, Charge: Housewares, $37.63

    a. Use the summation capabilities of the spreadsheet to determine the number of days in the billing period and the average daily balance.

    b. Find the finance charge (the interest) that is owed on June 11. Assume the monthly rate is 0.75%.

    c. Find the balance that is owed on June 11.

SECTION 4.6 • AMORTIZATION AND THE COST OF HOME OWNERSHIP

OBJECTIVES

1. Understand mortgage options.

2. Compute the monthly payment and interest costs for a mortgage.

3. Prepare a partial loan amortization schedule.

4. Compute payments and interest for other kinds of installment loans.

1 | Understand mortgage options.

In 2006, the median U.S. home price jumped to $206,000, up a stunning 15% in a year and 55% over five years. (*Source*: National Association of Realtors) Americans now brag about having bought their home in the 1990s the way they used to boast about having bought Microsoft stock in the 1980s. The deeper implication of this real estate boom is the notion that a house is no longer just a home: Real estate has become as much about nest feathering as it is about nesting. And when love and money collide, things can get a little crazy. In this section, we focus on the cost of home ownership and the mathematics underlying America's raucous house party.

Mortgages

A **mortgage** is a long-term loan (perhaps up to 30, 40, or even 50 years) for the purpose of buying a home, and for which the property is pledged as security for payment. If payments are not made on the loan, the lender gets to take possession of the property. The **down payment** is the portion of the sale price of the home that the buyer initially pays to the seller. The minimum required down payment is computed as a percentage of the sale price. For example, suppose you decide to buy a $220,000 home that requires you to pay the seller 10% of the sale price. You must pay 10% of $220,000, which is $0.10 \times \$220,000$, or $22,000, to the seller. Thus, $22,000 is the down payment. The **amount of the mortgage** is the difference between the sale price and the down payment. For your $220,000 home, the amount of the mortgage is $220,000 − $22,000, or $198,000.

There are many types of lenders and types of mortgages to choose from. Many banks, savings associations, mortgage companies, and credit unions provide mortgage loans. Some companies, called **mortgage brokers**, offer to find you a mortgage lender willing to make you a loan. Computer loan origination systems, or CLOs, are computer terminals sometimes available in real estate offices to help buyers sort through the various types of loans offered by different lenders.

Monthly payments for a mortgage depend on the amount of the mortgage, or the principal, the interest rate, and the time of the mortgage. Mortgages can have a fixed interest rate or a variable interest rate. **Fixed-rate mortgages** have the same monthly payment during the entire time of the loan. **Variable-rate mortgages**, also known as **adjustable-rate mortgages** (ARMs), have payment amounts that change from time to time depending on changes in the interest rate. ARMS are less predictable than fixed-rate mortgages. They start out at lower rates than fixed-rate mortgages. Caps limit how high rates can go over the term of the loan.

There are many other mortgage options. One option involves a short-term loan in which only the interest is paid, followed by a final payment (called a "balloon payment") for the entire loan amount. This kind of mortgage might appeal to a buyer who plans to sell the house in a short period of time. Some buyers are eligible for a mortgage insured through the Federal Housing Administration (FHA) or guaranteed by the Department of Veteran Affairs or similar programs operated by cities or states. These programs require a smaller down payment than standard loans.

2 | Compute the monthly payment and interest costs for a mortgage.

Computation Involved with Buying a Home

Although monthly payments for a mortgage depend on the amount of the mortgage, the time of the loan, and the interest rate, the rate is not the only cost of a mortgage. Most lending institutions require the buyer to pay one or more **points** at the time of closing—that is, the time at which the mortgage begins. A point is a one-time charge that equals 1% of the loan amount. For example, two points means that the buyer must pay 2% of the loan amount at closing. Often, a buyer can pay fewer points in exchange for a higher interest rate or more points for a lower rate. A document, called the **Truth-in-Lending Disclosure Statement**, shows the buyer the APR for the mortgage. The APR takes into account the interest rate and points.

A monthly mortgage payment is used to repay the principal plus interest. In addition, lending institutions can require that part of the monthly payment be deposited into an **escrow account**, an account used by the lender to pay real estate taxes and insurance. Interest is paid to the buyer on the amount in an escrow account.

We can use formulas for compound interest and the value of an annuity to determine the amount of mortgage payments for fixed-rate mortgages. Suppose that you borrow P dollars at interest rate r over t years.

> The lender expects A dollars at the end of t years.

> You save the A dollars in an annuity by paying PMT dollars n times per year.

$$A = P\left(1 + \frac{r}{n}\right)^{nt}$$

$$A = \frac{PMT\left[\left(1 + \frac{r}{n}\right)^{nt} - 1\right]}{\frac{r}{n}}$$

To find your regular payment amount, PMT, we set the amount the lender expects to receive equal to the amount you will save in the annuity:

$$P\left(1 + \frac{r}{n}\right)^{nt} = \frac{PMT\left[\left(1 + \frac{r}{n}\right)^{nt} - 1\right]}{\frac{r}{n}}.$$

Solving this equation for PMT, we obtain a formula for the loan payment for any installment loan, including payments on fixed-rate mortgages.

STUDY TIP

Because the formula in the box assumes the same number of yearly payments and yearly compounding periods, the actual payments may differ slightly from those calculated using the formula.

LOAN PAYMENT FORMULA FOR INSTALLMENT LOANS

The regular payment amount, PMT, required to repay a loan of P dollars paid n times per year over t years at an annual rate r is given by

$$PMT = \frac{P\left(\frac{r}{n}\right)}{1 - \left(1 + \frac{r}{n}\right)^{-nt}}.$$

EXAMPLE 1 COMPUTING THE MONTHLY PAYMENT AND INTEREST COSTS FOR A MORTGAGE

The price of a home is $195,000. The bank requires a 10% down payment and two points at the time of closing. The cost of the home is financed with a 30-year fixed-rate mortgage at 7.5%.

a. Find the required down payment.

b. Find the amount of the mortgage.

   c. How much must be paid for the two points at closing?

   d. Find the monthly payment (excluding escrowed taxes and insurance).

   e. Find the total interest paid over 30 years.

SOLUTION

   a. The required down payment is 10% of $195,000 or

$$0.10 \times \$195,000 = \$19,500.$$

   b. The amount of the mortgage is the difference between the price of the home and the down payment.

$$\boxed{\text{Amount of the mortgage}} = \boxed{\text{sale price}} - \boxed{\text{down payment}}$$

$$= \$195,000 - \$19,500$$

$$= \$175,500$$

   c. To find the cost of two points on a mortgage of $175,500, find 2% of $175,500.

$$0.02 \times \$175,500 = \$3510$$

The down payment ($19,500) is paid to the seller and the cost of two points ($3510) is paid to the lending institution.

   d. We are interested in finding the monthly payment for a $175,500 mortgage at 7.5% for 30 years. We use the loan payment formula for installment loans.

P, the mortgage amount, is $175,500.   Fixed rate, r, is 7.5%.

12 payments per year

The mortgage time, t, is 30 years.

$$PMT = \frac{P\left(\frac{r}{n}\right)}{1 - \left(1 + \frac{r}{n}\right)^{-nt}} = \frac{175{,}500\left(\frac{0.075}{12}\right)}{1 - \left(1 + \frac{0.075}{12}\right)^{-12(30)}}$$

$$= \frac{1096.875}{1 - (1.00625)^{-360}} \approx 1227$$

The monthly mortgage payment for principal and interest is approximately $1227.00. (Keep in mind that this payment does not include escrowed taxes and insurance.)

   e. The total cost of interest over 30 years is equal to the difference between the total of all monthly payments and the amount of the mortgage. The total of all monthly payments is equal to the amount of the monthly payment multiplied by the number of payments. We found the amount of each monthly payment in (d): $1227. The number of payments is equal to the number of months in a year, 12, multiplied by the number of years in the mortgage, 30: $12 \times 30 = 360$. Thus, the total of all montlhly payments $= \$1227 \times 360$.

Now we can calculate the interest over 30 years.

$$\boxed{\text{Total interest paid}} = \boxed{\text{total of all monthly payments}} \; \boxed{\text{minus}} \; \boxed{\text{amount of the mortgage.}}$$

$$= \$1227 \times 360 - \$175,500$$

$$= \$441,720 - \$175,500 = \$266,220$$

The total interest paid over 30 years is approximately $266,220.   ○

BLITZER BONUS

The Point Is, Don't Ignore Points

WHAT A FIXED-RATE
$100,000 MORTGAGE AT
7% REALLY COSTS

Points	APR 30 years	APR 15 years
1	7.10%	7.16%
2	7.20%	7.33%
3	7.30%	7.49%
4	7.41%	7.66%
5	7.52%	7.83%

In Example 1, the $175,500 mortgage was financed with a 30-year fixed rate at 7.5%. The total interest paid over 30 years was approximately $266,220.

a. Use the loan payment formula for installment loans to find the monthly payment if the time of the mortgage is reduced to 15 years. Round to the nearest dollar.

b. Find the total interest paid over 15 years.

c. How much interest is saved by reducing the mortgage from 30 to 15 years?

3 Prepare a partial loan amortization schedule.

Loan Amortization Schedules

When a loan is paid off through a series of regular payments, it is said to be **amortized**, which literally means "killed off." In working Check Point 1(c), were you surprised that nearly $150,000 was saved when the mortgage was amortized over 15 years rather than over 30 years? What adds to the interest cost is the long period over which the loan is financed. **Although each payment is the same, with each successive payment the interest portion decreases and the principal portion increases.** The interest is computed using the simple interest formula $I = Prt$. The principal, P, is equal to the balance of the loan, which changes each month. The rate, r, is the annual interest rate of the mortgage loan. Because a payment is made each month, the time, t, is

$$\frac{1 \text{ month}}{12 \text{ months}} = \frac{1 \text{ month}}{12 \text{ months}}$$

or $\frac{1}{12}$ of a year.

A document showing important information about the status of the mortgage is called a **loan amortization schedule**. Typically, this document includes the number of the most recent payment and those of any previous monthly payments, the interest for each monthly payment, the principal payment for each monthly payment, and the balance of the loan.

EXAMPLE 2	PREPARING A LOAN AMORTIZATION SCHEDULE

Prepare a loan amortization schedule for the first two months of the mortgage loan shown in the following table:

LOAN AMORTIZATION SCHEDULE

Annual % rate: 9.5%
Amount of Mortgage: $130,000   **Monthly payment: $1357.50**
Number of Monthly Payments: 180   **Term: Years 15, Months 0**

Payment Number	Interest Payment	Principal Payment	Balance of Loan
1			
2			

SOLUTION We begin with payment number 1.

$$\text{Interest for the month} = Prt = \$130{,}000 \times 0.095 \times \frac{1}{12} \approx \$1029.17$$

$$\text{Principal payment} = \text{Monthly payment} - \text{Interest payment}$$

$$= \$1357.50 - \$1029.17 = \$328.33$$

$$\text{Balance of loan} = \text{Principal balance} - \text{Principal payment}$$

$$= \$130{,}000 - \$328.33 = \$129{,}671.67$$

Bittersweet Interest

Early mortgage payments illustrate that it can be discouraging to realize how much goes toward interest and how little goes toward paying off the principal. Although you get socked with tons of interest in the early years of a loan, the one bright side to the staggering cost of a mortgage is the **mortgage interest tax deduction**. To make the cost of owning a home more affordable, the tax code permits deducting all the mortgage interest (but not the principal) that you pay per year on the loan. Table 4.7 illustrates how this tax loophole reduces the cost of the mortgage.

TABLE 4.7 TAX DEDUCTIONS FOR A $100,000 MORTGAGE AT 7% FOR A TAXPAYER IN THE 28% TAX BRACKET

Year	Interest	Tax Savings	Net Cost of Mortgage
1	$6968	$1951	$5017
2	$6895	$1931	$4964
3	$6816	$1908	$4908
4	$6732	$1885	$4847
5	$6641	$1859	$4782

Now, starting with a loan balance of $129,671.67, we repeat these computations for the second month.

$$\text{Interest for the month} = Prt = \$129{,}671.67 \times 0.095 \times \frac{1}{12} = \$1026.57$$

$$\text{Principal payment} = \text{Monthly payment} - \text{Interest payment}$$

$$= \$1357.50 - \$1026.57 = \$330.93$$

$$\text{Balance of loan} = \text{Principal balance} - \text{Principal payment}$$

$$= \$129{,}671.67 - \$330.93 = \$129{,}340.74$$

The results of these computations are included in Table 4.6, a partial loan amortization schedule. By using the simple interest formula month-to-month on the loan's balance, a complete loan amortization schedule for all 180 payments can be calculated.

TABLE 4.6 LOAN AMORTIZATION SCHEDULE

Annual % rate: 9.5%
Amount of Mortgage: $130,000
Number of Monthly Payments: 180
Monthly payment: $1357.50
Term: Years 15, Months 0

Payment Number	Interest Payment	Principal Payment	Balance of Loan
1	$1029.17	$328.33	$129,671.67
2	1026.57	330.93	129,340.74
3	1023.96	333.54	129,007.22
4	1021.32	336.18	128,671.04
30	944.82	412.68	118,931.35
31	941.55	415.95	118,515.52
125	484.62	872.88	60,340.84
126	477.71	879.79	59,461.05
179	21.26	1336.24	1347.74
180	9.76	1347.74	

Many lenders supply a loan amortization schedule like the one in Example 2. Such a schedule shows how the buyer pays slightly less in interest and more in principal for each payment over the entire life of the loan.

Prepare a loan amortization schedule for the first two months of the mortgage loan shown in the following table:

Annual % rate: 7.0%
Amount of Mortgage: $200,000
Number of Monthly Payments: 240
Monthly payment: $1550.00
Term: Years 20, Months 0

Payment Number	Interest Payment	Principal Payment	Balance of Loan
1			
2			

4 | Compute payments and interest for other kinds of installment loans.

Monthly Payments and Interest Costs for Other Kinds of Installment Loans

The loan payment formula can be used to determine how much your regular payments will be on installment loans other than mortgages, including car loans and student loans. The portions of each payment going toward the principal and toward the interest will vary as the loan balance declines. Near the beginning of the loan term, the portion going toward the interest will be relatively high and the portion going toward the principal will be relatively low. As the loan term continues, the principal portion will gradually increase and the interest portion will gradually decrease.

EXAMPLE 3   COMPARING CAR LOANS

You decide to take a $20,000 loan for a new car. You can select one of the following loans, each requiring regular monthly payments:

Installment Loan A: 3-year loan at 7%

Installment Loan B: 5-year loan at 9%.

a. Find the monthly payments and the total interest for Loan A.

b. Find the monthly payments and the total interest for Loan B.

c. Compare the monthly payments and total interest for the two loans.

SOLUTION For each loan, we use the loan payment formula to compute the monthly payments.

a. We first determine monthly payments and total interest for Loan A.

P, the loan amount, is $20,000. — Rate, r, is 7%. — 12 payments per year — The loan is for 3 years.

$$PMT = \frac{P\left(\frac{r}{n}\right)}{1 - \left(1 + \frac{r}{n}\right)^{-nt}} = \frac{20{,}000\left(\frac{0.07}{12}\right)}{1 - \left(1 + \frac{0.07}{12}\right)^{-12(3)}} \approx 618$$

The monthly payments are approximately $618.
Now we calculate the interest over 3 years, or 36 months.

Total interest over 3 years = Total of all monthly payments minus amount of the loan.

$$= \$618 \times 36 - \$20{,}000$$
$$= \$2248$$

The total interest paid over 3 years is approximately $2248.

b. Next, we determine monthly payments and total interest for Loan B.

P, the loan amount, is $20,000. — Rate, r, is 9%. — 12 payments per year — The loan is for 5 years.

$$PMT = \frac{P\left(\frac{r}{n}\right)}{1 - \left(1 + \frac{r}{n}\right)^{-nt}} = \frac{20{,}000\left(\frac{0.09}{12}\right)}{1 - \left(1 + \frac{0.09}{12}\right)^{-12(5)}} \approx 415$$

The monthly payments are approximately $415.

Now we calculate the interest over 5 years, or 60 months.

$$\underbrace{\text{Total interest over 5 years}} = \underbrace{\text{Total of all monthly payments}} \underbrace{\text{minus}} \underbrace{\text{amount of the loan.}}$$

$$= \quad \$415 \quad \times \quad 60 \quad - \quad \$20,000$$

$$= \quad \$4900$$

The total interest paid over 5 years is approximately \$4900.

c. Table 4.8 compares the monthly payments and total interest for the two loans.

TABLE 4.8 COMPARING CAR LOANS

\$20,000 loan	Monthly Payment	Total Interest
3-year loan at 7%	\$618	\$2248
5-year loan at 9%	\$415	\$4900

Monthly payments are less with the longer-term loan.   Interest is more with the longer-term loan.

CHECK POINT 3 You decide to take a \$15,000 loan for a new car. You can select one of the following loans, each requiring regular monthly payments:

Installment Loan A: 4-year loan at 8%

Installment Loan B: 6-year loan at 10%

a. Find the monthly payments and the total interest for Loan A.

b. Find the monthly payments and the total interest for Loan B.

c. Compare the monthly payments and total interest for the two loans.

EXERCISE SET 4.6 ●●●●●●

• Practice and Application Exercises

In all exercises, use

$$PMT = \frac{P\left(\dfrac{r}{n}\right)}{1 - \left(1 + \dfrac{r}{n}\right)^{-nt}}$$

to determine the regular payment amount, rounded to the nearest dollar.

Exercises 1–8 involve home mortgages.

1. The price of a home is \$220,000. The bank requires a 20% down payment and three points at the time of closing. The cost of the home is financed with a 30-year fixed-rate mortgage at 7%.

  a. Find the required down payment.

  b. Find the amount of the mortgage.

  c. How much must be paid for the three points at closing?

  d. Find the monthly payment (excluding escrowed taxes and insurance).

  e. Find the total cost of interest over 30 years.

2. The price of a condominium is \$180,000. The bank requires a 5% down payment and one point at the time of closing. The cost of the condominium is financed with a 30-year fixed-rate mortgage at 8%.

  a. Find the required down payment.

  b. Find the amount of the mortgage.

  c. How much must be paid for the one point at closing?

  d. Find the monthly payment (excluding escrowed taxes and insurance).

  e. Find the total cost of interest over 30 years.

3. The price of a small cabin is \$100,000. The bank requires a 5% down payment. The buyer is offered two mortgage options: 20-year fixed at 8% or 30-year fixed at 8%. Calculate the amount of interest paid for each option. How much does the buyer save in interest with the 20-year option?

4. The price of a home is \$160,000. The bank requires a 15% down payment. The buyer is offered two mortgage options: 15-year fixed at 8% or 30-year fixed at 8%. Calculate the amount of interest paid for each option. How much does the buyer save in interest with the 15-year option?

5. In terms of paying less in interest, which is more economical for a \$150,000 mortgage: a 30-year fixed-rate at 8% or a 20-year fixed-rate at 7.5%? How much is saved in interest?

6. In terms of paying less in interest, which is more economical for a $90,000 mortgage: a 30-year fixed-rate at 8% or a 15-year fixed-rate at 7.5%? How much is saved in interest?

In Exercises 7–8, which mortgage loan has the greater total cost (closing costs + the amount paid for points + total cost of interest)? By how much?

7. A $120,000 mortgage with two loan options:

Mortgage A: 30-year fixed at 7% with closing costs of $2000 and one point

Mortgage B: 30-year fixed at 6.5% with closing costs of $1500 and four points

8. A $250,000 mortgage with two loan options:

Mortgage A: 30-year fixed at 7.25% with closing costs of $2000 and one point

Mortgage B: 30-year fixed at 6.25% with closing costs of costs of $350 and four points

Exercises 9–18 involve installment loans other than mortgages.

9. Your credit card has a balance of $4200 and an annual interest rate of 18%. You decide to pay off the balance over two years. If there are no further purchases charged to the card,

a. How much must you pay each month?

b. How much total interest will you pay?

10. Your credit card has a balance of $3600 and an annual interest rate of 16.5%. You decide to pay off the balance over two years. If there are no further purchases charged to the card,

a. How much must you pay each month?

b. How much total interest will you pay?

11. To pay off the $4200 credit-card balance in Exercise 9, you can get a bank loan at 10.5% with a term of three years.

a. How much will you pay each month? How does this compare with your credit-card payment in Exercise 9?

b. How much total interest will you pay? How does this compare with your total credit-card interest in Exercise 9?

12. To pay off the $3600 credit-card balance in Exercise 10, you can get a bank loan at 9.5% with a term of three years.

a. How much will you pay each month? How does this compare with your credit-card payment in Exercise 10?

b. How much total interest will you pay? How does this compare with your total credit-card interest in Exercise 10?

13. Rework Exercise 9 if you decide to pay off the balance over one year, rather than two. How much more must you pay each month and how much less will you pay in total interest?

14. Rework Exercise 10 if you decide to pay off the balance over one year rather than two. How much more must you pay each month and how much less will you pay in total interest?

15. You borrow $10,000 for four years at 8% toward the purchase of a car.

a. Find the monthly payments and the total interest for the loan.

b. Prepare a loan amortization schedule for the first three months of the car loan. Round entries to the nearest cent.

Payment Number	Interest	Principal	Loan Balance
1			
2			
3			

16. You borrow $30,000 for four years at 8% toward the purchase of a car.

a. Find the monthly payments and the total interest for the loan.

b. Prepare a loan amortization schedule for the first three months of the car loan. Use the table in Exercise 15(b) and round entries to the nearest cent.

17. A student graduates from college with a loan of $40,000. The interest rate is 8.5% and the loan term is 20 years.

a. Find the monthly payments and the total interest for the loan.

b. Prepare a loan amortization schedule for the first three months of the student loan. Use the table in Exercise 15(b) and round entries to the nearest cent.

c. If the interest rate remains at 8.5% and the loan term is reduced to ten years, how much more must the student pay each month and how much less will be paid in total interest?

18. A student graduates from college with a loan of $50,000. The interest rate is 7.5% and the loan term is 20 years.

a. Find the monthly payments and the total interest for the loan.

b. Prepare a loan amortization schedule for the first three months of the student loan. Use the table in Exercise 15(b) and round entries to the nearest cent.

c. If the interest rate remains at 7.5% and the loan term is reduced to ten years, how much more must the student pay each month and how much less will be paid in total interest?

• Writing in Mathematics

19. What is a mortgage?

20. What is a down payment?

21. How is the amount of a mortgage determined?

22. Describe why a buyer would select a 30-year fixed-rate mortgage instead of a 15-year fixed-rate mortgage if interest rates are $\frac{1}{4}$% to $\frac{1}{2}$% lower on a 15-year mortgage.

23. Describe one advantage and one disadvantage of an adjustable-rate mortgage over a fixed-rate mortgage.

24. What is a loan amortization schedule?

25. Describe what happens to the portions of payments going to principal and interest over the life of an installment loan.

26. Describe one advantage and one disadvantage of home ownership over renting.

• Critical Thinking Exercises

27. Use the discussion that precedes the box on page 492 to prove the loan payment formula shown in the box. Work with the equation in which the amount the lender expects to receive is equal to the amount saved in the annuity. Multiply both sides of this equation by $\frac{r}{n}$ and then solve for PMT by dividing both sides by the appropriate expression. Finally, divide the numerator and the denominator of the resulting formula for PMT by $\left(1 + \frac{r}{n}\right)^{nt}$ to obtain the form of the loan payment formula shown in the box.

28. The unpaid balance of an installment loan is equal to the present value of the remaining payments. The unpaid balance, P, is given by

$$P = PMT \frac{1 - \left(1 + \frac{r}{n}\right)^{-nt}}{\frac{r}{n}},$$

where PMT is the regular payment amount, r is the annual interest rate, n is the number of payments per year, and t is the number of years remaining in the mortgage.

a. Use the loan payment formula to derive the unpaid balance formula.

b. The price of a home is \$180,000. The bank requires a 10% down payment. After the down payment, the balance is financed with a 30-year fixed-rate mortgage at 6.3%. Determine the unpaid balance after ten years.

• Group Exercise

29. Group members should go to the Internet and select a car that they might like to buy. Price the car and its options. Then find two loans with the best rates, but with different terms. For each loan, calculate the monthly payments and total interest. Select one of the loans and prepare a partial or complete amortization schedule.

●●●●●●● CHAPTER SUMMARY, REVIEW, AND TEST

● SUMMARY   DEFINITIONS AND CONCEPTS   EXAMPLES

4.1 Percent, Sales Tax, and Income Tax

a. Percent means per hundred. Thus, $97\% = \frac{97}{100}$.

b. To express a fraction as a percent, divide the numerator by the denominator, move the decimal point in the quotient two places to the right, and add a percent sign.   Ex. 1, p. 182

c. To express a decimal number as a percent, move the decimal point two places to the right and add a percent sign.   Ex. 2, p. 183

d. To express a percent as a decimal number, move the decimal point two places to the left and remove the percent sign.   Ex. 3, p. 183

e. The percent formula, $A = PB$, means A is P percent of B.

f. Sales tax amount = tax rate × item's cost   Ex. 4, p. 184

g. Discount amount = discount rate × original price   Ex. 5, p. 184

h. Calculating Income Tax   Ex. 6, p. 186
  1. Determine adjusted gross income:

    Adjusted gross income = Gross income − Adjustments.

  2. Determine taxable income:

    Taxable income = Adjusted gross income − (Exemptions + Deductions).

  3. Determine the income tax:

    Income tax = Tax computation − Tax credits.

  See details in the box on page 185.

i. The fraction for percent increase (or decrease) is

$$\frac{\text{amount of increase (or decrease)}}{\text{original amount}}.$$

Find the percent increase (or decrease) by expressing this fraction as a percent.

4.2   Simple Interest

a. Interest is the price we are paid for lending money or pay for borrowing money. The amount deposited or borrowed is the principal. The charge for interest, given as a percent, is the rate, assumed to be per year.

b. Simple interest involves interest calculated only on the principal and is computed using $I = Prt$.

c. The future value, A, of P dollars at simple interest rate r for t years is $A = P(1 + rt)$.

d. Discounted loans deduct the interest, called the discount, from the loan amount at the time the loan is made.

4.3   Compound Interest

a. Compound interest involves interest computed on the original principal as well as on any accumulated interest. The amount in an account for one compounding period per year is $A = P(1 + r)^t$. For n compoundings per year, the amount is $A = P\left(1 + \frac{r}{n}\right)^{nt}$. For continuous compounding, the amount is $A = Pe^{rt}$, where $e \approx 2.72$.

b. Calculating Present Value
If A dollars are to be accumulated in t years in an account that pays rate r compounded n times per year, then the present value, P, that needs to be invested now is given by

$$P = \frac{A}{\left(1 + \dfrac{r}{n}\right)^{nt}}.$$

c. Effective Annual Yield
Effective annual yield is defined in the box on page 202. The effective annual yield, Y, for an account that pays rate r compounded n times per year is given by

$$Y = \left(1 + \frac{r}{n}\right)^n - 1.$$

4.4   Annuities, Stocks, and Bonds

a. An annuity is a sequence of equal payments made at equal time periods. The value of an annuity is the sum of all deposits plus all interest paid.

b. The value of an annuity after t years is

$$A = \frac{P[(1 + r)^t - 1]}{r} \quad \text{or} \quad A = \frac{P\left[\left(1 + \dfrac{r}{n}\right)^{nt} - 1\right]}{\dfrac{r}{n}},$$

depending on whether interest is compounded once a year or n times per year. See the box on page 207 and the box on page 208.

c. The formula

Ex. 4, p. 210

$$P = \frac{A\left(\dfrac{r}{n}\right)}{\left[\left(1 + \dfrac{r}{n}\right)^{nt} - 1\right]}$$

gives the deposit, P, into an annuity at the end of each compounding period needed to achieve a value of A dollars after t years. See the box on page 209.

d. The return on an investment is the percent increase in the investment.

e. Investors purchase stock, shares of ownership in a company. The shares indicate the percent of ownership. Trading refers to buying and selling stock. Investors make money by selling a stock for more money than they paid for it. They can also make money while they own stock if a company distributes all or part of its profits as dividends. Each share of stock is paid the same dividend.

f. Investors purchase a bond, lending money to the company from which they purchase the bond. The company commits itself to pay the price an investor pays for the bond at the time it was purchased, called its face value, along with interest payments at a given rate.

g. Reading stock tables is explained on pages 212–213.

Ex. 5, p. 213

4.5 Installment Buying

a. A fixed installment loan is paid off with a series of equal periodic payments. An open-end installment loan is paid off with variable monthly payments. Credit card loans are open-end installment loans.

b. The terms of fixed installment loans—the amount financed, the total installment price, and the finance charge—are explained in the box on page 219.

Ex. 1, p. 219

c. The interest rate per year on a loan is called the annual percentage rate (APR). The box on page 220 shows how to find the APR for a fixed installment loan.

Ex. 2, p. 220

d. Unearned interest is the amount by which the original finance charge is reduced when a fixed installment loan is paid off early. The two methods for computing unearned interest—the actuarial method and the rule of 78—are explained in the box on page 221.

Ex. 3, p. 221; Ex. 4, p. 222

e. Open-end installment loans, such as credit cards, calculate interest using the simple interest formula $I = Prt$. The methods for determining the interest, the unpaid balance method, the previous balance method, and the average daily balance method, are described in the box on page 225.

Ex. 5, p. 224; Ex. 6, p. 225

4.6 Amortization and the Cost of Home Ownership

a. A mortgage is a long-term loan for the purpose of buying a home, and for which the property is pledged as security for payment. The term of the mortgage is the number of years until final payoff. The down payment is the portion of the sale price of the home that the buyer initially pays. The amount of the mortgage is the difference between the sale price and the down payment.

b. Fixed-rate mortgages have the same monthly payment during the entire time of the loan. Variable-rate mortgages, or adjustable-rate mortgages, have payment amounts that change from time to time depending on changes in the interest rate.

c. A point is a one-time charge that equals 1% of the amount of a mortgage loan.

d. Loan Payment Formula for Installment Loans

Ex. 1, p. 230; Ex. 3, p. 234

$$PMT = \frac{P\left(\dfrac{r}{n}\right)}{1 - \left(1 + \dfrac{r}{n}\right)^{-nt}}$$

PMT is the regular payment amount required to repay a loan of P dollars paid n times per year over t years at an annual interest rate r.

e. Amortizing a loan is the process of making regular payments on the principal and interest until the loan is paid off. A document containing the payment number, payment toward the interest, payment toward the principal, and balance of the loan is called a loan amortization schedule. Such a schedule shows how the buyer pays slightly less in interest and more in principal for each payment over the entire life of the loan.

Ex. 2, p. 232

REVIEW EXERCISES

4.1

In Exercises 1–3, express each fraction as a percent.

1. $\frac{4}{5}$ 2. $\frac{1}{8}$ 3. $\frac{3}{4}$

In Exercises 4–6, express each decimal as a percent.

4. 0.72   5. 0.0035   6. 4.756

In Exercises 7–12, express each percent as a decimal.

7. 65%   8. 99.7%   9. 150%

10. 3%   11. 0.65%   12. $\frac{1}{4}$%

13. What is 8% of 120?

14. Suppose that the local sales tax rate is 6% and you purchase a backpack for $24.

    a. How much tax is paid?

    b. What is the backpack's total cost?

15. A television with an original price of $850 is on sale at 35% off.

    a. What is the discount amount?

    b. What is the television's sale price?

16. Use the 2005 marginal tax rates in Table 4.1 on page 186 to calculate the income tax owed by the following person:

    - Single, no dependents
    - Gross income: $40,000
    - $2500 paid to a tax-deferred IRA
    - $6500 mortgage interest
    - $1800 property taxes
    - No tax credits

17. A college that had 40 students for each lecture course increased the number to 45 students. What is the percent increase in the number of students in a lecture course?

18. A dictionary regularly sells for $56.00. The sale price is $36.40. Find the percent decrease of the sale price from the regular price.

19. Consider the following statement:

    My portfolio fell 10% last year, but then it rose 10% this year, so at least I recouped my losses.

    Is this statement true? In particular, suppose you invested $10,000 in the stock market last year. How much money would be left in your portfolio with a 10% fall and then a 10% rise? If there is a loss, what is the percent decrease, to the nearest tenth of a percent, in your portfolio?

4.2

In Exercises 20–23, find the simple interest. (Assume 360 days in a year.)

	Principal	Rate	Time
20.	$6000	3%	1 year
21.	$8400	5%	6 years
22.	$20,000	8%	9 months
23.	$36,000	15%	60 days

24. In order to pay for tuition and books, a student borrows $3500 for four months at 10.5% interest.

a. How much interest must the student pay?

b. Find the future value of the loan.

In Exercises 25–29, use the formula for future value at simple interest, $A = P(1 + rt)$, to find the missing quantity. Round dollar amounts to the nearest cent and rates to the nearest tenth of a percent.

25. $A = ?, P = \$12,000, r = 8.2\%, t = 9$ months

26. $A = \$5750, P = \$5000, r = ?, t = 2$ years

27. $A = \$16,000, P = ?, r = 6.5\%, t = 3$ years

28. You plan to buy a $12,000 sailboat in four years. How much should you invest now, at 7.3% simple interest, to have enough for the boat in four years? (Round up to the nearest cent.)

29. You borrow $1500 from a friend and promise to pay back $1800 in six months. What simple interest rate will you pay?

30. You borrow $1800 on a 7% discounted loan for a period of 9 months.

    a. What is the loan's discount?

    b. Determine the net amount of money you will receive.

    c. What is the loan's actual interest rate, to the nearest tenth of a percent?

4.3

In Exercises 31–33, the principal represents an amount of money deposited in a savings account that provides the lender compound interest at the given rate.

a. Use the formula $A = P(1 + r)^t$ for one compounding period per year or $A = P\left(1 + \frac{r}{n}\right)^{nt}$ for n compounding periods per year to find how much money, to the nearest cent, there will be in the account after the given number of years.

b. Find the interest earned.

	Principal	Rate	Compoundings per Year	Time
31.	$7000	3%	1	5 years
32.	$30,000	2.5%	4	10 years
33.	$2500	4%	12	20 years

34. Use $A = P\left(1 + \frac{r}{n}\right)^{nt}$ and $A = Pe^{rt}$ to solve this exercise. Suppose that you have $14,000 to invest. Which investment yields the greater return over 10 years: 7% compounded monthly or 6.85% compounded continuously? How much more (to the nearest dollar) is yielded by the better investment?

Solve Exercises 35–36 using the present value formula

$$P = \frac{A}{\left(1 + \frac{r}{n}\right)^{nt}}.$$

Round answers to the nearest cent.

35. How much money should parents deposit today in an account that earns 10% compounded monthly so that it will accumulate to $100,000 in 18 years for their child's college education?

36. How much money should be deposited today in an account that earns 5% compounded quarterly so that it will accumulate to $75,000 in 35 years for retirement?

37. You deposit $2000 in an account that pays 6% interest compounded quarterly.

   a. Find the future value, to the nearest cent, after one year.

   b. Use the future value formula for simple interest to determine the effective annual yield. Round to the nearest tenth of a percent.

Use the effective annual yield formula

$$Y = \left(1 + \frac{r}{n}\right)^n - 1$$

to solve Exercises 38–39.

38. What is the effective annual yield, to the nearest hundredth of a percent, of an account paying 5.5% compounded quarterly? What does your answer mean?

39. Which investment is the better choice: 6.25% compounded monthly or 6.3% compounded annually?

4.4

In Exercises 40–41, use the formula

$$A = \frac{P[(1 + r)^t - 1]}{r} \quad \text{or} \quad A = \frac{P\left[\left(1 + \dfrac{r}{n}\right)^{nt} - 1\right]}{\dfrac{r}{n}}$$

to find the value of each annuity. Round to the nearest dollar.

40. You spend $10 per week on lottery tickets, averaging $520 per year. Instead of buying tickets, if you deposited the $520 at the end of each year in an annuity paying 6% compounded annually,

   a. How much would you have after 20 years?

   b. Find the interest.

41. To save for retirement, you decide to deposit $100 at the end of each month in an IRA that pays 5.5% compounded monthly.

   a. How much will you have from the IRA after 30 years?

   b. Find the interest.

42. You would like to have $25,000 to use as a down payment for a home in five years by making regular deposits at the end of every three months in an annuity that pays 7.25% compounded quarterly.

   a. Use the formula

$$P = \frac{A\left(\dfrac{r}{n}\right)}{\left[\left(1 + \dfrac{r}{n}\right)^{nt} - 1\right]}$$

   to determine the amount of each deposit. Round up to the nearest dollar.

   b. How much of the $25,000 comes from deposits and how much comes from interest?

Exercises 43–50, refer to the stock table for Harley Davidson (the motorcycle company). Where necessary, round dollar amounts to the nearest cent.

52-Week					Yld	
High	Low	Stock	SYM	Div	%	PE
64.06	26.13	Harley Dav	HDI	.16	.3	41

Vol				Net
100s	Hi	Lo	Close	Chg
5458	61.25	59.25	61	+1.75

43. What were the high and low prices for a share for the past 52 weeks?

44. If you owned 900 shares of this stock last year, what dividend did you receive?

45. What is the annual return for the dividends alone?

46. How many shares of this company's stock were traded yesterday?

47. What were the high and low prices for a share yesterday?

48. What was the price at which a share traded when the stock exchange closed yesterday?

49. What was the change in price for a share of stock from the market close two days ago to yesterday's market close?

50. Compute the company's annual earnings per share using

$$\text{Annual earnings per share} = \frac{\text{Yesterday's closing price per share}}{\text{PE ratio}}.$$

51. Explain the difference between investing in a stock and investing in a bond.

4.5

52. The cost of a new car is $16,500. You can finance the purchase by paying $500 down and $350 per month for 60 months.

   a. Determine the amount financed.

   b. Determine the total installment price.

   c. Determine the finance charge.

   d. Use Table 4.5 on page 220 to find the APR for this loan.

53. Use the actuarial method formula

$$u = \frac{kRV}{100 + V}$$

   to solve this problem. In Exercise 52, instead of making the forty-eighth payment, the borrower decides to pay the remaining balance and terminate the loan for the car.

   a. How much interest is saved by repaying the loan early?

   b. What is the total amount due on the day of the loan's termination?

54. Use the rule of 78 formula

$$u = \frac{k(k + 1)}{n(n + 1)} \times F$$

   to solve this problem. In Exercise 52, instead of making the forty-eighth payment, the borrower decides to pay the remaining balance and terminate the loan for the car.

   a. How much interest is saved by repaying the loan early?

   b. What is the total amount due on the day of the loan's termination?

55. Describe the difference between the answers in Exercises 53 and 54. Which method saves the borrower more money?

56. The terms of a particular credit card are based on the unpaid balance method. The monthly interest rate is 1.5% on the unpaid balance on the first day of the billing period less payments and credits. Here are some of the details in the June 1–June 30 itemized billing:

June 1 Unpaid Balance: $1300

Payment Received June 4: $200

Purchases Charged to the Account: airline ticket, $380; car repair, $120; groceries, $140

Last Day of the Billing Period: June 30

Due Date: July 9

  a. Find the interest due on the payment due date.

  b. Find the total balance owed on the last day of the billing period.

  c. Terms for the credit card require a $10 minimum monthly payment if the balance due is less than $360. Otherwise, the minimum monthly payment is $\frac{1}{36}$ of the balance due, rounded to the nearest whole dollar. What is the minimum monthly payment due by July 9?

57. A credit card has a monthly rate of 1.8%. In the March 1–March 31 itemized billing, the March 1 unpaid balance is $3600. A payment of $2000 was received on March 6. There are no purchases or cash advances in this billing period. The payment due date is April 9. Find the interest due on this date using

  a. the unpaid balance method.

  b. the previous balance method.

  c. the average daily balance method.

4.6

In Exercises 58–62, use

$$PMT = \frac{P\left(\dfrac{r}{n}\right)}{1 - \left(1 + \dfrac{r}{n}\right)^{-nt}}$$

to determine the regular payment amount, rounded to the nearest dollar.

58. The price of a home is $240,000. The bank requires a 20% down payment and two points at the time of closing. The cost of the home is financed with a 30-year fixed-rate mortgage at 7%.

  a. Find the required down payment.

  b. Find the amount of the mortgage.

  c. How much must be paid for the two points at closing?

  d. Find the monthly payment (excluding escrowed taxes and insurance).

  e. Find the total cost of interest over 30 years.

59. In terms of paying less in interest, which is more economical for a $70,000 mortgage: a 30-year fixed-rate at 8.5% or a 20-year fixed-rate at 8%? How much is saved in interest? Discuss one advantage and one disadvantage for each mortgage option.

60. You need a loan of $100,000 to buy a home. Here are your options:

Option A: 30-year fixed-rate at 8.5% with no closing costs and no points

Option B: 30-year fixed-rate at 7.5% with closing costs of $1300 and three points.

  a. Determine your monthly payments for each option and discuss how you would decide between the two options.

  b. Which mortgage loan has the greater total cost (closing costs + the amount paid for points + total cost of interest)? By how much?

61. You decide to take a $15,000 loan for a new car. You can select one of the following loans, each requiring regular monthly payments:

Loan A: 3-year loan at 7.2%

Loan B: 5-year loan at 8.1%.

  a. Find the monthly payments and the total interest for Loan A.

  b. Find the monthly payments and the total interest for Loan B.

  c. Compare the monthly payments and interest for the longer-term loan to the monthly payments and interest for the shorter-term loan.

62. The bar graph shows credit-card debt per U.S. household from 1995 through 2004.

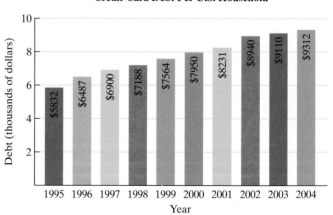

Credit-Card Debt Per U.S. Household

Source: CardWeb.com

In 2004, the average credit-card debt was $9312. Suppose your card has this balance and an annual interest rate of 18%. You decide to pay off the balance over two years. If there are no further purchases charged to the card,

  a. How much must you pay each month?

  b. How much total interest will you pay?

  c. Prepare an amortization schedule for the first three months of payments. Round entries to the nearest cent.

Payment Number	Interest	Principal	Balance
1			
2			
3			

SUMMARY OF FINANCIAL MANAGEMENT FORMULAS

Simple Interest

$$I = Prt$$

$$A = P(1 + rt)$$

Compound Interest

$$A = P(1 + r)^t$$

$$A = P\left(1 + \frac{r}{n}\right)^{nt}$$

$$P = \frac{A}{\left(1 + \frac{r}{n}\right)^{nt}}$$

$$Y = \left(1 + \frac{r}{n}\right)^n - 1$$

Annuities

$$A = \frac{P[(1 + r)^t - 1]}{r}$$

$$A = \frac{P\left[\left(1 + \frac{r}{n}\right)^{nt} - 1\right]}{\frac{r}{n}}$$

$$P = \frac{A\left(\frac{r}{n}\right)}{\left[\left(1 + \frac{r}{n}\right)^{nt} - 1\right]}$$

Amortization

$$PMT = \frac{P\left(\frac{r}{n}\right)}{1 - \left(1 + \frac{r}{n}\right)^{-nt}}$$

●●●●●●● CHAPTER 4 TEST

The box summarizes the financial management formulas you have worked with throughout the chapter. Where applicable, use the appropriate formula to solve an exercise in this test. Unless otherwise stated, round dollar amounts to the nearest cent and rates to the nearest tenth of a percent.

1. A CD player with an original price of $120 is on sale at 15% off.

   a. What is the amount of the discount?

   b. What is the sale price of the CD player?

2. Use the 2005 marginal tax rates in Table 4.1 on page 186 to calculate the income tax owed by the following person:

   • Single, no dependents

   • Gross income: $36,500

   • $2000 paid to a tax-deferred IRA

   • $4700 mortgage interest

   • $1300 property taxes

   • No tax credits

3. You purchased shares of stock for $2000 and sold them for $3500. Find the percent increase, or your return, on this investment.

4. You borrow $2400 for three months at 12% simple interest. Find the amount of interest paid and the future value of the loan.

5. You borrow $2000 from a friend and promise to pay back $3000 in two years. What simple interest rate will you pay?

6. In six months, you want to have $7000 worth of remodeling done to your home. How much should you invest now, at 9% simple interest, to have enough money for the project? (Round up to the nearest cent.)

7. Find the effective annual yield, to the nearest hundredth of a percent, of an account paying 4.5% compounded quarterly. What does your answer mean?

8. To save money to use as a down payment for a home in five years, you deposit $6000 in an account that pays 6.5% compounded monthly.

   a. How much, to the nearest dollar, will you have as a down payment after five years?

   b. Find the interest.

9. Instead of making the lump-sum deposit of $6000 described in Exercise 8, you decide to deposit $100 at the end of each month in an annuity that pays 6.5% compounded monthly.

   a. How much, to the nearest dollar, will you have as a down payment after five years?

   b. Find the interest.

   c. Why is less interest earned from this annuity than from the lump-sum deposit in Exercise 8? With less interest earned, why would one select the annuity rather than the lump-sum deposit?

10. You would like to have $3000 in four years for a special vacation by making a lump-sum investment in an account that pays 9.5% compounded semiannually. How much should you deposit now? Round up to the nearest dollar.

11. How much should you deposit at the end of each month in an IRA that pays 6.25% compounded monthly to have $1,500,000 when you retire in 40 years? How much of the $1.5 million comes from interest?

Use the stock table for AT&T to solve Exercises 12–14.

52-Week					Yld	
High	Low	Stock	SYM	Div	%	PE
26.50	24.25	AT & T	PNS	2.03	7.9	18

Vol				Net
100s	Hi	Lo	Close	Chg
961	25.75	25.50	25.75	+0.13

12. What were the high and low prices for a share yesterday?

13. If you owned 1000 shares of this stock last year, what dividend did you receive?

14. Suppose that you bought 600 shares of AT&T, paying the price per share at which a share traded when the stock exchange closed yesterday. If the broker charges 2.5% of the price paid for all 600 shares, find the broker's commission.

In Exercises 15–20, the cost of a new car is $16,000, which can be financed by paying $3000 down and $300 per month for 60 months.

15. Determine the amount financed.

16. Determine the total installment price.

17. Determine the finance charge.

18. Use Table 4.5 on page 220 to find the APR for this loan.

19. Use the rule of 78 formula

$$u = \frac{k(k + 1)}{n(n + 1)} \times F$$

to solve this problem. Instead of making the thirty-sixth payment, the borrower decides to pay the remaining balance and terminate the loan for the car. How much interest is saved by repaying the loan early?

20. Use the answer from Exercise 19 to find the total amount due on the day of the loan's termination.

Use the information at the top of the next column to solve Exercises 21–23. The terms of a particular credit card are based on the unpaid balance method. The monthly interest rate is 2% on the unpaid balance on the first day of the billing period less payments and credits. Here are some of the details in the November 1–November 30 itemized billing:

November 1 Unpaid Balance: $880
Payment Received November 5: $100
Purchases Charged to the Account: clothing, $350; gasoline, $70; groceries, $120
Last Day of the Billing Period: November 30
Due Date: December 8

21. Find the interest due on the payment due date.

22. Find the total balance owed on the last day of the billing period.

23. Terms for the credit card require a $10 minimum monthly payment if the balance due is less than $360. Otherwise, the minimum monthly payment is $\frac{1}{36}$ of the balance due, rounded to the nearest whole dollar. What is the minimum monthly payment due by December 8?

24. A credit card has a monthly rate of 1.6%. In the September 1–September 30 itemized billing, the September 1 unpaid balance is $2400. A payment of $1500 was received on September 4. There are no purchases or cash advances in this billing period. The payment due date is October 10. Find the interest due on this date using the average daily balance method.

Use this information to solve Exercises 25–29. The price of a home is $120,000. The bank requires a 10% down payment and two points at the time of closing. The cost of the home is financed with a 30-year fixed-rate mortgage at 8.5%.

25. Find the required down payment. Round to the nearest dollar.

26. Find the amount of the mortgage.

27. How much must be paid for the two points at closing?

28. Find the monthly payment (excluding escrowed taxes and insurance).

29. Find the total cost of interest over 30 years.

30. A student graduates from college with a loan of $20,000. The interest rate is 6.8% and the loan term is ten years.

   a. Find the monthly payments, rounded to the nearest dollar, and the total interest for the loan.

   b. Prepare a loan amortization schedule for the first two months of the student loan. Round entries to the nearest cent.

Payment Number	Interest	Principal	Balance
1			
2			

The Metric System

When you leave the United States, whether you travel to Canada, Mexico, or most other places in the world, you may see metric measurements being used. Clothing sizes may be given in centimeters, gasoline may be sold in liters, and speed limit signs may be given in kilometers per hour. Each day in the United States we see and use metric measurements. For example, soda is sold in liters, medicines are measured in milligrams, and tire sizes are given in millimeters. An understanding of the metric system will help you both at home and when you travel outside the United States.

●●●●●●
Everywhere outside the United States you may see traffic signs given in metric units.

SECTION 5.1 • BASIC TERMS AND CONVERSIONS WITHIN THE METRIC SYSTEM

OBJECTIVES

1. The advantages of using the metric system

2. The basic units used in the metric system

3. Conversions within the metric system

4. Determining length, area, volume, mass, and temperature in the metric system

5. Dimensional analysis and converting to and from the metric system

The sciences use metric measurements.

Have you ever taken a science course? If so, you most likely worked with metric measurements. For example, in chemistry you may have worked with liter containers, and in physics you may have worked with a mass in kilograms rather than a weight in pounds. Have you ever asked yourself why the sciences use metric measurement? In this section, we will explain some benefits of using the metric system.

TECHNOLOGY

LOST IN SPACE

The missing *Mars Climate Orbiter*

In September 1999, the United States lost a $125 million spacecraft, the *Mars Climate Orbiter,* as it approached Mars. Two spacecraft teams, one at NASA's Jet Propulsion Laboratory (JPL) and the other at a Lockheed Martin facility, were unknowingly exchanging some vital information in different measurement units. The spacecraft team at Lockheed sent some measurements to the spacecraft team at JPL using U.S. customary units. The JPL team assumed the information it received was in metric units. The mix-up in units led to the JPL scientists giving the spacecraft's computer the wrong information, which led to the spacecraft entering the Martian atmosphere, where it burned up. NASA has taken steps to prevent this error from ever happening again.

Most countries of the world use the *Système international d'unités* or *SI system*. The SI system is generally referred to as the *metric system* in the United States. The metric system was named for the Greek word *metron,* meaning "measure." The standard units in the metric system have gone through many changes since the system was first developed in France during the French Revolution. For example, one unit of measure, the meter, was first defined as one ten-millionth of the distance between the North Pole and the equator. Later, the meter was defined as 1,650,763.73 wavelengths of the orange–red line of krypton 86. Since 1893, the meter has been defined as the distance traveled by light in a vacuum in $\frac{1}{299,792,458}$ of a second.

Two systems of weights and measures exist side by side in the United States today, the *U.S. customary system* and the metric system. The metric system is used predominantly in the automotive, construction, farm equipment, computer, and bottling industries and in health-related professions. Furthermore, almost every industry that ships internationally uses at least some metric measures.

In this chapter, we will discuss the metric measurements of length, area, volume, mass, and temperature. Using the metric system has many advantages. Some of them are summarized here.

1. The metric system is the worldwide accepted standard measurement system. All industrial nations that trade internationally, except the United States, use the metric system as the official system of measurement.

2. There is only one basic unit of measurement for each physical quantity. In the U.S. customary system, many units are often used to represent the same physical quantity. For example, when discussing length, we use inches, feet, yards, miles, and so on. Converting from one of these units to the other is often a tedious task (consider changing 12 miles to inches). In the metric system, we can make many conversions by simply moving the decimal point.

3. The SI system is based on the number 10, and there is less need for fractions because most quantities can be expressed as decimals.

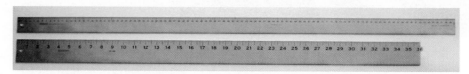

A meter (top figure) is a little longer than a yard (bottom figure).

One- and two-liter bottles

Basic Terms

Because the official definitions of many metric terms are quite technical, we present them informally.

The *meter* (m) is commonly used to measure *length* in the metric system. One meter is a little more than a yard. A door is about 2 meters high.

The *kilogram* (kg) is commonly used to measure *mass*. (The difference between mass and weight is discussed in Section 5.3.) One kilogram is about 2.2 pounds. A newborn baby may have a mass of about 3 kilograms. The gram (g), a unit of mass derived from the kilogram, is used to measure small amounts. A nickel has a mass of about 5 grams.

The *liter* (ℓ) is commonly used to measure *volume*. One liter is a little more than a quart. The gas tank of a compact car may hold 50 liters of gasoline.

Thus,

$$1 \text{ m} \approx 1 \text{ yd}$$
$$1 \text{ kg} \approx 2.2 \text{ lb}$$
$$1 \ \ell \approx 1 \text{ qt}$$

The term *degree Celsius* (°C) is used to measure temperature. The freezing point of water is 0°C, and the boiling point of water is 100°C. The temperature on a warm day may be 30°C.

$$0°C = 32°F \quad \text{Water freezes}$$
$$22°C = 71.6°F \quad \text{Comfortable room temperature}$$
$$37°C = 98.6°F \quad \text{Body temperature}$$
$$100°C = 212°F \quad \text{Water boils}$$

Prefixes

The metric system is based on the number 10 and therefore is a decimal system. Prefixes are used to denote a multiple or part of a base unit. Table 5.1 summarizes the more commonly used prefixes and their meanings. In the table, where we mention "base units" we mean metric units without prefixes, such as meter, gram, or liter. From Table 5.1, we can determine that a *deka*meter represents 10 meters and a *centi*meter represents $\frac{1}{100}$ of a meter. Also, 1 kiloliter = 1000 liters, 1 kilogram = 1000 grams, and 1 milliliter = $\frac{1}{1000}$ liter, and so on.

In the metric system, a comma is commonly used the way we use a decimal point (see the photo on the left, taken in Prague, Czech Republic), and a decimal point is used the way we use a comma (see the photo on the right, taken in Vienna, Austria).

TABLE 5.1	METRIC PREFIXES	
Prefix	**Symbol**	**Meaning**
kilo	k	1000 × base unit
hecto	h	100 × base unit
deka	da	10 × base unit
—	—	base unit
deci	d	$\frac{1}{10}$ of base unit
centi	c	$\frac{1}{100}$ of base unit
milli	m	$\frac{1}{1000}$ of base unit

The computer's hard drive can store 400 gigabytes (400 GB) of information.

In the metric system, groups of three digits in large numbers are often separated by a space, not a comma. For example, thirty thousand is written 30 000 and nine million is written 9 000 000. Groups of three digits to the right of the decimal point are also separated by spaces. For example, 16 millionths is written 0,000 016 in many countries of the world. We will use the decimal point in this book and write 0.000 016. In this section, we will separate groups of three digits using spaces. Note, however, that the space between groups of three digits is usually omitted if there are only four digits to the left or right of the decimal point. Thus, we will write three thousand as 3000 and five ten-thousandths as 0.0005.

For scientific work that involves very large and very small quantities, the following prefixes are also used: *mega* (M) is one million times the base unit, *giga* (G) is one billion times the base unit, *tera* (T) is one trillion times the base unit, *micro* (μ, the Greek letter mu) is one millionth of the base unit, *nano* (n) is one billionth of the base unit, and *pico* (p) is one trillionth of the base unit.

In this book, the abbreviations or symbols for units of measure are not pluralized, but full names are. For example, 5 milliliters is symbolized as 5 mℓ, not 5 mℓs. Some countries that use the metric system do not use an "s" in their abbreviations, whereas others do.

Conversions within the Metric System

We will use Table 5.2 to help demonstrate how to change from one metric unit to another metric unit using the meter as our base unit (for example, meters to kilometers, and so on).

The meters in Table 5.2 can be replaced by grams, liters, or any other base unit of the metric system. Regardless of which unit we choose, the procedure is the same. For purposes of explanation, we have used the meter.

TABLE 5.2 CHANGING METRIC UNITS

Measure of length	kilometer	hectometer	dekameter	meter	decimeter	centimeter	millimeter
Symbol	km	hm	dam	m	dm	cm	mm
Number of meters	1000 m	100 m	10 m	1 m	0.1 m	0.01 m	0.001 m

Table 5.2 shows that 1 hectometer equals 100 meters and 1 millimeter is 0.001 (or $\frac{1}{1000}$) meter. The millimeter is the smallest unit in the table. A centimeter is 10 times as large as a millimeter, a decimeter is 10 times as large as a centimeter, a meter is 10 times as large as a decimeter, and so on. Because each unit is 10 times as large as the unit on its right, converting from one unit to another is simply a matter of multiplying or dividing by powers of 10.

Our neighbors in Canada (and also Mexico) use the metric system. As you will learn shortly, the distance to the Botanical Gardens is about 0.6 mile and the distance to Niagara-on-the-Lake is about 9 miles from the sign.

CHANGING UNITS WITHIN THE METRIC SYSTEM

1. To change from a smaller unit to a larger unit (for example, from meters to kilometers), move the decimal point in the original quantity one place to the left for each larger unit of measurement until you obtain the desired unit of measurement.

2. To change from a larger unit to a smaller unit (for example, from kilometers to meters), move the decimal point in the original quantity one place to the right for each smaller unit of measurement until you obtain the desired unit of measurement.

EXAMPLE 1   CHANGING UNITS

a) Convert 375.6 m to km.

b) Convert 14 g to cg.

c) Convert 0.76 ℓ to mℓ.

d) Convert 240 daℓ to kℓ.

TECHNOLOGY

ADDITIONAL METRIC PREFACES

Many publications about the metric system are available free from the U.S. government. You may contact the National Institute of Standards and Technology (under the U.S. Department of Customs), through the Web site at www.nist.gov/, or you may write to the institute's office (Gaithersburg, MD 20899). Two worthwhile publications are *Metric Style Guide for the News Media* and *A Brief History of Measurement Systems*. The following interesting chart was selected and modified from the latter.

METRIC PREFIXES

Multiples and Submultiples	Prefixes	Symbols
1 000 000 000 000 000 000 000 000 = 10^{24}	yotta	Y
1 000 000 000 000 000 000 000 = 10^{21}	zetta	Z
1 000 000 000 000 000 000 = 10^{18}	exa	E
1 000 000 000 000 000 = 10^{15}	peta	P
1 000 000 000 000 = 10^{12}	tera	T
1 000 000 000 = 10^{9}	giga	G
1 000 000 = 10^{6}	mega	M
1000 = 10^{3}	kilo	k
100 = 10^{2}	hecto	h
10 = 10^{1}	deka	da*
1 = 10^{0}		
0.1 = 10^{-1}	deci	d
0.01 = 10^{-2}	centi	c
0.001 = 10^{-3}	milli	m
0.000 001 = 10^{-6}	micro	μ
0.000 000 001 = 10^{-9}	nano	n
0.000 000 000 001 = 10^{-12}	pico	p
0.000 000 000 000 001 = 10^{-15}	femto	f
0.000 000 000 000 000 001 = 10^{-18}	atto	a
0.000 000 000 000 000 000 001 = 10^{-21}	zepto	z
0.000 000 000 000 000 000 000 001 = 10^{-24}	yocto	y

*Some countries use D for deka.

SOLUTION

a) Table 5.2 shows that dekameters, hectometers, and kilometers are all larger units of measurements than meters. Kilometers appear three places to the left of meters in the table. Therefore, to change a measure from meters to kilometers, we must move the decimal point in the given number three places to the left, or

$$375.6 \text{ m} = 0.3756 \text{ km}$$

Note that since we are changing from a smaller unit of measurement (meter) to a larger unit of measurement (kilometer), the answer will be a smaller number of units.

b) Grams are a larger unit of measurement than centigrams. To convert grams to centigrams, we move the decimal point two places to the right, or

$$14 \text{ g} = 1400 \text{ cg}$$

Note that since we are changing from a larger unit of measurement (gram) to a smaller unit of measurement (centigram), the answer will be a larger number of units.

c) 0.76 ℓ = 760 mℓ

d) 240 daℓ = 2.40 kℓ

EXAMPLE 2   TWO MORE CONVERSIONS

a) Convert 305 mm to hectometers.

b) Convert 6.34 dam to decimeters.

SOLUTION

a) Table 5.2 shows that hectometers are five places to the left of millimeters. Therefore, to make the conversion, we must move the decimal point in the given number five places to the left, or

$$305 \text{ mm} = 0.003\ 05 \text{ hm}$$

b) Table 5.2 shows that decimeters are two places to the right of dekameters. Therefore, to make the conversion, we must move the decimal point in the given number two places to the right, or

$$6.34 \text{ dam} = 634 \text{ dm}$$

EXAMPLE 3   A METRIC ROAD SIGN

The sign in the photo, from Prague, Czech Republic, shows that there is a Subway sandwich shop 750 meters to the right.

a) Determine the distance in kilometers.

b) Determine the distance in centimeters.

SOLUTION

a) We must move the decimal point three places to the left to change from meters to kilometers. Therefore,

$$750 \text{ m} = 0.750 \text{ km}$$

b) We must move the decimal point two places to the right to change from meters to centimeters. Therefore,

$$750 \text{ m} = 75\ 000 \text{ cm}$$

EXAMPLE 4   COMPARING LENGTHS

Arrange in order from smallest to largest length: 3.4 m, 3421 mm, and 104 cm.

SOLUTION

To be compared, these lengths should all be in the same units of measure. Let's convert all the measures to millimeters, the smallest units of the lengths being compared.

$$3.4 \text{ m} = 3400 \text{ mm} \qquad 3421 \text{ mm} \qquad 104 \text{ cm} = 1040 \text{ mm}$$

Since the lengths, in millimeters, from smallest to largest are 1040, 3400, 3421, the lengths arranged in order from smallest to largest are 104 cm, 3.4 m, and 3421 mm.

EXERCISE SET 5.1 ●●●●●●

• Concept/Writing Exercises

1. What is the name commonly used for the Système international d'unités in the United States?

2. What is the name of the system of measurement primarily used in the United States today?

3. List three advantages of the metric system.

4. What metric unit is commonly used to measure

 a) length?   **b)** mass?

 c) volume?   **d)** temperature?

5. a) Explain how to convert from one metric unit of length to a different metric unit of length. Then use this procedure in parts (b) and (c).

b) Convert 214.6 cm to kilometers.

c) Convert 60.8 hm to decimeters.

6. What is the name of the prefix that is

    a) a million times the basic unit?

    b) one millionth of the base unit?

7. Without referring to any table, name as many of the metric system prefixes as you can and give their meanings. If you don't already know all the prefixes in Table 5.1, memorize them now.

8. a) How many times greater is 1 dam than 1 dm?

    b) Convert 1 dam to decimeters.

    c) Convert 1 dm to dekameters.

9. a) How many times greater is 1 hectometer than 1 centimeter?

    b) Convert 1 hm to centimeters.

    c) Convert 1 cm to hectometers.

10. a) What is the freezing temperature of water in the metric system?

    b) What is the boiling point of water in the metric system?

    c) What is normal human body temperature in the metric system?

• Practice the Skills

In Exercises 11–16, fill in the blank.

11. One meter is a little longer than a _____.

12. One kilogram is a little more than _____ pounds.

13. One nickel has a mass of about _____ grams.

14. The temperature on a warm day may be _____ °C.

15. A comfortable room temperature may be _____ °C.

16. A door may be _____ meters high.

In Exercises 17–22, match the prefix with the one letter, a–f, that gives the meaning of the prefix.

17. Milli   **a)** $\dfrac{1}{100}$ of base unit

18. Kilo   **b)** $\dfrac{1}{1000}$ of base unit

19. Hecto   **c)** 100 times base unit

20. Deka   **d)** 1000 times base unit

21. Deci   **e)** 10 times base unit

22. Centi   **f)** $\dfrac{1}{10}$ of base unit

23. Complete the following.

    a) 1 hectogram = _____ grams

    b) 1 milligram = _____ gram

    c) 1 kilogram = _____ grams

    d) 1 centigram = _____ gram

    e) 1 dekagram = _____ grams

    f) 1 decigram = _____ gram

24. Complete the following.

    a) 1 dekaliter = _____ liters

    b) 1 centiliter = _____ liter

    c) 1 milliliter = _____ liter

    d) 1 deciliter = _____ liter

    e) 1 kiloliter = _____ liters

    f) 1 hectoliter = _____ liters

In Exercises 25–30, without referring to any of the tables or your notes, give the symbol and the equivalent in grams for the unit.

25. Centigram   **26.** Milligram   **27.** Decigram

28. Dekagram   **29.** Hectogram   **30.** Kilogram

Maximum Mass *In Exercises 31 and 32, use the photo taken in Canada, which shows the maximum mass for vehicles allowed on the street.*

31. What is the maximum mass in grams?

32. What is the maximum mass in milligrams?

In Exercises 33–42, fill in the missing values.

33. 5 m = _____ mm

34. 35.7 hg = _____ g

35. 0.085 hℓ = _____ kℓ

36. 8 dam = _____ m

37. 242.6 cm = _____ hm

38. 1.34 mℓ = _____ ℓ

39. 2435 mg = _____ hg

40. 14.27 kℓ = _____ ℓ

41. 1.34 hm = _____ cm

42. 0.000 062 kg = _____ mg

In Exercises 43–50, convert the given unit to the unit indicated.

43. 32.5 kg to hectograms

44. 7.3 m to millimeters

45. 895 ℓ to milliliters

46. 24 dm to kilometers

47. 140 cg to grams

48. 6049 mm to meters

49. 40 302 mℓ to dekaliters

50. 0.034 mℓ to liters

In Exercises 51–56, arrange the quantities in order from smallest to largest.

51. 2.3 dam, 0.47 km, 590 cm

52. 514 hm, 62 km, 680 m

53. 1.4 kg, 1600 g, 16 300 dg

54. 4.3 ℓ, 420 cℓ, 0.045 kℓ

55. 2.6 km, 203 000 mm, 52.6 hm

56. 0.032 kℓ, 460 dℓ, 48 000 cℓ

• Problem Solving

57. *Who Ran Faster* Jim ran 100 m, and Bob ran 100 yd in the same length of time. Who ran faster? Explain.

58. *Walking* Would you be walking faster if you walked 1 dam in 10 min or 1 hm in 10 min? Explain.

59. *Water Removal* One pump removes 1 daℓ of water in 1 min, and another pump removes 1 dℓ of water in 1 min. Which pump removes water faster? Explain.

60. *Balance* If 5 kg are placed on one side of a balance and a 15 lb weight is placed on the other side, which way would the balance tip? Explain.

61. *Framing a Masterpiece* The painting by Picasso, including the frame, measures 74 cm by 99 cm.

a) How many centimeters of framing were needed to frame the painting?

b) How many millimeters of framing were needed to frame the painting?

62. *Calcium Tablets* Sean takes two 250 mg chewable calcium tablets each day.

a) How many milligrams of calcium will Sean take in a week?

b) How many grams of calcium will Sean take in a week?

63. *Gas Consumption* Dale Ewen drove 1200 km and used 187 ℓ of gasoline. What was his average rate of gas use for the trip

a) in kilometers per liter?

b) in meters per liter?

64. *Track and Field* The high school has a 400-m oval track. If Patty Burgess runs around the track eight times, how many kilometers has she traveled?

65. *Liters of Soda* A bottle of soda contains

a) How many milliliters are contained in a six-bottle carton?

b) How many liters does the amount in part (a) equal?

c) At $2.45 for the carton of soda, what is its cost per liter?

66. *Turkey Dinner* After a turkey is cooked it weighs 6.9 kg.

a) What is its weight in grams?

b) If Marie Sinclair cuts off one-third of the turkey and places it in the freezer, how many decigrams of turkey has she placed in the freezer?

67. *A Home Run* A baseball diamond is a square whose sides are about 27 m in length.

a) How many meters does a batter run if he hits a home run?

b) How many kilometers?

c) How many millimeters?

68. *Fill 'er Up* In Europe, gas may cost the equivalent of about $1.63 (American) per liter. What will be the cost of filling the gas tank of a car that has a capacity of 37.7 ℓ?

69. *Tennis Stadium* This photo taken at the Roland Garros Tennis Stadium in Paris shows the distances from the Roland Garros Stadium to tennis stadiums where the other three grand slams of tennis are played.

a) How much further is Melbourne Park (in Australia) than Flushing Meadows (in New York)?

b) What is the distance determined in part (a) in meters?

70. *Elevator* A sign in an elevator in Mexico City indicates that the maximum load is 375 kg. If the mass of the five people in the elevator are 92 kg, 100 kg, 62 kg, 96 kg, and 128 kg, by how much is the maximum load exceeded?

• Challenge Exercises/Group Activities

In Exercises 71–74, fill in the blank to make a true statement.

71. 1 gigameter = _____ megameters

72. 1 nanogram = _____ micrograms

73. 1 teraliter = _____ picoliters

74. 1 megagram = _____ nanograms

Calcium The recommended daily amount of calcium for an American adult is 0.8 g. In Exercises 75–78, how much of the food indicated must an adult eat to satisfy the entire daily allowance using only that food?

75. Eggs: 1 egg contains 27 mg calcium.

76. Milk: 1 cup contains 288 mg calcium.

77. Broccoli: 1 cup (cooked) contains 195 mg calcium.

78. Raisin bran: 49 g contains 1.6 mg calcium.

Large and Small Numbers One advantage of the metric system is that by using the proper prefix, you can write large and small numbers without large groups of zeroes. In Exercises 79–84, write an equivalent metric measurement without using any zeroes. For example, you can write 3000 m without zeroes as 3 km and 0.0003 hm as 3 cm.

79. 7000 cm   **80.** 4000 mm

81. 0.000 06 hg   **82.** 3000 dm

83. 0.02 kℓ   **84.** 500 cm

• Recreational Mathematics

In Exercises 85–94, unscramble the word to make a metric unit of measurement.

85. magr   **86.** migradec

87. rteli   **88.** raktileed

89. terem   **90.** leritililm

91. reketolim   **92.** timenceret

93. greseed sulesic   **94.** togmeharc

• Internet/Research Activities

95. Write a report on the development of the metric system in Europe. Indicate which individual people had the most influence in its development.

96. Write a report on why you believe many Americans oppose switching to the metric system. Give your opinion about whether the United States will eventually switch to the metric system and, if so, when it might do so.

SECTION 5.2 • LENGTH, AREA, AND VOLUME

When shipped overseas, U.S. cars will give gas mileage, the car's weight, and other measurements in metric units.

When U.S. companies send their cars overseas, the gas mileage given on the car's window sticker is usually given in liters per hundred kilometers ($\frac{1}{100}$ km) rather than miles per gallon. Other measurements, such as the car's length and weight, are also given in metric measurements. When clothing manufacturers ship clothing overseas, the clothing sizes will be given in metric units, such as centimeters. Can you convert a pants waist size of 38 inches to centimeters? In this chapter, you will learn how to make conversions to and from the metric system.

This section and the next section are designed to help you *think metric*, that is, to become acquainted with day-to-day usage of metric units. In this section, we consider length, area, and volume.

TECHNOLOGY

1 Yard = 3 Feet = 36 Inches = . . .

In the U.S. Customary system, 27 different units of length are used. How many of them can you name? Don't forget rod, mil, paris line, toise, cubit, and light-year. The different units can be found in the *CRC Handbook of Chemistry and Physics* or at the website www.hbcpnetbase.com.

Length

The basic unit of length in the metric system is the meter. In all English-speaking countries except the United States, *meter* is spelled "metre." Until 1960, the meter was officially defined by the length of a platinum bar kept in a vault in France. The modern definition of the meter is based on the speed of light, a constant that has been defined with great precision. Other commonly used units of length are the kilometer, centimeter, and millimeter. The meter, which is a little longer than 1 yard, is used to measure things that we normally measure in yards and feet. A man whose height is about 2 meters is a tall man. A tractor trailer unit (an 18-wheeler) is about 18 meters long.

The kilometer is used to measure what we normally measure in miles. For example, the distance from New York to Seattle is about 5120 kilometers. One kilometer is about 0.6 mile, and 1 mile is about 1.6 kilometers.

Centimeters and millimeters are used to measure what we normally measure in inches. The centimeter is a little less than $\frac{1}{2}$ inch (see Fig. 5.1), and the millimeter is a little less than $\frac{1}{20}$ inch. A millimeter is about the thickness of a dime. A book may measure 20 cm by 25 cm with a thickness of about 3 cm. Millimeters are often used in scientific work and other areas in which small quantities must be measured. The length of a small insect may be measured in millimeters.

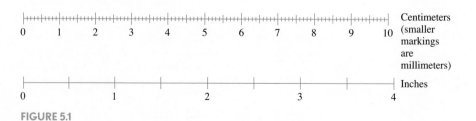

Centimeters (smaller markings are millimeters)

Inches

FIGURE 5.1

The Ted Williams statue outside
Fenway Park, Boston

EXAMPLE 1   CHOOSING AN APPROPRIATE UNIT OF LENGTH

Determine which metric unit of length you would use to express the following.

a) The height of the Ted Williams statue shown in the photo.

b) The length of your arm

c) The length of a flea

d) The height of the Sears Tower in Chicago

e) The diameter of a half-dollar

f) The distance between Amarillo, Texas, and Detroit, Michigan.

g) The diameter of a round wastepaper basket

h) The diameter of a pencil

i) Your waist size

j) Your height

SOLUTION

a) Meters or centimeters   b) Centimeters

c) Millimeters   d) Meters

e) Centimeters or millimeters   f) Kilometers

g) Centimeters   h) Millimeters

i) Centimeters   j) Meters or centimeters

In some parts of this solution, more than one possible answer is listed. Measurements can often be made by using more than one unit. For example, if someone asks your height, you might answer $5\frac{1}{2}$ feet or 66 inches. Both answers are correct.

Area

In Chapter 6, we provide formulas and discuss procedures for finding the area and volume of many geometric figures. The procedures and formulas for finding area and volume are the same regardless of whether the units are metric units or customary units. When finding areas and volumes, each side of the figure must be given in (or converted to) the same unit.

The area enclosed in a square with 1-centimeter sides (Fig. 5.2) is $1 \text{ cm} \times 1 \text{ cm} = 1 \text{ cm}^2$. A square whose sides are 2 cm (Fig. 5.3) has an area of $2 \text{ cm} \times 2 \text{ cm} = 2^2 \text{ cm}^2 = 4 \text{ cm}^2$.

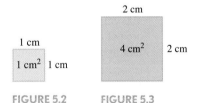

FIGURE 5.2   FIGURE 5.3

Areas are always expressed in square units, such as square centimeters, square kilometers, or square meters. When finding areas, be careful that all the numbers being multiplied are expressed in the same units.

In the metric system, the square centimeter replaces the square inch. The square meter replaces the square foot and square yard. In the future, you might purchase carpet or other floor covering by the square meter instead of by the square foot.

For measuring large land areas, the metric system uses a square unit 100 meters on each side (a square hectometer). This unit is called a *hectare* (pronounced "hectair" and symbolized ha). A hectare is about 2.5 acres. One square mile of land contains about 260 hectares. Very large units of area are measured in square kilometers. One square kilometer is about $\frac{4}{10}$ square mile.

Yellowstone National Park,
Wyoming, see Example 2(a)

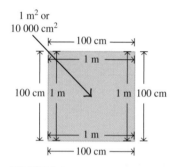

1 m² or
10 000 cm²

FIGURE 5.4

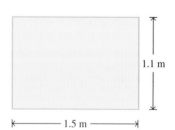

1.1 m

1.5 m

FIGURE 5.5

EXAMPLE 2   CHOOSING AN APPROPRIATE UNIT OF AREA

Determine which metric unit of area you would use to measure the area of the following.

a) Yellowstone National Park (see photo)
b) The top of a kitchen table
c) The floor of the classroom
d) A person's property with an average-sized lot
e) A newspaper page
f) A baseball field
g) An ice-skating rink
h) A dime
i) A lens in eyeglasses
j) A dollar bill

SOLUTION

a) Square kilometers or hectares   b) Square meters
c) Square meters   d) Square meters or hectares
e) Square centimeters   f) Hectares or square meters
g) Square meters   h) Square millimeters or square centimeters
i) Square centimeters   j) Square centimeters

To find the area, A, of a square, we use the formula $A = s^2$, where s is the length of a side of the square. The area can also be found by the formula area = side × side. We use this information in Example 3.

EXAMPLE 3   CONVERTING SQUARE METERS TO SQUARE CENTIMETERS

A square meter is how many times as large as a square centimeter?

SOLUTION

A square meter is a square whose sides are 1 meter long. Since 1 m equals 100 cm, we can replace 1 m with 100 cm (see Fig. 5.4). The area of $1 \text{ m}^2 = 1 \text{ m} \times 1 \text{ m} = 100 \text{ cm} \times 100 \text{ cm} = 10\,000 \text{ cm}^2$. Thus, the area of one square meter is 10,000 times the area of one square centimeter. This technique can be used to convert from any square unit to a different square unit.

EXAMPLE 4   TABLE TOP

Find the area of a rectangular table top if its length is 1.5 m and its width is 1.1 m (see Fig. 5.5).

SOLUTION
To find the area, we use the formula

$$\text{Area} = \text{length} \times \text{width}$$

or

$$A = l \times w$$

FIGURE 5.6

Substituting values for l and w, we have

$$A = 1.5 \text{ m} \times 1.1 \text{ m}$$
$$= 1.65 \text{ m}^2$$

Notice that the area is measured in square meters.

EXAMPLE 5   A QUARTER

A quarter has a diameter of about 2.4 cm (Fig. 5.6). Find the surface area of one side of a quarter.

SOLUTION

The formula for the area of a circle is $A = \pi r^2$, where π is *approximately* 3.14. The radius, r, is one-half the diameter. Since the diameter is about 2.4 cm, the radius is about 1.2 cm. Substituting values for π and r, we get the following.

$$A = \pi r^2$$
$$\approx 3.14(1.2 \text{ cm})^2$$
$$\approx 4.52 \text{ cm}^2$$

Thus, the area is approximately 4.52 square centimeters. Recall from earlier chapters that the symbol $\approx$ means "is approximately equal to."

Volume

When a figure has only two dimensions—length and width—we can find its area. When a figure has three dimensions—length, width, and height—we can find its volume. The volume of an item can be considered the space occupied by the item.

In the metric system, volume may be expressed in terms of liters or cubic meters, depending on what is being measured. In all English-speaking countries except the United States, *liter* is spelled "litre."

The volume of liquids is expressed in liters. A liter is a little larger than a quart. Liters are used in place of pints, quarts, and gallons. A liter can be divided into 1000 equal parts, each of which is called a milliliter. Figure 5.7 illustrates a 50 mℓ graduated cylinder. In chemistry, 1000 mℓ and other metric graduated cylinders are often used. Milliliters are used to express the volume of very small amounts of liquid. Drug dosages are often expressed in milliliters. An 8 oz cup will hold about 240 mℓ of liquid.

The kiloliter, 1000 liters, is used to represent the volume of large amounts of liquid. Tank trucks carrying gasoline to service stations hold about 10.5 kℓ of gasoline.

Cubic meters are used to express the volume of large amounts of solid and gaseous material. The volume of a dump truck's load of topsoil is measured in cubic meters. The volume of natural gas used to heat a house may soon be measured in cubic meters instead of cubic feet.

The liquid in a liter container will fit exactly in a cubic decimeter (Fig. 5.8). Note that $1 \ell = 1000 \text{ m}\ell$ and that $1 \text{ dm}^3 = 1000 \text{ cm}^3$. Because $1 \ell = 1 \text{ dm}^3$, *1 mℓ must equal 1 cm^3*. Other useful facts are illustrated in Table 5.3. Thus, within the metric system, conversions are much simpler than in the U.S. customary system. For example, how would you change cubic feet of water into gallons of water?

FIGURE 5.7

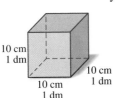

1 liter = 1000 mℓ 1 dm^3 = 1000 cm^3

FIGURE 6.8

TABLE 5.3		
Volume in Cubic Units		**Volume in Liters**
1 cm^3	=	1 mℓ
1 dm^3	=	1 ℓ
1 m^3	=	1 kℓ

See Example 6(a)

EXAMPLE 6   CHOOSING AN APPROPRIATE UNIT OF VOLUME

Determine which metric unit of volume you would use to measure the volume of the following.

a) The water in a swimming pool

b) A carton of milk

c) A truckload of topsoil

d) A drug dosage

e) Sand in a paper cup

f) A dime

g) Water in a drinking glass

h) Water in a full bath tub

i) The storage area of a sports utility vehicle with the back seats folded down or removed.

j) Concrete used to lay the foundation for a basement

SOLUTION

a) Kiloliters or liters   b) Liters

c) Cubic meters   d) Milliliters

e) Cubic centimeters   f) Cubic millimeters

g) Milliliters   h) Liters

i) Cubic meters   j) Cubic meters

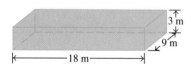

FIGURE 5.9

EXAMPLE 7   SWIMMING POOL VOLUME

A swimming pool is 18 m long and 9 m wide, and it has a uniform depth of 3 m (Fig. 5.9). Find (a) the volume of the pool in cubic meters and (b) the volume of water in the pool in kiloliters.

SOLUTION

a) To find the volume in cubic meters, we use the formula

$$V = l \times w \times h$$

Substituting values for l, w, and h we have

$$V = 18 \text{ m} \times 9 \text{ m} \times 3 \text{ m}$$
$$= 486 \text{ m}^3$$

b) Since $1 \text{ m}^3 = 1 \text{ k}\ell$, the pool will hold 486 kℓ of water.

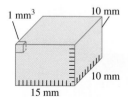

FIGURE 5.10

EXAMPLE 8   CHOOSE AN APPROPRIATE UNIT

Select the most appropriate answer. The volume of a shoe box is approximately

a) 1500 mm^3.   b) 6500 ℓ.   c) 6500 cm^3.

SOLUTION   A shoe box is not a liquid, so its volume is not expressed in liters. Thus, (b) is not the answer. The volume of the rectangular solid in Fig. 5.10 is approximately 1500 mm^3, so (a) is not an appropriate answer. A shoe box may measure about 33 cm $\times$ 18 cm $\times$ 11 cm, or 6534 cm^3. Therefore, 6500 cm^3 or (c) is the most appropriate answer.

When the volume of a liquid is measured, the abbreviation cc is often used instead of cm³ to represent cubic centimeters. For example, a nurse may give a patient an injection of 3 cc or 3 mℓ of the drug ampicillin.

EXAMPLE 9   MEASURING MEDICINE

A nurse must give a patient 3 cc of the drug gentamicin mixed in 100 cc of a normal saline solution.

a) How many milliliters of the drug will the nurse administer?

b) What is the total volume of the drug and saline solution in milliliters?

SOLUTION

a) Because 1 cc is equal in volume to 1 mℓ, the nurse will administer 3 mℓ of the drug.

b) The total volume is 3 + 100 or 103 cc, which is equal to 103 mℓ.

EXAMPLE 10   A HOT-WATER HEATER

A hot-water heater, in the shape of a right circular cylinder, has a radius of 50 cm and a height of 148 cm. What is the capacity, in liters, of the hot-water heater?

FIGURE 5.11

SOLUTION The hot-water heater is illustrated in Fig. 5.11. The formula for the volume of a right circular cylinder is $V = \pi r^2 h$, where π is approximately 3.14. Since we want the capacity in liters, we will express all the measurements in meters. The volume will then be given in cubic meters, which can be easily converted to liters. Thus, 50 cm = 0.5 m, and 148 cm = 1.48 m.

$$V = \pi r^2 h$$
$$\approx 3.14(0.5)^2(1.48)$$
$$\approx 3.14(0.25)(1.48) \approx 1.1618 \text{ m}^3$$

We want the volume in liters, so we must change the answer from cubic meters to liters.

$$1 \text{ m}^3 = 1000 \text{ } \ell$$

So,

$$1.1618 \text{ m}^3 = 1.1618 \times 1000 = 1161.8 \text{ } \ell$$

EXAMPLE 11   COMPARING VOLUME UNITS

a) How many times larger is a cubic meter than a cubic centimeter?

b) How many times larger is a cubic dekameter than a cubic meter?

SOLUTION

a) The procedure used to determine the answer is similar to that used in Example 3 in this section. First we draw a cubic meter, which is a cube 1 m long by 1 m wide by 1 m high. In Fig. 5.12, we represent each meter as 100 centimeters. The volume of the cube is its length times its width times its height, or

$$V = l \times w \times h$$
$$= 100 \text{ cm} \times 100 \text{ cm} \times 100 \text{ cm} = 1\,000\,000 \text{ cm}^3$$

TECHNOLOGY

METRICS AND MEDICINE
Both milliliters and cubic centimeters are commonly used in medicine. In the United States, cubic centimeters are commonly denoted cc rather than the cm^3 used in the metric system. A patient's intake and output of fluids and intravenous injections are commonly measured in cubic centimeters. Drug dosage is measured in milliliters.

The following question is from a nursing exam. Can you determine the correct answer?

In caring for a patient after delivery, you are to give 12 units of Pitocin (in 1000 cc of intravenous fluid). The ampule is labeled 10 units per 0.5 mℓ. How much of the solution would you draw and give?
a) 0.6 cc
b) 1.2 cc
c) 6.0 cc
d) 9.6 cc

Answer: (a)

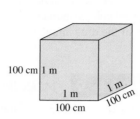

FIGURE 5.12

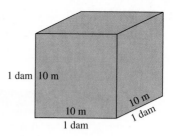

FIGURE 5.13

Since $1 \text{ m}^3 = 1\,000\,000 \text{ cm}^3$, a cubic meter is one million times larger than a cubic centimeter.

b) Work part (b) in a similar manner (Fig. 5.13). A dekameter is 10 meters. Thus,

$$V = l \times w \times h$$
$$= 10 \text{ m} \times 10 \text{ m} \times 10 \text{ m} = 1000 \text{ m}^3$$

Since $1 \text{ dam}^3 = 1000 \text{ m}^3$, a cubic dekameter is one thousand times larger than a cubic meter.

EXERCISE SET 5.2 ●●●●●●

• Concept/Writing Exercises

In Exercises 1–12, an object has been measured and the measurement has been written with the unit indicated. Indicate what was measured: length, area, or volume.

1. m^3 2. mm   3. ha   4. cm

5. cc   6. ℓ   7. cm^3 8. kℓ

9. m^2 10. dℓ   11. km   12. cm^2

13. Estimate, in centimeters, the length of this book.

14. Estimate your height in (a) centimeters and (b) meters.

15. Estimate, in meters, the length of the classroom in which your mathematics course is held.

16. Estimate, in square centimeters, the surface area of this book.

17. Estimate, in square centimeters, the surface area of a dollar bill.

18. Estimate, in centimeters, the length of your arm.

19. One liter of liquid has the equivalent volume of which of the following: a cubic centimeter, a cubic decimeter, or a cubic meter?

20. One cubic meter has the equivalent volume of which of the following liquid measures: a liter, a milliliter, or a kiloliter?

21. One milliliter of liquid has the equivalent volume of which of the following: a cubic centimeter, a cubic decimeter, or a cubic meter?

22. Which metric measurement is used to measure very large areas of land?

23. Is the hectare a measure of length, area, or volume?

24. A hectare has an area of about how many acres: 2.5, 25, or 250?

• Practice the Skills

In Exercises 25–36, indicate the metric unit of measurement that you would use to express the following.

25. The length of a pencil

26. The distance between cities

27. The diameter of a dime

28. The diameter of a Frisbee

29. The length of a newborn infant

30. The diameter of a helicopter landing pad

31. The distance between freeway exits

32. The width of an Olympic-size swimming pool

33. The height of a cereal box

34. The length of a butterfly

35. The distance to the moon

36. The height of an adult male

In Exercises 37–44, choose the best answer.

37. The length of a tennis court is about how long?

    a) 36 cm   **b)** 36 km   **c)** 36 m

38. A U.S. postage stamp is about how wide and how long?

    a) 2 cm $\times$ 3 cm   **b)** 2 mm $\times$ 3 mm

    c) 2 hm $\times$ 3 hm

39. The distance between Los Angeles and San Diego could be how far?

    a) 130 cm   **b)** 130 m   **c)** 130 km

40. A grown woman is about how tall?

    a) 160 cm   **b)** 160 mm   **c)** 160 dm

41. The width of a ruler is about how wide?

    a) 4 mm   **b)** 4 cm   **c)** 4 dm

42. The diameter of a coffee cup is about which of the following?

    a) 8 mm   **b)** 8 cm   **c)** 8 dm

43. The Sears Tower in Chicago is about how tall?

    a) 375 cm   **b)** 375 km   **c)** 375 m

44. The length of the New River Gorge Bridge near Fayetteville, West Virginia is about how long?

    a) 1000 dam   **b)** 1000 m   **c)** 1000 cm

New River Gorge Bridge

In Exercises 45–50, (a) estimate the item in metric units and (b) measure it with a metric ruler. Record your result.

45. The width of a card from a deck of cards

46. The width of a classroom door

47. The length of a car

48. The diameter of a can of soda

49. The height of a milk carton

50. The thickness of 10 sheets of paper.

In Exercises 51–56, replace the customary measure (shown in parentheses) with the appropriate metric measure.

51. Give him a _____ (inch), and he will take a _____ (mile).

52. There was a crooked man and he walked a crooked _____ (mile).

53. One hundred _____ (yard) dash.

54. I wouldn't touch a skunk with a 10-_____ (foot) pole.

55. I found a _____ (inch) worm.

56. This is a _____ (mile)stone in my life.

In Exercises 57–66, indicate the metric unit of measurement you would use to express the area of the following.

57. A small television screen

58. The floor of your classroom

59. A kitchen table

60. A building lot for a house

61. A baseball field

62. A postage stamp

63. A ceiling tile

64. Disney World

65. A professional basketball court

66. The city of San Antonio, Texas

Riverwalk, San Antonio, Texas

In Exercises 67–74, choose the best answer.

67. A U.S. postage stamp has an area of about

    a) 5 cm^2.   **b)** 5 mm^2.   **c)** 5 dm^2.

68. The area of a city lot is about

    a) 800 m^2.   **b)** 800 hm^2.   **c)** 800 cm^2.

69. The area of a city lot is about

    a) $\frac{1}{8}$ m^2.   **b)** $\frac{1}{8}$ ha.   **c)** $\frac{1}{8}$ km^2.

70. The area of a floor tile is about

    a) 930 m^2.   **b)** 930 km^2.   **c)** 930 cm^2.

71. The area of one side of a $1 bill is about

    a) 100 cm^2.   **b)** 100 m^2.   **c)** 100 mm^2.

72. The area of the screen of a tabletop TV is about

    a) 1200 dm^2.   **b)** 1200 mm^2.   **c)** 1200 cm^2.

73. The area of Grand Canyon National Park is about

    a) 4900 m^2 **b)** 4900 cm^2 **c)** 4900 km^2

74. The area of a U.S. flag is about

    a) 2.2 cm^2.   **b)** 2.2 m^2.   **c)** 2.2 km^2.

In Exercises 75–80, (a) estimate the area of the item in metric units and (b) measure it in metric units and compute its area.

75. A typical photograph

76. The cover of this book

77. A $20 bill

78. The top of your teacher's desk

79. The bottom of a 12 oz soda can

80. The face of a penny

In Exercises 81–90, determine the metric unit that would best be used to measure the volume of the following.

81. Water in a hot-water heater

82. Liquid in an eye dropper

83. Water flowing over Niagara Falls per minute

84. Oil needed to change the oil in your car

85. A bag of topsoil

86. A truckload of ready-mix concrete

87. Water coming out of a drinking fountain in 1 minute

88. Soda in a bottle of soda

89. Air in a hot air balloon

90. Air in a soccer ball

In Exercises 91–98, choose the best answer to indicate the volume of the following.

91. A shoe box

    a) 7780 mm^3 **b)** 7780 dm^3 **c)** 7780 cm^3

92. Water that could fit in a thimble

    a) 3 mℓ **b)** 3 ℓ **c)** 3 dℓ

93. Water in a 24-ft-diameter above-ground circular swimming pool

    a) 55 ℓ **b)** 55 mℓ **c)** 55 kℓ

94. Soda in a can of soda

    a) 355 ℓ **b)** 355 mℓ **c)** 355 m^3

95. A carry-on suitcase

    a) 0.04 cm^3 **b)** 0.04 mm^3 **c)** 0.04 m^3

96. Juice that can be squeezed out of an orange

    a) 120 kℓ **b)** 120 mℓ **c)** 120 ℓ

97. Air in a balloon with a diameter of 4 meters

    a) 30 m^3 **b)** 30 cm^3 **c)** 30 km^3

98. Air in a soccer ball

    a) 5 000 m^3 **b)** 5 000 cm^3 **c)** 5 000 mm^3

In Exercises 99–102, (a) estimate the volume in metric units and (b) compute the actual volume of the item.

99. Air in a cardboard box that is 61 cm long, 61 cm wide, and 41 cm tall (Use $V = lwh$.)

100. Water in a water bed that is 2 m long, 1.5 m wide, and 25 cm deep

101. Oil in a barrel that has a height of 1 m and a diameter of 0.5 m (Use $V = \pi r^2 h$.)

102. Water in a cylindrical tank that is 40 cm in diameter and 2 m high

Problem Solving

103. *Area* Use a metric ruler to measure the length and width of the sides of the rectangle. Then compute the area of the rectangle. Give your answers in metric units.

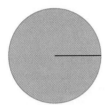

104. *Area* Use a metric ruler to find the radius of the circle. Then compute the area of the circle. Give your answers in metric units.

105. *Helipad* A helicopter landing area, generally in the shape of a circle, is called a helipad. A specific helipad is a circle of radius 10.2 meters. Determine the area of the helipad. Use the formula $A = \pi r^2$.

106. *Painting* The total area of a framed painting including the matting is 2540 cm² (see photo). If the length and width of the actual painting are 37 cm and 28 cm, respectively, determine the area of the matting.

107. *A Walkway* A rectangular building 50 m by 70 m is surrounded by a walk 1.5 m wide.

a) Find the area of the region covered by the building and the walk.

b) Find the area of the walk.

108. *Farmland* Mrs. Manecki has purchased a farm that is in the shape of a rectangle. The dimensions of the piece of land are 1.4 km by 3.75 km.

a) How many square kilometers of land did she purchase?

b) If 1 km² equals 100 ha, determine the amount of land she purchased in hectares.

109. *Gymnasium* The Boys and Girls Club is planning on having a large rectangular gymnasium built. The dimensions of the gymnasium are to be 62.4 m by 50.5 m.

a) Determine the area of the gymnasium in square meters.

b) If 1 m² equals 0.0001 ha, determine the area of the gymnasium in hectares.

110. *Volume of Water* **a)** What is the volume of water in a rectangular swimming pool that is 18 m long and 10 m wide and has an average depth of 2.5 m? Give your answer in cubic meters.

b) How many kiloliters of water will the pool hold?

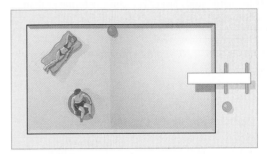

111. *Cost of Paint* The first coat of paint for the outside of a building requires 1 ℓ of paint for each 10 m². The second coat requires 1 ℓ for every 15 m². If the paint costs $4.75 per liter, what will be the cost of two coats of paint for the four outside walls of a building 20 m long, 12 m wide, and 6 m high?

112. *Volume of a Can* A can of soup has a diameter of 8.0 cm and a height of 12.5 cm. Determine the volume of the can in cubic centimeters.

113. *Fish Tank Volume* A rectangular fish tank is 70 cm long, 40 cm wide, and 20 cm high.

a) How many cubic centimeters of water will the tank hold?

b) How many milliliters of water will the tank hold?

c) How many liters of water will the tank hold?

114. *Hot-Water Heater* A cylindrical shaped hot-water heater has a diameter of 0.56 m and a height of 1.17 m. If the hot-water heater is filled, determine the volume of water in the hot-water heater in

    a) cubic meters.

    b) liters.

115. How many times larger is a square dekameter than a square meter?

116. How many times larger is a square kilometer than a square dekameter?

117. How many times larger is a cubic meter than a cubic decimeter?

118. How many times larger is a cubic centimeter than a cubic millimeter?

In Exercises 119–126, replace the question mark with the appropriate value.

119. $1 \text{ cm}^2 = ? \text{ mm}^2$ **120.** $1 \text{ hm}^2 = ? \text{ cm}^2$

121. $1 \text{ km}^2 = ? \text{ hm}^2$ **122.** $1 \text{ cm}^2 = ? \text{ m}^2$

123. $1 \text{ mm}^3 = ? \text{ dm}^3$ **124.** $1 \text{ dm}^3 = ? \text{ mm}^3$

125. $1 \text{ m}^3 = ? \text{ cm}^3$ **126.** $1 \text{ hm}^3 = ? \text{ km}^3$

In Exercises 127–130, fill in the blank.

127. $218 \text{ cm}^3 = $ ____ $\text{m}\ell$ **128.** $435 \text{ cm}^3 = $ ____ ℓ

129. $76 \text{ k}\ell = $ ____ m^3 **130.** $4.2 \ell = $ ____ cm^3

Glacier In Exercises 131 and 132, assume that a part of a rectangular glacier that contains 60 cubic meters of ice calves (or breaks) off and falls into the ocean.

A glacier in Alaska

131. When the ice that has fallen into the ocean melts, determine the approximate amount of water, in kiloliters, obtained from the ice.

132. When the ice melts, determine the approximate amount of water, in cubic centimeters, obtained from the ice.

Challenge Problems/Group Activities

133. Starting with a straight piece of wood of sufficient size, construct a meterstick. Indicate decimeters, centimeters, and millimeters on the meterstick. Use the centimeter measure in Fig. 5.1 as a guide.

134. Construct a metric tape measure from a piece of tape or rope and then determine your waist measurement.

In Exercises 135 and 136, fill in the blank to make a true statement.

135. $6.7 \text{ k}\ell = $ ____ dm^3 **136.** $1.4 \text{ ha} = $ ____ cm^2

137. *Conversions* In Example 3, we illustrated how to change an area in a metric unit to an area measured with a different metric unit.

    a) Using Example 3 as a guide, change 1 square mile to square inches.

    b) Is converting from one unit of area to a different unit of area generally easier in the metric system or the U.S. customary system? Explain.

138. *Conversions* In Example 11, we illustrated how to change a volume in one metric unit to a volume measured with a different metric unit.

    a) Using Example 11 as a guide, change 6 yd^3 (a volume 1 yard by 2 yards by 3 yards) into cubic inches.

    b) Is converting from one unit of volume to a different unit of volume generally easier in the metric system or the U.S. customary system? Explain.

• Recreational Mathematics

139. *Water Usage* **a)** How much water do we use daily? On the average, people in the United States use more water than people anywhere else in the world. Take a guess at the number of liters of water used per day per person in the United States.

    b) Now take a guess at the number of liters used per day per person in the United Kingdom.

    Compare your answers to those given in the answer section.

• Internet/Research Activities

140. *The Meter* The definition of the meter has changed several times throughout history. Write a one- to two-page report on the history of the meter, from when it was first named to the present.

SECTION 5.3 • MASS AND TEMPERATURE

This astronaut, while floating in space, has mass but no weight.

Suppose you go on a trip to Canada. When you turn on the television, the weatherperson says the temperature today will be sunny and 28°Celsius. How do you dress to go outside? Should you wear shorts or a sweater or a jacket? What is the temperature in degrees Fahrenheit?

On your television, you are watching U.S. astronauts floating in space. Do these floating astronauts have any weight? Do they have any mass? In this section, we will explore these two important metric measurements, temperature and mass.

Mass

Weight and mass are not the same. *Mass* is a measure of the amount of matter in an object. It is determined by the molecular structure of the object, and it will not change from place to place. Weight is a measure of the gravitational pull on an object. For example, the gravitational pull of Earth is about six times as great as the gravitational pull of the moon. Thus, a person on the moon weighs about $\frac{1}{6}$ as much as on Earth, even though the person's mass remains the same. In space, where there is no gravity, a person has no weight.

Even on Earth, the gravitational pull varies from point to point. The closer you are to Earth's center, the greater the gravitational pull. Thus, a person weighs very slightly less on a mountain than in a nearby valley. Because the mass of an object does not vary with location, scientists generally use mass rather than weight.

Although weight and mass are not the same, on Earth they are proportional to each other (the greater the weight, the greater the mass). Therefore, for our purposes, we can treat weight and mass as the same.

The *kilogram* is the basic unit of mass in the metric system. It is about 2.2 pounds. The official kilogram is a cylinder of platinum–iridium alloy kept by the International Bureau of Weights and Measures, located in Sèvres, near Paris. (See the Technology in the margin on the next page.)

Items that we normally measure in pounds are usually measured in kilograms in other parts of the world. For example, an average-sized man has a mass of about 75 kg.

The *gram* (a unit that is 0.001 kg) is relatively small and is used for items normally measured in ounces. A nickel has a mass of about 5 g, a cube of sugar has a mass of about 2 g, and a large paper clip has a mass of about 1 g.

The *milligram* is used extensively in the medical and scientific fields as well as in the pharmaceutical industry. Nearly all bottles of tablets are now labeled in either milligrams or grams.

The *metric tonne* (t) is used to express the mass of heavy items. One metric tonne equals 1000 kg. A metric ton is a little larger than our customary ton of 2000 lb. The mass of a large truck may be expressed in metric tonnes.

See Exercise 1(a)

TECHNOLOGY

THE KILOGRAM

Since 1889, a single platinum–iridium bar has been sealed in an airtight jar in the International Bureau of Weights and Measures in Sèvres, France.

Nicknamed "Le Grand K," this bar constitutes the one and only true kilogram. Of all the standard international units of measure, the kilogram remains the only one whose definition relies on a physical artifact. All the other units have their definitions rooted in constants of nature, such as the speed of light or atomic vibrations.

The kilogram has varied by as much as 0.05 part per million in the last 100 years. The cause of that variance remains unknown.

Some scientists want to redefine the kilogram in a way that will make the standard absolute, unchanging, and accessible to anyone, anywhere.

EXAMPLE 1   CHOOSING THE APPROPRIATE UNIT

Determine which metric unit you would use to express the mass of the following.

a) A 1-year-old child   b) An orca (or killer whale)
c) A teaspoon   d) A box of cereal
e) A laptop computer   f) A fly
g) A frog   h) A refrigerator

SOLUTION

a) Kilograms   b) Metric tonnes
c) Grams   d) Grams
e) Grams or kilograms   f) Milligrams
g) Grams   h) Kilograms

One kilogram of water has a volume of exactly 1 liter. In fact, 1 liter is defined to be the volume of 1 kilogram of water at a specified temperature and pressure. Thus, mass and volume are easily interchangeable in the metric system. Converting from weight to volume is not nearly as convenient in the U.S. customary system. For example, how would you change pounds of water to cubic feet or gallons of water in our customary system?

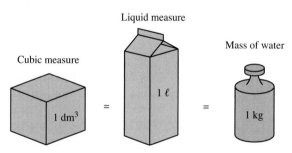

FIGURE 5.14 One cubic decimeter of water has the volume of one liter and the mass of one kilogram.

Since $1 \text{ dm}^3 = 1000 \text{ cm}^3$, $1\ell = 1000 \text{ m}\ell$, and $1\text{kg} = 1000\text{g}$, we have the following relationship.

$$1000 \text{ cm}^3 = 1000 \text{ m}\ell = 1000 \text{ g}$$
$$\text{or,} \quad 1 \text{ cm}^3 = 1 \text{ m}\ell = 1 \text{ g}$$

Figure 5.14 illustrates the relationship between volume of water in cubic decimeters, in liters, and mass in kilograms. Table 5.4 expands on this relationship between the volume and mass of water.

TABLE 5.4 VOLUME AND MASS OF WATER				
Volume in Cubic Units		**Volume in Liters**		**Mass of Water**
1 cm^3	=	$1 \text{ m}\ell$	=	1 g
1 dm^3	=	1ℓ	=	1 kg
1 m^3	=	$1 \text{ k}\ell$	=	1 t (1000 kg)

EXAMPLE 2 VOLUME OF A FISH TANK

A fish tank is 1 m long, 50 cm high, and 250 mm wide (Fig. 5.15).

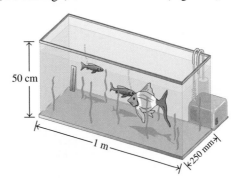

FIGURE 5.15

a) Determine the number of liters of water the tank holds.

b) What is the mass of the water in kilograms?

SOLUTION

a) We must convert all the measurements to the same units. Let's convert them all to meters: 50 cm is 0.5 m, and 250 mm is 0.25 m.

$$V = l \times w \times h$$
$$= 1 \times 0.25 \times 0.5$$
$$= 0.125 \text{ m}^3$$

Since 1 m³ of water $= 1$ kℓ of water,

$$0.125 \text{ m}^3 = 0.125 \text{ k}\ell, \text{ or } 125 \ \ell \text{ of water}$$

b) Since 1 ℓ has a mass of 1 kg, 125 ℓ has a mass of 125 kg of water.

To convince yourself of the advantages of the metric system, do a similar problem involving the U.S. customary system of measurement, such as Challenge Problems/ Group Activities Exercise 75 at the end of this section.

Temperature

The Celsius scale is used to measure temperatures in the metric system. Figure 5.16 shows a thermometer with the Fahrenheit scale on the left and the Celsius scale on the right.

The Celsius scale was named for Swedish astronomer Anders Celsius (1701–1744), who first devised it in 1742. On the Celsius scale, water freezes at 0°C and boils at 100°C. In the past, the Celsius thermometer was called a "centigrade thermometer." Recall that *centi* means $\frac{1}{100}$, and there are 100 degrees between the freezing point of water and the boiling point of water. Thus, 1°C is $\frac{1}{100}$ of this interval. Table 5.5 gives some common temperatures in both degrees Celsius (°C) and degrees Fahrenheit (°F).

At a temperature of $-40°$ the Celsius and Fahrenheit temperatures are the same. That is, $-40°C = -40°F$. See Exercise 74.

EXAMPLE 3 METRIC TEMPERATURES

Choose the best answer. (Refer to the dual-scale thermometer in Fig. 5.16.)

a) Chicago, Illinois, on New Year's Day might have a temperature of

   i) $-10°C$.   ii) $20°C$.   iii) $45°C$.

°F	°C
210	100
200	
190	90
180	80
170	
160	70
150	
140	60
130	
120	50
110	
100	40
90	30
80	
70	20
60	
50	10
40	
30	0
20	
10	−10
0	−20
−10	

FIGURE 5.16

TABLE 5.5

Celsius Temperature		Fahrenheit Temperature
−18°C	A very cold day	0°F
0°C	Freezing point of water	32°F
10°C	A warm winter day	50°F
20°C	A mild spring day	68°F
30°C	A warm summer day	86°F
37°C	Body temperature	98.6°F
100°C	Boiling point of water	212°F
177°C	Oven temperature for baking	351°F

b) Washington, D.C., on July 4 might have a temperature of

   i) 15°C.   ii) 30°C.   iii) 40°C.

c) The oven temperature for baking a cake might be

   i) 60°C.   ii) 100°C.   iii) 175°C.

SOLUTION

a) A temperature of 20°C is possible if it is a very mild winter, but 45°C is much too hot. The best answer for a normal winter is −10°C.

b) The best estimate is 30°C. A temperature of 15°C is too chilly, and 40°C is too hot for July 4.

c) A cake bakes at temperatures well above boiling, so the only reasonable answer is 175°C.

Comparing the temperature in Table 5.5, we see that the Celsius scale has 100° from the boiling point of water to the freezing point of water and the Fahrenheit scale has 180° from the boiling point of water to the freezing point of water. Therefore, one Celsius degree represents a greater change in temperature than one Fahrenheit degree does. In fact, one Celsius degree is the same as $\frac{180}{100}$, or $\frac{9}{5}$ Fahrenheit degrees. When converting from one system to the other system, use the following formulas.

FROM CELSIUS TO FAHRENHEIT

$$F = \frac{9}{5}C + 32$$

FROM FAHRENHEIT TO CELSIUS

$$C = \frac{5}{9}(F - 32)$$

TECHNOLOGY

IT'S A METRIC WORLD

The United States is the only westernized country not currently using the metric system as its primary system of measurement. The only countries in the world besides the United States not committed to using the metric system are Liberia and Myanmar (although Liberia and Myanmar use it in practice); see Fig. 5.17.

The European Union (EU) adopted a directive that requires all exporters to EU nations to indicate the dimensions of their products in metric units. Currently, U.S. manufacturers who export goods are doing so. Little by little, the United States is using more metric measurements. For example, soft drinks come in liter bottles and prescription drug dosages are given in metric units. Maybe in the not too distant future gasoline will be measured in liters, not gallons, as it is in Canada and Mexico.

FIGURE 5.17

EXAMPLE 4   CONVERT TO °C

A typical setting for home thermostats is 72°F. What is the equivalent temperature on the Celsius thermometer?

SOLUTION We use the formula $C = \frac{5}{9}(F - 32)$ to convert from °F to °C. Substituting $F = 72$ gives

$$C = \frac{5}{9}(72 - 32)$$

$$= \frac{5}{9}(40)$$

$$\approx 22.2$$

Thus, the equivalent temperature of 72°F is about 22.2°C.

EXAMPLE 5   CONVERT TO °F

If the temperature outdoors is 28°C, will you need to wear a sweater if going outdoors?

SOLUTION We use the formula $F = \frac{9}{5}C + 32$ to convert from °C to °F. Substituting $C = 28$ yields

$$F = \frac{9}{5}(28) + 32$$

$$= 50.4 + 32$$

$$= 82.4$$

Since the temperature is about 82.4°F, you will not need to wear a sweater.

EXERCISE SET 5.3 ●●●●●●

• Concept/Writing Exercises

1. What is the basic unit of mass in the metric system?

2. The mass of a nickel is about how many grams?

3. One kilogram is a little more than how many pounds?

4. What unit of mass is used to express the mass of very heavy items?

5. Give an estimate of the average temperature, in degrees Celsius, in Florida in August.

6. Give an estimate of the average temperature, in degrees Celsius, in North Dakota in February.

7. Give an estimate, in degrees Celsius, of what you would consider an ideal outdoor temperature.

8. **a)** Is a person's mass the same in space as on Earth? Explain.

   b) Is a person's weight the same in space as on Earth? Explain.

• Practice the Skills

In Exercises 9–18, indicate the metric unit of measurement that would best express the mass of the following.

9. A woman

10. A dime

11. A pair of eyeglasses

12. A box of cereal

13. A new pencil

14. A sports utility vehicle

15. A refrigerator

16. A mosquito

17. A full-grown whale

18. A calculator

In Exercises 19–24, select the best answer.

19. The mass of a 5 lb bag of flour is about how much?

   a) 2.27 g   **b)** 2.27 kg   **c)** 2.27 dag

20. The mass of a tea bag is about how much?

   a) 4 mg   **b)** 4 kg   **c)** 4 g

21. The mass of a coffee pot filled with coffee is about how much?

   a) 1.4 mg   **b)** 1.4 kg   **c)** 1.4 g

22. The mass of a box of cornflakes is about how much?

   a) 0.45 t   **b)** 0.45 g   **c)** 0.45 kg

23. The mass of a full-grown elephant is about how much?

   a) 2800 g   **b)** 2800 kg   **c)** 2800 dag

24. The mass of a full-size car is about how much?

   a) 1 962 000 hg   **b)** 380 kg   **c)** 1.6 t

In Exercises 25–28, estimate the mass of the item. If a scale with metric measure is available, find the mass.

25. Your body

26. A telephone book

27. A gallon of water

28. A tomato

In Exercises 29–38, choose the best answer. Use Table 5.5 and Fig. 5.16 to help select your answers.

29. Freezing rain is most likely to occur at a temperature of

   a) −25°C.   **b)** 32°C.   **c)** 0°C.

Rochester, New York

30. The thermostat for an air conditioner was set for 80°F. This setting is closest to

   a) 2°C.   **b)** 27°C.   **c)** 57°C.

31. The temperature of the water in a certain lake is 5°C. You could

   a) ice fish.

   b) dress warmly and walk along the lake.

   c) swim in the lake.

32. What might be the temperature at which a refrigerator is set?

   a) 30°C   **b)** 5°C   **c)** 0°C

33. The temperature in Phoenix, Arizona on a summer day might be

   a) 15°C   **b)** 20°C   **c)** 40°C

34. The weather forecast calls for a high of 32°C. You should plan to wear

   a) a down-lined jacket.

   b) a sweater.

   c) a bathing suit.

35. What might be the temperature of an apple pie baking in the oven?

   a) 90°C   **b)** 100°C   **c)** 177°C

36. The temperature of the water in a car's radiator when the car's engine is operating at its normal temperature might be

   a) 70°C.   **b)** 300°C.   **c)** 110°C.

37. The temperature of water in a hot tub might be

   a) 30°C.   **b)** 50°C.   **c)** 40°C.

38. The temperature of the snow in a snowman might be

   a) −15°C   **b)** −5°C   **c)** 5°C

In Exercises 39–52, convert each temperature as indicated. When appropriate, give your answer to the nearest tenth of a degree.

39. 25°C = ____°F   **40.** −5°C = ____°F

41. 92°F = ____°C   **42.** −10°F = ____°C

43. 0°F = ____°C   **44.** 98°F = ____°C

45. 37°C = ____°F   **46.** −4°C = ____°F

47. 13°F = ____°C   **48.** 75°F = ____°C

49. 0°C = ____°F   **50.** 50°C = ____°F

51. −20°F = ____°C   **52.** 425°F = ____°C

In Exercises 53 and 54, use the photo of a seismographic pool in Yellowstone National Park in Wyoming. The pool is heated by volcanic activity under Earth's surface.

53. Convert 165°F to degrees Celsius to verify that it is approximately 74°C.

54. Convert 74°C to degrees Fahrenheit to verify that it is approximately 165°F.

In Exercises 55–60, use the following graph, which shows the daily low and high temperatures, in degrees Celsius, for the week in the Outback in Australia. The week illustrated was unseasonably warm. Determine the following temperatures in degrees Fahrenheit.

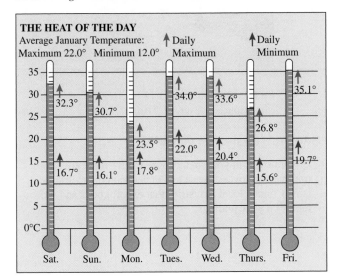

THE HEAT OF THE DAY
Average January Temperature:
Maximum 22.0° Minimum 12.0°

55. The average January maximum temperature

56. The maximum temperature for the week

57. The maximum temperature on Friday

58. The maximum temperature on Saturday

59. The range of temperatures on Monday

60. The range of temperatures on Tuesday

• Problem Solving

The photo shows the cost of popcorn and sabu dhana at a farm market in the country of Fiji. Use the information in the photo to answer Exercises 61 and 62.

61. *Popcorn* Determine the cost, in dollars, of 8.1 kg of popcorn if popcorn cost $2.50 per kg.

62. *Sabu Dhana* Determine the cost, in dollars, of 5.2 kg of sabu dhana if sabu cost $2.60 per kg. (Sabu dhana is a by-product of the tapioca root.)

63. *Salt and Soda* A mixture of 45 g of salt and 29 g of baking soda is poured into 370 mℓ of water. What is the total mass of the mixture in grams?

64. *Jet Fuel* A jet can travel about 1 km on 17 kg of fuel. How many metric tonnes of fuel will the jet use flying nonstop between Baltimore and Los Angeles, a distance of about 4320 km?

65. *A Storage Tank* The dimensions of a storage tank are length 16 m, width 12 m, and height 12 m. If the tank is filled with water, determine

a) the volume of water in the tank in cubic meters.

b) the number of kiloliters of water the tank will hold.

c) the mass of the water in metric tonnes.

66. *A Water Heater* A hot-water heater in the shape of a right circular cylinder has a radius of 50 cm and a height of 150 cm. If the tank is filled with water, determine

a) the volume of water in the tank in cubic meters.

b) the number of liters of water the tank will hold.

c) the mass of the water in kilograms.

67. *Is There a Problem?* A temperature display at a bank flashes the temperature in degrees Fahrenheit and then flashes the temperature in degrees Celsius. If it flashes 78°F, then 20°C, is there a problem with the display? Explain.

68. *Fever or Chills?* Maria's body temperature is 38.2°C. Should she take an aspirin or put on a sweater? Explain.

In Exercises 69–72, convert as indicated.

69. 4.2 kg = ____ t

70. 9.52 t = ____ kg

71. 17.4 t = ____ g

72. 1 460 000 mg = ____ t

• Challenge Problems/Group Activities

73. *Gatorade* Gatorade is poured into a plastic bottle that holds 1.2 ℓ of liquid. The bottle is then placed in a freezer. When the bottle is removed from the freezer, the plastic is cut away, leaving just the frozen Gatorade.

a) What is the approximate mass of the frozen Gatorade in grams?

b) What is the approximate volume of the frozen Gatorade in cubic centimeters?

74. Show that −40°C = −40°F.

In Example 2, we showed how to find the volume and mass of water in a fish tank. Exercise 75 demonstrates how much more complicated solving a similar problem is in the U.S. customary system.

75. *Fish Tank* A fish tank is 1 yd long by 1.5 ft high by 15 in. wide.

a) Determine the volume of water in the fish tank in cubic feet.

b) Determine the weight of the water in pounds. One cubic foot of water weighs about 62.5 lb.

c) If 1 gal of water weighs about 8.3 lb, how many gallons will the tank hold?

• Recreational Mathematics

76. *Balance the Scale* Determine the quantity needed to replace the question mark to make the scale balance. The weight times the distance on both sides of the fulcrum (the triangle) must be the same to make the scale balance.

77. *Interesting Facts* The 2006 *Guinness Book of World Records* provides some interesting facts.

a) The lowest temperature ever recorded in the United States was −62.11°C on January 23, 1971, in Prospect Creek, Alaska. What is this temperature in degrees Fahrenheit?

b) International Falls, Minnesota, has the lowest annual mean (average) temperature in the United States (including Alaska). Its mean annual temperature is about 2.5°C. What is this temperature in degrees Fahrenheit?

c) The highest temperature produced in a laboratory was about 918,000,000°F. What is this temperature in degrees Celsius?

Ice Box Day, International Falls, Minnesota, see Exercise 77(b)

• Internet/Research Activity

78. Do industries in your area export goods? If so, are they training employees to use and understand the metric system? Contact local industries that export goods and write a report on your findings.

SECTION 5.4 • DIMENSIONAL ANALYSIS AND CONVERSIONS TO AND FROM THE METRIC SYSTEM

Can you determine the length, in feet, of the Smart Car?

Pictured here is a Smart Car, commonly driven throughout Europe and soon to be sold in the United States. Some of the specifications of the Smart Car shown are length, 2500 mm; width, 1515 mm; maximum speed, 135 km/hr; gross weight, 990 kg; 0–100 km/hr, 18.3 sec; engine size, 698 cc: and fuel economy, 4.8 ℓ/100 km. Can you change these specifications to U.S. customary system measurements? To determine the Smart Car's specifications, you will need to know how to convert measurements from the metric system to the U.S. customary system. We will explain how to do so in this section.

You may sometimes need to change units of measurement in the metric system to equivalent units in the U.S. customary system. To do so, use *dimensional analysis*, which is a

John Quincy Adams, 6th president of
the United States

We all realize how important the
abilities to read and to write are.
Yet do we realize how important
an understanding of measurements is in our daily lives? As John
Quincy Adams wrote in his report
to the U.S. Congress in 1821:
"Weights and measures may be
ranked among the necessities of
life to every individual of human
society. They enter into the economical arrangements and daily
concerns of every family. They are
necessary to every occupation of
human industry."

procedure used to convert from one unit of measurement to a different unit of measurement. To perform dimensional analysis, you must first understand what is meant by a unit
fraction. A *unit fraction* is any fraction in which the numerator and denominator contain
different units and the value of the fraction is 1. From Table 5.6, we can obtain many unit
fractions involving U.S. customary units.

TABLE 5.6 U.S. CUSTOMARY UNITS
1 foot = 12 inches
1 yard = 3 feet
1 mile = 5280 feet
1 pound = 16 ounces
1 ton = 2000 pounds
1 cup (liquid) = 8 fluid ounces
1 pint = 2 cups
1 quart = 2 pints
1 gallon = 4 quarts
1 minute = 60 seconds
1 hour = 60 minutes
1 day = 24 hours
1 year = 365 days

Examples of Unit Fractions

$$\frac{12 \text{ in.}}{1 \text{ ft}} \qquad \frac{1 \text{ ft}}{12 \text{ in.}} \qquad \frac{16 \text{ oz}}{1 \text{ lb}} \qquad \frac{1 \text{ lb}}{16 \text{ oz}} \qquad \frac{60 \text{ min}}{1 \text{ hr}} \qquad \frac{1 \text{ hr}}{60 \text{ min}}$$

In each of these examples, the numerator equals the denominator, so the value of the fraction is 1.

To convert an expression from one unit of measurement to a different unit, multiply the
given expression by the unit fraction (or fractions) that will result in the answer having the
units you are seeking. When two fractions are being multiplied and the same unit appears
in the numerator of one fraction and in the denominator of the other fraction, that common
unit may be divided out and eliminated. For example, suppose we want to convert 30
inches to feet. We consider the following:

$$30 \text{ in.} = ? \text{ ft}$$

Since inches are given, we will need to eliminate them. Thus, inches will need to appear in
the denominator of the unit fraction. We need to convert to feet, so feet will need to appear
in the numerator of the unit fraction. If we multiply a quantity in inches by a unit fraction
containing feet/inches, the inches will divide out as follows, leaving feet. In the following
illustration we have omitted the numbers in the unit fraction so we can concentrate on
the units.

$$(\cancel{\text{in.}})\left(\frac{\text{ft}}{\cancel{\text{in.}}}\right) = \text{ft}$$

Thus, to convert 30 inches to feet, we do the following.

$$30 \text{ in.} = (30 \, \cancel{\text{in.}})\left(\frac{1 \text{ ft}}{12 \, \cancel{\text{in.}}}\right) = \frac{30}{12}\text{ft} = 2.5 \text{ ft}$$

In Examples 1 through 3, we will give examples that do not involve the metric system.
After that, we will use dimensional analysis to make conversions to and from the metric
system.

EXAMPLE 1   USING DIMENSIONAL ANALYSIS

A container contains 26 ounces of salt. Convert 26 ounces to pounds.

SOLUTION   One pound is 16 ounces. Therefore, we write

$$26 \text{ oz} = (26 \text{ oz})\left(\frac{1 \text{ lb}}{16 \text{ oz}}\right) = \frac{26}{16}\text{lb} = 1.625 \text{ lb}$$

Thus, 26 oz equals 1.625 lb.

EXAMPLE 2   MEXICAN PESOS

On November 4, 2006, $1 U.S. could be exchanged for about 10.87 Mexican pesos. What was the amount in U.S. dollars of 2500 pesos?

SOLUTION

$$2500 \text{ pesos} = 2500 \text{ pesos}\left(\frac{\$1.00}{10.87 \text{ pesos}}\right) = \$\frac{2500}{10.87} \approx \$229.99$$

Thus, 2500 pesos had a value of about $229.99.

If more than one unit needs to be changed, more than one multiplication may be needed, as illustrated in Example 3.

EXAMPLE 3   USING SEVERAL UNIT FRACTIONS

Convert 60 miles per hour to feet per second.

SOLUTION   Let's consider the units given and where we want to end up. We are given $\frac{\text{mi}}{\text{hr}}$ and wish to end with $\frac{\text{ft}}{\text{sec}}$. Thus, we need to change miles into feet and hours into seconds. Because two units need to be changed, we will need to multiply the given quantity by two unit fractions, one for each conversion. First we show how to convert the units of measurement from miles per hour to feet per second:

$$\left(\frac{\text{mi}}{\text{hr}}\right)\left(\frac{\text{ft}}{\text{mi}}\right)\left(\frac{\text{hr}}{\text{sec}}\right) \qquad \text{gives an answer in} \qquad \frac{\text{ft}}{\text{sec}}$$

Now we multiply the given quantity by the appropriate unit fractions to obtain the answer:

$$60\frac{\text{mi}}{\text{hr}} = \left(60\frac{\text{mi}}{\text{hr}}\right)\left(\frac{5280 \text{ ft}}{1 \text{ mi}}\right)\left(\frac{1 \text{ hr}}{3600 \text{ sec}}\right) = \frac{(60)(5280)}{(1)(3600)}\frac{\text{ft}}{\text{sec}}$$

$$= 88\frac{\text{ft}}{\text{sec}}$$

Note that $\left(60\dfrac{\text{mi}}{\text{hr}}\right)\left(\dfrac{1 \text{ hr}}{3600 \text{ sec}}\right)\left(\dfrac{5280 \text{ ft}}{1 \text{ mi}}\right)$ will give the same answer.

Conversions to and from the Metric System

Now we will apply dimensional analysis to the metric system.

Table 5.7 is used in making conversions to and from the metric system. The values given in Table 5.7 on page 275 are often approximations. A more exact table of conversion factors may be found in many science books at your college's library or on the Internet. However, we can use this table to obtain many unit fractions.

Mexican currency

TABLE 5.7 CONVERSIONS TABLE

Length

1 inch (in.) = 2.54 centimeters (cm)
1 foot (ft) = 30   centimeters (cm)
1 yard (yd) = 0.9   meter (m)
1 mile (mi) = 1.6   kilometers (km)

Area

1 square inch (in.^{2}) = 6.5   square centimeters (cm^2)
1 square foot (ft^2) = 0.09 square meter (m^2)
1 square yard (yd^2) = 0.8   square meter (m^2)
1 square mile (mi^2) = 2.6   square kilometers (km^2)
1 acre   = 0.4   hectare (ha)

Volume

1 teaspoon (tsp)   =   5 milliliters (mℓ)
1 tablespoon (tbsp) =   15 milliliters (mℓ)
1 fluid ounce (fl oz) =   30 milliliters (mℓ)
1 cup (c)   = 0.24 liter (ℓ)
1 pint (pt)   = 0.47 liter (ℓ)
1 quart (qt)   = 0.95 liter (ℓ)
1 gallon (gal)   = 3.8 liters (ℓ)
1 cubic foot (ft^3) = 0.03 cubic meter (m^3)
1 cubic yard (yd^3) = 0.76 cubic meter (m^3)

Weight (Mass)

1 ounce (oz) =   28 grams (g)
1 pound (lb) = 0.45 kilogram (kg)
1 ton (T)   = 0.9 tonne (t)

Table 5.7 shows that 1 in. = 2.54 cm. From this equality, we can write the two unit fractions

$$\frac{1 \text{ in.}}{2.54 \text{ cm}} \quad \text{or} \quad \frac{2.54 \text{ cm}}{1 \text{ in.}}$$

Examples of other unit fractions from Table 5.7 are

$$\frac{1 \text{ yd}}{0.9 \text{ m}}, \quad \frac{0.9 \text{ m}}{1 \text{ yd}}, \quad \frac{1 \text{ gal}}{3.8 \ \ell}, \quad \frac{3.8 \ \ell}{1 \text{ gal}}, \quad \frac{1 \text{ lb}}{0.45 \text{ kg}}, \quad \text{and} \quad \frac{0.45 \text{ kg}}{1 \text{ lb}}$$

To change from a metric unit to a customary unit or vice versa, multiply the given quantity by the unit fraction whose product will result in the units you are seeking. For example, to convert 5 in. to centimeters, multiply 5 in. by a unit fraction with centimeters in the numerator and inches in the denominator.

$$5 \text{ in.} = (5 \text{ in.})\left(\frac{2.54 \text{ cm}}{1 \text{ in.}}\right)$$
$$= 5(2.54) \text{ cm}$$
$$= 12.7 \text{ cm}$$

EXAMPLE 4   VOLUME AND LENGTH CONVERSIONS

a) A recipe requires $3\frac{1}{2}$ cups of chicken broth. How many liters does this amount equal?
b) A man measures 1.86 m (see photo). What is his height in feet?

See Example 4(b)

SOLUTION

a) In Table 5.7, under the heading of volume, we see that 1 cup = 0.24 ℓ. Thus, the unit fractions involving cups and liters are

$$\frac{1 \text{ cup}}{0.24 \text{ } \ell} \quad \text{or} \quad \frac{0.24 \text{ } \ell}{1 \text{ cup}}$$

We need to convert from cups to liters. Since $3\frac{1}{2}$ is 3.5 in decimal form, we write

$$3.5 \text{ cups} = 3.5 \text{ cups}\left(\frac{0.24 \text{ } \ell}{1 \text{ cup}}\right) = (3.5)(0.24) \text{ } \ell = 0.84 \text{ } \ell$$

b) In Table 5.7, under the heading of length, we see that there is no conversion given from meters to feet. There are a number of ways this example could be worked. One method is to convert meters to yards and then convert yards to feet. The procedure is shown below.

$$1.86 \text{ m} = (1.86 \text{ m})\left(\frac{1 \text{ yd}}{0.9 \text{ m}}\right)\left(\frac{3 \text{ ft}}{1 \text{ yd}}\right)$$
$$= \frac{(1.86)(3)}{0.9} \text{ ft}$$
$$= 6.2 \text{ ft}$$

Thus, the man is 6.2 ft.

Land for sale in Fiji, measured in hectares, see Example 5

EXAMPLE 5   AREA CONVERSION

The photo shows an area of 31.46 hectares for sale. Find the area in acres.

SOLUTION From Table 5.7, we determine that 1 acre = 0.4 ha. Thus,

$$31.46 \text{ ha} = (31.46 \text{ ha})\left(\frac{1 \text{ acre}}{0.4 \text{ ha}}\right) = \frac{31.46}{0.4} \text{ acres} = 78.65 \text{ acres}$$

EXAMPLE 6   WEIGHT (MASS) CONVERSION

The photo shows that peppers (in New Zealand) cost $3.75 per kilogram. Determine the cost per pound for the peppers.

SOLUTION First we will determine the number of pounds that is equivalent to 1 kilogram. From Table 5.7, we obtain the unit fraction

$$\frac{0.45 \text{ kg}}{1 \text{ lb}}$$

Next, we use this unit fraction to determine the pepper's cost per pound.

$$\frac{\$3.75}{1 \text{ kg}} = \left(\frac{\$3.75}{1 \text{ kg}}\right)\left(\frac{0.45 \text{ kg}}{1 \text{ lb}}\right)$$
$$= \$3.75(0.45) \text{ per pound}$$
$$\approx \$1.69 \text{ per pound}$$

Therefore, the peppers cost about $1.69 per pound.

See Example 6

EXAMPLE 7   ADMINISTERING A MEDICINE

A nurse must administer 4 cc of codeine elixir to a patient.

a) How many milliliters of the drug will be administered?

b) How many ounces is this dosage equivalent to?

SOLUTION

a) Since 1 cc = 1 mℓ, the nurse will administer 4 mℓ of the drug.

b) Since 1 fl oz = 30 mℓ,

$$4 \text{ m}\ell = (4 \text{ m}\ell)\left(\frac{1 \text{ fl oz}}{30 \text{ m}\ell}\right) = \frac{4}{30}\text{fl oz} \approx 0.13 \text{ fl oz}$$

Suppose we want to convert 150 millimeters to inches. Table 5.7 does not have a conversion factor from millimeters to inches, but it does have one for inches to centimeters. Because 1 inch = 2.54 centimeters and 1 centimeter = 10 millimeters, we can reason that 1 inch = 25.4 millimeters. Therefore, unit fractions we may use are as follows.

$$\frac{1 \text{ in.}}{25.4 \text{ mm}} \quad \text{or} \quad \frac{25.4 \text{ mm}}{1 \text{ in.}}$$

We can solve the problem as follows.

$$150 \text{ mm} = (150 \text{ mm})\left(\frac{1 \text{ in.}}{25.4 \text{ mm}}\right) = \frac{150}{25.4}\text{in.}$$
$$\approx 5.91 \text{ in.}$$

If we wish, we can use dimensional analysis using two unit fractions to make the conversion. The procedure follows:

$$150 \text{ mm} = (150 \text{ mm})\left(\frac{1 \text{ cm}}{10 \text{ mm}}\right)\left(\frac{1 \text{ in.}}{2.54 \text{ cm}}\right) = \frac{150}{(10)(2.54)}\text{in.}$$
$$\approx 5.91 \text{ in.}$$

EXAMPLE 8   SOUTHERNMOST POINT

The photo shows that the southernmost point in the continental United States, in Key West, Florida, is 90 miles away from Cuba. Determine this distance in kilometers.

SOLUTION   We need to convert miles to kilometers. From Table 5.7, we find the unit fractions.

$$\frac{1 \text{ mi}}{1.6 \text{ km}} \quad \text{or} \quad \frac{1.6 \text{ km}}{1 \text{ mi}}$$

Since we are converting 90 miles to kilometers, the miles in the unit fraction must go in the denominator. Thus, we use the unit fraction 1.6 km/1 mi.

$$90 \text{ mi} = 90 \text{ mi}\left(\frac{1.6 \text{ km}}{1 \text{ mi}}\right) = 144 \text{ km}$$

Therefore, 90 miles is equal to 144 kilometers.

Key West, Florida

EXAMPLE 9   UNDERSTANDING THE LABEL

The label on a bottle of Vicks Formula 44D Cough Syrup indicates that the active ingredient is dextromethorphan hydrobromide and that 5 mℓ (or 1 teaspoon) contains 10 mg of this ingredient. If the recommended dosage for adults is 3 teaspoons, determine the following.

a) How many milliliters of cough medicine should be taken?

b) How many milligrams of the active ingredient should be taken?

c) If the bottle contains 8 fluid ounces of medicine, how many milligrams of the active ingredient are in the bottle?

SOLUTION

a) Since each teaspoon contains 5 mℓ and 3 teaspoons should be taken, 15 mℓ of the cough medicine should be taken.

$$3 \text{ tsp} = (3 \text{ tsp})\left(\frac{5 \text{ m}\ell}{1 \text{ tsp}}\right) = 15 \text{ m}\ell$$

b) Since each teaspoon contains 10 mg of the active ingredient, 30 mg of the active ingredient should be taken.

$$3 \text{ tsp} = (3 \text{ tsp})\left(\frac{10 \text{ mg}}{1 \text{ tsp}}\right) = 30 \text{ mg}$$

c) Table 5.7 shows that each fluid ounce contains 30 mℓ. Since each 5 mℓ contains 10 mg of the active ingredient, we can work the problem as follows.

$$8 \text{ fl oz} = (8 \text{ fl oz})\left(\frac{30 \text{ m}\ell}{1 \text{ fl oz}}\right)\left(\frac{10 \text{ mg}}{5 \text{ m}\ell}\right) = \frac{8(30)(10)}{5} \text{ mg} = 480 \text{ mg}$$

Therefore, there are 480 mg (or 0.48 g) of the active ingredient in the bottle of cough syrup.

EXAMPLE 10   DETERMINING DOSAGE BY WEIGHT

Drug dosage is often administered according to a patient's weight. For example, 30 mg of the drug vancomicin is to be given for each kilogram of a person's weight. If Martha Greene, who weighs 136 lb, is to be given the drug, what dosage should she be given?

SOLUTION   First we need to convert Martha's weight into kilograms. From Table 5.7, we see that 1 lb = 0.45 kg. We obtain our unit fraction from this information. Then we need to determine the number of milligrams of the drug for Martha's weight in kilograms. To do so, write the given ratio of 30 mg of the drug for each kilogram as $\frac{30 \text{ mg}}{1 \text{ kg}}$. Note that this ratio is not a unit fraction since the numerator and denominator are not equivalent. The answer may be found as follows.

$$136 \text{ lb} = (136 \text{ lb})\left(\frac{0.45 \text{ kg}}{1 \text{ lb}}\right)\left(\frac{30 \text{ mg}}{1 \text{ kg}}\right) = (136)(0.45)(30) \text{ mg} = 1836 \text{ mg}$$

Thus, 1836 mg, or 1.836 g, of the drug should be given.

EXERCISE SET 5.4 ●●●●●● ●

• Concept/Writing Exercises

1. What is dimensional analysis?

2. What is a unit fraction?

3. Give a unit fraction that relates seconds and minutes. Explain how you determined the unit fraction.

4. Give a unit fraction that relates feet and yards. Explain how you determined the unit fraction.

5. When converting from kilograms to pounds, which unit fraction would you use? Explain.

$$\frac{1 \text{ lb}}{0.45 \text{ kg}} \quad \text{or} \quad \frac{0.45 \text{ kg}}{1 \text{ lb}}$$

6. When converting from centimeters to feet, which unit fraction would you use? Explain.

$$\frac{1 \text{ ft}}{30 \text{ cm}} \quad \text{or} \quad \frac{30 \text{ cm}}{1 \text{ ft}}$$

7. When converting from gallons to liters, which unit fraction would you use? Explain.

$$\frac{1 \text{ gal}}{3.8 \ \ell} \quad \text{or} \quad \frac{3.8 \ \ell}{1 \text{ gal}}$$

8. When converting from square yards to square meters, which unit fraction would you use? Explain.

$$\frac{1 \text{ yd}^2}{0.8 \text{ m}^2} \quad \text{or} \quad \frac{0.8 \text{ m}^2}{1 \text{ yd}^2}$$

• Practice the Skills

In Exercises 9–24, convert the quantity to the indicated units. When appropriate, give your answer to the nearest hundredth.

9. 62 in. to centimeters

10. 9 lb to kilograms

11. 4.2 ft to meters

12. 427 g to ounces

13. 120 kg to pounds

14. 20 yd² to square meters

15. 39 mi to kilometers

16. 765 mm to inches

17. 675 ha to acres

18. 192 oz to grams

19. 15.6 ℓ to pints

20. 4 T to tonnes

21. 3.8 km² to square miles

22. 25.6 mℓ to fluid ounces

23. 120 lb to kilograms

24. 6.2 acres to hectares

In Exercises 25–32, replace the measurement(s) indicated in blue with an equivalent metric measure(s). For example, a foot could be replaced with 30 cm.

25. More bounce to the *ounce*.

26. An *ounce* of prevention is worth a *pound* of cure.

27. He demanded his *pound* of flesh.

28. *Five foot two* and eyes of blue.

29. Give him an *inch* and he'll take a *mile*.

30. A miss is as good as a *mile*.

31. The longest *yard*.

32. First down and *10 yards* to go.

In Exercises 33–36, use the part of the scorecard that shows the distance in meters for the first four holes of the Mill-brook Resort Golf Course in Queenstown, New Zealand. Determine the distances indicated.

HOLE	BLACK Tees	BLUE Tees	HANDICAP	PAR			WHITE Tees	RED Tees
1	505	505	3	5			466	414
2	185	175	15	3			137	91
3	366	357	11	4			344	287
4	396	376	7	4			376	303

33. Hole 1, black tees, in yards

34. Hole 2, blue tees, in yards

35. Hole 3, white tees, in feet

36. Hole 4, red tees, in feet

• Problem Solving

37. *Speed Limit* The photo shows that the speed limit is 60 kph. Determine the speed in miles per hour.

38. *How Far?* Carol Ann Harle's new car traveled 105 mi on 5 gal of gasoline. How many kilometers can Carol Ann's car travel with the same amount of gasoline?

39. *Buying Carpet* Victoria Montoya is buying outdoor carpet for her lanai, which is 6 yd by 9 yd. The carpeting is sold in square meters. How many square meters of carpeting will she need?

40. *Cincinnati to Columbus* The distance from Cincinnati, Ohio, to Columbus, Ohio, is about 110 mi. What is the distance in kilometers?

41. *The QEW* Part of the Queen Elizabeth Way in Canada has a speed limit of 80 kph. What is the speed in miles per hour?

42. *Milliliters in a Glass* A glass holds 8 fl oz. How many milliliters will it hold?

43. *Poison Dart Frog* A full-grown strawberry poison dart frog (see photo) has a weight of about 6 g. What is its weight in ounces?

44. *Swimming Pool* A swimming pool holds 12,500 gal of water. What is this volume in kiloliters?

45. *Building a Basement* A basement is to be 50 ft long, 30 ft wide, and 8 ft high. How much dirt will have to be removed when this basement is built? Answer in cubic meters.

46. *Area of Yosemite National Park* Yosemite National Park has an area of 1189 mi^2. What is its area in square kilometers?

47. *Cost of Rice* If rice costs $1.10 per kilogram, determine the cost of 1 pound of rice.

48. *Weight Restriction* The weight restriction on a road in France is 3.5 t.

a) How many tons does this weight equal?

b) How many pounds?

49. *Capacity of a Tank Truck* A tank truck holds 34.5 kℓ of gasoline. How many gallons does it hold?

50. *Cost per Gram* A 0.25 oz bottle of Chanel perfume costs $80. What is the cost per gram?

51. *Car's Engine* A specific car's engine has a capacity of 5.7 ℓ of oil. How many quarts of oil does the engine have?

52. *A Precious Stone* One gram is the same as 5 carats. David Erich's new ring contains a precious stone that is $\frac{1}{8}$ carat. Find the weight of the stone in grams.

53. *Death Valley Elevation* The lowest elevation in the United States is -282 ft at Badwater in Death Valley, California. Determine this elevation in

a) centimeters.

b) meters.

54. *Sign in Costa Rica* Using the sign in the photo belowt, determine the distance to Lecheria #2 in

a) kilometers.

b) feet.

55. *Square Meters to Square Feet* One meter is about 3.3 ft. Use this information to determine

a) the equivalent of one square meter in square feet.

b) the equivalent of one cubic meter in cubic feet.

56. *Acres to Hectares* One acre is about 0.4 hectare.

a) Use this information to determine the equivalent of 15.3 acres in hectares.

b) If 1 hectare is 10 000 m^2, determine the area of the 15.3 acres in square meters.

57. *Dosage for a Child* The recommended dosage of the drug codeine for pediatric patients is 1 mg per kilogram of a child's weight. What dosage of codeine should be given to April Adam, who weighs 56 lb?

58. *Dosage for a Man* For each kilogram of a person's weight, 1.5 mg of the antibiotic drug gentamicin is to be administered. If Ron Gigliotti weighs 170 lb, how much of the drug should he receive?

59. *Ampicillin* The recommended dosage of the drug ampicillin for pediatric patients is 200 mg per kilogram of a patient's weight. If Janine Baker weighs 76 lb, how much ampicillin should she receive?

60. *Medicine for a Dog* For each kilogram of weight of a dog, 5 mg of the drug bretylium is to be given. If Blaster, an Irish setter, weighs 82 lb, how much of the drug should be given?

61. *Active Ingredients* The label on the bottle of Triaminic expectorant indicates that each teaspoon (5 mℓ) contains 12.5 mg of the active ingredient phenylpropanolamine hydrochloride.

a) Determine the amount of the active ingredient in the recommended adult dosage of 2 teaspoons.

b) Determine the quantity of the active ingredient in a 12 oz bottle.

62. *Stomach Ache Remedy* The label on the bottle of Maximum Strength Pepto-Bismol indicates that each tablespoon contains 236 mg of the active ingredient bismuth subsalicyate.

a) Determine the amount of the active ingredient in the recommended dosage of 2 tablespoons.

b) If the bottle contains 8 fl oz, determine the quantity of the active ingredient in the bottle.

63. *Disney Magic* The Disney Magic Cruise Ship is 964 feet long, has a weight of 85,000 tons, and can travel 28 mph.

a) Determine the length of the ship in meters.

b) Determine the weight in tonnes.

c) Determine the speed in kilometers per hour.

64. *Making Cookies* Change all the measurements in the cookie recipe to metric units. Do not forget pan size, temperature, and size of cookies.

Magic Cookie Bar

$\frac{1}{2}$ c graham cracker crumbs
12 oz nuts
8 oz chocolate pieces
$1\frac{1}{3}$ c flaked coconut
$1\frac{1}{3}$ c condensed milk

Coat the bottom of a 9 in. × 13 in. pan with melted margarine. Add rest of ingredients one by one: crumbs, nuts, chocolate, and coconut. Pour condensed milk over all. Bake at 350°F for 25 minutes. Allow to cool 15 minutes before cutting. Makes about two dozen $1\frac{1}{2}$ in. by 3 in. bars.

65. *Peppers* The photo on the top right shows that in Rome, Italy, peppers cost 2 euros (€) per kilogram.

a) Determine the cost per pound, in euros, for the peppers.

b) If 1 € can be converted to $1.30 U.S., determine the cost, in U.S. dollars, of 1 pound of peppers.

See Exercise 65

66. *Curry* The photo shows Indian curry for sale at a street market in Albi, France.

a) Indian curry cost 7 € per 100 grams. Determine the price, in euros, of 1 kg of curry.

b) Determine the cost in euros of 1 pound of curry.

c) If 1 € can be converted to $1.30 U.S., determine the cost, in U.S. dollars, of 1 pound of curry.

• Challenge Problems/Group Activities

67. *Nursing Question* The following question was selected from a nursing exam. Can you answer it?

In caring for a patient after delivery, you are to give 0.2 mg Ergotrate Maleate. The ampule is labeled $\frac{1}{300}$ grain/mℓ. How much would you draw and give? (60 mg = 1 grain)

a) 15 cc   b) 1.0 cc   c) 0.5 cc   d) 0.01 cc

68. *How Much Beef* Paul Gosse is planning a picnic and plans on purchasing 0.18 kg of ground beef for each 100 lb of weight of guests who will be in attendance. If he expects 15 people whose average weight is 130 lb, how many pounds of beef should he purchase?

69. *An Auto Engine* The displacement of automobile engines is measured in liters. A 2007 Ford Explorer has a 4.0 ℓ engine.

a) Determine the displacement of the engine in cubic centimeters.

b) Determine the displacement of the engine in cubic inches.

• **Recreational Mathematics**

In Exercises 70–75, answer the question, What metric unit am I?

70. I am a length greater than a yard, but less than a kitchen tabletop.

71. I am a weight greater than a calculator, but less than a large bottle of ketchup.

72. I am an area greater than an acre, but less than a square kilometer.

73. I am a liquid volume greater than a quart, but less than a gallon.

74. I am a weight greater than a ton, but less than a full-grown elephant.

75. I am a length greater than an inch, but less than a yard.

In Exercises 76–85, try to solve the puzzle. What is

76. 1 millionth of a mouthwash?

77. 2000 pounds of Chinese soup?

78. 448 grams of cake?

79. 1000 aches?

80. 1 million bicycles?

81. 1 million phones?

82. 10 cards?

83. 2000 mockingbirds?

84. 1 millionth of a fish?

85. 10 rations?

●●●●●● CHAPTER SUMMARY, REVIEW, AND TEST

● SUMMARY   DEFINITIONS AND CONCEPTS

Important Facts
Metric Units

Prefix	Symbol	Meaning
kilo	k	$1000 \times$ base unit
hecto	h	$100 \times$ base unit
deka	da	$10 \times$ base unit
—	—	base unit
deci	d	$\frac{1}{10}$ of base unit
centi	c	$\frac{1}{100}$ of base unit
milli	m	$\frac{1}{1000}$ of base unit

Water

Volume in Cubic Units		Volume in Liters		Mass of Water
1 cm^3	=	1 mℓ	=	1g
1 dm^3	=	1 ℓ	=	1 kg
1 m^3	=	1 kℓ	=	1 t (1000 kg)

Temperature

$$^\circ C = \frac{5}{9}(^\circ F - 32)$$

$$^\circ F = \frac{9}{5}{}^\circ C + 32$$

REVIEW EXERCISES

5.1

In Exercises 1–6, indicate the meaning of the prefix.

1. Centi	**2.** Kilo	**3.** Milli
4. Hecto	**5.** Deka	**6.** Deci

In Exercises 7–12, change the given quantity to that indicated.

7. 40 mg to grams

8. 3.2 ℓ to centiliters

9. 0.0016 cm to millimeters

10. 1 000 000 mg to kilograms

11. 4.62 kℓ to liters

12. 192.6 dag to decigrams

In Exercises 13 and 14, arrange the quantities from smallest to largest.

13. 2.67 kℓ, 3000 mℓ, 14 630 cℓ

14. 0.047 km, 4700 m, 47 000 cm

5.2, 5.3

In Exercises 15–24, indicate the metric unit of measurement that would best express the following.

15. The diameter of a pizza

16. The mass of a cellular telephone

17. The temperature of the sun's surface

18. The diameter of a quarter

19. The area of a room of a house

20. The volume of a glass of milk

21. The length of an ant

22. The mass of a car

23. The distance from Miami, Florida, to Los Angeles, California

24. The height a dolphin can jump

In Exercises 25 and 26, (a) first estimate the following in metric units and then (b) measure with a metric ruler. Record your results.

25. Your height

26. The length of a new pencil

In Exercises 27–32, select the best answer.

27. The length of the distance between New York City and Boston, Massachusetts, is about

   a) 3100 m.   **b)** 3100 km.   **c)** 310 km.

28. The mass of a full-grown border collie is about

   a) 600 g.   **b)** 20 kg.   **c)** 100 kg.

29. The volume of a gallon of gasoline is about

   a) 0.1 kℓ.   **b)** 0.5 ℓ.   **c)** 4 ℓ.

30. The area of a large vegetable garden in a person's yard may be

   a) 200 m².   **b)** 0.5 ha.   **c)** 0.02 km².

31. The temperature on a hot summer day in Georgia may be

   a) 34°C.   **b)** 55°C.   **c)** 25°C.

32. The height of a giant sequoia tree is about

   a) 300 m.   **b)** 3000 cm.   **c)** 0.3 m.

33. Convert 3600 kg to tonnes.

34. Convert 4.3 t to grams.

35. The temperature on the thermostat shown is 24°C. What is the Fahrenheit temperature?

36. If the room temperature is 68°F, what is the Celsius temperature?

37. If your outdoor thermometer shows a temperature of −6°F, what is the Celsius temperature?

38. If Lynn Colgin's body temperature is 39°C, what is her Fahrenheit temperature?

39. Measure, in centimeters, each of the line segments, then compute the area of the figure.

40. Measure, in centimeters, the radius of the circle, then compute the area of the circle.

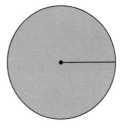

41. a) *A Swimming Pool's Volume* What is the volume of water in a full rectangular swimming pool that is 10 m long and 4 m wide and has an average depth of 2 m? Answer in cubic meters.

b) What is the mass of the water in kilograms?

42. *Computer Monitor* A rectangular computer monitor's screen measures 33.7 cm by 26.7 cm. Determine the area in

a) square centimeters.

b) square meters.

43. *Volume of a Fish Tank* A small fish tank measures 80 cm long, 40 cm wide, and 30 cm high.

a) What is its volume in cubic centimeters?

b) What is its volume in cubic meters?

c) How many milliliters of water will the tank hold?

d) How many kiloliters of water will the tank hold?

44. A square kilometer is a square with length and width both 1 km. How many times larger is a square kilometer than a square dekameter?

5.4

In Exercises 45–58, change the given quantity to the indicated quantity. When appropriate, round answers to the nearest hundredth.

45. 25 cm = _____ in.

46. 105 kg = _____ lb

47. 83 yd = _____ m

48. 100 m = _____ yd

49. 45 mph = _____ kph

50. 60 ℓ = _____ qt

51. 20 gal = _____ ℓ

52. 60 m^3 = _____ yd^3

53. 83 cm^2 = _____ in.^{2}

54. 4 qt = _____ ℓ

55. 15 yd^3 = _____ m^3

56. 62 mi = _____ km

57. 27 cm = _____ ft

58. $3\frac{1}{4}$ in. = _____ mm

59. *Building a Chimney* Anne Kelly bought 700 bricks to build a chimney. Each brick has a mass of 1.5 kg.

a) What is the total mass of the bricks in kilograms?

b) What is the total weight of the bricks in pounds?

60. *Carpeting a Room* Patricia Burgess is buying new carpet for her family room. The room is 15 ft wide and 24 ft long. The carpeting is sold only in square meters. How many square meters of carpeting will she need? Round your answer to the nearest tenth of a square meter.

61. *Milk Tank* A cylindrical milk tank can store 50,000 gal of milk.

a) Determine the volume in kiloliters.

b) Estimate the weight of the milk in kilograms. Assume that milk has the same weight as water.

62. *The Speed Limit* The speed limit on a certain road is 65 mph. What is the speed limit in

a) kilometers per hour?

b) meters per hour?

63. *A Water Tank* A rectangular tank used to test leaks in tires is 90 cm long by 70 cm wide by 40 cm deep.

a) Determine the number of liters of water the tank holds.

b) What is the mass of the water in kilograms?

64. *Oranges* If the cost of oranges is $3.50 per kilogram, determine the cost of 1 lb of oranges.

●●●●●●● CHAPTER 5 TEST

1. Change 497 cℓ to daℓ.

2. Change 273 hm to cm.

3. How many times greater is a kilometer than a dekameter?

4. *Jogging* A high school track is an oval that measures 400 m around. If Dave Camp jogs around the track six times, how many kilometers has he gone?

In Exercises 5–9, choose the best answer.

5. The length of this page is about

   a) 10 cm.

   b) 25 cm.

   c) 60 cm.

6. The surface area of the top of a kitchen table is about

   a) 2 m^2.

   b) 200 cm^2.

   c) 2000 cm^2.

7. The amount of gasoline that an automobile's gas tank can hold is about

   a) 200 ℓ.

   b) 20 ℓ.

   c) 75 ℓ.

8. The mass of a cell phone is about

   a) 0.1 t.

   b) 2 kg.

   c) 150 g.

9. The outside temperature on a snowy day is about

   a) 18°C.

   b) −2°C.

   c) −40°C.

10. How many times greater is a square meter than a square centimeter?

11. How many times greater is a cubic meter than a cubic millimeter?

12. Convert 225 oz. to grams.

13. *Distance* The photo of the sign shows distances, in kilometers, from Positano, Italy, to other nearby Italian cities. How far, in miles, is Salerno from the sign?

14. Change −15°F to degrees Celsius.

15. Change 20°C to degrees Fahrenheit.

16. *Elevator* A sign in an elevator in Nice, France, indicates that its maximum capacity is 4 persons or 300 kg. Determine the maximum capacity in

   a) grams.

   b) pounds.

17. *At the Aquarium* A fish tank at an aquarium is 20 m long by 20 m wide by 8 m deep.

   a) Determine the volume of the tank in cubic meters.

   b) Determine the number of liters of water the tank holds.

   c) Determine the weight of the water in kilograms.

18. *Cost of Paint* The first coat of paint for the outside walls of a building requires 1 ℓ of paint for each 10 m^2 of wall surface. The second coat requires 1 ℓ for every 15 m^2. If the paint costs $3.50 per liter, what will be the cost of two coats of paint for the four outside walls of a building 20 m long, 15 m wide, and 6 m high?

●●●●●●● GROUP PROJECTS

HEALTH AND MEDICINE

Throughout this chapter, we have shown the importance of the metric system in the medical professions. The following two questions involve applications of the metric system to medicine.

1. a) Twenty milligrams of the drug lincomycin is to be given for each kilogram of a person's weight. The drug is to be mixed with 250 cc of a normal saline solution, and the mixture is to be administered intravenously over a 1 hr period. Clyde Dexter, who weighs 196 lb, is to be given the drug. Determine the dosage of the drug he will be given.

   b) At what rate per minute should the 250 cc solution be administered?

2. a) At a pharmacy, a parent asks a pharmacist why her child needs such a small dosage of a certain medicine. The pharmacist explains that a general formula may be used to estimate a child's dosage of certain medicines. The formula is

$$\text{Child's dose*} = \frac{\left(\begin{array}{c}\text{child's weight} \\ \text{in kilograms}\end{array}\right)}{67.5 \text{ kg}} \times \text{adult dose}$$

   What is the amount of medicine you would give a 60 lb child if the adult dosage of the medicine is 70 mg?

   b) At what weight, in pounds, would the child receive an adult dose?

TRAVELING TO OTHER COUNTRIES

3. Dale Pollinger is a buyer at General Motors and travels frequently on business to foreign countries. He always plans ahead and does his holiday shopping overseas, where he can purchase items not easily found in the United States.

   a) On a trip to Tokyo, he decides to buy a kimono for his sister, Kathy. To determine the length of a kimono, one measures, in centimeters, the distance from the bottom of a person's neck to 5 cm above the floor. If the distance from the bottom of Kathy's neck to the floor is 5 ft 2 in., calculate the length of the kimono that Dale should purchase.

   b) If the conversion rate at the time is 1 U.S. dollar = 117.25 yen and the kimono cost 8695.5 yen, determine the cost of the kimono in U.S. dollars.

   c) On a trip to Mexico City, Mexico, Dale finds a small replica of a Mayan castle that he wants to purchase for his wife, Sue. He is going directly from Mexico to Rome, so he wants to mail the castle back to the United States. The mailing rate from Mexico to the United States is 10 pesos per hundred grams. Determine the mailing cost, in U.S. dollars, if the castle weighs 6 lb and the exchange rate is 1 peso = 0.092 U.S. dollar.

   d) This question has three parts. While traveling to Italy, Dale finds that unleaded gasoline cost 1.238 € per liter.

Positano, Italy on the Amalfi Coast

   1) How much will it cost him, in euros, to fill the 53 ℓ gas tank of his rented car? 2) If the exchange rate is 1 euro = $1.17 U.S., what will it cost in U.S. dollars to fill the tank? 3) What is the cost, in U.S. dollars, of a gallon of gasoline at this gas station?

Many objects we encounter each day can be described in terms of geometry. Spherical baseballs hit on square baseball "diamonds," cylindrical cans of soda, and rectangular computer screens are all examples of geometric objects we frequently encounter. In addition to these items, scientists also use geometry to conduct research and create items that improve our lives. For example, the antenna on your cell phone is an example of a geometric object known as a fractal. In this chapter, we will study many geometric objects that we see in our everyday lives.

●●●●●●
Baseballs and baseball diamonds are examples of geometric shapes

SECTION 6.1 ● POINTS, LINES, PLANES, AND ANGLES

Billiard games involve many geometric concepts.

Playing billiards involves many geometric concepts. In this section, we will introduce the geometric terms *points, lines, planes*, and *angles*. In a typical billiard game, each of these terms is evident. The billiard balls rest on specific points on the table, which is part of a plane. After being struck with a cue, the ball travels along a path that is part of a line. Angles are involved in the path the ball takes when the ball hits a table bumper or another ball. The concepts we will discuss in this section form an important basis for the study of geometry.

Human beings recognized shapes, sizes, and physical forms long before geometry was developed. Geometry as a science is said to have begun in the Nile Valley of ancient Egypt. The Egyptians used geometry to measure land and to build pyramids and other structures.

The word *geometry* is derived from two Greek words, *ge*, meaning earth, and *metron*, meaning measure. Thus, geometry means "earth measure" or "measurement of the earth."

Unlike the Egyptians, the Greeks were interested in more than just the applied aspects of geometry. The Greeks attempted to apply their knowledge of logic to geometry. In about 600 B.C., Thales of Miletus was the first to be credited with using deductive methods to develop geometric concepts. Another outstanding Greek mathematician, Pythagoras, continued the systematic development of geometry that Thales had begun.

In about 300 B.C., Euclid (see Blitzer Bonus on page 289) collected and summarized much of the Greek mathematics of his time. In a set of 13 books called *Elements*, Euclid laid the foundation for plane geometry, which is also called *Euclidean geometry*.

Euclid is credited with being the first mathematician to use the *axiomatic method* in developing a branch of mathematics. First, Euclid introduced *undefined terms* such as point, line, plane, and angle. He related these to physical space by such statements as "A line is length without breadth" so that we may intuitively understand them. Because such statements play no further role in his system, they constitute primitive or undefined terms.

Second, Euclid introduced certain *definitions*. The definitions are introduced when needed and are often based on the undefined terms. Some terms that Euclid introduced and defined include triangle, right angle, and hypotenuse.

Third, Euclid stated certain primitive propositions called *postulates* (now called *axioms**) about the undefined terms and definitions. The reader is asked to accept these statements as true on the basis of their "obviousness" and their relationship with the physical world. For example, the Greeks accepted all right angles as being equal, which is Euclid's fourth postulate.

Fourth, Euclid proved, using deductive reasoning (see Section 1.1), other propositions called *theorems*. One theorem that Euclid proved is known as the Pythagorean theorem: "The sum of the areas of the squares constructed on the arms of a right triangle is equal to

---

*The concept of the axiom has changed significantly since Euclid's time. Now any statement may be designated as an axiom, whether it is self-evident or not. All axioms are *accepted* as true. A set of axioms forms the foundation for a mathematical system.

the area of the square constructed on the hypotenuse." He also proved that the sum of the angles of a triangle is 180°.

Using only 10 axioms, Euclid deduced 465 propositions (or theorems) in plane and solid geometry, number theory, and Greek geometric algebra.

Point and Line

Three basic terms in geometry are *point*, *line*, and *plane*. These three terms are not given a formal definition, but we recognize points, lines, and planes when we see them.

Let's consider some properties of a line. Assume that a line means a straight line unless otherwise stated.

1. A line is a set of points. Each point is on the line and the line passes through each point. When we wish to refer to a specific point, we will label it with a single capital letter. For example, in Figure 6.1(a) three points are labled A, B, and C, respectively.
2. Any two distinct points determine a unique line. Figure 6.1(a) illustrates a line. The arrows at both ends of the line indicate that the line continues in each direction. The line in Fig. 6.1(a) may be symbolized with any two points on the line by placing a line with a double-sided arrow above the letters that correspond to the points, such as $\overleftrightarrow{AB}$, $\overleftrightarrow{BA}$, $\overleftrightarrow{AC}$, $\overleftrightarrow{CA}$, $\overleftrightarrow{BC}$, or $\overleftrightarrow{CB}$.
3. Any point on a line separates the line into three parts: the point itself and two *half lines* (neither of which includes the point). For example, in Fig. 6.1(a) point B separates the line into the point B and two half lines. Half line BA, symbolized $\overset{\circ}{\overleftarrow{BA}}$, is illustrated in Fig. 6.1(b). The open circle above the B indicates that point B is not included in the half line. Figure 6.1(c) illustrates half line BC, symbolized $\overset{\circ}{\overrightarrow{BC}}$.

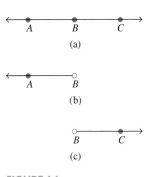

FIGURE 6.1

Look at the half line $\overset{\circ}{\overrightarrow{AB}}$ in Fig. 6.2(b) on page 290. If the *end point*, A, is included with the set of points on the half line, the result is called a *ray*. Ray AB, symbolized $\overrightarrow{AB}$, is illustrated in Fig. 6.2(c). Ray BA, symbolized $\overrightarrow{BA}$, is illustrated in Fig. 6.2(d).

A *line segment* is that part of a line between two points, including the end points. Line segment AB, symbolized $\overline{AB}$, is illustrated in Fig. 6.2(e).

An open line segment is the set of points on a line between two points, excluding the end points. Open line segment AB, symbolized $\overset{\circ\,\circ}{AB}$, is illustrated in Fig. 6.2(f).

Figure 6.2(g) illustrates two half open line segments, symbolized $\overset{\circ}{AB}$ and $\overset{\;\circ}{AB}$.

The intersection (symbolized $\cap$) of two sets is the set of elements (points in this case) common to both sets.

Consider the rays $\overrightarrow{AB}$ and $\overrightarrow{BA}$ in Fig. 6.3(a). The intersection of $\overrightarrow{AB}$ and $\overrightarrow{BA}$ is $\overline{AB}$. Thus, $\overrightarrow{AB} \cap \overrightarrow{BA} = \overline{AB}$.

The union (symbolized $\cup$) of two sets is the set of elements (points in this case) that belong to either of the sets or both sets. The union of $\overrightarrow{AB}$ and $\overrightarrow{BA}$ is $\overleftrightarrow{AB}$ (Fig. 6.3b). Thus, $\overrightarrow{AB} \cup \overrightarrow{BA} = \overleftrightarrow{AB}$.

Description	Diagram	Symbol
(a) Line AB		$\overleftrightarrow{AB}$
(b) Half line AB		$\overrightarrow{AB}$
(c) Ray AB		$\overrightarrow{AB}$
(d) Ray BA		$\overrightarrow{BA}$
(e) Line segment AB		$\overline{AB}$
(f) Open line segment AB		$\overline{AB}$
(g) Half open line segments AB		$\overline{AB}$ $\overline{AB}$

FIGURE 6.2

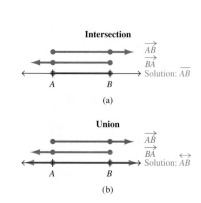

Intersection

Solution: $\overline{AB}$

(a)

Union

Solution: $\overleftrightarrow{AB}$

(b)

FIGURE 6.3

TECHNOLOGY

COMPASS AND STRAIGHTEDGE CONSTRUCTIONS

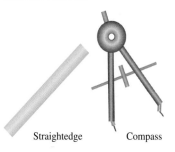

Straightedge   Compass

Geometric constructions were central to ancient Greek mathematics. Although these constructions are often referred to as *Euclidean constructions*, they were used centuries before Euclid wrote his classic work, *Elements*. The tools *allowed* in geometric constructions are a pencil, an unmarked straightedge, and a drawing compass. The straightedge is used to draw line segments, and the compass is used to draw circles and arcs. The Internet has many sites devoted to classic geometric constructions. Exercise 105 shows you how to construct a triangle with sides of equal length (an equilateral triangle).

EXAMPLE 1   UNIONS AND INTERSECTIONS OF PARTS OF A LINE

Using line AD, determine the solution to each part.

a) $\overrightarrow{AB} \cap \overrightarrow{DC}$ b) $\overrightarrow{AB} \cup \overrightarrow{DC}$ c) $\overline{AB} \cap \overrightarrow{CD}$ d) $\overline{AD} \cup \overleftarrow{CA}$

SOLUTION

a) $\overrightarrow{AB} \cap \overrightarrow{DC}$

Ray AB and ray DC are shown below. The intersection of these two rays is that part of line AD that is a part of *both* ray AB and ray DC. The intersection of ray AB and ray DC is line segment AD.

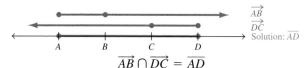

$\overrightarrow{AB}$
$\overrightarrow{DC}$
Solution: $\overline{AD}$

$$\overrightarrow{AB} \cap \overrightarrow{DC} = \overline{AD}$$

b) $\overrightarrow{AB} \cup \overrightarrow{DC}$

Once again ray AB and ray DC are shown below. The union of these two rays is that part of line AD that is part of *either* ray AB or ray DC. The union of ray AB and ray DC is the entire line AD.

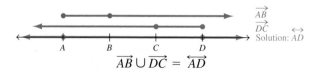

$\overrightarrow{AB}$
$\overrightarrow{DC}$
Solution: $\overleftrightarrow{AD}$

$$\overrightarrow{AB} \cup \overrightarrow{DC} = \overleftrightarrow{AD}$$

c) $\overline{AB} \cap \overrightarrow{CD}$

Line segment AB and ray CD have no points in common, so their intersection is empty.

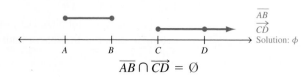

$\overline{AB}$
$\overrightarrow{CD}$
Solution: ϕ

$$\overline{AB} \cap \overrightarrow{CD} = \varnothing$$

d) $\overline{AD} \cup \overset{\circ}{CA}$

The union of line segment AD and half line CA is ray DA (or equivalently, $\overrightarrow{DB}$ or $\overrightarrow{DC}$).

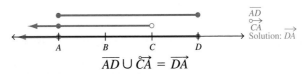

$$\overline{AD} \cup \overset{\circ}{CA} = \overrightarrow{DA}$$

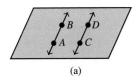

(a)

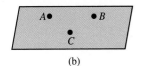

(b)

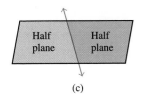

(c)

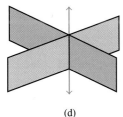

(d)

FIGURE 6.4

Plane

The term *plane* is one of Euclid's undefined terms. For our purposes, we can think of a plane as a two-dimensional surface that extends infinitely in both directions, like an infinitely large blackboard. Euclidean geometry is called *plane geometry* because it is the study of two-dimensional figures in a plane.

Two lines in the same plane that do not intersect are called *parallel lines*. Figure 6.4(a) illustrates two parallel lines in a plane ($\overleftrightarrow{AB}$ is parallel to $\overleftrightarrow{CD}$).

Properties of planes include the following:

1. Any three points that are not on the same line (noncollinear points) determine a unique plane (Fig. 6.4b).
2. A line in a plane divides the plane into three parts, the line and two half planes (Fig. 6.4c).
3. Any line and a point not on the line determine a unique plane.
4. The intersection of two distinct planes is a line (Fig. 6.4d).

Two planes that do not intersect are said to be *parallel planes*. For example, in Fig. 6.5 plane ABE is parallel to plane GHF.

Two lines that do not lie in the same plane and do not intersect are called *skew lines*. Figure 6.5 illustrates many skew lines (for example, $\overleftrightarrow{AB}$ and $\overleftrightarrow{CD}$).

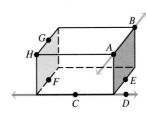

FIGURE 6.5

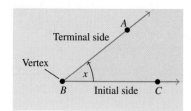

FIGURE 6.6

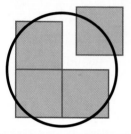
Angles

An *angle*, denoted $\angle$, is the union of two rays with a common end point (Fig. 6.6):

$$\overrightarrow{BA} \cup \overrightarrow{BC} = \angle ABC \text{ (or } \angle CBA)$$

An angle can be formed by the rotation of a ray about a point. An angle has an initial side and a terminal side. The initial side indicates the position of the ray prior to rotation; the terminal side indicates the position of the ray after rotation. The point common to both rays is called the *vertex* of the angle. The letter designating the vertex is always the middle one of the three letters designating an angle. The rays that make up the angle are called its *sides*.

There are several ways to name an angle. The angle in Fig. 6.6 may be denoted

$$\angle ABC, \quad \angle CBA, \quad \text{or} \quad \angle B$$

An angle divides a plane into three distinct parts: the angle itself, its interior, and its exterior. In Fig. 6.6, the angle is represented by the blue lines, the interior of the angle is shaded pink, and the exterior is shaded green.

The *measure of an angle*, symbolized m, is the amount of rotation from its initial side to its terminal side. In Fig. 6.6, the letter x represents the measure of $\angle ABC$; therefore, we may write $m\angle ABC = x$.

Angles can be measured in *degrees*, radians, or gradients. In this text, we will discuss only the degree unit of measurement. The symbol for degrees is the same as the symbol for temperature degrees. An angle of 45 degrees is written 45°. A *protractor* is used to measure angles. The angle shown being measured by the protractor in Fig. 6.7 is 50°.

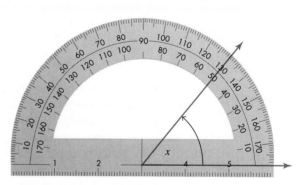

FIGURE 6.7

EXAMPLE 2   UNION AND INTERSECTION

Refer to Fig. 6.8. Determine the following.

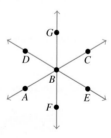

FIGURE 6.8

a) $\overleftrightarrow{AC} \cap \overleftrightarrow{DE}$ b) $\overrightarrow{AB} \cup \overrightarrow{CB}$ c) $\overrightarrow{BE} \cup \overrightarrow{BF}$ d) $\angle DBG \cap \angle CBG$

SOLUTION

a) $\overleftrightarrow{AC} \cap \overleftrightarrow{DE} = \{B\}$ b) $\overrightarrow{AB} \cup \overrightarrow{CB} = \overleftrightarrow{AC}$

c) $\overrightarrow{BE} \cup \overrightarrow{BF} = \angle EBF$ d) $\angle DBG \cap \angle CBG = \overrightarrow{BG}$

Consider a circle whose circumference is divided into 360 equal parts. If we draw a line from each mark on the circumference to the center of the circle, we get 360 wedge-shaped pieces. The measure of an angle formed by the straight sides of each wedge-shaped piece is defined to be 1°.

Angles are classified by their degree measurement, as shown in the following summary. A *right angle* has a measure of 90°, an *acute angle* has a measure less than 90°, an *obtuse angle* has a measure greater than 90° but less than 180°, and a *straight angle* has a measure of 180°.

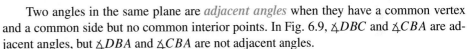

Right Angle	**Acute Angle**	**Obtuse Angle**	**Straight Angle**
$x = 90°$ The symbol ∟ is used to indicate right angles.	$0° < x < 90°$	$90° < x < 180°$	$x = 180°$

Two angles in the same plane are *adjacent angles* when they have a common vertex and a common side but no common interior points. In Fig. 6.9, $\angle DBC$ and $\angle CBA$ are adjacent angles, but $\angle DBA$ and $\angle CBA$ are not adjacent angles.

Two angles are called *complementary angles* if the sum of their measures is 90°. Two angles are called *supplementary angles* if the sum of their measures is 180°.

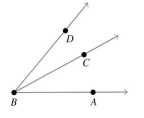

FIGURE 6.9

EXAMPLE 3   DETERMINING COMPLEMENTARY AND SUPPLEMENTARY ANGLES

In Fig. 6.10, we see that $m\angle ABC = 25°$.

a) $\angle ABC$ and $\angle CBD$ are complementary angles. Determine $m\angle CBD$.

b) $\angle ABC$ and $\angle CBE$ are supplementary angles. Determine $m\angle CBE$.

SOLUTION

a) The sum of two complementary angles must be 90°, so

$$m\angle ABC + m\angle CBD = 90°$$
$$25° + m\angle CBD = 90°$$
$$m\angle CBD = 90° - 25° = 65° \quad \text{Subtract 25° from each side of the equation.}$$

b) The sum of two supplementary angles must be 180°, so

$$m\angle ABC + m\angle CBE = 180°$$
$$25° + m\angle CBE = 180°$$
$$m\angle CBE = 180° - 25° = 155° \quad \text{Subtract 25° from each side of the equation.}$$

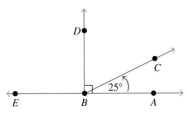

FIGURE 6.10

EXAMPLE 4   DETERMINING COMPLEMENTARY ANGLES

If $\angle ABC$ and $\angle CBD$ are complementary angles and $m\angle ABC$ is 26° less than $m\angle CBD$, determine the measure of each angle (Fig. 6.11).

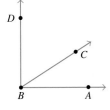

FIGURE 6.11

SOLUTION Let $m\angle CBD = x$. Then $m\angle ABC = x - 26$ since it is 26° less than $m\angle CBD$. Because these angles are complementary, we have

$$m\angle CBD + m\angle ABC = 90°$$
$$x + (x - 26) = 90°$$
$$2x - 26 = 90°$$
$$2x = 116°$$
$$x = 58°$$

Therefore, $m\angle CBD = 58°$ and $m\angle ABC = 58° - 26°$, or 32°. Note that $58° + 32° = 90°$, which is what we expected.

EXAMPLE 5   DETERMINING SUPPLEMENTARY ANGLES

If $\angle ABC$ and $\angle ABD$ are supplementary and $m\angle ABC$ is five times larger than $m\angle ABD$, determine $m\angle ABC$ and $m\angle ABD$ (Fig. 6.12).

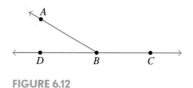

FIGURE 6.12

SOLUTION Let $m\angle ABD = x$, then $m\angle ABC = 5x$. Since these angles are supplementary, we have

$$m\angle ABD + m\angle ABC = 180°$$
$$x + 5x = 180°$$
$$6x = 180°$$
$$x = 30°$$

Thus, $m\angle ABD = 30°$ and $m\angle ABC = 5(30°) = 150°$. Note that $30° + 150° = 180°$, which is what we expected.

When two straight lines intersect, the nonadjacent angles formed are called *vertical angles*. In Fig. 6.13, $\angle 1$ and $\angle 3$ are vertical angles, and $\angle 2$ and $\angle 4$ are vertical angles. We can show that vertical angles have the same measure, that is, they are equal. For example, Fig. 6.13 shows that

$$m\angle 1 + m\angle 2 = 180°. \qquad \text{Why?}$$
$$m\angle 2 + m\angle 3 = 180°. \qquad \text{Why?}$$

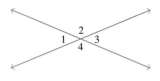

FIGURE 6.13

Since $\angle 2$ has the same measure in both cases, $m\angle 1$ must equal $m\angle 3$.

> Vertical angles have the same measure.

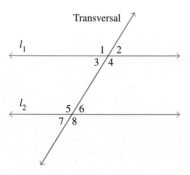

FIGURE 6.14

A line that intersects two different lines, l_1 and l_2, at two different points is called a *transversal*. Figure 6.14 illustrates that when two parallel lines are cut by a transversal, eight angles are formed. Angles 3, 4, 5, and 6 are called *interior angles*, and angles 1, 2, 7, and 8 are called *exterior angles*. Eight pairs of supplementary angles are formed. Can you list them?

Special names are given to the angles formed by a transversal crossing two parallel lines. We describe these angles below.

Name	Description	Illustration	Pairs of Angles Meeting Criteria
Alternate interior angles	Interior angles on opposite sides of the transversal	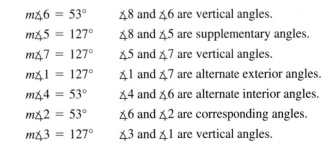	∡3 and ∡6 ∡4 and ∡5
Alternate exterior angles	Exterior angles on opposite sides of the transversal		∡1 and ∡8 ∡2 and ∡7
Corresponding angles	One interior and one exterior angle on the same side of the transversal		∡1 and ∡5 ∡2 and ∡6 ∡3 and ∡7 ∡4 and ∡8

When two parallel lines are cut by a transversal,

1. alternate interior angles have the same measure.
2. alternate exterior angles have the same measure.
3. corresponding angles have the same measure.

EXAMPLE 6   DETERMINING ANGLE MEASURES

Figure 6.15 shows two parallel lines cut by a transversal. Determine the measure of ∡1 through ∡7.

SOLUTION

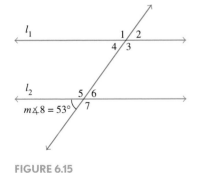

FIGURE 6.15

$m∡6 = 53°$ ∡8 and ∡6 are vertical angles.

$m∡5 = 127°$ ∡8 and ∡5 are supplementary angles.

$m∡7 = 127°$ ∡5 and ∡7 are vertical angles.

$m∡1 = 127°$ ∡1 and ∡7 are alternate exterior angles.

$m∡4 = 53°$ ∡4 and ∡6 are alternate interior angles.

$m∡2 = 53°$ ∡6 and ∡2 are corresponding angles.

$m∡3 = 127°$ ∡3 and ∡1 are vertical angles.

In Example 6, the angles could have been determined in alternate ways. For example, we mentioned $m∡1 = 127°$ because ∡1 and ∡7 are alternate exterior angles. We could have also stated that $m∡1 = 127°$ because ∡1 and ∡5 are corresponding angles.

EXERCISE SET 6.1 ●●●○●○

• Concept/Writing Exercises

1. **a)** What are the four key parts in the axiomatic method used by Euclid?

   b) Discuss each of the four parts.

2. What is the difference between an axiom and a theorem?

3. What are skew lines?

4. What are parallel lines?

5. What are adjacent angles?

6. What are complementary angles?

7. What are supplementary angles?

8. What is a straight angle?

9. What is an obtuse angle?

10. What is a right angle?

11. What is an acute angle?

12. Draw two intersecting lines. Identify the two pairs of vertical angles.

• Practice the Skills

In Exercises 13–20, identify the figure as a line, half line, ray, line segment, open line segment, or half open line segment. Denote the figure by its appropriate symbol.

13.

14.

15.

16.

17.

18.

19.

20.

In Exercises 21–32, use the figure to find the following:

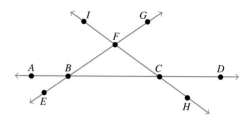

21. ⊿$ABF \cap$⊿GBC

22. $\overrightarrow{FE} \cup \overrightarrow{FG}$

23. $\overrightarrow{BC} \cup \overleftrightarrow{CD}$

24. $\overline{AB} \cup \overline{BD}$

25. ⊿$ICA \cap \overleftrightarrow{EG}$

26. ⊿$IFG \cap$⊿EFH

27. $\overleftrightarrow{AB} \cap \overline{HC}$

28. $\overleftrightarrow{BD} \cap \overleftrightarrow{CB}$

29. $\overrightarrow{FG} \cup \overrightarrow{FC}$

30. $\overline{BC} \cup \overline{CF} \cup \overline{FB}$

31. $\overleftrightarrow{BD} \cup \overleftrightarrow{CB}$

32. $\{C\} \cap \overleftrightarrow{CH}$

In Exercises 33–44, use the figure to find each of the following.

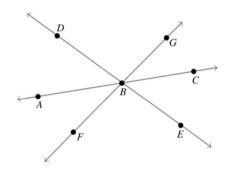

33. $\overleftrightarrow{DE} \cap \overleftrightarrow{FG}$

34. $\overline{BD} \cup \overline{BE}$

35. ⊿$GBC \cap$⊿CBE

36. $\overleftrightarrow{DE} \cup \overline{BE}$

37. ⊿$ABE \cup \overleftrightarrow{AB}$

38. $\overrightarrow{BF} \cup \overline{BE}$

39. $\overrightarrow{FG} \cap \overrightarrow{BF}$

40. $\overline{BE} \cup \overline{BD}$

41. $\overleftrightarrow{AC} \cap \overline{AC}$

42. $\overleftrightarrow{AC} \cap \overline{BE}$

43. $\overrightarrow{EB} \cap \overline{BE}$

44. $\overrightarrow{FB} \cup \overline{BG}$

In Exercises 45–52, classify the angle as acute, right, straight, obtuse, or none of these angles.

45.

46.

47.

48.

49.

50.

51.

52.

In Exercises 53–58, find the complementary angle of the given angle.

53. $26°$

54. $89°$

55. $32\frac{3}{4}°$

56. $31\frac{2}{5}°$

57. $64.7°$

58. $0.01°$

In Exercises 59–64, find the supplementary angle of the given angle.

59. $89°$

60. $8°$

61. $20.5°$

62. $148.7°$

63. $43\frac{5}{7}°$

64. $64\frac{7}{16}°$

In Exercises 65–70, match the names of the angles with the corresponding figure in parts (a)–(f).

65. Vertical angles

66. Corresponding angles

67. Complementary angles

68. Supplementary angles

69. Alternate exterior angles

70. Alternate interior angles

a)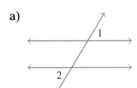

b)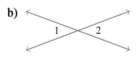

c)

d)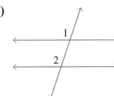

e)

f)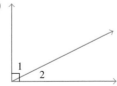

• Problem Solving

71. MODELING - *Complementary Angles* If ∡1 and ∡2 are complementary angles and if the measure of ∡1 is eight more than the measure of ∡2, determine the measures of ∡1 and ∡2.

72. MODELING - *Complementary Angles* The difference between the measures of two complementary angles is $16°$. Determine the measures of the two angles.

73. MODELING - *Supplementary Angles* The difference between the measures of two supplementary angles is $88°$. Determine the measures of the two angles.

74. MODELING - *Supplementary Angles* If ∡1 and ∡2 are supplementary angles and if the measure of ∡2 is 17 times the measure of ∡1, determine the measures of the two angles.

In Exercises 75–78, parallel lines are cut by the transversal shown. Determine the measures of ∡1 through ∡7.

75.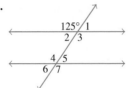

76.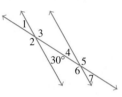

77.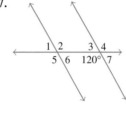

78.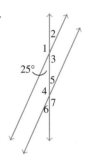

In Exercises 79–82, the angles are complementary angles. Determine the measures of ∡1 and ∡2.

79.

80.

81.

82.

In Exercises 83–86, the angles are supplementary angles. Determine the measures of ∡1 and ∡2.

83.

84.

85.

86.

87. a) How many lines can be drawn through a given point?

b) How many planes can be drawn through a given point?

88. What is the intersection of two distinct nonparallel planes?

89. How many planes can be drawn through a given line?

90. a) Will three noncollinear points *A*, *B*, and *C* always determine a plane? Explain.

    b) Is it possible to determine more than one plane with three noncollinear points? Explain.

    c) How many planes can be constructed through three collinear points?

The figure suggests a number of lines and planes. The lines may be described by naming two points, and the planes may be described by naming three points. In Exercises 91–98, use the figure to name the following.

91. Two parallel planes

92. Two parallel lines

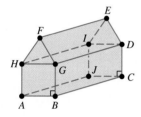

93. Two lines that intersect at right angles

94. Two planes that intersect at right angles

95. Three planes whose intersection is a single point

96. Three planes whose intersection is a line

97. A line and a plane whose intersection is a point

98. A line and a plane whose intersection is a line

In Exercises 99–104, determine whether the statement is always true, sometimes true, or never true. Explain your answer.

99. Two lines that are both parallel to a third line must be parallel to each other.

100. A triangle contains exactly two acute angles.

101. Vertical angles are complementary angles.

102. Alternate exterior angles are supplementary angles.

103. Alternate interior angles are complementary angles.

104. A triangle contains two obtuse angles.

• Challenge Problems/Group Activities

105. Use a straightedge and a compass to construct a triangle with sides of equal length (an equilateral triangle) by doing the following:

a) Use the straightedge to draw a line segment of any length and label the end points *A* and *B* (Fig. a).

b) Place one end of the compass at point *A* and the other end at point *B* and draw an arc as shown (Fig. b).

c) Now turn the compass around and draw another arc as shown. Label the point of intersection of the two arcs *C* (Fig. c).

d) Draw line segments *AC* and *BC*. This completes the construction of equilateral triangle *ABC* (Fig. d).

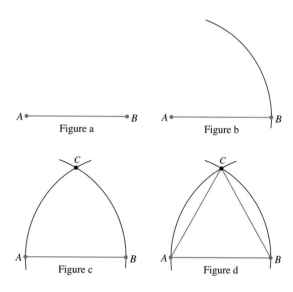

106. If lines *l* and *m* are parallel lines and if lines *l* and *n* are skew lines, is it true that lines *m* and *n* must also be skew? (*Hint:* Look at Fig. 6.5 on page 291.) Explain your answer and include a sketch to support your answer.

107. Two lines are *perpendicular* if they intersect at right angles. If lines *l* and *m* are perpendicular and if lines *m* and *n* are perpendicular, is it true that lines *l* and *n* must also be perpendicular? Explain your answer and include a sketch to support your answer.

108. Suppose you have three distinct lines, all lying in the same plane. Find all the possible ways in which the three lines can be related. Sketch each case (four cases).

• Recreational Mathematics

109. If two straight lines intersect at a point, determine the sum of the measures of the 4 angles formed.

110. ∡*ABC* and ∡*CBD* are complementary and *m*∡*CBD* is twice the *m*∡*ABC*. ∡*ABD* and ∡*DBE* are supplementary angles.

a) Draw a sketch illustrating ∡*ABC*, ∡*CBD*, and ∡*DBE*.

b) Determine *m*∡*ABC*.

c) Determine *m*∡*CBD*.

d) Determine *m*∡*DBE*.

• **Internet/Research Activities**

111. Using the Internet and other sources, write a research paper on Euclid's contributions to geometry.

112. Using the Internet and other sources, write a research paper on the three classic geometry problems of Greek antiquity (see the Technology Box on page 292).

113. Search the Internet or other sources such as a geometry textbook to study the geometric constructions that use a straightedge and a compass only. Prepare a poster demonstrating five of these basic constructions.

SECTION 6.2 • POLYGONS

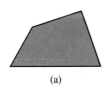

The shapes of these road signs are examples of polygons.

What shape would you use to best describe the following road signs: a stop sign, a yield sign, a speed limit sign? In this section, we will study the shapes of these and other geometric figures that can be classified as *polygons*.

A *polygon* is a closed figure in a plane determined by three or more straight line segments. Examples of polygons are given in Fig. 6.16.

The straight line segments that form the polygon are called its *sides*, and a point where two sides meet is called a *vertex* (plural *vertices*). The union of the sides of a polygon and its interior is called a *polygonal region*. A *regular polygon* is one whose sides are all the same length and whose interior angles all have the same measure. Figures 6.16(b) and (d) are regular polygons.

(a)   (b)   (c)   (d)

FIGURE 6.16

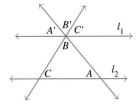

FIGURE 6.17

Polygons are named according to their number of sides. The names of some polygons are given in Table 6.1.

One of the most important polygons is the triangle. The sum of the measures of the interior angles of a triangle is 180°. To illustrate, consider triangle ABC given in Fig. 6.17. The triangle is formed by drawing two transversals through two parallel lines l_1 and l_2 with the two transversals intersecting at a point on l_1.

TABLE 6.1

Number of Sides	Name	Number of Sides	Name
3	Triangle	8	Octagon
4	Quadrilateral	9	Nonagon
5	Pentagon	10	Decagon
6	Hexagon	12	Dodecagon
7	Heptagon	20	Icosagon

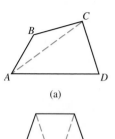

(a)

(b)

(c)

FIGURE 6.18

In Fig. 6.17, notice that $\angle A$ and $\angle A'$ are corresponding angles. Recall from Section 6.1 that corresponding angles are equal, so $m\angle A = m\angle A'$. Also, $\angle C$ and $\angle C'$ are corresponding angles; therefore, $m\angle C = m\angle C'$. Next, we notice that $\angle B$ and $\angle B'$ are vertical angles. In Section 6.1, we learned that vertical angles are equal; therefore, $m\angle B = m\angle B'$. Figure 6.17 shows that $\angle A'$, $\angle B'$, and $\angle C'$ form a straight angle; therefore, $m\angle A' + m\angle B' + m\angle C' = 180°$. Since $m\angle A = m\angle A'$, $m\angle B = m\angle B'$, and $m\angle C = m\angle C'$, we can reason that $m\angle A + m\angle B + m\angle C = 180°$. This example illustrates that the sum of the interior angles of a triangle is 180°.

Consider the quadrilateral $ABCD$ (Fig. 6.18a). Drawing a straight line segment between any two vertices forms two triangles. Since the sum of the measures of the angles of a triangle is 180°, the sum of the measures of the interior angles of a quadrilateral is $2 \cdot 180°$, or 360°.

Now let's examine a pentagon (Fig. 6.18b). We can draw two straight line segments to form three triangles. Thus, the sum of the measures of the interior angles of a five-sided figure is $3 \cdot 180°$, or 540°. Figure 6.18(c) shows that four triangles can be drawn in a six-sided figure. Table 6.2 summarizes this information.

TABLE 6.2

Sides	Triangles	Sum of the Measures of the Interior Angles
3	1	$1(180°) = 180°$
4	2	$2(180°) = 360°$
5	3	$3(180°) = 540°$
6	4	$4(180°) = 720°$

If we continue this procedure, we can see that for an n-sided polygon the sum of the measures of the interior angles is $(n - 2)180°$.

> The **sum** of the measures of the interior angles of an n-sided polygon is $(n - 2)180°$.

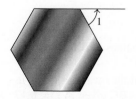

FIGURE 6.19

EXAMPLE 1　　ANGLES OF A HEXAGON

The surfaces of the heads of many bolts are in the shape of regular hexagons. A regular hexagon is a six-sided figure with all the sides the same length and all interior angles with the same measure. See Fig. 6.19. Determine

a) the measure of an interior angle.

b) the measure of exterior $\angle 1$.

SOLUTION

a) Using the formula $(n - 2)180°$, we can determine the sum of the measures of the interior angles of a hexagon as follows.

$$
\begin{aligned}
\text{Sum} &= (6 - 2)180° \\
&= 4(180°) \\
&= 720°
\end{aligned}
$$

The measure of an interior angle of a regular polygon can be determined by dividing the sum of the interior angles by the number of angles.

The measure of an interior angle of a regular hexagon is determined as follows:

$$\text{Measure} = \frac{720°}{6} = 120°$$

b) Since $\angle 1$ is the supplement of an interior angle,

$$m\angle 1 = 180° - 120° = 60°$$

To discuss area in the next section, we must be able to identify various types of triangles and quadrilaterals. The following is a summary of certain types of triangles and their characteristics.

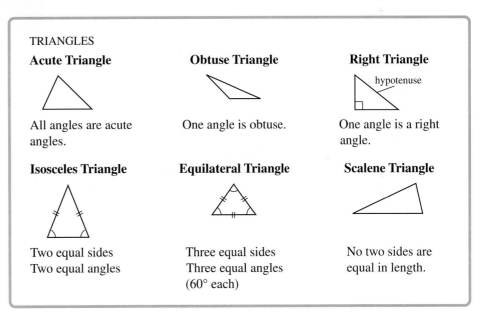

TRIANGLES

Acute Triangle — All angles are acute angles.

Obtuse Triangle — One angle is obtuse.

Right Triangle — hypotenuse — One angle is a right angle.

Isosceles Triangle — Two equal sides, Two equal angles

Equilateral Triangle — Three equal sides, Three equal angles (60° each)

Scalene Triangle — No two sides are equal in length.

Similar Figures

In everyday living, we often have to deal with geometric figures that have the "same shape" but are of different sizes. For example, an architect will make a small-scale drawing of a floor plan or a photographer will make an enlargement of a photograph. Figures that have the same shape but may be of different sizes are called *similar figures*. Two similar figures are illustrated in Fig. 6.20.

Similar figures have *corresponding angles* and *corresponding sides*. In Fig. 6.20, triangle *ABC* has angles *A*, *B*, and *C*. Their respective corresponding angles in triangle *DEF* are angles *D*, *E*, and *F*. Sides $\overline{AB}$, $\overline{BC}$, and $\overline{AC}$ in triangle *ABC* have corresponding sides $\overline{DE}$, $\overline{EF}$, and $\overline{DF}$, respectively, in triangle *DEF*.

> Two polygons are **similar** if their corresponding angles have the same measure and the lengths of their corresponding sides are in proportion.

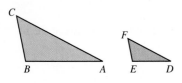

FIGURE 6.20

In Figure 6.20, $\angle A$ and $\angle D$ have the same measure, $\angle B$ and $\angle E$ have the same measure, and $\angle C$ and $\angle F$ have the same measure. Also, the lengths of corresponding sides of similar triangles are in proportion.

When we refer to the line segment AB, we place a line over the AB and write $\overline{AB}$. **When we refer to the *length* of a line segment, we do not place a bar above the two letters.** Thus, when we refer to the *length* of line segment $\overline{AB}$, we write AB (without the bar on top of the two letters). For example, if we write $AB = 12$, we are indicating the length of line segment $\overline{AB}$ is 12. When setting up proportions, as is shown below, we will be comparing the lengths of corresponding sides of similar figures, and so we will not be using the bar above the letters of the line segments. The proportion below shows that the lengths of the corresponding sides of the similar triangles in Figure 6.20 are in proportion.

$$\frac{AB}{DE} = \frac{BC}{EF} = \frac{AC}{DF}$$

EXAMPLE 2   SIMILAR FIGURES

Consider the similar figures in Fig. 6.21.

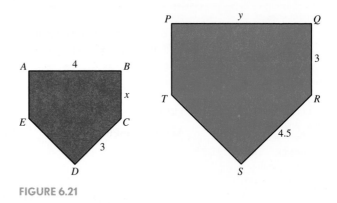

FIGURE 6.21

Determine
a) the length of side $\overline{BC}$.   b) the length of side $\overline{PQ}$.

SOLUTION

a) We will represent the length of side $\overline{BC}$ with the variable x. Because the corresponding sides of similar figures must be in proportion, we can write a proportion to determine the length of side $\overline{BC}$. Corresponding sides $\overline{CD}$ and $\overline{RS}$ are known, so we use them as one ratio in the proportion. The side corresponding to $\overline{BC}$ is $\overline{QR}$.

$$\frac{BC}{QR} = \frac{CD}{RS}$$
$$\frac{x}{3} = \frac{3}{4.5}$$

Now we solve for x.

$$x \cdot 4.5 = 3 \cdot 3$$
$$4.5x = 9$$
$$x = 2$$

Thus, the length of side $\overline{BC}$ is 2 units.

b) We will represent the length of side $\overline{PQ}$ with the variable y. The side corresponding to $\overline{PQ}$ is $\overline{AB}$. We will work part (b) in a manner similar to part (a).

$$\frac{PQ}{AB} = \frac{RS}{CD}$$
$$\frac{y}{4} = \frac{4.5}{3}$$

$$y \cdot 3 = 4 \cdot 4.5$$
$$3y = 18$$
$$y = 6$$

Thus, the length of side $\overline{PQ}$ is 6 units.

EXAMPLE 3 USING SIMILAR TRIANGLES TO FIND THE HEIGHT OF A TREE

Saraniti Walker plans to remove a tree from her back yard. She needs to know the height of the tree. Saraniti is 5 ft tall and determines that when her shadow is 8 ft long, the shadow of the tree is 50 ft long (see Fig. 6.22). How tall is the tree?

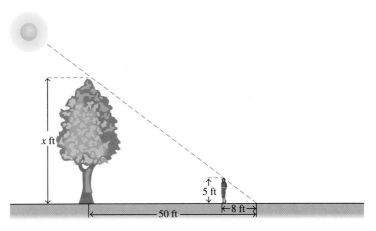

FIGURE 6.22

SOLUTION We will let x represent the height of the tree. From Fig. 6.22, we can see that the triangle formed by the sun's rays, Saraniti, and her shadow is similar to the triangle formed by the sun's rays, the tree, and its shadow. To find the height of the tree, we will set up and solve the following proportion:

$$\frac{\text{Height of the tree}}{\text{Height of Saraniti}} = \frac{\text{length of tree's shadow}}{\text{length of Saraniti's shadow}}$$

$$\frac{x}{5} = \frac{50}{8}$$
$$8x = 250$$
$$x = 31.25$$

Therefore, the tree is 31.25 ft tall.

Congruent Figures

If the corresponding sides of two similar figures are the same length, the figures are called *congruent figures*. Corresponding angles of congruent figures have the same measure, and the corresponding sides are equal in length. Two congruent figures coincide when placed one upon the other.

FIGURE 6.23

EXAMPLE 4   CONGRUENT TRIANGLES

Triangles *ABC* and *DEF* in Fig. 6.23 are congruent. Determine
a) the length of side $\overline{DF}$.
b) the length of side $\overline{AB}$.
c) $m\angle FDE$.
d) $m\angle ACB$.
e) $m\angle ABC$.

SOLUTION Because $\triangle ABC$ is congruent to $\triangle DEF$, we know that the corresponding side lengths are equal and corresponding angle measures are equal.
a) $DF = AC = 12$
b) $AB = DE = 7$
c) $m\angle FDE = m\angle CAB = 65°$
d) $m\angle ACB = m\angle DFE = 34°$
e) The sum of the angles of a triangle is 180°. Since $m\angle BAC = 65°$ and $m\angle ACB = 34°$, $m\angle ABC = 180° - 65° - 34° = 81°$.

Earlier we learned that *quadrilaterals* are four-sided polygons, the sum of whose interior angles is 360°. Quadrilaterals may be classified according to their characteristics, as illustrated in the summary box below.

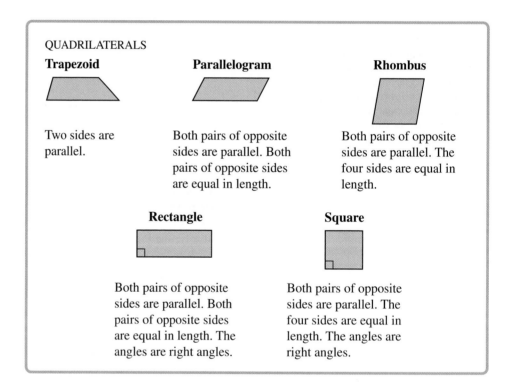

QUADRILATERALS

Trapezoid

Two sides are parallel.

Parallelogram

Both pairs of opposite sides are parallel. Both pairs of opposite sides are equal in length.

Rhombus

Both pairs of opposite sides are parallel. The four sides are equal in length.

Rectangle

Both pairs of opposite sides are parallel. Both pairs of opposite sides are equal in length. The angles are right angles.

Square

Both pairs of opposite sides are parallel. The four sides are equal in length. The angles are right angles.

EXAMPLE 5   ANGLES OF A TRAPEZOID

Trapezoid *ABCD* is shown in Fig. 6.24.
a) Determine the measure of the interior angle, *x*.
b) Determine the measure of the exterior angle, *y*.

SOLUTION

a) We know that each of the two right angles in trapezoid *ABCD* has a measure of 90°. We also know that the sum of the interior angles in any quadrilateral is 360°. Therefore, we have

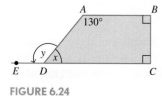

FIGURE 6.24

$$m\angle DAB + m\angle ABC + m\angle BCD + m\angle x = 360°$$
$$130° + 90° + 90° + m\angle x = 360°$$
$$310° + m\angle x = 360°$$
$$m\angle x = 50°$$

Thus, the measure of the interior angle, *x*, is 50°.

b) Angle *x* and angle *y* are supplementary angles. Therefore, $m\angle x + m\angle y = 180°$ and $m\angle y = 180° - m\angle x = 180° - 50° = 130°$. Thus, the measure of the exterior angle, *y*, is 130°.

Note that in Example 5 part (b) we could also have determined the measure of angle *y* as follows. By the definition of a trapezoid, sides $\overline{AB}$ and $\overline{CD}$ must be parallel. Therefore, side $\overline{AD}$ may be considered a transversal and $\angle BAD$ and $\angle ADE$ are alternate interior angles. Recall from Section 6.1 that alternate interior angles are equal. Thus, $m\angle BAD = m\angle ADE$ and $m\angle y = 130°$.

EXERCISE SET 6.2 ●●●●●●

• Concept/Writing Exercises

1. What is a polygon?

2. What distinguishes regular polygons from other polygons?

3. List six different types of triangles and in your own words describe the characteristics of each.

4. List five different types of quadrilaterals and in your own words describe the characteristics of each.

5. What are congruent figures?

6. What are similar figures?

In Exercises 7–14, (a) name the polygon. If the polygon is a quadrilateral, give its specific name. (b) State whether or not the polygon is a regular polygon.

7.
8.
9.
10.
11.
12.
13.
14.

In Exercises 15–22, identify the triangle as (a) scalene, isosceles, or equilateral and as (b) acute, obtuse, or right. The parallel markings (the two small parallel lines) on two or more sides indicate that the marked sides are of equal length.

15.
16.
17.
18.
19.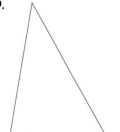
20.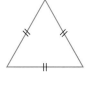

21.

22.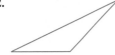

In Exercises 23–28, identify the quadrilateral.

23.

24.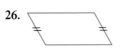

25.

26.

27.

28.

In Exercises 29–32, find the measure of ∡x.

29.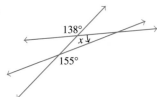

30.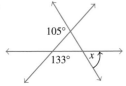

31.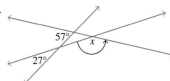

32.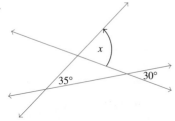

In Exercises 33–34, lines l_1 and l_2 are parallel. Determine the measures of ∡1 through ∡12.

33.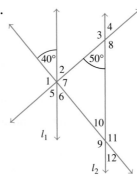

34.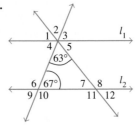

In Exercises 35–40, determine the sum of the measures of the interior angles of the indicated polygon.

35. Hexagon

36. Heptagon

37. Octagon

38. Decagon

39. Icosagon

40. Dodecagon

In Exercises 41–46, (a) determine the measure of an interior angle of the named regular polygon. (b) If a side of the polygon is extended, determine the supplementary angle of an interior angle. See Example 1.

41. Triangle

42. Quadrilateral

43. Pentagon

44. Nonagon

45. Decagon

46. Icosagon

In Exercises 47–52, the figures are similar. Find the length of side x and side y.

47.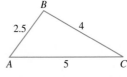

48.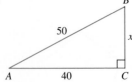

49.
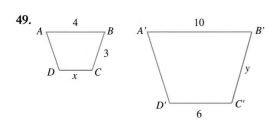

50.
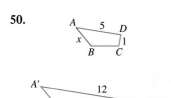

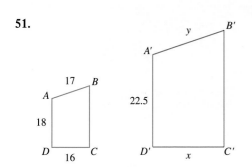

51.
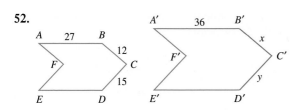

52.

In Exercises 53–56, triangles ABC and DEC are similar figures. Determine the length of

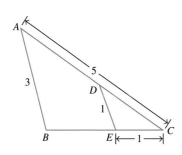

53. side $\overline{BC}$.

54. side $\overline{DC}$.

55. side $\overline{AD}$.

56. side $\overline{BE}$.

In Exercises 57–62, find the length of the sides and the measures of the angles for the congruent triangles ABC and A'B'C'.

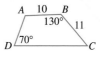
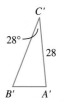

57. The length of side $\overline{AC}$

58. The length of side $\overline{A'B'}$

59. The length of side $\overline{B'C'}$

60. $\angle B'A'C'$

61. $\angle ACB$

62. $\angle ABC$

In Exercises 63–68, determine the length of the sides and the measures of the angles for the congruent quadrilaterals ABCD and A'B'C'D'.

63. The length of side $\overline{AD}$

64. The length of side $\overline{B'C'}$

65. The length of side $\overline{A'B'}$

66. $\angle BCD$ **67.** $\angle A'D'C'$

68. $\angle DAB$

• **Problem Solving**

In Exercises 69–72, determine the measure of the angle. In the figure, $\angle ABC$ makes an angle of 125° with the floor and l_1 and l_2 are parallel.

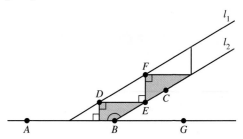

69. $\angle GBC$ **70.** $\angle EDF$

71. $\angle DFE$ **72.** $\angle DEC$

73. *Height of a Silo* Steve Runde is buying a farm and needs to determine the height of a silo on the farm. Steve, who is 6 ft tall, notices that when his shadow is 9 ft long, the shadow of the silo is 105 ft long (see diagram). How tall is the silo? Note that the diagram is not to scale.

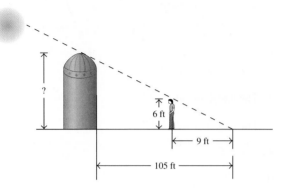

74. Angles on a Picnic Table The legs of a picnic table form an isosceles triangle as indicated in the figure. If $\angle ABC = 80°$, determine $m\angle x$ and $m\angle y$ so that the top of the table will be parallel to the ground.

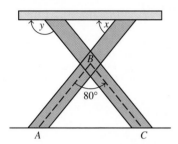

75. Distances in Minnesota A triangle can be formed by drawing line segments on a map of Minnesota connecting the cities of Austin, Rochester, and St. Paul (see figure). If the actual distance from Austin to Rochester is approximately 44 miles, use the lengths of the line segments indicated in the figure along with similar triangles to approximate

a) the actual distance from St. Paul to Austin. ≈ 113.14 mi

b) the actual distance from St. Paul to Rochester.

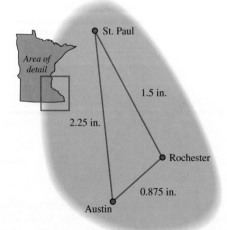

76. Distances in Illinois A triangle can be formed by drawing line segments on a map of Illinois connecting the cities of Rockford, Chicago, and Bloomington (see figure below). If the actual distance from Chicago to Rockford is approximately 90 miles, use the lengths of the line segments indicated in the figure along with similar triangles to approximate

a) the actual distance from Chicago to Bloomington.

b) the actual distance from Bloomington to Rockford.

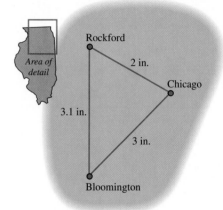

Challenge Problems/Group Activities

Scaling Factor Examine the similar triangles ABC and A'B'C' in the figure below.

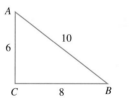

If we calculate the ratios $\frac{AB}{A'B'}$, $\frac{BC}{B'C'}$, and $\frac{CA}{C'A'}$, we see that each of these ratios is equal to 2. We call this common ratio the **scaling factor** of $\triangle ABC$ with respect to $\triangle A'B'C'$. If we calculate the reciprocal ratios $\frac{A'B'}{AB}$, $\frac{B'C'}{BC}$, and $\frac{C'A'}{CA}$, we see that each of these ratios is equal to $\frac{1}{2}$. We call this common ratio the scaling factor of $\triangle A'B'C'$ with respect to $\triangle ABC$. Every pair of similar figures has two scaling factors that show the relationship between the corresponding side lengths. Notice that the length of each side of $\triangle ABC$ is two times the length of the corresponding side in $\triangle A'B'C'$. We can also state that the length of each side of $\triangle A'B'C'$ is one-half the length of the corresponding side of $\triangle ABC$.

77. In the figure, $\triangle DEF$ is similar to $\triangle D'E'F'$. The length of the sides of $\triangle DEF$ is shown in the figure. If the scaling factor of $\triangle DEF$ with respect to $\triangle D'E'F'$ is 3, determine the length of the sides of triangle $\triangle D'E'F'$.

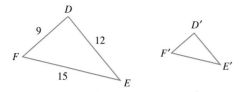

78. In the figure, quadrilateral $EFGH$ is similar to quadrilateral $E'F'G'H'$. The length of the sides of quadrilateral $EFGH$ is shown in the figure. If the scaling factor of quadrilateral $E'F'G'H'$ with respect to quadrilateral $EFGH$ is $\frac{1}{3}$, determine the length of the sides of quadrilateral $E'F'G'H'$.

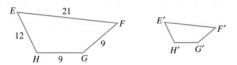

79. *Height of a Wall* You are asked to measure the height of an inside wall of a warehouse. No ladder tall enough to measure the height is available. You borrow a mirror from a salesclerk and place it on the floor. You then move away from the mirror until you can see the reflection of the top of the wall in it, as shown in the figure.

a) Explain why triangle HFM is similar to triangle TBM. (*Hint:* In the reflection of light the angle of incidence equals the angle of reflection. Thus, $\angle HMF = \angle TMB$.)

b) If your eyes are $5\frac{1}{2}$ ft above the floor and you are $2\frac{1}{2}$ ft from the mirror and the mirror is 20 ft from the wall, how high is the wall?

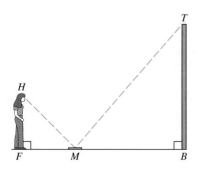

• Recreational Mathematics

80. *Distance Across a Lake*

a) In the figure, $m\angle CED = m\angle ABC$. Explain why triangles ABC and DEC must be similar.

b) Determine the distance across the lake, DE.

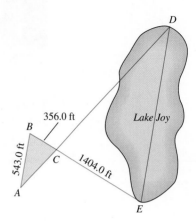

• Internet/Research Activities

81. Using the Internet and history of mathematics texts, write a paper on the history and use of the theodolite, a surveying instrument.

82. Using the Internet and other sources, write a paper on the use of geometry in the photographic process. Include discussions on the use of similar figures.

SECTION 6.3 • PERIMETER AND AREA

We will study the perimeter and area of rectangles, such as those on which basketball games are played.

If you were to walk around the outside edge of a basketball court, how far would you walk? If you had to place floor tiles that each measured 1 foot by 1 foot on a basketball court, how many tiles would you need? In this section, we will study the geometric concepts of perimeter and area that are used to answer these and other questions.

Perimeter and Area

The *perimeter*, P, of a two-dimensional figure is the sum of the lengths of the sides of the figure. In Figs. 6.25 and 6.26, the sums of the lengths of the red line segments are the perimeters. Perimeters are measured in the same units as the sides. For example, if the sides of a figure are measured in feet, the perimeter will be measured in feet.

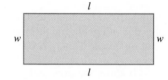

FIGURE 6.25   FIGURE 6.26

The *area*, A, is the region within the boundaries of the figure. The blue color in Figs. 6.25 and 6.26 indicates the areas of the figures. Area is measured in square units. For example, if the sides of a figure are measured in inches, the area of the figure will be measured in square inches (in.^2). (See Table 5.7 on page 275 for common units of area in the U.S. customary and metric systems.)

Consider the rectangle in Fig. 6.26. Two sides of the rectangle have length l, and two sides of the rectangle have width w. Thus, if we add the lengths of the four sides to get the perimeter, we find $P = l + w + l + w = 2l + 2w$.

PERIMETER OF A RECTANGLE

$$P = 2l + 2w$$

Consider a rectangle of length 5 units and width 3 units (Fig. 6.27). Counting the number of 1-unit by 1-unit squares within the figure we obtain the area of the rectangle, 15 square units. The area can also be obtained by multiplying the number of units of length by the number of units of width, or 5 units $\times$ 3 units = 15 square units. We can find the area of a rectangle by the formula area = length $\times$ width.

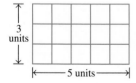

FIGURE 6.27

AREA OF A RECTANGLE

$$A = l \times w$$

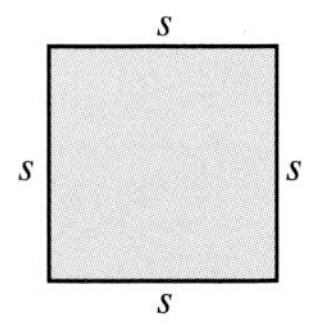

FIGURE 6.28

Using the formula for the area of a rectangle, we can determine the formulas for the areas of other figures.

A square (Fig. 6.28) is a rectangle that contains four equal sides. Therefore, the length equals the width. If we call both the length and the width of the square s, then

$$A = l \times w, \quad \text{so} \quad A = s \times s = s^2$$

> **AREA OF A SQUARE**
>
> $$A = s^2$$

A parallelogram with height h and base b is shown in Fig. 6.29(a).

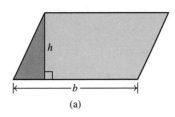

(a)　　　　　　　　　(b)

FIGURE 6.29

If we were to cut off the red portion of the parallelogram on the left, Fig. 6.29(a), and attach it to the right side of the figure, the resulting figure would be a rectangle, Fig. 6.29(b). Since the area of the rectangle is $b \times h$, the area of the parallelogram is also $b \times h$.

> **AREA OF A PARALLELOGRAM**
>
> $$A = b \times h$$

Consider the triangle with height, h, and base, b, shown in Fig. 6.30(a). Using this triangle and a second identical triangle, we can construct a parallelogram, Fig. 6.30(b). The area of the parallelogram is bh. The area of the triangle is one-half that of the parallelogram. Therefore, the area of the triangle is $\frac{1}{2}(\text{base})(\text{height})$.

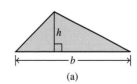

(a)

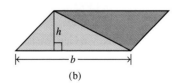

(b)

FIGURE 6.30

> **AREA OF A TRIANGLE**
>
> $$A = \frac{1}{2}bh$$

Now consider the trapezoid shown in Fig. 6.31(a). We can partition the trapezoid into two triangles by drawing diagonal $\overline{DB}$, as in Fig. 6.31(b). One triangle has base $\overline{AB}$ (called b_2) with height $\overline{DE}$, and the other triangle has base $\overline{DC}$ (called b_1) with height $\overline{FB}$. Note that the line used to measure the height of the triangle need not be inside the triangle. Be-

cause heights $\overline{DE}$ and $\overline{FB}$ are equal, both triangles have the same height, h. The area of triangles DCB and ADB are $\frac{1}{2}b_1h$ and $\frac{1}{2}b_2h$, respectively. The area of the trapezoid is the sum of the areas of the triangles, $\frac{1}{2}b_1h + \frac{1}{2}b_2h$, which can be written $\frac{1}{2}h(b_1 + b_2)$.

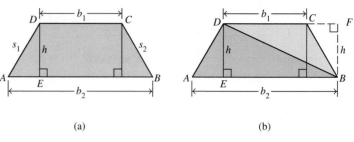

(a)   (b)

FIGURE 6.31

AREA OF A TRAPEZOID

$$A = \tfrac{1}{2}h(b_1 + b_2)$$

Following is a summary of the perimeters and areas of selected figures.

PERIMETERS AND AREAS

Triangle

$P = s_1 + s_2 + s_3 \ (s_3 = b)$
$A = \tfrac{1}{2}bh$

Square

$P = 4s$
$A = s^2$

Rectangle

$P = 2l + 2w$
$A = lw$

Parallelogram

$P = 2b + 2w$
$A = bh$

Trapezoid

$P = s_1 + s_2 + b_1 + b_2$
$A = \tfrac{1}{2}h(b_1 + b_2)$

EXAMPLE 1   SODDING A BACKYARD

Kevin Geis wishes to replace the grass (sod) in his backyard. One pallet of Milberger's sod costs \$130 and covers 450 square feet. If Kevin's backyard is rectangular in shape with a length of 90 feet and width of 60 feet, determine

a) the area of the backyard.

b) how many pallets of sod Kevin needs to purchase.

c) the cost of the sod purchased.

SOLUTION

a) The area of the backyard is

$$A = l \cdot w = 90 \cdot 60 = 5400 \text{ ft}^2$$

The area of the backyard is in square feet because both the length and width are measured in feet.

b) To determine the number of pallets of sod Kevin needs, divide the area of the backyard by the area covered by one pallet of sod.

$$\frac{\text{Area of backyard}}{\text{Area covered by one pallet}} = \frac{5400}{450} = 12$$

Kevin needs to purchase 12 pallets of sod.

c) The cost of 12 pallets of sod is $12 \times \$130$, or $1560.

Pythagorean Theorem

The Pythagorean Theorem is an important tool for finding the perimeter and area of triangles.

> PYTHAGOREAN THEOREM
> The sum of the squares of the lengths of the legs of a right triangle equals the square of the length of the hypotenuse.
>
> $$\text{leg}^2 + \text{leg}^2 = \text{hypotenuse}^2$$
>
> Symbolically, if a and b represent the lengths of the legs and c represents the length of the hypotenuse (the side opposite the right angle), then
>
> $$a^2 + b^2 = c^2$$
>
>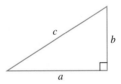

EXAMPLE 2 CROSSING A MOAT

The moat surrounding a castle is 18 ft wide and the wall by the moat of the castle is 24 ft high (see Fig. 6.32). If an invading army wishes to use a ladder to cross the moat and reach the top of the wall, how long must the ladder be?

SOLUTION The moat, the castle wall, and the ladder form a right triangle. The moat and the castle wall form the legs of the triangle (sides a and b), and the ladder forms the hypotenuse (side c). By the Pythagorean theorem,

$$c^2 = a^2 + b^2$$
$$c^2 = (18)^2 + (24)^2$$
$$c^2 = 324 + 576$$
$$c^2 = 900$$
$$\sqrt{c^2} = \sqrt{900}$$
$$c = 30$$

Take the square root of both sides of the equation.

Therefore, the ladder would need to be at least 30 ft long.

BLITZER BONUS

Pythagorean Theorem

The Pythagorean theorem is one of the most famous theorems of all time. One book, *Pythagorean Propositions*, contains 370 different proofs of the Pythagorean theorem. U.S. President James A. Garfield gave one notable proof. The Pythagorean theorem has found its way into popular culture as well. In the movie *The Wizard of Oz*, the scarecrow incorrectly recites the Pythagorean theorem once the wizard grants him his diploma. In the play *The Pirates of Penzance*, the Major General refers to the Pythagorean theorem when he sings "I'm teeming with a lot o' news, with many cheerful facts about the square of the hypotenuse." Lewis Carroll, author of *Through the Looking Glass* and *Alice's Adventures in Wonderland*, stated that the Pythagorean theorem "is as dazzlingly beautiful now as it was in the day when Pythagoras discovered it." Actually, the Pythagorean theorem was known to the ancient Babylonians in about 1600 B.C., 1000 years before Pythagoras, and it continues to play a huge role in mathematics.

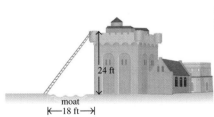

24 ft

moat
18 ft

FIGURE 6.32

Circumference
$C = 2\pi r$

Radius

Area
$A = \pi r^2$

Diameter

FIGURE 6.33

TECHNOLOGY

CITY PLANNING

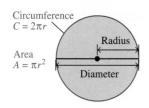

The Roman poet Virgil tells the story of Queen Dido, who fled to Africa after her brother murdered her husband. There, she begged for some land from King Iarbus, telling him she only needed as much land as the hide of an ox would enclose. Being very clever, she decided that the greatest area would be enclosed if she tore the hide into thin strips and formed the strips into a circle. On this land she founded the city of Byrsa (the Greek word for "hide"), later known as Carthage in present-day Tunisia.

Circles

A commonly used plane figure that is not a polygon is a *circle*. A *circle* is a set of points equidistant from a fixed point called the center. A *radius*, *r*, of a circle is a line segment from the center of the circle to any point on the circle (Fig. 6.33). A *diameter*, *d*, of a circle is a line segment through the center of a circle with both end points on the circle. Note that the diameter of the circle is twice its radius. The *circumference* is the length of the simple closed curve that forms the circle. The formulas for the area and circumference of a circle are given in Fig. 6.33. Π is approximately 3.14. If your calculator contains a $\boxed{\pi}$ key, you should use that key when working calculations involving pi.

EXAMPLE 3   COMPARING PIZZAS

Victoria Montoya wishes to order a large cheese pizza. She can choose among three pizza parlors in town: Antonio's, Brett's, and Dorsey's. Antonio's large cheese pizza is a round 16-in.-diameter pizza that sells for $15. Brett's large cheese pizza is a round 14-in.-diameter pizza that sells for $12. Dorsey's large cheese pizza is a square 12-in. by 12-in. pizza that sells for $10. All three pizzas have the same thickness. To get the most for her money, from which pizza parlor should Victoria order her pizza?

SOLUTION   To determine the best value, we will calculate the cost per square inch of pizza for each of the three pizzas. To do so, we will divide the cost of each pizza by its area. The areas of the two round pizzas can be determined using the formula for the area of a circle, $A = \pi r^2$. Since the radius is half the diameter, we will use $r = 8$ and $r = 7$ for Antonio's and Brett's large pizzas, respectively. The area for the square pizza can be determined using the formula for the area of a square, $A = s^2$. We will use $s = 12$.

$$\text{Area of Antonio's pizza} = \pi r^2 \approx (3.14)(8)^2 \approx 3.14(64) \approx 200.96 \text{ in.}^{2*}$$
$$\text{Area of Brett's pizza} = \pi r^2 \approx (3.14)(7)^2 \approx 3.14(49) \approx 153.86 \text{ in.}^{2*}$$
$$\text{Area of Dorsey's pizza} = s^2 = (12)^2 = 144 \text{ in.}^2$$

Now, to find the cost per square inch of pizza, we will divide the cost of the pizza by the area of the pizza.

$$\text{Cost per square inch of Antonio's pizza} \approx \frac{\$15}{200.96 \text{ in.}^2} \approx \$0.0746$$

Thus, Antonio's pizza costs about $0.0746, or about 7.5 cents, per square inch.

$$\text{Cost per square inch of Brett's pizza} \approx \frac{\$12}{153.86 \text{ in.}^2} \approx \$0.0780$$

Thus, Brett's pizza costs about $0.0780, or about 7.8 cents, per square inch.

$$\text{Cost per square inch of Dorsey's pizza} = \frac{\$10}{144 \text{ in.}^2} \approx \$0.0694$$

Thus, Dorsey's pizza costs about $0.0694, or about 6.9 cents, per square inch.
Since the cost per square inch of pizza is the lowest for Dorsey's pizza, Victoria would get the most pizza for her money by ordering her pizza from Dorsey's.

---

*If you use the $\boxed{\pi}$ key on your calculator, your answers will be slightly more accurate.

Andrew J. Wiles

In 1637, Pierre de Fermat, an amateur French mathematician, scribbled a note in the margin of the book *Arithmetica* by Diophantus. The note would haunt mathematicians for centuries. Fermat stated that the generalized form of the Pythagorean theorem, $a^n + b^n = c^n$, has no positive integer solutions where $n > 2$. Fermat's note concluded, "I have a truly marvelous demonstration of this proposition, which this margin is too narrow to contain." This conjecture became known as Fermat's last theorem. A formal proof of this conjecture escaped mathematicians until on September 19, 1994, Andrew J. Wiles of Princeton University announced he had found a proof. It took Wiles more than 8 years of work to accomplish the task. Wiles was awarded the Wolfskehl prize at Göttingen University in Germany in acknowledgment of his achievement.

EXAMPLE 4   APPLYING LAWN FERTILIZER

Steve May plans to fertilize his lawn. The shapes and dimensions of his lot, house, driveway, pool, and rose garden are shown in Fig. 6.34. One bag of fertilizer costs $26.95 and covers 5000 ft^2. Determine how many bags of fertilizer Steve needs and the total cost of the fertilizer.

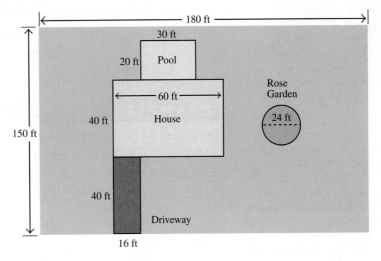

FIGURE 6.34

SOLUTION The total area of the lot is $150 \cdot 180$, or 27,000 ft^2. To determine the area to be fertilized, subtract the area of house, driveway, pool, and rose garden from the total area.

$$\text{Area of house} = 60 \cdot 40 = 2400 \text{ ft}^2$$
$$\text{Area of driveway} = 40 \cdot 16 = 640 \text{ ft}^2$$
$$\text{Area of pool} = 20 \cdot 30 = 600 \text{ ft}^2$$

The diameter of the rose garden is 24 ft, so its radius is 12 ft.

$$\text{Area of rose garden} = \pi r^2 = \pi(12)^2 \approx 3.14(144) \approx 452.16 \text{ ft}^2$$

The total area of the house, driveway, pool, and rose garden is approximately $2400 + 640 + 600 + 452.16$, or 4092.16 ft^2. The area to be fertilized is $27,000 - 4092.16$ ft^2, or 22,907.84 ft^2. The number of bags of fertilizer is found by dividing the total area to be fertilized by the number of square feet covered per bag.

The number of bags of fertilizer is $\dfrac{22,907.84}{5000}$, or about 4.58 bags. Therefore, Steve needs five bags. At $29.95 per bag, the total cost is $5 \times \$29.95$, or $149.75.

EXAMPLE 5   CONVERTING BETWEEN SQUARE FEET AND SQUARE INCHES

a) Convert 1 ft^2 to square inches.
b) Convert 37 ft^2 to square inches.
c) Convert 432 in.^{2} to square feet.
d) Convert 2196 in.^{2} to square feet.

Pierre de Fermat

Pierre de Fermat (1601–1665) is considered one of the greatest mathematicians of the seventeenth century. Fermat (pronounced Fair-MAH), however, was a lawyer by trade and considered mathematics a hobby. Although he is mostly known for his famous "last theorem" (see the Technology Box on page 315), Fermat also made many contributions to mathematics through his correspondence with leading mathematicians of Europe. Although Fermat published very little himself, his letters to other mathematicians influenced virtually all branches of mathematical study in his time, including analytic geometry, calculus, probability, and number theory.

SOLUTION

a) 1 ft = 12 in. Therefore, 1 ft^2 = 12 in. $\times$ 12 in. = 144 in.^{2}.

b) From part (a), we know that 1 ft^2 = 144 in.^{2}. Therefore, 37 ft^2 = 37 $\times$ 144 in.^{2} = 5328 in.^{2}.

c) In part (b), we converted from square feet to square inches by *multiplying* the number of square feet by 144. Now, to convert from square inches to square feet we will *divide* the number of square inches by 144. Therefore, 432 in.^{2} = $\frac{432}{144}$ ft^2 = 3 ft^2.

d) As in part (c), we will divide the number of square inches by 144. Therefore, 2196 in.^{2} = $\frac{2196}{144}$ ft^2 = 15.25 ft^2.

EXAMPLE 6   INSTALLING CERAMIC TILE

Debra Levy wishes to purchase ceramic tile for her family room, which measures 30 ft $\times$ 27 ft. The cost of the tile, including installation, is $21 per square yard.

a) Find the area of Debra's family room in square *yards*.

b) Determine Debra's cost of the ceramic tile for her family room.

SOLUTION

a) The area of the family room in square feet is $30 \cdot 27 = 810$ ft^2. Since 1 yd = 3 ft, 1 yd^2 = 3 ft $\times$ 3 ft = 9 ft^2. To find the area of the family room in square yards, divide the area in square feet by 9 ft^2.

$$\text{Area in square yards} = \frac{810}{9} = 90$$

Therefore, the area is 90 yd^2.

b) The cost of 90 yd^2 of ceramic tile, including installation, is $90 \cdot \$21 = \$1890$.

When multiplying units of length, be sure that the units are the same. You can multiply feet by feet to get square feet or yards by yards to get square yards. However, you cannot get a valid answer if you multiply numbers expressed in feet by numbers expressed in yards.

EXERCISE SET 6.3 ●●●●●●

• Concept/Writing Exercises

1. a) Describe in your own words how to determine the *perimeter* of a two-dimensional figure.

   b) Describe in your own words how to determine the *area* of a two-dimensional figure.

   c) Draw a rectangle with a length of 6 units and a width of 2 units. Determine the area and perimeter of this rectangle.

2. What is the relationship between the *radius* and the *diameter* of a circle?

3. a) How do you convert an area from square yards into square feet?

   b) How do you convert an area from square feet into square yards?

4. a) How do you convert an area from square feet into square inches?

   b) How do you convert an area from square inches into square feet?

• Practice the Skills

In Exercises 5–8, find the area of the triangle.

5.
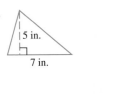
5 in.
7 in.

6.

6 yd
2 ft

7.
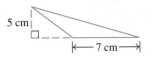
5 cm
←— 7 cm —→

8.

2 m
√3 m

In Exercises 9–14, determine (a) the area and (b) the perimeter of the quadrilateral.

9.

10 ft
21 ft

10.
7 in.
9 in.
14 in.

11.
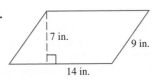
20 cm
27 cm
3 m

12.
2 yd
6 ft

13.
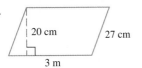
5 in.
25 in.   2 ft   25 in.
19 in.

14.
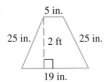
16 in.
13 in.   12 in.   13 in.
6 in.

In Exercises 15–18, determine (a) the area and (b) the circumference of the circle. Use the 🔲π key on your calculator and round your answer to the nearest hundredth.

15.
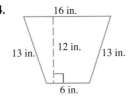
4 m

16.

28 yd

17.
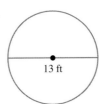
13 ft

18.
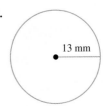
13 mm

In Exercises 19–22, (a) use the Pythagorean theorem to determine the length of the unknown side of the triangle, (b) determine the perimeter of the triangle, and (c) determine the area of the triangle.

19.
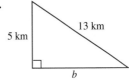
c   15 yd
8 yd

20.
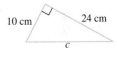
15 in.   12 in.
a

21.
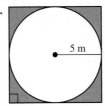
5 km   13 km
b

22.

10 cm   24 cm
c

• Problem Solving

In Exercises 23–32, find the shaded area. When appropriate, use the 🔲π key on your calculator and round your answer to the nearest hundredth.

23.
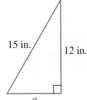
5 m

24.
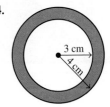
3 cm
4 cm

25.
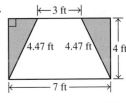
←— 4 in. —→
4 in.

26.
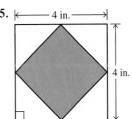
←3 ft→
4.47 ft   4.47 ft   4 ft
←— 7 ft —→

27.
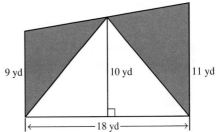
9 yd   10 yd   11 yd
←————— 18 yd —————→

28.

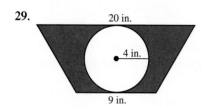

29.

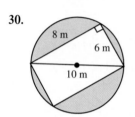

30.

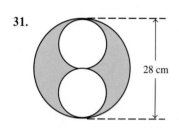

31.

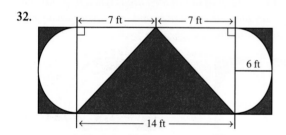

32.

One square yard equals 9 ft². Use this information to convert the following.

33. 207 ft² to square yards   **34.** 15.2 ft² to square yards

35. 14.7 yd² to square feet   **36.** 15.2 yd² to square feet

One square meter equals 10,000 cm². Use this information to convert the following.

37. 23.4 m² to square centimeters

38. 0.375 m² to square centimeters

39. 8625 cm² to square meters

40. 608 cm² to square meters

Nancy Wallin has just purchased a new house that is in need of new flooring. In Exercises 41–46, use the measurements given on the floor plans of Nancy's house to obtain the answer.

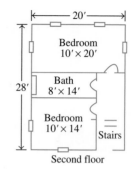

Second floor

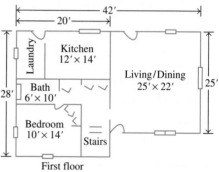

First floor

41. *Cost of Hardwood Flooring* The cost of Mannington Chestnut hardwood flooring is $10.86 per square foot if Nancy installs the flooring herself or $13.86 per square foot if she has the flooring installed by the flooring company. Determine the cost for hardwood flooring in the living/dining room if

  a) Nancy installs it herself.

  b) Nancy has it installed by the flooring company.

42. *Cost of Laminate Flooring* The cost of Pergo Select Helsinki Birch laminate flooring is $5.89 per square foot if Nancy installs the flooring herself or $8.89 per square foot if she has the flooring installed by the flooring company. Determine the cost for the flooring in the living/dining room if

  a) Nancy installs it herself.

  b) Nancy has it installed by the flooring company.

43. *Cost of Ceramic Tile* The cost of Mohawk Porcelain ceramic tile is $8.50 per square foot. This price includes the cost of installation. Determine the cost for Nancy to have this ceramic tile installed in the kitchen and in both bathrooms.

44. *Cost of Linoleum* The cost of Armstrong Solarian Woodcut linoleum is $5.00 per square foot. This price includes the cost of installation. Determine the cost for Nancy to have this linoleum installed in the kitchen and in both bathrooms.

45. *Cost of Berber Carpeting* The cost of Bigelow Commodore Berber carpeting is $6.06 per square foot. This price includes the cost of installation. Determine the cost for Nancy to have this carpeting installed in all three bedrooms.

46. *Cost of Saxony Carpeting* The cost of DuPont Stainmaster Saxony carpeting is $5.56 per square foot. This price includes the cost of installation. Determine the cost for Nancy to have this carpeting installed in all three bedrooms.

47. *Cost of a Lawn Service* Clarence and Rose Cohen's home lot is illustrated here. Clarence and Rose wish to hire Picture Perfect Lawn Service to cut their lawn. How much will it cost Clarence and Rose to have their lawn cut if Picture Perfect charges $0.02 per square yard?

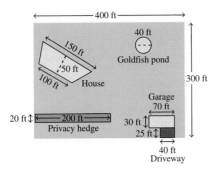

48. *Cost of a Lawn Service* Jim and Wendy Scott's home lot is illustrated here. The Scotts wish to hire a lawn service to cut their lawn. M&M Lawn Service charges $0.02 per square yard of lawn. How much will it cost the Scotts to have their lawn cut?

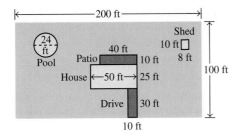

49. *Area of a Basketball Court* A National Basketball Association (NBA) basketball court is a rectangle that is 94 ft long and 50 ft wide.

a) If you were to walk around the outside edge of a basketball court, how far would you walk?

b) If you had to place floor tiles that each measured 1 foot by 1 foot on a basketball court, how many tiles would you need?

50. *Quartz Countertops* Larry Shedden wishes to have three Cambria Windsor quartz countertops installed in his new kitchen. The countertops are rectangular and have the following dimensions: $3\frac{1}{2}$ ft $\times$ 6 ft, $2\frac{1}{2}$ ft $\times$ 8 ft, and 3 ft $\times$ $11\frac{1}{2}$ ft. The cost of the countertops is $87 per square foot, which includes the cost of installation.

a) Determine the total area of the three countertops.

b) Determine the total cost to have all three countertops installed.

51. *Ladder on a Wall* Lorrie Morgan places a 29 ft ladder against the side of a building with the bottom of the ladder 20 ft away from the building (see figure). How high up on the wall does the ladder reach?

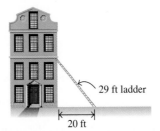

52. *Docking a Boat* Brian Murphy is bringing his boat into a dock that is 9 ft above the water level (see figure). If a 41 ft rope is attached to the dock on one side and to the boat on the other side, determine the horizontal distance from the dock to the boat.

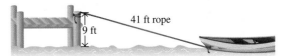

53. *The Green Monster* In Fenway Park, home of baseball's Boston Red Sox, the left field wall is known as the *Green Monster*. The distance from home plate down the third baseline to the bottom of the wall is 310 feet (see photo). In left field, at the end of the baseline, the Green Monster is perpendicular to the ground and is 37 feet tall. Determine the distance from home plate to the top of the Green Monster along the third baseline. Round your answer to the nearest foot.

Challenge Problems/Group Activities

54. *Plasma Television* The screen of a plasma television is in the shape of a rectangle with a diagonal of length 43 in. If the height of the screen is 21 in., determine the width of the screen.

55. *Doubling the Sides of a Square* In the figure below, an original square with sides of length s is shown. Also shown is a larger square with sides double in length, or $2s$.

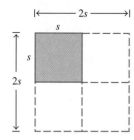

a) Express the area of the original square in terms of s.

b) Express the area of the larger square in terms of s.

c) How many times larger is the area of the square in part (b) than the area of the square in part (a)?

56. *Doubling the Sides of a Parallelogram* In the figure below, an original parallelogram with base b and height h is shown. Also shown is a larger parallelogram with base and height double in length, or $2b$ and $2h$, respectively.

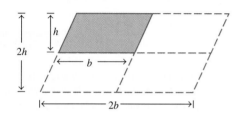

a) Express the area of the original parallelogram in terms of b and h.

b) Express the area of the larger parallelogram in terms of b and h.

c) How many times larger is the area of the parallelogram in part (b) than the area of the parallelogram in part (a)?

57. *Heron's Formula* A second formula for determining the area of a triangle (called Heron's formula) is

$$A = \sqrt{s(s-a)(s-b)(s-c)}$$

where $s = \frac{1}{2}(a + b + c)$ and a, b, and c are the lengths of the sides of the triangle. Use Heron's formula to determine the area of right triangle ABC and check your answer using the formula $A = \frac{1}{2}ab$.

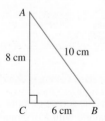

58. *Expansion of $(a + b)^2$* In the figure, one side of the largest square has length $a + b$. Therefore, the area of the largest square is $(a + b)^2$. Answer the following questions to find a formula for the expansion of $(a + b)^2$.

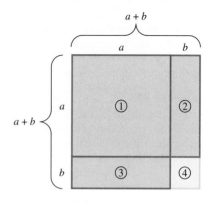

a) What is the area of the square marked ① ?

b) What is the area of the rectangle marked ② ?

c) What is the area of the rectangle marked ③ ?

d) What is the area of the square marked ④ ?

e) Add the four areas found in parts (a) through (d) to write a formula for the expansion of $(a + b)^2$.

• Recreational Mathematics

59. *Sports Areas* Use the Internet to research the official dimensions of the playing surface of your favorite sport and determine the area of the playing surface. Choices may include a basketball court, volleyball court, tennis court, racquetball court, hockey rink, football field, soccer field, lacrosse field, and a baseball diamond.

60. *Scarecrow's Error* In the movie *The Wizard of Oz*, once the scarecrow gets his diploma he states the following: "In an isosceles triangle, the sum of the square roots of the two equal sides is equal to the square root of the third side." Discuss why this statement is incorrect.

Internet/Research Activities

For Exercises 61–63, references include the Internet, history of mathematics textbooks, and encyclopedias.

61. Research the proof of the Pythagorean theorem provided by President James Garfield. Write a brief paper and make a poster of this proof and the associated diagrams.

62. The early Babylonians and Egyptians did not know about π and had to devise techniques to approximate the area of a circle. Do research and write a paper on the techniques these societies used to approximate the area of a circle.

63. Write a paper on the contributions of Heron of Alexandria to geometry.

SECTION 6.4 • VOLUME AND SURFACE AREA

The amount of paint in a can refers to volume, and the amount of wall space that the paint covers refers to surface area.

On the label of a can of Color Place paint is the following sentence: "One gallon will cover about 400 sq. ft." This sentence refers to the two main geometric topics that we will cover in this section. *One gallon* refers to volume of the paint in the can, and *400 sq. ft* refers to the surface area that the paint will cover.

When discussing a one-dimensional figure such as a line, we can find its length. When discussing a two-dimensional figure such as a rectangle, we can find its area and its perimeter. When discussing a three-dimensional figure such as a cube, we can find its volume and its surface area. *Volume* is a measure of the capacity of a three-dimensional figure. *Surface area* is the sum of the areas of the surfaces of a three-dimensional figure. Volume refers to the amount of material that you can put *inside* a three-dimensional figure, and surface area refers to the total area that is on the *outside* surface of the figure.

Solid geometry is the study of three-dimensional solid figures, also called *space figures*. Volumes of three-dimensional figures are measured in cubic units such as cubic feet or cubic meters. Surface areas of three-dimensional figures are measured in square units such as square feet or square meters.

Rectangular Solids, Cylinders, Cones, and Spheres

We will begin our discussion with the *rectangular solid*. If the length of the solid is 5 units, the width is 2 units, and the height is 3 units, the total number of cubes is 30 (Fig. 6.35). Thus, the volume is 30 cubic units. The volume of a rectangular solid can also be found by multiplying its length times width times height; in this case, 5 units $\times$ 2 units $\times$ 3 units = 30 cubic units. In general, the volume of any rectangular solid is $V = l \times w \times h$.

The surface area of the rectangular solid in Fig. 6.35 is the sum of the area of the surfaces of the rectangular solid. Notice that each surface of the rectangular solid is a rectangle. The left and right side of the rectangular solid each has an area of 5 units $\times$ 3 units, or 15 square units. The front and back sides of the rectangular solid each has an area of 2 units $\times$ 3 units, or 6 square units. The top and bottom sides of the rectangular solid each has an area of 5 units $\times$ 2 units, or 10 square units. Therefore, the surface area of the rectangular solid is $2(5 \times 3) + 2(2 \times 3) + 2(5 \times 2) = 2(15) + 2(6) + 2(10) = 30 + 12 + 20 = 62$ square units. In general, the surface area of any rectangular solid is $SA = 2lw + 2wh + 2lh$.

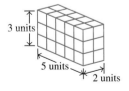

3 units

5 units

2 units

FIGURE 6.35

> **VOLUME AND SURFACE AREA OF A RECTANGULAR SOLID**
>
> $$V = lwh \qquad SA = 2lw + 2wh + 2lh$$

A *cube* is a rectangular solid with the same length, width, and height. If we call the length of the side of the cube s and use the volume and surface area formulas for a rectangular solid, substituting s in for l, w, and h, we obtain $V = s \cdot s \cdot s = s^3$ and $SA = 2 \cdot s \cdot s + 2 \cdot s \cdot s + 2 \cdot s \cdot s = 2s^2 + 2s^2 + 2s^2 = 6s^2$.

> **VOLUME AND SURFACE AREA OF A CUBE**
>
> $$V = s^3 \qquad SA = 6s^2$$

Now consider the right circular cylinder shown in Fig. 6.36(a). When we use the term *cylinder* in this book, we mean a right circular cylinder. The volume of the cylinder is found by multiplying the area of the circular base, πr^2, by the height, h, to get $V = \pi r^2 h$.

The surface area of the cylinder is the sum of the area of the top, the area of the bottom, and the area of the side of the cylinder. Both the top and bottom of the cylinder are circles with an area of πr^2. To determine the area of the side of the cylinder, examine Fig. 6.36(b) and (c).

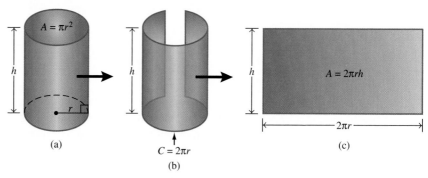

FIGURE 6.36

Notice how when flattened, the side of the cylinder is a rectangle whose length is the circumference of the base of the cylinder and whose width is the height of the cylinder. Thus, the side of the cylinder has an area of $2\pi r \cdot h$, or $2\pi rh$. Therefore, the surface area of the cylinder is $\pi r^2 + \pi r^2 + 2\pi rh$, or $SA = 2\pi rh + 2\pi r^2$.

> **VOLUME AND SURFACE AREA OF A CYLINDER**
>
> $$V = \pi r^2 h \qquad SA = 2\pi rh + 2\pi r^2$$

Now consider the right circular cone illustrated in Fig. 6.37. When we use the term *cone* in this book, we mean a right circular cone. The volume of a cone is less than the volume of a cylinder that has the same base and the same height. In fact, the volume of the cone is one-third the volume of the cylinder. The formula for the surface area of a cone is the sum of the area of the circular base of the cone, πr^2, and the area of the side of the cone, $\pi r \sqrt{r^2 + h^2}$, or $SA = \pi r^2 + \pi r \sqrt{r^2 + h^2}$. The derivation of the area of the side of the cone is beyond the scope of this book.

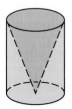

FIGURE 6.37

> **VOLUME AND SURFACE AREA OF A CONE**
>
> $$V = \tfrac{1}{3}\pi r^2 h \qquad SA = \pi r^2 + \pi r \sqrt{r^2 + h^2}$$

The next shape we will discuss in this section is the *sphere*. Baseballs, tennis balls, and so on have the shape of a sphere. The formulas for the volume and surface area of a sphere are as follows. The derivation of the volume and surface area of a sphere are beyond the scope of this book.

VOLUME AND SURFACE AREA OF A SPHERE

$$V = \tfrac{4}{3}\pi r^3 \qquad SA = 4\pi r^2$$

Following is a summary of the formulas for the volumes and surface areas of the three-dimensional figures we have discussed thus far.

VOLUMES AND SURFACE AREAS

Rectangular Solid   **Cube**   **Cylinder**

$V = lwh$ $V = s^3$ $V = \pi r^2 h$
$SA = 2lw + 2wh + 2lh$ $SA = 6s^2$ $SA = 2\pi rh + 2\pi r^2$

Cone   **Sphere**

$V = \tfrac{1}{3}\pi r^2 h$ $V = \tfrac{4}{3}\pi r^3$
$SA = \pi r^2 + \pi r\sqrt{r^2 + h^2}$ $SA = 4\pi r^2$

E X A M P L E   1   VOLUME AND SURFACE AREA

Determine the volume and surface area of each of the following three-dimensional figures. When appropriate, use the $\boxed{\pi}$ key on your calculator and round your answer to the nearest hundredths.

(a)   (b)

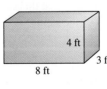

(c)   (d)

SOLUTION

a) $V = lwh = 8 \cdot 3 \cdot 4 = 96 \text{ ft}^3$
    $SA = 2lw + 2wh + 2lh = 2 \cdot 8 \cdot 3 + 2 \cdot 3 \cdot 4 + 2 \cdot 8 \cdot 4$
    $\qquad\qquad\qquad\qquad = 48 + 24 + 64 = 136 \text{ ft}^2$

b) $V = \pi r^2 h = \pi \cdot 5^2 \cdot 9 = 225\pi \approx 706.86 \text{ in.}^3$
    $SA = 2\pi rh + 2\pi r^2 = 2\pi \cdot 5 \cdot 9 + 2\pi \cdot 5^2$
    $\qquad\qquad\qquad = 90\pi + 50\pi = 140\pi \approx 439.82 \text{ in.}^2$

c) $V = \frac{1}{3}\pi r^2 h = \frac{1}{3}\pi \cdot 3^2 \cdot 4 = \frac{1}{3}\pi \cdot 9 \cdot 4 = 12\pi \text{ m}^3 \approx 37.70 \text{ m}^3$
    $SA = \pi r^2 + \pi r\sqrt{r^2 + h^2} = \pi \cdot 3^2 + \pi \cdot 3 \cdot \sqrt{3^2 + 4^2}$
    $\qquad\qquad\qquad\qquad = \pi \cdot 9 + \pi \cdot 3 \cdot \sqrt{25}$
    $\qquad\qquad\qquad\qquad = \pi \cdot 9 + \pi \cdot 3 \cdot 5 = 9\pi + 15\pi$
    $\qquad\qquad\qquad\qquad = 24\pi \approx 75.40 \text{ m}^2$

d) $V = \frac{4}{3}\pi r^3 = \frac{4}{3} \cdot \pi \cdot 6^3 = \frac{4}{3} \cdot \pi \cdot 216 = 288\pi \approx 904.78 \text{ cm}^3$
    $SA = 4\pi r^2 = 4 \cdot \pi \cdot 6^2 = 4 \cdot \pi \cdot 36 = 144\pi \approx 452.39 \text{ cm}^2$

EXAMPLE 2   REPLACING A SAND VOLLEYBALL COURT

Joan Lind is the manager at the Colony Apartments and needs to replace the sand in the rectangular sand volleyball court. The court is 30 ft wide by 60 ft long, and the sand has a uniform depth of 18 in. (see figure below). Sand sells for $15 per cubic yard.

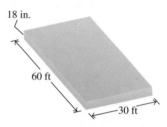

a) How many cubic yards of sand does Joan need?

b) How much will the sand cost?

SOLUTION

a) Since we are asked to find the volume in cubic yards, we will convert each measurement to yards. There are 3 ft in a yard. Thus, 30 ft equals $\frac{30}{3}$ or 10 yd, and 60 ft equals $\frac{60}{3}$ or 20 yd. There are 36 in. in a yard, so 18 in. equals $\frac{18}{36}$, or $\frac{1}{2}$ yd. The amount of sand needed is determined using the formula for the volume of a rectangular solid, $V = l \cdot w \cdot h$. In this case, the height of the rectangular solid can be considered the depth of the sand.

$$V = l \cdot w \cdot h = 10 \cdot 20 \cdot \tfrac{1}{2} = 100 \text{ yd}^3$$

Note that since the measurements for length, width, and height are each in terms of yards, the answer is in terms of cubic yards.

b) One cubic yard of sand costs $15, so 100 yd^3 will cost 100 × $15, or $1500.

EXAMPLE 3   HOMECOMING FLOAT

The basketball team at Southwestern High School is building a float for the homecoming parade. On the float is a large papier-mâché basketball that has a radius of 4.5 ft. Team members need to know the surface area of the basketball so that they can determine how much paint they will need to buy to paint the basketball.

a) Determine the surface area of the basketball.

b) If 1 quart of paint covers approximately 100 sq ft, how many quarts of paint will team members need to buy?

SOLUTION

a) The basketball has the shape of a sphere. We will use the formula for the surface area of a sphere: $SA = 4\pi r^2 = 4 \cdot \pi \cdot (4.5)^2 = 81\pi \approx 254.47$ sq ft.

b) Since each quart of paint will cover about 100 sq ft, they will need about $\dfrac{254.47}{100} = 2.5447$ quarts. Since you cannot buy a portion of a quart of paint, the team will need to buy 3 quarts of paint to paint the basketball.

EXAMPLE 4   SILAGE STORAGE

Gordon Langeneger has three silos on his farm. The silos are each in the shape of a right circular cylinder (see Fig. 6.38). One silo has a 12 ft diameter and is 40 ft tall. The second silo has a 14 ft diameter and is 50 ft tall. The third silo has an 18 ft diameter and is 60 ft tall.

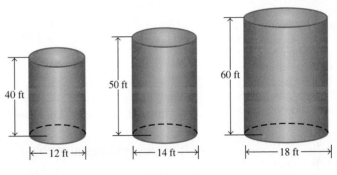

FIGURE 6.38

a) What is the total capacity of the three silos in cubic feet?

b) If Gordon fills all three of his silos and then feeds his cattle 150 ft³ of silage per day, in how many days will all three silos be empty?

SOLUTION

a) The capacity of each silo can be determined using the formula for the volume of a right circular cylinder, $V = \pi r^2 h$. Since the radius is half the diameter, the radii for the three silos are 6 ft, 7 ft, and 9 ft, respectively. Now let's determine the volumes.

$$\text{Volume of the first silo} = \pi r^2 h = \pi \cdot 6^2 \cdot 40$$
$$\approx 3.14 \cdot 36 \cdot 40 \approx 4521.6 \text{ ft}^3$$
$$\text{Volume of the second silo} = \pi r^2 h = \pi \cdot 7^2 \cdot 50$$
$$\approx 3.14 \cdot 49 \cdot 50 \approx 7693.0 \text{ ft}^3$$
$$\text{Volume of the third silo} = \pi r^2 h = \pi \cdot 9^2 \cdot 60$$
$$\approx 3.14 \cdot 81 \cdot 60 \approx 15{,}260.4 \text{ ft}^3$$

Therefore, the total capacity of all three silos is about

$$4521.6 + 7693.0 + 15{,}260.4 \approx 27{,}475.0 \text{ ft}^3.$$

b) To find how long it takes to empty all three silos, we will divide the total capacity by 150 ft³, the amount fed to Gordon's cattle every day.

$$\frac{27{,}475}{150} \approx 183.17$$

Thus, the silos will be empty in about 183 days.

Polyhedra, Prisms, and Pyramids

Now let's discuss polyhedra. A *polyhedron* (plural is *polyhedra*) is a closed surface formed by the union of polygonal regions. Figure 6.39 illustrates some polyhedra.

Polyhedra

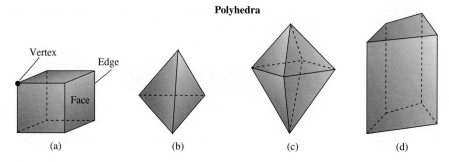

(a)   (b)   (c)   (d)

FIGURE 6.39

Each polygonal region is called a *face* of the polyhedron. The line segment formed by the intersection of two faces is called an *edge*. The point at which two or more edges intersect is called a *vertex*. In Fig. 6.39(a), there are 6 faces, 12 edges, and 8 vertices. Note that

Number of vertices − number of edges + number of faces = 2

8   −   12   +   6   = 2

This formula, credited to Leonhard Euler, is true for any polyhedron.

> **EULER'S POLYHEDRON FORMULA**
>
> Number of vertices − number of edges + number of faces = 2

We suggest that you verify that this formula holds for Fig. 6.39(b), (c), and (d).

EXAMPLE 5   USING EULER'S POLYHEDRON FORMULA

A certain polyhedron has 13 vertices and 8 faces. Determine the number of edges on the polyhedron.

SOLUTION Since we are seeking the number of edges, we will let x represent the number of edges on the polyhedron. Next, we will use Euler's polyhedron formula to set up an equation:

Number of vertices − number of edges + number of faces = 2

13   − x +   8   = 2

$$21 - x = 2$$
$$-x = -19$$
$$x = 19$$

Therefore, the polyhedron has 19 edges.

PLATONIC SOLIDS

Tetrahedron: 4 faces, 4 vertices, 6 edges

Cube: 6 faces, 8 vertices, 12 edges

Octahedron: 8 faces, 6 vertices, 12 edges

Dodecahedron: 12 faces, 20 vertices, 30 edges

Icosahedron: 20 faces, 12 vertices, 30 edges

A platonic solid is a polyhedron whose faces are all regular polygons of the same size and shape. There are exactly five platonic solids, as shown above. Platonic solids, also called regular polyhedra, are named after the ancient Greek philosopher Plato and are included in Euclid's *Elements* (see the Blitzer Bonus on page 289). The figures above show each of the platonic solids, along with the number of faces, vertices, and edges for each.

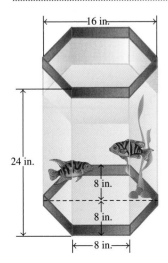

FIGURE 6.41

A *platonic solid*, also known as a *regular polyhedron*, is a polyhedron whose faces are all regular polygons of the same size and shape. There are exactly five platonic solids. All five platonic solids are illustrated in the Technology Box at left.

A *prism* is a special type of polyhedron whose bases are congruent polygons and whose sides are parallelograms. These parallelogram regions are called the *lateral faces* of the prism. If all the lateral faces are rectangles, the prism is said to be a *right prism*. The prisms illustrated in Fig. 6.40 are all right prisms. When we use the word *prism* in this book, we are referring to a right prism.

Prisms

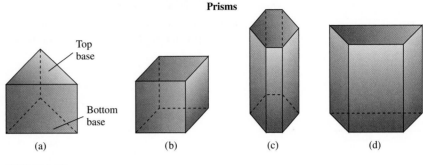

FIGURE 6.40

The volume of any prism can be found by multiplying the area of the base, *B*, by the height, *h*, of the prism.

VOLUME OF A PRISM

$$V = Bh$$

where *B* is the area of a base and *h* is the height.

EXAMPLE 6   VOLUME OF A HEXAGONAL PRISM FISH TANK

Frank Nicolzaao's fish tank is in the shape of a hexagonal prism as shown in Fig. 6.41. Use the dimensions shown in the figure and the fact that 1 gal = 231 in.³ to

a) determine the volume of the fish tank in cubic inches.

b) determine the volume of the fish tank in gallons (round your answer to the nearest gallon).

SOLUTION

a) First we will need to calculate the area of the hexagonal base of the fish tank. Notice from Fig. 6.41 that by drawing a diagonal as indicated, the base can be divided into two identical trapezoids. To find the area of the hexagonal base, we will calculate the area of one of these trapezoids and then multiply by 2.

$$\text{Area of one trapezoid} = \tfrac{1}{2}h(b_1 + b_2)$$
$$= \tfrac{1}{2}(8)(16 + 8) = 96 \text{ in.}^2$$
$$\text{Area of the hexagonal base} = 2(96) = 192 \text{ in.}^2$$

Now to determine the volume of the fish tank, we will use the formula for the volume of a prism, $V = Bh$. We already determined that the area of the base, *B*, is 192 in.²

$$V = B \cdot h = 192 \cdot 24 = 4608 \text{ in.}^3$$

In the above calculation, the area of the base, *B*, was measured in square inches and the height was measured in inches. The product of square inches and inches is cubic inches, or in.³.

b) To determine the volume of the fish tank in gallons, we will divide the volume of the fish tank in cubic inches by 231.

$$V = \frac{4608}{231} \approx 19.95 \text{ gal}$$

Thus, the volume of the fish tank is approximately 20 gal.

EXAMPLE 7   VOLUMES INVOLVING PRISMS

Determine the volume of the remaining solid after the cylinder, triangular prism, and square prism have been cut from the solid (Fig. 6.42).

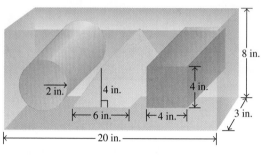

FIGURE 6.42

SOLUTION To determine the volume of the remaining solid, first determine the volume of the rectangular solid. Then subtract the volume of the two prisms and the cylinder that were cut out.

$$
\begin{aligned}
\text{Volume of rectangular solid} &= l \cdot w \cdot h \\
&= 20 \cdot 3 \cdot 8 = 480 \text{ in.}^3 \\
\text{Volume of circular cylinder} &= \pi r^2 h \\
&\approx (3.14)(2^2)(3) \\
&\approx (3.14)(4)(3) \approx 37.68 \text{ in.}^3 \\
\text{Volume of triangular prism} &= \text{area of the base} \cdot \text{height} \\
&= \tfrac{1}{2}(6)(4)(3) = 36 \text{ in.}^3 \\
\text{Volume of square prism} &= s^2 \cdot h \\
&= 4^2 \cdot 3 = 48 \text{ in.}^3 \\
\text{Volume of solid} &\approx 480 - 37.68 - 36 - 48 \\
&\approx 358.32 \text{ in.}^3
\end{aligned}
$$

Another special category of polyhedra is the *pyramid*. Unlike prisms, pyramids have only one base. The figures illustrated in Fig. 6.43 on the following page are pyramids. Note that all but one face of a pyramid intersect at a common vertex.

If a pyramid is drawn inside a prism, as shown in Fig. 6.44, the volume of the pyramid is less than that of the prism. In fact, the volume of the pyramid is one-third the volume of the prism.

VOLUME OF A PYRAMID

$$V = \tfrac{1}{3}Bh$$

where B is the area of the base and h is the height.

Pyramids

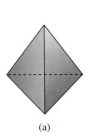

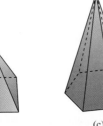

(a)   (b)   (c)   (d)

FIGURE 6.43

FIGURE 6.44

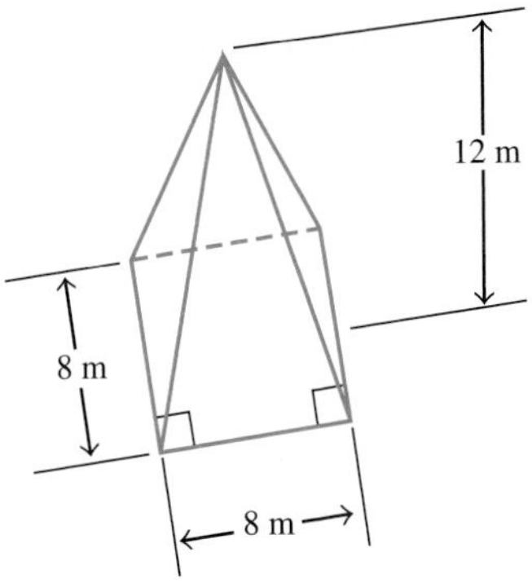

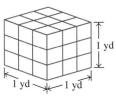

FIGURE 6.45

EXAMPLE 8   VOLUME OF A PYRAMID

Find the volume of the pyramid shown in Fig. 6.45.

SOLUTION First find the area of the base of the pyramid. Since the base of the pyramid is a square,

$$\text{Area of base} = s^2 = 8^2 = 64 \text{ m}^2$$

Now use this information to find the volume of the pyramid.

$$V = \tfrac{1}{3} \cdot B \cdot h$$
$$= \tfrac{1}{3} \cdot 64 \cdot 12$$
$$= 256 \text{ m}^3$$

Thus, the volume of the pyramid is 256 m³.

Cubic Unit Conversions

In certain situations, converting volume from one cubic unit to a different cubic unit might be necessary. For example, when purchasing topsoil you might have to change the amount of topsoil from cubic feet to cubic yards prior to placing your order. Example 9 shows how that may be done.

EXAMPLE 9   CUBIC YARDS AND CUBIC FEET

a) Convert 1 yd³ to cubic feet. (See Fig. 6.46.)

b) Convert 18.5 yd³ to cubic feet.

c) Convert 1302.75 ft³ to cubic yards.

FIGURE 6.46

SOLUTION

a) We know that 1 yd = 3ft. Thus, 1 yd³ = 3 ft × 3 ft × 3 ft = 27 ft³.

b) In part (a), we learned that 1 yd³ = 27ft³. Thus, 18.5 yd³ = 18.5 × 27 = 499.5 ft³.

c) In part (b), we converted from cubic yards to cubic feet by *multiplying* the number of cubic yards by 27. Now, to convert from cubic feet to cubic yards we will *divide* the number of cubic feet by 27. Therefore, 1302.75 ft³ = $\frac{1302.75}{27}$ yd³ = 48.25 yd³.

EXAMPLE 10   FILLING IN A SWIMMING POOL

Julianne Peterson recently purchased a home with a rectangular swimming pool. The pool is 30 ft long and 15 ft wide, and it has a uniform depth of 4.5 ft. Julianne lives in a cold climate, so she plans to fill the pool in with dirt to make a flower garden. How many cubic yards of dirt will Julianne have to purchase to fill in the swimming pool?

SOLUTION   To find the amount of dirt, we will use the formula for the volume of a rectangular solid:

$$V = lwh$$
$$= (30)(15)(4.5)$$
$$= 2025 \text{ ft}^3$$

Now we must convert this volume from cubic feet to cubic yards. In Example 9, we learned that $1 \text{ yd}^3 = 27 \text{ ft}^3$. Therefore, $2025 \text{ ft}^3 = \frac{2025}{27} = 75 \text{ yd}^3$. Thus, Julianne needs to purchase 75 yd^3 of dirt to fill in her swimming pool.

EXERCISE SET 6.4 ●●●●●●

• Concept/Writing Exercises

1. **a)** Define *volume*.

   b) Define *surface area*.

2. What is solid geometry?

3. What is the difference between a polyhedron and a regular polyhedron?

4. What is the difference between a prism and a right prism?

5. In your own words, explain the difference between a prism and a pyramid.

6. In your own words, state Euler's polyhedron formula.

• Practice the Skills

In Exercises 7–16, determine (a) the volume and (b) the surface area of the three-dimensional figure. When appropriate, use the $\boxed{\pi}$ key on your calculator and round your answer to the nearest hundredth.

7.

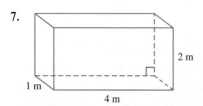

2 m
1 m
4 m

8.

6 yd
2 yd
3 yd

9.

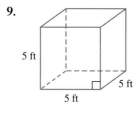

5 ft
5 ft
5 ft

10.

7 cm
7 cm
7 cm

11.

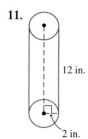

12 in.
2 in.

12.

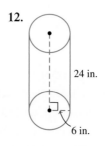

24 in.
6 in.

13.

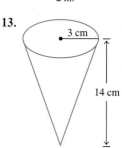

3 cm
14 cm

14.

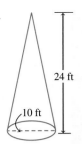

24 ft

10 ft

15.

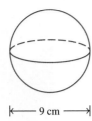

|← 9 cm →|

16.

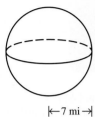

|← 7 mi →|

In Exercises 17–20, determine the volume of the three-dimensional figure. When appropriate, round your answer to the nearest hundredth.

17.

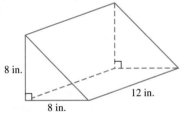

8 in.

8 in.

12 in.

18.

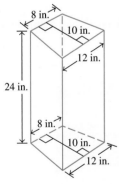

8 in.

10 in.

12 in.

24 in.

8 in.

10 in.

12 in.

19.

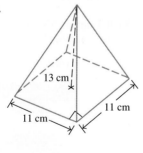

13 cm

11 cm

11 cm

20.

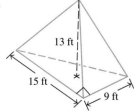

13 ft

15 ft

9 ft

In Exercises 21–28, determine the volume of the shaded region. When appropriate, use the [π] key on your calculator and round your answer to the nearest hundredth.

21.

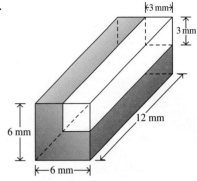

|←3 mm→|

3 mm

12 mm

6 mm

|← 6 mm →|

22.

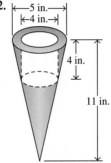

|←5 in.→|

|←4 in.→|

4 in.

11 in.

23.

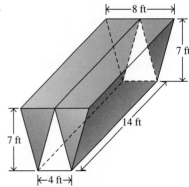

|← 8 ft →|

7 ft

14 ft

7 ft

|←4 ft→|

24.

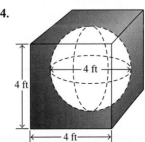

4 ft

|← 4 ft →|

4 ft

25.

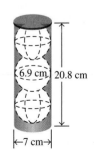

6.9 cm   20.8 cm

|←7 cm→|

26.

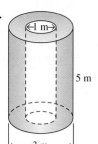

27.

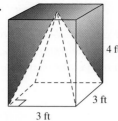

28.

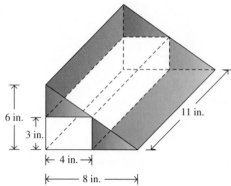

In Exercises 29–32, use the fact that 1 yd³ equals 27 ft³ to make the conversion.

29. 9 yd³ to cubic feet   **30.** 7.25 yd³ to cubic feet

31. 153 ft³ to cubic yards   **32.** 2457 ft³ to cubic yards

In Exercises 33–36, use the fact that 1 m³ equals 1,000,000 cm³ to make the conversion.

33. 3.7 m³ to cubic centimeters

34. 17.6 m³ to cubic centimeters

35. 7,500,000 cm³ to cubic meters

36. 7,300,000 cm³ to cubic meters

37. *Ice-Cream Comparison* The Louisburg Creamery packages its homemade ice cream in tubs and in boxes. The tubs are in the shape of a right cylinder with a radius of 3 in. and height of 5 in. The boxes are in the shape of a cube with each side measuring 5 in. Determine the volume of each container.

38. *Volume of a Freezer* The dimensions of the interior of an upright freezer are height 46 in., width 25 in., and depth 25 in. Determine the volume of the freezer

a) in cubic inches.   b) in cubic feet.

39. *CD Case* A compact disc case is a rectangular solid that is 142 mm long, 125 mm wide, and 10 mm high. Determine its surface area.

40. *Globe Surface Area* The Everest model globe has a diameter of 20 in. Determine the surface area of this globe. Round your answer to the nearest hundredth.

41. *Volume of a Bread Pan* A bread pan is 12 in. × 4 in. × 3 in. How many quarts does it hold, if 1 in.³ ≈ 0.01736 qt?

42. *Gasoline Containers* Mark Russo has two right cylindrical containers for storing gasoline. One has a diameter of 10 in. and a height of 12 in. The other has a diameter of 12 in. and a height of 10 in.

a) Which container holds the greater amount of gasoline, the taller one or the one with the greater diameter?

b) What is the difference in volume?

43. *A Fish Tank*

a) How many cubic centimeters of water will a rectangular fish tank hold if the tank is 80 cm long, 50 cm wide, and 30 cm high?

b) If 1 cm³ holds 1 mℓ of liquid, how many milliliters will the tank hold?

c) If 1ℓ = 1000 mℓ, how many liters will the tank hold?

44. *The Pyramid of Cheops* The Pyramid of Cheops in Egypt has a square base measuring 720 ft on a side. Its height is 480 ft. What is its volume?

45. *Engine Capacity* The engine in a 1957 Chevrolet Corvette has eight cylinders. Each cylinder is a right cylinder with a bore (diameter) of 3.875 in. and a stroke (height) of 3 in. Determine the total displacement (volume) of this engine.

46. *Rose Garden Topsoil* Marisa Raffaele wishes to plant a rose garden in her backyard. The rose garden will be in the shape of a 9 ft by 18 ft rectangle. Marisa wishes to add a 4 in. layer of organic topsoil on top of the rectangular area. The topsoil sells for $32.95 per cubic yard. Determine

a) how many cubic yards of topsoil Marisa will need.

b) how much the topsoil will cost.

47. *Pool Toys* A Wacky Noodle Pool Toy, frequently referred to as a "noodle," is a cylindrical flotation device made from cell foam (see photo). One style of noodle is a cylinder that has a diameter of 2.5 in. and a length of 5.5 ft. Determine the volume of this style of noodle in

a) cubic inches.

b) cubic feet.

48. *Comparing Cake Pans* When baking a cake, you can choose between a round pan with a 9 in. diameter and a 7 in. × 9 in. rectangular pan.

a) Determine the area of the base of each pan.

b) If both pans are 2 in. deep, determine the volume of each pan.

c) Which pan has the larger volume?

49. *Cake Icing* A bag used to apply icing to a cake is in the shape of a cone with a diameter of 3 in. and a height of 6 in. How much icing will this bag hold when full?

50. *Flower Box* The flower box shown at the top of the right-hand column is 4 ft long, and its ends are in the shape of a trapezoid. The upper and lower bases of the trapezoid measure 12 in. and 8 in., respectively, and the height is 9 in. Find the volume of the flower box

a) in cubic inches.

b) in cubic feet.

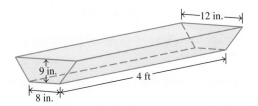

In Exercises 51–56, find the missing value indicated by the question mark. Use the following formula.

$$\left(\begin{array}{c}\text{Number of}\\\text{vertices}\end{array}\right) - \left(\begin{array}{c}\text{number of}\\\text{edges}\end{array}\right) + \left(\begin{array}{c}\text{number}\\\text{of faces}\end{array}\right) = 2$$

	Number of Vertices	Number of Edges	Number of Faces
51.	8	?	4
52.	12	16	?
53.	?	8	4
54.	7	12	?
55.	11	?	5
56.	?	10	4

• Challenge Problems/Group Activities

57. *Earth and Moon Comparisons* The diameter of Earth is approximately 12,756.3 km. The diameter of the moon is approximately 3474.8 km. Assume that both Earth and the moon are spheres.

a) Determine the surface area of Earth.

b) Determine the surface area of the moon.

c) How many times larger is the surface area of Earth than the surface area of the moon?

d) Determine the volume of Earth.

e) Determine the volume of the moon.

f) How many times larger is the volume of Earth than the volume of the moon?

58. *Packing Orange Juice* A box is packed with six cans of orange juice. The cans are touching each other and the sides of the box, as shown. What percent of the volume of the interior of the box is not occupied by the cans?

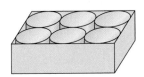

59. ***Doubling the Edges of a Cube*** In this exercise, we will explore what happens to the volume of a cube if we double the length of each edge of the cube.

   a) Choose a number between 1 and 10 and call this number s.

   b) Calculate the volume of a cube with the length of each edge equal to s.

   c) Now double s and call this number t.

   d) Calculate the volume of a cube with the length of each edge equal to t.

   e) Repeat parts (a) through (d) for a different value of s.

   f) Compare the results from part (b) with the results from part (d) and explain what happens to the volume of a cube if we double the length of each edge.

60. ***Doubling the Radius of a Sphere*** In this exercise, we will explore what happens to the volume of a sphere if we double the radius of the sphere.

   a) Choose a number between 1 and 10 and call this number r.

   b) Calculate the volume of a sphere with radius r (use the $\boxed{\pi}$ key on your calculator).

   c) Now double r and call this number t.

   d) Calculate the volume of a sphere with radius t.

   e) Repeat parts (a) through (d) for a different value of r.

   f) Compare the results from part (b) with the results from part (d) and explain what happens to the volume of a sphere if we double the radius.

61. a) Explain how to demonstrate, using the cube shown below, that

$$(a + b)^3 = a^3 + 3a^2b + 3ab^2 + b^3$$

   b) What is the volume in terms of a and b of each numbered piece in the figure?

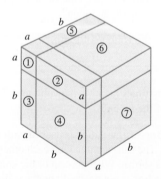

   c) An eighth piece is not illustrated. What is its volume?

• Recreational Mathematics

62. ***More Pool Toys*** Wacky Noodle Pool Toys (see Exercise 47) come in many different shapes and sizes.

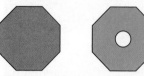

Base for part (a)   Base for part (b)

   a) Determine the volume, in cubic inches, of a noodle that is in the shape of a 5.5-ft-long solid octagonal prism whose base has an area of 5 in.^{2}.

   b) Determine the volume, in cubic inches, of a hollow noodle that has the same shape as the noodle described in part (a) except that a right circular cylinder of diameter 0.75 in. has been removed from the center.

• Internet/Research Activities

63. ***Air-Conditioner Selection*** Calculate the volume of the room in which you sleep or study. Go to a store that sells room air conditioners and find out how many cubic feet can be cooled by the different models available. Describe the model that would be the proper size for your room. What is the initial cost? How much does that model cost to operate? If you moved to a room that had twice the amount of floor space and the same height, would the air conditioner you selected still be adequate? Explain.

64. Pappus of Alexandria (ca. A.D. 350) was the last of the well-known ancient Greek mathematicians. Write a paper on his life and his contributions to mathematics.

65. ***Platonic Solids*** Construct cardboard models of one or more of the platonic solids. Visit the web site www.mathsnet.net/geometry/solid/platonic.html or similar web sites for patterns to follow.

SECTION 6.5 • TRANSFORMATIONAL GEOMETRY, SYMMETRY, AND TESSELLATIONS

Capital letters can be used to display symmetry.

Consider the capital letters of the alphabet. Now consider a kindergarten-age child who is practicing to write capital letters. Usually, children will write some of the letters "backwards." However, some letters cannot be made backwards. For example, the capital letter A would look the same backwards as it does forwards, but the capital letters B and C would look different backwards than they do forwards. The capital letters that appear the same forwards as they do backwards have a property called *symmetry* that we will define and study in this section. Symmetry is part of another branch of geometry known as *transformational geometry*.

In our study of geometry, we have thus far focused on definitions, axioms, and theorems that are used in the study of *Euclidean geometry*. We will now introduce a second type of geometry called *transformational geometry*. In *transformational geometry*, we study various ways to move a geometric figure without altering the shape or size of the figure. When discussing transformational geometry, we often use the term *rigid motion*.

> The act of moving a geometric figure from some starting position to some ending position without altering its shape or size is called a **rigid motion** (or **transformation**).

Consider trapezoid *ABCD* in Figure 6.47. If we move each point on this trapezoid 4 units to the right and 3 units up, the trapezoid is in the location specified by trapezoid *A′B′C′D′*. This figure illustrates one type of rigid motion. When studying rigid motions, we are only concerned about the starting and ending positions of the figure and not what happens in between. When discussing rigid motions of two-dimensional figures, there are four basic types of rigid motions: reflections, rotations, translations, and glide reflections. We call these four types of rigid motions the *basic rigid motions in a plane*. After we discuss the four rigid motions we will discuss symmetry of geometric figures and tessellations.

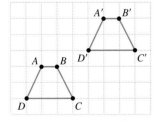

FIGURE 6.47

Reflections

The first rigid motion we will study is *reflection*. In our everyday life, we are quite familiar with the concept of reflection. In transformational geometry, a reflection is an image of a geometric figure that appears on the opposite side of a designated line.

> A **reflection** is a rigid motion that moves a geometric figure to a new position such that the figure in the new position is a mirror image of the figure in the starting position. In two dimensions, the figure and its mirror image are equidistant from a line called the **reflection line** or the **axis of reflection**.

Figure 6.48 shows trapezoid *ABCD*, a reflection line *l*, and the reflected trapezoid *A′B′C′D′*. Notice that vertex *A* is 6 units to the *left* of reflection line *l* and that vertex *A′* is 6 units to the *right* of reflection line *l*. Next notice that vertex *B* is 2 units to the *left* of *l* and that vertex *B′* is 2 units to the *right* of *l*. A similar relationship holds true for vertices *C* and *C′* and for vertices *D* and *D′*. It is important to see that the trapezoid is not simply *moved* to the other side of the reflection line, but instead it is *reflected*. Notice in the trapezoid *ABCD* that the longer base $\overline{BC}$ is on the *right* side of the trapezoid, but in the reflected trapezoid *A′B′C′D′* the longer base $\overline{B'C'}$ is on the *left* side of the trapezoid. Finally, notice the colors of the sides of the two trapezoids. Side $\overline{AB}$ in trapezoid *ABCD* and side $\overline{A'B'}$ in the reflected trapezoid are both blue. Side $\overline{BC}$ and side $\overline{B'C'}$ are both red, sides $\overline{CD}$ and $\overline{C'D'}$ are both gold, and sides $\overline{DA}$ and $\overline{D'A'}$ are both green. In this section, we will occasionally use such color coding to help you visualize the effect of a rigid transformation on a figure.

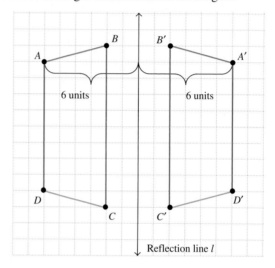

FIGURE 6.48

EXAMPLE 1 REFLECTION OF A SQUARE

Construct the reflection of square *ABCD*, shown in Fig. 6.49, about reflection line *l*.

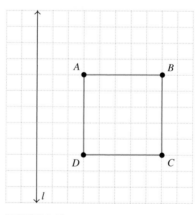

FIGURE 6.49

SOLUTION The reflection of square *ABCD* will be called *A′B′C′D′*. To determine the position of the reflection, we first examine vertex *A* in Fig. 6.49. Notice that vertex *A* is 3 units to the *right* of line *l*. Thus, in the reflected square *A′B′C′D′*, vertex *A′* must also be 3 units away from, but to the *left* of, reflection line *l*. Next, notice that vertex *B* is 8 units to the right of *l*. Thus, in the reflected square *A′B′C′D′*, vertex *B′* must also be 8 units away from, but to the *left* of, reflection line *l*. Next, notice that vertices *C* and *D* are 8 units and 3 units, respectively, to the *right* of *l*. Thus, vertices *C′* and *D′* must be 8 units and 3 units, respectively, to the *left* of *l*. Figure 6.50 shows vertices *A′*, *B′*, *C′*, and *D′*. Finally, we draw line segments between vertices *A′* and *B′*, *B′* and *C′*, *C′* and *D′*, and *D′* and *A′* to form the sides of the reflection, square *A′B′C′D′*, as illustrated in Fig. 6.50.

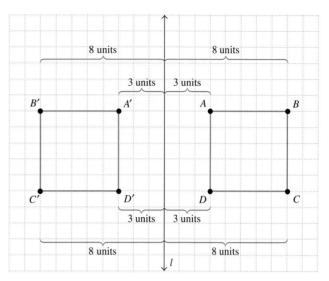

FIGURE 6.50

In Example 1, the reflection line did not intersect the figure being reflected. We will now study an example in which the reflection line goes directly through the figure to be reflected.

EXAMPLE 2   REFLECTION OF A HEXAGON

Construct the reflection of hexagon *ABCDEF*, shown in Fig. 6.51, about reflection line *l*.

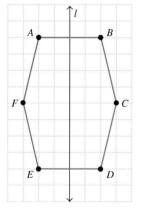

FIGURE 6.51

SOLUTION From Fig. 6.51, we see that vertex *A* in hexagon *ABCDEF* is 2 units to the left of reflection line *l*. Thus, vertex *A′* in the reflected hexagon will be 2 units to the right of *l* (see Fig. 6.52). Notice that vertex *A′* of the reflected hexagon is in the same location as vertex *B* of hexagon *ABCDEF* in Fig. 6.51.

We next see that vertex *B* in hexagon *ABCDEF* is 2 units to the right of *l*. Thus, vertex *B′* in the reflected hexagon will be 2 units to the left of *l*. Notice that vertex *B′* of the reflected hexagon is in the same location as vertex *A* of hexagon *ABCDEF*. We continue this process to determine the locations of vertices *C′*, *D′*, *E′*, and *F′* of the reflected hexagon. Notice once again that each vertex of the reflected hexagon is in the same location as a vertex of hexagon *ABCDEF*. Finally, we draw the line segments to complete the reflected hexagon *A′B′C′D′E′F′* (see Fig. 6.52). For this example, we see that other than the vertex labels, the positions of the hexagon before and after the reflection are identical.

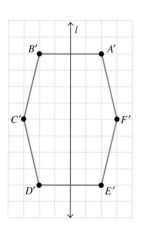

FIGURE 6.52

In Example 2, the reflection line was in the center of the hexagon in the original position. As a result, the reflection line was also in the center of the reflected hexagon. In this particular case the reflected hexagon lies directly on top of the hexagon in its original position. We will revisit reflections such as that in Example 2 again when we discuss *reflective symmetry* later in this section.

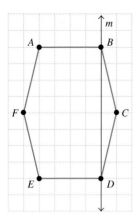

FIGURE 6.53

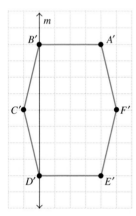

FIGURE 6.54

Now consider hexagon *ABCDEF* in Fig. 6.53 and its reflection about line *m*, hexagon *A'B'C'D'E'F'* in Fig. 6.54. Notice that the positions of the hexagon before and after the reflection, relative to line *m*, are not the same. Furthermore, if we line up reflection line *m* in Fig. 6.53 and Fig. 6.54, we would see that hexagon *ABCDEF* and hexagon *A'B'C'D'E'F'* are in different positions.

Translations

The next rigid motion we will discuss is the *translation*. In a translation, we simply move a figure along a straight line to a new position.

> A **translation** (or **glide**) is a rigid motion that moves a geometric figure by sliding it along a straight line segment in the plane. The direction and length of the line segment completely determine the translation.

After conducting a translation, we say the figure was *translated* to a new position.

A concise way to indicate the direction and the distance that a figure is moved during a translation is with a *translation vector*. In mathematics, vectors are typically represented with boldface letters. For example, in Fig. 6.55 we see trapezoid *ABCD* and a translation vector, **v**, which is pointing to the right and upward. This translation vector indicates a translation of 9 units to the right and 4 units upward. Notice that in Fig. 6.55 the translated vector appears on the right side of the polygon. The placement of the translation vector does not matter. Therefore, the translation vector could have been placed to the left, above, or below the polygon, and the translation would not change. When trapezoid *ABCD* is translated using **v**, every point on trapezoid *ABCD* is moved 9 units to the right and 4 units upward. This movement is demonstrated for vertex *A* in Fig. 6.56(a). Figure 6.56(b) shows trapezoid *ABCD* and the translated trapezoid *A'B'C'D'*. Notice in Fig. 6.56(b) that every point on trapezoid *A'B'C'D'* is 9 units to the right and 4 units up from its corresponding point on trapezoid *ABCD*.

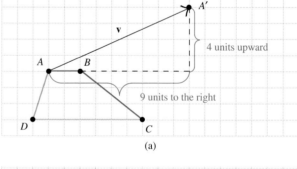

(a)

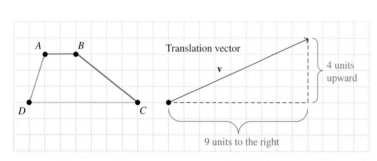

FIGURE 6.55

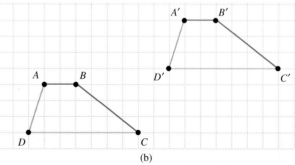

(b)

FIGURE 6.56

EXAMPLE 3   A TRANSLATED PARALLELOGRAM

Given parallelogram *ABCD* and translation vector, **v**, shown in Fig. 6.57, construct the translated parallelogram *A'B'C'D'*.

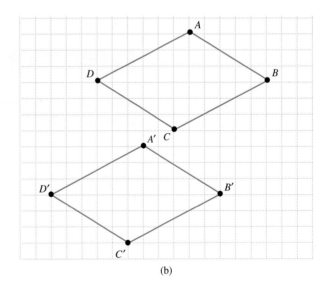

FIGURE 6.57

SOLUTION The translated figure will be a parallelogram of the same size and shape as parallelogram *ABCD*. We notice that the translation vector, **v**, points 7 units downward and 3 units to the left. We next examine vertex *A*. To determine the location of vertex *A'* of the translated parallelogram, start at vertex *A* of parallelogram *ABCD* and move down 7 units and to the left 3 units. We label this vertex *A'* (see Fig. 6.58a). We determine vertices *B'*, *C'*, and *D'* in a similar manner by moving down 7 units and to the left 3 units from vertices *B, C,* and *D*, respectively. Figure 6.58(b) shows parallelogram *ABCD* and the translated parallelogram *A'B'C'D'*. Notice in Fig. 6.58(b) that every point on parallelogram *A'B'C'D'* is 7 units down and 3 units to the left of its corresponding point on parallelogram *ABCD*.

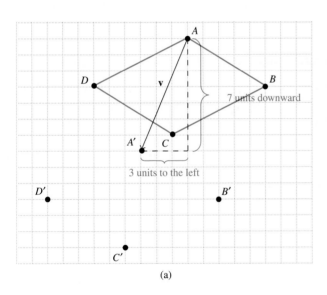

(a)

FIGURE 6.58

(b)

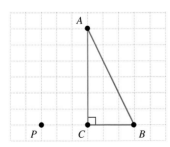

FIGURE 6.59

Rotations

The next rigid motion we will discuss is *rotation*. To help visualize a rotation, examine Fig. 6.59, which shows right triangle *ABC* and point *P* about which right triangle *ABC* is to be rotated.

Imagine that this page was removed from this book and attached to a bulletin board with a single pin through point *P*. Next imagine rotating the page 90° in the *counterclockwise* direction. The triangle would now appear as triangle *A'B'C'* shown in Fig. 6.60. Next, imagine rotating the original triangle 180° in a counterclockwise direction. The triangle would now appear as triangle *A"B"C"* shown in Fig. 6.61.

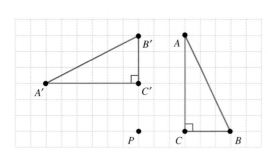

FIGURE 6.60

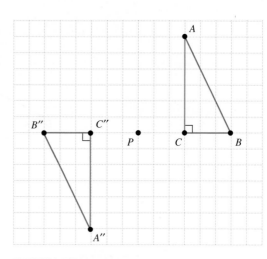

FIGURE 6.61

Now that we have an intuitive idea of how to determine a rotation, we give the definition of rotation.

> A **rotation** is a rigid motion performed by rotating a geometric figure in the plane about a specific point, called the **rotation point** or the **center of rotation**. The angle through which the object is rotated is called the **angle of rotation**.

We will measure angles of rotation using degrees. In mathematics, generally, *counterclockwise angles have positive degree measures and clockwise angles have negative degree measures*.

EXAMPLE 4   A ROTATED RECTANGLE

Given rectangle *ABCD* and rotation point *P*, shown in Fig. 6.62, construct rectangles that result from rotations through

a) 90°.   b) 180°.   c) 270°.

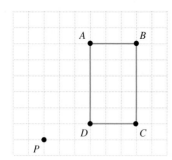

FIGURE 6.62

SOLUTION

a) First, since 90 is a *positive* number, we will rotate the figure in a counterclockwise direction. We also note that the rotated rectangle will be the same size and shape as rectangle *ABCD*. To get an idea of what the rotated rectangle will look like, pick up this book and rotate it counterclockwise 90°. Figure 6.63 shows rectangle *ABCD* and rectangle *A′B′C′D′* which is rectangle *ABCD* rotated 90° about point *P*. Notice how line segment *AB* in rectangle *ABCD* is horizontal, but in the rotated rectangle in Fig. 6.63 line segment *A′B′* is vertical. Also notice that in rectangle *ABCD* vertex *D* is 3 units to the *right* and 1 unit *above* rotation point *P*, but in the rotated rectangle, vertex *D′* is 3 units *above* and 1 unit to the *left* of rotation point *P*.

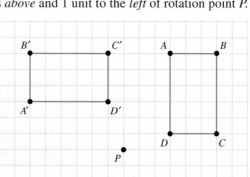

FIGURE 6.63

b) To gain some perspective on a 180° rotation, again pick up this book, but this time rotate the book 180° in the counterclockwise direction. The rotated rectangle $A''B''C''D''$ is shown along with the rectangle $ABCD$ in Fig. 6.64.

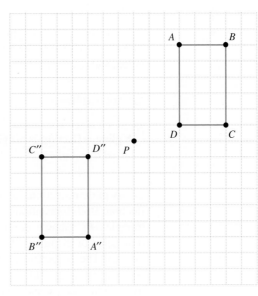

FIGURE 6.64

c) To gain some perspective on a 270° rotation, rotate this book 270° in the counterclockwise direction. The rotated rectangle $A'''B'''C'''D'''$ is shown along with rectangle $ABCD$ in Fig. 6.65.

Thus far in our examples of rotations, the rotation point was outside the figure being rotated. We now will study an example where the rotation point is inside the figure to be rotated.

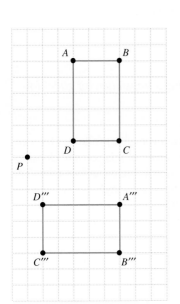

FIGURE 6.65

FIGURE 6.66

FIGURE 6.67

EXAMPLE 5   A ROTATION POINT INSIDE A POLYGON

Given polygon $ABCDEFGH$ and rotation point P, shown in Fig. 6.66, construct polygons that result from rotations through

a) 90°.   b) 180°.

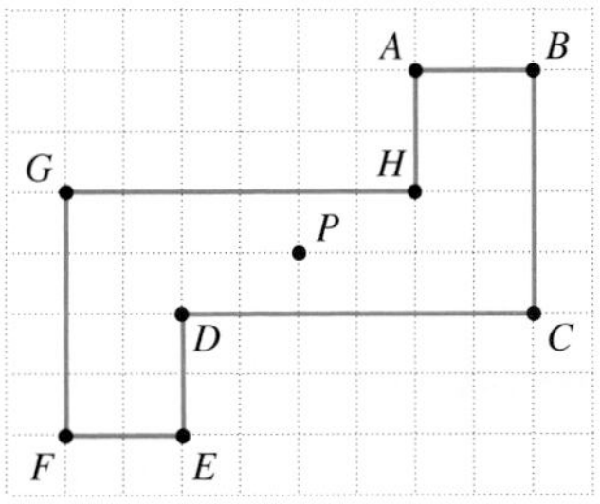

SOLUTION

a) We will rotate the polygon 90° in a counterclockwise direction. The resulting polygon will be the same size and shape as polygon $ABCDEFGH$. To visualize what the rotated polygon will look like, pick up this book and rotate it counterclockwise 90°. Figure 6.67 shows the polygon $ABCDEFGH$, in pale blue, and the rotated polygon $A'B'C'D'E'F'G'H'$, in deeper blue. Notice how line segments $\overline{AB}$, $\overline{CD}$, $\overline{EF}$, and $\overline{GH}$ in polygon $ABCDEFGH$ are *horizontal*, but in the rotated polygon $A'B'C'D'E'F'G'H'$, line segments $\overline{A'B'}$, $\overline{C'D'}$, $\overline{E'F'}$, and $\overline{G'H'}$ are *vertical*. Also notice in polygon $ABCDEFGH$ that line segment $\overline{GH}$ is 1 unit *above* rotation point P, but in the rotated polygon, line segment $\overline{G'H'}$ is 1 unit to the *left* of rotation point P.

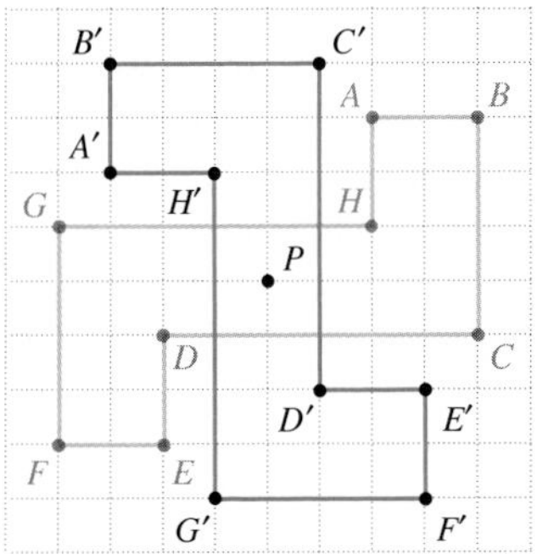

b) To visualize the polygon obtained through a 180° rotation, we can pick up this book and rotate it 180° in the counterclockwise direction. Notice from Fig. 6.68 that vertex A'' of the rotated polygon is in the same position as vertex E of polygon $ABCDEFGH$. Also notice from Fig. 6.68 that vertex B'' of the rotated polygon is in the same position as vertex F of polygon $ABCDEFGH$. In fact, each of the vertices in the rotated polygon is in the same position as a different vertex in polygon $ABCDEFGH$. From

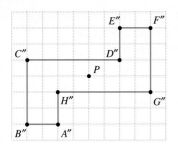

FIGURE 6.68

Fig. 6.68 we see that, other than vertex labels, the position of rotated polygon $A''B''C''D''E''F''G''H''$ is the same as the position of polygon $ABCDEFGH$.

The polygon used in Example 5 will be discussed again later when we discuss *rotational symmetry*. The three rigid motions we have discussed thus far are reflection, translation, and rotation. Now we will discuss the fourth rigid motion, *glide reflection*.

Glide Reflections

> A **glide reflection** is a rigid motion formed by performing a *translation* (or *glide*) followed by a *reflection*.

A glide reflection, as its name suggests, is a translation (or glide) followed by a reflection. Both translations and reflections were discussed earlier in this section. Consider triangle ABC (shown in blue), translation vector **v**, and reflection line l in Fig. 6.69. The translation of triangle ABC, obtained using translation vector **v**, is triangle $A'B'C'$ (shown in red). The reflection of triangle $A'B'C'$ about reflection line l is triangle $A''B''C''$ (shown in green). Thus, triangle $A''B''C''$ is the glide reflection of triangle ABC using translation vector **v** and reflection line l.

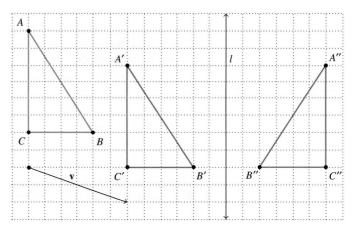

FIGURE 6.69

EXAMPLE 6   A GLIDE REFLECTION OF A PARALLELOGRAM

Construct a glide reflection of parallelogram $ABCD$, shown in Fig. 6.70, using translation vector **v** and reflection line l.

SOLUTION To construct the glide reflection of parallelogram $ABCD$, first translate the parallelogram 2 units to the left and 5 units up as indicated by translation vector **v**. This translated parallelogram is labeled $A'B'C'D'$, shown in red in Fig. 6.71(a). Next, we will reflect parallelogram $A'B'C'D'$ about reflection line l. Parallelogram $A'B'C'D'$, shown in red, and the reflected parallelogram, labeled $A''B''C''D''$, shown in green, are shown in Fig. 6.71(b). The glide reflection of the parallelogram $ABCD$ is parallelogram $A''B''C''D''$.

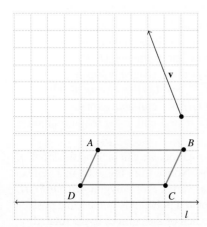

FIGURE 6.70

Symmetry

We are now ready to discuss symmetry. Our discussion of symmetry involves a rigid motion of an object.

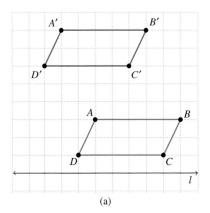

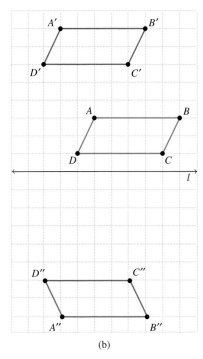

FIGURE 6.71

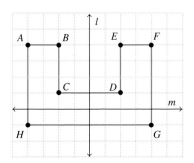

FIGURE 6.73

A **symmetry** of a geometric figure is a rigid motion that moves the figure back onto itself. That is, the beginning position and ending position of the figure must be identical.

Suppose we start with a figure in a specific position and perform a rigid motion on this figure. If the position of the figure after the rigid motion is identical to the position of the figure before the rigid motion (if the beginning and ending positions of the figure coincide), then the rigid motion is a symmetry and we say that the figure has symmetry. For a two-dimensional figure, there are four types of symmetries: reflective symmetry, rotational symmetry, translational symmetry, and glide reflective symmetry. In this textbook, however, we will only discuss reflective symmetry and rotational symmetry.

Consider the polygon and reflection line l shown in Fig. 6.72(a). If we use the rigid motion of reflection and reflect the polygon $ABCDEFGH$ about line l, we get polygon $A'B'C'D'E'F'G'H'$. Notice that the ending position of the polygon is identical to the starting position, as shown in Fig. 6.72(b). Compare Fig. 6.72(a) with Fig. 6.72(b). Although the vertex labels are different, the reflected polygon is in the same position as the polygon in the original position. Thus, we say that the polygon has *reflective symmetry* about line l. We refer to line l as a *line of symmetry*.

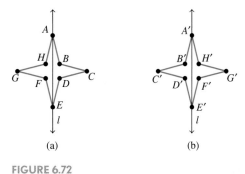

FIGURE 6.72

Recall Example 2 on page 337 in which hexagon $ABCDEF$ was reflected about reflection line l. Examine the hexagon in the original position (Fig. 6.51) and the hexagon in the final position after being reflected about line l (Fig. 6.52). Other than the labels of the vertices, the beginning and ending positions of the hexagon are identical. Therefore, hexagon $ABCDEF$ has reflective symmetry about line l.

EXAMPLE 7 REFLECTIVE SYMMETRIES OF POLYGONS

Determine whether the polygon shown in Fig. 6.73 has reflective symmetry about each of the following lines.

a) Line l b) Line m

SOLUTION

a) Examine the reflection of the polygon about line l as seen in Fig. 6.74(a). Notice that other than the vertex labels, the beginning and ending positions of the polygon are identical. Thus, the polygon has reflective symmetry about line l.

b) Examine the reflection of the polygon about line m as seen in Fig. 6.74(b). Notice that the position of the reflected polygon is different from the original position of the polygon. Thus, the polygon does not have reflective symmetry about line m.

We will now discuss a second type of symmetry, rotational symmetry. Consider the polygon and rotation point P shown in Fig. 6.75(a). The rigid motion of rotation of polygon $ABCDEFGH$ through a $90°$ angle about point P gives polygon $A'B'C'D'E'F'G'H'$

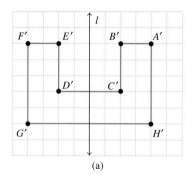

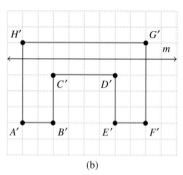

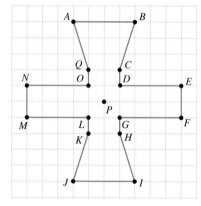

FIGURE 6.74

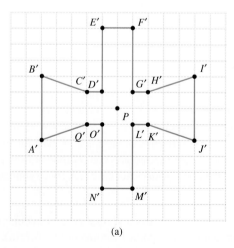

FIGURE 6.76

shown in Fig. 6.75(b). Compare Fig. 6.75(a) with Fig. 6.75(b). Although the vertex labels are different, the position of the polygon before and after the rotation is identical. Thus, we say that the polygon has 90° *rotational symmetry* about point P. We refer to point P as the *point of symmetry*.

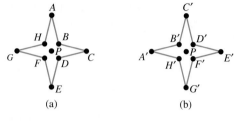

FIGURE 6.75

Recall Example 5 on page 341 in which polygon *ABCDEFGH* was rotated 90° about point P in part (a) and 180° in part (b). First examine the polygon in the original position in Fig. 6.66 on page 341 and the 90° rotated polygon in Fig. 6.67 on page 341. Notice the position of the polygon after the 90° rotation is different from the original position of the polygon. Therefore, polygon *ABCDEFGH* in Fig. 6.67 does not have 90° rotational symmetry about point P. Now examine the 180° rotated polygon in Fig. 6.68 on page 341. Notice that other than the vertex labels, the position of the two polygons *ABCDEFGH* and *A'B'C'D'E'F'G'H'* is identical with respect to rotation about point P. Therefore, polygon *ABCDEFGH* in Fig. 6.66 has 180° rotational symmetry about point P.

EXAMPLE 8   ROTATIONAL SYMMETRIES

Determine whether the polygon shown in Fig. 6.76 has rotational symmetry about point P for rotations through each of the following angles.

a) 90°   b) 180°

SOLUTION

a) To determine whether the polygon has 90° counterclockwise rotational symmetry about point P we rotate the polygon 90° as shown in Fig. 6.77(a). Compare Fig. 6.77(a) with Fig. 6.76. Notice that the position of the polygon after the rotation in Fig. 6.77(a) is different than the original position of the polygon (Fig. 6.76). Therefore, the polygon does not have 90° rotational symmetry.

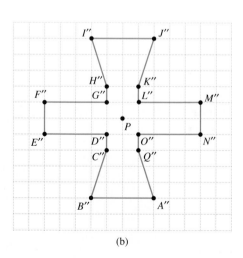

FIGURE 6.77

b) To determine whether the polygon has 180° counterclockwise rotational symmetry about the point P, we rotate the polygon 180° as shown in Fig. 6.77(b). Compare Fig. 6.77(b) with Fig. 6.76. Notice that other than vertex labels, the position of the polygon after the rotation in Fig. 6.77(b) is identical to the position of the polygon before the rotation (Fig. 6.76). Therefore, the polygon has 180° rotational symmetry.

Tessellations

A fascinating application of transformational geometry is the creation of *tessellations*.

> A **tessellation** (or **tiling**) is a pattern consisting of the repeated use of the same geometric figures to entirely cover a plane, leaving no gaps. The geometric figures used are called the **tessellating shapes** of the tessellation.

Figure 6.78 shows an example of a tessellation from ancient Egypt. Perhaps the most famous person to incorporate tessellations into his work is M. C. Escher (see Blitzer Bonus at left).

FIGURE 6.78

The simplest tessellations use one single regular polygon as the tessellating shape. Recall that a *regular polygon* is one whose sides are all the same length and whose interior angles all have the same measure. A tessellation that uses one single regular polygon as the tessellating shape is called a *regular tessellation*. It can be shown that only three regular tessellations exist: those that use an equilateral triangle, a square, or a regular hexagon as the tessellating shape. Figure 6.79 shows each of these regular tessellations. Notice that each tessellation can be obtained from a single tessellating shape through the use of reflections, translations, or rotations.

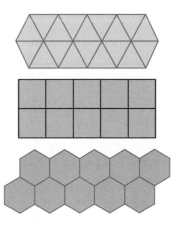

FIGURE 6.79

We will now learn how to create unique tessellations. We will do so by constructing a unique tessellating shape from a square. We could also construct other tessellating shapes using an equilateral triangle or a regular hexagon. If you wish to follow along with our construction, you will need some lightweight cardboard, a ruler, cellophane tape, and a pair of scissors. We will start by measuring and cutting out a square 2 in. by 2 in. from the cardboard. We next cut the square into two parts by cutting it from top to bottom using any kind of cut. One example is shown in Fig. 6.80. We then rearrange the pieces and tape the two vertical edges together as shown in Fig. 6.81. Next we cut this new shape into two parts by cutting it from left to right using any kind of cut as shown in Fig. 6.82. We then rearrange the pieces and tape the two horizontal edges together as shown in Fig. 6.83. This completes our tessellating shape.

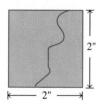

FIGURE 6.80

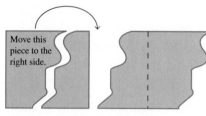

FIGURE 6.81

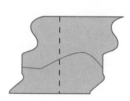

FIGURE 6.82

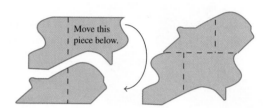

FIGURE 6.83

We now set the cardboard tessellating shape in the middle of a blank piece of paper (the tessellating shape can be rotated to any position as a starting point) and trace the outline of the shape onto the paper. Next move the tessellating shape so that it lines up with the figure already drawn and trace the outline again. Continue to do that until the page is completely covered. Once the page is covered with the tessellation, we can add some interesting colors or even some unique sketches to the tessellation. Figure 6.84 shows one tessellation created using the tessellation shape in Fig. 6.83. In Fig. 6.84, the tessellation shape was rotated about 45° counterclockwise.

An infinite number of different tessellations can be created using the method described by altering the cuts made. We could also create different tessellations using an equilateral triangle, a regular hexagon, or other types of polygons. There are also other, more complicated ways to create the tessellating shape. The Internet has many sites devoted to the creation of tessellations by hand. Many computer programs that generate tessellations are also available.

FIGURE 6.84

EXERCISE SET 6.5 ●●●●●●

• Concept/Writing Exercises

1. In the study of transformational geometry, what is a rigid motion? List the four rigid motions studied in this section.

2. What is transformational geometry?

3. In terms of transformational geometry, describe a reflection.

4. Describe how to construct a reflection of a given figure about a given line.

5. In terms of transformational geometry, describe a rotation.

6. Describe how to construct a rotation of a given figure, about a given point, through a given angle.

7. In terms of transformational geometry, describe a translation.

8. Describe how to construct a translation of a given figure using a translation vector.

9. In terms of transformational geometry, describe a glide reflection.

10. Describe how to construct a glide reflection of a given figure using a given translation vector and a given reflection line.

11. Describe what it means for a figure to have reflective symmetry about a given line.

12. Describe what it means for a figure to have rotational symmetry about a given point.

13. What is a tessellation?

14. Describe one way to make a unique tessellation from a 2-in. by 2-in. cardboard square.

• Practice the Skills/Problem Solving

In Exercises 15–22, use the given figure and lines of reflection to construct the indicated reflections. Show the figure in the positions both before and after the reflection.

In Exercises 15 and 16, use the following figure. Construct

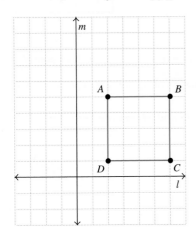

15. the reflection of square *ABCD* about line *m*.

16. the reflection of square *ABCD* about line *l*.

In Exercises 17 and 18, use the following figure. Construct

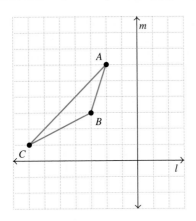

17. the reflection of triangle *ABC* about line *l*.

18. the reflection of triangle *ABC* about line *m*.

In Exercises 19 and 20, use the following figure. Construct

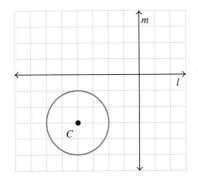

19. the reflection of circle *C* about line *l*.

20. the reflection of circle *C* about line *m*.

In Exercises 21 and 22, use the following figure. Construct

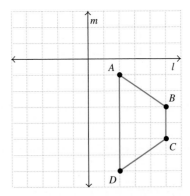

21. the reflection of trapezoid *ABCD* about line *m*.

22. the reflection of the trapezoid *ABCD* about line *l*.

*In Exercises 23–30, use the translation vectors, **v** and **w** shown below, to construct the translations indicated in the exercises. Show the figure in the positions both before and after the translation.*

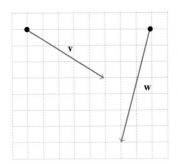

In Exercises 23 and 24, use the following figure. Construct

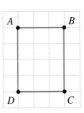

23. the translation of rectangle *ABCD* using translation vector **v**.

24. the translation of rectangle *ABCD* using translation vector **w**.

In Exercises 25 and 26, use the following figure. Construct

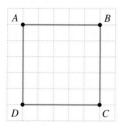

25. the translation of square *ABCD* using translation vector **w**.

26. the translation of square *ABCD* using translation vector **v**.

In Exercises 27 and 28, use the following figure. Construct

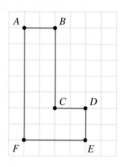

27. the translation of polygon *ABCDEF* using translation vector **v**.

28. the translation of polygon *ABCDEF* using translation vector **w**.

In Exercises 29 and 30, use the following figure. Construct

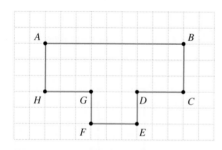

29. the translation of polygon *ABCDEFGH* using translation vector **w**.

30. the translation of polygon *ABCDEFGH* using translation vector **v**.

In Exercises 31–38, use the given figure and rotation point P to construct the indicated rotations. Show the figure in the positions both before and after the rotation.

In Exercises 31 and 32, use the following figure. Construct

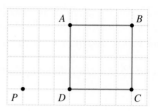

31. a 90° rotation of square *ABCD* about point *P*.

32. a 180° rotation of square *ABCD* about point *P*.

In Exercises 33 and 34, use the following figure. Construct

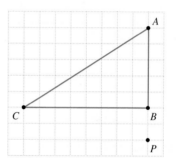

33. a 180° rotation of triangle *ABC* about point *P*.

34. a 270° rotation of triangle *ABC* about point *P*.

In Exercises 35 and 36, use the following figure. Construct

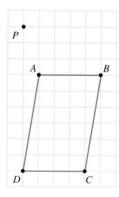

35. a 270° rotation of parallelogram *ABCD* about point *P*.

36. a 180° rotation of parallelogram *ABCD* about point *P*.

In Exercises 37 and 38, use the following figure. Construct

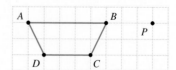

37. a 90° rotation of trapezoid *ABCD* about point *P*.

38. a 270° rotation of trapezoid *ABCD* about point *P*.

In Exercises 39–46, use the given figure, translation vectors **v** *and* **w**, *and reflection lines l and m to construct the indicated glide reflections. Show the figure in the positions before and after the glide reflection.*

In Exercises 39 and 40, use the following figure. Construct

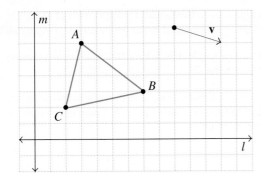

39. a glide reflection of triangle *ABC* using vector **v** and reflection line *l*.

40. a glide reflection of triangle *ABC* using vector **v** and reflection line *m*.

In Exercises 41 and 42, use the following figure. Construct

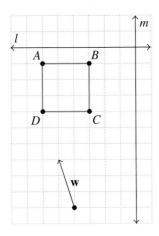

41. a glide reflection of square *ABCD* using vector **w** and reflection line *l*.

42. a glide reflection of square *ABCD* using vector **w** and reflection line *m*.

In Exercises 43 and 44, use the following figure. Construct

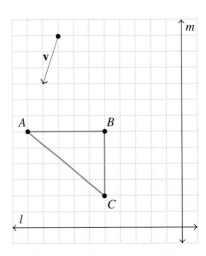

43. a glide reflection of triangle *ABC* using vector **v** and reflection line *l*.

44. a glide reflection of triangle *ABC* using vector **v** and reflection line *m*.

In Exercises 45 and 46, use the following figure. Construct

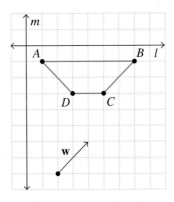

45. a glide reflection of trapezoid *ABCD* using vector **w** and reflection line *l*.

46. a glide reflection of trapezoid *ABCD* using vector **w** and reflection line *m*.

47. a) Reflect triangle *ABC*, shown below, about line *l*. Label the reflected triangle *A'B'C'*.

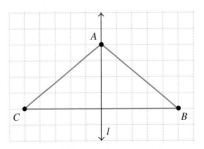

b) Other than vertex labels, is the position of triangle *A'B'C'* identical to the position of triangle *ABC*?

c) Does triangle *ABC* have reflective symmetry about line *l*?

48. a) Reflect rectangle *ABCD*, shown below, about line *l*. Label the reflected rectangle *A′B′C′D′*.

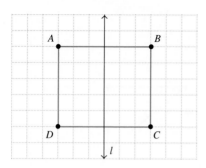

b) Other than vertex labels, is the position of rectangle *A′B′C′D′* identical to the position of rectangle *ABCD*?

c) Does rectangle *ABCD* have reflective symmetry about line *l*?

49. a) Reflect parallelogram *ABCD*, shown below, about line *l*. Label the reflected parallelogram *A′B′C′D′*.

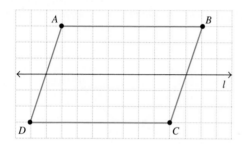

b) Other than vertex labels, is the position of parallelogram *A′B′C′D′* identical to the position of parallelogram *ABCD*?

c) Does parallelogram *ABCD* have reflective symmetry about line *l*?

50. a) Reflect square *ABCD*, shown below, about line *l*. Label the reflected square *A′B′C′D′*.

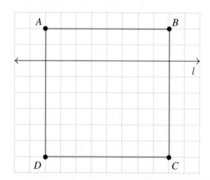

b) Other than vertex labels, is the position of square *A′B′C′D′* identical to the position of square *ABCD*?

c) Does square *ABCD* have reflective symmetry about line *l*?

51. a) Rotate rectangle *ABCD*, shown below, 90° about point *P*. Label the rotated rectangle *A′B′C′D′*.

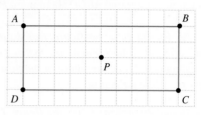

b) Other than vertex labels, is the position of rectangle *A′B′C′D′* identical to the position of rectangle *ABCD*?

c) Does rectangle *ABCD* have 90° rotational symmetry about point *P*?

d) Now rotate the rectangle in the original position, rectangle *ABCD*, 180° about point *P*. Label the rotated rectangle *A″B″C″D″*.

e) Other than vertex labels, is the position of rectangle *A″B″C″D″* identical to the position of rectangle *ABCD*?

f) Does rectangle *ABCD* have 180° rotational symmetry about point *P*?

52. a) Rotate parallelogram *ABCD*, shown below, 90° about point *P*. Label the rotated parallelogram *A′B′C′D′*.

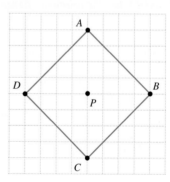

b) Other than vertex labels, is the position of parallelogram *A′B′C′D′* identical to the position of parallelogram *ABCD*?

c) Does parallelogram *ABCD* have 90° rotational symmetry about point *P*?

d) Now rotate the parallelogram in the original position, parallelogram *ABCD*, shown above, 180° about point *P*. Label the rotated parallelogram *A″B″C″D″*.

e) Other than vertex labels, is the position of parallelogram *A″B″C″D″* identical to the position of parallelogram *ABCD*?

f) Does parallelogram *ABCD* have 180° rotational symmetry about point *P*?

53. Consider the following figure.

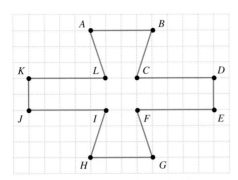

a) Insert a vertical line *m* through the figure so the figure has reflective symmetry about line *m*.

b) Insert a horizontal line *l* through the figure so the figure has reflective symmetry about line *l*.

c) Insert a point *P* within the figure so the figure has 180° rotational symmetry about point *P*.

d) Is it possible to insert a point *P* within the figure so the figure has 90° rotational symmetry about point *P*? Explain your answer.

54. Consider the following figure.

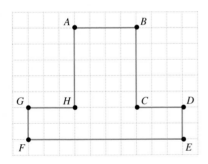

a) Insert a vertical line *m* through the figure so the figure has reflective symmetry about line *m*.

b) Is it possible to insert a horizontal line *l* through the figure so the figure has reflective symmetry about line *l*? Explain your answer.

c) Is it possible to insert a point *P* within the figure so the figure has 90° rotational symmetry about point *P*? Explain your answer.

d) Is it possible to insert a point *P* within the figure so the figure has 180° rotational symmetry about point *P*? Explain your answer.

Challenge Problems/Group Activities

55. *Glide Reflection, Order* Examine the figure below and then do the following:

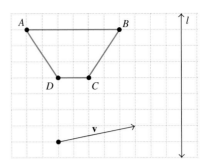

a) Determine a glide reflection of trapezoid *ABCD* by first applying translation vector **v** and then reflecting about the line *l*. Label the glide reflection *A'B'C'D'*.

b) In this step, we will reverse the order of the translation and the reflection. First reflect trapezoid *ABCD* about the line *l* and then translate the reflection using vector **v**. Label the resulting figure *A"B"C"D"*.

c) Is figure *A'B'C'D'* in the same position as figure *A"B"C"D"*?

d) What can be said about the order of the translation and the reflection used in a glide reflection? Is the figure obtained in part (a) or part (b) the glide reflection?

56. *Tessellation with a Square* Create a unique tessellation from a square piece of cardboard by using the method described on page 346. Be creative using color and sketches to complete your tessellation.

57. *Tessellation with a Hexagon* Using the method described on page 346, create a unique tessellation using a regular hexagon like the one shown below. Be creative using color and sketches to complete your tessellation.

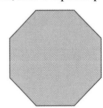

58. *Tessellation with an Octagon?* a) Trace the regular octagon, shown below, onto a separate piece of paper.

b) Try to create a regular tessellation by tracing this octagon repeatedly. Attempt to cover the entire piece of paper where no two octagons overlap each other. What conclusion can you draw about using a regular octagon as a tessellating shape?

59. *Tessellation with a Pentagon?* Repeat Exercise 58 using the regular pentagon below instead of a regular octagon.

• Recreational Mathematics

60. Examine each capital letter in the alphabet and determine which letters have reflective symmetry about a horizontal line through the center of the letter.

61. Examine each capital letter in the alphabet and determine which letters have reflective symmetry about a vertical line through the center of the letter.

62. Examine each capital letter in the alphabet and determine which letters have 180° rotational symmetry about a point in the center of the letter.

• Internet/Research Activities

63. In the study of biology, reflective symmetry is called *bilateral symmetry* and rotational symmetry is called *radial symmetry*. Do research and write a report on the role symmetry plays in the study of biology.

64. Write a paper on the mathematics displayed in the artwork of M. C. Escher. Include such topics as tessellations, optical illusions, perspective, and non-Euclidean geometry.

SECTION 6.6 • TOPOLOGY

How many different colors are needed so that no two bordering states share the same color?

Examine the outline of the map of the continental United States shown above. Now suppose you were given four crayons, each of a different color. Could you color this map with the four crayons in a way so that no two bordering states have the same color? In this section, we will discuss this question and many other questions that are relevant to the branch of mathematics known as *topology*.

The branch of mathematics called *topology* is sometimes referred to as "rubber sheet geometry" because it deals with bending and stretching of geometric figures.

One of the first pioneers of topology was the German astronomer and mathematician August Ferdinand Möbius (1790–1866). A student of Gauss, Möbius was the director of the University of Leipzig's observatory. He spent a great deal of time studying geometry and he played an essential part in the systematic development of projective geometry. He is best known for his studies of the properties of one-sided surfaces, including the one called the Möbius strip.

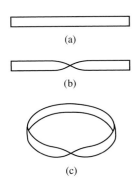

(a)

(b)

(c)

FIGURE 6.85

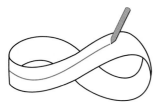

FIGURE 6.86

FIGURE 6.87

FIGURE 6.88

FIGURE 6.89

Limericks from unknown writers:

"A mathematician confided
That a Möbius band is one-sided,
And you'll get quite a laugh
If you cut one in half
For it stays in one piece when divided."

"A mathematician named Klein
Thought the Möbius band was divine.
He said, 'If you glue
the edges of two
You'll get a weird bottle like mine.'"

Möbius Strip

If you place a pencil on one surface of a sheet of paper and do not remove it from the sheet, you must cross the edge to get to the other surface. Thus, a sheet of paper has one edge and two surfaces. The sheet retains these properties even when crumpled into a ball. The *Möbius strip*, also called a *Möbius band*, is a one-sided, one-edged surface. You can construct one, as shown in Fig. 6.85, by (a) taking a strip of paper, (b) giving one end a half twist, and (c) taping the ends together.

The Möbius strip has some very interesting properties. To better understand these properties, perform the following experiments.

Experiment 1 Make a Möbius strip using a strip of paper and tape as illustrated in Fig. 6.85. Place the point of a felt-tip pen on the edge of the strip (Fig. 6.86). Pull the strip slowly so that the pen marks the edge; do not remove the pen from the edge. Continue pulling the strip and observe what happens.

Experiment 2 Make a Möbius strip. Place the tip of a felt-tip pen on the surface of the strip (Fig. 6.87). Pull the strip slowly so that the pen marks the surface. Continue and observe what happens.

Experiment 3 Make a Möbius strip. Use scissors to make a small slit in the middle of the strip. Starting at the slit, cut along the strip, keeping the scissors in the middle of the strip (Fig. 6.88). Continue cutting and observe what happens.

Experiment 4 Make a Möbius strip. Make a small slit at a point about one-third of the width of the strip. Cut along the strip, keeping the scissors the same distance from the edge (Fig. 6.89). Continue cutting and observe what happens.

If you give a strip of paper several twists, you get variations on the Möbius strip. To a topologist, the important distinction is between an odd number of twists, which leads to a one-sided surface, and an even number of twists, which leads to a two-sided surface. All strips with an odd number of twists are topologically the same as a Möbius strip, and all strips with an even number of twists are topologically the same as an ordinary cylinder, which has no twists.

Klein Bottle

Another topological object is the punctured *Klein bottle*; see Fig. 6.90. This object, named after Felix Klein (1849–1925), resembles a bottle but only has one side.

A punctured Klein bottle can be made by stretching a hollow piece of glass tubing. The neck is then passed through a hole and joined to the base.

Look closely at the model of the Klein bottle shown in Fig. 6.90. The punctured Klein bottle has only one edge and no outside or inside because it has just one side. Figure 6.91 shows a Klein bottle blown in glass by Alan Bennett of Bedford, England.

FIGURE 6.91 *Klein bottle,* A one-sided surface, blown in glass by Alan Bennett.

FIGURE 6.90

Paper-strip Klein bottle

Imagine trying to paint a Klein bottle. You start on the "outside" of the large part and work your way down the narrowing neck. When you cross the self-intersection, you have to pretend temporarily that it is not there, so you continue to follow the neck, which is now inside the bulb. As the neck opens up, to rejoin the bulb, you find that you are now painting the inside of the bulb! What appear to be the inside and outside of a Klein bottle connect together seamlessly since it is one-sided.

If a Klein bottle is cut along a curve, the results are two (one-twist) Möbius strips, see Fig. 6.92. Thus, a Klein bottle could also be made by gluing together two Möbius strips along the edges.

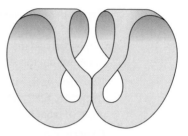

FIGURE 6.92 Two Möbius strips result from cutting a Klein bottle along a curve.

Maps

Maps have fascinated topologists for years because of the many challenging problems they present. Mapmakers have known for a long time that regardless of the complexity of the map and whether it is drawn on a flat surface or a sphere, only *four colors* are needed to differentiate each country (or state) from its immediate neighbors. Thus, every map can be drawn by using only four colors, and no two countries with a common border will have the same color. Regions that meet at only one point (such as the states of Arizona, Colorado, Utah, and New Mexico) are not considered to have a common border. In Fig. 6.93(a), no two states with a common border are marked with the same color.

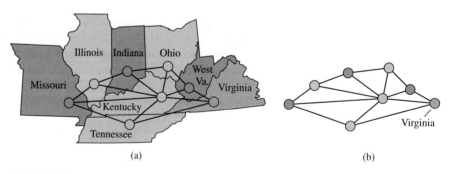

FIGURE 6.93

The "four-color" problem was first suggested by a student of Augustus DeMorgan in 1852. In 1976, Kenneth Appel and Wolfgang Haken of the University of Illinois—using their ingenuity, logic, and 1200 hours of computer time—succeeded in proving that only four colors are needed to draw a map. They solved the four-color map problem by reducing any map to a series of points and connecting line segments. They replaced each country with a point. They connected two countries having a common border with a straight line; see Fig. 6.93(b). They then showed that the points of any graph in the plane could be colored by using only four colors in such a way that no two points connected by the same line were the same color.

Mathematicians have shown that, on different surfaces, more than four colors may be needed to draw a map. For example, a map drawn on a Möbius strip requires a maximum of six colors, as in Fig. 6.94(a). A map drawn on a torus (the shape of a doughnut) requires a maximum of seven colors, as in Fig. 6.94(b).

(a)

(b)

FIGURE 6.94

Jordan Curves

A *Jordan curve* is a topological object that can be thought of as a circle twisted out of shape; see Fig. 6.95 (a)–(d). Like a circle, it has an inside and an outside. To get from one side to the other, at least one line must be crossed. Consider the Jordan curve in Fig. 6.95(d). Are points *A* and *B* inside or outside the curve?

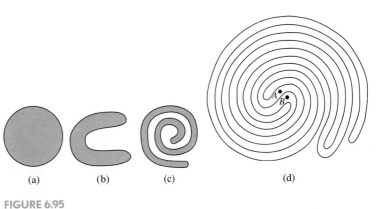

(a)   (b)   (c)   (d)

FIGURE 6.95

A quick way to tell whether the two dots are inside or outside the curve is to draw a straight line from each dot to a point that is clearly outside the curve. If the straight line crosses the curve an even number of times, the dot is outside. If the straight line crosses the curve an odd number of times, the dot is inside the curve. Can you explain why this procedure works? Determine whether point *A* and point *B* are inside or outside the curve (see Exercises 21 and 22 at the end of this section).

Topological Equivalence

Someone once said that a topologist is a person who does not know the difference between a doughnut and a coffee cup. Two geometric figures are said to be *topologically equivalent* if one figure can be elastically twisted, stretched, bent, or shrunk into the other figure without puncturing or ripping the original figure. If a doughnut is made of elastic material, it can be stretched, twisted, bent, shrunk, and distorted until it resembles a coffee cup with a handle, as shown in Fig. 6.96. Thus, the doughnut and the coffee cup are topologically equivalent.

In topology, figures are classified according to their *genus*. The *genus* of an object is determined by the number of holes that go *through* the object. A cup and a doughnut each have one hole and are of genus 1 (and are therefore topologically equivalent). Notice that the cup's handle is considered a hole, whereas the opening at the rim of the cup is not considered a hole. For our purposes, we will consider an object's opening a hole if you could pour liquid *through* the opening. For example, a typical bowling ball has three openings in the surface into which you can put your fingers when preparing to roll the ball, but liquid

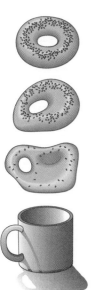

FIGURE 6.96

cannot be poured *through* any of these openings. Therefore, a bowling ball has genus 0 and is topologically equivalent to a marble. Figure 6.97 illustrates the genus of several objects.

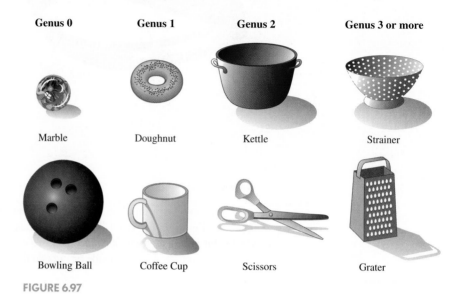

Genus 0	Genus 1	Genus 2	Genus 3 or more
Marble	Doughnut	Kettle	Strainer
Bowling Ball	Coffee Cup	Scissors	Grater

FIGURE 6.97

EXERCISE SET 6.6 ●●●●●●

• Concept/Writing Exercises

1. Explain why topology is sometimes referred to as "rubber sheet geometry."

2. What is a Möbius strip?

3. Explain how to make a Möbius strip.

4. What is a Klein bottle?

5. What is the maximum number of colors needed to create a map on a flat surface if no two regions colored the same are to share a common border?

6. What is the maximum number of colors needed to create a map if no two regions colored the same are to share a common border if the surface is a

   a) Möbius strip?

   b) torus?

7. What is a Jordan curve?

8. When testing to determine whether a point is inside or outside a Jordan curve, explain why if you count an odd number of lines, the point is inside the curve, and if you count an even number of lines, the point is outside the curve.

9. How is the genus of a figure determined?

10. When are two figures topologically equivalent?

• Practice the Skills

In Exercises 11–16, color the map by using a maximum of four colors so that no two regions with a common border have the same color.

11.

12.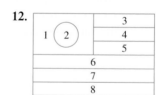

13.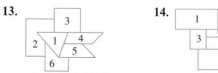

14.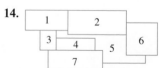

15.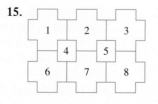

16.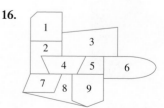

Using the Four-Color Theorem In Exercises 17–20, maps show certain areas of the United States, Canada, and Mexico. Shade in the states (or provinces) using a maximum of four colors so that no two states (or provinces) with a common border have the same color.

17.

18.

19.

20.

21. Determine whether point *A* in Fig. 6.95(d) on page 355 is inside or outside the Jordan curve.

22. Determine whether point *B* in Fig. 6.95(d) is inside or outside the Jordan curve.

At right is a Jordan curve. In Exercises 23–28, determine if the point is inside or outside the curve.

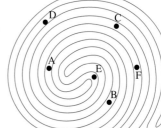

23. Point *F*

24. Point *E*

25. Point *D*

26. Point *C*

27. Point *B*

28. Point *A*

In Exercises 29–40, give the genus of the object. If the object has a genus larger than 5, write "larger than 5."

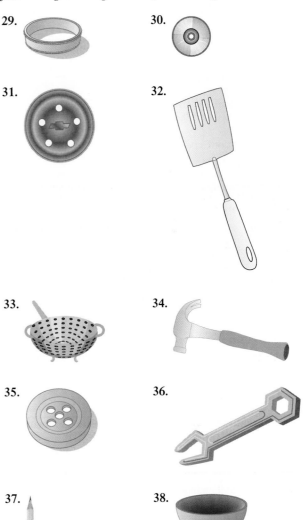

29.

30.

31.

32.

33.

34.

35.

36.

37.

38.

39.

40.

41. Name at least three objects not mentioned in this section that have

a) genus 0.

b) genus 1.

c) genus 2.

d) genus 3 or more.

42. Use the result of Experiment 1 on page 353 to find the number of edges on a Möbius strip.

43. Use the result of Experiment 2 on page 353 to find the number of surfaces on a Möbius strip.

44. How many separate strips are obtained in Experiment 3 on page 353?

45. How many separate strips are obtained in Experiment 4 on page 353?

46. Make a Möbius strip. Cut it one-third of the way from the edge, as in Experiment 4. You should get two loops, one going through the other. Determine whether either (or both) of these loops is itself a Möbius strip.

47. a) Take a strip of paper, give it one full twist, and connect the ends. Is the result a Möbius strip with only one side? Explain.

b) Determine the number of edges, as in Experiment 1.

c) Determine the number of surfaces, as in Experiment 2.

d) Cut the strip down the middle. What is the result?

48. Take a strip of paper, make one whole twist and another half twist, and then tape the ends together. Test by a method of your choice to determine whether this has the same properties as a Möbius strip.

• Challenge Problems/Group Activities

49. Using clay (or glazing compound), make a doughnut. Without puncturing or tearing the doughnut, reshape it into a topologically equivalent figure, a cup with a handle.

50. Using at most four colors, color the map of South America. Do not use the same color for any two countries that share a common border.

Source: www.mapsofworld.com
<http://www.mapsofworld.com>
used with permission.

51. Using at most four colors, color the following map of the counties of New Mexico. Do not use the same color for any two counties that share a common border.

• Recreational Mathematics

52. ***An Interesting Surface*** Construct the following surface using two strips of paper, scissors, and tape. Then answer the following questions.

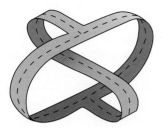

a) How many sides does this surface have?

b) How many edges does this surface have?

c) Attempt to cut the surface "in half" by making a small slit in the middle of the paper surface. Then cut along the surface (see dashed line in the figure), keeping the scissors the same distance from the edge. In your own words, describe what happens.

Although the surface shown in the figure above shares some of the same traits as a Möbius strip, this surface is not topologically equivalent to the Möbius strip.

• Internet/Research Activities

53. Use the Internet to find a map of your state that shows the outline of all the counties within your state. Print this map and, using at most four colors, color it. Do not use the same color for any two counties that share a common border.

54. The short story *Paul Bunyan versus the Conveyor Belt* (1947) by William Hazlett Upson focuses on a conveyor belt in the shape of a Möbius strip. The story can be found in several books that include mathematical essays. Read Upson's short story and write a 200-word description of what Paul Bunyan does to the conveyor belt. Confirm the outcome of the story by repeating Paul's actions with a paper Möbius strip.

SECTION 6.7 · NON-EUCLIDEAN GEOMETRY AND FRACTAL GEOMETRY

Many branches of geometry are needed to accurately represent space.

Ponder the following question: Given a line *l* and a point *P* not on the line *l*, how many lines can you draw through *P* that are parallel to *l*?

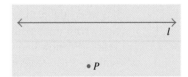

You may answer that only one line may be drawn through *P* parallel to *l*. This answer would be correct *provided* the setting of the problem is in a plane and not on the surface of a curved object. The study of this question led to the development of several new branches of geometry. It is now believed all of these branches of geometry, taken together, can be used to accurately represent space. In this section, we will study the geometry of surfaces other than the geometry of the plane.

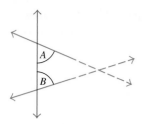

FIGURE 6.98

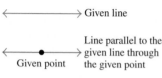

Given line

Line parallel to the
given line through
the given point

Given point

FIGURE 6.99

Non-Euclidean Geometry

In Section 6.1, we stated that postulates or axioms are statements to be accepted as true. In his book *Elements*, Euclid's fifth postulate was, "If a straight line falling on two straight lines makes the interior angles on the same side less than two right angles, the two straight lines, if produced indefinitely, meet on that side on which the angles are less than the two right angles."

Euclid's fifth axiom may be better understood by observing Fig. 6.98. The sum of angles *A* and *B* is less than the sum of two right angles (180°). Therefore, the two lines will meet if extended.

John Playfair (1748–1819), a Scottish physicist and mathematician, wrote a geometry book that was published in 1795. In his book, Playfair gave a logically equivalent interpretation of Euclid's fifth postulate. This version is often referred to as Playfair's postulate or the Euclidean parallel postulate.

THE EUCLIDEAN PARALLEL POSTULATE

Given a line and a point not on the line, one and only one line can be drawn through the given point parallel to the given line (Fig. 6.99)

The Euclidean parallel postulate may be better understood by looking at Fig. 6.99. Many mathematicians after Euclid believed that this postulate was not as self-evident as the other nine postulates given by Euclid. Others believed that this postulate could be proved from the other nine postulates and therefore was not needed at all. Of the many attempts to prove that the fifth postulate was not needed, the most noteworthy one was presented by Girolamo Saccheri (1667–1733), a Jesuit priest in Italy. In the course of his elaborate chain of deductions, Saccheri proved many of the theorems of what is now called hyperbolic geometry. However, Saccheri did not realize what he had done. He believed that Euclid's geometry was the only "true" geometry and concluded that his own work was in error. Thus, Saccheri narrowly missed receiving credit for a great achievement: the founding of *non-Euclidean geometry*.

Over time, geometers became more and more frustrated at their inability to prove Euclid's fifth postulate. One of them, a Hungarian named Farkos Bolyai, in a letter to his son, Janos Bolyai, wrote, "I entreat you leave the science of parallels alone. . . . I have traveled past all reefs of this infernal dead sea and have always come back with a broken mast and torn sail." The son, refusing to heed his father's advice, continued to think about parallels until, in 1823, he saw the whole truth and enthusiastically declared, "I have created a new universe from nothing." He recognized that geometry branches in two directions, depending on whether Euclid's fifth postulate is applied. He recognized two different geometries and published his discovery as a 24-page appendix to a textbook written by his father. The famous mathematician George Bruce Halsted called it "the most extraordinary two dozen pages in the whole history of thought." Farkos Bolyai proudly presented a copy of his son's work to his friend Carl Friedrich Gauss, then Germany's greatest mathematician, whose reply to the father had a devastating effect on the son. Gauss wrote, "I am unable to praise this work. . . . To praise it would be to praise myself. Indeed, the whole content of the work, the path taken by your son, the results to which he is led, coincides almost entirely with my meditations which occupied my mind partly for the last thirty or thirty-five years." We now know from his earlier correspondence that Gauss had indeed been familiar with *hyperbolic geometry* even before Janos was born. In his letter, Gauss also indicated that it was his intention not to let his theory be published during his lifetime, but to record it so that the theory would not perish with him. It is believed that the reason Gauss did not publish his work was that he feared being ridiculed by other prominent mathematicians of his time.

At about the same time as Bolyai's publication, Nikolay Ivanovich Lobachevsky, a Russian, published a paper that was remarkably like Bolyai's, although it was quite independent of it. Lobachevsky made a deeper investigation and wrote several books. In marked contrast to Bolyai, who received no recognition during his lifetime, Lobachevsky received great praise and became a professor at the University of Kazan.

Mapping the Brain

Medical researchers and mathematicians are currently attempting to capture an image of the three-dimensional human brain on a two-dimensional map. In some respects, the task is like capturing the image of Earth on a two-dimensional map, but because of the many folds and fissures on the surface of the brain, the task is much more complex. Points of the brain that are at different depths can appear too close in a flat image. Therefore, to develop an accurate mapping, researchers use topology, hyperbolic geometry, and elliptical geometry to create an image known as a *conformal mapping*. Researchers use conformal mappings to precisely identify the parts of the brain that correspond to specific functions.

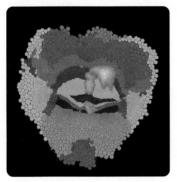

Photograph courtesy of Dr. Monica K. Hurdal (mhurdal@math.fsu.edu) Dept. of Mathematics, Florida State University

After the initial discovery, little attention was paid to the subject until 1854, when G. F. Bernhard Riemann (1826–1866), a student of Gauss, suggested a second type of non-Euclidean geometry, which is now called *spherical*, *elliptical*, or *Riemannian geometry*. The hyperbolic geometry of his predecessors was synthetic; that is, it was not based on or related to any concrete model when it was developed. Riemann's geometry was closely related to the theory of surfaces. A *model* may be considered a physical interpretation of the undefined terms that satisfies the axioms. A model may be a picture or an actual physical object.

The two types of non-Euclidean geometries we have mentioned are elliptical geometry and hyperbolic geometry. The major difference among the three geometries lies in the fifth axiom. The fifth axiom of the three geometries is summarized here.

THE FIFTH AXIOM OF GEOMETRY

Euclidean	**Elliptical**	**Hyperbolic**
Given a line and a point not on the line, one and only one line can be drawn parallel to the given line through the given point.	Given a line and a point not on the line, no line can be drawn through the given point parallel to the given line.	Given a line and a point not on the line, two or more lines can be drawn through the given point parallel to the given line.

To understand the fifth axiom of the two non-Euclidean geometries, remember that the term *line* is undefined. Thus, a line can be interpreted differently in different geometries. A model for Euclidean geometry is a plane, such as a blackboard (Fig. 6.100a). A model for elliptical geometry is a sphere (Fig. 6.100b). A model for hyperbolic geometry is a pseudosphere (Fig. 6.100c). A pseudosphere is similar to two trumpets placed bell to bell. Obviously, a line on a plane cannot be the same as a line on either of the other two figures.

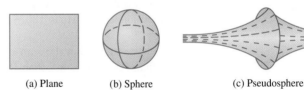

(a) Plane   (b) Sphere   (c) Pseudosphere

FIGURE 6.100

Elliptical Geometry

A circle on the surface of a sphere is called a great circle if it divides the sphere into two equal parts. If we were to cut through a sphere along a great circle, we would have two identical pieces. If we interpret a line to be a great circle, then the two red curves in Fig. 6.101(a) are lines. Figure 6.101(a) shows that the fifth axiom of elliptical geometry is true. Two great circles on a sphere must intersect; hence, there can be no parallel lines (Fig. 6.101a).

If we were to construct a triangle on a sphere, the sum of its angles would be greater than 180° (Fig. 6.101b). The theorem "The sum of the measures of the angles of a triangle is greater than 180°" has been proven by means of the axioms of elliptical geometry. The sum of the measures of the angles varies with the area of the triangle and gets closer to 180° as the area decreases.

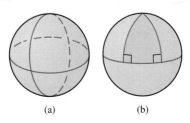

(a)   (b)

FIGURE 6.101

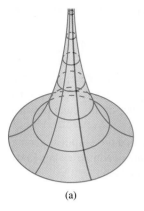

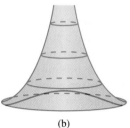

FIGURE 6.102

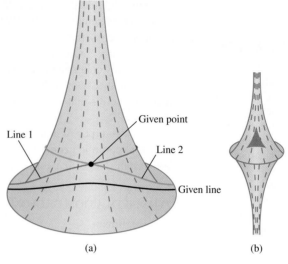

FIGURE 6.103

Hyperbolic Geometry

Lines in hyperbolic geometry* are represented by geodesics on the surface of a pseudosphere. A *geodesic* is the shortest and least-curved arc between two points on a surface. Figure 6.102 shows two different lines represented by geodesics on the surface of a pseudosphere. For simplicity of the diagrams, we only show one of the "bells" of the pseudosphere.

Figure 6.103(a) illustrates the fifth axiom of hyperbolic geometry. The diagram illustrates one way that, through the given point, two lines are drawn parallel to the given line. If we were to construct a triangle on a pseudosphere, the sum of the measures of the angles would be less than 180° (Fig. 6.103b). The theorem "The sum of the measures of the angles of a triangle is less than 180°" has been proven by means of the axioms of hyperbolic geometry.

We have stated that the sum of the measures of the angles of a triangle is 180°, is greater than 180°, and is less than 180°. Which statement is correct? Each statement is correct *in its own geometry*. Many theorems hold true for all three geometries; vertical angles still have the same measure, we can uniquely bisect a line segment with a straightedge and compass alone, and so on.

The many theorems based on the fifth postulate may differ in each geometry. It is important for you to realize that each theorem proved is true *in its own geometry* because

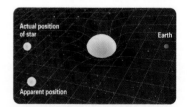
*A formal discussion of hyperbolic geometry is beyond the scope of this text.

"The Great Architect of the universe now appears to be a great mathematician."
British physicist Sir James Jeans

Fractal images

each is logically deduced from the given set of axioms of the geometry. No one system is the "best" system. Euclidean geometry may appear to be the one to use in the classroom, where the blackboard is flat. In discussions involving Earth as a whole, however, elliptical geometry may be the most useful since Earth is a sphere. If the object under consideration has the shape of a saddle or pseudosphere, hyperbolic geometry may be the most useful.

Fractal Geometry

We are familiar with one-, two-, and three-dimensional figures. Many objects, however, are difficult to categorize as one-, two-, or three-dimensional. For example, how would you classify the irregular shapes we see in nature, such as a coastline, or the bark on a tree, or a mountain, or a path followed by lightning? For a long time mathematicians assumed that making realistic geometric models of natural shapes and figures was almost impossible, but the development of *fractal geometry* now makes it possible. Both color photos on the next page were made by using fractal geometry. The discovery and study of fractal geometry has been one of the most popular mathematical topics in recent times.

The word *fractal* (from the Latin word *fractus*, "broken up, fragmented") was first used in the mid-1970s by mathematician Benoit Mandelbrot to describe shapes that had several common characteristics, including some form of "self-similarity," as will be seen shortly in the Koch snowflake.

Typical fractals are extremely irregular curves or surfaces that "wiggle" enough so that they are not considered one-dimensional. Fractals do not have integer dimensions; their dimensions are between 1 and 2. For example, a fractal may have a dimension of 1.26. Fractals are developed by applying the same rule over and over again, with the end point of each simple step becoming the starting point for the next step, in a process called *recursion*.

Using the recursive process, we will develop a famous fractal called the *Koch snowflake* named after Helga von Koch, a Swedish mathematician who first discovered its remarkable characteristics. The Koch snowflake illustrates a property of all fractals called *self-similarity*; that is, each smaller piece of the curve resembles the whole curve.

To develop the Koch snowflake:

1. Start with an equilateral triangle (step 1, Fig. 6.104).
2. Whenever you see an edge —— replace it with ⌐⌐ (steps 2–4).

What is the perimeter of the snowflake in Fig. 6.104, and what is its area? A portion of the boundary of the Koch snowflake known as the Koch curve or the snowflake curve is represented in Fig. 6.105.

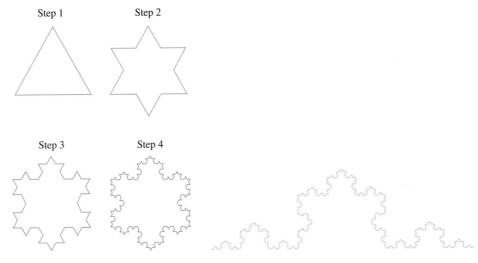

Step 1   Step 2

Step 3   Step 4

FIGURE 6.104   **FIGURE 6.105**

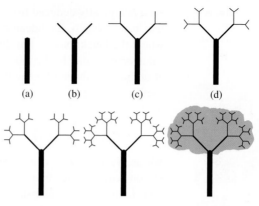

FIGURE 6.106 The fractal tree

The Koch curve consists of infinitely many pieces of the form 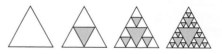 . Notice that after each step, the perimeter is $\frac{4}{3}$ times the perimeter of the previous step. Therefore, the Koch snowflake has an infinite perimeter. It can be shown that the area of the snowflake is 1.6 times the area of the starting equilateral triangle. Thus, the area of the snowflake is finite. The Koch snowflake has a finite area enclosed by an infinite boundary! This fact may seem difficult to accept, but it is true. However, the Koch snowflake, like other fractals, is not an everyday run-of-the-mill geometric shape.

Let us look at a few more fractals made using the recursive process. We will now construct what is known as a *fractal tree*. Start with a tree trunk (Fig. 6.106a). Draw two branches, each one a bit smaller than the trunk (Fig. 6.106b). Draw two branches from each of those branches, and continue; see Fig. 6.106(c) and (d). Ideally, we continue the process forever.

If you take a little piece of any branch and zoom in on it, it will look exactly like the original tree. Fractals are *scale independent*, which means that you cannot really tell whether you are looking at something very big or something very small because the fractal looks the same whether you are close to it or far from it.

In Figs. 6.107 and 6.108, we develop two other fractals through the process of recursion. Figure 6.107 shows a fractal called the Sierpinski triangle, and Fig. 6.108 shows a fractal called the Sierpinski carpet. Both fractals are named after Waclaw Sierpinski, a Polish mathematician who is best known for his work with fractals and space-filling curves.

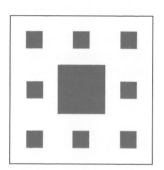

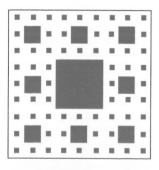

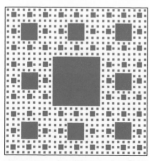

FIGURE 6.108 Sierpinski carpet

FIGURE 6.107 Sierpinski triangle

Fractals provide a way to study natural forms such as coastlines, trees, mountains, galaxies, polymers, rivers, weather patterns, brains, lungs, and blood supply. Fractals also help explain that which appears chaotic. The blood supply in the body is one example. The branching of arteries and veins appears chaotic, but closer inspection reveals that the same type of branching occurs for smaller and smaller blood vessels, down to the capillaries. Thus, fractal geometry provides a geometric structure for chaotic processes in nature. The study of chaotic processes is called *chaos theory*.

Fractals nowadays have a potentially important role to play in characterizing weather systems and in providing insight into various physical processes such as the occurrence of earthquakes or the formation of deposits that shorten battery life. Some scientists view fractal statistics as a doorway to unifying theories of medicine, offering a powerful glimpse of what it means to be healthy.

Fractals lie at the heart of current efforts to understand complex natural phenomena. Unraveling their intricacies could reveal the basic design principles at work in our world. Until recently, there was no way to describe fractals. Today, we are beginning to see such features everywhere. Tomorrow, we may look at the entire universe through a fractal lens.

EXERCISE SET 6.7 ●●●●●●

• Concept/Writing Exercises

In Exercises 1–6, describe the accomplishments of the mathematician.

1. Benoit Mandelbrot

2. G. F. Bernhard Riemann

3. Nikolay Ivanovich Lobachevsky

4. Carl Friedrich Gauss

5. Janos Bolyai

6. Girolamo Saccheri

7. State the fifth axiom of

   a) Euclidean geometry.

   b) elliptical geometry.

   c) hyperbolic geometry.

8. State the theorem concerning the sum of the measures of the angles of a triangle in

   a) Euclidean geometry.

   b) hyperbolic geometry.

   c) elliptical geometry.

9. What model is often used in describing and explaining Euclidean geometry?

10. What model is often used in describing and explaining elliptical geometry?

11. What model is often used in describing and explaining hyperbolic geometry?

12. What do we mean when we say that no one axiomatic system of geometry is "best"?

13. List the three types of curvature of space and the types of geometry that correspond to them.

14. List at least five natural forms that appear chaotic that we can study using fractals.

• Practice the Skills

In the following, we show a fractal-like figure made using a recursive process with the letter "M." In Exercises 15–18, use this fractal-like figure as a guide in constructing fractal-like figures with the letter given. Show three steps, as is done here.

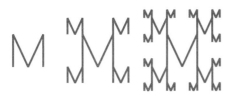

15. I   16. V   17. H   18. W

19. **a)** Develop a fractal by beginning with a square and replacing each side ⎯⎯ with a ⌐⌐ . Repeat this process twice.

    b) If you continue this process, will the fractal's perimeter be finite or infinite? Explain.

    c) Will the fractal's area be finite or infinite? Explain.

• Problem Solving/Group Activity

20. In forming the Koch snowflake in Figure 6.104 on page 363, the perimeter becomes greater at each step in the process. If each side of the original triangle is 1 unit, a general formula for the perimeter, L, of the snowflake at any step, n, may be found by the formula

$$L = 3\left(\frac{4}{3}\right)^{n-1}$$

For example, at the first step when $n = 1$, the perimeter is 3 units, which can be verified by the formula as follows:

$$L = 3\left(\frac{4}{3}\right)^{1-1} = 3\left(\frac{4}{3}\right)^{0} = 3 \cdot 1 = 3$$

At the second step, when $n = 2$, we find the perimeter as follows:

$$L = 3\left(\frac{4}{3}\right)^{2-1} = 3\left(\frac{4}{3}\right) = 4$$

Thus, at the second step the perimeter of the snowflake is 4 units.

a) Use the formula to complete the following table.

Step	Perimeter
1	
2	
3	
4	
5	
6	

b) Use the results of your calculations to explain why the perimeter of the Koch snowflake is infinite.

c) Explain how the Koch snowflake can have an infinite perimeter, but a finite area.

• Internet/Research Activities

In Exercises 21–23, references include the Internet, books on art, encyclopedias, and history of mathematics books.

21. To complete his masterpiece *Circle Limit III*, M. C. Escher studied a model of hyperbolic geometry called the *Poincaré disk*. Write a paper on the Poincaré disk and how it was used in Escher's art. Include representations of *infinity* and the concepts of *point* and *line* in hyperbolic geometry.

Escher's *Circle Limit III*

22. To transfer his two-dimensional tiling known as *Symmetry Work 45* to a sphere, M. C. Escher used the spherical geometry of Bernhard Riemann. Write a paper on Escher's use of geometry to complete this masterpiece.

23. Go to the web site *Fantastic Fractals* at www.fantastic-fractals.com and study the information about fractals given there. Print copies, in color if a color printer is available, of the Mandlebrot set and the Julia set.

●●●●●○○ CHAPTER SUMMARY, REVIEW, AND TEST

● S U M M A R Y   DEFINITIONS AND CONCEPTS

Important Facts

The sum of the measures of the angles of a triangle is 180°.

The sum of the measures of the angles of a quadrilateral is 360°.

The sum of the measures of the interior angles of an n-sided polygon is $(n - 2)180°$.

TRIANGLE

$P = s_1 + s_2 + s_3 (s_3 = b)$
$A = \frac{1}{2}bh$

SQUARE

$P = 4s$
$A = s^2$

RECTANGLE

$P = 2l + 2w$
$A = lw$

PARALLELOGRAM

$P = 2b + 2w$
$A = bh$

TRAPEZOID

$P = s_1 + s_2 + b_1 + b_2$
$A = \frac{1}{2}h(b_1 + b_2)$

PYTHAGOREAN THEOREM

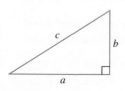

$a^2 + b^2 = c^2$

CIRCLE

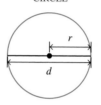

$A = \pi r^2; C = 2\pi r \text{ or } C = \pi d$

CUBE

$V = s^3$
$SA = 6s^2$

RECTANGULAR SOLID

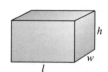

$V = lwh$
$SA = 2lw + 2wh + 2lh$

CYLINDER

$V = \pi r^2 h$
$SA = 2\pi rh + 2\pi r^2$

CONE

$V = \frac{1}{3}\pi r^2 h$
$SA = \pi r^2 + \pi r\sqrt{r^2 + h^2}$

SPHERE

$V = \frac{4}{3}\pi r^3$
$SA = 4\pi r^2$

PRISM

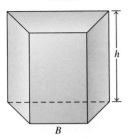

$V = Bh$, where B is the area of the base

PYRAMID

$V = \frac{1}{3}Bh$, where B is the area of the base

FIFTH POSTULATE IN EUCLIDEAN GEOMETRY

Given a line and a point not on the line, only one line can be drawn through the given point parallel to the given line.

FIFTH POSTULATE IN ELLIPTICAL GEOMETRY

Given a line and a point not on the line, no line can be drawn through the given point parallel to the given line.

FIFTH POSTULATE IN HYPERBOLIC GEOMETRY

Given a line and a point not on the line, two or more lines can be drawn through the given point parallel to the given line.

REVIEW EXERCISES

6.1

In Exercises 1–6, use the figure shown to determine the following.

1. $\angle ABF \cap \angle CBH$

2. $\overleftrightarrow{AB} \cap \overleftrightarrow{DC}$

3. $\overline{BF} \cup \overline{FC} \cup \overline{BC}$

4. $\overrightarrow{BH} \cup \overrightarrow{HB}$

5. $\overleftrightarrow{HI} \cap \overrightarrow{EG}$

6. $\overrightarrow{CF} \cap \overrightarrow{CG}$

7. $m\angle A = 23.7°$. Determine the measure of the complement of $\angle A$.

8. $m\angle B = 124.7°$. Determine the measure of the supplement $\angle B$.

6.2

In Exercises 9–12, use the similar triangles ABC and A'B'C shown to determine the following.

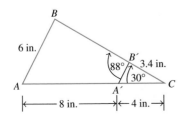

9. The length of $\overline{BC}$

10. The length of $\overline{A'B'}$

11. $m\angle BAC$

12. $m\angle ABC$

13. In the following figure, l_1 and l_2 are parallel lines. Determine $m\angle 1$ through $m\angle 6$.

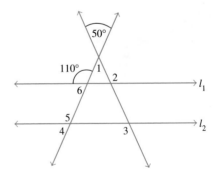

14. Determine the sum of the measures of the interior angles of a pentagon.

6.3

In Exercises 15–18, determine (a) the area and (b) the perimeter of the figure.

15.

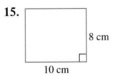

16.

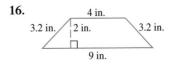

17.
9 in. 7 in.
12 in.

18.
3 km
4 km

19. Determine (a) the area and (b) the circumference of the circle. Use the $\boxed{\pi}$ key on a calculator and round your answer to the nearest hundredth.

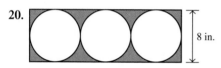
13 cm

In Exercises 20 and 21, determine the shaded area. When appropriate, use the $\boxed{\pi}$ key on your calculator and round your answer to the nearest hundredth.

20.
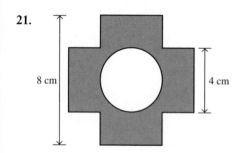
8 in.

21.
8 cm   4 cm

22. *Cost of Kitchen Tile* Determine the total cost of covering a 14 ft by 16 ft kitchen floor with ceramic tile. The cost of the tile selected is $5.25 per square foot.

6.4

In Exercises 23–26, determine (a) the volume and (b) the surface area of the figure. When appropriate, use the $\boxed{\pi}$ key on your calculator and round your answer to the nearest hundredth.

24.
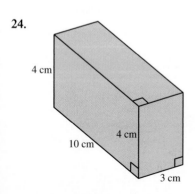
4 cm
4 cm
10 cm
3 cm

24.
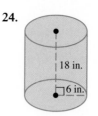
18 in.
6 in.

25.
12 mm
16 mm

26.
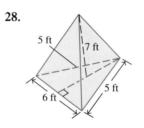
4 ft

In Exercises 27 and 28, determine the volume of the figure.

27.
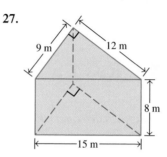
9 m   12 m
8 m
15 m

28.
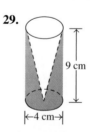
5 ft   7 ft
5 ft
6 ft

In Exercises 29 and 30, determine the volume of the shaded area. When appropriate, use the $\boxed{\pi}$ key and round your answer to the nearest hundredth.

29.
9 cm
4 cm

30.
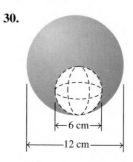
6 cm
12 cm

31. *Water Trough* Steven Dale has a water trough whose ends are trapezoids and whose sides are rectangles, as illustrated. He is afraid that the base it is sitting on will not support the weight of the trough when it is filled with water. He knows that the base will support 4800 lb.

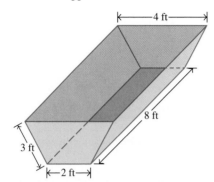

a) If the trough is filled with water, determine the number of cubic feet of water contained in the trough.

b) Determine the total weight, assuming that the trough weighs 375 lb and the water weighs 62.4 lb per cubic foot. Is the base strong enough to support the trough filled with water?

c) If 1 gal of water weighs 8.3 lb, how many gallons of water will the trough hold?

6.5

In Exercises 32 and 33, use the given triangle and reflection lines to construct the indicated reflections. Show the triangle in the positions both before and after the reflection.

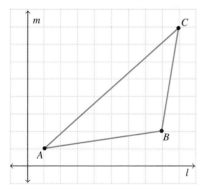

32. Construct the reflection of triangle *ABC* about line *l*.

33. Construct the reflection of triangle *ABC* about line *m*.

*In Exercises 34 and 35, use translation vectors **v** and **w** to construct the indicated translations. Show the parallelogram in the positions both before and after the translation.*

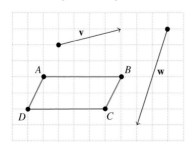

34. Construct the translation of parallelogram *ABCD* using translation vector **v**.

35. Construct the translation of parallelogram *ABCD* using translation vector **w**.

In Exercises 36–38, use the given figure and rotation point P to construct the indicated rotations. Show the trapezoid in the positions both before and after the rotation.

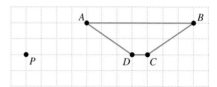

36. Construct a 90° rotation of trapezoid *ABCD* about point *P*.

37. Construct a 180° rotation of trapezoid *ABCD* about point *P*.

38. Construct a 270° rotation of trapezoid *ABCD* about point *P*.

*In Exercises 39 and 40, use the given figure, translation vector **v**, and reflection lines l and m to construct the indicated glide reflections. Show the triangle in the positions both before and after the glide reflection.*

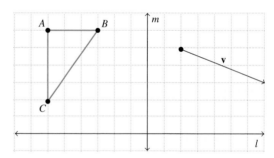

39. Construct a glide reflection of triangle *ABC* using vector **v** and reflection line *l*.

40. Construct a glide reflection of triangle *ABC* using vector **v** and reflection line *m*.

In Exercises 41 and 42, use the following figure to answer the following questions.

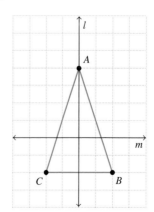

41. Does triangle *ABC* have reflective symmetry about line *l*? Explain.

42. Does triangle *ABC* have reflective symmetry about line *m*? Explain.

In Exercises 43 and 44, use the following figure to answer the following questions.

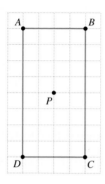

43. Does rectangle *ABCD* have 90° rotational symmetry about point *P*? Explain.

44. Does rectangle *ABCD* have 180° rotational symmetry about point *P*? Explain.

6.7

45. Give an example of an object that has

a) genus 0.

b) genus 1.

c) genus 2.

d) genus 3 or more.

46. The map shows the states of Germany. Shade in the states using a maximum of four colors so that no two states with a common border have the same color.

47. Determine whether point *A* is inside or outside the Jordan curve.

6.7

48. State the fifth axiom of Euclidean, elliptical, and hyperbolic geometry.

49. Develop a fractal by beginning with a square and replacing each side ——— with a ⎍ . Repeat this process twice.

50. Construct a Koch snowflake by beginning with an equilateral triangle and replacing each side with a ⋀ . Repeat this process twice.

●●●●●○○ CHAPTER 6 TEST

*In Exercises 1–4, use the figure to describe the following
sets of points.*

1. $\overleftrightarrow{AF} \cap \overleftrightarrow{EF}$

2. $\overline{BC} \cup \overline{CD} \cup \overline{BD}$

3. $\measuredangle EDF \cap \measuredangle BDC$

4. $\overrightarrow{AC} \cup \overrightarrow{BA}$

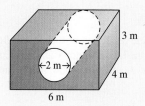

5. $m\measuredangle A = 12.4°$. Determine the measure of the complement
of $\measuredangle A$.

6. $m\measuredangle B = 51.7°$. Determine the measure of the supplement of
$\measuredangle B$.

7. In the figure, determine the measure of $\measuredangle x$.

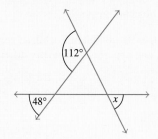

8. Determine the sum of the measures of the interior angles of
a decagon.

9. Triangles ABC and $A'B'C'$ are similar figures. Determine
the length of side $\overline{B'C'}$.

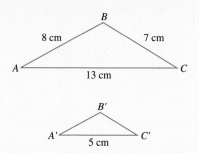

10. Right triangle ABC (see top of right-hand column) has one
leg of length 5 in. and a hypotenuse of length 13 in.

   a) Determine the length of the other leg.

   b) Determine the perimeter of the triangle.

   c) Determine the area of the triangle.

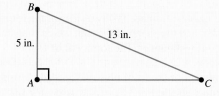

11. Determine (a) the volume and (b) the surface area of a
sphere of diameter 14 cm.

12. Determine the volume of the shaded area. Use the $\boxed{\pi}$ key
on your calculator and round your answer to the nearest
hundredth.

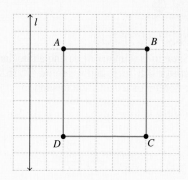

13. Determine the volume of the pyramid.

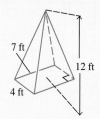

14. Construct a reflection of square $ABCD$, shown below, about
line l. Show the square in the positions both before and
after the reflection.

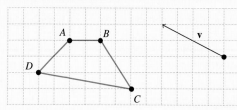

15. Construct a translation of quadrilateral $ABCD$, shown below,
using translation vector **v**. Show the quadrilateral in the positions both before and after the translation.

16. Construct a 180° rotation of triangle *ABC*, shown below, about rotation point *P*. Show the triangle in the positions both before and after the rotation.

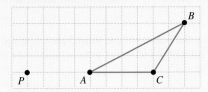

17. Construct a glide reflection of rectangle *ABCD*, shown below, using translation vector **v** and reflection line *l*. Show the rectangle in the positions both before and after the glide reflection.

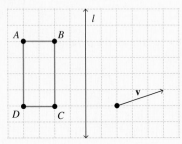

18. Use the figure below to answer the following questions.

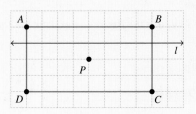

a) Does rectangle *ABCD* have reflective symmetry about line *l*? Explain.

b) Does rectangle *ABCD* have 180° rotational symmetry about point *P*? Explain.

19. What is a Möbius strip?

20. a) Sketch an object of genus 1.

b) Sketch an object of genus 2.

21. Explain how the fifth axiom in Euclidean geometry, elliptical geometry, and hyperbolic geometry differ.

●●●●●● GROUP PROJECTS

SUPPORTING A HOT TUB

1. Samantha Saraniti is thinking of buying a circular hot tub 12 ft in diameter, 4 ft deep, and weighing 475 lb. She wants to place the hot tub on a deck built to support 30,000 lb.

a) Determine the volume of the water in the hot tub in cubic feet.

b) Determine the number of gallons of water the hot tub will hold. (*Note:* 1 ft³ ≈ 7.5 gal.)

c) Determine the weight of the water in the hot tub. (*Hint:* Fresh water weighs about 62.4 lb/ft³.)

d) Will the deck support the weight of the hot tub and water?

e) Will the deck support the weight of the hot tub, water, and four people, whose average weight is 115 lb?

DESIGNING A RAMP

2. David and Sandra Jessee are planning to build a ramp so that the front entrance of their home is wheelchair accessible. The ramp will be 3 feet wide. It will rise 2 in. for each foot of length of horizontal distance. Where the ramp meets the porch, the ramp must be 2 ft high. To provide stability for the ramp, the Jessees will install a slab of concrete 4 in. thick and 6 in. longer and wider than the ramp (see accompanying figure). The top of the slab will be level with the ground. The ramp may be constructed of concrete or pressure-treated lumber. You are to estimate the cost of materials for constructing the slab, the ramp of concrete, and the ramp of pressure-treated lumber.

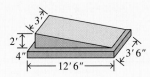

Slab

a) Determine the length of the base of the ramp.

b) Determine the dimensions of the concrete slab on which the ramp will set.

c) Determine the volume of the concrete in cubic yards needed to construct the slab.

d) If ready-mix concrete costs $45 per cubic yard, determine the cost of the concrete needed to construct the slab.

Concrete Ramp

e) To build the ramp of concrete, a form in the shape of the ramp must be framed. The two sides of the form are triangular, and the shape of the end, which is against the porch, is rectangular. The form will be framed from ¾ in. plywood, which comes in 4 ft × 8 ft sheets. Determine the number of sheets of plywood needed. Assume that the entire sheet(s) will be used to make the sides and the end of the form and that there is no waste.

f) If the plywood costs $18.95 for a 4 ft × 8 ft sheet, determine the cost of the plywood.

g) To brace the form, the Jessees will need two boards 2 in. × 4 in. × 8 ft (referred to as 8 ft 2 × 4's) and six pieces of lumber 2 in. × 4 in. × 3 ft. These six pieces of lumber will be cut from 8 ft 2 × 4 boards. Determine the number of 8 ft 2 × 4 boards needed.

h) Determine the cost of the 8 ft 2 × 4 boards needed in part (g) if one board costs $2.14.

i) Determine the volume, in cubic yards, of concrete needed to fill the form.

j) Determine the cost of the concrete needed to fill the form.

k) Determine the total cost of materials for building the ramp of concrete by adding the results in parts (d), (f), (h), and (j).

Wooden Ramp

l) Determine the length of the top of the ramp.

m) The top of the ramp will be constructed of $\frac{5}{4}$ in. × 6 in. × 10 ft pressure-treated lumber. The boards will be butted end to end to make the necessary length and will be supported from underneath by a wooden frame. Determine the number of boards needed to cover the top of the ramp. The boards are laid lengthwise on the ramp.

n) Determine the cost of the boards to cover the top of the ramp if the price of a 10 ft length is $6.47.

o) To support the top of the ramp, the Jessees will need 10 pieces of 8 ft 2 × 4's. The price of a pressure-treated 8 ft 2 × 4 is $2.44. Determine the cost of the supports.

p) Determine the cost of the materials for building a wooden ramp by adding the amounts from parts (d), (n), and (o).

q) Are the materials for constructing a concrete ramp or a wooden ramp less expensive?

CHAPTER

7

Set Theory

You want to organize a blood drive on campus with the local Red Cross. The Red Cross asked you whether the number of potential donors warrants a commitment to provide medical staff for the blood drive. So you took a survey to obtain information. Your survey asked students two questions:

1. Would you be willing to donate blood?
2. Would you be willing to help serve a free breakfast to blood donors?

Now the survey results are in. How will you organize and present the results to the Red Cross in an efficient manner?

The need to sort and organize information obtained through surveys is related to our need to find order and meaning by classifying things into collections, called *sets*. In this chapter, we analyze a variety of collections, ranging from sets of television's most popular shows to sets of places with the greatest number of shark attacks, and even collections of famous people on whom the FBI kept files.

The problem of organizing and presenting the results of the blood drive survey appears as Example 1 in Section 7.5. In Exercise Set 7.4, you'll find TV's most popular shows (Exercises 93–98) and Jaws on the attack (Exercise 105). The set of famous Americans watched by the FBI is divided into smaller collections, called *subsets*, in Exercise 21 of the Chapter 7 Test.

SECTION 7.1 ● BASIC SET CONCEPTS

We tend to place things in categories, allowing us to order and structure the world. For example, you can categorize yourself by your age, your ethnicity, your academic major, or your gender. Our minds cannot find order and meaning without creating collections. Mathematicians call such collections *sets*. A **set** is a collection of objects whose contents can be clearly determined. The objects in a set are called the **elements**, or **members**, of the set.

A set must be **well defined**, meaning that its contents can be clearly determined. Using this criterion, the collection of actors who have won Academy Awards is a set. We can always determine whether or not a particular actor is an element of this collection. By contrast, consider the collection of great actors. Whether or not a person belongs to this collection is a matter of how we interpret the word *great*. In this text, we will only consider collections that form well-defined sets.

Methods for Representing Sets

1 | Use three methods to represent sets.

An example of a set is the set of the days of the week, whose elements are Monday, Tuesday, Wednesday, Thursday, Friday, Saturday, and Sunday.

Capital letters are generally used to name sets. Let's use W to represent the set of the days of the week.

Three methods are commonly used to designate a set. One method is a **word description**. We can describe set W as the set of the days of the week. A second method is the **roster method**. This involves listing the elements of a set inside a pair of braces, { }. The braces at the beginning and end indicate that we are representing a set. The roster form uses commas to separate the elements of the set. Thus, we can designate the set W by listing its elements:

$W = \{\text{Monday, Tuesday, Wednesday, Thursday, Friday, Saturday, Sunday}\}.$

Grouping symbols such as parentheses, ( ), and square brackets, [ ], are not used to represent sets. Only commas are used to separate the elements of a set. Separators such as colons or semicolons are not used. Finally, the order in which the elements are listed in a set is not important. Thus, another way of expressing the set of the days of the week is

$W = \{\text{Saturday, Sunday, Monday, Tuesday, Wednesday, Thursday, Friday}\}.$

EXAMPLE 1   REPRESENTING A SET USING A DESCRIPTION

Write a word description of the set

$P = \{\text{Washington, Adams, Jefferson, Madison, Monroe}\}.$

SOLUTION Set P is the set of the first five presidents of the United States.

Write a word description of the set

$$L = \{a, b, c, d, e, f\}.$$

EXAMPLE 2   REPRESENTING A SET USING THE ROSTER METHOD

Set C is the set of U.S. coins with a value of less than a dollar. Express this set using the roster method.

SOLUTION $C = \{$penny, nickel, dime, quarter, half-dollar$\}$

 Set M is the set of months beginning with the letter A. Express this set using the roster method.

The third method for representing a set is with **set-builder notation**. Using this method, the set of the days of the week can be expressed as

$$W = \{x \mid x \text{ is a day of the week}\}.$$

| Set W | is | the set of | all elements x | such that |

We read this notation as "Set W is the set of all elements x such that x is a day of the week." Before the vertical line is the variable x, which represents an element in general. After the vertical line is the condition x must meet in order to be an element of the set.

STUDY TIP

Any letter can be used to represent the variable in set-builder notation. Thus, $\{x \mid x \text{ is a day of the week}\}$, $\{y \mid y \text{ is a day of the week}\}$, and $\{z \mid z \text{ is a day of the week}\}$ all represent the same set.

Table 7.1 contains two examples of sets, each represented with a word description, the roster method, and set-builder notation.

TABLE 7.1 SETS USING THREE DESIGNATIONS

Word Description	Roster Method	Set-Builder Notation
B is the set of members of the Beatles in 1963.	$B = \{$George Harrison, John Lennon, Paul McCartney, Ringo Starr$\}$	$B = \{x \mid x \text{ was a member of the Beatles in 1963}\}$
S is the set of states whose names begin with the letter A.	$S = \{$Alabama, Alaska, Arizona, Arkansas$\}$	$S = \{x \mid x \text{ is a U.S. state whose name begins with the letter A}\}$

EXAMPLE 3   CONVERTING FROM SET-BUILDER TO ROSTER NOTATION

Express set

$$A = \{x \mid x \text{ is a month that begins with the letter M}\}$$

using the roster method.

SOLUTION   Set A is the set of all elements x such that x is a month beginning with the letter M. There are two such months, namely March and May. Thus,

$$A = \{\text{March, May}\}.$$

The Beatles climbed to the top of the British music charts in 1963, conquering the United States a year later.

CHECK POINT 3 Express the set

$$O = \{x \mid x \text{ is a positive odd number less than } 10\}$$

using the roster method.

The representation of some sets by the roster method can be rather long, or even impossible, if we attempt to list every element. For example, consider the set of all lowercase letters of the English alphabet. If L is chosen as a name for this set, we can use set-builder notation to represent L as follows:

$$L = \{x \mid x \text{ is a lowercase letter of the English alphabet}\}.$$

A complete listing using the roster method is rather tedious:

$$L = \{a, b, c, d, e, f, g, h, i, j, k, l, m, n, o, p, q, r, s, t, u, v, w, x, y, z\}.$$

We can shorten the listing in set L by writing

$$L = \{a, b, c, d, \ldots, z\}.$$

The three dots after the element d, called an *ellipsis*, indicate that the elements in the set continue in the same manner up to and including the last element z.

BLITZER BONUS

The Loss of Sets

John Tenniel, colored by Fritz Kredel

Have you ever considered what would happen if we suddenly lost our ability to recall categories and the names that identify them? This is precisely what happened to Alice, the heroine of Lewis Carroll's *Through the Looking Glass*, as she walked with a fawn in "the woods with no names."

So they walked on together through the woods, Alice with her arms clasped lovingly round the soft neck of the Fawn, till they came out into another open field, and here the Fawn gave a sudden bound into the air, and shook itself free from Alice's arm. "I'm a Fawn!" it cried out in a voice of delight. "And, dear me! you're a human child!" A sudden look of alarm came into its beautiful brown eyes, and in another moment it had darted away at full speed.

By realizing that Alice is a member of the set of human beings, which in turn is part of the set of dangerous things, the fawn is overcome by fear. Thus, the fawn's experience is determined by the way it structures the world into sets with various characteristics.

2 Define and recognize the empty set.

The Empty Set

Consider the following sets:

$$\{x \mid x \text{ is a fawn that speaks}\}$$
$$\{x \mid x \text{ is a number greater than } 10 \text{ and less than } 4\}.$$

Can you see what these sets have in common? They both contain no elements. There are no fawns that speak. There are no numbers that are both greater than 10 and also less than 4. Sets such as these that contain no elements are called the *empty set*, or the *null set*.

> **THE EMPTY SET**
> The **empty set**, also called the **null set**, is the set that contains no elements. The empty set is represented by $\{\ \}$ or $\varnothing$.

Notice that { } and Ø have the same meaning. However, the empty set is not represented by {Ø}. This notation represents a set containing the element Ø.

EXAMPLE 4   RECOGNIZING THE EMPTY SET

Which one of the following is the empty set?

a. {0}   **b.** 0

c. $\{x \mid x$ is a number less than 4 or greater than 10$\}$

d. $\{x \mid x$ is a square with exactly three sides$\}$

SOLUTION

a. {0} is a set containing one element, 0. Because this set contains an element, it is not the empty set.

b. 0 is a number, not a set, so it cannot possibly be the empty set. It does, however, represent the number of members of the empty set.

c. $\{x \mid x$ is a number less than 4 or greater than 10$\}$ contains all numbers that are either less than 4, such as 3, or greater than 10, such as 11. Because some elements belong to this set, it cannot be the empty set.

d. $\{x \mid x$ is a square with exactly three sides$\}$ contains no elements. There are no squares with exactly three sides. This set is the empty set.

 Which one of the following is the empty set?

a. $\{x \mid x$ is a number less than 3 or greater than 5$\}$

b. $\{x \mid x$ is a number less than 3 and greater than 5$\}$

c. nothing   **d.** {Ø}

The Musical Sounds of the Empty Set

John Cage (1912–1992), the American avant-garde composer, translated the empty set into the quietest piece of music ever written. His piano composition *4'33"* requires the musician to sit frozen in silence at a piano stool for 4 minutes, 33 seconds, or 273 seconds. (The significance of 273 is that at approximately −273°C, all molecular motion stops.) The set

$$\{x \mid x \text{ is a musical sound from } 4'33''\}$$

is the empty set. There are no musical sounds in the composition. Mathematician Martin Gardner wrote, "I have not heard *4'33"* performed, but friends who have tell me it is Cage's finest composition."

3 | Use the symbols ∈ and ∉.

Notations for Set Membership

We now consider two special notations that indicate whether or not a given object belongs to a set.

THE NOTATIONS ∈ AND ∉

The symbol ∈ is used to indicate that an object is an element of a set. The symbol ∈ is used to replace the words "is an element of."

The symbol ∉ is used to indicate that an object is *not* an element of a set. The symbol ∉ is used to replace the words "is not an element of."

EXAMPLE 5   USING THE SYMBOLS ∈ AND ∉

Determine whether each statement is true or false:

a. $r \in \{a, b, c, \ldots, z\}$ **b.** $7 \notin \{1, 2, 3, 4, 5\}$ **c.** $\{a\} \in \{a, b\}$.

SOLUTION

a. Because r is an element of the set $\{a, b, c, \ldots, z\}$, the statement

$$r \in \{a, b, c, \ldots, z\}$$

is true.

Observe that an element can belong to a set in roster notation when three dots appear even though the element is not listed.

b. Because 7 is not an element of the set $\{1, 2, 3, 4, 5\}$, the statement

$$7 \notin \{1, 2, 3, 4, 5\}$$

is true.

c. Because $\{a\}$ is a set and the set $\{a\}$ is not an element of the set $\{a, b\}$, the statement

$$\{a\} \in \{a, b\}$$

is false.

Determine whether each statement is true or false:

a. $8 \in \{1, 2, 3, \ldots, 10\}$

b. $r \notin \{a, b, c, z\}$

c. $\{Monday\} \in \{x \mid x \text{ is a day of the week}\}$.

4 | Apply set notation to sets of natural numbers.

Sets of Natural Numbers

For the remainder of this section, we will focus on the set of numbers used for counting:

$$\{1, 2, 3, 4, 5, 6, 7, 8, 9, 10, 11, \ldots\}.$$

The set of counting numbers is also called the set of **natural numbers**. We represent this set by the bold face letter **N**.

THE SET OF NATURAL NUMBERS

$$\mathbf{N} = \{1, 2, 3, 4, 5, \ldots\}$$

The three dots, or ellipsis, after the 5 indicate that there is no final element and that the listing goes on forever.

EXAMPLE 6   REPRESENTING SETS OF NATURAL NUMBERS

Express each of the following sets using the roster method:

a. Set A is the set of natural numbers less than 5.

b. Set B is the set of natural numbers greater than or equal to 25.

c. $E = \{x \mid x \in \mathbf{N} \text{ and } x \text{ is even}\}$.

SOLUTION

a. The natural numbers less than 5 are 1, 2, 3, and 4. Thus, set A can be expressed using the roster method as

$$A = \{1, 2, 3, 4\}.$$

b. The natural numbers greater than or equal to 25 are 25, 26, 27, 28, and so on. Set B in roster form is

$$B = \{25, 26, 27, 28, \ldots\}.$$

The three dots show that the listing goes on forever.

c. The set-builder notation

$$E = \{x \mid x \in \mathbf{N} \text{ and } x \text{ is even}\}$$

indicates that we want to list the set of all x such that x is an element of the set of natural numbers and x is even. The set of numbers that meet both conditions is the set of even natural numbers. The set in roster form is

$$E = \{2, 4, 6, 8, \dots\}.$$

 Express each of the following sets using the roster method:

a. Set A is the set of natural numbers less than or equal to 3.

b. Set B is the set of natural numbers greater than 14.

c. $O = \{x \mid x \in \mathbf{N} \text{ and } x \text{ is odd}\}$.

Inequality symbols are frequently used to describe sets of natural numbers. Table 7.2 reviews basic inequality notation.

TABLE 7.2 INEQUALITY NOTATION AND SETS

Inequality Symbol and Meaning	Example — Set-Builder Notation	Roster Method
$x < a$ — x is less than a.	$\{x \mid x \in \mathbf{N} \text{ and } x < 4\}$ — x is a natural number less than 4.	$\{1, 2, 3\}$
$x \leq a$ — x is less than or equal to a.	$\{x \mid x \in \mathbf{N} \text{ and } x \leq 4\}$ — x is a natural number less than or equal to 4.	$\{1, 2, 3, 4\}$
$x > a$ — x is greater than a.	$\{x \mid x \in \mathbf{N} \text{ and } x > 4\}$ — x is a natural number greater than 4.	$\{5, 6, 7, 8, \dots\}$
$x \geq a$ — x is greater than or equal to a.	$\{x \mid x \in \mathbf{N} \text{ and } x \geq 4\}$ — x is a natural number greater than or equal to 4.	$\{4, 5, 6, 7, \dots\}$
$a < x < b$ — x is greater than a and less than b.	$\{x \mid x \in \mathbf{N} \text{ and } 4 < x < 8\}$ — x is a natural number greater than 4 and less than 8.	$\{5, 6, 7\}$
$a \leq x \leq b$ — x is greater than or equal to a and less than or equal to b.	$\{x \mid x \in \mathbf{N} \text{ and } 4 \leq x \leq 8\}$ — x is a natural number greater than or equal to 4 and less than or equal to 8.	$\{4, 5, 6, 7, 8\}$
$a \leq x < b$ — x is greater than or equal to a and less than b.	$\{x \mid x \in \mathbf{N} \text{ and } 4 \leq x < 8\}$ — x is a natural number greater than or equal to 4 and less than 8.	$\{4, 5, 6, 7\}$
$a < x \leq b$ — x is greater than a and less than or equal to b.	$\{x \mid x \in \mathbf{N} \text{ and } 4 < x \leq 8\}$ — x is a natural number greater than 4 and less than or equal to 8.	$\{5, 6, 7, 8\}$

STUDY TIP

A page of sheet music, filled with symbols and notations, *represents* a piece of music. Similarly, the symbols and notations throughout this book are representations of mathematical ideas. Mathematical notation no more *is* mathematics than musical notation *is* music. As you become familiar with various mathematical notations, the ideas represented by the symbols can then live and breathe in your mind.

EXAMPLE 7   REPRESENTING SETS OF NATURAL NUMBERS

Express each of the following sets using the roster method:

a. $\{x \mid x \in \mathbf{N} \text{ and } x \leq 100\}$

b. $\{x \mid x \in \mathbf{N} \text{ and } 70 \leq x < 100\}$.

SOLUTION

a. $\{x \mid x \in \mathbf{N} \text{ and } x \leq 100\}$ represents the set of natural numbers less than or equal to 100. This set can be expressed using the roster method as

$$\{1, 2, 3, 4, \ldots, 100\}.$$

b. $\{x \mid x \in \mathbf{N} \text{ and } 70 \leq x < 100\}$ represents the set of natural numbers greater than or equal to 70 and less than 100. This set in roster form is $\{70, 71, 72, 73, \ldots, 99\}$.

 Express each of the following sets using the roster method:

a. $\{x \mid x \in \mathbf{N} \text{ and } x < 200\}$ **b.** $\{x \mid x \in \mathbf{N} \text{ and } 50 < x \leq 200\}$.

---

5 | Determine a set's cardinal number.

Cardinality and Equivalent Sets

The number of elements in a set is called the **cardinal number**, or **cardinality**, of the set. For example, the set {a, e, i, o, u} contains five elements and therefore has the cardinal number 5. We can also say that the set has a cardinality of 5.

> **DEFINITION OF A SET'S CARDINAL NUMBER**
> The **cardinal number** of set A, represented by $n(A)$, is the number of distinct elements in set A. The symbol $n(A)$ is read "n of A."

Notice that the cardinal number of a set refers to the number of *distinct*, or different, elements in the set. **Repeating elements in a set neither adds new elements to the set nor changes its cardinality.** For example, $A = \{3, 5, 7\}$ and $B = \{3, 5, 5, 7, 7, 7\}$ represent the same set with three distinct elements, 3, 5, and 7. Thus, $n(A) = 3$ and $n(B) = 3$.

EXAMPLE 8   DETERMINING A SET'S CARDINAL NUMBER

Find the cardinal number of each of the following sets:

a. $A = \{7, 9, 11, 13\}$

b. $B = \{0\}$

c. $C = \{13, 14, 15, \ldots, 22, 23\}$

d. $\varnothing$.

SOLUTION The cardinal number for each set is found by determining the number of elements in the set.

a. $A = \{7, 9, 11, 13\}$ contains four distinct elements. Thus, the cardinal number of set A is 4. We also say that set A has a cardinality of 4, or $n(A) = 4$.

b. $B = \{0\}$ contains one element, namely 0. The cardinal number of set B is 1. Therefore, $n(B) = 1$.

c. Set $C = \{13, 14, 15, \ldots, 22, 23\}$ lists only five elements. However, the three dots indicate that the natural numbers from 16 through 21 are also in the set. Counting the elements in the set, we find that there are 11 natural numbers in set C. The cardinality of set C is 11, and $n(C) = 11$.

d. The empty set, $\varnothing$, contains no elements. Thus, $n(\varnothing) = 0$.

 Find the cardinal number of each of the following sets:

a. $A = \{6, 10, 14, 15, 16\}$ **b.** $B = \{872\}$

c. $C = \{9, 10, 11, \ldots, 15, 16\}$ **d.** $D = \{\ \}$.

6 | Recognize equivalent sets.

Sets that contain the same number of elements are said to be *equivalent*.

> **DEFINITION OF EQUIVALENT SETS**
> Set A is **equivalent** to set B means that set A and set B contain the same number of elements. For equivalent sets, $n(A) = n(B)$.

Here is an example of two equivalent sets:

$$n(A) = n(B) = 5$$

$$A = \{x \mid x \text{ is a vowel}\} \quad = \quad \{a, e, i, o, u\}$$
$$B = \{x \mid x \in \mathbf{N} \text{ and } 3 \leq x \leq 7\} = \{3, 4, 5, 6, 7\}.$$

It is not necessary to count elements and arrive at 5 to determine that these sets are equivalent. The lines with arrowheads, $\updownarrow$, indicate that each element of set A can be paired with exactly one element of set B and each element of set B can be paired with exactly one element of set A. We say that the sets can be placed in a **one-to-one correspondence**.

> **ONE-TO-ONE CORRESPONDENCES AND EQUIVALENT SETS**
> 1. If set A and set B can be placed in a one-to-one correspondence, then A is equivalent to B: $n(A) = n(B)$.
> 2. If set A and set B cannot be placed in a one-to-one correspondence, then A is not equivalent to B: $n(A) \neq n(B)$.

EXAMPLE 9   DETERMINING IF SETS ARE EQUIVALENT

Table 7.3 shows the celebrities who hosted NBC's *Saturday Night Live* most frequently and the number of times each starred on the show. Let

A = the set of the five most frequent hosts on *Saturday Night Live*

B = the set of the number of times each of the five
         most frequent *Saturday Night Live* hosts starred on the show.

Are these sets equivalent? Explain.

SOLUTION   Let's begin by expressing each set in roster form.

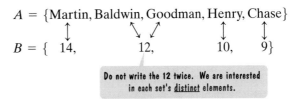

$$A = \{\text{Martin, Baldwin, Goodman, Henry, Chase}\}$$
$$B = \{\quad 14, \qquad 12, \qquad 10, \quad 9\}$$

Do not write the 12 twice. We are interested in each set's <u>distinct</u> elements.

There are two ways to determine that these sets are not equivalent.

Method 1. Trying to Set Up a One-to-One Correspondence

The lines with arrowheads indicate that the correspondence between the sets is not one-to-one. The elements Baldwin and Goodman from set A are both paired with the element 12 from set B. These sets are not equivalent.

Method 2. Counting Elements

Set A contains five distinct elements: $n(A) = 5$. Set B contains four distinct elements: $n(B) = 4$. Because the sets do not contain the same number of elements, they are not equivalent.

○

TABLE 7.3 MOST FREQUENT HOSTS OF *SATURDAY NIGHT LIVE*

Celebrity	Number of Shows Hosted
Steve Martin	14
Alec Baldwin	12
John Goodman	12
Buck Henry	10
Chevy Chase	9

Source: NBC Universal

TABLE 7.4 TOP FIVE LANGUAGES SPOKEN BY THE YOUTH OF 2050

Language	Estimated Number (in millions) of 15–24-Year-Old Speakers
Chinese	166
Hindu/Urdu	74
Arabic	72
English	65
Spanish	63

Source: David Graddol, *The Future of English?*, British Council

7 Distinguish between finite and infinite sets.

8 Recognize equal sets.

Table 7.4 shows the top five languages that will be spoken by the youth of 2050 and the number, in millions, of 15–24-year-old speakers. Let

$A =$ the set of the five languages spoken by the greatest number of 15–24-year-olds in 2050

$B =$ the set of the number of 15–24-year-old speakers, in millions, of each of the top five languages spoken by the youth of 2050.

Are these sets equivalent? Without counting elements in the sets, explain your answer.

Finite and Infinite Sets

Example 9 illustrated that to compare the cardinalities of two sets, pair off their elements. If there is not a one-to-one correspondence, the sets have different cardinalities and are not equivalent. Although this idea is obvious in the case of *finite sets*, some unusual conclusions emerge when dealing with *infinite sets*.

> **FINITE SETS AND INFINITE SETS**
> Set A is a **finite set** if $n(A) = 0$ (that is, A is the empty set) or $n(A)$ is a natural number. A set whose cardinality is not 0 or a natural number is called an **infinite set**.

An example of an infinite set is the set of natural numbers, $\mathbf{N} = \{1, 2, 3, 4, 5, 6, \dots\}$, where the ellipsis indicates that there is no last, or final, element. Does this set have a cardinality? The answer is yes, albeit one of the strangest numbers you've ever seen. The set of natural numbers is assigned the infinite cardinal number $\aleph_0$ (read: "aleph-null," aleph being the first letter of the Hebrew alphabet). What follows is a succession of mind-boggling results, including a hierarchy of different infinite numbers in which $\aleph_0$ is the smallest infinity:

$$\aleph_0 < \aleph_1 < \aleph_2 < \aleph_3 < \aleph_4 < \aleph_5 \dots .$$

These ideas, which are impossible for our imaginations to grasp, are developed in Section 7.2 and the Blitzer Bonus at the end of that section.

Equal Sets

We conclude this section with another important concept of set theory, equality of sets.

> **DEFINITION OF EQUALITY OF SETS**
> Set A is **equal** to set B means that set A and set B contain exactly the same elements, regardless of order or possible repetition of elements. We symbolize the equality of sets A and B using the statement $A = B$.

For example, if $A = \{w, x, y, z\}$ and $B = \{z, y, w, x\}$, then $A = B$ because the two sets contain exactly the same elements.

Because equal sets contain the same elements, they also have the same cardinal number. For example, the equal sets $A = \{w, x, y, z\}$ and $B = \{z, y, w, x\}$ have four elements each. Thus, both sets have the same cardinal number: 4. Notice that a possible one-to-one correspondence between the equal sets A and B can be obtained by pairing each element with itself:

$$A = \{w, \ x, \ y, \ z\}$$
$$B = \{z, \ y, \ w, \ x\}$$

This illustrates an important point: **If two sets are equal, then they must be equivalent.**

EXAMPLE 10   DETERMINING WHETHER SETS ARE EQUAL

Determine whether each statement is true or false:

a. $\{4, 8, 9\} = \{8, 9, 4\}$ **b.** $\{1, 3, 5\} = \{0, 1, 3, 5\}.$

SOLUTION

a. The sets $\{4, 8, 9\}$ and $\{8, 9, 4\}$ contain exactly the same elements. Therefore, the statement

$$\{4, 8, 9\} = \{8, 9, 4\}$$

is true.

b. As we look at the given sets, $\{1, 3, 5\}$ and $\{0, 1, 3, 5\}$, we see that 0 is an element of the second set, but not the first. The sets do not contain exactly the same elements. Therefore, the sets are not equal. This means that the statement

$$\{1, 3, 5\} = \{0, 1, 3, 5\}$$

is false.

 Determine whether each statement is true or false:

a. $\{O, L, D\} = \{D, O, L\}$ **b.** $\{4, 5\} = \{5, 4, \emptyset\}.$

STUDY TIP

In English, the words *equal* and *equivalent* often mean the same thing. This is not the case in set theory. **Equal sets** contain the **same elements**. **Equivalent sets** contain the **same number of elements**. If two sets are equal, then they must be equivalent. However, if two sets are equivalent, they are not necessarily equal.

EXERCISE SET 7.1 ●●●●●●

• Practice Exercises

In Exercises 1–6, determine which collections are not well defined and therefore not sets.

1. The collection of U.S. presidents

2. The collection of part-time and full-time students currently enrolled at your college

3. The collection of the five worst U.S. presidents

4. The collection of elderly full-time students currently enrolled at your college

5. The collection of natural numbers greater than one million

6. The collection of even natural numbers greater than 100

In Exercises 7–14, write a description of each set. (More than one correct description may be possible.)

7. {Mercury, Venus, Earth, Mars, Jupiter, Saturn, Uranus, Neptune}

8. {Saturday, Sunday}

9. {January, June, July}

10. {April, August}

11. $\{6, 7, 8, 9, \dots\}$

12. $\{9, 10, 11, 12, \dots\}$

13. $\{6, 7, 8, 9, \dots, 20\}$

14. $\{9, 10, 11, 12, \dots, 25\}$

In Exercises 15–32, express each set using the roster method.

15. The set of the four seasons in a year

16. The set of months of the year that have exactly 30 days

17. $\{x \mid x$ is a month that ends with the letters b-e-r$\}$

18. $\{x \mid x$ is a letter of the alphabet that follows d and comes before j$\}$

19. The set of natural numbers less than 4

20. The set of natural numbers less than or equal to 6

21. The set of odd natural numbers less than 13

22. The set of even natural numbers less than 10

23. $\{x \mid x \in \mathbf{N}$ and $x \leq 5\}$

24. $\{x \mid x \in \mathbf{N}$ and $x \leq 4\}$

25. $\{x \mid x \in \mathbf{N}$ and $x > 5\}$

26. $\{x \mid x \in \mathbf{N}$ and $x > 4\}$

27. $\{x \mid x \in \mathbf{N}$ and $6 < x \leq 10\}$

28. $\{x \mid x \in \mathbf{N}$ and $7 < x \leq 11\}$

29. $\{x \mid x \in \mathbf{N}$ and $10 \leq x < 80\}$

30. $\{x \mid x \in \mathbf{N}$ and $15 \leq x < 60\}$

31. $\{x | x + 5 = 7\}$ **32.** $\{x | x + 3 = 9\}$

In Exercises 33–46, determine which sets are the empty set.

33. $\{\varnothing, 0\}$ **34.** $\{0, \varnothing\}$

35. $\{x | x$ is a woman who served as U.S. president before 2000$\}$

36. $\{x | x$ is a living U.S. president born before 1700$\}$

37. $\{x | x$ is the number of women who served as U.S. president before 2000$\}$

38. $\{x | x$ is the number of living U.S. presidents born before 1700$\}$

39. $\{x | x$ is a U.S. state whose name begins with the letter X$\}$

40. $\{x | x$ is a month of the year whose name begins with the letter X$\}$

41. $\{x | x < 2$ and $x > 5\}$

42. $\{x | x < 3$ and $x > 7\}$

43. $\{x | x \in \mathbf{N}$ and $2 < x < 5\}$

44. $\{x | x \in \mathbf{N}$ and $3 < x < 7\}$

45. $\{x | x$ is a number less than 2 or greater than 5$\}$

46. $\{x | x$ is a number less than 3 or greater than 7$\}$

In Exercises 47–66, determine whether each statement is true or false.

47. $3 \in \{1, 3, 5, 7\}$ **48.** $6 \in \{2, 4, 6, 8, 10\}$

49. $12 \in \{1, 2, 3, \ldots, 14\}$ **50.** $10 \in \{1, 2, 3, \ldots, 16\}$

51. $5 \in \{2, 4, 6, \ldots, 20\}$ **52.** $8 \in \{1, 3, 5, \ldots 19\}$

53. $11 \notin \{1, 2, 3, \ldots, 9\}$ **54.** $17 \notin \{1, 2, 3, \ldots, 16\}$

55. $37 \notin \{1, 2, 3, \ldots, 40\}$ **56.** $26 \notin \{1, 2, 3, \ldots, 50\}$

57. $4 \notin \{x | x \in \mathbf{N}$ and x is even$\}$

58. $2 \in \{x | x \in \mathbf{N}$ and x is odd$\}$

59. $13 \notin \{x | x \in \mathbf{N}$ and $x < 13\}$

60. $20 \notin \{x | x \in \mathbf{N}$ and $x < 20\}$

61. $16 \notin \{x | x \in \mathbf{N}$ and $15 \le x < 20\}$

62. $19 \notin \{x | x \in \mathbf{N}$ and $16 \le x < 21\}$

63. $\{3\} \in \{3, 4\}$ **64.** $\{7\} \in \{7, 8\}$

65. $-1 \notin \mathbf{N}$ **66.** $-2 \notin \mathbf{N}$

In Exercises 67–80, find the cardinal number for each set.

67. $A = \{17, 19, 21, 23, 25\}$

68. $A = \{16, 18, 20, 22, 24, 26\}$

69. $B = \{2, 4, 6, \ldots, 30\}$

70. $B = \{1, 3, 5, \ldots, 21\}$

71. $C = \{x | x$ is a day of the week that begins with the letter A$\}$

72. $C = \{x | x$ is a month of the year that begins with the letter W$\}$

73. $D = \{five\}$

74. $D = \{six\}$

75. $A = \{x | x$ is a letter in the word *five*$\}$

76. $A = \{x | x$ is a letter in the word *six*$\}$

77. $B = \{x | x \in \mathbf{N}$ and $2 \le x < 7\}$

78. $B = \{x | x \in \mathbf{N}$ and $3 \le x < 10\}$

79. $C = \{x | x < 4$ and $x \ge 12\}$

80. $C = \{x | x < 5$ and $x \ge 15\}$

In Exercises 81–90,

   a. *Are the sets equivalent? Explain.*

   b. *Are the sets equal? Explain.*

81. A is the set of students at your college. B is the set of students majoring in business at your college.

82. A is the set of states in the United States. B is the set of people who are now governors of the states in the United States.

83. $A = \{1, 2, 3, 4, 5\}$
$B = \{0, 1, 2, 3, 4\}$

84. $A = \{1, 3, 5, 7, 9\}$
$B = \{2, 4, 6, 8, 10\}$

85. $A = \{1, 1, 1, 2, 2, 3, 4\}$
$B = \{4, 3, 2, 1\}$

86. $A = \{0, 1, 1, 2, 2, 2, 3, 3, 3, 3\}$
$B = \{3, 2, 1, 0\}$

87. $A = \{x | x \in \mathbf{N}$ and $6 \le x < 10\}$
$B = \{x | x \in \mathbf{N}$ and $9 < x \le 13\}$

88. $A = \{x | x \in \mathbf{N}$ and $12 < x \le 17\}$
$B = \{x | x \in \mathbf{N}$ and $20 \le x < 25\}$

89. $A = \{x | x \in \mathbf{N}$ and $100 \le x \le 105\}$
$B = \{x | x \in \mathbf{N}$ and $99 < x < 106\}$

90. $A = \{x | x \in \mathbf{N}$ and $200 \le x \le 206\}$
$B = \{x | x \in \mathbf{N}$ and $199 < x < 207\}$

In Exercises 91–96, determine whether each set is finite or infinite.

91. $\{x | x \in \mathbf{N}$ and $x \ge 100\}$

92. $\{x | x \in \mathbf{N}$ and $x \ge 50\}$

93. $\{x | x \in \mathbf{N}$ and $x \le 1{,}000{,}000\}$

94. $\{x | x \in \mathbf{N}$ and $x \le 2{,}000{,}000\}$

95. The set of natural numbers less than 1

96. The set of natural numbers less than 0

• Practice Plus

In Exercises 97–100, express each set using set-builder notation. Use inequality notation to express the condition x must meet in order to be a member of the set. (More than one correct inequality may be possible.)

97. $\{61, 62, 63, 64, \ldots\}$

98. $\{36, 37, 38, 39, \ldots\}$

99. $\{61, 62, 63, 64, \ldots, 89\}$

100. $\{36, 37, 38, 39, \ldots, 59\}$

In Exercises 101–104, give examples of two sets that meet the given conditions. If the conditions are impossible to satisfy, explain why.

101. The two sets are equivalent but not equal.

102. The two sets are equivalent and equal.

103. The two sets are equal but not equivalent.

104. The two sets are neither equivalent nor equal.

• Application Exercises

The bar graph shows the countries with the greatest percentage of their population having used marijuana. In Exercises 105–112, use the information given by the graph to represent each set by the roster method, or use the appropriate notation to indicate that the set is the empty set.

Reefer Madness: Countries with the Greatest Marijuana Use

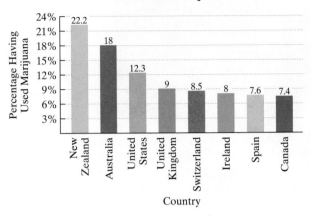

Source: Organization for Economic Cooperation and Development

105. The set of countries in which the percentage using marijuana exceeds 12%

106. The set of countries in which the percentage using marijuana exceeds 9%

107. The set of countries in which the percentage using marijuana is at least 8% and at most 18%

108. The set of countries in which the percentage using marijuana is at least 8.5% and at most 20%

109. $\{x \mid x$ is a country in which $8\% \leq$ percentage using marijuana $< 12.3\%\}$

110. $\{x \mid x$ is a country in which $7.6\% \leq$ percentage using marijuana $< 9\%\}$

111. $\{x \mid x$ is a country in which percentage using marijuana $> 22.2\%\}$

112. $\{x \mid x$ is a country in which percentage using marijuana $\geq 22.2\%\}$

A study of 900 working women in Texas showed that their feelings changed throughout the day. The line graph shows 15 different times in a day and the average level of happiness for the women at each time. Based on the information given by the graph, represent each of the sets in Exercises 113–116 using the roster method.

Average Level of Happiness at Different Times of Day

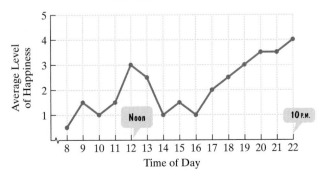

Source: D. Kahneman et al. "A Survey Method for Characterizing Daily Life Experience," *Science.*

113. $\{x \mid x$ is a time of the day when the average level of happiness is 3$\}$

114. $\{x \mid x$ is a time of the day when the average level of happiness is 1$\}$

115. $\{x \mid x$ is a time of the day when 3 < average level of happiness < 4$\}$

116. $\{x \mid x$ is a time of the day when 3 < average level of happiness ≤ 4$\}$

117. Do the results of Exercise 113 or 114 indicate a one-to-one correspondence between the set representing the time of day and the set representing average level of happiness? Are these sets equivalent?

• Writing in Mathematics

118. What is a set?

119. Describe the three methods used to represent a set. Give an example of a set represented by each method.

120. What is the empty set?

121. Explain what is meant by *equivalent sets.*

122. Explain what is meant by *equal sets.*

123. Use cardinality to describe the difference between a finite set and an infinite set.

• Critical Thinking Exercises

124. Which one of the following is true?
 a. Two sets can be equal but not equivalent.
 b. Any set in roster notation that contains three dots must be an infinite set.
 c. $n(\varnothing) = 1$
 d. Some sets that can be written in set-builder notation cannot be written in roster form.

125. Which one of the following is true?
 a. The set of fractions between 0 and 1 is an infinite set.
 b. The set of multiples of 4 between 0 and 4,000,000,000 is an infinite set.
 c. If the elements in a set cannot be counted in a trillion years, the set is an infinite set.
 d. Because 0 is not a natural number, it can be deleted from any set without changing the set's cardinality.

126. In a certain town, a barber shaves all those men and only those men who do not shave themselves. Consider each of the following sets:

$A = \{x \mid x$ is a man of the town who shaves himself$\}$

$B = \{x \mid x$ is a man of the town who does not shave himself$\}$.

The one and only barber in the town is Sweeney Todd. If s represents Sweeney Todd,

 a. is $s \in A$?

 b. is $s \in B$?

SECTION 7.2 • SUBSETS

OBJECTIVES

1. Recognize subsets and use the notation ⊆.

2. Recognize proper subsets and use the notation ⊂.

3. Determine the number of subsets of a set.

4. Apply concepts of subsets and equivalent sets to infinite sets.

TABLE 7.5 PERCENTAGE OF TATTOOED AMERICANS, BY AGE GROUP	
Age Group	**Percent Tattooed**
18–24	13%
25–29	36%
30–39	28%
40–49	14%
50–64	10%
65+	7%

Source: Harris Interactive

1 │ Recognize subsets and use the notation ⊆.

Emerging from their often unsavory reputation of the recent past, tattoos have gained increasing prominence as a form of body art and self-expression. A Harris poll conducted in 2003 estimated that 30 million Americans, or 16% of the adult population, have at least one tattoo.

Table 7.5 shows the percentage of Americans, by age group, with tattoos. The categories in the table divide the set of tattooed Americans into smaller sets, called *subsets*, based on age. The age subsets can be broken into still-smaller subsets. For example, tattooed Americans ages 25–29 can be categorized by gender, political party affiliation, race/ethnicity, or any other area of interest. This suggests numerous possible subsets of the set of Americans with tattoos. Every American in each of these subsets is also a member of the set of tattooed Americans.

Subsets

Situations in which all the elements of one set are also elements of another set are described by the following definition:

DEFINITION OF A SUBSET OF A SET
Set *A* is a **subset** of set *B*, expressed as

$$A \subseteq B,$$

if every element in set *A* is also an element in set *B*.

Let's apply this definition to the set of people ages 25–29 in Table 7.5.

The set of tattooed Americans in the 25-29 age group   is a subset of   the set of all tattooed Americans.

$$\{x \mid x \text{ is a tattooed American and } 25 \leq x\text{'s age} \leq 29\} \quad \subseteq \quad \{x \mid x \text{ is a tattooed American}\}$$

Every person in this set, to the left of the subset symbol,   is also a member of this set, to the right of the subset symbol.

The notation $A \not\subseteq B$ means that A **is not a subset** of B. Set A is not a subset of set B if there is at least one element of set A that is not an element of set B. For example, consider the following sets:

$$A = \{1, 2, 3\} \quad \text{and} \quad B = \{1, 2\}.$$

Can you see that 3 is an element of set A that is not in set B? Thus, set A is not a subset of set B: $A \not\subseteq B$.

We can show that $A \subseteq B$ by showing that every element of set A also occurs as an element of set B. We can show that $A \not\subseteq B$ by finding one element of set A that is not in set B.

EXAMPLE 1   USING THE SYMBOLS $\subseteq$ AND $\not\subseteq$

Write $\subseteq$ or $\not\subseteq$ in each blank to form a true statement:

a. $A = \{1, 3, 5, 7\}$
$B = \{1, 3, 5, 7, 9, 11\}$
A_____B

b. $A = \{x \mid x$ is a letter in the word *proof*$\}$
$B = \{y \mid y$ is a letter in the word *roof*$\}$
A_____B

c. $A = \{x \mid x$ is a planet of Earth's solar system$\}$
$B = \{$Mercury, Venus, Earth, Mars, Jupiter, Saturn, Uranus, Neptune$\}$
A_____B.

SOLUTION

a. All the elements of $A = \{1, 3, 5, 7\}$ are also contained in $B = \{1, 3, 5, 7, 9, 11\}$. Therefore, set A is a subset of set B:

$$A \subseteq B.$$

b. Let's write the set of letters in the word *proof* and the set of letters in the word *roof* in roster form. In each case, we consider only the distinct elements, so there is no need to repeat the o.

$$A = \{p, r, o, f\} \qquad B = \{r, o, f\}$$

The element p is in set A but not in set B.

Because there is an element in set A that is not in set B, set A is not a subset of set B:

$$A \not\subseteq B.$$

c. All the elements of
$$A = \{x \mid x \text{ is a planet of the Earth's solar system}\}$$
are contained in
$$B = \{\text{Mercury, Venus, Earth, Mars, Jupiter, Saturn, Uranus, Neptune}\}.$$
Furthermore, the sets are equal $(A = B)$. Because all elements in set A are also in set B, set A is a subset of set B:

$$A \subseteq B.$$

 CHECK POINT 1   Write $\subseteq$ or $\not\subseteq$ in each blank to form a true statement:

a. $A = \{1, 3, 5, 6, 9, 11\}$
$B = \{1, 3, 5, 7\}$
A_____B

b. $A = \{x \mid x$ is a letter in the word *roof*$\}$
$B = \{y \mid y$ is a letter in the word *proof*$\}$
A_____B

c. $A = \{x \mid x$ is a day of the week$\}$
$B = \{$Monday, Tuesday, Wednesday, Thursday, Friday, Saturday, Sunday$\}$
A_____B.

Neptune

Uranus

Saturn

Jupiter

Mars
Earth
Venus
Mercury

The eight planets in Earth's solar system

No, we did not forget Pluto. In 2006, based on the requirement that a planet must dominate its own orbit (Pluto is slave to Neptune's orbit), the International Astronomical Union removed Pluto from the list of planets and decreed that it belonged to a new category of heavenly body, a "dwarf planet."

2 | Recognize proper subsets and use the notation ⊂.

Proper Subsets

In Example 1(c) and Check Point 1(c), the given equal sets illustrate that **every set is a subset of itself**. If A is any set, then $A \subseteq A$ because it is obvious that each element of A is a member of A.

If we know that set A is a subset of set B and we exclude the possibility of equal sets, then set A is called a *proper subset* of set B, written $A \subset B$.

> **DEFINITION OF A PROPER SUBSET OF A SET**
> Set A is a **proper subset** of set B, expressed as $A \subset B$, if set A is a subset of set B and sets A and B are not equal ($A \neq B$).

Try not to confuse the symbols for subset, $\subseteq$, and proper subset, $\subset$. Because the lower half of the subset symbol in $A \subseteq B$ suggests an equal sign, it is *possible* that sets A and B are equal, although they do not have to be. By contrast, the missing lower line for the proper subset symbol in $A \subset B$ indicates that sets A and B *cannot* be equal.

STUDY TIP

- The notation for "is a subset of," $\subseteq$, is similar to the notation for "is less than or equal to," $\leq$. Because the notations share similar ideas, $A \subseteq B$ applies to finite sets only if set A is smaller than or equal to set B.

- The notation for "is a proper subset of," $\subset$, is similar to the notation for "is less than," $<$. Because the notations share similar ideas, $A \subset B$ applies to finite sets only if set A is smaller than set B.

EXAMPLE 2 USING THE SYMBOLS ⊆ AND ⊂

Write $\subseteq$, $\subset$, or both in each blank to form a true statement:

a. $A = \{x \mid x \text{ is a person and } x \text{ lives in San Francisco}\}$
$B = \{x \mid x \text{ is a person and } x \text{ lives in California}\}$
A_____B

b. $A = \{2, 4, 6, 8\}$
$B = \{2, 8, 4, 6\}$
A_____B.

SOLUTION

a. Every person living in San Francisco is also a person living in California. Because each person in set A is contained in set B, set A is a subset of set B:

$$A \subseteq B.$$

Can you see that the two sets do not contain the same elements and, consequently, are not equal? A person living in California outside San Francisco is in set B, but not in set A. Because the sets are not equal, set A is a proper subset of set B:

$$A \subset B.$$

The symbols $\subseteq$ and $\subset$ can both be placed in the blank to form a true statement.

b. Every number in $A = \{2, 4, 6, 8\}$ is contained in $B = \{2, 8, 4, 6\}$, so set A is a subset of set B:

$$A \subseteq B.$$

Because the sets contain the same elements and are equal, set A is *not* a proper subset of set B. The symbol $\subset$ cannot be placed in the blank if we want to form a true statement. (Because set A is not a proper subset of set B, it is correct to write $A \not\subset B$.)

○

Write ⊆, ⊂, or both in each blank to form a true statement:

    a. $A = \{2, 4, 6, 8\}$

       $B = \{2, 8, 4, 6, 10\}$

       A_____B

    b. $A = \{x \mid x \text{ is a person and } x \text{ lives in Atlanta}\}$

       $B = \{x \mid x \text{ is a person and } x \text{ lives in Georgia}\}$

       A_____B.

STUDY TIP

Do not confuse the symbols ∈ and ⊆. The symbol ∈ means "is an element of" and the symbol ⊆ means "is a subset of." Notice the difference between the following true statements:

$$4 \in \{4, 8\} \qquad \{4\} \subseteq \{4, 8\}.$$

4 is an element of the set {4, 8}.   The set containing 4 is a subset of the set {4, 8}.

Subsets and the Empty Set

The meaning of $A \subseteq B$ leads to some interesting properties of the empty set.

EXAMPLE 3   THE EMPTY SET AS A SUBSET

Let $A = \{ \ \}$ and $B = \{1, 2, 3, 4, 5\}$. Is $A \subseteq B$?

SOLUTION A is not a subset of B ($A \nsubseteq B$) if there is at least one element of set A that is not an element of set B. Because A represents the empty set, there are no elements in set A, period, much less elements in A that do not belong to B. Because we cannot find an element in $A = \{ \ \}$ that is not contained in $B = \{1, 2, 3, 4, 5\}$, this means that $A \subseteq B$. Equivalently, $\emptyset \subseteq B$. ○

 Let $A = \{ \ \}$ and $B = \{6, 7, 8\}$. Is $A \subseteq B$?

Example 3 illustrates the principle that **the empty set is a subset of every set**. Furthermore, the empty set is a proper subset of every set except itself.

> **THE EMPTY SET AS A SUBSET**
>
> **1.** For any set B, $\emptyset \subseteq B$.
> **2.** For any set B other than the empty set, $\emptyset \subset B$.

3   Determine the number of subsets of a set.

The Number of Subsets of a Given Set

If a set contains n elements, how many subsets can be formed? Let's observe some special cases, namely sets with $0, 1, 2,$ and 3 elements. We can use inductive reasoning to arrive at a general conclusion. We begin by listing subsets and counting the number of subsets in our list. This is shown in Table 7.6 on the next page.

TABLE 7.6 THE NUMBER OF SUBSETS: SOME SPECIAL CASES

Set	Number of Elements	List of All Subsets	Number of Subsets
{ }	0	{ }	1
{a}	1	{a}, { }	2
{a, b}	2	{a, b}, {a}, {b}, { }	4
{a, b, c}	3	{a, b, c}, {a, b}, {a, c}, {b, c}, {a}, {b}, {c}, { }	8

Table 7.6 suggests that when we increase the number of elements in the set by one, the number of subsets doubles. The number of subsets appears to be a power of 2.

Number of elements	0	1	2	3
Number of subsets	$1 = 2^0$	$2 = 2^1$	$4 = 2 \times 2 = 2^2$	$8 = 2 \times 2 \times 2 = 2^3$

The power of 2 is the same as the number of elements in the set. Using inductive reasoning, if the set contains n elements, then the number of subsets that can be formed is 2^n.

NUMBER OF SUBSETS

The number of subsets of a set with n elements is 2^n.

For a given set, we know that every subset except the set itself is a proper subset. In Table 7.6, we included the set itself when counting the number of subsets. If we want to find the number of proper subsets, we must exclude counting the given set, thereby decreasing the number by 1.

NUMBER OF PROPER SUBSETS

The number of proper subsets of a set with n elements is $2^n - 1$.

EXAMPLE 4 FINDING THE NUMBER OF SUBSETS AND PROPER SUBSETS

Find the number of subsets and the number of proper subsets for each set:

a. {a, b, c, d, e}

b. $\{x | x \in \mathbf{N}$ and $9 \le x \le 15\}$.

SOLUTION

a. A set with n elements has 2^n subsets. Because the set {a, b, c, d, e} contains 5 elements, there are $2^5 = 2 \times 2 \times 2 \times 2 \times 2 = 32$ subsets. Of these, we must exclude counting the given set as a proper subset, so there are $2^5 - 1 = 32 - 1 = 31$ proper subsets.

b. We can write $\{x | x \in \mathbf{N}$ and $9 \le x \le 15\}$ in roster form as {9, 10, 11, 12, 13, 14, 15}. Because this set contains 7 elements, there are $2^7 = 2 \times 2 \times 2 \times 2 \times 2 \times 2 \times 2 = 128$ subsets. Of these, there are $2^7 - 1 = 128 - 1 = 127$ proper subsets.

Find the number of subsets and the number of proper subsets for each set:

a. {a, b, c, d}   **b.** $\{x | x \in \mathbf{N}$ and $3 \le x \le 8\}$.

**Smartest Dogs
Rank/Breed**

1. Border collie

2. Poodle

3. German shepherd

4. Golden retriever
Source: The Intelligence of Dogs

EXAMPLE 5   FINDING THE NUMBER OF SUBSETS AND PROPER SUBSETS

According to *The Intelligence of Dogs* by Stanley Coren, the four smartest breeds of dogs are

1. Border collie
2. Poodle
3. German shepherd
4. Golden retriever.

A man is trying to decide whether to buy a dog. He can afford up to four dogs, but may buy fewer or none at all. However, if the man makes a purchase, he will buy one or more of the four smartest breeds. The kennel has only one dog from each breed—that is, one border collie, one poodle, one German shepherd, and one golden retriever.

a. Consider the set that represents these breeds:

{border collie, poodle, German shepherd, golden retriever}.

Find the number of subsets of this set. What does this number represent in practical terms?

b. List all the subsets and describe what they represent for the prospective dog owner.

c. How many of the subsets are proper subsets?

SOLUTION

a. A set with n elements has 2^n subsets. Because the set of breeds contains four elements, the number of subsets is $2^4 = 2 \times 2 \times 2 \times 2 = 16$. In practical terms, there are 16 different ways to make a selection.

b. Purchase no dogs: $\emptyset$

Purchase one dog: {border collie}, {poodle}, {German shepherd}, {golden retriever}

Purchase two dogs: {border collie, poodle}, {border collie, German shepherd}, {border collie, golden retriever}, {poodle, German shepherd}, {poodle, golden retriever}, {German shepherd, golden retriever}

Purchase three dogs: {border collie, poodle, German shepherd}, {border collie, poodle, golden retriever}, {border collie, German shepherd, golden retriever}, {poodle, German shepherd, golden retriever}

Purchase four dogs: {border collie, poodle, German shepherd, golden retriever}

As predicted in part(a), 16 different selections are possible.

c. Every set except

{border collie, poodle, German shepherd, golden retriever}

is a proper subset of the given set. There are $16 - 1$, or 15, proper subsets. Although we obtained this number by counting, we can also use the fact that the number of proper subsets of a set with n elements is $2^n - 1$. Because the set of breeds contains four elements, there are $2^4 - 1$ proper subsets:

$2^4 - 1 = (2 \times 2 \times 2 \times 2) - 1 = 16 - 1 = 15$ proper subsets.

CHECK POINT 5 You recently purchased three books, shown by the set

$$\{\textit{The Da Vinci Code}, \textit{The Lord of the Rings}, \textit{America} (\textit{The Book})\}.$$

Now you are deciding which books, if any, to take on vacation. You have enough room to pack up to three books, but may take fewer or none at all.

a. Find the number of subsets of the given set. What does this number represent in practical terms?

b. List all the subsets and describe what they represent in terms of vacation reading.

c. How many of the subsets are proper subsets?

---

4 Apply concepts of subsets and equivalent sets to infinite sets.

"Infinity is where things happen that don't."

W. W. Sawyer, *Prelude to Mathematics*, Penguin Books, 1960

The Number of Subsets of Infinite Sets

In Section 7.1, we mentioned that the infinite set of natural numbers, $\{1, 2, 3, 4, 5, 6, \ldots\}$, is assigned the transfinite cardinal number $\aleph_0$ (read "aleph-null"). Equivalently, there are $\aleph_0$ natural numbers.

Once we accept the cardinality of sets with infinitely many elements, a surreal world emerges in which there is no end to an ascending hierarchy of infinities. Because the set of natural numbers contains $\aleph_0$ elements, it has $2^{\aleph_0}$ subsets, where $2^{\aleph_0} > \aleph_0$. Denoting $2^{\aleph_0}$ by $\aleph_1$, we have $\aleph_1 > \aleph_0$. Because the set of subsets of the natural numbers contains $\aleph_1$ elements, it has $2^{\aleph_1}$ subsets, where $2^{\aleph_1} > \aleph_1$. Denoting $2^{\aleph_1}$ by $\aleph_2$, we now have $\aleph_2 > \aleph_1 > \aleph_0$. Continuing in this manner, $\aleph_0$ is the "smallest" transfinite cardinal number in an infinite hierarchy of different infinities!

BLITZER BONUS

Cardinal Numbers of Infinite Sets

P. J. Crook, *Time and Time Again* 1981. Courtesy Barry Friedman Limited, New York.

The mirrors in the painting *Time and Time Again* have the effect of repeating the image infinitely many times, creating an endless tunnel of mirror images. There is something quite fascinating about the idea of endless infinity. Did you know that for thousands of years religious leaders warned that human beings should not examine the nature of the infinite? Religious teaching often equated infinity with the concept of a Supreme Being. One of the last victims of the Inquisition, Giordano Bruno, was burned at the stake for his explorations into the characteristics of infinity. It was not until the 1870s that the German mathematician Georg Cantor (1845–1918) began a careful analysis of the mathematics of infinity.

It was Cantor who assigned the transfinite cardinal number $\aleph_0$ to the set of natural numbers. He used one-to-one correspondences to establish some surprising equivalences between the set of natural numbers and its proper subsets. Here are two examples:

Natural Numbers: $\{1, 2, 3, 4, \ 5, \ 6, \ \ldots, \ n, \ldots\}$

Even Natural Numbers: $\{2, 4, 6, 8, 10, 12, \ldots, 2n, \ldots\}$

Each natural number, n, is paired with its double, $2n$, in the set of even natural numbers.

Natural Numbers: $\{1, 2, 3, 4, 5, 6, \ldots, n, \ldots\}$

Odd Natural Numbers: $\{1, 3, 5, 7, 9, 11, \ldots, 2n - 1, \ldots\}$

Each natural number, n, is paired with 1 less than its double, $2n - 1$, in the set of odd natural numbers.

These one-to-one correspondences indicate that the set of even natural numbers and the set of odd natural numbers are equivalent to the set of all natural numbers. In fact, an infinite set, such as the natural numbers, can be *defined* as any set that can be placed in a one-to-one correspondence with a proper subset of itself. This definition boggles the mind because it implies that part of a set has the same number of objects as the entire set. There are $\aleph_0$ even natural numbers, $\aleph_0$ odd natural numbers, and $\aleph_0$ natural numbers. Because the even and odd natural numbers combined make up the entire set of natural numbers, we are confronted with an unusual statement of transfinite arithmetic:

$$\aleph_0 + \aleph_0 = \aleph_0.$$

As Cantor continued studying infinite sets, his observations grew stranger and stranger. It was Cantor who showed that some infinite sets contain more elements than others. This was too much for his colleagues, who considered this work ridiculous. Cantor's mentor, Leopold Kronecker, told him, "Look at the crazy ideas that are now surfacing with your work with infinite sets. How can one infinity be greater than another? Best to ignore such inconsistencies. By considering these monsters and infinite numbers mathematics, I will make sure that you never gain a faculty position at the University of Berlin." Although Cantor was not burned at the stake, universal condemnation of his work resulted in numerous nervous breakdowns. His final days, sadly, were spent in a psychiatric hospital. However, Cantor's work later regained the respect of mathematicians. Today, he is seen as a great mathematician who demystified infinity.

EXERCISE SET 7.2 ●●●●●●

• Practice Exercises

In Exercises 1–12, write $\subseteq$ or $\not\subseteq$ in each blank so that the resulting statement is true.

1. $\{1, 2, 5\}$ _____ $\{1, 2, 3, 4, 5, 6, 7\}$

2. $\{2, 3, 7\}$ _____ $\{1, 2, 3, 4, 5, 6, 7\}$

3. $\{-3, 0, 3\}$ _____ $\{-3, -1, 1, 3\}$

4. $\{-4, 0, 4\}$ _____ $\{-4, -3, -1, 1, 3, 4\}$

5. $\{$Monday, Friday$\}$ _____
$\{$Saturday, Sunday, Monday, Tuesday, Wednesday$\}$

6. $\{$Mercury, Venus, Earth$\}$ _____
$\{$Venus, Earth, Mars, Jupiter$\}$

7. $\{x \mid x$ is a key on a piano$\}$ _____
$\{x \mid x$ is a black key on a piano$\}$

8. $\{x \mid x$ is a dog$\}$ _____ $\{x \mid x$ is a pure-bred dog$\}$

9. $\{$c, o, n, v, e, r, s, a, t, i, o, n$\}$ _____
$\{$v, o, i, c, e, s, r, a, n, t, o, n$\}$

10. $\{$r, e, v, o, l, u, t, i, o, n$\}$ _____ $\{$t, o, l, o, v, e, r, u, i, n$\}$

11. $\left\{\frac{4}{7}, \frac{9}{13}\right\}$ _____ $\left\{\frac{7}{4}, \frac{13}{9}\right\}$

12. $\left\{\frac{1}{2}, \frac{1}{3}\right\}$ _____ $\{2, 3, 5\}$

In Exercises 13–22, determine whether $\subseteq$, $\subset$, both, or neither can be placed in each blank to form a true statement.

13. $\{$V, C, R$\}$ _____ $\{$V, C, R, S$\}$

14. $\{$F, I, N$\}$ _____ $\{$F, I, N, K$\}$

15. $\{0, 2, 4, 6, 8\}$ _____ $\{8, 0, 6, 2, 4\}$

16. $\{9, 1, 7, 3, 4\}$ _____ $\{1, 3, 4, 7, 9\}$

17. $\{x \mid x$ is a person living in Alabama$\}$ _____
$\{y \mid y$ is a person living in the American South$\}$

18. $\{x \mid x$ is a person living in Massachusetts$\}$ _____
$\{y \mid y$ is a person living in a New England state$\}$

19. $\{x \mid x$ is a person living in Washington, D.C.$\}$ _____
$\{y \mid y$ is a person living in the U.S. capital$\}$

20. $\{x \mid x$ is a person living in London$\}$ _____
$\{y \mid y$ is a person living in the capital of England$\}$

21. $\{x \mid x$ is a person living in Alabama$\}$ _____
$\{y \mid y$ is a person living in Birmingham$\}$

22. $\{x \mid x$ is a person living in Massachusetts$\}$ _____
$\{y \mid y$ is a person living in Boston$\}$

In Exercises 23–36, determine whether each statement is true or false. If the statement is false, explain why.

23. Ralph $\in \{$Ralph, Alice, Trixie, Norton$\}$

24. Canada $\in \{$Mexico, United States, Canada$\}$

25. Ralph $\subseteq \{$Ralph, Alice, Trixie, Norton$\}$

26. Canada $\subseteq \{$Mexico, United States, Canada$\}$

27. $\{$Ralph$\} \subseteq \{$Ralph, Alice, Trixie, Norton$\}$

28. $\{$Canada$\} \subseteq \{$Mexico, United States, Canada$\}$

29. $\varnothing \in \{$Archie, Edith, Mike, Gloria$\}$

30. $\varnothing \subseteq \{$Charlie Chaplin, Groucho Marx, Woody Allen$\}$

31. $\{4\} \in \{\{4\}, \{8\}\}$ **32.** $\{1\} \in \{\{1\}, \{3\}\}$

33. $\{1, 4\} \not\subseteq \{4, 1\}$ **34.** $\{1, 4\} \not\subset \{4, 1\}$

35. $0 \notin \varnothing$ **36.** $0 \not\subseteq \varnothing$

In Exercises 37–42, list all the subsets of the given set.

37. {border collie, poodle}   **38.** {Romeo, Juliet}

39. {t, a, b}   **40.** {I, II, III}

41. {0}   **42.** Ø

In Exercises 43–50, calculate the number of subsets and the number of proper subsets for each set.

43. {2, 4, 6, 8}   **44.** $\left\{\frac{1}{2}, \frac{1}{3}, \frac{1}{4}, \frac{1}{5}\right\}$

45. {2, 4, 6, 8, 10, 12}   **46.** {a, b, c, d, e, f}

47. {x|x is a day of the week}

48. {x|x is a U.S. coin worth less than a dollar}

49. {x|x ∈ **N**   and   2 < x < 6}

50. {x|x ∈ **N**   and   2 ≤ x ≤ 6}

• Practice Plus

In Exercises 51–64, determine whether each statement is true or false. If the statement is false, make the necessary change(s) to produce a true statement.

51. The set {1, 2, 3, ..., 1000} has 2^{1000} proper subsets.

52. The set {1, 2, 3, ..., 10,000} has $2^{10,000}$ proper subsets.

53. {x|x ∈ **N** and 30 < x < 50} ⊆ {x|x ∈ **N** and 30 ≤ x ≤ 50}

54. {x|x ∈ **N** and 20 ≤ x ≤ 60} ⊄ {x|x ∈ **N** and 20 < x < 60}

55. Ø ⊄ {Ø, {Ø}}   **56.** {Ø} ⊄ {Ø, {Ø}}

57. Ø ∈ {Ø, {Ø}}   **58.** {Ø} ∈ {Ø, {Ø}}

59. If A ⊆ B and d ∈ A, then d ∈ B.

60. If A ⊆ B and B ⊆ C, then A ⊆ C.

61. If set A is equivalent to the set of natural numbers, then $n(A) = \aleph_0$.

62. If set A is equivalent to the set of even natural numbers, then $n(A) = \aleph_0$.

63. The set of subsets of {a, e, i, o, u} contains 64 elements.

64. The set of subsets of {a, b, c, d, e, f} contains 128 elements.

• Application Exercises

Sets and subsets allow us to order and structure data. In the data shown below, the set of tattooed Americans is divided into subsets categorized by party affiliation. These subsets are further broken down into subsets categorized by gender. All numbers in the branching tree diagram are based on the number of people per 10,000 American adults.

**Breakdown of Tattooed Americans
by Party Affiliation and Gender**

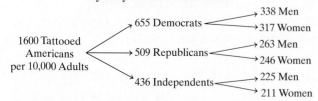

Source: Harris Interactive

Let

T = the set of tattooed Americans

R = the set of tattooed Republicans

D = the set of tattooed Democrats

M = the set of tattooed Democratic men

W = the set of tattooed Democratic women.

In Exercises 65–74, determine whether each statement is true or false. If the statement is false, make the necessary change(s) to produce a true statement.

65. D ∈ T   **66.** R ∈ T

67. M ⊂ T   **68.** W ⊂ T

69. If x ∈ D, then x ∈ W.   **70.** If x ∈ D, then x ∈ M.

71. If x ∈ R, then x ∉ D.   **72.** If x ∈ D, then x ∉ R.

73. The set of elements in M and W combined is equal to set D.

74. The set of elements in M and W combined is equivalent to set D.

Use the formula for the number of subsets of a set with n elements to solve Exercises 75–80.

75. Houses in Euclid Estates are all identical. However, a person can purchase a new house with some, all, or none of a set of options. This set includes {pool, screened-in balcony, lake view, alarm system, upgraded landscaping}. How many options are there for purchasing a house in this community?

76. A cheese pizza can be ordered with some, all, or none of the following set of toppings: {beef, ham, mushrooms, sausage, peppers, pepperoni, olives, prosciutto, onion}. How many different variations are available for ordering a pizza?

77. Based on more than 1500 ballots sent to film notables, the American Film Institute rated the top U.S. movies. The Institute selected *Citizen Kane* (1941), *Casablanca* (1942), *The Godfather* (1972), *Gone With the Wind* (1939), *Lawrence of Arabia* (1962), and *The Wizard of Oz* (1939) as the top six films. Suppose that you have all six films on video and decide to view some, all, or none of these films. How many viewing options do you have?

78. A small town has four police cars. If a radio dispatcher receives a call, depending on the nature of the situation, no cars, one car, two cars, three cars, or all four cars can be sent. How many options does the dispatcher have for sending the police cars to the scene of the caller?

79. According to the U.S. Census Bureau, the most ethnically diverse U.S. cities are New York City, Los Angeles, Miami, Chicago, Washington, D.C., Houston, San Diego, and Seattle. If you decide to visit some, all, or none of these cities, how many travel options do you have?

80. Some of the movies with all-time box office grosses include

Titanic ($601 million), *Star Wars: Episode IV—A New Hope* ($461 million), *Shrek 2* ($441 million),

E. T. the Extra-Terrestrial ($435 million),

Star Wars: Episode I—The Phantom Menace ($431 million),

Spider-Man ($404 million), and

The Lord of the Rings: The Return of the King ($377 million).

Suppose that you have all seven films on video and decide, over the course of a week, to view some, all, or none of these films. How many viewing options do you have?

• Writing in Mathematics

81. Explain what is meant by a subset.

82. What is the difference between a subset and a proper subset?

83. Explain why the empty set is a subset of every set.

84. Describe the difference between the symbols $\in$ and $\subseteq$. Explain how each symbol is used.

85. Describe the formula for finding the number of subsets for a given set. Give an example.

86. Describe how to find the number of proper subsets for a given set. Give an example.

• Critical Thinking Exercises

87. Which one of the following is true?
   a. The set {3} has 2^3, or eight, subsets.
   b. All sets have subsets.
   c. Every set has a proper subset.
   d. The set {3, {1, 4}} has eight subsets.

88. Suppose that a nickel, a dime, and a quarter are on a table. You may select some, all, or none of the coins. Specify all of the different amounts of money that can be selected.

89. If a set has 127 proper subsets, how many elements are there in the set?

• Group Exercises

90. This activity is a group research project and should result in a presentation made by group members to the entire class. Georg Cantor was certainly not the only genius in history who faced criticism during his lifetime, only to have his work acclaimed as a masterpiece after his death. Describe the life and work of three other people, including at least one mathematician, who faced similar circumstances.

91. Research useful Web sites and present a report on infinite sets and their cardinalities. Explain why the sets of whole numbers, integers, and rational numbers each have cardinal number $\aleph_0$. Be sure to define these sets and show the one-to-one correspondences between each set and the set of natural numbers. Then explain why the set of real numbers does not have cardinal number $\aleph_0$ by describing how a real number can always be left out in a pairing with the natural numbers. Spice up the more technical aspects of your report with ideas you discovered about infinity that you find particularly intriguing.

SECTION 7.3 • VENN DIAGRAMS AND SET OPERATIONS

OBJECTIVES

1. Understand the meaning of a universal set.

2. Understand the basic ideas of a Venn diagram.

3. Use Venn diagrams to visualize relationships between two sets.

4. Find the complement of a set.

5. Find the intersection of two sets.

6. Find the union of two sets.

7. Perform operations with sets.

8. Determine sets involving set operations from a Venn diagram.

9. Understand the meaning of *and* and *or*.

10. Use the formula for $n(A \cup B)$.

Sí TV, a 24-hour cable channel targeted to young U.S. Latinos, was launched in 2004 and is now in more than 15 million households. Its motto: "Speak English. Live Latin." As Latino spending power steadily rises, corporate America has discovered that Hispanic Americans, particularly young spenders between the ages of 14 and 34, want to be spoken to in English, even as they stay true to their Latino identity.

What is the primary language spoken at home by U.S. Hispanics? In this section, we use sets to analyze the answer to this question. By doing so, you will see how sets and their visual representations provide precise ways of organizing, classifying, and describing a wide variety of data.

1 Understand the meaning of a universal set.

Languages Spoken at Home by U.S. Hispanics

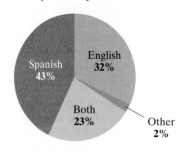

FIGURE 7.1
Source: Time, August 22, 2005

2 Understand the basic ideas of a Venn diagram.

STUDY TIP

The size of the circle representing set *A* in a Venn diagram has nothing to do with the number of elements in set *A*.

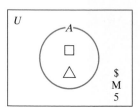

FIGURE 7.3

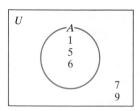

FIGURE 7.4

3 Use Venn diagrams to visualize relationships between two sets.

Universal Sets and Venn Diagrams

The circle graph in Figure 7.1 categorizes America's 40 million Hispanics by the primary language spoken at home. The graph's sectors define four sets:

- the set of U.S. Hispanics who speak Spanish at home
- the set of U.S. Hispanics who speak English at home
- the set of U.S. Hispanics who speak both Spanish and English at home
- the set of U.S. Hispanics who speak neither Spanish nor English at home.

In discussing sets, it is convenient to refer to a general set that contains all elements under discussion. This general set is called the *universal set*. A **universal set**, symbolized by *U*, is a set that contains all the elements being considered in a given discussion or problem. Thus, a convenient universal set for the sets described above is

$$U = \text{the set of U.S. Hispanics.}$$

Notice how this universal set restricts our attention so that we can divide it into the four subsets shown by the circle graph in Figure 7.1.

We can obtain a more thorough understanding of sets and their relationship to a universal set by considering diagrams that allow visual analysis. **Venn diagrams**, named for the British logician John Venn (1834–1923), are used to show the visual relationship among sets.

Figure 7.2 is a Venn diagram. The universal set is represented by a region inside a rectangle. Subsets within the universal set are depicted by circles, or sometimes by ovals or other shapes. In this Venn diagram, set *A* is represented by the light blue region inside the circle.

The dark blue region in Figure 7.2 represents the set of elements in the universal set *U* that are not in set *A*. By combining the regions shown by the light blue shading and the dark blue shading, we obtain the universal set, *U*.

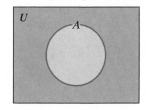

FIGURE 7.2

EXAMPLE 1   DETERMINING SETS FROM A VENN DIAGRAM

Use the Venn diagram in Figure 7.3 to determine each of the following sets:

a. *U*   **b.** *A*   **c.** the set of elements in *U* that are not in *A*.

SOLUTION

a. Set *U*, the universal set, consists of all the elements within the rectangle. Thus, $U = \{\square, \Delta, \$, M, 5\}$.

b. Set *A* consists of all the elements within the circle. Thus, $A = \{\square, \Delta\}$.

c. The set of elements in *U* that are not in *A*, shown by the set of all the elements outside the circle, is $\{\$, M, 5\}$.

 Use the Venn diagram in Figure 7.4 to determine each of the following sets:

   a. *U*

   b. *A*

   c. the set of elements in *U* that are not in *A*.

Representing Two Sets in a Venn Diagram

There are a number of different ways to represent two subsets of a universal set in a Venn diagram. To help understand these representations, let's revisit the scenario that opened the chapter.

You need to determine whether there is sufficient support on campus to have a blood drive. You take a survey to obtain information, asking students

   Would you be willing to donate blood?

   Would you be willing to help serve a free breakfast to blood donors?

Set *A* represents the set of students willing to donate blood. Set *B* represents the set of students willing to help serve breakfast to donors. Possible survey results include the following:

- No students willing to donate blood are willing to serve breakfast, and vice versa.
- All students willing to donate blood are willing to serve breakfast.
- The same students who are willing to donate blood are willing to serve breakfast.
- Some of the students willing to donate blood are willing to serve breakfast.

We begin by using Venn diagrams to visualize these results. To do so, we consider four basic relationships and their visualizations.

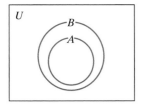

FIGURE 7.5

Relationship 1: Disjoint Sets Two sets that have no elements in common are called **disjoint sets**. Two disjoint sets, *A* and *B*, are shown in the Venn diagram in Figure 7.5. Disjoint sets are represented as circles that do not overlap. No elements of set *A* are elements of set *B*, and vice versa.

If set *A* represents the set of students willing to donate blood and set *B* represents the set of students willing to serve breakfast to donors, the set diagram illustrates

> No students willing to donate blood are willing to serve breakfast, and vice versa.

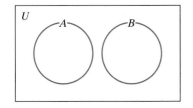

FIGURE 7.6

Relationship 2: Proper Subsets If set *A* is a proper subset of set *B* ($A \subset B$), the relationship is shown in the Venn diagram in Figure 7.6. All elements of set *A* are elements of set *B*. If an *x* representing an element is placed inside circle *A*, it automatically falls inside circle *B*.

If set *A* represents the set of students willing to donate blood and set *B* represents the set of students willing to serve breakfast to donors, the set diagram illustrates

> All students willing to donate blood are willing to serve breakfast.

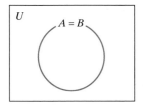

FIGURE 7.7

Relationship 3: Equal Sets If $A = B$, then set *A* contains exactly the same elements as set *B*. This relationship is shown in the Venn diagram in Figure 7.7. Because all elements in set *A* are in set *B*, and vice versa, this diagram illustrates that when $A = B$, then $A \subseteq B$ and $B \subseteq A$.

If set *A* represents the set of students willing to donate blood and set *B* represents the set of students willing to serve breakfast to donors, the set diagram illustrates

> The same students who are willing to donate blood are willing to serve breakfast.

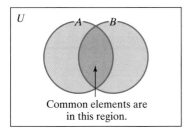

FIGURE 7.8

Relationship 4: Sets with Some Common Elements In mathematics, the word *some* means *there exists at least one*. If set *A* and set *B* have at least one element in common, then the circles representing the sets must overlap. This is illustrated in the Venn diagram in Figure 7.8.

If set *A* represents the set of students willing to donate blood and set *B* represents the set of students willing to serve breakfast to donors, the presence of at least one student in the dark blue region in Figure 7.8 illustrates

> Some students willing to donate blood are willing to serve breakfast.

In Figure 7.9 on the next page, we've numbered each of the regions in the Venn diagram in Figure 7.8. Let's make sure we understand what these regions represent in terms of the campus blood drive scenario. Remember that *A* is the set of blood donors and *B* is the set of breakfast servers.

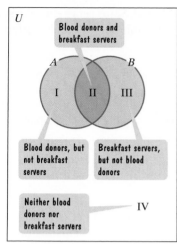

A: Set of blood donors
B: Set of breakfast servers

FIGURE 7.9

In Figure 7.9, we'll start with the innermost region, region II, and work outward to region IV.

Region II	This region represents the set of students willing to donate blood and serve breakfast. The elements that belong to both set A and set B are in this region.
Region I	This region represents the set of students willing to donate blood, but not serve breakfast. The elements that belong to set A but not to set B are in this region.
Region III	This region represents the set of students willing to serve breakfast, but not donate blood. The elements that belong to set B but not to set A are in this region.
Region IV	This region represents the set of students surveyed who are not willing to donate blood and are not willing to serve breakfast. The elements that belong to the universal set U that are not in sets A or B are in this region.

EXAMPLE 2   DETERMINING SETS FROM A VENN DIAGRAM

Use the Venn diagram in Figure 7.10 to determine each of the following sets:

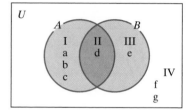

a. U **b.** B

c. the set of elements in A but not B

d. the set of elements in U that are not in B

e. the set of elements in both A and B.

FIGURE 7.10

SOLUTION

a. Set U, the universal set, consists of all elements within the rectangle. Taking the elements in regions I, II, III, and IV, we obtain $U = \{a, b, c, d, e, f, g\}$.

b. Set B consists of the elements in regions II and III. Thus, $B = \{d, e\}$.

c. The set of elements in A but not B, found in region I, is $\{a, b, c\}$.

d. The set of elements in U that are not in B, found in regions I and IV, is $\{a, b, c, f, g\}$.

e. The set of elements in both A and B, found in region II, is $\{d\}$.

Use the Venn diagram in Figure 7.10 to determine each of the following sets:

a. A; **b.** the set of elements in B but not A; **c.** the set of elements in U that are not in A; **d.** the set of elements in U that are not in A or B.

The Complement of a Set

4 | Find the complement of a set.

In arithmetic, we use operations such as addition and multiplication to combine numbers. We now turn to three set operations, called *complement, intersection*, and *union*. We begin by defining a set's complement.

> **DEFINITION OF THE COMPLEMENT OF A SET**
> The **complement** of set A, symbolized by A', is the set of all elements in the universal set that are *not* in A. This idea can be expressed in set-builder notation as follows:
> $$A' = \{x \mid x \in U \text{ and } x \notin A\}.$$

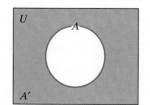

FIGURE 7.11

The shaded region in Figure 7.11 represents the complement of set A, or A'. This region lies outside circle A, but within the rectangular universal set.

In order to find A', a universal set U must be given. A fast way to find A' is to cross out the elements in U that are given to be in set A. A' is the set that remains.

EXAMPLE 3   FINDING A SET'S COMPLEMENT

Let $U = \{1, 2, 3, 4, 5, 6, 7, 8, 9\}$ and $A = \{1, 3, 4, 7\}$. Find A'.

SOLUTION Set A' contains all the elements of set U that are not in set A. Because set A contains the elements 1, 3, 4, and 7, these elements cannot be members of set A':

$$\{\cancel{1}, 2, \cancel{3}, \cancel{4}, 5, 6, \cancel{7}, 8, 9\}.$$

Thus, set A' contains 2, 5, 6, 8, and 9:

$$A' = \{2, 5, 6, 8, 9\}.$$

A Venn diagram illustrating A and A' is shown in Figure 7.12.

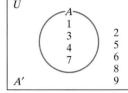

FIGURE 7.12

CHECK POINT 3 Let $U = \{a, b, c, d, e\}$ and $A = \{a, d\}$. Find A'.

---

5 | Find the intersection of two sets.

The Intersection of Sets

If A and B are sets, we can form a new set consisting of all elements that are in both A and B. This set is called the *intersection* of the two sets.

> ### DEFINITION OF THE INTERSECTION OF SETS
> The **intersection** of sets A and B, written $A \cap B$, is the set of elements common to both set A and set B. This definition can be expressed in set-builder notation as follows:
> $$A \cap B = \{x | x \in A \quad \text{and} \quad x \in B\}.$$

In Example 4, we are asked to find the intersection of two sets. This is done by listing the common elements of both sets. Because the intersection of two sets is also a set, we enclose these elements with braces.

EXAMPLE 4   FINDING THE INTERSECTION OF TWO SETS

Find each of the following intersections:

a. $\{7, 8, 9, 10, 11\} \cap \{6, 8, 10, 12\}$
b. $\{1, 3, 5, 7, 9\} \cap \{2, 4, 6, 8\}$
c. $\{1, 3, 5, 7, 9\} \cap \varnothing$.

SOLUTION

a. The elements common to $\{7, 8, 9, 10, 11\}$ and $\{6, 8, 10, 12\}$ are 8 and 10. Thus,

$$\{7, 8, 9, 10, 11\} \cap \{6, 8, 10, 12\} = \{8, 10\}.$$

The Venn diagram in Figure 7.13 illustrates this situation.

b. The sets $\{1, 3, 5, 7, 9\}$ and $\{2, 4, 6, 8\}$ have no elements in common. Thus,

$$\{1, 3, 5, 7, 9\} \cap \{2, 4, 6, 8\} = \varnothing.$$

The Venn diagram in Figure 7.14 illustrates this situation. The sets are disjoint.

c. There are no elements in $\varnothing$, the empty set. This means that there can be no elements belonging to both $\{1, 3, 5, 7, 9\}$ and $\varnothing$. Therefore,

$$\{1, 3, 5, 7, 9\} \cap \varnothing = \varnothing.$$

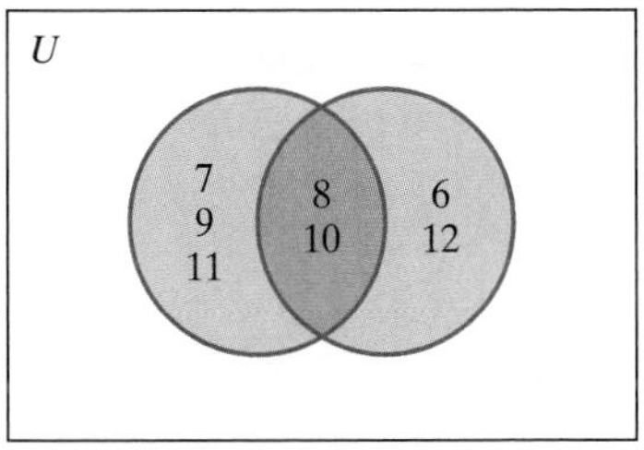

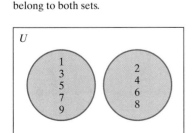

FIGURE 7.13 The numbers 8 and 10 belong to both sets.

FIGURE 7.14 These disjoint sets have no common elements.

4 Find each of the following intersections:

    a. $\{1, 3, 5, 7, 10\} \cap \{6, 7, 10, 11\}$

    b. $\{1, 2, 3\} \cap \{4, 5, 6, 7\}$

    c. $\{1, 2, 3\} \cap \varnothing.$

6 | Find the union of two sets.

The Union of Sets

Another set that we can form from sets A and B consists of elements that are in A or B or in both sets. This set is called the *union* of the two sets.

> ### DEFINITION OF THE UNION OF SETS
>
> The **union** of sets A and B, written $A \cup B$, is the set of elements that are members of set A or of set B or of both sets. This definition can be expressed in set-builder notation as follows:
>
> $$A \cup B = \{x \mid x \in A \quad \text{or} \quad x \in B\}.$$

We can find the union of set A and set B by listing the elements of set A. Then, we include any elements of set B that have not already been listed. Enclose all elements that are listed with braces. This shows that the union of two sets is also a set.

EXAMPLE 5   FINDING THE UNION OF TWO SETS

Find each of the following unions:

    a. $\{7, 8, 9, 10, 11\} \cup \{6, 8, 10, 12\}$

    b. $\{1, 3, 5, 7, 9\} \cup \{2, 4, 6, 8\}$

    c. $\{1, 3, 5, 7, 9\} \cup \varnothing.$

STUDY TIP

When finding the union of two sets, some elements may appear in both sets. List these common elements only once, *not twice*, in the union of the sets.

SOLUTION This example uses the same sets as in Example 4. However, this time we are finding the unions of the sets, rather than their intersections.

    a. To find $\{7, 8, 9, 10, 11\} \cup \{6, 8, 10, 12\}$, start by listing all the elements from the first set, namely 7, 8, 9, 10, and 11. Now list all the elements from the second set that are not in the first set, namely 6 and 12. The union is the set consisting of all these elements. Thus,

$$\{7, 8, 9, 10, 11\} \cup \{6, 8, 10, 12\} = \{6, 7, 8, 9, 10, 11, 12\}.$$

    b. To find $\{1, 3, 5, 7, 9\} \cup \{2, 4, 6, 8\}$, list the elements from the first set, namely 1, 3, 5, 7, and 9. Now add to the list the elements in the second set that are not in the first set. This includes every element in the second set, namely 2, 4, 6, and 8. The union is the set consisting of all these elements, so

$$\{1, 3, 5, 7, 9\} \cup \{2, 4, 6, 8\} = \{1, 2, 3, 4, 5, 6, 7, 8, 9\}.$$

    c. To find $\{1, 3, 5, 7, 9\} \cup \varnothing$, list the elements from the first set, namely 1, 3, 5, 7, and 9. Because there are no elements in $\varnothing$, the empty set, there are no additional elements to add to the list. Thus,

$$\{1, 3, 5, 7, 9\} \cup \varnothing = \{1, 3, 5, 7, 9\}.$$

        ○

Examples 4 and 5 illustrate the role that the empty set plays in intersection and union.

> ### THE EMPTY SET IN INTERSECTION AND UNION
>
> For any set A,
>
>   **1.** $A \cap \varnothing = \varnothing$
>
>   **2.** $A \cup \varnothing = A.$

CHECK POINT 5 Find each of the following unions:

    a. $\{1, 3, 5, 7, 10\} \cup \{6, 7, 10, 11\}$

    b. $\{1, 2, 3\} \cup \{4, 5, 6, 7\}$

    c. $\{1, 2, 3\} \cup \varnothing$.

7 | Perform operations with sets.

STUDY TIP

The words *union* and *intersection* are helpful in distinguishing these two operations. Union, as in a marriage union, suggests joining things, or uniting them. Intersection, as in the intersection of two crossing streets, brings to mind the area common to both, suggesting things that overlap.

Performing Set Operations

Some problems involve more than one set operation. The set notation specifies the order in which we perform these operations. **Always begin by performing any operations inside parentheses.** Here are two examples involving sets we will find in Example 6.

- Finding $(A \cup B)'$

  Step 1. Parentheses indicate to first find the union of A and B.

  Step 2. Find the complement of $A \cup B$.

- Finding $A' \cap B'$

  Step 1. Find the complement of A.

  Step 2. Find the complement of B.

  Step 3. Find the intersection of A' and B'.

EXAMPLE 6   PERFORMING SET OPERATIONS

Given

$$U = \{1, 2, 3, 4, 5, 6, 7, 8, 9, 10\}$$
$$A = \{1, 3, 7, 9\}$$
$$B = \{3, 7, 8, 10\},$$

find each of the following sets:

    a. $(A \cup B)'$ **b.** $A' \cap B'$.

SOLUTION

a. To find $(A \cup B)'$ we will first work inside the parentheses and determine $A \cup B$. Then we'll find the complement of $A \cup B$, namely $(A \cup B)'$.

$$A \cup B = \{1, 3, 7, 9\} \cup \{3, 7, 8, 10\}$$ These are the given sets.

$$= \{1, 3, 7, 8, 9, 10\}$$ Join (unite) the elements, listing the common elements (3 and 7) only once.

Now find $(A \cup B)'$, the complement of $A \cup B$.

$$(A \cup B)' = \{1, 3, 7, 8, 9, 10\}'$$

$$= \{2, 4, 5, 6\}$$ List the elements in the universal set that are not listed in $\{1, 3, 7, 8, 9, 10\}$: $\{\not{1}, 2, \not{3}, 4, 5, 6, \not{7}, \not{8}, \not{9}, \not{10}\}$.

b. To find $A' \cap B'$, we must first identify the elements in A' and B'. Set A' is the set of elements of U that are not in set A:

$$A' = \{2, 4, 5, 6, 8, 10\}.$$ List the elements in the universal set that are not listed in $A = \{1, 3, 7, 9\}$: $\{\not{1}, 2, \not{3}, 4, 5, 6, \not{7}, 8, \not{9}, 10\}$.

Set B' is the set of elements of U that are not in set B:

$$B' = \{1, 2, 4, 5, 6, 9\}.$$ List the elements in the universal set that are not listed in $B = \{3, 7, 8, 10\}$: $\{1, 2, \not{3}, 4, 5, 6, \not{7}, \not{8}, 9, \not{10}\}$.

Now we can find $A' \cap B'$, the set of elements belonging to both A' and to B':

$$A' \cap B' = \{2, 4, 5, 6, 8, 10\} \cap \{1, 2, 4, 5, 6, 9\}$$

$$= \{2, 4, 5, 6\}.$$

The numbers 2, 4, 5, and 6 are common to both sets.

 CHECK POINT 6 Given $U = \{a, b, c, d, e\}$, $A = \{b, c\}$, and $B = \{b, c, e\}$, find each of the following sets:

   a. $(A \cup B)'$ **b.** $A' \cap B'$.

8 Determine sets involving set operations from a Venn diagram.

EXAMPLE 7   DETERMINING SETS FROM A VENN DIAGRAM

The Venn diagram in Figure 7.15 percolates with interesting numbers. Use the diagram to determine each of the following sets:

   a. $A \cup B$ **b.** $(A \cup B)'$ **c.** $A \cap B$

   d. $(A \cap B)'$ **e.** $A' \cap B$ **f.** $A \cup B'$.

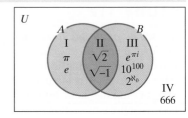

FIGURE 7.15

SOLUTION

Set to Determine	Description of Set	Regions in Venn Diagram	Set in Roster Form
a. $A \cup B$	set of elements in A or B or both	I, II, III	$\{\pi, e, \sqrt{2}, \sqrt{-1}, e^{\pi i}, 10^{100}, 2^{\aleph_0}\}$
b. $(A \cup B)'$	set of elements in U that are not in $A \cup B$	IV	$\{666\}$
c. $A \cap B$	set of elements in both A and B	II	$\{\sqrt{2}, \sqrt{-1}\}$
d. $(A \cap B)'$	set of elements in U that are not in $A \cap B$	I, III, IV	$\{\pi, e, e^{\pi i}, 10^{100}, 2^{\aleph_0}, 666\}$
e. $A' \cap B$	set of elements that are not in A and are in B	III	$\{e^{\pi i}, 10^{100}, 2^{\aleph_0}\}$
f. $A \cup B'$	set of elements that are in A or not in B or both	I, II, IV	$\{\pi, e, \sqrt{2}, \sqrt{-1}, 666\}$

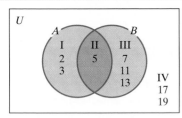

FIGURE 7.16

 CHECK POINT 7 Use the Venn diagram in Figure 7.16 to determine each of the following sets:

   a. $A \cap B$ **b.** $(A \cap B)'$ **c.** $A \cup B$

   d. $(A \cup B)'$ **e.** $A' \cup B$ **f.** $A \cap B'$.

9 Understand the meaning of *and* and *or*.

Sets and Precise Use of Everyday English

Set operations and Venn diagrams provide precise ways of organizing, classifying, and describing the vast array of sets and subsets we encounter every day. Let's see how this applies to the sets from the beginning of this section:

$$U = \text{the set of U.S. Hispanics}$$

$$S = \text{the set of U.S. Hispanics who speak Spanish at home}$$

$$E = \text{the set of U.S. Hispanics who speak English at home.}$$

When describing collections in everyday English, the word **or** refers to the **union** of sets. Thus, U.S. Hispanics who speak Spanish or English at home means those who speak Spanish or English or both. The word **and** refers to the **intersection** of sets. Thus, U.S. Hispanics who speak Spanish and English at home means those who speak both languages.

In Figure 7.17, we revisit the circle graph showing languages spoken at home by U.S. Hispanics. To the right of the circle graph, we've organized the data using a Venn diagram. The voice balloons indicate how the Venn diagram provides a more accurate understanding of the subsets and their data.

Languages Spoken at Home by U.S. Hispanics

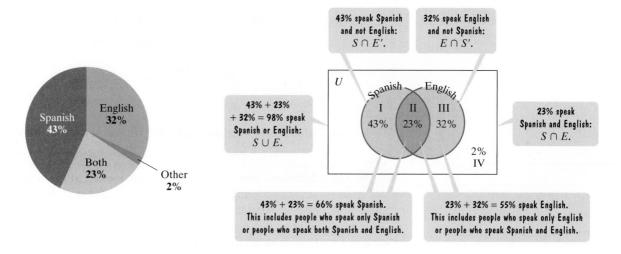

FIGURE 7.17 Comparing a circle graph and a Venn diagram
Source: Time, August 22, 2005

10 | Use the formula for $n(A \cup B)$.

The Cardinal Number of the Union of Two Finite Sets

Can the number of elements in A or B, $n(A \cup B)$, be determined by adding the number of elements in A and the number of elements in B, $n(A) + n(B)$? The answer is no. Figure 7.18 illustrates that by doing this, we are counting elements in both sets, $A \cap B$, or region II, twice.

To find the number of elements in the union of finite sets A and B, add the number of elements in A and the number of elements in B. Then subtract the number of elements common to both sets. We perform this subtraction so that we do not count the number of elements in the intersection twice, once for $n(A)$, and again for $n(B)$.

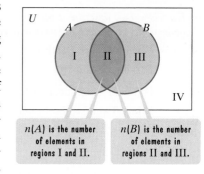

FIGURE 7.18

FORMULA FOR THE CARDINAL NUMBER OF THE UNION OF TWO FINITE SETS

$$n(A \cup B) = n(A) + n(B) - n(A \cap B)$$

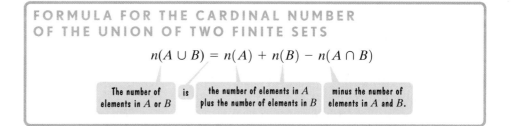

EXAMPLE 8   USING THE FORMULA FOR $n(A \cup B)$

Some of the results of the campus blood drive survey indicated that 490 students were willing to donate blood, 340 students were willing to help serve a free breakfast to blood donors, and 120 students were willing to donate blood and serve breakfast. How many students were willing to donate blood or serve breakfast?

SOLUTION Let A = the set of students willing to donate blood and B = the set of students willing to serve breakfast. We are interested in how many students were willing to donate blood or serve breakfast. Thus, we need to determine $n(A \cup B)$.

number of blood donors or breakfast servers   number of blood donors   number of breakfast servers   number of blood donors and breakfast servers

$$n(A \cup B) = n(A) + n(B) - n(A \cap B)$$

$$= 490 + 340 - 120$$

$$= 830 - 120$$

$$= 710$$

We see that 710 students were willing to donate blood or serve a free breakfast.

CHECK POINT 8 The admissions department at a college looked at the registration of 500 of its students and found the following results: 244 students were registered in a mathematics class, 230 students were registered in an English class, and 89 students were registered in a math class and an English class. How many students were registered in a math class or an English class?

EXERCISE SET 7.3 ●●●●●●

• Practice Exercises

In Exercises 1–4, describe a universal set U that includes all elements in the given sets. Answers may vary.

1. A = {Bach, Mozart, Beethoven}

   B = {Brahms, Schubert}

2. A = {William Shakespeare, Charles Dickens}

   B = {Mark Twain, Robert Louis Stevenson}

3. A = {Pepsi, Sprite}

   B = {Coca Cola, Seven-Up}

4. A = {Acura RSX, Toyota Camry, Mitsubishi Lancer}

   B = {Dodge Ram, Chevrolet Impala}

In Exercises 5–8, let U = {a, b, c, d, e, f, g}, A = {a, b, f, g}, B = {c, d, e}, C = {a, g}, and D = {a, b, c, d, e, f}. Use the roster method to write each of the following sets.

5. A' 6. B' 7. C' 8. D'

In Exercises 9–12, let U = {1, 2, 3, 4, ..., 20}, A = {1, 2, 3, 4, 5}, B = {6, 7, 8, 9}, C = {1, 3, 5, 7, ..., 19}, and D = {2, 4, 6, 8, ..., 20}. Use the roster method to write each of the following sets.

9. A' 10. B' 11. C' 12. D'

In Exercises 13–16, let U = {1, 2, 3, 4, ...}, A = {1, 2, 3, 4, ..., 20}, B = {1, 2, 3, 4, ..., 50}, C = {2, 4, 6, 8, ...}, and D = {1, 3, 5, 7, ...}. Use the roster method to write each of the following sets.

13. A' 14. B' 15. C' 16. D'

In Exercises 17–40, let

$$U = \{1, 2, 3, 4, 5, 6, 7\}$$
$$A = \{1, 3, 5, 7\}$$
$$B = \{1, 2, 3\}$$
$$C = \{2, 3, 4, 5, 6\}.$$

Find each of the following sets.

17. $A \cap B$	18. $B \cap C$	19. $A \cup B$	20. $B \cup C$
21. A'	22. B'	23. $A' \cap B'$	24. $B' \cap C$
25. $A \cup C'$	26. $B \cup C'$	27. $(A \cap C)'$	28. $(A \cap B)'$
29. $A' \cup C'$	30. $A' \cup B'$	31. $(A \cup B)'$	32. $(A \cup C)'$
33. $A \cup \varnothing$	34. $C \cup \varnothing$	35. $A \cap \varnothing$	36. $C \cap \varnothing$
37. $A \cup U$	38. $B \cup U$	39. $A \cap U$	40. $B \cap U$

In Exercises 41–66, let

$$U = \{a, b, c, d, e, f, g, h\}$$
$$A = \{a, g, h\}$$
$$B = \{b, g, h\}$$
$$C = \{b, c, d, e, f\}.$$

Find each of the following sets.

41. $A \cap B$	42. $B \cap C$	43. $A \cup B$	44. $B \cup C$
45. A'	46. B'	47. $A' \cap B'$	48. $B' \cap C$
49. $A \cup C'$	50. $B \cup C'$	51. $(A \cap C)'$	52. $(A \cap B)'$
53. $A' \cup C'$	54. $A' \cup B'$	55. $(A \cup B)'$	56. $(A \cup C)'$
57. $A \cup \varnothing$	58. $C \cup \varnothing$	59. $A \cap \varnothing$	60. $C \cap \varnothing$
61. $A \cup U$	62. $B \cup U$	63. $A \cap U$	64. $B \cap U$
65. $(A \cap B) \cup B'$	66. $(A \cup B) \cap B'$		

In Exercises 67–78, use the Venn diagram to represent each set in roster form.

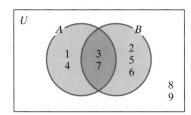

67. A **68.** B **69.** U **70.** $A \cup B$
71. $A \cap B$ **72.** A' **73.** B' **74.** $(A \cap B)'$
75. $(A \cup B)'$ **76.** $A' \cap B$ **77.** $A \cap B'$ **78.** $A \cup B'$

In Exercises 79–92, use the Venn diagram to determine each set or cardinality.

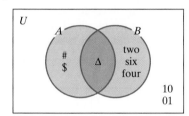

79. B **80.** A **81.** $A \cup B$
82. $A \cap B$ **83.** $n(A \cup B)$ **84.** $n(A \cap B)$
85. $n(A')$ **86.** $n(B')$ **87.** $(A \cap B)'$
88. $(A \cup B)'$ **89.** $A' \cap B$ **90.** $A \cap B'$
91. $n(U) - n(B)$ **92.** $n(U) - n(A)$

Use the formula for the cardinal number of the union of two sets to solve Exercise 93–96.

93. Set A contains 17 elements, set B contains 20 elements, and 6 elements are common to sets A and B. How many elements are in $A \cup B$?

94. Set A contains 30 elements, set B contains 18 elements, and 5 elements are common to sets A and B. How many elements are in $A \cup B$?

95. Set A contains 8 letters and 9 numbers. Set B contains 7 letters and 10 numbers. Four letters and 3 numbers are common to both sets A and B. Find the number of elements in set A or set B.

96. Set A contains 12 numbers and 18 letters. Set B contains 14 numbers and 10 letters. One number and 6 letters are common to both sets A and B. Find the number of elements in set A or set B.

• Practice Plus

In Exercises 97–104, let

$U = \{x \mid x \in \mathbf{N} \text{ and } x < 9\}$

$A = \{x \mid x \text{ is an odd natural number and } x < 9\}$

$B = \{x \mid x \text{ is an even natural number and } x < 9\}$

$C = \{x \mid x \in \mathbf{N} \text{ and } 1 < x < 6\}.$

Find each of the following sets.

97. $A \cup B$ **98.** $B \cup C$ **99.** $A \cap U$ **100.** $A \cup U$
101. $A \cap C'$ **102.** $A \cap B'$ **103.** $(B \cap C)'$ **104.** $(A \cap C)'$

In Exercises 105–108, use the Venn diagram to determine each set or cardinality.

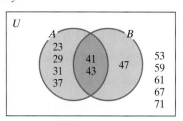

105. $A \cup (A \cup B)'$
106. $(A' \cap B) \cup (A \cap B)$
107. $n(U)[n(A \cup B) - n(A \cap B)]$
108. $n(A \cap B)[n(A \cup B) - n(A')]$

• Application Exercises

A math tutor working with a small group of students asked each student when he or she had studied for class the previous weekend. Their responses are shown in the Venn diagram.

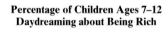
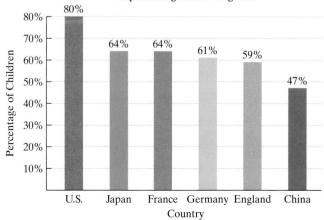

In Exercises 109–116, use the Venn diagram to list the elements of each set in roster form.

109. The set of students who studied Saturday

110. The set of students who studied Sunday

111. The set of students who studied Saturday or Sunday

112. The set of students who studied Saturday and Sunday

113. The set of students who studied Saturday and not Sunday

114. The set of students who studied Sunday and not Saturday

115. The set of students who studied neither Saturday nor Sunday

116. The set of students surveyed by the math tutor

The bar graph shows the percentage of children in the world's leading industrial countries who daydream about being rich.

Percentage of Children Ages 7–12 Daydreaming about Being Rich

Country	Percentage
U.S.	80%
Japan	64%
France	64%
Germany	61%
England	59%
China	47%

Source: Roper Starch Worldwide for A.B.C. Research

In Exercises 117–122, use the information in the graph on the previous page to place the indicated country in the correct region of the following Venn diagram.

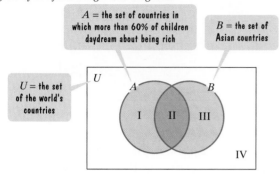

A = the set of countries in which more than 60% of children daydream about being rich

B = the set of Asian countries

U = the set of the world's countries

117. U.S.　　**118.** Japan　　**119.** France　　**120.** Germany
121. England　　　　　　**122.** China

A **palindromic number** *is a natural number whose value does not change if its digits are reversed. Examples of palindromic numbers are 11, 454, and 261,162. In Exercises 123–132, use this definition to place the indicated natural number in the correct region of the following Venn diagram.*

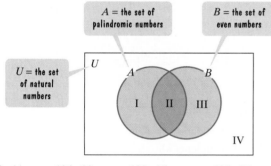

A = the set of palindromic numbers

B = the set of even numbers

U = the set of natural numbers

123. 11　　**124.** 22　　**125.** 15　　**126.** 17
127. 454　　**128.** 101　　**129.** 9558　　**130.** 9778
131. 9559　　**132.** 9779

As a result of cultural expectations about what is appropriate behavior for each gender, boys and girls differ substantially in their toy preferences. The graph shows the percentage of boys and girls asking for various types of toys in letters to Santa Claus. Use the information in the graph to write each set in Exercises 133–138 in roster form or express the set as ∅.

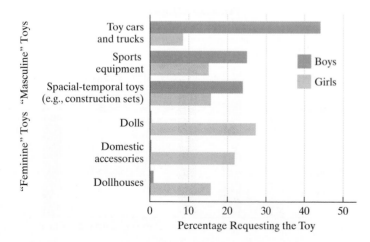

Toys Requested by Children

"Masculine" Toys / "Feminine" Toys (vertical axis label)

Toy cars and trucks
Sports equipment
Spacial-temporal toys (e.g., construction sets)
Dolls
Domestic accessories
Dollhouses

Boys
Girls

Percentage Requesting the Toy

Source: Richard, J.G., & Simpson, C.H. (1982). Children, gender and social structure: An analysis of the contents of letters to Santa Claus. *Child Development,* 53, 429–436.

133. $\{x \mid x$ is a toy requested by more than 10% of the boys$\} \cap$ $\{x \mid x$ is a toy requested by less than 20% of the girls$\}$

134. $\{x \mid x$ is a toy requested by fewer than 5% of the boys$\} \cap$ $\{x \mid x$ is a toy requested by fewer than 20% of the girls$\}$

135. $\{x \mid x$ is a toy requested by more than 10% of the boys$\} \cup$ $\{x \mid x$ is a toy requested by less than 20% of the girls$\}$

136. $\{x \mid x$ is a toy requested by fewer than 5% of the boys$\} \cup$ $\{x \mid x$ is a toy requested by fewer than 20% of the girls$\}$

137. The set of toys requested by more than 40% of the boys and more than 10% of the girls

138. The set of toys requested by more than 40% of the boys or more than 10% of the girls

139. A winter resort took a poll of its 350 visitors to see which winter activities people enjoyed. The results were as follows: 178 people liked to ski, 154 people liked to snowboard, and 49 people liked to ski and snowboard. How many people in the poll liked to ski or snowboard?

140. A pet store surveyed 200 pet owners and obtained the following results: 96 people owned cats, 97 people owned dogs, and 29 people owned cats and dogs. How many people in the survey owned cats or dogs?

• Writing in Mathematics

141. Describe what is meant by a universal set. Provide an example.

142. What is a Venn diagram and how is it used?

143. Describe the Venn diagram for two disjoint sets. How does this diagram illustrate that the sets have no common elements?

144. Describe the Venn diagram for proper subsets. How does this diagram illustrate that the elements of one set are also in the second set?

145. Describe the Venn diagram for two equal sets. How does this diagram illustrate that the sets are equal?

146. Describe the Venn diagram for two sets with common elements. How does the diagram illustrate this relationship?

147. Describe what is meant by the complement of a set.

148. Is it possible to find a set's complement if a universal set is not given? Explain your answer.

149. Describe what is meant by the intersection of sets. Give an example.

150. Describe what is meant by the union of sets. Give an example.

151. Describe how to find the cardinal number of the union of two finite sets.

• Critical Thinking Exercises

152. Which one of the following is true?
  a. $n(A \cup B) = n(A) + n(B)$
  b. $A \cap A' = \emptyset$
  c. $(A \cup B) \subseteq A$
  d. If $A \subseteq B$, then $A \cap B = B$.

153. Which one of the following is true?

  a. $A \cap U = U$

  b. $A \cup \varnothing = \varnothing$

  c. If $A \subseteq B$, then $A \cap B = \varnothing$.

  d. If $B \subseteq A$, then $A \cap B = B$.

In Exercises 154–157, if $A \neq B$, draw a Venn diagram that correctly illustrates the relationship between the sets.

154. $A \cap B = A$ **155.** $A \cap B = B$

156. $A \cup B = A$ **157.** $A \cup B = B$

SECTION 7.4 • SET OPERATIONS AND VENN DIAGRAMS WITH THREE SETS

OBJECTIVES

1. Perform set operations with three sets.
2. Use Venn diagrams with three sets.
3. Use Venn diagrams to prove equality of sets.

Our bodies are fragile and complex, vulnerable to disease, and easily damaged. The imminent mapping of the human genome—all 140,000 genes—could lead to rapid advances in treating heart disease, cancer, Alzheimer's, and AIDS. Neural stem cell research could make it possible to repair brain damage and even re-create whole parts of the brain. There appears to be no limit to the parts of our bodies that can be replaced. By contrast, at the start of the twentieth century, we lacked a basic understanding of the different types of human blood. The discovery of blood types, which can be illustrated by a Venn diagram with three sets, rescued surgery patients from random, often lethal, transfusions. In this sense, the Venn diagram that you encounter in this section reinforces our optimism that life does improve, and that we are better off today than we were one hundred years ago.

1 | Perform set operations with three sets.

Set Operations with Three Sets

We now know how to find the union and intersection of two sets. We also know how to find a set's complement. In Example 1, we apply set operations to situations containing three sets.

EXAMPLE 1   SET OPERATIONS WITH THREE SETS

Given

$$U = \{1, 2, 3, 4, 5, 6, 7, 8, 9\}$$
$$A = \{1, 2, 3, 4, 5\}$$
$$B = \{1, 2, 3, 6, 8\}$$
$$C = \{2, 3, 4, 6, 7\},$$

find each of the following sets:

a. $A \cup (B \cap C)$

b. $(A \cup B) \cap (A \cup C)$

c. $A \cap (B \cup C')$.

SOLUTION Before determining each set, let's be sure we perform the operations in the correct order. Remember that we begin by performing any set operations inside parentheses.

• Finding $A \cup (B \cap C)$

> Step 1. Find the intersection of B and C.

> Step 2. Find the union of A and $(B \cap C)$.

• Finding $(A \cup B) \cap (A \cup C)$

> Step 1. Find the union of A and B.

> Step 2. Find the union of A and C.

> Step 3. Find the intersection of $(A \cup B)$ and $(A \cup C)$.

• Finding $A \cap (B \cup C')$

> Step 1. Find the complement of C.

> Step 2. Find the union of B and C'.

> Step 3. Find the intersection of A and $(B \cup C')$.

$U = \{1, 2, 3, 4, 5, 6, 7, 8, 9\}$
$A = \{1, 2, 3, 4, 5\}$
$B = \{1, 2, 3, 6, 8\}$
$C = \{2, 3, 4, 6, 7\}$

The given sets (repeated)

a. To find $A \cup (B \cap C)$, first find the set within the parentheses, $B \cap C$:
$$B \cap C = \{1, 2, 3, 6, 8\} \cap \{2, 3, 4, 6, 7\} = \{2, 3, 6\}.$$

> Common elements are 2, 3, and 6.

Now finish the problem by finding $A \cup (B \cap C)$:
$$A \cup (B \cap C) = \{1, 2, 3, 4, 5\} \cup \{2, 3, 6\} = \{1, 2, 3, 4, 5, 6\}.$$

> List all elements in A and then add the only unlisted element in $B \cap C$, namely 6.

b. To find $(A \cup B) \cap (A \cup C)$, first find the sets within parentheses. Start with $A \cup B$:
$$A \cup B = \{1, 2, 3, 4, 5\} \cup \{1, 2, 3, 6, 8\} = \{1, 2, 3, 4, 5, 6, 8\}.$$

> List all elements in A and then add the unlisted elements in B, namely 6 and 8.

Now find $A \cup C$:
$$A \cup C = \{1, 2, 3, 4, 5\} \cup \{2, 3, 4, 6, 7\} = \{1, 2, 3, 4, 5, 6, 7\}.$$

> List all elements in A and then add the unlisted elements in C, namely 6 and 7.

Now finish the problem by finding $(A \cup B) \cap (A \cup C)$:
$$(A \cup B) \cap (A \cup C) = \{1, 2, 3, 4, 5, 6, 8\} \cap \{1, 2, 3, 4, 5, 6, 7\} = \{1, 2, 3, 4, 5, 6\}.$$

> Common elements are 1, 2, 3, 4, 5, and 6.

c. As in parts (a) and (b), to find $A \cap (B \cup C')$, begin with the set in parentheses. First we must find C', elements in U that are not in C:
$$C' = \{1, 5, 8, 9\}. \quad \text{List the elements in } U \text{ that are not in}$$
$$C = \{2, 3, 4, 6, 7\}: \{1, \cancel{2}, \cancel{3}, \cancel{4}, 5, \cancel{6}, \cancel{7}, 8, 9\}.$$

Now we can identify elements of $B \cup C'$:

$$B \cup C' = \{1, 2, 3, 6, 8\} \cup \{1, 5, 8, 9\} = \{1, 2, 3, 5, 6, 8, 9\}.$$

List all elements in B and then add the unlisted elements in C', namely 5 and 9.

Now finish the problem by finding $A \cap (B \cup C')$:

$$A \cap (B \cup C') = \{1, 2, 3, 4, 5\} \cap \{1, 2, 3, 5, 6, 8, 9\} = \{1, 2, 3, 5\}.$$

Common elements are 1, 2, 3, and 5.

CHECK POINT 1 Given $U = \{a, b, c, d, e, f\}$, $A = \{a, b, c, d\}$, $B = \{a, b, d, f\}$, and $C = \{b, c, f\}$, find each of the following sets:

a. $A \cup (B \cap C)$

b. $(A \cup B) \cap (A \cup C)$

c. $A \cap (B \cup C')$.

---

2 | Use Venn diagrams with three sets.

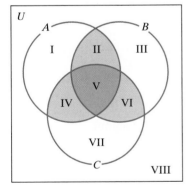

FIGURE 7.19 Three intersecting sets separate the universal set into eight regions.

Venn Diagrams with Three Sets

Venn diagrams can contain three or more sets, such as the diagram in Figure 7.19. The three sets in the figure separate the universal set, U, into eight regions. The numbering of these regions is arbitrary—that is, we can number any region as I, any region as II, and so on. Here is a description of each region, starting with the innermost region, region V, and working outward to region VIII.

The Region Shown in Dark Blue

Region V   This region represents elements that are common to sets A, B, and C: $A \cap B \cap C$.

The Regions Shown in Light Blue

Region II   This region represents elements in both sets A and B that are not in set C: $(A \cap B) \cap C'$.

Region IV   This region represents elements in both sets A and C that are not in set B: $(A \cap C) \cap B'$.

Region VI   This region represents elements in both sets B and C that are not in set A: $(B \cap C) \cap A'$.

The Regions Shown in White

Region I   This region represents elements in set A that are in neither sets B nor C: $A \cap (B' \cap C')$.

Region III   This region represents elements in set B that are in neither sets A nor C: $B \cap (A' \cap C')$.

Region VII   This region represents elements in set C that are in neither sets A nor B: $C \cap (A' \cap B')$.

Region VIII   This region represents elements in the universal set U that are not in sets A, B, or C: $A' \cap B' \cap C'$.

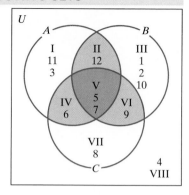

EXAMPLE 2   DETERMINING SETS FROM A VENN DIAGRAM WITH THREE INTERSECTING SETS

Use the Venn diagram in Figure 7.20 to determine each of the following sets:

a. A b. $A \cup B$ c. $B \cap C$

d. C' e. $A \cap B \cap C$.

FIGURE 7.20

SOLUTION

Set to Determine	Description of Set	Regions in Venn Diagram	Set in Roster Form
a. A	set of elements in A	I, II, IV, V	$\{11, 3, 12, 6, 5, 7\}$
b. $A \cup B$	set of elements in A or B or both	I, II, III, IV, V, VI	$\{11, 3, 12, 1, 2, 10, 6, 5, 7, 9\}$
c. $B \cap C$	set of elements in both B and C	V, VI	$\{5, 7, 9\}$
d. C'	set of elements in U that are not in C	I, II, III, VIII	$\{11, 3, 12, 1, 2, 10, 4\}$
e. $A \cap B \cap C$	set of elements in A and B and C	V	$\{5, 7\}$

 Use the Venn diagram in Figure 7.20 to determine each of the following sets:

a. C b. $B \cup C$ c. $A \cap C$

d. B' e. $A \cup B \cup C$.

In Example 2, we used a Venn diagram showing elements in the regions to determine various sets. Now we are going to reverse directions. We'll use sets A, B, C, and U to determine the elements in each region of a Venn diagram.

To construct a Venn diagram illustrating the elements in A, B, C, and U, **start by placing elements into the innermost region and work outward**. Because the four inner regions represent various intersections, find $A \cap B, A \cap C, B \cap C$, and $A \cap B \cap C$. Then use these intersections, and the given sets to place the various elements into regions. This procedure is illustrated in Example 3.

EXAMPLE 3   DETERMINING A VENN DIAGRAM FROM SETS

Construct a Venn diagram illustrating the following sets:

$$A = \{a, d, e, g, h, i, j\}$$
$$B = \{b, e, g, h, l\}$$
$$C = \{a, c, e, h\}$$
$$U = \{a, b, c, d, e, f, g, h, i, j, k, l\}.$$

SOLUTION We begin by finding four intersections. In each case, common elements are shown in red.

- $A \cap B = \{a, d, e, g, h, i, j\} \cap \{b, e, g, h, l\} = \{e, g, h\}$
- $A \cap C = \{a, d, e, g, h, i, j\} \cap \{a, c, e, h\} = \{a, e, h\}$

- $B \cap C = \{b, e, g, h, l\} \cap \{a, c, e, h\} = \{e, h\}$
- $A \cap B \cap C = \{e, g, h\} \cap \{a, c, e, h\} = \{e, h\}$

This is $A \cap B$ from above.

Now we can place elements into regions, starting with the innermost region, region V, and working outward.

STEP 1

$A \cap B \cap C$:
Region V

$A \cap B \cap C = \{e, h\}$
Place e and h into V.

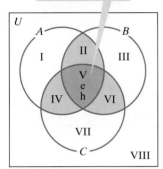

STEP 2

$A \cap B$:
Regions II and V

$A \cap B = \{e, g, h\}$
With e and h in V,
place g into II.

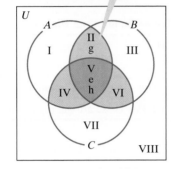

STEP 3

$A \cap C$:
Regions IV and V

$A \cap C = \{a, e, h\}$
With e and h in V,
place a into IV.

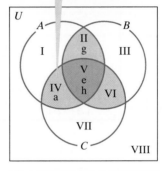

STEP 4

$B \cap C$:
Regions V and VI

$B \cap C = \{e, h\}$
With e and h in V,
place no letters into VI.

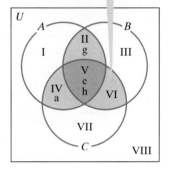

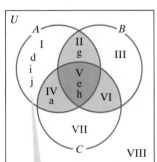

A:
Regions I, II, IV, V

$A = \{a, d, e, g, h, i, j\}$
With a, e, g, and h already placed
in A, place d, i, and j into I.

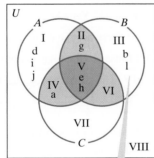

B:
Regions II, III, V, VI

$B = \{b, e, g, h, l\}$
With e, g, and h already placed
in B, place b and l into III.

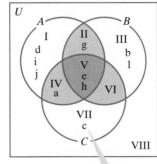

C:
Regions IV, V, VI, VII

$C = \{a, c, e, h\}$
With a, e, and h already
placed in C, place c into VII.

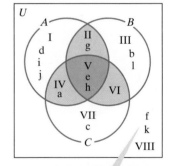

U:
Regions I–VIII

$U = \{a, b, c, d, e, f, g, h, i, j, k, l\}$
With all letters, except f and k, already
placed in U, place f and k into VIII.

STEP 5   **STEP 6**   **STEP 7**   **STEP 8**

The completed Venn diagram in step 8 illustrates the given sets.

CHECK POINT **3**   Construct a Venn diagram illustrating the following sets:

$$A = \{1, 3, 6, 10\}$$
$$B = \{4, 7, 9, 10\}$$
$$C = \{3, 4, 5, 8, 9, 10\}$$
$$U = \{1, 2, 3, 4, 5, 6, 7, 8, 9, 10\}.$$

3 Use Venn diagrams to prove equality of sets.

STUDY TIP

Here are two forms of reasoning .

- **Inductive Reasoning:** Starts with individual observations and works to a general conjecture (or educated guess)
- **Deductive Reasoning:** Starts with general cases and works to the proof of a specific statement (or theorem)

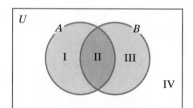

FIGURE 7.21

Proving the Equality of Sets

In Section 7.3, you were given two sets and asked to find $(A \cap B)'$ and $A' \cup B'$. In the example, $(A \cap B)'$ and $A' \cup B'$ resulted in the same set. This occurs regardless of which sets we choose for A and B. Examining these individual cases and applying inductive reasoning, a conjecture (or educated guess) is that $(A \cap B)' = A' \cup B'$.

We can apply deductive reasoning to *prove* the statement $(A \cap B)' = A' \cup B'$ for *all* sets A and B. To prove that $(A \cap B)'$ and $A' \cup B'$ are equal, we use a Venn diagram. If both sets represent the same regions in this general diagram, then this proves that they are equal. Example 4 shows how this is done.

EXAMPLE 4   PROVING THE EQUALITY OF SETS

Use the Venn diagram in Figure 7.21 to prove that

$$(A \cap B)' = A' \cup B'.$$

SOLUTION Begin with the regions represented by $(A \cap B)'$.

Set	Regions in the Venn Diagram
A	I, II
B	II, III
$A \cap B$	II (This is the region common to A and B.)
$(A \cap B)'$	I, III, IV (These are the regions in U that are not in $A \cap B$.)

Next, find the regions represented by $A' \cup B'$.

Set	Regions in the Venn Diagram
A'	III, IV (These are the regions not in A.)
B'	I, IV (These are the regions not in B.)
$A' \cup B'$	I, III, IV (These are the regions obtained by uniting the regions representing A' and B'.)

Both $(A \cap B)'$ and $A' \cup B'$ are represented by the same regions, I, III, and IV, of the Venn diagram. This result proves that

$$(A \cap B)' = A' \cup B'$$

for all sets A and B.

○

Can you see how we applied deductive reasoning in Example 4? We started with the two general sets in the Venn diagram in Figure 7.21 and worked to the specific conclusion that $(A \cap B)'$ and $A' \cup B'$ represent the same regions in the diagram. Thus, the statement $(A \cap B)' = A' \cup B'$ is a theorem.

 Use the Venn diagram in Figure 7.21 to solve this exercise.

a. Which region is represented by $(A \cup B)'$?

b. Which region is represented by $A' \cap B'$?

c. Based on parts (a) and (b), what can you conclude?

The statements proved in Example 4 and Check Point 4 are known as *De Morgan's laws*, named for the British logician Augustus De Morgan (1806–1871).

DE MORGAN'S LAWS

$(A \cap B)' = A' \cup B'$:   The complement of the intersection of two sets is the union of the complements of those sets.

$(A \cup B)' = A' \cap B'$:   The complement of the union of two sets is the intersection of the complements of those sets.

EXAMPLE 5   PROVING THE EQUALITY OF SETS

Use a Venn diagram to prove that

$$A \cup (B \cap C) = (A \cup B) \cap (A \cup C).$$

SOLUTION Use a Venn diagram with three sets A, B, and C, drawn in Figure 7.22. Begin with the regions represented by $A \cup (B \cap C)$.

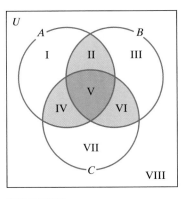

FIGURE 7.22

Set	Regions in the Venn Diagram
A	I, II, IV, V
$B \cap C$	V, VI (These are the regions common to B and C.)
$A \cup (B \cap C)$	I, II, IV, V, VI (These are the regions obtained by uniting the regions representing A and $B \cap C$.)

Next, find the regions represented by $(A \cup B) \cap (A \cup C)$.

Set	Regions in the Venn Diagram
A	I, II, IV, V
B	II, III, V, VI
C	IV, V, VI, VII
$A \cup B$	I, II, III, IV, V, VI (Unite the regions representing A and B.)
$A \cup C$	I, II, IV, V, VI, VII (Unite the regions representing A and C.)
$(A \cup B) \cap (A \cup C)$	I, II, IV, V, VI (These are the regions common to $A \cup B$ and $A \cup C$.)

Both $A \cup (B \cap C)$ and $(A \cup B) \cap (A \cup C)$ are represented by the same regions, I, II, IV, V, and VI, of the Venn diagram. This result proves that

$$A \cup (B \cap C) = (A \cup B) \cap (A \cup C)$$

for all sets A, B, and C. Thus, the statement is a theorem.

  Use the Venn diagram in Figure 7.22 to solve this exercise.

  a. Which regions are represented by $A \cap (B \cup C)$?

  b. Which regions are represented by $(A \cap B) \cup (A \cap C)$?

  c. Based on parts (a) and (b), what can you conclude?

BLITZER BONUS

Blood Types and Venn Diagrams

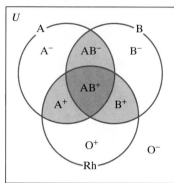

FIGURE 7.23 Human blood types

In the early 1900s, the Austrian immunologist Karl Landsteiner discovered that all blood is not the same. Blood serum drawn from one person often clumped when mixed with the blood cells of another. The clumping was caused by different antigens, proteins, and carbo-hydrates that trigger antibodies and fight infection. Landsteiner classified blood types based on the presence or absence of the antigens A, B, and Rh in red blood cells. The Venn diagram in Figure 7.23 contains eight regions representing the eight common blood groups.

In the Venn diagram, blood with the Rh antigen is labeled positive and blood lacking the Rh antigen is labeled negative. The region where the three circles intersect represents type AB$^+$, indicating that a person with this blood type has the antigens A, B, and Rh. Observe that type O blood (both positive and negative) lacks A and B antigens. Type O$^-$ lacks all three antigens, A, B, and Rh.

In blood transfusions, the recipient must have all or more of the antigens present in the donor's blood. This discovery rescued surgery patients from random, often lethal, transfusions. This knowledge made the massive blood drives during World War I possible. Eventually, it made the modern blood bank possible as well.

EXERCISE SET 7.4 ●●●●●●

• Practice Exercises

In Exercises 1–12, let

$$U = \{1, 2, 3, 4, 5, 6, 7\}$$
$$A = \{1, 3, 5, 7\}$$
$$B = \{1, 2, 3\}$$
$$C = \{2, 3, 4, 5, 6\}.$$

Find each of the following sets.

1. $A \cup (B \cap C)$
2. $A \cap (B \cup C)$
3. $(A \cup B) \cap (A \cup C)$
4. $(A \cap B) \cup (A \cap C)$
5. $A' \cap (B \cup C')$
6. $C' \cap (A \cup B')$
7. $(A' \cap B) \cup (A' \cap C')$
8. $(C' \cap A) \cup (C' \cap B')$
9. $(A \cup B \cup C)'$
10. $(A \cap B \cap C)'$
11. $(A \cup B)' \cap C$
12. $(B \cup C)' \cap A$

In Exercises 13–24, let

$$U = \{a, b, c, d, e, f, g, h\}$$
$$A = \{a, g, h\}$$
$$B = \{b, g, h\}$$
$$C = \{b, c, d, e, f\}.$$

Find each of the following sets.

13. $A \cup (B \cap C)$
14. $A \cap (B \cup C)$
15. $(A \cup B) \cap (A \cup C)$
16. $(A \cap B) \cup (A \cap C)$
17. $A' \cap (B \cup C')$
18. $C' \cap (A \cup B')$

19. $(A' \cap B) \cup (A' \cap C')$
20. $(C' \cap A) \cup (C' \cap B')$
21. $(A \cup B \cup C)'$
22. $(A \cap B \cap C)'$
23. $(A \cup B)' \cap C$
24. $(B \cup C)' \cap A$

In Exercises 25–32, use the Venn diagram shown to answer each question.

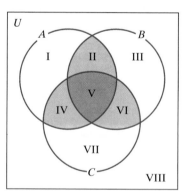

25. Which regions represent set B?
26. Which regions represent set C?
27. Which regions represent $A \cup C$?
28. Which regions represent $B \cup C$?
29. Which regions represent $A \cap B$?
30. Which regions represent $A \cap C$?
31. Which regions represent B'?
32. Which regions represent C'?

In Exercises 33–44, use the Venn diagram to represent each set in roster form.

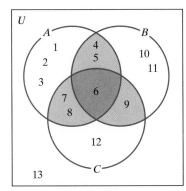

33. A

34. B

35. $A \cup B$

36. $B \cup C$

37. $(A \cup B)'$

38. $(B \cup C)'$

39. $A \cap B$

40. $A \cap C$

41. $A \cap B \cap C$

42. $A \cup B \cup C$

43. $(A \cap B \cap C)'$

44. $(A \cup B \cup C)'$

In Exercises 45–48, construct a Venn diagram illustrating the given sets.

45. $A = \{4, 5, 6, 8\}, B = \{1, 2, 4, 5, 6, 7\},$
$C = \{3, 4, 7\}, U = \{1, 2, 3, 4, 5, 6, 7, 8, 9\}$

46. $A = \{a, e, h, i\}, B = \{b, c, e, f, h, i\},$
$C = \{e, f, g\}, U = \{a, b, c, d, e, f, g, h, i\}$

47. $A = \{+, -, \times, \div, \rightarrow, \leftrightarrow\}$
$B = \{\times, \div, \rightarrow\}$
$C = \{\wedge, \vee, \rightarrow, \leftrightarrow\}$
$U = \{+, -, \times, \div, \wedge, \vee, \rightarrow, \leftrightarrow, \sim\}$

48. $A = \{x_3, x_9\}$
$B = \{x_1, x_2, x_3, x_5, x_6\}$
$C = \{x_3, x_4, x_5, x_6, x_9\}$
$U = \{x_1, x_2, x_3, x_4, x_5, x_6, x_7, x_8, x_9\}$

Use the Venn diagram shown to solve Exercises 49–52.

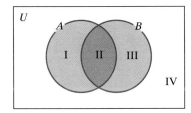

49. a. Which region is represented by $A \cap B$?

b. Which region is represented by $B \cap A$?

c. Based on parts (a) and (b), what can you conclude?

50. a. Which regions are represented by $A \cup B$?

b. Which regions are represented by $B \cup A$?

c. Based on parts (a) and (b), what can you conclude?

51. a. Which region(s) is/are represented by $(A \cap B)'$?

b. Which region(s) is/are represented by $A' \cap B'$?

c. Based on parts (a) and (b), are $(A \cap B)'$ and $A' \cap B'$ equal for all sets A and B? Explain your answer.

52. a. Which region(s) is/are represented by $(A \cup B)'$?

b. Which region(s) is/are represented by $A' \cup B'$?

c. Based on parts (a) and (b), are $(A \cup B)'$ and $A' \cup B'$ equal for all sets A and B? Explain your answer.

In Exercises 53–58, use the Venn diagram for Exercises 49–52 in the previous column to determine whether the given sets are equal for all sets A and B.

53. $A' \cup B, \quad A \cap B'$

54. $A' \cap B, \quad A \cup B'$

55. $(A \cup B)', \quad (A \cap B)'$

56. $(A \cup B)', \quad A' \cap B$

57. $(A' \cap B)', \quad A \cup B'$

58. $(A \cup B')', \quad A' \cap B$

Use the Venn diagram shown to solve Exercises 59–62.

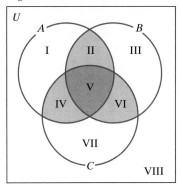

59. a. Which regions are represented by $(A \cap B) \cup C$?

b. Which regions are represented by $(A \cup C) \cap (B \cup C)$?

c. Based on parts (a) and (b), what can you conclude?

60. a. Which regions are represented by $(A \cup B) \cap C$?

b. Which regions are represented by $(A \cap C) \cup (B \cap C)$?

c. Based on parts (a) and (b), what can you conclude?

61. a. Which regions are represented by $A \cap (B \cup C)$?

b. Which regions are represented by $A \cup (B \cap C)$?

c. Based on parts (a) and (b), are $A \cap (B \cup C)$ and $A \cup (B \cap C)$ equal for all sets A, B, and C? Explain your answer.

62. a. Which regions are represented by $C \cup (B \cap A)$?

b. Which regions are represented by $C \cap (B \cup A)$?

c. Based on parts (a) and (b), are $C \cup (B \cap A)$ and $C \cap (B \cup A)$ equal for all sets A, B, and C? Explain your answer.

In Exercises 63–68, use the Venn diagram shown above to determine which statements are true for all sets A, B, and C, and, consequently, are theorems.

63. $A \cap (B \cup C) = (A \cap B) \cup C$

64. $A \cup (B \cap C) = (A \cup B) \cap C$

65. $B \cup (A \cap C) = (A \cup B) \cap (B \cup C)$

66. $B \cap (A \cup C) = (A \cap B) \cup (B \cap C)$

67. $A \cap (B \cup C)' = A \cap (B' \cap C')$

68. $A \cup (B \cap C)' = A \cup (B' \cup C')$

• Practice Plus

69. a. Let $A = \{c\}, B = \{a, b\}, C = \{b, d\}$, and $U = \{a, b, c, d, e, f\}$. Find $A \cup (B' \cap C')$ and $(A \cup B') \cap (A \cup C')$.

b. Let $A = \{1, 3, 7, 8\}, B = \{2, 3, 6, 7\}, C = \{4, 6, 7, 8\}$, and $U = \{1, 2, 3, \ldots, 8\}$. Find $A \cup (B' \cap C')$ and $(A \cup B') \cap (A \cup C')$.

c. Based on your results in parts (a) and (b), use inductive reasoning to write a conjecture that relates $A \cup (B' \cap C')$ and $(A \cup B') \cap (A \cup C')$.

d. Use deductive reasoning to determine whether your conjecture in part (c) is a theorem.

70. a. Let $A = \{3\}, B = \{1, 2\}, C = \{2, 4\}$, and $U = \{1, 2, 3, 4, 5, 6\}$. Find $(A \cup B)' \cap C$ and $A' \cap (B' \cap C)$.

b. Let $A = \{d, f, g, h\}, B = \{a, c, f, h\}, C = \{c, e, g, h\}$, and $U = \{a, b, c, \ldots, h\}$. Find $(A \cup B)' \cap C$ and $A' \cap (B' \cap C)$.

c. Based on your results in parts (a) and (b), use inductive reasoning to write a conjecture that relates $(A \cup B)' \cap C$ and $A' \cap (B' \cap C)$.

d. Use deductive reasoning to determine whether your conjecture in part (c) is a theorem.

In Exercises 71–78, use the symbols $A, B, C, \cap, \cup,$ and $',$ as necessary, to describe each shaded region. More than one correct symbolic description may be possible.

71.

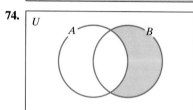

72.

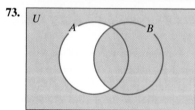

73.

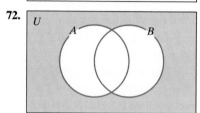

74.

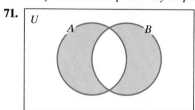

75.

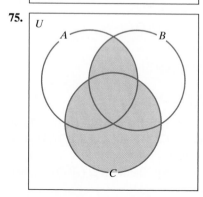

76.

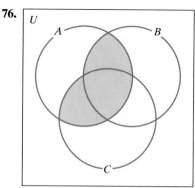

77.

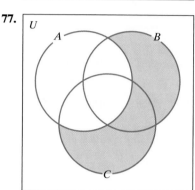

78.

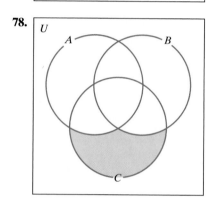

• Application Exercises

A math tutor working with a small study group has classified students in the group by whether or not they scored 90% or above on each of three tests. The results are shown in the Venn diagram.

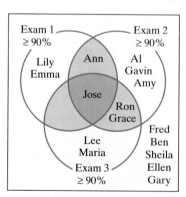

In Exercises 79–90, use the Venn diagram to represent each set in roster form.

79. The set of students who scored 90% or above on exam 2

80. The set of students who scored 90% or above on exam 3

81. The set of students who scored 90% or above on exam 1 and exam 3

82. The set of students who scored 90% or above on exam 1 and exam 2

83. The set of students who scored 90% or above on exam 1 and not on exam 2

84. The set of students who scored 90% or above on exam 3 and not on exam 1

85. The set of students who scored 90% or above on exam 1 or not on exam 2

86. The set of students who scored 90% or above on exam 3 or not on exam 1

87. The set of students who scored 90% or above on *exactly one* test

88. The set of students who scored 90% or above on *at least two* tests

89. The set of students who scored 90% or above on exam 2 and not on exam 1 and exam 3

90. The set of students who scored 90% or above on exam 1 and not on exam 2 and exam 3

91. Use the Venn diagram shown at the bottom of the previous page to describe a set of students that is the empty set.

92. Use the Venn diagram shown at the bottom of the previous page to describe the set {Fred, Ben, Sheila, Ellen, Gary}.

The chart shows the most popular shows on television in 2003, 2004, and 2005.

MOST POPULAR TELEVISION SHOWS

2003	2004	2005
1. *Friends*	1. *Friends*	1. *CSI*
2. *CSI*	2. *CSI*	2. *American Idol*
3. *E.R.*	3. *American Idol*	3. *Desperate Housewives*
4. *Everybody Loves Raymond*	4. *Apprentice*	4. *Without a Trace*
5. *Law and Order*	5. *Desperate Housewives*	5. *Survivor*
6. *Survivor*	6. *E.R.*	6. *Grey's Anatomy*

Source: Nielsen Media Research

In Exercises 93–98, use the Venn diagram to indicate in which region, I through VIII, each television show should be placed.

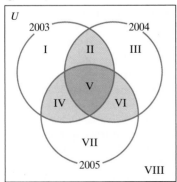

93. *Friends*

94. *Desperate Housewives*

95. *CSI*

96. *60 Minutes*

97. *Everybody Loves Raymond*

98. *Grey's Anatomy*

The chart shows the top single recordings of all time.

TOP SINGLE RECORDINGS

Title	Artist or Group	Sales	Year Released
"Candle in the Wind"	Elton John	37 million	1997
"White Christmas"	Bing Crosby	30 million	1942
"Rock Around the Clock"	Bill Haley and His Comets	17 million	1954
"I Want to Hold Your Hand"	The Beatles	12 million	1963
"It's Now or Never"	Elvis Presley	10 million	1960
"Hey Jude"	The Beatles	10 million	1968
"I Will Always Love You"	Whitney Houston	10 million	1992
"Hound Dog"	Elvis Presley	9 million	1956
"Diana"	Paul Anka	9 million	1957
"I'm a Believer"	The Monkees	8 million	1966

Source: RIAA

In Exercises 99–104, use the Venn diagram to indicate in which region, I through VIII, each recording should be placed.

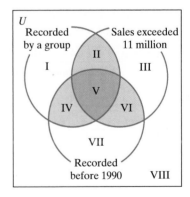

99. "Candle in the Wind"

100. "White Christmas"

101. "I Want to Hold Your Hand"

102. "Hey Jude"

103. "Diana"

104. "I'm a Believer"

105. The chart shows the ten places where the greatest number of people have been attacked by sharks.

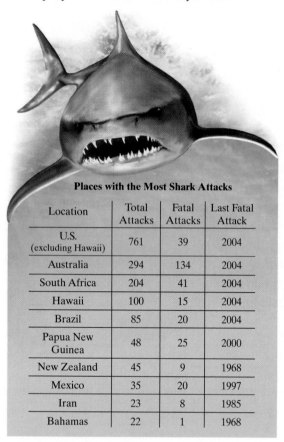

Places with the Most Shark Attacks

Location	Total Attacks	Fatal Attacks	Last Fatal Attack
U.S. (excluding Hawaii)	761	39	2004
Australia	294	134	2004
South Africa	204	41	2004
Hawaii	100	15	2004
Brazil	85	20	2004
Papua New Guinea	48	25	2000
New Zealand	45	9	1968
Mexico	35	20	1997
Iran	23	8	1985
Bahamas	22	1	1968

Source: International Shark Attack File

Let U = the set of locations shown in the chart, A = the set of locations with at least 100 total attacks, B = the set of locations with no more than 40 fatal attacks, and C = the set of locations where the last fatal attack occurred in 2004. Use the information in the chart to construct a Venn diagram that illustrates these sets.

106. The chart shows the ten films nominated for the most Oscars.

FILMS WITH THE MOST OSCAR NOMINATIONS

Film	Nominations	Awards	Year
All About Eve	14	6	1950
Titanic	14	11	1997
Gone with the Wind	13	8	1939
From Here to Eternity	13	8	1953
Shakespeare in Love	13	7	1998
Mary Poppins	13	5	1964
Who's Afraid of Virginia Woolf?	13	5	1966
Forrest Gump	13	6	1994
The Lord of the Rings: The Fellowship of the Ring	13	4	2001
Chicago	13	6	2004

Source: Academy of Motion Picture Arts and Sciences

Using abbreviated film titles, let U = {*Eve, Titanic, Wind, Eternity, Love, Poppins, Woolf, Gump, Ring, Chicago*}, A = the set of films nominated for 14 Oscars, B = the set of films that won at least 7 Oscars, and C = the set of films that won Oscars after 1965. Use the information in the chart to construct a Venn diagram that illustrates these sets.

• Writing in Mathematics

107. If you are given four sets, A, B, C, and U, describe what is involved in determining $(A \cup B)' \cap C$. Be as specific as possible in your description.

108. Describe how a Venn diagram can be used to prove that $(A \cup B)'$ and $A' \cap B'$ are equal sets.

• Critical Thinking Exercises

The eight blood types discussed in the Blitzer Bonus on page 416 are shown once again in the Venn diagram. In blood transfusions, the set of antigens in a donor's blood must be a subset of the set of antigens in a recipient's blood. Thus, the recipient must have all or more of the antigens present in the donor's blood. Use this information to solve Exercises 109–112.

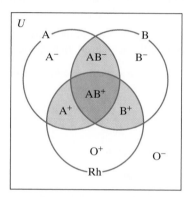

Human blood types

109. What is the blood type of a universal recipient?

110. What is the blood type of a universal donor?

111. Can an A$^+$ person donate blood to an A$^-$ person?

112. Can an A$^-$ person donate blood to an A$^+$ person?

• Group Exercises

113. Each group member should find out his or her blood type. (If you cannot obtain this information, select a blood type that you find appealing!) Read the introduction to Exercises 109–112. Referring to the Venn diagram for these exercises, each group member should determine all other group members to whom blood can be donated and from whom it can be received.

114. The group should define three sets, each of which categorizes U, the set of students in the group, in different ways. Examples include the set of students with blonde hair, the set of students no more than 23 years old, and the set of students whose major is undecided. Once you have defined the sets, construct a Venn diagram with three intersecting sets and eight regions. Each student should determine which region he or she belongs to. Illustrate the sets by writing each first name in the appropriate region.

SECTION 7.5 • SURVEY PROBLEMS

OBJECTIVES

1. Use Venn diagrams to visualize a survey's results.

2. Use survey results to complete Venn diagrams and answer questions about the survey.

Mexico's 2006 election, its closest-ever race for president, exposed an emerging trend in Latin America: a sharpening divide between the rich and the poor. Although Mexico's economy expanded by 4.4% in 2004 and 3% in 2005, at the end of 2005, almost half of the country's 107 million people still lived in poverty. (*Source: Newsweek*, July 17, 2006) Figure 7.24 shows that Mexicans tend to see societal injustice, rather than personal laziness, as the primary cause of poverty.

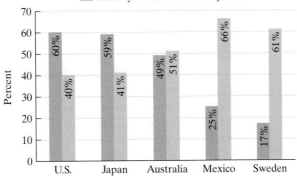

FIGURE 7.24 Percentages for each country may not add to 100% because less frequently identified primary causes of poverty were omitted from the graph.
Source: Ronald Inglehart et al., *World Values Surveys and European Values Surveys*

Suppose a survey is taken that asks randomly selected adults in the United States and Mexico the following question:

Do you agree or disagree that the primary cause of poverty is societal injustice?

In this section, you will see how sets and Venn diagrams are used to tabulate information collected in such a survey. In survey problems, it is helpful to remember that **and** means **intersection**, **or** means **union**, and **not** means **complement**. Furthermore, *but* means the same thing as *and*. Thus, **but** means **intersection**.

1 | Use Venn diagrams to visualize a survey's results.

Visualizing the Results of a Survey

In Section 7.1, we defined the cardinal number of set A, denoted by $n(A)$, as the number of elements in set A. Venn diagrams are helpful in determining a set's cardinality.

EXAMPLE 1	USING A VENN DIAGRAM TO VISUALIZE THE RESULTS OF A SURVEY

We return to the campus survey in which students were asked two questions:

Would you be willing to donate blood?
Would you be willing to help serve a free breakfast to blood donors?

Set A represents the set of students willing to donate blood. Set B represents the set of students willing to help serve breakfast to donors. The survey

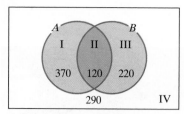

A: Set of students willing to
  donate blood
B: Set of students willing to
  serve breakfast to donors

FIGURE 7.25 Results of a survey

results are summarized in Figure 7.25. Use the diagram to answer the following questions:

a. How many students are willing to donate blood?
b. How many students are willing to help serve a free breakfast to blood donors?
c. How many students are willing to donate blood and serve breakfast?
d. How many students are willing to donate blood or serve breakfast?
e. How many students are willing to donate blood but not serve breakfast?
f. How many students are willing to serve breakfast but not donate blood?
g. How many students are neither willing to donate blood nor serve breakfast?
h. How many students were surveyed?

SOLUTION

a. The number of students willing to donate blood can be determined by adding the numbers in regions I and II. Thus, $n(A) = 370 + 120 = 490$. There are 490 students willing to donate blood.

b. The number of students willing to help serve a free breakfast to blood donors can be determined by adding the numbers in regions II and III. Thus, $n(B) = 120 + 220 = 340$. There are 340 students willing to help serve breakfast.

c. The number of students willing to donate blood and serve breakfast appears in region II, the region representing the intersection of the two sets. Thus, $n(A \cap B) = 120$. There are 120 students willing to donate blood and serve breakfast.

d. The number of students willing to donate blood or serve breakfast is found by adding the numbers in regions I, II, and III, representing the union of the two sets. We see that $n(A \cup B) = 370 + 120 + 220 = 710$. Therefore, 710 students in the survey are willing to donate blood or serve breakfast.

e. The region representing students who are willing to donate blood but not serve breakfast, $A \cap B'$, is region I. We see that 370 of the students surveyed are willing to donate blood but not serve breakfast.

f. Region III represents students willing to serve breakfast but not donate blood: $B \cap A'$. We see that 220 students surveyed are willing to help serve breakfast but not donate blood.

g. Students who are neither willing to donate blood nor serve breakfast, $A' \cap B'$, fall within the universal set, but outside circles A and B. These students fall in region IV, where the Venn diagram indicates that there are 290 elements. There are 290 students in the survey who are neither willing to donate blood nor serve breakfast.

h. We can find the number of students surveyed by adding the numbers in regions I, II, III, and IV. Thus, $n(U) = 370 + 120 + 220 + 290 = 1000$. There were 1000 students surveyed.

○

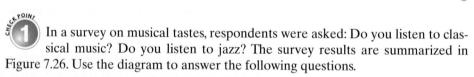

In a survey on musical tastes, respondents were asked: Do you listen to classical music? Do you listen to jazz? The survey results are summarized in Figure 7.26. Use the diagram to answer the following questions.

a. How many respondents listened to classical music?
b. How many respondents listened to jazz?
c. How many respondents listened to both classical music and jazz?
d. How many respondents listened to classical music or jazz?
e. How many respondents listened to classical music but not jazz?
f. How many respondents listened to jazz but not classical music?
g. How many respondents listened to neither classical music nor jazz?
h. How many people were surveyed?

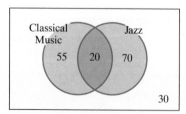

FIGURE 7.26

2
Use survey results to complete Venn diagrams and answer questions about the survey.

Solving Survey Problems

Venn diagrams are used to solve problems involving surveys. Here are the steps needed to solve survey problems:

> ### SOLVING SURVEY PROBLEMS
> 1. Use the survey's description to define sets and draw a Venn diagram.
> 2. Use the survey's results to determine the cardinality for each region in the Venn diagram. **Start with the intersection of the sets, the innermost region, and work outward.**
> 3. Use the completed Venn diagram to answer the problem's questions.

EXAMPLE 2 SURVEYING PEOPLE'S ATTITUDES

A survey is taken that asks 2000 randomly selected U.S. and Mexican adults the following question:

Do you agree or disagree that the primary cause of poverty is societal injustice?

The results of the survey showed that

1060 people agreed with the statement.
400 Americans agreed with the statement.

Source: World Values Surveys

If half the adults surveyed were Americans,

a. How many Mexicans agreed with the statement?
b. How many Mexicans disagreed with the statement?

SOLUTION

Step 1. Define sets and draw a Venn diagram. The Venn diagram in Figure 7.27 shows two sets. Set $U.S.$ is the set of Americans surveyed. Set A (labeled "Agree") is the set of people surveyed who agreed with the statement. By representing the Americans surveyed with circle $U.S.$, we do not need a separate circle for the Mexicans. The group of people outside circle $U.S.$ must be the set of Mexicans. Similarly, by visualizing the set of people who agreed with the statement as circle A, we do not need a separate circle for those who disagreed. The group of people outside the A (Agree) circle must be the set of people disagreeing with the statement.

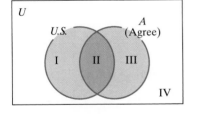

FIGURE 7.27

Step 2. Determine the cardinality for each region in the Venn diagram, starting with the innermost region and working outward. We are given the following cardinalities:

There were 2000 people surveyed: $n(U) = 2000$.
Half the people surveyed were Americans: $n(U.S.) = 1000$.
The number of people who agreed with the statement was 1060: $n(A) = 1060$.
There were 400 Americans who agreed with the statement: $n(U.S. \cap A) = 400$.

Now let's use these numbers to determine the cardinality of each region, starting with region II, moving outward to regions I and III, and ending with region IV.

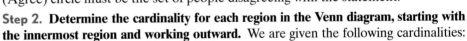

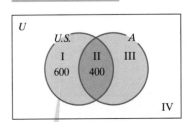

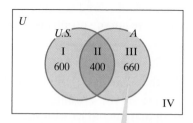

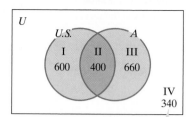

Is the Primary Cause of Poverty Societal Injustice?

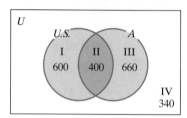

FIGURE 7.28

Step 3. Use the completed Venn diagram to answer the problem's questions. The completed Venn diagram that illustrates the survey's results is shown in Figure 7.28.

a. The Mexicans who agreed with the statement are those members of the set of people who agreed who are not Americans, shown in region III. This means that 660 Mexicans agreed that societal injustice is the primary cause of poverty.

b. The Mexicans who disagreed with the statement can be found outside the circles of people who agreed and people who are Americans. This corresponds to region IV, whose cardinality is 340. Thus, 340 Mexicans disagreed that societal injustice is the primary cause of poverty.

CHECK POINT **2** In a Gallup poll, 2000 U.S. adults were selected at random and asked to agree or disagree with the following statement:

Job opportunities for women are not equal to those for men.

The results of the survey showed that

1190 people agreed with the statement.

700 women agreed with the statement.

Source: The People's Almanac

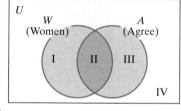

If half the people surveyed were women,

a. How many men agreed with the statement?

b. How many men disagreed with the statement?

When tabulating survey results, more than two circles within a Venn diagram are often needed. For example, consider a *Time*/CNN poll that sought to determine how Americans felt about reserving a certain number of college scholarships exclusively for minorities and women. Respondents were asked the following question:

Do you agree or disagree with the following statement: Colleges should reserve a certain number of scholarships exclusively for minorities and women?

Source: Time Almanac

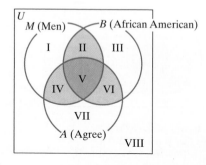

FIGURE 7.29

Suppose that we want the respondents to the poll to be identified by gender (man or woman), ethnicity (African American or other), and whether or not they agreed with the statement. A Venn diagram into which the results of the survey can be tabulated is shown in Figure 7.29.

Based on our work in Example 2, we only used one circle in the Venn diagram to indicate the gender of the respondent. We used M for men, so the set of women respondents, M', consists of the regions outside circle M. Similarly, we used B for the set of African-American respondents, so the regions outside circle B account for all other ethnicities. Finally, we used A for the set of respondents who agreed with the statement. Those who disagreed lie outside circle A.

In the next example, we create a Venn diagram with three intersecting sets to illustrate a survey's results. In our final example, we use this Venn diagram to answer questions about the survey.

EXAMPLE 3   CONSTRUCTING A VENN DIAGRAM FOR A SURVEY

Sixty people were contacted and responded to a movie survey. The following information was obtained:

a. 6 people liked comedies, dramas, and science fiction.
b. 13 people liked comedies and dramas.
c. 10 people liked comedies and science fiction.
d. 11 people liked dramas and science fiction.
e. 26 people liked comedies.
f. 21 people liked dramas.
g. 25 people liked science fiction.

Use a Venn diagram to illustrate the survey's results.

SOLUTION The set of people surveyed is a universal set with 60 elements containing three subsets:

$$C = \text{the set of those who like comedies}$$
$$D = \text{the set of those who like dramas}$$
$$S = \text{the set of those who like science fiction.}$$

We draw these sets in Figure 7.30. Now let's use the numbers in (a) through (g), as well as the fact that 60 people were surveyed, which we call condition (h), to determine the cardinality of each region in the Venn diagram.

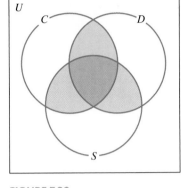

FIGURE 7.30

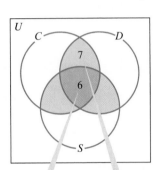

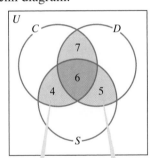

(a) 6 people liked comedies, drama, and science fiction: $n(C \cap D \cap S) = 6$.

(b) 13 people liked comedies and drama: $n(C \cap D) = 13$. With 6 counted, there are $13 - 6 = 7$ people in this region.

(c) 10 people liked comedies and science fiction: $n(C \cap S) = 10$. With 6 counted, there are $10 - 6 = 4$ people in this region.

(d) 11 people liked drama and science fiction: $n(D \cap S) = 11$. With 6 counted, there are $11 - 6 = 5$ people in this region.

(e) 26 people liked comedies: $n(C) = 26$. With $7 + 6 + 4 = 17$ counted, there are $26 - 17 = 9$ people in this region.

(f) 21 people liked dramas: $n(D) = 21$. With $7 + 6 + 5 = 18$ counted, there are $21 - 18 = 3$ people in this region.

(g) 25 people liked science fiction: $n(S) = 25$. With $4 + 6 + 5 = 15$ counted, there are $25 - 15 = 10$ people in this region.

(h) 60 people were surveyed: $n(U) = 60$. With $9 + 7 + 3 + 4 + 6 + 5 + 10 = 44$ counted, there are $60 - 44 = 16$ people in this region.

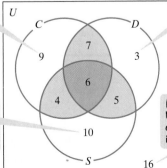

With a cardinality in each region, we have completed the Venn diagram that illustrates the survey's results.

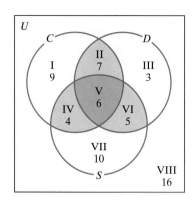

U

FIGURE 7.31

CHECK POINT 3 A survey of 250 memorabilia collectors showed the following results: 108 collected baseball cards. 92 collected comic books. 62 collected stamps. 29 collected baseball cards and comic books. 5 collected baseball cards and stamps. 2 collected comic books and stamps. 2 collected all three types of memorabilia. Use a Venn diagram to illustrate the survey's results.

EXAMPLE 4   USING A SURVEY'S VENN DIAGRAM

The Venn diagram in Figure 7.31 shows the results of the movie survey in Example 3. How many of those surveyed liked

a. comedies, but neither dramas nor science fiction?
b. dramas and science fiction, but not comedies?
c. dramas or science fiction, but not comedies?
d. exactly one movie style?
e. at least two movie styles?
f. none of the movie styles?

SOLUTION

a. Those surveyed who liked comedies, but neither dramas nor science fiction, are represented in region I. There are 9 people in this category.

$$C \cap (D' \cap S')$$

b. Those surveyed who liked dramas and science fiction, but not comedies, are represented in region VI. There are 5 people in this category.

$$(D \cap S) \cap C'$$

c. We are interested in those surveyed who liked dramas or science fiction, but not comedies:

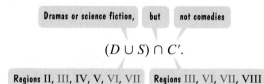

Dramas or science fiction, but not comedies

$$(D \cup S) \cap C'.$$

Regions II, III, IV, V, VI, VII   Regions III, VI, VII, VIII

The intersection of the regions in the voice balloons consists of the common regions shown in red, III, VI, and VII. There are $3 + 5 + 10 = 18$ elements in these regions. There are 18 people who liked dramas or science fiction, but not comedies.

d. Those surveyed who liked exactly one movie style are represented in regions I, III, and VII. There are $9 + 3 + 10 = 22$ elements in these regions. Thus, 22 people liked exactly one movie style.

e. Those surveyed who liked at least two movie styles are people who liked two or more types of movies. People who liked two movie styles are represented in regions II, IV, and VI. Those who liked three movie styles are represented in region V. Thus, we add the number of elements in regions II, IV, V, and VI: $7 + 4 + 6 + 5 = 22$. Thus, 22 people liked at least two movie styles.

f. Those surveyed who liked none of the movie styles are represented in region VIII. There are 16 people in this category.

CHECK POINT 4 Use the Venn diagram you constructed in Check Point 3 to determine how many of those surveyed collected

a. comic books, but neither baseball cards nor stamps.
b. baseball cards and stamps, but not comic books.
c. baseball cards or stamps, but not comic books.
d. exactly two types of memorabilia.
e. at least one type of memorabilia.
f. none of the types of memorabilia.

EXERCISE SET 7.5 ●●●●●○○

• Practice Exercises

Use the accompanying Venn diagram, which shows the number of elements in regions I through IV, to answer the questions in Exercises 1–8.

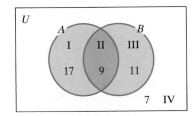

1. How many elements belong to set A?
2. How many elements belong to set B?
3. How many elements belong to set A but not set B?
4. How many elements belong to set B but not set A?
5. How many elements belong to set A or set B?
6. How many elements belong to set A and set B?
7. How many elements belong to neither set A nor set B?
8. How many elements are there in the universal set?

Use the accompanying Venn diagram, which shows the number of elements in region II, to answer Exercises 9–10.

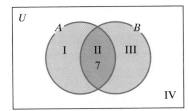

9. If $n(A) = 21$, $n(B) = 29$, and $n(U) = 48$, find the number of elements in each of regions I, III, and IV.
10. If $n(A) = 23$, $n(B) = 27$, and $n(U) = 53$, find the number of elements in each of regions I, III, and IV.

Use the accompanying Venn diagram, which shows the cardinality of each region, to answer Exercises 11–26.

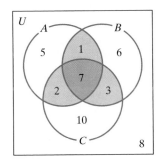

11. How many elements belong to set B?
12. How many elements belong to set A?
13. How many elements belong to set A but not set C?
14. How many elements belong to set B but not set A?
15. How many elements belong to set A or set C?
16. How many elements belong to set A or set B?
17. How many elements belong to set A and set C?
18. How many elements belong to set A and set B?

19. How many elements belong to set B and set C, but not to set A?
20. How many elements belong to set A and set C, but not to set B?
21. How many elements belong to set B or set C, but not to set A?
22. How many elements belong to set A or set C, but not to set B?
23. Considering sets A, B, and C, how many elements belong to exactly one of these sets?
24. Considering sets A, B, and C, how many elements belong to exactly two of these sets?
25. Considering sets A, B, and C, how many elements belong to at least one of these sets?
26. Considering sets A, B, and C, how many elements belong to at least two of these sets?

The accompanying Venn diagram shows the number of elements in region V. In Exercises 27–28, use the given cardinalities to determine the number of elements in each of the other seven regions.

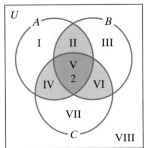

27. $n(U) = 30$, $n(A) = 11$, $n(B) = 8$, $n(C) = 14$, $n(A \cap B) = 3$, $n(A \cap C) = 5$, $n(B \cap C) = 3$
28. $n(U) = 32$, $n(A) = 21$, $n(B) = 15$, $n(C) = 14$, $n(A \cap B) = 6$, $n(A \cap C) = 7$, $n(B \cap C) = 8$

• Practice Plus

In Exercises 29–32, use the Venn diagram and the given conditions to determine the number of elements in each region, or explain why the conditions are impossible to meet.

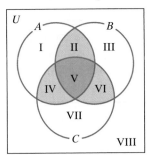

29. $n(U) = 38$, $n(A) = 26$, $n(B) = 21$, $n(C) = 18$, $n(A \cap B) = 17$, $n(A \cap C) = 11$, $n(B \cap C) = 8$, $n(A \cap B \cap C) = 7$
30. $n(U) = 42$, $n(A) = 26$, $n(B) = 22$, $n(C) = 25$, $n(A \cap B) = 17$, $n(A \cap C) = 11$, $n(B \cap C) = 9$, $n(A \cap B \cap C) = 5$

(In Exercises 31–32, continue to refer to the Venn diagram at the bottom of the previous page.)

31. $n(U) = 40, n(A) = 10, n(B) = 11, n(C) = 12,$
$n(A \cap B) = 6, n(A \cap C) = 9, n(B \cap C) = 7,$
$n(A \cap B \cap C) = 2$

32. $n(U) = 25, n(A) = 8, n(B) = 9, n(C) = 10,$
$n(A \cap B) = 6, n(A \cap C) = 9, n(B \cap C) = 8,$
$n(A \cap B \cap C) = 5$

• Application Exercises

As discussed in the text on page 424, a poll asked respondents if they agreed with the statement

Colleges should reserve a certain number of scholarships exclusively for minorities and women.

Hypothetical results of the poll are tabulated in the Venn diagram. Use these cardinalities to solve Exercises 33–38.

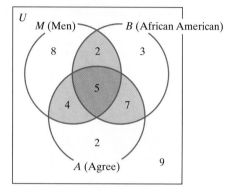

33. How many respondents agreed with the statement?

34. How many respondents disagreed with the statement?

35. How many women agreed with the statement?

36. How many people who are not African American agreed with the statement?

37. How many women who are not African American disagreed with the statement?

38. How many men who are not African American disagreed with the statement?

39. A pollster conducting a telephone poll of a city's residents asked two questions:

   1. Do you currently smoke cigarettes?

   2. Regardless of your answer to question 1, would you support a ban on smoking in all city parks?

   a. Construct a Venn diagram that allows the respondents to the poll to be identified by whether or not they smoke cigarettes and whether or not they support the ban.

   b. Write the letter b in every region of the diagram that represents smokers polled who support the ban.

   c. Write the letter c in every region of the diagram that represents nonsmokers polled who support the ban.

   d. Write the letter d in every region of the diagram that represents nonsmokers polled who do not support the ban.

40. A pollster conducting a telephone poll at a college campus asked students two questions:

   1. Do you binge drink three or more times per month?

   2. Regardless of your answer to question 1, are you frequently behind in your school work?

   a. Construct a Venn diagram that allows the respondents to the poll to be identified by whether or not they binge drink and whether or not they frequently fall behind in school work.

   b. Write the letter b in every region of the diagram that represents binge drinkers who are frequently behind in school work.

   c. Write the letter c in every region of the diagram that represents students polled who do not binge drink but who are frequently behind in school work.

   d. Write the letter d in every region of the diagram that represents students polled who do not binge drink and who do not frequently fall behind in their school work.

41. A pollster conducting a telephone poll asked three questions:

   1. Are you religious?

   2. Have you spent time with a person during his or her last days of a terminal illness?

   3. Should assisted suicide be an option for terminally ill people?

   a. Construct a Venn diagram with three circles that can assist the pollster in tabulating the responses to the three questions.

   b. Write the letter b in every region of the diagram that represents all religious persons polled who are not in favor of assisted suicide for the terminally ill.

   c. Write the letter c in every region of the diagram that represents the people polled who do not consider themselves religious, who have not spent time with a terminally ill person during his or her last days, and who are in favor of assisted suicide for the terminally ill.

   d. Write the letter d in every region of the diagram that represents the people polled who consider themselves religious, who have not spent time with a terminally ill person during his or her last days, and who are not in favor of assisted suicide for the terminally ill.

   e. Write the letter e in a region of the Venn diagram other than those in parts (b)–(d) and then describe who in the poll is represented by this region.

42. A poll asks respondents the following question:

   Do you agree or disagree with this statement: In order to address the trend in diminishing male enrollment, colleges should begin special efforts to recruit men?

   a. Construct a Venn diagram with three circles that allows the respondents to be identified by gender (man or woman), education level (college or no college), and whether or not they agreed with the statement.

   b. Write the letter b in every region of the diagram that represents men with a college education who agreed with the statement.

   c. Write the letter c in every region of the diagram that represents women who disagreed with the statement.

   d. Write the letter d in every region of the diagram that represents women without a college education who agreed with the statement.

   e. Write the letter e in a region of the Venn diagram other than those in parts (b)–(d) and then describe who in the poll is represented by this region.

In Exercises 43–48, construct a Venn diagram and determine the cardinality for each region. Use the completed Venn diagram to answer the questions.

43. A survey of 75 college students was taken to determine where they got the news about what's going on in the world. Of those surveyed, 29 students got the news from newspapers, 43 from television, and 7 from both newspapers and television.

Of those surveyed,

a. How many got the news from only newspapers?

b. How many got the news from only television?

c. How many got the news from newspapers or television?

d. How many did not get the news from either newspapers or television?

44. A survey of 120 college students was taken at registration. Of those surveyed, 75 students registered for a math course, 65 for an English course, and 40 for both math and English.

Of those surveyed,

a. How many registered only for a math course?

b. How many registered only for an English course?

c. How many registered for a math course or an English course?

d. How many did not register for either a math course or an English course?

45. A survey of 80 college students was taken to determine the musical styles they listened to. Forty-two students listened to rock, 34 to classical, and 27 to jazz. Twelve students listened to rock and jazz, 14 to rock and classical, and 10 to classical and jazz. Seven students listened to all three musical styles.

Of those surveyed,

a. How many listened to only rock music?

b. How many listened to classical and jazz, but not rock?

c. How many listened to classical or jazz, but not rock?

d. How many listened to music in exactly one of the musical styles?

e. How many listened to music in at least two of the musical styles?

f. How many did not listen to any of the musical styles?

46. A survey of 180 college men was taken to determine participation in various campus activities. Forty-three students were in fraternities, 52 participated in campus sports, and 35 participated in various campus tutorial programs. Thirteen students participated in fraternities and sports, 14 in sports and tutorial programs, and 12 in fraternities and tutorial programs. Five students participated in all three activities.

Of those surveyed,

a. How many participated in only campus sports?

b. How many participated in fraternities and sports, but not tutorial programs?

c. How many participated in fraternities or sports, but not tutorial programs?

d. How many participated in exactly one of these activities?

e. How many participated in at least two of these activities?

f. How many did not participate in any of the three activities?

47. An anonymous survey of college students was taken to determine behaviors regarding alcohol, cigarettes, and illegal drugs. The results were as follows: 894 drank alcohol regularly, 665 smoked cigarettes, 192 used illegal drugs, 424 drank alcohol regularly and smoked cigarettes, 114 drank alcohol regularly and used illegal drugs, 119 smoked cigarettes and used illegal drugs, 97 engaged in all three behaviors, and 309 engaged in none of these behaviors.

(*Source:* Jamie Langille, University of Nevada Las Vegas)

a. How many students were surveyed?

Of those surveyed,

b. How many drank alcohol regularly or smoked cigarettes?

c. How many used illegal drugs only?

d. How many drank alcohol regularly and smoked cigarettes, but did not use illegal drugs?

e. How many drank alcohol regularly or used illegal drugs, but did not smoke cigarettes?

f. How many engaged in exactly two of these behaviors?

g. How many engaged in at least one of these behaviors?

48. In the August 2005 issue of *Consumer Reports*, readers suffering from depression reported that alternative treatments were less effective than prescription drugs. Suppose that 550 readers felt better taking prescription drugs, 220 felt better through meditation, and 45 felt better taking St. John's wort. Furthermore, 95 felt better using prescription drugs and meditation, 17 felt better using prescription drugs and St. John's wort, 35 felt better using meditation and St. John's wort, 15 improved using all three treatments, and 150 improved using none of these treatments. (Hypothetical results are partly based on percentages given in *Consumer Reports*.)

a. How many readers suffering from depression were included in the report?

Of those included in the report,

b. How many felt better using prescription drugs or meditation?

c. How many felt better using St. John's wort only?

d. How many improved using prescription drugs and meditation, but not St. John's wort?

e. How many improved using prescription drugs or St. John's wort, but not meditation?

f. How many improved using exactly two of these treatments?

g. How many improved using at least one of these treatments?

• Writing in Mathematics

49. Suppose that you are drawing a Venn diagram to sort and tabulate the results of a survey. If results are being tabulated along gender lines, explain why only a circle representing women is needed, rather than two separate circles representing the women surveyed and the men surveyed.

50. Suppose that you decide to use two sets, *M* and *W*, to sort and tabulate the responses for men and women in a survey. Describe the set of people represented by regions II and IV in the Venn diagram shown. What conclusion can you draw?

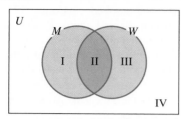

• **Critical Thinking Exercises**

51. Which one of the following is true?

    a. In a survey, 110 students were taking mathematics, 90 were taking psychology, and 20 were taking neither. Thus, 220 students were surveyed.

    b. If $A \cap B = \emptyset$, then $n(A \cup B) = n(A) + n(B)$.

    c. When filling in cardinalities for regions in a two-set Venn diagram, the innermost region, the intersection of the two sets, should be the last region to be filled in.

    d. $n(A')$ cannot be obtained by subtracting $n(A)$ from $n(U)$.

52. In a survey of 150 students, 90 were taking mathematics and 30 were taking psychology.

    a. What is the least number of students who could have been taking both courses?

    b. What is the greatest number of students who could have been taking both courses?

    c. What is the greatest number of students who could have been taking neither course?

53. A person applying for the position of college registrar submitted the following report to the college president on 90 students: 31 take math; 28 take chemistry; 42 take psychology; 9 take math and chemistry; 10 take chemistry and psychology; 6 take math and psychology; 4 take all three subjects; and 20 take none of these courses. The applicant was not hired. Explain why.

• **Group Exercise**

54. This group activity is intended to provide practice in the use of Venn diagrams to sort responses to a survey. The group will determine the topic of the survey. Although you will not actually conduct the survey, it might be helpful to imagine carrying out the survey using the students on your campus.

    a. In your group, decide on a topic for the survey.

    b. Devise three questions that the pollster will ask to the people who are interviewed.

    c. Construct a Venn diagram that will assist the pollster in sorting the answers to the three questions. The Venn diagram should contain three intersecting circles within a universal set and eight regions.

    d. Describe what each of the regions in the Venn diagram represents in terms of the questions in your poll.

●●●●●○● **CHAPTER SUMMARY, REVIEW, AND TEST**

● **S U M M A R Y**   **DEFINITIONS AND CONCEPTS**   EXAMPLES

7.1 Basic Set Concepts

a. A set is a collection of objects whose contents can be clearly determined. The objects in a set are called the elements, or members, of the set.

b. Sets can be designated by word descriptions, the roster method (a listing within braces, separating elements with commas), or set-builder notation:

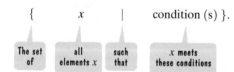

| Ex. 1, p. 376;
Ex. 2, p. 377;
Ex. 3, p. 377

c. The empty set, or the null set, represented by { } or ∅, is a set that contains no elements.   Ex. 4, p. 379

d. The symbol ∈ means that an object is an element of a set. The symbol ∉ means that an object is not an element of a set.   Ex. 5, p. 380

e. The set of natural numbers is **N** = {1, 2, 3, 4, 5, ... }. Inequality symbols, summarized in Table 7.2 on page 381, are frequently used to describe sets of natural numbers.   Ex. 6, p. 380; Ex. 7, p. 382

f. The cardinal number of a set A, $n(A)$, is the number of distinct elements in set A. Repeating elements in a set neither adds new elements to the set nor changes its cardinality.   Ex. 8, p. 382

g. Equivalent sets have the same number of elements, or the same cardinality. A one-to-one correspondence between sets A and B means that each element in A can be paired with exactly one element in B, and vice versa. If two sets can be placed in a one-to-one correspondence, then they are equivalent.   Ex. 9, p. 383

h. Set A is a finite set if $n(A) = 0$ or if $n(A)$ is a natural number. A set that is not finite is an infinite set.

i. Equal sets have exactly the same elements, regardless of order or possible repetition of elements. If two sets are equal, then they must be equivalent.

Ex. 10, p. 385

7.2   Subsets

a. Set A is a subset of set B, expressed as $A \subseteq B$, if every element in set A is also in set B. The notation $A \nsubseteq B$ means that set A is not a subset of set B, so there is at least one element of set A that is not an element of set B.

Ex. 1, p. 389

b. Set A is a proper subset of set B, expressed as $A \subset B$, if A is a subset of B and $A \neq B$.

Ex. 2, p. 390

c. The empty set is a subset of every set.

Ex. 3, p. 391

d. A set with n elements has 2^n subsets and $2^n - 1$ proper subsets.

Ex. 4, p. 392;
Ex. 5, p. 393

7.3   Venn Diagrams and Set Operations

a. A universal set, symbolized by U, is a set that contains all the elements being considered in a given discussion or problem.

Ex. 1, p. 398

b. Venn Diagrams: Representing Two Subsets of a Universal Set

Ex. 2, p. 400

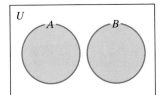

No A are B.
A and B are disjoint.

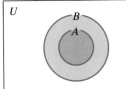

All A are B.
$A \subset B$

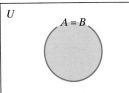

A and B are
equal sets.

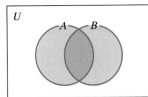

Some (at least
one) A are B.

c. A' (the complement of set A), which can be read A prime or **not** A, is the set of all elements in the universal set that are not in A.

Ex. 3, p. 401

d. $A \cap B$ (A intersection B), which can be read set A **and** set B, is the set of elements common to both set A and set B.

Ex. 4, p. 401

e. $A \cup B$ (A union B), which can be read set A **or** set B, is the set of elements that are members of set A or of set B or of both sets.

Ex. 5, p. 402

f. Some problems involve more than one set operation. Begin by performing any operations inside parentheses.

Ex. 6, p. 403

g. Elements of sets involving a variety of set operations can be determined from Venn diagrams.

Ex. 7, p. 404

h. Cardinal Number of the Union of Two Sets

Ex. 8, p. 405

$$n(A \cup B) = n(A) + n(B) - n(A \cap B)$$

7.4   Set Operations and Venn Diagrams with Three Sets

a. When using set operations involving three sets, begin by performing operations within parentheses.

Ex. 1, p. 409

b. The figure below shows a Venn diagram with three intersecting sets that separate the universal set, U, into eight regions. Elements of sets involving a variety of set operations can be determined from this Venn diagram.

Ex. 2, p. 412

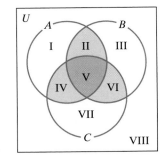

c. To construct a Venn diagram illustrating the elements in $A, B, C,$ and $U,$ first find $A \cap B$, $A \cap C$, $B \cap C$,   Ex. 3, p. 412
and $A \cap B \cap C$. Then place elements into the eight regions shown at the bottom of the previous page,
starting with the innermost region, region V, and working outward to region VIII.

d. If two specific sets represent the same regions of a general Venn diagram, then this deductively   Ex. 4, p. 414
proves that the two sets are equal.   Ex. 5, p. 415

7.5 Survey Problems

a. Venn diagrams can be used to organize information collected in surveys. When interpreting cardinal-   Ex. 1, p. 421
ities in such diagrams, *and* and *but* mean intersection, *or* means union, and *not* means complement.

b. To solve a survey problem,   Ex. 2, p. 423;

1. Define sets and draw a Venn diagram.   Ex. 3, p. 425;
Ex. 4, p. 426

2. Fill in the cardinality of each region, starting with the innermost region and working outward.

3. Use the completed diagram to answer the problem's questions.

REVIEW EXERCISES

7.1

In Exercises 1–2, write a description of each set. (More than one correct description may be possible.)

1. {Tuesday, Thursday}

2. $\{1, 2, 3, \ldots, 10\}$

In Exercises 3–5, express each set using the roster method.

3. $\{x \mid x$ is a letter in the word *miss*$\}$

4. $\{x \mid x \in \mathbf{N}$ and $8 \le x < 13\}$

5. $\{x \mid x \in \mathbf{N}$ and $x \le 30\}$

In Exercises 6–7, determine which sets are the empty set.

6. $\{\varnothing\}$

7. $\{x \mid x < 4$ and $x \ge 6\}$

In Exercises 8–9, fill in the blank with either $\in$ or $\notin$ to make each statement true.

8. 93_____$\{1, 2, 3, 4, \ldots, 99, 100\}$

9. {d}_____{a, b, c, d, e}

In Exercises 10–11, find the cardinal number for each set.

10. $A = \{x \mid x$ is a month of the year$\}$

11. $B = \{18, 19, 20, \ldots, 31, 32\}$

In Exercises 12–13, fill in the blank with either = or $\ne$ to make each statement true.

12. $\{0, 2, 4, 6, 8\}$_____$\{8, 2, 6, 4\}$

13. $\{x \mid x \in \mathbf{N}$ and $x > 7\}$_____$\{8, 9, 10, \ldots, 100\}$

In Exercises 14–15, determine if the pairs of sets are equivalent, equal, both, or neither.

14. $A = \{x \mid x$ is a lowercase letter that comes before f in the English alphabet$\}$
$B = \{2, 4, 6, 8, 10\}$

15. $A = \{x \mid x \in \mathbf{N}$ and $3 < x < 7\}$
$B = \{4, 5, 6\}$

In Exercises 16–17, determine whether each set is finite or infinite.

16. $\{x \mid x \in \mathbf{N}$ and $x < 50,000\}$

17. $\{x \mid x \in \mathbf{N}$ and x is even$\}$

7.2

In Exercises 18–20, write $\subseteq$ or $\nsubseteq$ in each blank so that the resulting statement is true.

18. {penny, nickel, dime}
_____{half-dollar, quarter, dime, nickel, penny}

19. $\{-1, 0, 1\}$_____$\{-3, -2, -1, 1, 2, 3\}$

20. $\varnothing$_____$\{x \mid x$ is an odd natural number$\}$

In Exercises 21–22, determine whether $\subseteq$, $\subset$, both, or neither can be placed in each blank to form a true statement.

21. $\{1, 2\}$_____$\{1, 1, 2, 2\}$

22. $\{x \mid x$ is a person living in the United States$\}$
_____$\{y \mid y$ is a person living on planet Earth$\}$

In Exercises 23–29, determine whether each statement is true or false. If the statement is false, explain why.

23. Texas $\in$ {Oklahoma, Louisiana, Georgia, South Carolina}

24. $4 \subseteq \{2, 4, 6, 8, 10, 12\}$

25. $\{e, f, g\} \subset \{d, e, f, g, h, i\}$

26. $\{\ominus, \varnothing\} \subset \{\varnothing, \ominus\}$

27. $\{3, 7, 9\} \subseteq \{9, 7, 3, 1\}$

28. {six} has 2^6 subsets.

29. $\varnothing \subseteq \{\ \}$

30. List all subsets for the set $\{1, 5\}$. Which one of these subsets is not a proper subset?

In Exercises 31–32, find the number of subsets and the number of proper subsets for each set.

31. $\{2, 4, 6, 8, 10\}$

32. $\{x \mid x$ is a month that begins with the letter J$\}$

7.3

In   Exercises   33–37,   let   U = {1, 2, 3, 4, 5, 6, 7, 8},
A = {1, 2, 3, 4},   and   B = {1, 2, 4, 5}.   Find   each   of   the
following sets.

33. $A \cap B$ **34.** $A \cup B'$ **35.** $A' \cap B$

36. $(A \cup B)'$ **37.** $A' \cap B'$

In Exercises 38–45, use the Venn diagram to represent each set in
roster form.

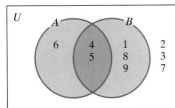

38. A **39.** B' **40.** $A \cup B$

41. $A \cap B$ **42.** $(A \cap B)'$ **43.** $(A \cup B)'$

44. $A \cap B'$ **45.** U

46. Set A contains 25 elements, set B contains 17 elements, and 9 elements are common to sets A and B. How many elements are in $A \cup B$?

7.4

In Exercises 47–48, let

$$U = \{1, 2, 3, 4, 5, 6, 7, 8\}$$
$$A = \{1, 2, 3, 4\}$$
$$B = \{1, 2, 4, 5\}$$
$$C = \{1, 5\}.$$

Find each of the following sets.

47. $A \cup (B \cap C)$ **48.** $(A \cap C)' \cup B$

In Exercises 49–54, use the Venn diagram to represent each set in
roster form.

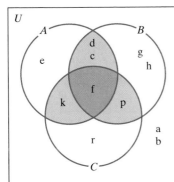

49. $A \cup C$ **50.** $B \cap C$ **51.** $(A \cap B) \cup C$

52. $A \cap C'$ **53.** $(A \cap C)'$ **54.** $A \cap B \cap C$

55. Construct a Venn diagram illustrating the following sets: $A = \{q, r, s, t, u\}, B = \{p, q, r\}, C = \{r, u, w, y\}$, and $U = \{p, q, r, s, t, u, v, w, x, y\}$.

56. Use a Venn diagram with two intersecting circles to prove that $(A \cup B)' = A' \cap B'$.

57. Use a Venn diagram with three intersecting circles to determine whether the following statement is a theorem:

$$A \cap (B \cup C) = A \cup (B \cap C).$$

58. The U.S. Committee for Refugees and Immigrants issues grades for treatment of refugees. Here are its grades for selected countries, as well as for the European Union:

	Detaining Refugees	Allowing Refugees to Work	Allowing Refugees to Move Freely
United States	D	A	A
European Union	D	B	A
Saudi Arabia	B	D	C
South Africa	F	C	B
Chad	B	B	C
Iran	F	F	C
Russia	F	F	F

Source: U.S. Committee for Refugees and Immigrants

Considering D or F a failing grade, the data can be organized in the following Venn diagram:

Failing in the Treatment of Refugees

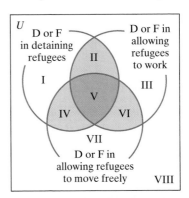

Use the data to determine the region in the Venn diagram into which each of the following countries should be placed.

a. United States

b. Saudi Arabia

c. Chad

d. Iran

e. Russia

7.5

59. A pollster conducting a telephone survey of college students asked two questions:

    1. Are you a registered Republican?

    2. Are you in favor of the death penalty?

a. Construct a Venn diagram with two circles that can assist the pollster in tabulating the responses to the two questions.

b. Write the letter b in every region of the diagram that represents students polled who are registered Republicans who are not in favor of the death penalty.

c. Write the letter c in every region of the diagram that represents students polled who are not registered Republicans and who are in favor of the death penalty.

In Exercises 60–61, construct a Venn diagram and determine the cardinality for each region. Use the completed Venn diagram to answer the questions.

60. A survey of 1000 American adults was taken to analyze their investments. Of those surveyed, 650 had invested in stocks, 550 in bonds, and 400 in both stocks and bonds. Of those surveyed,

   a. How many invested in only stocks?

   b. How many invested in stocks or bonds?

   c. How many did not invest in either stocks or bonds?

61. A survey of 200 students at a nonresidential college was taken to determine how they got to campus during the fall term. Of those surveyed, 118 used cars, 102 used public transportation, and 70 used bikes. Forty-eight students used cars and public transportation, 38 used cars and bikes, and 26 used public transportation and bikes. Twenty-two students used all three modes of transportation. Of those surveyed,

   a. How many used only public transportation?

   b. How many used cars and public transportation, but not bikes?

   c. How many used cars or public transportation, but not bikes?

   d. How many used exactly two of these modes of transportation?

   e. How many did not use any of the three modes of transportation to get to campus?

●●●●●● CHAPTER 7 TEST

1. Express the following set using the roster method:

$$\{x \mid x \in \mathbf{N} \text{ and } 17 < x \leq 24\}.$$

In Exercises 2–9, determine whether each statement is true or false. If the statement is false, explain why.

2. $\{6\} \in \{1, 2, 3, 4, 5, 6, 7\}$

3. If $A = \{x \mid x \text{ is a day of the week}\}$ and $B = \{2, 4, 6, \ldots, 14\}$, then sets A and B are equivalent.

4. $\{2, 4, 6, 8\} = \{8, 8, 6, 6, 4, 4, 2\}$

5. $\{d, e, f, g\} \subseteq \{a, b, c, d, e, f\}$

6. $\{3, 4, 5\} \subset \{x \mid x \in \mathbf{N} \text{ and } x < 6\}$

7. $14 \notin \{1, 2, 3, 4, \ldots, 39, 40\}$

8. $\{a, b, c, d, e\}$ has 25 subsets.

9. The empty set is a proper subset of any set, including itself.

10. List all subsets for the set $\{6, 9\}$. Which of these subsets is not a proper subset?

In Exercises 11–15, let

$$U = \{a, b, c, d, e, f, g\}$$
$$A = \{a, b, c, d\}$$
$$B = \{c, d, e, f\}$$
$$C = \{a, e, g\}.$$

Find each of the following sets or cardinalities.

11. $A \cup B$

12. $(B \cap C)'$

13. $A \cap C'$

14. $(A \cup B) \cap C$

15. $n(A \cup B')$

In Exercises 16–18, use the Venn diagram to represent each set in roster form.

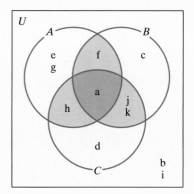

16. A'

17. $A \cap B \cap C$

18. $(A \cap B) \cup (A \cap C)$

19. Construct a Venn diagram illustrating the following sets: $A = \{1, 4, 5\}$, $B = \{1, 5, 6, 7\}$, and $U = \{1, 2, 3, 4, 5, 6, 7\}$.

20. Use the Venn diagram shown to determine whether the following statement is a theorem:

$$A' \cap (B \cup C) = (A' \cap B) \cup (A' \cap C).$$

Show work clearly as you develop the regions represented by each side of the statement.

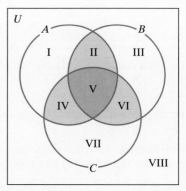

21. Here is a list of some famous people on whom the FBI kept files:

Famous Person	Length of FBI File
Bud Abbott (entertainer)	14 pages
Charlie Chaplin (entertainer)	2063 pages
Albert Einstein (scientist)	1800 pages
Martin Luther King, Jr. (civil rights leader)	17,000 pages
Elvis Presley (entertainer)	663 pages
Jackie Robinson (athlete)	131 pages
Eleanor Roosevelt (first lady; U.N. representative)	3000 pages
Frank Sinatra (entertainer)	1275 pages

Source: Paul Grobman, *Vital Statistics*, Plume, 2005

The data can be organized in the following Venn diagram:

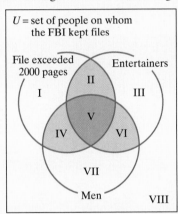

Use the data to determine the region in the Venn diagram into which each of the following people should be placed.

a. Chaplin

b. Einstein

c. King

d. Roosevelt

e. Sinatra

22. A winter resort took a poll of its 350 visitors to see which winter activities people enjoyed. The results were as follows: 178 liked to ski, 154 liked to snowboard, 57 liked to ice skate, 49 liked to ski and snowboard, 15 liked to ski and ice skate, 2 liked to snowboard and ice skate, and 2 liked all three activities.

a. Use a Venn diagram to illustrate the survey's results.

Use the Venn diagram to determine how many of those surveyed enjoyed

b. exactly one of these activities.

c. none of these activities.

d. at least two of these activities.

e. snowboarding and ice skating, but not skiing.

f. snowboarding or ice skating, but not skiing.

g. only skiing.

Counting Methods and Probability Theory

Two of America's best-loved presidents, Abraham Lincoln and John F. Kennedy, are linked by a bizarre series of coincidences:

- Lincoln was elected president in 1860. Kennedy was elected president in 1960.
- Lincoln's assassin, John Wilkes Booth, was born in 1839. Kennedy's assassin, Lee Harvey Oswald, was born in 1939.
- Lincoln's secretary, named Kennedy, warned him not to go to the theater on the night he was shot. Kennedy's secretary, named Lincoln, warned him not to go to Dallas on the day he was shot.
- Booth shot Lincoln in a theater and ran into a warehouse. Oswald shot Kennedy from a warehouse and ran into a theater.
- Both Lincoln and Kennedy were shot from behind, with their wives present.
- Andrew Johnson, who succeeded Lincoln, was born in 1808. Lyndon Johnson, who succeeded Kennedy, was born in 1908.

Source: Edward Burger and Michael Starbird, *Coincidences, Chaos, and All That Math Jazz,* W. W. Norton and Company, 2005.

Amazing coincidences? A cosmic conspiracy? Not really. In this chapter, you will see how the mathematics of uncertainty and risk, called probability theory, numerically describes situations in which to expect the unexpected. By assigning numbers to things that are extraordinarily unlikely, we can logically analyze coincidences without erroneous beliefs that strange and mystical events are occurring. We'll even see how wildly inaccurate our intuition can be about the likelihood of an event by examining an "amazing" coincidence that is nearly certain.

Coincidences are discussed in the Blitzer Bonus on page 488. Coincidences that are nearly certain are developed in Exercise 83 of Exercise Set 8.7.

SECTION 8.1 • THE FUNDAMENTAL COUNTING PRINCIPLE

O B J E C T I V E

1. Use the Fundamental Counting Principle to determine the number of possible outcomes in a given situation.

Have you ever imagined what your life would be like if you won the lottery? What changes would you make? Before you fantasize about becoming a person of leisure with a staff of obedient elves, think about this: The probability of winning top prize in the lottery is about the same as the probability of being struck by lightning. There are millions of possible number combinations in lottery games, and only one way of winning the grand prize. Determining the probability of winning involves calculating the chance of getting the winning combination from all possible outcomes. In this section, we begin preparing for the surprising world of probability by looking at methods for counting possible outcomes.

1 | Use the Fundamental Counting Principle to determine the number of possible outcomes in a given situation.

The Fundamental Counting Principle with Two Groups of Items

It's early morning, you're groggy, and you have to select something to wear for your 8 A.M. class. (What *were* you thinking when you signed up for a class at that hour?!) Fortunately, your "lecture wardrobe" is rather limited—just two pairs of jeans to choose from (one blue, one black) and three T-shirts to choose from (one beige, one yellow, and one blue). Your early-morning dilemma is illustrated in Figure 8.1.

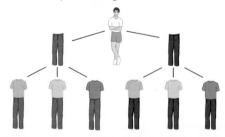

FIGURE 8.1 Selecting a wardrobe

The **tree diagram**, so named because of its branches, shows that you can form six different outfits from your two pairs of jeans and three T-shirts. Each pair of jeans can be combined with one of three T-shirts. Notice that the total number of outfits can be obtained by multiplying the number of choices for the jeans, 2, by the number of choices for the T-shirts, 3:

$$2 \cdot 3 = 6.$$

We can generalize this idea to any two groups of items—not just jeans and T-shirts—with the **Fundamental Counting Principle**.

> THE FUNDAMENTAL COUNTING PRINCIPLE
> If you can choose one item from a group of M items and a second item from a group of N items, then the total number of two-item choices is $M \cdot N$.

EXAMPLE 1	APPLYING THE FUNDAMENTAL COUNTING PRINCIPLE

The Greasy Spoon Restaurant offers 6 appetizers and 14 main courses. In how many ways can a person order a two-course meal?

SOLUTION Choosing from one of 6 appetizers and one of 14 main courses, the total number of two-course meals is

$$6 \cdot 14 = 84.$$

A person can order a two-course meal in 84 different ways.

 A restaurant offers 10 appetizers and 15 main courses. In how many ways can you order a two-course meal?

EXAMPLE 2	APPLYING THE FUNDAMENTAL COUNTING PRINCIPLE

This is the semester that you will take your required psychology and social science courses. Because you decide to register early, there are 15 sections of psychology from which you can choose. Furthermore, there are 9 sections of social science that are available at times that do not conflict with those for psychology. In how many ways can you create two-course schedules that satisfy the psychology-social science requirement?

SOLUTION The number of ways that you can satisfy the requirement is found by multiplying the number of choices for each course. You can choose your psychology course from 15 sections and your social science course from 9 sections. For both courses you have

$$15 \cdot 9, \text{ or } 135$$

choices. Thus, you can satisfy the psychology-social science requirement in 135 ways.

 Rework Example 2 given that the number of sections of psychology and nonconflicting sections of social science each decrease by 5.

The Fundamental Counting Principle with More Than Two Groups of Items

Whoops! You forgot something in choosing your lecture wardrobe—shoes! You have two pairs of sneakers to choose from—one black and one red, for that extra fashion flair! Your possible outfits, including sneakers, are shown in Figure 8.2.

The number of possible ways of playing the first four moves on each side in a game of chess is 318,979,564,000.

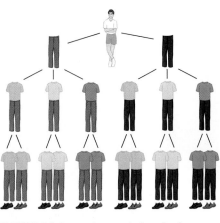

FIGURE 8.2 Increasing wardrobe selections

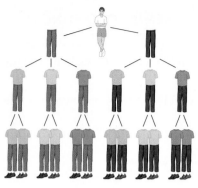

FIGURE 8.2 (repeated)

The tree diagram shows that you can form 12 outfits from your two pairs of jeans, three T-shirts, and two pairs of sneakers. Notice that the number of outfits can be obtained by multiplying the number of choices for jeans, 2, the number of choices for T-shirts, 3, and the number of choices for sneakers, 2:

$$2 \cdot 3 \cdot 2 = 12.$$

Unlike your earlier dilemma, you are now dealing with *three* groups of items. The Fundamental Counting Principle can be extended to determine the number of possible outcomes in situations in which there are three or more groups of items.

> **THE FUNDAMENTAL COUNTING PRINCIPLE**
> The number of ways in which a series of successive things can occur is found by multiplying the number of ways in which each thing can occur.

For example, if you own 30 pairs of jeans, 20 T-shirts, and 12 pairs of sneakers, you have

$$30 \cdot 20 \cdot 12 = 7200$$

choices for your wardrobe.

EXAMPLE 3   OPTIONS IN PLANNING A COURSE SCHEDULE

Next semester you are planning to take three courses—math, English, and humanities. Based on time blocks and highly recommended professors, there are 8 sections of math, 5 of English, and 4 of humanities that you find suitable. Assuming no scheduling conflicts, how many different three-course schedules are possible?

SOLUTION This situation involves making choices with three groups of items.

We use the Fundamental Counting Principle to find the number of three-course schedules. Multiply the number of choices for each of the three groups.

$$8 \cdot 5 \cdot 4 = 160$$

Thus, there are 160 different three-course schedules.

CHECK POINT 3 A pizza can be ordered with two choices of size (medium or large), three choices of crust (thin, thick, or regular), and five choices of toppings (ground beef, sausage, pepperoni, bacon, or mushrooms). How many different one-topping pizzas can be ordered?

EXAMPLE 4   CAR OF THE FUTURE

Car manufacturers are now experimenting with lightweight three-wheel cars, designed for one person, and considered ideal for city driving. Intrigued? Suppose you could order such a car with a choice of 9 possible colors, with or without air conditioning, electric or gas powered, and with or without an onboard computer. In how many ways can this car be ordered with regard to these options?

SOLUTION This situation involves making choices with four groups of items.

Color	Air conditioning	Power	Computer
9 choices	2 choices: with or without	2 choices: electric or gas	2 choices: with or without

Source: Corbin Motors
(www.Corbinmotors.com)

We use the Fundamental Counting Principle to find the number of ordering options. Multiply the number of choices for each of the four groups.

$$9 \cdot 2 \cdot 2 \cdot 2 = 72$$

Thus, the car can be ordered in 72 different ways.

CHECK POINT 4 The car in Example 4 is now available in 10 possible colors. The options involving air conditioning, power, and an onboard computer still apply. Furthermore, the car is available with or without a global positioning system (for pinpointing your location at every moment). In how many ways can this car be ordered in terms of these options?

EXAMPLE 5   A MULTIPLE-CHOICE TEST

You are taking a multiple-choice test that has ten questions. Each of the questions has four answer choices, with one correct answer per question. If you select one of these four choices for each question and leave nothing blank, in how many ways can you answer the questions?

SOLUTION This situation involves making choices with ten questions.

Question 1	Question 2	Question 3	⋯	Question 9	Question 10
4 choices	4 choices	4 choices		4 choices	4 choices

We use the Fundamental Counting Principle to determine the number of ways that you can answer the questions on the test. Multiply the number of choices, 4, for each of the ten questions.

$$4 \cdot 4 \cdot 4 \cdot 4 \cdot 4 \cdot 4 \cdot 4 \cdot 4 \cdot 4 \cdot 4 = 4^{10} = 1{,}048{,}576 \qquad \text{Use a calculator: } 4 \boxed{y^x} 10 \boxed{=}.$$

Thus, you can answer the questions in 1,048,576 different ways.

Are you surprised that there are over one million ways of answering a ten-question multiple-choice test? Of course, there is only one way to answer the test and receive a perfect score. The probability of guessing your way into a perfect score involves calculating the chance of getting a perfect score, just one way, from all 1,048,576 possible outcomes. In short, prepare for the test and do not rely on guessing!

CHECK POINT 5 You are taking a multiple-choice test that has six questions. Each of the questions has three answer choices, with one correct answer per question. If you select one of these three choices for each question and leave nothing blank, in how many ways can you answer the questions?

EXAMPLE 6   TELEPHONE NUMBERS IN THE UNITED STATES

Telephone numbers in the United States begin with three-digit area codes followed by seven-digit local telephone numbers. Area codes and local telephone numbers cannot begin with 0 or 1. How many different telephone numbers are possible?

SOLUTION This situation involves making choices with ten groups of items.

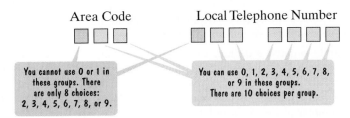

Area Code   Local Telephone Number

You cannot use 0 or 1 in these groups. There are only 8 choices: 2, 3, 4, 5, 6, 7, 8, or 9.

You can use 0, 1, 2, 3, 4, 5, 6, 7, 8, or 9 in these groups. There are 10 choices per group.

Here are the choices for each of the ten groups of items:

Area Code	Local Telephone Number
8 10 10	8 10 10 10 10 10 10 .

We use the Fundamental Counting Principle to determine the number of different telephone numbers that are possible. The total number of telephone numbers possible is

$$8 \cdot 10 \cdot 10 \cdot 8 \cdot 10 \cdot 10 \cdot 10 \cdot 10 \cdot 10 \cdot 10 = 6,400,000,000.$$

There are six billion four hundred million different telephone numbers that are possible.

CHECK POINT 6   An electronic gate can be opened by entering five digits on a keypad containing the digits $0, 1, 2, 3, \ldots, 8, 9$. How many different keypad sequences are possible if the digit 0 cannot be used as the first digit?

EXERCISE SET 8.1 ●●●●●●

• Practice and Application Exercises

Solve Exercises 1–6 using the Fundamental Counting Principle with two groups of items.

1. A restaurant offers 8 appetizers and 10 main courses. In how many ways can a person order a two-course meal?

2. The model of the car you are thinking of buying is available in nine different colors and three different styles (hatchback, sedan, or station wagon). In how many ways can you order the car?

3. A popular brand of pen is available in three colors (red, green, or blue) and four writing tips (bold, medium, fine, or micro). How many different choices of pens do you have with this brand?

4. In how many ways can a casting director choose a female lead and a male lead from five female actors and six male actors?

5. A student is planning a two-part trip. The first leg of the trip is from San Francisco to New York, and the second leg is from New York to Paris. From San Francisco to New York, travel options include airplane, train, or bus. From New York to Paris, the options are limited to airplane or ship. In how many ways can the two-part trip be made?

6. For a temporary job between semesters, you are painting the parking spaces for a new shopping mall with a letter of the alphabet and a single digit from 1 to 9. The first parking space is A1 and the last parking space is Z9. How many parking spaces can you paint with distinct labels?

Solve Exercises 7–22 using the Fundamental Counting Principle with three or more groups of items.

7. An ice cream store sells two drinks (sodas or milk shakes), in four sizes (small, medium, large, or jumbo), and five flavors (vanilla, strawberry, chocolate, coffee, or pistachio). In how many ways can a customer order a drink?

8. A pizza can be ordered with three choices of size (small, medium, or large), four choices of crust (thin, thick, crispy, or regular), and six choices of toppings (ground beef, sausage, pepperoni, bacon, mushrooms, or onions). How many one-topping pizzas can be ordered?

9. A restaurant offers the following limited lunch menu.

Main Course	Vegetables	Beverages	Desserts
Ham	Potatoes	Coffee	Cake
Chicken	Peas	Tea	Pie
Fish	Green beans	Milk	Ice cream
Beef		Soda	

If one item is selected from each of the four groups, in how many ways can a meal be ordered? Describe two such orders.

10. An apartment complex offers apartments with four different options, designated by A through D.

A	B	C	D
one bedroom	one bathroom	first floor	lake view
two bedrooms	two bathrooms	second floor	golf course view
three bedrooms			no special view

How many apartment options are available? Describe two such options.

11. Shoppers in a large shopping mall are categorized as male or female, over 30 or 30 and under, and cash or credit card shoppers. In how many ways can the shoppers be categorized?

12. There are three highways from city A to city B, two highways from city B to city C, and four highways from city C to city D. How many different highway routes are there from city A to city D?

13. A person can order a new car with a choice of six possible colors, with or without air conditioning, with or without automatic transmission, with or without power windows, and with or without a CD player. In how many different ways can a new car be ordered with regard to these options?

14. A car model comes in nine colors, with or without air conditioning, with or without a sun roof, with or without automatic transmission, and with or without antilock brakes. In how many ways can the car be ordered with regard to these options?

15. You are taking a multiple-choice test that has five questions. Each of the questions has three answer choices, with one correct answer per question. If you select one of these three choices for each question and leave nothing blank, in how many ways can you answer the questions?

16. You are taking a multiple-choice test that has eight questions. Each of the questions has three answer choices, with one correct answer per question. If you select one of these three choices for each question and leave nothing blank, in how many ways can you answer the questions?

17. In the original plan for area codes in 1945, the first digit could be any number from 2 through 9, the second digit was either 0 or 1, and the third digit could be any number except 0. With this plan, how many different area codes are possible?

18. The local seven-digit telephone numbers in Inverness, California, have 669 as the first three digits. How many different telephone numbers are possible in Inverness?

19. License plates in a particular state display two letters followed by three numbers, such as AT-887 or BB-013. How many different license plates can be manufactured for this state?

20. How many different four-letter radio station call letters can be formed if the first letter must be W or K?

21. A stock can go up, go down, or stay unchanged. How many possibilities are there if you own seven stocks?

22. A social security number contains nine digits, such as 074-66-7795. How many different social security numbers can be formed?

• Writing in Mathematics

23. Explain the Fundamental Counting Principle.

24. Figure 8.2 on page 439 shows that a tree diagram can be used to find the total number of outfits. Describe one advantage of using the Fundamental Counting Principle rather than a tree diagram.

25. Write an original problem that can be solved using the Fundamental Counting Principle. Then solve the problem.

• Critical Thinking Exercises

26. How many four-digit odd numbers are there? Assume that the digit on the left cannot be 0.

27. In order to develop a more appealing hamburger, a franchise used taste tests with 12 different buns, 30 sauces, 4 types of lettuce, and 3 types of tomatoes. If the taste test was done at one restaurant by one tester who took 10 minutes to eat each hamburger, approximately how long would it take the tester to eat all possible hamburgers?

• Group Exercise

28. The group should select real-world situations where the Fundamental Counting Principle can be applied. These can involve the number of possible student ID numbers on your campus, the number of possible phone numbers in your community, the number of meal options at a local restaurant, the number of ways a person in the group can select outfits for class, the number of ways a condominium can be purchased in a nearby community, and so on. Once situations have been selected, group members should determine in how many ways each part of the task can be done. Group members will need to obtain menus, find out about telephone-digit requirements in the community, count shirts, pants, shoes in closets, visit condominium sales offices, and so on. Once the group reassembles, apply the Fundamental Counting Principle to determine the number of available options in each situation. Because these numbers may be quite large, use a calculator.

SECTION 8.2 • PERMUTATIONS

OBJECTIVES

1. Use the Fundamental Counting Principle to count permutations.

2. Evaluate factorial expressions.

3. Use the permutations formula.

4. Find the number of permutations of duplicate items.

Ladies and gentlemen: Please give a huge round of applause for

    U2!   Bruce Springsteen and the E Street Band!
    Aerosmith!   The Rolling Stones!

You are in charge of planning one of the most anticipated concert tours of the decade. All four of these groups will appear in concert, which will be seen in a pay-per-view cable special by millions of people throughout the world. One of your jobs is to determine the order in which the groups will perform. Each group will perform once. How many different ways can you put together this four-group concert?

You are familiar with the work of all these musicians *and* you know the Fundamental Counting Principle! (Who could be better qualified for this job?) You can choose any of the four groups as the first performer. Once you've chosen the first

1   Use the Fundamental Counting Principle to count permutations.

group, you'll have three groups left to choose from for the second performer. You'll then have two groups left to choose from for the third performance. After the first three performers are determined, you'll have only one group left for the final appearance in the concert. This situation can be shown as follows:

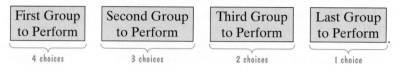

First Group to Perform	Second Group to Perform	Third Group to Perform	Last Group to Perform
4 choices	3 choices	2 choices	1 choice

We use the Fundamental Counting Principle to find the number of ways you can put together the concert. Multiply the choices:

$$4 \cdot 3 \cdot 2 \cdot 1 = 24.$$

Thus, there are 24 different ways to arrange the concert. One of the 24 possible arrangements is

Aerosmith–Bruce Springsteen–U2–The Rolling Stones.

Such an ordered arrangement is called a *permutation* of the four rock groups.
   A **permutation** is an ordered arrangement of items that occurs when

- No item is used more than once. (Each rock group performs exactly once.)
- The order of arrangement makes a difference. (It will make a difference in terms of how the concert is received if the Rolling Stones are the first group or the last group to perform.)

EXAMPLE 1   COUNTING PERMUTATIONS

Based on their long-standing contribution to rock music, you decide that the Rolling Stones should be the last group to perform at the four-group U2, Bruce Springsteen, Aerosmith, Rolling Stones concert. Given this decision, in how many ways can you put together the concert?

SOLUTION You can now choose any one of the three groups, U2, Bruce Springsteen and the E Street Band, or Aerosmith, as the opening act. Once you've chosen the first group, you'll have two groups left to choose from for the second performance. You'll then have just one group left to choose for the third performance. There is also just one choice for the closing act—the Rolling Stones. This situation can be shown as follows:

The Rolling Stones

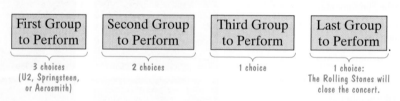

First Group to Perform	Second Group to Perform	Third Group to Perform	Last Group to Perform
3 choices (U2, Springsteen, or Aerosmith)	2 choices	1 choice	1 choice: The Rolling Stones will close the concert.

We use the Fundamental Counting Principle to find the number of ways you can put together the concert. Multiply the choices:

$$3 \cdot 2 \cdot 1 \cdot 1 = 6.$$

Thus, there are six different ways to arrange the concert if the Rolling Stones are the final group to perform.

○

CHECK POINT 1 For the concert in Example 1, suppose that U2 is to be the opening act and the Rolling Stones are to be the last group to perform. In how many ways can you put together the concert?

EXAMPLE 2   COUNTING PERMUTATIONS

You need to arrange seven of your favorite books along a small shelf. How many different ways can you arrange the books, assuming that the order of the books makes a difference to you?

SOLUTION You may choose any of the seven books for the first position on the shelf. This leaves six choices for second position. After the first two positions are filled, there are five books to choose from for third position, four choices left for the fourth position, three choices left for the fifth position, then two choices for the sixth position, and only one choice for the last position. This situation can be shown as follows:

First Shelf Position	Second Shelf Position	Third Shelf Position	Fourth Shelf Position	Fifth Shelf Position	Sixth Shelf Position	Seventh Shelf Position
7 choices	6 choices	5 choices	4 choices	3 choices	2 choices	1 choice

We use the Fundamental Counting Principle to find the number of ways you can arrange the seven books along the shelf. Multiply the choices:

$$7 \cdot 6 \cdot 5 \cdot 4 \cdot 3 \cdot 2 \cdot 1 = 5040.$$

Thus, you can arrange the books in 5040 ways. There are 5040 different possible permutations.

CHECK POINT 2 In how many ways can you arrange five books along a shelf, assuming that the order of the books makes a difference?

Factorial Notation

The product in Example 2,

$$7 \cdot 6 \cdot 5 \cdot 4 \cdot 3 \cdot 2 \cdot 1$$

is given a special name and symbol. It is called 7 **factorial**, and written 7!. Thus,

$$7! = 7 \cdot 6 \cdot 5 \cdot 4 \cdot 3 \cdot 2 \cdot 1.$$

In general, if n is a positive integer, then $n!$ (n factorial) is the product of all positive integers from n down through 1. For example,

$$1! = 1$$
$$2! = 2 \cdot 1 = 2$$
$$3! = 3 \cdot 2 \cdot 1 = 6$$
$$4! = 4 \cdot 3 \cdot 2 \cdot 1 = 24$$
$$5! = 5 \cdot 4 \cdot 3 \cdot 2 \cdot 1 = 120$$
$$6! = 6 \cdot 5 \cdot 4 \cdot 3 \cdot 2 \cdot 1 = 720.$$

2 | Evaluate factorial expressions.

FACTORIALS FROM 0 THROUGH 20

0!	1
1!	1
2!	2
3!	6
4!	24
5!	120
6!	720
7!	5040
8!	40,320
9!	362,880
10!	3,628,800
11!	39,916,800
12!	479,001,600
13!	6,227,020,800
14!	87,178,291,200
15!	1,307,674,368,000
16!	20,922,789,888,000
17!	355,687,428,096,000
18!	6,402,373,705,728,000
19!	121,645,100,408,832,000
20!	2,432,902,008,176,640,000

As n increases, $n!$ grows very rapidly. Factorial growth is more explosive than exponential growth.

FACTORIAL NOTATION

If n is a positive integer, the notation $n!$ (read "n factorial") is the product of all positive integers from n down through 1.

$$n! = n(n - 1)(n - 2) \cdots (3)(2)(1)$$

0! (zero factorial), by definition, is 1.

$$0! = 1$$

EXAMPLE 3   USING FACTORIAL NOTATION

Evaluate the following factorial expressions without using the factorial key on your calculator:

a. $\dfrac{8!}{5!}$ **b.** $\dfrac{26!}{21!}$ **c.** $\dfrac{500!}{499!}$.

TECHNOLOGY

Most calculators have a key or menu item for calculating factorials. Here are the keystrokes for finding 9!:

MANY SCIENTIFIC CALCULATORS:

9 $\boxed{x!}$ $\boxed{=}$

MANY GRAPHING CALCULATORS:

9 $\boxed{!}$ $\boxed{\text{ENTER}}$.

Because $n!$ becomes quite large as n increases, your calculator will display these larger values in scientific notation.

SOLUTION

a. We can evaluate the numerator and the denominator of $\frac{8!}{5!}$. However, it is easier to use the following simplification:

$$\frac{8!}{5!} = \frac{8 \cdot 7 \cdot 6 \cdot \boxed{5 \cdot 4 \cdot 3 \cdot 2 \cdot 1}}{\boxed{5 \cdot 4 \cdot 3 \cdot 2 \cdot 1}} = \frac{8 \cdot 7 \cdot 6 \cdot \boxed{5!}}{\boxed{5!}} = \frac{8 \cdot 7 \cdot 6 \cdot \cancel{5!}}{\cancel{5!}} = 8 \cdot 7 \cdot 6 = 336.$$

b. Rather than write out 26!, the numerator of $\frac{26!}{21!}$, as the product of all integers from 26 down to 1, we can express 26! as

$$26! = 26 \cdot 25 \cdot 24 \cdot 23 \cdot 22 \cdot 21!.$$

In this way, we can cancel 21! in the numerator and the denominator of the given expression.

$$\frac{26!}{21!} = \frac{26 \cdot 25 \cdot 24 \cdot 23 \cdot 22 \cdot 21!}{21!} = \frac{26 \cdot 25 \cdot 24 \cdot 23 \cdot 22 \cdot \cancel{21!}}{\cancel{21!}}$$

$$= 26 \cdot 25 \cdot 24 \cdot 23 \cdot 22 = 7,893,600$$

c. In order to cancel identical factorials in the numerator and the denominator of $\frac{500!}{499!}$, we can express 500! as $500 \cdot 499!$.

$$\frac{500!}{499!} = \frac{500 \cdot 499!}{499!} = \frac{500 \cdot \cancel{499!}}{\cancel{499!}} = 500$$

 Evaluate without using a calculator's factorial key:

a. $\dfrac{9!}{6!}$ **b.** $\dfrac{16!}{11!}$ **c.** $\dfrac{100!}{99!}$.

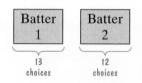 Use the permutations formula.

A Formula for Permutations

You are the coach of a little league baseball team. There are 13 players on the team (and lots of parents hovering in the background, dreaming of stardom for their little "Barry Bonds"). You need to choose a batting order having 9 players. The order makes a difference, because, for instance, if bases are loaded and "Little Barry" is fourth or fifth at bat, his possible home run will drive in three additional runs. How many batting orders can you form?

You can choose any of 13 players for the first person at bat. Then you will have 12 players from which to choose the second batter, then 11 from which to choose the third batter, and so on. The situation can be shown as follows:

Batter 1	Batter 2	Batter 3	Batter 4	Batter 5	Batter 6	Batter 7	Batter 8	Batter 9
13 choices	12 choices	11 choices	10 choices	9 choices	8 choices	7 choices	6 choices	5 choices

The total number of batting orders is

$$13 \cdot 12 \cdot 11 \cdot 10 \cdot 9 \cdot 8 \cdot 7 \cdot 6 \cdot 5 = 259,459,200.$$

Nearly 260 million batting orders are possible for your 13-player little league team. Each batting order is a permutation because the order of the batters makes a difference. The number of permutations of 13 players taken 9 at a time is 259,459,200.

We can obtain a formula for finding the number of permutations by rewriting our computation:

$$13 \cdot 12 \cdot 11 \cdot 10 \cdot 9 \cdot 8 \cdot 7 \cdot 6 \cdot 5$$

$$= \frac{13 \cdot 12 \cdot 11 \cdot 10 \cdot 9 \cdot 8 \cdot 7 \cdot 6 \cdot 5 \cdot \boxed{4 \cdot 3 \cdot 2 \cdot 1}}{\boxed{4 \cdot 3 \cdot 2 \cdot 1}} = \frac{13!}{4!} = \frac{13!}{(13-9)!}.$$

Thus, the number of permutations of 13 things taken 9 at a time is $\frac{13!}{(13-9)!}$. The special notation $_{13}P_9$ is used to replace the phrase "the number of permutations of 13 things taken 9 at a time." Using this new notation, we can write

$$_{13}P_9 = \frac{13!}{(13-9)!}.$$

The numerator of this expression is the factorial of the number of items, 13 team members: 13!. The denominator is also a factorial. It is the factorial of the difference between the number of items, 13, and the number of items in each permutation, 9 batters: $(13-9)!$.

The notation $_nP_r$ means the **number of permutations of n things taken r at a time**. We can generalize from the situation in which 9 batters were taken from 13 players. By generalizing, we obtain the following formula for the number of permutations if r items are taken from n items:

> **PERMUTATIONS OF n THINGS TAKEN r AT A TIME**
> The number of possible permutations if r items are taken from n items is
> $$_nP_r = \frac{n!}{(n-r)!}.$$

EXAMPLE 4   USING THE FORMULA FOR PERMUTATIONS

You and 19 of your friends have decided to form an Internet marketing consulting firm. The group needs to choose three officers—a CEO, an operating manager, and a treasurer. In how many ways can those offices be filled?

SOLUTION Your group is choosing $r = 3$ officers from a group of $n = 20$ people (you and 19 friends). The order in which the officers are chosen matters because the CEO, the operating manager, and the treasurer each have different responsibilities. Thus, we are looking for the number of permutations of 20 things taken 3 at a time. We use the formula

$$_nP_r = \frac{n!}{(n-r)!}$$

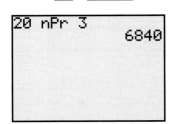
with $n = 20$ and $r = 3$.

$$_{20}P_3 = \frac{20!}{(20-3)!} = \frac{20!}{17!} = \frac{20 \cdot 19 \cdot 18 \cdot 17!}{17!} = \frac{20 \cdot 19 \cdot 18 \cdot \cancel{17!}}{\cancel{17!}} = 20 \cdot 19 \cdot 18 = 6840$$

Thus, there are 6840 different ways of filling the three offices.

A corporation has seven members on its board of directors. In how many different ways can it elect a president, vice-president, secretary, and treasurer?

EXAMPLE 5   USING THE FORMULA FOR PERMUTATIONS

You are working for The Sitcom Television Network. Your assignment is to help set up the television schedule for Monday evenings between 7 and 10 P.M. You need to schedule a show in each of six 30-minute time blocks, beginning with 7 to 7:30 and ending with 9:30 to 10:00. You can select from among the following situation comedies: *Home Improvement*, *Seinfeld*, *Mad About You*, *Cheers*, *Friends*, *Frasier*, *All in the Family*, *I Love Lucy*, *M*A*S*H*, *The Larry Sanders Show*, *The Jeffersons*, *Married with Children*, and *Happy Days*. How many different programming schedules can be arranged?

SOLUTION You are choosing $r = 6$ situation comedies from a collection of $n = 13$ classic sitcoms. The order in which the programs are aired matters. Family-oriented comedies have higher ratings when aired in earlier time blocks, such as 7 to 7:30. By contrast, comedies with adult themes do better in later time blocks. In short, we are looking for the number of permutations of 13 things taken 6 at a time. We use the formula

$$_nP_r = \frac{n!}{(n-r)!}$$

with $n = 13$ and $r = 6$.

$$_{13}P_6 = \frac{13!}{(13-6)!} = \frac{13!}{7!} = \frac{13 \cdot 12 \cdot 11 \cdot 10 \cdot 9 \cdot 8 \cdot \cancel{7!}}{\cancel{7!}} = 13 \cdot 12 \cdot 11 \cdot 10 \cdot 9 \cdot 8 = 1,235,520$$

There are 1,235,520 different programming schedules that can be arranged.   ○

 How many different programming schedules can be arranged by choosing 5 situation comedies from a collection of 9 classic sitcoms?

4 | Find the number of permutations of duplicate items.

Permutations of Duplicate Items

The number of permutations of the letters in the word SET is 3!, or 6. The six permutations are

SET,   STE,   EST,   ETS,   TES,   TSE.

Are there also six permutations of the letters in the name ANA? The answer is no. Unlike SET, with three distinct letters, ANA contains three letters, of which the two As are duplicates. If we rearrange the letters just as we did with SET, we obtain

ANA,   AAN,   NAA,   NAA,   ANA,   AAN.

Without the use of color to distinguish between the two As, there are only three distinct permutations: ANA, AAN, NAA.

There is a formula for finding the number of distinct permutations when duplicate items exist:

> **PERMUTATIONS OF DUPLICATE ITEMS**
> The number of permutations of n items, where p items are identical, q items are identical, r items are identical, and so on, is given by
> $$\frac{n!}{p!\, q!\, r! \ldots}.$$

For example, ANA contains three letters ($n = 3$), where two of the letters are identical ($p = 2$). The number of distinct permutations is

$$\frac{n!}{p!} = \frac{3!}{2!} = \frac{3 \cdot \cancel{2!}}{\cancel{2!}} = 3.$$

We saw that the three distinct permutations are ANA, AAN, and NAA.

TECHNOLOGY

Parentheses are necessary to enclose the factorials in the denominator when using a calculator to find

$$\frac{11!}{4!\,4!\,2!}.$$

| EXAMPLE 6 | USING THE FORMULA FOR PERMUTATIONS OF DUPLICATE ITEMS |

In how many distinct ways can the letters of the word MISSISSIPPI be arranged?

SOLUTION The word contains 11 letters ($n = 11$), where four Is are identical ($p = 4$), four Ss are identical ($q = 4$), and 2 Ps are identical ($r = 2$). The number of distinct permutations is

$$\frac{n!}{p!\,q!\,r!} = \frac{11!}{4!\,4!\,2!} = \frac{11 \cdot 10 \cdot 9 \cdot 8 \cdot 7 \cdot 6 \cdot 5 \cdot 4!}{4!\,4 \cdot 3 \cdot 2 \cdot 1 \cdot 2 \cdot 1} = 34{,}650$$

There are 34,650 distinct ways the letters in the word MISSISSIPPI can be arranged.

 6 In how many ways can the letters of the word OSMOSIS be arranged?

EXERCISE SET 8.2 ●●●●●●

• Practice and Application Exercises

Use the Fundamental Counting Principle to solve Exercises 1–12.

1. Six performers are to present their comedy acts on a weekend evening at a comedy club. How many different ways are there to schedule their appearances?

2. Five singers are to perform on a weekend evening at a night club. How many different ways are there to schedule their appearances?

3. In the *Cambridge Encyclopedia of Language* (Cambridge University Press, 1987), author David Crystal presents five sentences that make a reasonable paragraph regardless of their order. The sentences are as follows:

   Mark had told him about the foxes.
   John looked out of the window.
   Could it be a fox?
   However, nobody had seen one for months.
   He thought he saw a shape in the bushes.

   In how many different orders can the five sentences be arranged?

4. In how many different ways can a police department arrange eight suspects in a police lineup if each lineup contains all eight people?

5. As in Exercise 1, six performers are to present their comedy acts on a weekend evening at a comedy club. One of the performers insists on being the last stand-up comic of the evening. If this performer's request is granted, how many different ways are there to schedule the appearances?

6. As in Exercise 2, five singers are to perform at a night club. One of the singers insists on being the last performer of the evening. If this singer's request is granted, how many different ways are there to schedule the appearances?

7. You need to arrange nine of your favorite books along a small shelf. How many different ways can you arrange the books, assuming that the order of the books makes a difference to you?

8. You need to arrange ten of your favorite photographs on the mantel above a fireplace. How many ways can you arrange the photographs, assuming that the order of the pictures makes a difference to you?

In Exercises 9–10, use the five sentences that are given in Exercise 3.

9. How many different five-sentence paragraphs can be formed if the paragraph begins with "He thought he saw a shape in the bushes" and ends with "John looked out of the window"?

10. How many different five-sentence paragraphs can be formed if the paragraph begins with "He thought he saw a shape in the bushes" followed by "Mark had told him about the foxes"?

11. A television programmer is arranging the order that five movies will be seen between the hours of 6 P.M. and 4 A.M. Two of the movies have a G rating, and they are to be shown in the first two time blocks. One of the movies is rated NC-17, and it is to be shown in the last of the time blocks, from 2 A.M. until 4 A.M. Given these restrictions, in how many ways can the five movies be arranged during the indicated time blocks?

12. A camp counselor and six campers are to be seated along a picnic bench. In how many ways can this be done if the counselor must be seated in the middle and a camper who has a tendency to engage in food fights must sit to the counselor's immediate left?

In Exercises 13–32, evaluate each factorial expression.

13. $\dfrac{9!}{6!}$ 14. $\dfrac{12!}{10!}$ 15. $\dfrac{29!}{25!}$

16. $\dfrac{31!}{28!}$ 17. $\dfrac{19!}{11!}$ 18. $\dfrac{17!}{9!}$

19. $\dfrac{600!}{599!}$ 20. $\dfrac{700!}{699!}$ 21. $\dfrac{104!}{102!}$

22. $\dfrac{106!}{104!}$ 23. $7! - 3!$ 24. $6! - 3!$

25. $(7 - 3)!$ 26. $(6 - 3)!$ 27. $\left(\dfrac{12}{4}\right)!$

28. $\left(\dfrac{45}{9}\right)!$ 29. $\dfrac{7!}{(7 - 2)!}$ 30. $\dfrac{8!}{(8 - 5)!}$

31. $\dfrac{13!}{(13 - 3)!}$ 32. $\dfrac{17!}{(17 - 3)!}$

In Exercises 33–40, use the formula for $_nP_r$ to evaluate each expression.

33. $_9P_4$ **34.** $_7P_3$ **35.** $_8P_5$

36. $_{10}P_4$ **37.** $_6P_6$ **38.** $_9P_9$

39. $_8P_0$ **40.** $_6P_0$

Use the formula for $_nP_r$ to solve Exercises 41–48.

41. A club with ten members is to choose three officers— president, vice-president, and secretary-treasurer. If each office is to be held by one person and no person can hold more than one office, in how many ways can those offices be filled?

42. A corporation has seven members on its board of directors. In how many different ways can it elect a president, vice-president, secretary, and treasurer?

43. For a segment of a radio show, a disc jockey can play 7 records. If there are 13 records to select from, in how many ways can the program for this segment be arranged?

44. Suppose you are asked to list, in order of preference, the three best movies you have seen this year. If you saw 20 movies during the year, in how many ways can the three best be chosen and ranked?

45. In a race in which six automobiles are entered and there are no ties, in how many ways can the first three finishers come in?

46. In a production of *West Side Story*, eight actors are considered for the male roles of Tony, Riff, and Bernardo. In how many ways can the director cast the male roles?

47. Nine bands have volunteered to perform at a benefit concert, but there is only enough time for five of the bands to play. How many lineups are possible?

48. How many arrangements can be made using four of the letters of the word COMBINE if no letter is to be used more than once?

Use the formula for the number of permutations of duplicate items to solve Exercises 49–56.

49. In how many distinct ways can the letters of the word DALLAS be arranged?

50. In how many distinct ways can the letters of the word SCIENCE be arranged?

51. How many distinct permutations can be formed using the letters of the word TALLAHASSEE?

52. How many distinct permutations can be formed using the letters of the word TENNESSEE?

53. In how many ways can the digits in the number 5,446,666 be arranged?

54. In how many ways can the digits in the number 5,432,435 be arranged?

In Exercises 55–56, a signal can be formed by running different colored flags up a pole, one above the other.

55. Find the number of different signals consisting of eight flags that can be made using three white flags, four red flags, and one blue flag.

56. Find the number of different signals consisting of nine flags that can be made using three white flags, five red flags, and one blue flag.

• Writing in Mathematics

57. What is a permutation?

58. Explain how to find $n!$, where n is a positive integer.

59. Explain the best way to evaluate $\frac{900!}{899!}$ without a calculator.

60. Describe what $_nP_r$ represents.

61. Write a word problem that can be solved by evaluating $5!$.

62. Write a word problem that can be solved by evaluating $_7P_3$.

63. If 24 permutations can be formed using the letters in the word BAKE, why can't 24 permutations also be formed using the letters in the word BABE? How is the number of permutations in BABE determined?

• Critical Thinking Exercises

64. Ten people board an airplane that has 12 aisle seats. In how many ways can they be seated if they all select aisle seats?

65. Six horses are entered in a race. If two horses are tied for first place, and there are no ties among the other four horses, in how many ways can the six horses cross the finish line?

66. Performing at a concert are eight rock bands and eight jazz groups. How many ways can the program be arranged if the first, third, and eighth performers are jazz groups?

67. Five men and five women line up at a checkout counter in a store. In how many ways can they line up if the first person in line is a woman, and the people in line alternate woman, man, woman, man, and so on?

68. How many four-digit odd numbers less than 6000 can be formed using the digits 2, 4, 6, 7, 8, and 9?

69. Express $_nP_{n-2}$ without using factorials.

SECTION 8.3 • COMBINATIONS

OBJECTIVES

1. Distinguish between permutation and combination problems.

2. Solve problems involving combinations using the combinations formula.

As the twentieth century drew to a close, *Time* magazine presented a series of special issues on the most influential people of the century. In its issue on heroes and icons (June 14, 1999), *Time* discussed a number of people whose careers became more profitable after their tragic deaths, including Marilyn Monroe, James Dean, Jim Morrison, Kurt Cobain, and Selena.

Imagine that you ask your friends the following question: "Of these five people, which three would you select to be included in a documentary featuring the best of their work?" You are not asking your friends to rank their three favorite artists in any kind of order—they should merely select the three to be included in the documentary.

Marilyn Monroe, Actress (1927–1962)

1 | Distinguish between permutation and combination problems.

One friend answers, "Jim Morrison, Kurt Cobain, and Selena." Another responds, "Selena, Kurt Cobain, and Jim Morrison." These two people have the same artists in their group of selections, even if they are named in a different order. We are interested *in which artists are named, not the order in which they are named* for the documentary. Because the items are taken without regard to order, this is not a permutation problem. No ranking of any sort is involved.

Later on, you ask your roommate which three artists she would select for the documentary. She names Marilyn Monroe, James Dean, and Selena. Her selection is different from those of your two other friends because different entertainers are cited.

Mathematicians describe the group of artists given by your roommate as a *combination*. A **combination** of items occurs when

- The items are selected from the same group (the five stars who died young and tragically).
- No item is used more than once. (You may adore Selena, but your three selections cannot be Selena, Selena, and Selena.)
- The order of items makes no difference. (Morrison, Cobain, Selena is the same group in the documentary as Selena, Cobain, Morrison.)

Do you see the difference between a permutation and a combination? A permutation is an ordered arrangement of a given group of items. A combination is a group of items taken without regard to their order. **Permutation** problems involve situations in which **order matters**. **Combination** problems involve situations in which the **order** of items **makes no difference**.

James Dean, Actor (1931–1955)

Jim Morrison, Musician and Lead Singer of The Doors (1943–1971)

Kurt Cobain, Musician and Front Man for Nirvana (1967–1994)

Selena, Musician of Tejano Music (1971–1995)

EXAMPLE 1   DISTINGUISHING BETWEEN PERMUTATIONS AND COMBINATIONS

For each of the following problems, determine whether the problem is one involving permutations or combinations. (It is not necessary to solve the problem.)

a. Six students are running for student government president, vice-president, and treasurer. The student with the greatest number of votes becomes the president, the second highest vote-getter becomes vice-president, and the student who gets the third largest number of votes will be treasurer. How many different outcomes are possible for these three positions?

b. Six people are on the board of supervisors for your neighborhood park. A three-person committee is needed to study the possibility of expanding the park. How many different committees could be formed from the six people?

c. Baskin-Robbins offers 31 different flavors of ice cream. One of their items is a bowl consisting of three scoops of ice cream, each a different flavor. How many such bowls are possible?

SOLUTION

a. Students are choosing three student government officers from six candidates. The order in which the officers are chosen makes a difference because each of the offices (president, vice-president, treasurer) is different. Order matters. This is a problem involving permutations.

b. A three-person committee is to be formed from the six-person board of supervisors. The order in which the three people are selected does not matter because they are not filling different roles on the committee. Because order makes no difference, this is a problem involving combinations.

c. A three-scoop bowl of three different flavors is to be formed from Baskin-Robbin's 31 flavors. The order in which the three scoops of ice cream are put into the bowl is irrelevant. A bowl with chocolate, vanilla, and strawberry is exactly the same as a bowl with vanilla, strawberry, and chocolate. Different orderings do not change things, and so this is a problem involving combinations.

CHECK POINT 1 For each of the following problems, determine whether the problem is one involving permutations or combinations. (It is not necessary to solve the problem.)

a. How many ways can you select 6 free DVDs from a list of 200 DVDs?

b. In a race in which there are 50 runners and no ties, in how many ways can the first three finishers come in?

2 Solve problems involving combinations using the combinations formula.

A Formula for Combinations

We have seen that the notation $_nP_r$ means the number of permutations of n things taken r at a time. Similarly, the notation $_nC_r$ **means the number of combinations of n things taken r at a time**.

We can develop a formula for $_nC_r$ by comparing permutations and combinations. Consider the letters A, B, C, and D. The number of permutations of these four letters taken three at a time is

$$_4P_3 = \frac{4!}{(4-3)!} = \frac{4!}{1!} = \frac{4 \cdot 3 \cdot 2 \cdot 1}{1} = 24.$$

Here are the 24 permutations:

ABC,	ABD,	ACD,	BCD,
ACB,	ADB,	ADC,	BDC,
BAC,	BAD,	CAD,	CBD,
BCA,	BDA,	CDA,	CDB,
CAB,	DAB,	DAC,	DBC,
CBA,	DBA,	DCA,	DCB.

This column contains only one combination, ABC.	This column contains only one combination, ABD.	This column contains only one combination, ACD.	This column contains only one combination, BCD.

Because the order of items makes no difference in determining combinations, each column of six permutations represents one combination. There are a total of four combinations:

ABC,   ABD,   ACD,   BCD.

Thus, $_4C_3 = 4$: The number of combinations of 4 things taken 3 at a time is 4. With 24 permutations and only four combinations, there are 6, or 3!, times as many permutations as there are combinations.

In general, there are $r!$ times as many permutations of n things taken r at a time as there are combinations of n things taken r at a time. Thus, we find the number of combinations of n things taken r at a time by dividing the number of permutations of n things taken r at a time by $r!$.

$$_nC_r = \frac{_nP_r}{r!} = \frac{\frac{n!}{(n-r)!}}{r!} = \frac{n!}{(n-r)!\, r!}$$

COMBINATIONS OF n THINGS TAKEN r AT A TIME
The number of possible combinations if r items are taken from n items is

$$_nC_r = \frac{n!}{(n-r)!\, r!}.$$

EXAMPLE 2   USING THE FORMULA FOR COMBINATIONS

A three-person committee is needed to study ways of improving public transportation. How many committees could be formed from the eight people on the board of supervisors?

SOLUTION The order in which the three people are selected does not matter. This is a problem of selecting $r = 3$ people from a group of $n = 8$ people. We are looking for the number of combinations of eight things taken three at a time. We use the formula

$$_nC_r = \frac{n!}{(n-r)!\, r!}$$

with $n = 8$ and $r = 3$.

$$_8C_3 = \frac{8!}{(8-3)!\,3!} = \frac{8!}{5!\,3!} = \frac{8 \cdot 7 \cdot 6 \cdot 5!}{5! \cdot 3 \cdot 2 \cdot 1} = \frac{8 \cdot 7 \cdot 6 \cdot \cancel{5!}}{\cancel{5!} \cdot 3 \cdot 2 \cdot 1} = 56$$

Thus, 56 committees of three people each can be formed from the eight people on the board of supervisors.

2 You volunteer to pet-sit for your friend who has seven different animals. How many different pet combinations are possible if you take three of the seven pets?

EXAMPLE 3   USING THE FORMULA FOR COMBINATIONS

In poker, a person is dealt 5 cards from a standard 52-card deck. The order in which you are dealt the 5 cards does not matter. How many different 5-card poker hands are possible?

SOLUTION Because the order in which the 5 cards are dealt does not matter, this is a problem involving combinations. We are looking for the number of combinations of $n = 52$ cards drawn $r = 5$ at a time. We use the formula

$$_nC_r = \frac{n!}{(n-r)!\, r!}$$

with $n = 52$ and $r = 5$.

$$_{52}C_5 = \frac{52!}{(52-5)!\,5!} = \frac{52!}{47!\,5!} = \frac{52 \cdot 51 \cdot 50 \cdot 49 \cdot 48 \cdot \cancel{47!}}{\cancel{47!} \cdot 5 \cdot 4 \cdot 3 \cdot 2 \cdot 1} = 2{,}598{,}960$$

Thus, there are 2,598,960 different 5-card poker hands possible. It surprises many people that more than 2.5 million 5-card hands can be dealt from a mere 52 cards.

FIGURE 8.3 A royal flush

If you are a card player, it does not get any better than to be dealt the 5-card poker hand shown in Figure 8.3. This hand is called a *royal flush*. It consists of an ace, king, queen, jack, and 10, all of the same suit: all hearts, all diamonds, all clubs, or all spades. The probability of being dealt a royal flush involves calculating the number of ways of being dealt such a hand: just 4 of all 2,598,960 possible hands. In the next section, we move from counting possibilities to computing probabilities.

How many different 4-card hands can be dealt from a deck that has 16 different cards?

There are situations in which both the formula for combinations and the Fundamental Counting Principle are used together. Let's say that the U.S. Senate, with 100 members, consists of 54 Republicans and 46 Democrats. We want to form a committee of 3 Republicans and 2 Democrats.

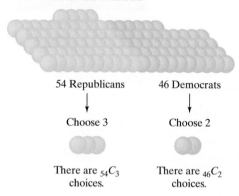

By the Fundamental Counting Principle, the number of ways of choosing 3 Republicans and 2 Democrats is given by

$$_{54}C_3 \cdot {}_{46}C_2.$$

In Example 4, we develop these ideas in more detail.

EXAMPLE 4 | USING THE FORMULA FOR COMBINATIONS AND THE FUNDAMENTAL COUNTING PRINCIPLE

The U.S. Senate of the 104th Congress consisted of 54 Republicans and 46 Democrats. How many committees can be formed if each committee must have 3 Republicans and 2 Democrats?

SOLUTION The order in which the members are selected does not matter. Thus, this is a problem involving combinations.

We begin with the number of ways of selecting 3 Republicans out of 54 Republicans without regard to order. We are looking for the number of combinations of $n = 54$ people taken $r = 3$ people at a time. We use the formula

$$_{n}C_r = \frac{n!}{(n-r)!\,r!}$$

with $n = 54$ and $r = 3$.

$$_{54}C_3 = \frac{54!}{(54-3)!\,3!} = \frac{54!}{51!\,3!} = \frac{54 \cdot 53 \cdot 52 \cdot \cancel{51!}}{\cancel{51!} \cdot 3 \cdot 2 \cdot 1} = \frac{54 \cdot 53 \cdot 52}{3 \cdot 2 \cdot 1} = 24{,}804$$

There are 24,804 choices for forming 3-member Republican committees.

Next, we find the number of ways of selecting 2 Democrats out of 46 Democrats without regard to order. We are looking for the number of combinations of $n = 46$ people taken $r = 2$ people at a time. Once again, we use the formula

$$_nC_r = \frac{n!}{(n-r)!\,r!}.$$

This time, $n = 46$ and $r = 2$.

$$_{46}C_2 = \frac{46!}{(46-2)!\,2!} = \frac{46!}{44!\,2!} = \frac{46 \cdot 45 \cdot 44!}{44! \cdot 2 \cdot 1} = 1035$$

There are 1035 choices for forming 2-member Democratic committees.

We use the Fundamental Counting Principle to find the number of committees that can be formed:

$$_{54}C_3 \cdot {}_{46}C_2 = 24{,}804 \cdot 1035 = 25{,}672{,}140.$$

Thus, 25,672,140 committees can be formed.

CHECK POINT 4 The U.S. Senate of the 107th Congress consisted of 50 Democrats, 49 Republicans, and one Independent. How many committees can be formed if each committee must have 3 Democrats and 2 Republicans?

EXERCISE SET 8.3 ●●●●●●

• Practice Exercises

In Exercises 1–4, does the problem involve permutations or combinations? Explain your answer. (It is not necessary to solve the problem.)

1. A medical researcher needs 6 people to test the effectiveness of an experimental drug. If 13 people have volunteered for the test, in how many ways can 6 people be selected?

2. Fifty people purchase raffle tickets. Three winning tickets are selected at random. If first prize is $1000, second prize is $500, and third prize is $100, in how many different ways can the prizes be awarded?

3. How many different four-letter passwords can be formed from the letters A, B, C, D, E, F, and G if no repetition of letters is allowed?

4. Fifty people purchase raffle tickets. Three winning tickets are selected at random. If each prize is $500, in how many different ways can the prizes be awarded?

In Exercises 5–20, use the formula for $_nC_r$ to evaluate each expression.

5. $_6C_5$ 6. $_8C_7$ 7. $_9C_5$ 8. $_{10}C_6$

9. $_{11}C_4$ 10. $_{12}C_5$ 11. $_8C_1$ 12. $_7C_1$

13. $_7C_7$ 14. $_4C_4$ 15. $_{30}C_3$ 16. $_{25}C_4$

17. $_5C_0$ 18. $_6C_0$ 19. $\dfrac{_7C_3}{_5C_4}$ 20. $\dfrac{_{10}C_3}{_6C_4}$

• Practice Plus

In Exercises 21–28, evaluate each expression.

21. $\dfrac{_7P_3}{3!} - {}_7C_3$ 22. $\dfrac{_{20}P_2}{2!} - {}_{20}C_2$ 23. $1 - \dfrac{_3P_2}{_4P_3}$

24. $1 - \dfrac{_5P_3}{_{10}P_4}$ 25. $\dfrac{_7C_3}{_5C_4} - \dfrac{98!}{96!}$ 26. $\dfrac{_{10}C_3}{_6C_4} - \dfrac{46!}{44!}$

27. $\dfrac{_4C_2 \cdot {}_6C_1}{_{18}C_3}$ 28. $\dfrac{_5C_1 \cdot {}_7C_2}{_{12}C_3}$

• Application Exercises

Use the formula for $_nC_r$ to solve Exercises 29–36.

29. An election ballot asks voters to select three city commissioners from a group of six candidates. In how many ways can this be done?

30. A four-person committee is to be elected from an organization's membership of 11 people. How many different committees are possible?

31. Of 12 possible books, you plan to take 4 with you on vacation. How many different collections of 4 books can you take?

32. There are 14 standbys who hope to get seats on a flight, but only 6 seats are available on the plane. How many different ways can the 6 people be selected?

33. You volunteer to help drive children at a charity event to the zoo, but you can fit only 8 of the 17 children present in your van. How many different groups of 8 children can you drive?

34. Of the 100 people in the U.S. Senate, 18 serve on the Foreign Relations Committee. How many ways are there to select Senate members for this committee (assuming party affiliation is not a factor in the selection)?

35. To win at LOTTO in the state of Florida, one must correctly select 6 numbers from a collection of 53 numbers (1 through 53). The order in which the selection is made does not matter. How many different selections are possible?

36. To win in the New York State lottery, one must correctly select 6 numbers from 59 numbers. The order in which the selection is made does not matter. How many different selections are possible?

In Exercises 37–46, solve by the method of your choice.

37. In a race in which six automobiles are entered and there are no ties, in how many ways can the first four finishers come in?

38. A book club offers a choice of 8 books from a list of 40. In how many ways can a member make a selection?

39. A medical researcher needs 6 people to test the effectiveness of an experimental drug. If 13 people have volunteered for the test, in how many ways can 6 people be selected?

40. Fifty people purchase raffle tickets. Three winning tickets are selected at random. If first prize is $1000, second prize is $500, and third prize is $100, in how many different ways can the prizes be awarded?

41. From a club of 20 people, in how many ways can a group of three members be selected to attend a conference?

42. Fifty people purchase raffle tickets. Three winning tickets are selected at random. If each prize is $500, in how many different ways can the prizes be awarded?

43. How many different four-letter passwords can be formed from the letters A, B, C, D, E, F, and G if no repetition of letters is allowed?

44. Nine comedy acts will perform over two evenings. Five of the acts will perform on the first evening. How many ways can the schedule for the first evening be made?

45. Using 15 flavors of ice cream, how many cones with three different flavors can you create if it is important to you which flavor goes on the top, middle, and bottom?

46. Baskin-Robbins offers 31 different flavors of ice cream. One of its items is a bowl consisting of three scoops of ice cream, each a different flavor. How many such bowls are possible?

Use the formula for $_nC_r$ and the Fundamental Counting Principle to solve Exercises 47–50.

47. In how many ways can a committee of four men and five women be formed from a group of seven men and seven women?

48. How many different committees can be formed from 5 professors and 15 students if each committee is made up of 2 professors and 10 students?

49. The U.S. Senate of the 109th Congress consisted of 55 Republicans, 44 Democrats, and 1 Independent. How many committees can be formed if each committee must have 4 Republicans and 3 Democrats?

50. A mathematics exam consists of 10 multiple-choice questions and 5 open-ended problems in which all work must be shown. If an examinee must answer 8 of the multiple-choice questions and 3 of the open-ended problems, in how many ways can the questions and problems be chosen?

Thousands of jokes have been told about marriage and divorce. Exercises 51–58 are based on the following observations:

- *"By all means, marry; if you get a good wife, you'll be happy. If you get a bad one, you'll become a philosopher." - Socrates*

- *"My wife and I were happy for 20 years. Then we met." - Rodney Dangerfield*

- *"Whatever you may look like, marry a man your own age. As your beauty fades, so will his eyesight." - Phyllis Diller*

- *"Why do Jewish divorces cost so much? Because they're worth it." - Henny Youngman*

- *"I think men who have a pierced ear are better prepared for marriage. They've experienced pain and bought jewelry." - Rita Rudner*

- *"For a while we pondered whether to take a vacation or get a divorce. We decided that a trip to Bermuda is over in two weeks, but a divorce is something you always have." - Woody Allen*

51. In how many ways can these six jokes be ranked from best to worst?

52. If Socrates's thoughts about marriage are excluded, in how many ways can the remaining five jokes be ranked from best to worst?

53. In how many ways can people select their three favorite jokes from these thoughts about marriage and divorce?

54. In how many ways can people select their two favorite jokes from these thoughts about marriage and divorce?

55. If the order in which these jokes are told makes a difference in terms of how they are received, how many ways can they be delivered if Socrates's comments are scheduled first and Dangerfield's joke is told last?

56. If the order in which these jokes are told makes a difference in terms of how they are received, how many ways can they be delivered if a joke by a woman (Rudner or Diller) is told first?

57. In how many ways can people select their favorite joke told by a woman (Rudner or Diller) and their two favorite jokes told by a man?

58. In how many ways can people select their favorite joke told by a woman (Rudner or Diller) and their three favorite jokes told by a man?

• Writing in Mathematics

59. What is a combination?

60. Explain how to distinguish between permutation and combination problems.

61. Write a word problem that can be solved by evaluating $_7C_3$.

• Critical Thinking Exercises

62. Write a word problem that can be solved by evaluating $_{10}C_3 \cdot _7C_2$.

63. A 6/53 lottery involves choosing 6 of the numbers from 1 through 53 and a 5/36 lottery involves choosing 5 of the numbers from 1 through 36. The order in which the numbers are chosen does not matter. Which lottery is easier to win? Explain your answer.

64. If the number of permutations of n objects taken r at a time is six times the number of combinations of n objects taken r at a time, determine the value of r. Is there enough information to determine the value of n? Why or why not?

65. In a group of 20 people, how long will it take each person to shake hands with each of the other persons in the group, assuming that it takes three seconds for each shake and only 2 people can shake hands at a time? What if the group is increased to 40 people?

66. A sample of 4 telephones is selected from a shipment of 20 phones. There are 5 defective telephones in the shipment. How many of the samples of 4 phones do not include any of the defective ones?

SECTION 8.4 • FUNDAMENTALS OF PROBABILITY

O B J E C T I V E S

1. Compute theoretical probability.

2. Compute empirical probability.

TABLE 8.1 THE HOURS OF SLEEP AMERICANS GET ON A TYPICAL NIGHT	
Hours of Sleep	**Number of Americans, in millions**
4 or less	12
5	27
6	75
7	90
8	81
9	9
10 or more	6

Total: 300

Source: Discovery Health Media

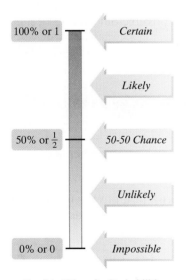

Possible Values for Probabilities

How many hours of sleep do you typically get each night? Table 8.1 indicates that 75 million out of 300 million Americans are getting six hours of sleep on a typical night. The *probability* of an American getting six hours of sleep on a typical night is $\frac{75}{300}$. This fraction can be reduced to $\frac{1}{4}$, or expressed as 0.25, or 25%. Thus, 25% of Americans get six hours of sleep each night.

We find a probability by dividing one number by another. Probabilities are assigned to an *event*, such as getting six hours of sleep on a typical night. Events that are certain to occur are assigned probabilities of 1, or 100%. For example, the probability that a given individual will eventually die is 1. Although Woody Allen whined, "I don't want to achieve immortality through my work. I want to achieve it through not dying," death (and taxes) are always certain. By contrast, if an event cannot occur, its probability is 0. Regrettably, the probability that Elvis will return and serenade us with one final reprise of "Don't Be Cruel" (and we hope we're not) is 0.

Probabilities of events are expressed as numbers ranging from 0 to 1, or 0% to 100%. The closer the probability of a given event is to 1, the more likely it is that the event will occur. The closer the probability of a given event is to 0, the less likely it is that the event will occur.

Theoretical Probability

1 | Compute theoretical probability.

You toss a coin. Although it is equally likely to land either heads up, denoted by *H*, or tails up, denoted by *T*, the actual outcome is uncertain. Any occurrence for which the outcome is uncertain is called an **experiment**. Thus, tossing a coin is an example of an experiment. The set of all possible outcomes of an experiment is the **sample space** of the experiment, denoted by *S*. The sample space for the coin-tossing experiment is

$$S = \{H, T\}.$$

Lands heads up   Lands tails up

An **event**, denoted by *E*, is any subset of a sample space. For example, the subset $E = \{T\}$ is the event of landing tails up when a coin is tossed.

Theoretical probability applies to situations like this, in which the sample space only contains equally likely outcomes, all of which are known. To calculate the theoretical probability of an event, we divide the number of outcomes resulting in the event by the total number of outcomes in the sample space.

COMPUTING THEORETICAL PROBABILITY

If an event E has $n(E)$ equally likely outcomes and its sample space S has $n(S)$ equally likely outcomes, the **theoretical probability** of event E, denoted by $P(E)$, is

$$P(E) = \frac{\text{number of outcomes in event } E}{\text{total number of possible outcomes}} = \frac{n(E)}{n(S)}.$$

How can we use this formula to compute the probability of a coin landing tails up? We use the following sets:

$$E = \{T\} \qquad S = \{H, T\}.$$

This is the event of landing tails up.

This is the sample space with all equally likely outcomes.

The probability of a coin landing tails up is

$$P(E) = \frac{\text{number of outcomes that result in tails up}}{\text{total number of possible outcomes}} = \frac{n(E)}{n(S)} = \frac{1}{2}.$$

Theoretical probability applies to many games of chance, including dice rolling, lotteries, card games, and roulette. We begin with rolling a die. Figure 8.4 illustrates that when a die is rolled, there are six equally likely possible outcomes. The sample space can be shown as

$$S = \{1, 2, 3, 4, 5, 6\}.$$

FIGURE 8.4 Outcomes when a die is rolled

EXAMPLE 1   COMPUTING THEORETICAL PROBABILITY

A die is rolled once. Find the probability of rolling

a. a 3.   **b.** an even number.   **c.** a number less than 5.
d. a number less than 10.   **e.** a number greater than 6.

SOLUTION The sample space is $S = \{1, 2, 3, 4, 5, 6\}$ with $n(S) = 6$. We will use 6, the total number of possible outcomes, in the denominator of each probability fraction.

a. The phrase "rolling a 3" describes the event $E = \{3\}$. This event can occur in one way: $n(E) = 1$.

$$P(3) = \frac{\text{number of outcomes that result in 3}}{\text{total number of possible outcomes}} = \frac{n(E)}{n(S)} \frac{1}{6}$$

The probability of rolling a 3 is $\frac{1}{6}$.

b. The phrase "rolling an even number" describes the event $E = \{2, 4, 6\}$. This event can occur in three ways: $n(E) = 3$.

$$P(\text{even number}) = \frac{\text{number of outcomes that result in an even number}}{\text{total number of possible outcomes}} = \frac{n(E)}{n(S)} = \frac{3}{6} = \frac{1}{2}$$

The probability of rolling an even number is $\frac{1}{2}$.

c. The phrase "rolling a number less than 5" describes the event $E = \{1, 2, 3, 4\}$. This event can occur in four ways: $n(E) = 4$.

$$P(\text{less than 5}) = \frac{\text{number of outcomes that are less than 5}}{\text{total number of possible outcomes}} = \frac{n(E)}{n(S)} = \frac{4}{6} = \frac{2}{3}$$

The probability of rolling a number less than 5 is $\frac{2}{3}$.

d. The phrase "rolling a number less than 10" describes the event $E = \{1, 2, 3, 4, 5, 6\}$. This event can occur in six ways: $n(E) = 6$. Can you see that all of the possible outcomes are less than 10? This event is certain to occur.

$$P(\text{less than 10}) = \frac{\text{number of outcomes that are less than 10}}{\text{total number of possible outcomes}} = \frac{n(E)}{n(S)} = \frac{6}{6} = 1$$

The probability of any certain event is 1.

e. The phrase "rolling a number greater than 6" describes an event that cannot occur, or the empty set. Thus, $E = \varnothing$ and $n(E) = 0$.

$$P(\text{greater than 6}) = \frac{\text{number of outcomes that are greater than 6}}{\text{total number of possible outcomes}} = \frac{n(E)}{n(S)} = \frac{0}{6} = 0$$

The probability of an event that cannot occur is 0.

In Example 1, there are six possible outcomes, each with a probability of $\frac{1}{6}$:

$$P(1) = \frac{1}{6} \quad P(2) = \frac{1}{6} \quad P(3) = \frac{1}{6} \quad P(4) = \frac{1}{6} \quad P(5) = \frac{1}{6} \quad P(6) = \frac{1}{6}.$$

The sum of these probabilities is 1: $\frac{1}{6} + \frac{1}{6} + \frac{1}{6} + \frac{1}{6} + \frac{1}{6} + \frac{1}{6} = 1$. In general, **the sum of the theoretical probabilities of all possible outcomes in the sample space is 1**.

  A die is rolled once. Find the probability of rolling

    a. a 2.

    b. a number less than 4.

    c. a number greater than 7.

    d. a number less than 7.

Our next example involves a standard 52-card bridge deck, illustrated in Figure 8.5. The deck has four suits: Hearts and diamonds are red, and clubs and spades are black. Each suit has 13 different face values—A(ace), 2, 3, 4, 5, 6, 7, 8, 9, 10, J(jack), Q(queen), and K(king). Jacks, queens, and kings are called **picture cards** or **face cards**.

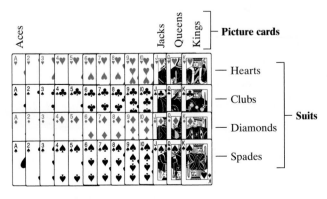

FIGURE 8.5 A standard 52-card bridge deck

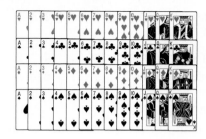

FIGURE 8.5 (repeated)

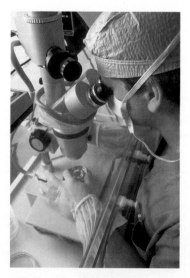

Genetic engineering offers some hope for cystic fibrosis patients. Geneticists can now isolate the *c* gene, the gene responsible for the disease. It is hoped that it will soon be possible to replace the defective *c* gene with a normal *C* gene.

EXAMPLE 2 PROBABILITY AND A DECK OF 52 CARDS

You are dealt one card from a standard 52-card deck. Find the probability of being dealt

a. a king.   **b.** a heart.   **c.** the king of hearts.

SOLUTION Because there are 52 cards in the deck, the total number of possible ways of being dealt a single card is 52. The number of outcomes in the sample space is 52: $n(S) = 52$. We use 52 as the denominator of each probability fraction.

a. Let E be the event of being dealt a king. Because there are four kings in the deck, this event can occur in four ways: $n(E) = 4$.

$$P(\text{king}) = \frac{\text{number of outcomes that result in a king}}{\text{total number of possible outcomes}} = \frac{n(E)}{n(S)} = \frac{4}{52} = \frac{1}{13}$$

The probability of being dealt a king is $\frac{1}{13}$.

b. Let E be the event of being dealt a heart. Because there are 13 hearts in the deck, this event can occur in 13 ways: $n(E) = 13$.

$$P(\text{heart}) = \frac{\text{number of outcomes that result in a heart}}{\text{total number of possible outcomes}} = \frac{n(E)}{n(S)} = \frac{13}{52} = \frac{1}{4}$$

The probability of being dealt a heart is $\frac{1}{4}$.

c. Let E be the event of being dealt the king of hearts. Because there is only one card in the deck that is the king of hearts, this event can occur in just one way: $n(E) = 1$.

$$P(\text{king of hearts}) = \frac{\text{number of outcomes that result in the king of hearts}}{\text{total number of possible outcomes}} = \frac{n(E)}{n(S)} = \frac{1}{52}$$

The probability of being dealt the king of hearts is $\frac{1}{52}$.

CHECK POINT 2 You are dealt one card from a standard 52-card deck. Find the probability of being dealt

a. an ace.   **b.** a red card.   **c.** a red king.

Probabilities play a valuable role in the science of genetics. Example 3 deals with cystic fibrosis, an inherited lung disease occurring in about 1 out of every 2000 births among Caucasians and in about 1 out of every 250,000 births among non-Caucasians.

EXAMPLE 3 PROBABILITIES IN GENETICS

Each person carries two genes that are related to the absence or presence of the disease cystic fibrosis. Most Americans have two normal genes for this trait and are unaffected by cystic fibrosis. However, 1 in 25 Americans carries one normal gene and one defective gene. If we use *c* to represent a defective gene and *C* a normal gene, such a carrier can be designated as *Cc*. Thus, *CC* is a person who neither carries nor has cystic fibrosis, *Cc* is a carrier who is not actually sick, and *cc* is a person sick with the disease. Table 8.2 shows the four equally likely outcomes for a child's genetic inheritance from two parents who are both carrying one cystic fibrosis gene. One copy of each gene is passed on to the child from the parents.

TABLE 8.2 CYSTIC FIBROSIS AND GENETIC INHERITANCE

		Second Parent	
		C	*c*
First	*C*	*CC*	*Cc*
Parent	*c*	*cC*	*cc*

Shown in the table are the four possibilities for a child whose parents each carry one cystic fibrosis gene.

If each parent carries one cystic fibrosis gene, what is the probability that their child will have cystic fibrosis?

SOLUTION Table 8.2 shows that there are four equally likely outcomes. The sample space is $S = \{CC, Cc, cC, cc\}$ and $n(S) = 4$. The phrase "will have cystic fibrosis" describes only the cc child. Thus, $E = \{cc\}$ and $n(E) = 1$.

$$P(\text{cystic fibrosis}) = \frac{\text{number of outcomes that result in cystic fibrosis}}{\text{total number of possible outcomes}} = \frac{n(E)}{n(S)} = \frac{1}{4}$$

If each parent carries one cystic fibrosis gene, the probability that their child will have cystic fibrosis is $\frac{1}{4}$.

○

CHECK POINT 3 Use Table 8.2 in Example 3 to solve this exercise. If each parent carries one cystic fibrosis gene, find the probability that their child will be a carrier of the disease who is not actually sick.

---

2 Compute empirical probability.

Empirical Probability

Theoretical probability is based on a set of equally likely outcomes and the number of elements in the set. By contrast, *empirical probability* applies to situations in which we observe how frequently an event occurs. We use the following formula to compute the empirical probability of an event:

> **COMPUTING EMPIRICAL PROBABILITY**
> The empirical probability of event E is
> $$P(E) = \frac{\text{observed number of times } E \text{ occurs}}{\text{total number of observed occurrences}}.$$

EXAMPLE 4   COMPUTING EMPIRICAL PROBABILITY

Table 8.3 shows the distribution, by marital status and gender, of the 212.5 million Americans ages 18 or older.

TABLE 8.3 MARITAL STATUS OF THE U.S. POPULATION, AGES 18 OR OLDER, IN MILLIONS

	Never Married	Married	Widowed	Divorced	Total
Male	28.6	62.1	2.7	9.0	102.4
Female	23.3	62.8	11.3	12.7	110.1
Total	51.9	124.9	14.0	21.7	212.5

Total male:
28.6 + 62.1 + 2.7 + 9.0 = 102.4

Total female:
23.3 + 62.8 + 11.3 + 12.7 = 110.1

Total never married:
28.6 + 23.3 = 51.9

Total widowed:
2.7 + 11.3 = 14.0

Total adult population:
102.4 + 110.1 = 212.5

Total married:
62.1 + 62.8 = 124.9

Total divorced:
9.0 + 12.7 = 21.7

Source: U.S. Census Bureau

STUDY TIP

Our selection from the U.S. adult population is *random*. This means that every person in the population has an equal chance of being chosen. We'll have much more to say about random selections in Chapter 9, Statistics.

If one person is randomly selected from the population described in Table 8.3, find the probability, to the nearest hundreth, that the person

a. is divorced.   **b.** is female.

SOLUTION

a. The probability of selecting a divorced person is the observed number of divorced people, 21.7 (million), divided by the total number of U.S. adults, 212.5 (million).

$$P(\text{selecting a divorced person from the U.S. adult population})$$

$$= \frac{\text{number of divorced people}}{\text{total number of U.S. adults}} = \frac{21.7}{212.5} \approx 0.10$$

The empirical probability of selecting a divorced person from the U.S. adult population is approximately 0.10.

b. Be sure to refer to Table 8.3 on the previous page. The probability of selecting a female is the observed number of females, 110.1 (million), divided by the total number of U.S. adults, 212.5 (million).

$$P(\text{selecting a female from the U.S. adult population})$$

$$= \frac{\text{number of females}}{\text{total number of U.S. adults}} = \frac{110.1}{212.5} \approx 0.52$$

The empirical probability of selecting a female from the U.S. adult population is approximately 0.52.

○

CHECK POINT 4 If one person is randomly selected from the population described in Table 8.3 on page 461, find the probability, expressed as a decimal rounded to the nearest hundredth, that the person

a. has never been married.   **b.** is male.

In certain situations, we can establish a relationship between the two kinds of probability. Consider, for example, a coin that is equally likely to land heads or tails. Such a coin is called a **fair coin**. Empirical probability can be used to determine whether a coin is fair. Suppose we toss a coin 10, 50, 100, 1000, 10,000, and 100,000 times. We record the number of heads observed, shown in Table 8.4. For each of the six cases in the table, the empirical probability of heads is determined by dividing the number of heads observed by the number of tosses.

TABLE 8.4 EMPIRICAL PROBABILITIES OF HEADS AS THE NUMBER OF TOSSES INCREASES

Number of Tosses	Number of Heads Observed	Empirical Probability of Heads, or $P(H)$
10	4	$P(H) = \frac{4}{10} = 0.4$
50	27	$P(H) = \frac{27}{50} = 0.54$
100	44	$P(H) = \frac{44}{100} = 0.44$
1000	530	$P(H) = \frac{530}{1000} = 0.53$
10,000	4851	$P(H) = \frac{4851}{10,000} = 0.4851$
100,000	49,880	$P(H) = \frac{49,880}{100,000} = 0.4988$

A pattern is exhibited by the empirical probabilities in the right-hand column of Table 8.4. As the number of tosses increases, the empirical probabilities tend to get closer to 0.5, the theoretical probability. These results give us no reason to suspect that the coin is not fair.

Table 8.4 illustrates an important principle when observing uncertain outcomes such as the event of a coin landing on heads. As an experiment is repeated more and more times, the empirical probability of an event tends to get closer to the theoretical probability of that event. This principle is known as the **law of large numbers**.

EXERCISE SET 8.4 ●●●●●○○

• Practice and Application Exercises

Exercises 1–54 involve theoretical probability. Use the theoretical probability formula to solve each exercise. Express each probability as a fraction reduced to lowest terms.

In Exercises 1–10, a die is rolled. The set of equally likely outcomes is {1, 2, 3, 4, 5, 6}. Find the probability of rolling

1. a 4.
2. a 5.
3. an odd number.
4. a number greater than 3.
5. a number less than 3.
6. a number greater than 4.
7. a number less than 7.
8. a number less than 8.
9. a number greater than 7.
10. a number greater than 8.

In Exercises 11–20, you are dealt one card from a standard 52-card deck. Find the probability of being dealt

11. a queen.
12. a jack.
13. a club.
14. a diamond.
15. a picture card.
16. a card greater than 3 and less than 7.
17. the queen of spades.
18. the ace of clubs.
19. a diamond and a spade.
20. a card with a green heart.

In Exercises 21–26, a fair coin is tossed two times in succession. The set of equally likely outcomes is {HH, HT, TH, TT}. Find the probability of getting

21. two heads.
22. two tails.
23. the same outcome on each toss.
24. different outcomes on each toss.
25. a head on the second toss.
26. at least one head.

In Exercises 27–34, you select a family with three children. If M represents a male child and F a female child, the set of equally likely outcomes for the children's genders is {MMM, MMF, MFM, MFF, FMM, FMF, FFM, FFF}. Find the probability of selecting a family with

27. exactly one female child.
28. exactly one male child.
29. exactly two male children.
30. exactly two female children.
31. at least one male child.
32. at least two female children.
33. four male children.
34. fewer than four female children.

In Exercises 35–40, a single die is rolled twice. The 36 equally likely outcomes are shown as follows:

	Second Roll					
	⚀	⚁	⚂	⚃	⚄	⚅
⚀	(1, 1)	(1, 2)	(1, 3)	(1, 4)	(1, 5)	(1, 6)
⚁	(2, 1)	(2, 2)	(2, 3)	(2, 4)	(2, 5)	(2, 6)
⚂	(3, 1)	(3, 2)	(3, 3)	(3, 4)	(3, 5)	(3, 6)
⚃	(4, 1)	(4, 2)	(4, 3)	(4, 4)	(4, 5)	(4, 6)
⚄	(5, 1)	(5, 2)	(5, 3)	(5, 4)	(5, 5)	(5, 6)
⚅	(6, 1)	(6, 2)	(6, 3)	(6, 4)	(6, 5)	(6, 6)

First Roll (labels on the left side)

Find the probability of getting

35. two even numbers.
36. two odd numbers.
37. two numbers whose sum is 5.
38. two numbers whose sum is 6.
39. two numbers whose sum exceeds 12.
40. two numbers whose sum is less than 13.

Use the spinner shown to answer Exercises 41–48. Assume that it is equally probable that the pointer will land on any one of the ten colored regions. If the pointer lands on a borderline, spin again.

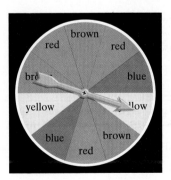

Find the probability that the spinner lands in

41. a red region.
42. a yellow region.
43. a blue region.
44. a brown region.
45. a region that is red or blue.
46. a region that is yellow or brown.
47. a region that is red and blue.
48. a region that is yellow and brown.

Exercises 49–54 deal with sickle cell anemia, an inherited disease in which red blood cells become distorted and deprived of oxygen. Approximately 1 in every 500 African-American infants is born with the disease; only 1 in 160,000 white infants has the disease. A person with two sickle cell genes will have the disease, but a person with only one sickle cell gene will have a mild, non-fatal anemia called sickle cell trait. (Approximately 8%–10% of the African-American population has this trait.)

		Second Parent	
		S	*s*
First	*S*	*SS*	*Ss*
Parent	*s*	*sS*	*ss*

If we use s to represent a sickle cell gene and S a healthy gene, the table shows the four possibilities for the children of two Ss parents. Each parent has only one sickle cell gene, so each has the relatively mild sickle cell trait. Find the probability that these parents give birth to a child who

49. has sickle cell anemia.   **50.** has sickle cell trait.

51. is healthy.

In Exercises 52–54, use the following table that shows the four possibilities for the children of one healthy, SS, parent, and one parent with sickle cell trait, Ss.

		Second Parent (with Sickle Cell Trait)	
		S	*s*
Healthy	*S*	*SS*	*Ss*
First Parent	*S*	*SS*	*Ss*

Find the probability that these parents give birth to a child who

52. has sickle cell anemia.   **53.** has sickle cell trait.
54. is healthy.

The table shows the distribution, by age and gender, of the 29.3 million Americans who live alone. Use the data in the table to solve Exercises 55–60.

NUMBER OF PEOPLE IN THE UNITED STATES LIVING ALONE, IN MILLIONS

	Ages 15–24	Ages 25–34	Ages 35–44	Ages 45–64	Ages 65–74	Ages ≥75	Total
Male	0.7	2.2	2.6	4.3	1.3	1.4	12.5
Female	0.8	1.6	1.6	5.0	2.9	4.9	16.8
Total	1.5	3.8	4.2	9.3	4.2	6.3	29.3

Source: U.S. Census Bureau

Find the probability, expressed as a decimal rounded to the nearest hundredth, that a randomly selected American living alone is

55. male.   **56.** female.

57. in the 25–34 age range.

58. in the 35–44 age range.

59. a woman in the 15–24 age range.

60. a man in the 45–64 age range.

The table shows the number of Americans who moved in 2004, categorized by where they moved and whether they were an owner or a renter. Use the data in the table, expressed in millions, to solve Exercises 61–66.

NUMBER OF PEOPLE IN THE UNITED STATES WHO MOVED IN 2004, IN MILLIONS

	Moved to Same State	Moved to Different State	Moved to Different Country
Owner	11.7	2.8	0.3
Renter	18.7	4.5	1.0

Source: U.S. Census Bureau

Find the probability, expressed as a decimal rounded to the nearest hundredth, that a randomly selected American who moved in 2004 was

61. an owner.

62. a renter.

63. a person who moved within the same state.

64. a person who moved to a different country.

65. a renter who moved to a different state.

66. an owner who moved to a different state.

• Writing in Mathematics

67. What is the sample space of an experiment? What is an event?

68. How is the theoretical probability of an event computed?

69. Describe the difference between theoretical probability and empirical probability.

70. Give an example of an event whose probability must be determined empirically rather than theoretically.

71. Use the definition of theoretical probability to explain why the probability of an event that cannot occur is 0.

72. Use the definition of theoretical probability to explain why the probability of an event that is certain to occur is 1.

73. Write a probability word problem whose answer is one of the following fractions: $\frac{1}{6}$ or $\frac{1}{4}$ or $\frac{1}{3}$.

74. The president of a large company with 10,000 employees is considering mandatory cocaine testing for every employee. The test that would be used is 90% accurate, meaning that it will detect 90% of the cocaine users who are tested, and that 90% of the nonusers will test negative. This also means that the test gives 10% false positive. Suppose that 1% of the employees actually use cocaine. Find the probability that someone who tests positive for cocaine use is, indeed, a user.

Hint: Find the following probability fraction:

the number of employees who test positive
and are cocaine users
――――――――――――――――――――.
the number of employes who test positive

This fraction is given by

$$\frac{90\% \text{ of } 1\% \text{ of } 10,000}{\text{the number who test positive who actually use cocaine plus the number who test positive who do not use cocaine}}.$$

What does this probability indicate in terms of the percentage of employees who test positive who are not actually users? Discuss these numbers in terms of the issue of mandatory drug testing. Write a paper either in favor of or against mandatory drug testing, incorporating the actual percentage accuracy for such tests.

• Critical Thinking Exercises

75. The target in the figure shown in the next column contains four squares. If a dart thrown at random hits the target, find the probability that it will land in an orange region.

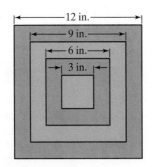

76. Some three-digit numbers, such as 101 and 313, read the same forward and backward. If you select a number from all three-digit numbers, find the probability that it will read the same forward and backward.

SECTION 8.5 • PROBABILITY WITH THE FUNDAMENTAL COUNTING PRINCIPLE, PERMUTATIONS, AND COMBINATIONS

OBJECTIVES

1. Compute probabilities with permutations.

2. Compute probabilities with combinations.

PROBABILITY OF DYING AT ANY GIVEN AGE

Age	Probability of Male Death	Probability of Female Death
10	0.00013	0.00010
20	0.00140	0.00050
30	0.00153	0.00050
40	0.00193	0.00095
50	0.00567	0.00305
60	0.01299	0.00792
70	0.03473	0.01764
80	0.07644	0.03966
90	0.15787	0.11250
100	0.26876	0.23969
110	0.39770	0.39043

Source: George Shaffner, *The Arithmetic of Life and Death*

George Tooker (b. 1920) "*Mirror II*"
1963, egg tempera on gesso panel, 20 × 20 in., 1968.4. Gift of R. H. Donnelley Erdman (PA 1956). Addison Gallery of American Art, Phillips Academy, Andover, Massachusetts. All Rights Reserved.

According to actuarial tables, there is no year in which death is as likely as continued life, at least until the age of 115. Until that age, the probability of dying in any one year ranges from a low of 0.00009 for a girl at age 11 to a high of 0.465 for either gender at age 114. For a healthy 30-year-old, how does the probability of dying this year compare to the probability of winning the top prize in a state lottery game? In this section, we provide the surprising answer to this question, as we study probability with the Fundamental Counting Principle, permutations, and combinations.

1 | Compute probabilities with permutations.

Probability with Permutations

We return to our concert tour with U2, Bruce Springsteen and the E Street Band, Aerosmith, and the Rolling Stones. Now, the two surviving members of the Beatles have agreed to join the tour! You really have your work cut out for you. In which order should the five groups in the concert perform? Because order makes a difference, this is a permutation situation. Example 1 is based on this scenario, and uses permutations to solve a probability problem.

EXAMPLE 1   PROBABILITY AND PERMUTATIONS

The five groups in the tour agree to determine the order of performance based on a random selection. Each band's name is written on one of five cards. The cards are placed in a hat and then five cards are drawn, one at a time. The order in which the cards are drawn determines the order in which the bands perform. What is the probability of the Rolling Stones performing fourth and the Beatles last?

SOLUTION We begin by applying the definition of probability to this situation.

P(Rolling Stones fourth, Beatles last)

$$= \frac{\text{number of permutations with Rolling Stones fourth, Beatles last}}{\text{total number of possible permutations}}$$

We can use the Fundamental Counting Principle to find the total number of possible permutations. This represents the number of ways you can put together the concert.

First Group to Perform	Second Group to Perform	Third Group to Perform	Fourth Group to Perform	Last Group to Perform
5 choices	4 choices	3 choices	2 choices	1 choice

There are $5 \cdot 4 \cdot 3 \cdot 2 \cdot 1$, or 120, possible permutations. Equivalently, the five groups can perform in 120 different orders.

We can also use the Fundamental Counting Principle to find the number of permutations with the Rolling Stones performing fourth and the Beatles performing last. You can choose any one of the three groups, U2, Bruce Springsteen and the E Street Band, or Aerosmith, as the opening act. This leaves two choices for the second group to perform, and only one choice for the third group to perform. There is only one choice for the fourth group—the Rolling Stones, and one choice for the closing act—the Beatles:

First Group to Perform	Second Group to Perform	Third Group to Perform	Fourth Group to Perform	Last Group to Perform
3 choices (U2, Springsteen, or Aerosmith)	2 choices	1 choice	1 choice: The Rolling Stones	1 choice: The Beatles

Thus, there are $3 \cdot 2 \cdot 1 \cdot 1 \cdot 1$, or 6 possible permutations. Equivalently, there are 6 lineups with the Rolling Stones performing fourth and the Beatles last.

Now we can return to our probability fraction.

P(Rolling Stones fourth, Beatles last)

$$= \frac{\text{number of permutations with Rolling Stones fourth, Beatles last}}{\text{total number of possible permutations}}$$

$$= \frac{6}{120} = \frac{1}{20}$$

The probability of the Rolling Stones performing fourth and the Beatles last is $\frac{1}{20}$. ○

 Use the information given in Example 1 to find the probability of U2 performing first, the Rolling Stones performing fourth, and the Beatles last.

2 | Compute probabilities with combinations.

In 2004, Americans spent $49.4 billion on lotteries set up by revenue-hungry states. Once prizes and administrative costs were paid, $15.1 billion was left in revenue for the states. Throughout the United States, 64% of lottery profits go to education funding.
Source: North American Association of State and Provincial Lotteries

Probability with Combinations

In 2006, 41 states and Washington, D.C., had lotteries, and several states were considering selling lottery tickets on the Internet. If your state has a lottery drawing each week, the probability that someone will win the top prize is relatively high. If there is no winner this week, it is virtually certain that eventually someone will be graced with millions of dollars. So, why are you so unlucky compared to this undisclosed someone? In Example 2, we provide an answer to this question.

| EXAMPLE 2 | PROBABILITY AND COMBINATIONS: WINNING THE LOTTERY |

Florida's lottery game, LOTTO, is set up so that each player chooses six different numbers from 1 to 53. If the six numbers chosen match the six numbers drawn randomly, the player wins (or shares) the top cash prize. (As of this writing, the top cash prize has ranged from $7 million to $106.5 million.) With one LOTTO ticket, what is the probability of winning this prize?

SOLUTION Because the order of the six numbers does not matter, this is a situation involving combinations. We begin with the formula for probability.

$$P(\text{winning}) = \frac{\text{number of ways of winning}}{\text{total number of possible combinations}}$$

We can use the combinations formula

$$_nC_r = \frac{n!}{(n-r)!\,r!}$$

to find the total number of possible combinations. We are selecting $r = 6$ numbers from a collection of $n = 53$ numbers.

$$_{53}C_6 = \frac{53!}{(53-6)!\,6!} = \frac{53!}{47!\,6!} = \frac{53 \cdot 52 \cdot 51 \cdot 50 \cdot 49 \cdot 48 \cdot \cancel{47!}}{\cancel{47!} \cdot 6 \cdot 5 \cdot 4 \cdot 3 \cdot 2 \cdot 1} = 22{,}957{,}480$$

There are nearly 23 million number combinations possible in LOTTO. If a person buys one LOTTO ticket, that person has selected only one combination of the six numbers. With one LOTTO ticket, there is only one way of winning.

Now we can return to our probability fraction.

$$P(\text{winning}) = \frac{\text{number of ways of winning}}{\text{total number of possible combinations}} = \frac{1}{22{,}957{,}480} \approx 0.0000000436$$

The probability of winning the top prize with one LOTTO ticket is $\frac{1}{22,957,480}$, or about 1 in 23 million.

Suppose that a person buys 5000 different tickets in Florida's LOTTO. Because that person has selected 5000 different combinations of the six numbers, the probability of winning is

$$\frac{5000}{22{,}957{,}480} \approx 0.000218.$$

The chances of winning top prize are about 218 in a million. At $1 per LOTTO ticket, it is highly probable that our LOTTO player will be $5000 poorer. Knowing a little probability helps a lotto.

2 People lose interest when they do not win at games of chance, including Florida's LOTTO. With drawings twice weekly instead of once, the game described in Example 2 was brought in to bring back lost players and increase ticket sales. The original LOTTO was set up so that each player chose six different numbers from 1 to 49, rather than from 1 to 53, with a lottery drawing only once a week. With one LOTTO ticket, what was the probability of winning the top cash prize in Florida's original LOTTO? Express the answer as a fraction and as a decimal correct to ten places.

BLITZER BONUS

Comparing the Probability of Dying to the Probability of Winning Florida's LOTTO

As a healthy nonsmoking 30-year-old, your probability of dying this year is approximately 0.001. Divide this probability by the probability of winning LOTTO with one ticket:

$$\frac{0.001}{0.0000000436} \approx 22{,}936.$$

A healthy 30-year-old is nearly 23,000 times more likely to die this year than to win Florida's lottery.

EXAMPLE 3   PROBABILITY AND COMBINATIONS

A club consists of five men and seven women. Three members are selected at random to attend a conference. Find the probability that the selected group consists of

a. three men.

b. one man and two women.

SOLUTION   The order in which the three people are selected does not matter, so this is a problem involving combinations.

12 Club Members

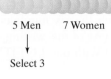

5 Men   7 Women

↓

Select 3

a. We begin with the probability of selecting three men.

$$P(3 \text{ men}) = \frac{\text{number of ways of selecting 3 men}}{\text{total number of possible combinations}}$$

First, we consider the denominator of the probability fraction. We are selecting $r = 3$ people from a total group of $n = 12$ people (five men and seven women). The total number of possible combinations is

$$_{12}C_3 = \frac{12!}{(12-3)!\,3!} = \frac{12!}{9!\,3!} = \frac{12 \cdot 11 \cdot 10 \cdot 9!}{9! \cdot 3 \cdot 2 \cdot 1} = 220.$$

Thus, there are 220 possible three-person selections.

Next, we consider the numerator of the probability fraction. We are interested in the number of ways of selecting three men from five men. We are selecting $r = 3$ men from a total group of $n = 5$ men. The number of possible combinations of three men is

$$_{5}C_3 = \frac{5!}{(5-3)!\,3!} = \frac{5!}{2!\,3!} = \frac{5 \cdot 4 \cdot 3!}{2 \cdot 1 \cdot 3!} = 10.$$

Thus, there are 10 ways of selecting three men from five men. Now we can fill in the numbers in the numerator and the denominator of our probability fraction.

$$P(3 \text{ men}) = \frac{\text{number of ways of selecting 3 men}}{\text{total number of possible combinations}} = \frac{10}{220} = \frac{1}{22}$$

The probability that the group selected to attend the conference consists of three men is $\frac{1}{22}$.

12 Club Members

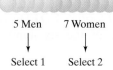

5 Men   7 Women

↓   ↓

Select 1   Select 2

b. We set up the fraction for the probability that the selected group consists of one man and two women.

$$P(1 \text{ man, 2 women}) = \frac{\text{number of ways of selecting 1 man and 2 women}}{\text{total number of possible combinations}}$$

The denominator of this fraction is the same as the denominator in part (a). The total number of possible combinations is found by selecting $r = 3$ people from $n = 12$ people: $_{12}C_3 = 220$.

Next, we move to the numerator of the probability fraction. The number of ways of selecting $r = 1$ man from $n = 5$ men is

$$_{5}C_1 = \frac{5!}{(5-1)!\,1!} = \frac{5!}{4!\,1!} = \frac{5 \cdot 4!}{4! \cdot 1} = 5.$$

The number of ways of selecting $r = 2$ women from $n = 7$ women is

$$_{7}C_2 = \frac{7!}{(7-2)!\,2!} = \frac{7!}{5!\,2!} = \frac{7 \cdot 6 \cdot 5!}{5! \cdot 2 \cdot 1} = 21.$$

By the Fundamental Counting Principle, the number of ways of selecting 1 man and 2 women is

$$_{5}C_1 \cdot {}_{7}C_2 = 5 \cdot 21 = 105.$$

Now we can fill in the numbers in the numerator and the denominator of our probability fraction.

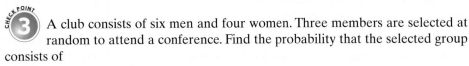

$$P(\text{1 man, 2 women}) = \frac{\text{number of ways of selecting 1 man and 2 women}}{\text{total number of possible combinations}} = \frac{{}_5C_1 \cdot {}_7C_2}{{}_{12}C_3} = \frac{105}{220} = \frac{21}{44}$$

The probability that the group selected to attend the conference consists of one man and two women is $\frac{21}{44}$.

CHECK POINT 3 A club consists of six men and four women. Three members are selected at random to attend a conference. Find the probability that the selected group consists of

    a. three men.

    b. two men and one woman.

EXERCISE SET 8.5 ●●●●●●

• Practice and Application Exercises

1. Martha, Lee, Nancy, Paul, and Armando have all been invited to a dinner party. They arrive randomly and each person arrives at a different time.

    a. In how many ways can they arrive?

    b. In how many ways can Martha arrive first and Armando last?

    c. Find the probability that Martha will arrive first and Armando last.

2. Three men and three women line up at a checkout counter in a store.

    a. In how many ways can they line up?

    b. In how many ways can they line up if the first person in line is a woman, and then the line alternates by gender—that is a woman, a man, a woman, a man, and so on?

    c. Find the probability that the first person in line is a woman and the line alternates by gender.

3. Six stand-up comics, A, B, C, D, E, and F, are to perform on a single evening at a comedy club. The order of performance is determined by random selection. Find the probability that

    a. Comic E will perform first.

    b. Comic C will perform fifth and comic B will perform last.

    c. The comedians will perform in the following order: D, E, C, A, B, F.

    d. Comic A or comic B will perform first.

4. Seven performers, A, B, C, D, E, F, and G, are to appear in a fund raiser. The order of performance is determined by random selection. Find the probability that

    a. D will perform first.

    b. E will perform sixth and B will perform last.

    c. They will perform in the following order: C, D, B, A, G, F, E.

    d. F or G will perform first.

5. A group consists of four men and five women. Three people are selected to attend a conference.

    a. In how many ways can three people be selected from this group of nine?

    b. In how many ways can three women be selected from the five women?

    c. Find the probability that the selected group will consist of all women.

6. A political discussion group consists of five Democrats and six Republicans. Four people are selected to attend a conference.

    a. In how many ways can four people be selected from this group of eleven?

    b. In how many ways can four Republicans be selected from the six Republicans?

    c. Find the probability that the selected group will consist of all Republicans.

7. To play the California lottery, a person has to correctly select 6 out of 51 numbers, paying $1 for each six-number selection. If the six numbers picked are the same as the ones drawn by the lottery, mountains of money are bestowed. What is the probability that a person with one combination of six numbers will win? What is the probability of winning if 100 different lottery tickets are purchased?

8. A state lottery is designed so that a player chooses five numbers from 1 to 30 on one lottery ticket. What is the probability that a player with one lottery ticket will win? What is the probability of winning if 100 different lottery tickets are purchased?

9. A box contains 25 transistors, 6 of which are defective. If 6 are selected at random, find the probability that

    a. all are defective.

    b. none are defective.

10. A committee of five people is to be formed from six lawyers and seven teachers. Find the probability that

    a. all are lawyers.

    b. none are lawyers.

11. A city council consists of six Democrats and four Republicans. If a committee of three people is selected, find the probability of selecting one Democrat and two Republicans.

12. A parent-teacher committee consisting of four people is to be selected from fifteen parents and five teachers. Find the probability of selecting two parents and two teachers.

Exercises 13–18 involve a deck of 52 cards. If necessary, refer to the picture of a deck of cards, Figure 8.5 on page 629.

13. A poker hand consists of five cards.

    a. Find the total number of possible five-card poker hands.

    b. A diamond flush is a five-card hand consisting of all diamonds. Find the number of possible diamond flushes.

    c. Find the probability of being dealt a diamond flush.

14. A poker hand consists of five cards.

    a. Find the total number of possible five-card poker hands.

    b. Find the number of ways in which four aces can be selected.

    c. Find the number of ways in which one king can be selected.

    d. Use the Fundamental Counting Principle and your answers from parts (b) and (c) to find the number of ways of getting four aces and one king.

    e. Find the probability of getting a poker hand consisting of four aces and one king.

15. If you are dealt 3 cards from a shuffled deck of 52 cards, find the probability that all 3 cards are picture cards.

16. If you are dealt 4 cards from a shuffled deck of 52 cards, find the probability that all 4 are hearts.

17. If you are dealt 4 cards from a shuffled deck of 52 cards, find the probability of getting two queens and two kings.

18. If you are dealt 4 cards from a shuffled deck of 52 cards, find the probability of getting three jacks and one queen.

• Writing in Mathematics

19. If people understood the mathematics involving probabilities and lotteries, as you now do, do you think they would continue to spend hundreds of dollars per year on lottery tickets? Explain your answer.

20. Write and solve an original problem involving probability and permutations.

21. Write and solve an original problem involving probability and combinations whose solution requires $\dfrac{_{14}C_{10}}{_{20}C_{10}}$.

• Critical Thinking Exercises

22. An apartment complex offers apartments with four different options, designated by A through D. There are an equal number of apartments with each combination of options.

A	B	C	D
one bedroom two bedrooms three bedrooms	one bathroom two bathrooms	first floor second floor	lake view golf course view no special view

    If there is only one apartment left, what is the probability that it is precisely what a person is looking for, namely two bedrooms, two bathrooms, first floor, and a lake or golf course view?

23. Reread Exercise 7. How much must a person spend so that the probability of winning the California lottery is $\frac{1}{2}$?

24. Suppose that it is a week in which the cash prize in Florida's LOTTO is promised to exceed $50 million. If a person purchases 22,957,480 tickets in LOTTO at $1 per ticket (all possible combinations), isn't this a guarantee of winning the lottery? Because the probability in this situation is 1, what's wrong with doing this?

25. The digits 1, 2, 3, 4, and 5 are randomly arranged to form a three-digit number. (Digits are not repeated.) Find the probability that the number is even and greater than 500.

26. In a five-card poker hand, what is the probability of being dealt exactly one ace and no picture cards?

• Group Exercise

27. Research and present a group report on state lotteries. Include answers to some or all of the following questions. As always, make the report interesting and informative. Which states do not have lotteries? Why not? How much is spent per capita on lotteries? What are some of the lottery games? What is the probability of winning top prize in these games? What income groups spend the greatest amount of money on lotteries? If your state has a lottery, what does it do with the money it makes? Is the way the money is spent what was promised when the lottery first began?

SECTION 8.6 • EVENTS INVOLVING *NOT* AND *OR*; ODDS

OBJECTIVES

1. Find the probability that an event will not occur.
2. Find the probability of one event or a second event occurring.
3. Understand and use odds.

You take your first trip to London. You are surprised to learn that the British gamble on everything. Shops with bookmakers are available everywhere for placing bets. In such a shop, you overhear a conversation about turning up the king of hearts in a deck of cards. You are expecting to hear something about a probability of $\frac{1}{52}$. Instead, you hear the phrase "51 to 1 against." Are you having difficulty understanding the British accents or did you miss something in your liberal arts math course? Whatever happened to probability?

No, it's not the accent. There are several ways to express the likelihood of an event. For example, we can discuss the probability of an event. We can also discuss *odds against* an event and *odds in favor* of an event. In this section, we expand our knowledge of probability and explain the meaning of odds.

1 | Find the probability that an event will not occur.

Probability of an Event Not Occurring

If we know $P(E)$, the probability of an event E, we can determine the probability that the event will not occur, denoted by $P(\text{not } E)$. The event *not E* is the **complement** of E because it is the set of all outcomes in the sample space S that are not outcomes in the event E. In any experiment, an event must occur or its complement must occur. Thus, the sum of the probability that an event will occur and the probability that it will not occur is 1:

$$P(E) + P(\text{not } E) = 1.$$

Solving for $P(E)$ or for $P(\text{not } E)$, we obtain the following formulas:

> **COMPLEMENT RULES OF PROBABILITY**
>
> - The probability that an event E will not occur is equal to 1 minus the probability that it will occur.
>
> $$P(\text{not } E) = 1 - P(E)$$
>
> - The probability that an event E will occur is equal to 1 minus the probability that it will not occur.
>
> $$P(E) = 1 - P(\text{not } E)$$
>
> Using set notation, if E' is the complement of E, then $P(E') = 1 - P(E)$ and $P(E) = 1 - P(E')$.

EXAMPLE 1

THE PROBABILITY OF AN EVENT NOT OCCURRING

If you are dealt one card from a standard 52-card deck, find the probability that you are not dealt a queen.

SOLUTION Because

$$P(\text{not } E) = 1 - P(E)$$

then

$$P(\text{not a queen}) = 1 - P(\text{queen}).$$

There are four queens in a deck of 52 cards. The probability of being dealt a queen is $\frac{4}{52} = \frac{1}{13}$. Thus,

$$P(\text{not a queen}) = 1 - P(\text{queen}) = 1 - \frac{1}{13} = \frac{13}{13} - \frac{1}{13} = \frac{12}{13}.$$

The probability that you are not dealt a queen is $\frac{12}{13}$.

 If you are dealt one card from a standard 52-card deck, find the probability that you are not dealt a diamond.

STUDY TIP

You can work Example 1 without using the formula for $P(\text{not } E)$. Here is how it's done:

$P(\text{not a queen})$

$= \dfrac{\text{number of ways a}}{\text{non-queen can occur}}$
$\overline{\text{total number of outcomes}}$

$= \dfrac{48}{52}$ With 4 queens, $52 - 4 = 48$ cards are not queens.

$= \dfrac{4 \cdot 12}{4 \cdot 13} = \dfrac{12}{13}.$

EXAMPLE 2

USING THE COMPLEMENT RULES

The circle graph in Figure 8.6 shows the distribution, by age group, of the 191 million car drivers in the United States, with all numbers rounded to the nearest million. If one driver is randomly selected from this population, find the probability that the person

a. is not in the 20–29 age group.

b. is less than 80 years old.

Express probabilities as simplified fractions.

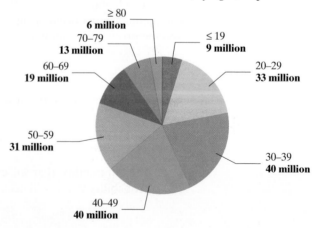

Number of U.S. Car Drivers, by Age Group

FIGURE 8.6
Source: U.S. Census Bureau

SOLUTION

a. We begin with the probability that a randomly selected driver is not in the 20–29 age group.

P(not in 20–29 age group)

$$= 1 - P(\text{in } 20\text{–}29 \text{ age group})$$

> The graph shows 33 million drivers in the 20–29 age group.

$$= 1 - \frac{33}{191}$$

> This number, 191 million drivers, was given, but can be obtained by adding the numbers in the eight sectors.

$$= \frac{191}{191} - \frac{33}{191} = \frac{158}{191}$$

The probability that a randomly selected driver is not in the 20–29 age group is $\frac{158}{191}$.

b. We could compute the probability that a randomly selected driver is less than 80 years old by adding the numbers in each of the seven sectors representing drivers less than 80 and dividing this sum by 191 (million). However, it is easier to use complements. The complement of selecting a driver less than 80 years old is selecting a driver 80 or older.

P(less than 80 years old)

$$= 1 - P(80 \text{ or older})$$

$$= 1 - \frac{6}{191}$$

> The graph shows 6 million drivers 80 or older.

$$= \frac{191}{191} - \frac{6}{191} = \frac{185}{191}$$

The probability that a randomly selected driver is less than 80 years old is $\frac{185}{191}$.

 2 If one driver is randomly selected from the population represented in Figure 8.6, find the probability, expressed as a simplified fraction, that the person

a. is not in the 50–59 age group.

b. is at least 20 years old.

2 Find the probability of one event or a second event occurring.

Or **Probabilities with Mutually Exclusive Events**

Suppose that you randomly select one card from a deck of 52 cards. Let A be the event of selecting a king and B be the event of selecting a queen. Only one card is selected, so it is impossible to get both a king and a queen. The events of selecting a king and a queen cannot occur simultaneously. They are called *mutually exclusive events*.

> **MUTUALLY EXCLUSIVE EVENTS**
> If it is impossible for events A and B to occur simultaneously, the events are said to be **mutually exclusive**.

In general, if A and B are mutually exclusive events, the probability that either A or B will occur is determined by adding their individual probabilities.

> **OR PROBABILITIES WITH MUTUALLY EXCLUSIVE EVENTS**
> If A and B are mutually exclusive events, then
> $$P(A \text{ or } B) = P(A) + P(B).$$
> Using set notation, $P(A \cup B) = P(A) + P(B)$.

| EXAMPLE 3 | THE PROBABILITY OF EITHER OF TWO MUTUALLY EXCLUSIVE EVENTS OCCURRING |

If one card is randomly selected from a deck of cards, what is the probability of selecting a king or a queen?

SOLUTION We find the probability that either of these mutually exclusive events will occur by adding their individual probabilities.

$$P(\text{king or queen}) = P(\text{king}) + P(\text{queen}) = \frac{4}{52} + \frac{4}{52} = \frac{8}{52} = \frac{2}{13}$$

The probability of selecting a king or a queen is $\frac{2}{13}$.

 3 If you roll a single, six-sided die, what is the probability of getting either a 4 or a 5?

Or Probabilities with Events That Are Not Mutually Exclusive

Consider the deck of 52 cards shown in Figure 8.7. Suppose that these cards are shuffled and you randomly select one card from the deck. What is the probability of selecting a diamond or a picture card (jack, queen, king)? Begin by adding their individual probabilities.

$$P(\text{diamond}) + P(\text{picture card}) = \frac{13}{52} + \frac{12}{52}$$

There are 13 diamonds in the deck of 52 cards.   There are 12 picture cards in the deck of 52 cards.

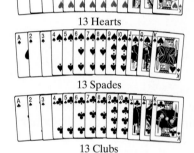

13 Diamonds

13 Hearts

13 Spades

13 Clubs

FIGURE 8.7 A deck of 52 cards

FIGURE 8.8 Three diamonds are picture cards.

However, this sum is not the probability of selecting a diamond or a picture card. The problem is that there are three cards that are *simultaneously* diamonds and picture cards, shown in Figure 8.8. The events of selecting a diamond and selecting a picture card are not mutually exclusive. It is possible to select a card that is both a diamond and a picture card.

The situation is illustrated in the Venn diagram in Figure 8.9. Why can't we find the probability of selecting a diamond or a picture card by adding their individual probabilities? The Venn diagram shows that three of the cards, the three diamonds that are picture cards, get counted twice when we add the individual probabilities. First the three cards get counted as diamonds, and then they get counted as picture cards. In order to avoid the error of counting the three cards twice, we need to subtract the probability of getting a diamond and a picture card, $\frac{3}{52}$, as follows:

$P(\text{diamond or picture card})$

$$= P(\text{diamond}) + P(\text{picture card}) - P(\text{diamond and picture card})$$

$$= \frac{13}{52} + \frac{12}{52} - \frac{3}{52} = \frac{13 + 12 - 3}{52} = \frac{22}{52} = \frac{11}{26}.$$

Thus, the probability of selecting a diamond or a picture card is $\frac{11}{26}$.

In general, if A and B are events that are not mutually exclusive, the probability that A or B will occur is determined by adding their individual probabilities and then subtracting the probability that A and B occur simultaneously.

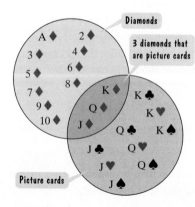

FIGURE 8.9

> *OR* **PROBABILITIES WITH EVENTS THAT ARE NOT MUTUALLY EXCLUSIVE**
>
> If A and B are not mutually exclusive events, then
> $$P(A \text{ or } B) = P(A) + P(B) - P(A \text{ and } B).$$
> Using set notation,
> $$P(A \cup B) = P(A) + P(B) - P(A \cap B).$$

EXAMPLE 4   AN *OR* PROBABILITY WITH EVENTS THAT ARE NOT MUTUALLY EXCLUSIVE

In a group of 25 baboons, 18 enjoy grooming their neighbors, 16 enjoy screeching wildly, while 10 enjoy grooming their neighbors and screeching wildly. If one baboon is selected at random from the group, find the probability that it enjoys grooming its neighbors or screeching wildly.

SOLUTION It is possible for a baboon in the group to enjoy both grooming its neighbors and screeching wildly. Ten of the brutes are given to engage in both activities. These events are not mutually exclusive.

$$P\left(\begin{array}{c}\text{grooming}\\\text{or screeching}\end{array}\right) = P(\text{grooming}) + P(\text{screeching}) - P\left(\begin{array}{c}\text{grooming}\\\text{and screeching}\end{array}\right)$$

$$= \frac{18}{25} + \frac{16}{25} - \frac{10}{25}$$

> 18 of the 25 baboons enjoy grooming.

> 16 of the 25 baboons enjoy screeching.

> 10 of the 25 baboons enjoy both.

$$= \frac{18 + 16 - 10}{25} = \frac{24}{25}$$

The probability that a baboon in the group enjoys grooming its neighbors or screeching wildly is $\frac{24}{25}$.

CHECK POINT 4 In a group of 50 students, 23 take math, 11 take psychology, and 7 take both math and psychology. If one student is selected at random, find the probability that the student takes math or psychology.

EXAMPLE 5   AN *OR* PROBABILITY WITH EVENTS THAT ARE NOT MUTUALLY EXCLUSIVE

Figure 8.10 illustrates a spinner. It is equally probable that the pointer will land on any one of the eight regions, numbered 1 through 8. If the pointer lands on a borderline, spin again. Find the probability that the pointer will stop on an even number or on a number greater than 5.

SOLUTION It is possible for the pointer to land on a number that is both even and greater than 5. Two of the numbers, 6 and 8, are even and greater than 5. These events are not mutually exclusive. The probability of landing on a number that is even or greater than 5 is calculated as follows:

$$P\left(\begin{array}{c}\text{even or}\\\text{greater than 5}\end{array}\right) = P(\text{even}) + P(\text{greater than 5}) - P\left(\begin{array}{c}\text{even and}\\\text{greater than 5}\end{array}\right)$$

$$= \frac{4}{8} + \frac{3}{8} - \frac{2}{8}$$

> Four of the eight numbers, 2, 4, 6, and 8, are even.

> Three of the eight numbers, 6, 7, and 8, are greater than 5.

> Two of the eight numbers, 6 and 8, are even and greater than 5.

$$= \frac{4 + 3 - 2}{8} = \frac{5}{8}.$$

The probability that the pointer will stop on an even number or a number greater than 5 is $\frac{5}{8}$.

FIGURE 8.10 It is equally probable that the pointer will land on any one of the eight regions.

CHECK POINT 5 Use Figure 8.10 to find the probability that the pointer will stop on an odd number or a number less than 5.

EXAMPLE 6 *OR* PROBABILITIES WITH REAL-WORLD DATA

Each year the Internal Revenue Service audits a sample of tax forms to verify their accuracy. Table 8.5 shows the number of tax returns filed and audited in 2003, by taxable income.

TABLE 8.5 TAX RETURNS FILED AND AUDITED, BY TAXABLE INCOME, 2003

	<$25,000	$25,000–$49,999	$50,000–$99,999	≥$100,000	Total
Audit	414,357	135,041	113,944	151,969	815,311
No audit	52,792,911	30,964,967	25,502,542	10,775,542	120,035,962
Total	53,207,268	31,100,008	25,616,486	10,927,511	120,851,273

Source: Internal Revenue Service

If one person is randomly selected from the population represented in Table 8.5, find the probability that

a. the taxpayer had a taxable income less than $25,000 or was audited.

b. the taxpayer had a taxable income less than $25,000 or at least $100,000.

Express probabilities as decimals rounded to the nearest hundredth.

SOLUTION

a. It is possible to select a taxpayer who both earned less than $25,000 and was audited. Thus, these events are not mutually exclusive.

P (less than $25,000 or audited)

$= P(\text{less than } \$25,000) + P(\text{audited}) - P(\text{less than } \$25,000 \text{ and audited})$

$= \dfrac{53,207,268}{120,851,273} + \dfrac{815,311}{120,851,273} - \dfrac{414,357}{120,851,273}$

> Of the 120,851,273 taxpayers, 53,207,268 had taxable incomes less than $25,000.

> Of the 120,851,273 taxpayers, 815,311 were audited.

> Of the 120,851,273 taxpayers, 414,357 earned less than $25,000 and were audited.

$= \dfrac{53,608,222}{120,851,273} \approx 0.44$

The probability that a taxpayer had a taxable income less than $25,000 or was audited is approximately 0.44.

b. A taxable income of *at least* $100,000 means $100,000 or more. Thus, it is not possible to select a taxpayer with both a taxable income of less than $25,000 and at least $100,000. These events are mutually exclusive.

$P(\text{less than } \$25,000 \text{ or at least } \$100,000)$

$= P(\text{less than } \$25,000) + P(\text{at least } \$100,000)$

$= \dfrac{53,207,268}{120,851,273} + \dfrac{10,927,511}{120,851,273}$

> Of the 120,851,273 taxpayers, 53,207,268 had taxable incomes less than $25,000.

> Of the 120,851,273 taxpayers, 10,927,511 had taxable incomes of $100,000 or more.

$= \dfrac{64,134,779}{120,851,273} \approx 0.53$

The probability that a taxpayer had a taxable income less than $25,000 or at least $100,000 is approximately 0.53.

CHECK POINT 6 If one person is randomly selected from the population represented in Table 8.5, find the probability, expressed as a decimal rounded to the nearest hundredth, that

    a. the taxpayer had a taxable income of at least $100,000 or was not audited.

    b. the taxpayer had a taxable income less than $25,000 or between $50,000 and $99,999, inclusive.

3 | Understand and use odds.

Odds

If we know the probability of an event E, we can also speak of the *odds in favor*, or the *odds against*, the event. The following definitions link together the concepts of odds and probabilities:

> **PROBABILITY TO ODDS**
>
> If $P(E)$ is the probability of an event E occurring, then
>
> **1.** The **odds in favor of E** are found by taking the probability that E will occur and dividing by the probability that E will not occur.
>
> $$\text{Odds in favor of } E = \frac{P(E)}{P(\text{not } E)}$$
>
> **2.** The **odds against E** are found by taking the probability that E will not occur and dividing by the probability that E will occur.
>
> $$\text{Odds against } E = \frac{P(\text{not } E)}{P(E)}$$
>
> The odds against E can also be found by reversing the ratio representing the odds in favor of E.

EXAMPLE 7   FROM PROBABILITY TO ODDS

You roll a single, six-sided die.

    a. Find the odds in favor of rolling a 2.

    b. Find the odds against rolling a 2.

SOLUTION Let E represent the event of rolling a 2. In order to determine odds, we must first find the probability of E occurring and the probability of E not occurring. With $S = \{1, 2, 3, 4, 5, 6\}$ and $E = \{2\}$, we see that

$$P(E) = \frac{1}{6}$$

$$\text{and} \quad P(\text{not } E) = 1 - \frac{1}{6} = \frac{6}{6} - \frac{1}{6} = \frac{5}{6}.$$

Now we are ready to construct the ratios for the odds in favor of E and the odds against E.

    a.
$$\text{Odds in favor of } E(\text{rolling a 2}) = \frac{P(E)}{P(\text{not } E)} = \frac{\frac{1}{6}}{\frac{5}{6}} = \frac{1}{6} \cdot \frac{6}{5} = \frac{1}{5}$$

STUDY TIP

When computing odds, the denominators of the two probabilities will always divide out.

The odds in favor of rolling a 2 are $\frac{1}{5}$. The ratio $\frac{1}{5}$ is usually written 1:5 and is read "1 to 5." Thus, the odds in favor of rolling a 2 are 1 to 5.

b. Now that we have the odds in favor of rolling a 2, namely $\frac{1}{5}$ or 1:5, we can find the odds against rolling a 2 by reversing this ratio. Thus,

$$\text{Odds against } E(\text{rolling a 2}) = \frac{5}{1} \quad \text{or} \quad 5:1.$$

The odds against rolling a 2 are 5 to 1.

 You are dealt one card from a 52-card deck.

    a. Find the odds in favor of getting a red queen.

    b. Find the odds against getting a red queen.

EXAMPLE 8   **FROM PROBABILITY TO ODDS**

The winner of a raffle will receive a new sports utility vehicle. If 500 raffle tickets were sold and you purchased ten tickets, what are the odds against your winning the car?

SOLUTION Let E represent the event of winning the SUV. Because you purchased ten tickets and 500 tickets were sold,

$$P(E) = \frac{10}{500} = \frac{1}{50} \quad \text{and} \quad P(\text{not } E) = 1 - \frac{1}{50} = \frac{50}{50} - \frac{1}{50} = \frac{49}{50}.$$

Now we are ready to construct the ratio for the odds against E (winning the SUV).

$$\text{Odds against } E = \frac{P(\text{not } E)}{P(E)} = \frac{\frac{49}{50}}{\frac{1}{50}} = \frac{49}{50} \cdot \frac{50}{1} = \frac{49}{1}$$

The odds against winning the SUV are 49 to 1, written 49:1.

8 The winner of a raffle will receive a two-year scholarship to the college of his or her choice. If 1000 raffle tickets were sold and you purchased five tickets, what are the odds against your winning the scholarship?

Odds enable us to play and bet fairly on games. For example, we have seen that the odds in favor of getting 2 when you roll a die are 1 to 5. Suppose this is a gaming situation and you bet $1 on a 2 turning up. In terms of your bet, there is one favorable outcome, rolling 2, and five unfavorable outcomes, rolling 1, 3, 4, 5, or 6. The odds in favor of getting 2, 1 to 5, compares the number of favorable outcomes, one, to the number of unfavorable outcomes, five.

Using odds in a gaming situation where money is waged, we can determine if the game is *fair*. If the odds in favor of an event E are a to b, the **game is fair** if a bet of $\$a$ is lost if event E does not occur, but a win of $\$b$ (as well as returning the bet of $\$a$) is realized if event E does occur. For example, the odds in favor of getting 2 on a die roll are 1 to 5. If you bet $1 on a 2 turning up and the game is fair, you should win $5 (and have your bet of $1 returned) if a 2 turns up.

Now that we know how to convert from probability to odds, let's see how to convert from odds to probability. Suppose that the odds in favor of event E occurring are a to b. This means that

$$\frac{P(E)}{P(\text{not } E)} = \frac{a}{b} \quad \text{or} \quad \frac{P(E)}{1 - P(E)} = \frac{a}{b}.$$

By solving the equation on the right for $P(E)$, we obtain the following formula for converting from odds to probability:

House Odds

The odds given at horse races and at all games of chance are usually *odds against*. The horse in Example 9, with odds of winning at 2 to 5, has odds against winning at 5 to 2. At a horse race, the odds on this particular horse are given simply as 5 to 2. These **house odds** tell a gambler what the payoff is on a bet. For every $2 bet on the horse, the gambler would win $5 if the horse won, in addition to having the $2 bet returned.

ODDS TO PROBABILITY

If the odds in favor of event E are a to b, then the probability of the event is given by

$$P(E) = \frac{a}{a + b}.$$

EXAMPLE 9   FROM ODDS TO PROBABILITY

The odds in favor of a particular horse winning a race are 2 to 5. What is the probability that this horse will win the race?

SOLUTION Because odds in favor, a to b, means a probability of $\frac{a}{a+b}$, then odds in favor, 2 to 5, means a probability of

$$\frac{2}{2+5} = \frac{2}{7}.$$

The probability that this horse will win the race is $\frac{2}{7}$.

CHECK POINT 9 The odds against a particular horse winning a race are 15 to 1. Find the odds in favor of the horse winning the race and the probability of the horse winning the race.

EXERCISE SET 8.6 ●●●●●●

• Practice and Application Exercises

In Exercises 1–6, you are dealt one card from a 52-card deck. Find the probability that you are not dealt

1. an ace. **2.** a 3. **3.** a heart. **4.** a club. **5.** a picture card. **6.** a red picture card.

In 5-card poker, played with a standard 52-card deck, $_{52}C_5$, or 2,598,960, different hands are possible. The probability of being dealt various hands is the number of different ways they can occur divided by 2,598,960. Shown in Exercises 7–10 are various types of poker hands and their probabilities. In each exercise, find the probability of not being dealt this type of hand.

Type of Hand	Illustration	Number of Ways the Hand Can Occur	Probability
7. Straight flush: 5 cards with consecutive numbers, all in the same suit (excluding royal flush)		36	$\frac{36}{2,598,960}$
8. Four of a kind: 4 cards with the same number, plus 1 additional card		624	$\frac{624}{2,598,960}$
9. Full house: 3 cards of one number and 2 cards of a second number		3744	$\frac{3744}{2,598,960}$
10. Flush: 5 cards of the same suit (excluding royal flush and straight flush)		5108	$\frac{5108}{2,598,960}$

The graph shows the probability of cardiovascular disease, by age and gender. Use the information in the graph to solve Exercises 11–12. Express all probabilities as decimals, estimated to two decimal places.

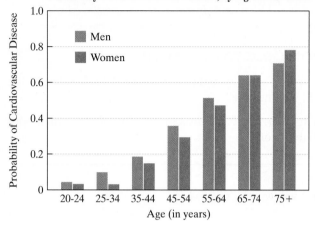

Probability of Cardiovascular Disease, by Age and Gender

Source: American Heart Association

11. a. What is the probability that a randomly selected man between the ages of 25 and 34 has cardiovascular disease?

b. What is the probability that a randomly selected man between the ages of 25 and 34 does not have cardiovascular disease?

12. a. What is the probability that a randomly selected woman, 75 or older, has cardiovascular disease?

b. What is the probability that a randomly selected woman, 75 or older, does not have cardiovascular disease?

The table shows the distribution, by annual income, of the 112 million households in the United States in 2003, with all numbers rounded to the nearest million. Use this distribution to solve Exercises 13–16.

INCOME DISTRIBUTION OF U.S. HOUSEHOLDS, IN MILLIONS

Annual Income	Number	Annual Income	Number
Less than $10,000	10	$35,000–$49,999	17
$10,000–$14,999	8	$50,000–$74,999	20
$15,000–$24,999	15	$75,000–$99,999	12
$25,000–$34,999	13	$100,000 or more	17

Source: U.S. Census Bureau

If one household is randomly selected from this population, find the probability, expressed as a simplified fraction, that

13. the household income is not in the $50,000–$74,999 range.

14. the household income is not in the $15,000–$24,999 range.

15. the household income is less than $100,000.

16. the household income is at least $10,000.

In Exercises 17–22, you randomly select one card from a 52-card deck. Find the probability of selecting

17. a 2 or a 3. **18.** a 7 or an 8.

19. a red 2 or a black 3. **20.** a red 7 or a black 8.

21. the 2 of hearts or the 3 of spades.

22. the 7 of hearts or the 8 of spades.

23. The mathematics faculty at a college consists of 8 professors, 12 associate professors, 14 assistant professors, and 10 instructors. If one faculty member is randomly selected, find the probability of choosing a professor or an instructor.

24. A political discussion group consists of 30 Republicans, 25 Democrats, 8 Independents, and 4 members of the Green party. If one person is randomly selected from the group, find the probability of choosing an Independent or a Green.

In Exercises 25–26, a single die is rolled. Find the probability of rolling

25. an even number or a number less than 5.

26. an odd number or a number less than 4.

In Exercises 27–30, you are dealt one card from a 52-card deck. Find the probability that you are dealt

27. a 7 or a red card.

28. a 5 or a black card.

29. a heart or a picture card.

30. a card greater than 2 and less than 7, or a diamond.

In Exercises 31–34, it is equally probable that the pointer on the spinner shown will land on any one of the eight regions, numbered 1 through 8. If the pointer lands on a borderline, spin again.

Find the probability that the pointer will stop on

31. an odd number or a number less than 6.

32. an odd number or a number greater than 3.

33. an even number or a number greater than 5.

34. an even number or a number less than 4.

Use this information to solve Exercises 35–38. The mathematics department of a college has 8 male professors, 11 female professors, 14 male teaching assistants, and 7 female teaching assistants. If a person is selected at random from the group, find the probability that the selected person is

35. a professor or a male.

36. a professor or a female.

37. a teaching assistant or a female.

38. a teaching assistant or a male.

39. In a class of 50 students, 29 are Democrats, 11 are business majors, and 5 of the business majors are Democrats. If one student is randomly selected from the class, find the probability of choosing a Democrat or a business major.

40. A student is selected at random from a group of 200 students in which 135 take math, 85 take English, and 65 take both math and English. Find the probability that the selected student takes math or English.

The table shows the educational attainment of the U.S. population, ages 25 and over, in 2004. Use the data in the table, expressed in millions, to solve Exercises 41–48.

EDUCATIONAL ATTAINMENT OF THE U.S. POPULATION, AGES 25 AND OVER, IN MILLIONS

	Less Than 4 Years High School	4 Years High School Only	Some College (Less than 4 years)	4 Years College (or More)	Total
Male	14	28	22	26	90
Female	14	32	26	25	97
Total	28	60	48	51	187

Source: U.S. Census Bureau

Find the probability, expressed as a simplified fraction, that a randomly selected American, aged 25 or over,

41. has not completed four years (or more) of college.

42. has not completed four years of high school.

43. has completed four years of high school only or less than four years of college.

44. has completed less than four years of high school or four years of high school only.

45. has completed four years of high school only or is a man.

46. has completed four years of high school only or is a woman.

Find the odds in favor and the odds against a randomly selected American, aged 25 and over, with

47. four years (or more) of college.

48. less than four years of high school.

The graph shows the distribution, by branch and gender, of the 1.43 million, or 1430 thousand, active-duty personnel in the U.S. military in 2003. Numbers are given in thousands and rounded to the nearest ten thousand. Use the data to solve Exercises 49–60.

Active Duty U.S. Military Personnel

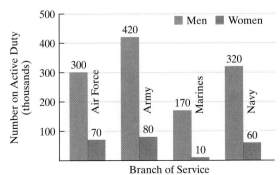

Source: U.S. Defense Department

If one person is randomly selected from the population represented in the bar graph in the previous column, find the probability, expressed as a simplified fraction, that the person

49. is not in the Army.

50. is not in the Marines.

51. is in the Navy or is a man.

52. is in the Army or is a woman.

53. is in the Air Force or the Marines.

54. is in the Army or the Navy.

Find the odds in favor and the odds against a randomly selected person from the population represented in the bar graph in the previous column being

55. in the Navy.

56. in the Army.

57. a woman in the Marines.

58. a woman in the Air Force.

59. a man.

60. a woman.

In Exercises 61–64, a single die is rolled. Find the odds

61. in favor of rolling a number greater than 2.

62. in favor of rolling a number less than 5.

63. against rolling a number greater than 2.

64. against rolling a number less than 5.

The circle graphs show the percentage of children in the United States whose parents are college graduates in one-parent households and two-parent households. Use the information shown to solve Exercises 65–66.

Percentage of U.S. Children Whose Parents Are College Graduates

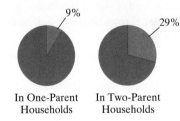

In One-Parent Households   In Two-Parent Households

Source: U.S. Census Bureau

65. a. What are the odds in favor of a child in a one-parent household having a parent who is a college graduate?

 b. What are the odds against a child in a one-parent household having a parent who is a college graduate?

66. a. What are the odds in favor of a child in a two-parent household having parents who are college graduates?

 b. What are the odds against a child in a two-parent household having parents who are college graduates?

In Exercises 67–76, one card is randomly selected from a deck of cards. Find the odds

67. in favor of drawing a heart.

68. in favor of drawing a picture card.

69. in favor of drawing a red card.

70. in favor of drawing a black card.

71. against drawing a 9.

72. against drawing a 5.

73. against drawing a black king.

74. against drawing a red jack.

75. against drawing a spade greater than 3 and less than 9.

76. against drawing a club greater than 4 and less than 10.

77. The winner of a raffle will receive a 21-foot outboard boat. If 1000 raffle tickets were sold and you purchased 20 tickets, what are the odds against your winning the boat?

78. The winner of a raffle will receive a 30-day all-expense-paid trip throughout Europe. If 5000 raffle tickets were sold and you purchased 30 tickets, what are the odds against your winning the trip?

Of the 38 plays attributed to Shakespeare, 18 are comedies, 10 are tragedies, and 10 are histories. In Exercises 79–86, one play is randomly selected from Shakespeare's 38 plays. Find the odds

79. in favor of selecting a comedy.

80. in favor of selecting a tragedy.

81. against selecting a history.

82. against selecting a comedy.

83. in favor of selecting a comedy or a tragedy.

84. in favor of selecting a tragedy or a history.

85. against selecting a tragedy or a history.

86. against selecting a comedy or a history.

87. If you are given odds of 3 to 4 in favor of winning a bet, what is the probability of winning the bet?

88. If you are given odds of 3 to 7 in favor of winning a bet, what is the probability of winning the bet?

89. Based on his skills in basketball, it was computed that when Michael Jordan shot a free throw, the odds in favor of his making it were 21 to 4. Find the probability that when Michael Jordan shot a free throw, he missed it. Out of every 100 free throws he attempted, on the average how many did he make?

90. The odds in favor of a person who is alive at age 20 still being alive at age 70 are 193 to 270. Find the probability that a person who is alive at age 20 will still be alive at age 70.

Exercises 91–92 give the odds against various flight risks. (Source: Men's Health, August 2005) Use these odds to determine the probability of the underlined event for those in flight.

91. odds against contracting an airborne disease: 999 to 1

92. odds against deep-vein thrombosis (blood clot in the leg): 28 to 1

• Writing in Mathematics

93. Explain how to find the probability of an event not occurring. Give an example.

94. What are mutually exclusive events? Give an example of two events that are mutually exclusive.

95. Explain how to find *or* probabilities with mutually exclusive events. Give an example.

96. Give an example of two events that are not mutually exclusive.

97. Explain how to find *or* probabilities with events that are not mutually exclusive. Give an example.

98. Explain how to find the odds in favor of an event if you know the probability that the event will occur.

99. Explain how to find the probability of an event if you know the odds in favor of that event.

• Critical Thinking Exercises

100. In Exercise 39, find the probability of choosing **a.** a Democrat who is not a business major; **b.** a student who is neither a Democrat nor a business major.

101. On New Year's Eve, the probability of a person driving while intoxicated or having a driving accident is 0.35. If the probability of driving while intoxicated is 0.32 and the probability of having a driving accident is 0.09, find the probability of a person having a driving accident while intoxicated.

102. The formula for converting from odds to probability is given in the box on page 479. Read the paragraph on the bottom of page 478 that precedes this box and derive the formula.

SECTION 8.7 • EVENTS INVOLVING *AND*; CONDITIONAL PROBABILITY

OBJECTIVES

1. Find the probability of one event and a second event occurring.

2. Compute conditional probabilities.

You are considering a job offer in South Florida. You were thrilled by images of Miami on MTV's *The Real World*. The job offer is just what you wanted and you are excited about living in the midst of Miami's tropical diversity. However, there is just one thing: the risk of hurricanes. If you expect to stay in Miami ten years and buy a home, what is the probability that South Florida will be hit by a hurricane at least once in the next ten years?

In this section, we look at the probability that an event occurs at least once by expanding our discussion of probability to events involving *and*.

1 | Find the probability of one event and a second event occurring.

And Probabilities with Independent Events

Consider tossing a fair coin two times in succession. The outcome of the first toss, heads or tails, does not affect what happens when you toss the coin a second time. For example, the occurrence of tails on the first toss does not make tails more likely or less likely to occur on the second toss. The repeated toss of a coin produces *independent events* because the outcome of one toss does not affect the outcome of others.

STUDY TIP

Do not confuse *independent events* and *mutually exclusive events*. Mutually exclusive events cannot occur at the same time. Independent events occur at different times, although they have no effect on each other.

> **INDEPENDENT EVENTS**
> Two events are **independent events** if the occurrence of either of them has no effect on the probability of the other.

When a fair coin is tossed two times in succession, the set of equally likely outcomes is

{heads heads, heads tails, tails heads, tails tails}.

We can use this set to find the probability of getting heads on the first toss and heads on the second toss:

$$P(\text{heads and heads}) = \frac{\text{number of ways two heads can occur}}{\text{total number of possible outcomes}} = \frac{1}{4}.$$

We can also determine the probability of two heads, $\frac{1}{4}$, without having to list all the equally likely outcomes. The probability of heads on the first toss is $\frac{1}{2}$. The probability of heads on the second toss is also $\frac{1}{2}$. The product of these probabilities, $\frac{1}{2} \cdot \frac{1}{2}$, results in the probability of two heads, namely $\frac{1}{4}$. Thus,

$$P(\text{heads and heads}) = P(\text{heads}) \cdot P(\text{heads}).$$

In general, if two events are independent, we can calculate the probability of the first occurring and the second occurring by multiplying their probabilities.

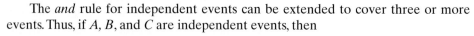

AND **PROBABILITIES WITH INDEPENDENT EVENTS**
If *A* and *B* are independent events, then

$$P(A \text{ and } B) = P(A) \cdot P(B).$$

EXAMPLE 1   INDEPENDENT EVENTS ON A ROULETTE WHEEL

Figure 8.11 shows a U.S. roulette wheel that has 38 numbered slots (1 through 36, 0, and 00). Of the 38 compartments, 18 are black, 18 are red, and 2 are green. A play has the dealer spin the wheel and a small ball in opposite directions. As the ball slows to a stop, it can land with equal probability on any one of the 38 numbered slots. Find the probability of red occurring on two consecutive plays.

SOLUTION   The wheel has 38 equally likely outcomes and 18 are red. Thus, the probability of red occurring on a play is $\frac{18}{38}$, or $\frac{9}{19}$. The result that occurs on each play is independent of all previous results. Thus,

$$P(\text{red and red}) = P(\text{red}) \cdot P(\text{red}) = \frac{9}{19} \cdot \frac{9}{19} = \frac{81}{361} \approx 0.224.$$

The probability of red occurring on two consecutive plays is $\frac{81}{361}$.

Some roulette players incorrectly believe that if red occurs on two consecutive plays, then another color is "due." Because the events are independent, the outcomes of previous spins have no effect on any other spins.

 Find the probability of green occurring on two consecutive plays on a roulette wheel.

The *and* rule for independent events can be extended to cover three or more events. Thus, if *A*, *B*, and *C* are independent events, then

$$P(A \text{ and } B \text{ and } C) = P(A) \cdot P(B) \cdot P(C).$$

EXAMPLE 2   INDEPENDENT EVENTS IN A FAMILY

The picture in the margin shows a family that had nine girls in a row. Find the probability of this occurrence.

SOLUTION   If two or more events are independent, we can find the probability of them all occurring by multiplying their probabilities. The probability of a baby girl is $\frac{1}{2}$, so the probability of nine girls in a row is $\frac{1}{2}$ used as a factor nine times.

$$P(\text{nine girls in a row}) = \frac{1}{2} \cdot \frac{1}{2} \cdot \frac{1}{2} \cdot \frac{1}{2} \cdot \frac{1}{2} \cdot \frac{1}{2} \cdot \frac{1}{2} \cdot \frac{1}{2} \cdot \frac{1}{2}$$

$$= \left(\frac{1}{2}\right)^9 = \frac{1}{512}$$

The probability of a run of nine girls in a row is $\frac{1}{512}$. (If another child is born into the family, this event is independent of the other nine and the probability of a girl is still $\frac{1}{2}$.)

 Find the probability of a family having four boys in a row.

FIGURE 8.11 A U.S. roulette wheel

TABLE 8.6 THE SAFFIR/SIMPSON HURRICANE SCALE

Category	Winds (Miles per Hour)
1	74–95
2	96–110
3	111–130
4	131–155
5	>155

Now let us return to the hurricane problem that opened this section. The Saffir/Simpson scale assigns numbers 1 through 5 to measure the disaster potential of a hurricane's winds. Table 8.6 describes the scale. According to the National Hurricane Center, the probability that South Florida will be hit by a category 1 hurricane or higher in any single year is $\frac{5}{19}$, or approximately 0.26. In Example 3, we explore the risks of living in "Hurricane Alley."

EXAMPLE 3   HURRICANES AND PROBABILITIES

If the probability that South Florida will be hit by a hurricane in any single year is $\frac{5}{19}$,

a. What is the probability that South Florida will be hit by a hurricane in three consecutive years?

b. What is the probability that South Florida will not be hit by a hurricane in the next ten years?

SOLUTION

a. The probability that South Florida will be hit by a hurricane in three consecutive years is

$$P(\text{hurricane and hurricane and hurricane})$$

$$= P(\text{hurricane}) \cdot P(\text{hurricane}) \cdot P(\text{hurricane}) = \frac{5}{19} \cdot \frac{5}{19} \cdot \frac{5}{19} = \frac{125}{6859} \approx 0.018.$$

b. We will first find the probability that South Florida will not be hit by a hurricane in any single year.

$$P(\text{no hurricane}) = 1 - P(\text{hurricane}) = 1 - \frac{5}{19} = \frac{14}{19} \approx 0.737$$

The probability of not being hit by a hurricane in a single year is $\frac{14}{19}$. Therefore, the probability of not being hit by a hurricane ten years in a row is $\frac{14}{19}$ used as a factor ten times.

$$P(\text{no hurricanes for ten years})$$

$$= P\left(\begin{array}{c}\text{no hurricane}\\ \text{for year 1}\end{array}\right) \cdot P\left(\begin{array}{c}\text{no hurricane}\\ \text{for year 2}\end{array}\right) \cdot P\left(\begin{array}{c}\text{no hurricane}\\ \text{for year 3}\end{array}\right) \cdot \ldots \cdot P\left(\begin{array}{c}\text{no hurricane}\\ \text{for year 10}\end{array}\right)$$

$$= \frac{14}{19} \cdot \frac{14}{19} \cdot \frac{14}{19} \cdot \ldots \cdot \frac{14}{19}$$

$$= \left(\frac{14}{19}\right)^{10} \approx (0.737)^{10} \approx 0.047$$

The probability that South Florida will not be hit by a hurricane in the next ten years is approximately 0.047.

Now we are ready to answer your question:

What is the probability that South Florida will be hit by a hurricane at least once in the next ten years?

Because $P(\text{not } E) = 1 - P(E)$,

$$P(\text{no hurricane for ten years}) = 1 - P(\text{at least one hurricane in ten years}).$$

> In our logic chapter, we saw that the negation of "at least one" is "no."

Equivalently,

$$P(\text{at least one hurricane in ten years}) = 1 - P(\text{no hurricane for ten years})$$

$$= 1 - 0.047 = 0.953.$$

With a probability of 0.953, it is nearly certain that South Florida will be hit by a hurricane at least once in the next ten years.

STUDY TIP

When solving probability problems, begin by deciding whether to use the *or* formulas or the *and* formulas.

• *Or* problems usually have the word *or* in the statement of the problem. These problems involve only one selection.

Example:

If one person is selected, find the probability of selecting a man or a Canadian.

• *And* problems often do not have the word *and* in the statement of the problem. These problems involve more than one selection.

Example:

If two people are selected, find the probability that both are men.

> ### THE PROBABILITY OF AN EVENT HAPPENING AT LEAST ONCE
>
> $$P(\text{event happening at least once}) = 1 - P(\text{event does not happen})$$

 If the probability that South Florida will be hit by a hurricane in any single year is $\frac{5}{19}$,

    a. What is the probability that South Florida will be hit by a hurricane in four consecutive years?

    b. What is the probability that South Florida will not be hit by a hurricane in the next four years?

    c. What is the probability that South Florida will be hit by a hurricane at least once in the next four years?

Express all probabilities as fractions and as decimals rounded to three places.

And Probabilities with Dependent Events

5 chocolate-covered cherries lie within the 20 pieces.

Chocolate lovers, please help yourselves! There are 20 mouth-watering tidbits to select from. What's that? You want 2? And you prefer chocolate-covered cherries? The problem is that there are only 5 chocolate-covered cherries, and it's impossible to tell what is inside each piece. They're all shaped exactly alike. At any rate, reach in, select a piece, enjoy, choose another piece, eat, and be well. There is nothing like savoring a good piece of chocolate in the midst of all this chit-chat about probability and hurricanes.

Another question? You want to know what your chances are of selecting 2 chocolate-covered cherries? Well, let's see. Five of the 20 pieces are chocolate-covered cherries, so the probability of getting one of them on your first selection is $\frac{5}{20}$, or $\frac{1}{4}$. Now, suppose that you did choose a chocolate-covered cherry on your first pick. Eat it slowly; there's no guarantee that you'll select your favorite on the second selection. There are now only 19 pieces of chocolate left. Only 4 are chocolate-covered cherries. The probability of getting a chocolate-covered cherry on your second try is 4 out of 19, or $\frac{4}{19}$. This is a different probability than the $\frac{1}{4}$ probability on your first selection. Selecting a chocolate-covered cherry the first time changes what is in the candy box. The probability of what you select the second time *is* affected by the outcome of the first event. For this reason, we say that these are *dependent events*.

> ### DEPENDENT EVENTS
> Two events are **dependent events** if the occurrence of one of them has an effect on the probability of the other.

Once a chocolate-covered cherry is selected, only 4 chocolate-covered cherries lie within the remaining 19 pieces.

The probability of selecting two chocolate-covered cherries in a row can be found by multiplying the $\frac{1}{4}$ probability on the first selection by the $\frac{4}{19}$ probability on the second selection:

$P(\text{chocolate-covered cherry and chocolate-covered cherry})$

$$= P(\text{chocolate-covered cherry}) \cdot P\left(\begin{array}{c}\text{chocolate-covered cherry} \\ \text{given that one was selected}\end{array}\right)$$

$$= \frac{1}{4} \cdot \frac{4}{19} = \frac{1}{19}.$$

The probability of selecting two chocolate-covered cherries in a row is $\frac{1}{19}$. This is a special case of finding the probability that each of two dependent events occurs.

> ### *AND* PROBABILITIES WITH DEPENDENT EVENTS
> If A and B are dependent events, then
> $$P(A \text{ and } B) = P(A) \cdot P(B \text{ given that } A \text{ has occurred}).$$

EXAMPLE 4	AN *AND* PROBABILITY WITH DEPENDENT EVENTS

Good news: You won a free trip to Madrid and can take two people with you, all expenses paid. Bad news: Ten of your cousins have appeared out of nowhere and are begging you to take them. You write each cousin's name on a card, place the cards in a hat, and select one name. Then you select a second name without replacing the first card. If three of your ten cousins speak Spanish, find the probability of selecting two Spanish-speaking cousins.

STUDY TIP

Example 4 can also be solved using the combinations formula.

P(two Spanish speakers)

$$= \frac{\text{number of ways of selecting 2 Spanish-speaking cousins}}{\text{number of ways of selecting 2 cousins}}$$

$$= \frac{{}_3C_2}{{}_{10}C_2}$$

> 2 Spanish speakers selected from 3 Spanish-speaking cousins

> 2 cousins selected from 10 cousins

$$= \frac{3}{45} = \frac{1}{15}$$

SOLUTION Because $P(A \text{ and } B) = P(A) \cdot P(B \text{ given that } A \text{ has occurred})$, then
P(two Spanish-speaking cousins)

$= P$(speaks Spanish and speaks Spanish)

$= P$(speaks Spanish) $\cdot P\left(\begin{array}{c}\text{speaks Spanish given that a Spanish-speaking}\\\text{cousin was selected first}\end{array}\right)$

$$= \frac{3}{10} \cdot \frac{2}{9}$$

> There are ten cousins, three of whom speak Spanish.

> After picking a Spanish-speaking cousin, there are nine cousins left, two of whom speak Spanish.

$$= \frac{6}{90} = \frac{1}{15} \approx 0.067.$$

The probability of selecting two Spanish-speaking cousins is $\frac{1}{15}$.

 4 You are dealt two cards from a 52-card deck. Find the probability of getting two kings.

The multiplication rule for dependent events can be extended to cover three or more dependent events. For example, in the case of three such events,

$P(A \text{ and } B \text{ and } C)$
$\quad = P(A) \cdot P(B \text{ given that } A \text{ occurred}) \cdot P(C \text{ given that } A \text{ and } B \text{ occurred}).$

EXAMPLE 5	AN *AND* PROBABILITY WITH THREE DEPENDENT EVENTS

Three people are randomly selected, one person at a time, from five freshmen, two sophomores, and four juniors. Find the probability that the first two people selected are freshmen and the third is a junior.

5 freshmen

2 sophomores

4 juniors

The given numbers (repeated)

SOLUTION

P(first two are freshmen and the third is a junior)

$= P(\text{freshman}) \cdot P\left(\begin{array}{c}\text{freshman given that a}\\\text{freshman was selected first}\end{array}\right) \cdot P\left(\begin{array}{c}\text{junior given that a freshman was}\\\text{selected first and a freshman was}\\\text{selected second}\end{array}\right)$

$= \dfrac{5}{11} \cdot \dfrac{4}{10} \cdot \dfrac{4}{9}$

> There are 11 people, five of whom are freshmen.

> After picking a freshman, there are 10 people left, four of whom are freshmen.

> After the first two selections, 9 people are left, four of whom are juniors.

| Compute conditional probabilities.

$= \dfrac{8}{99}$

The probability that the first two people selected are freshmen and the third is a junior is $\frac{8}{99}$.

Coincidences

The phone rings and it's the friend you were just thinking of. You're driving down the road and a song you were humming in your head comes on the radio. Although these coincidences seem strange, perhaps even mystical, they're not. Coincidences are bound to happen. Ours is a world in which there are a great many potential coincidences, each with a low probability of occurring. When these surprising coincidences happen, we are amazed and remember them. However, we pay little attention to the countless number of non-coincidences: How often do you think of your friend and she doesn't call, or how often does she call when you're not thinking about her? By noticing the hits and ignoring the misses, we incorrectly perceive that there is a relationship between the occurrence of two independent events.

Another problem is that we often underestimate the probabilities of coincidences in certain situations, acting with more surprise than we should when they occur. For example, in a group of only 23 people, the probability that two individuals share a birthday (same month and day) is greater than $\frac{1}{2}$. Above 50 people, the probability of any two people sharing a birthday approaches certainty. You can verify the probabilities behind the coincidence of shared birthdays in relatively small groups by working Exercise 83 in Exercise Set 8.7.

CHECK POINT 5 You are dealt three cards from a 52-card deck. Find the probability of getting three hearts.

Conditional Probability

We have seen that for any two dependent events A and B,

$$P(A \text{ and } B) = P(A) \cdot P(B \text{ given that } A \text{ occurs}).$$

The probability of B given that A occurs is called *conditional probability*, denoted by $P(B|A)$.

> **CONDITIONAL PROBABILITY**
>
> The probability of event B, assuming that the event A has already occurred, is called the **conditional probability** of B, given A. This probability is denoted by $P(B|A)$.

It is helpful to think of the conditional probability $P(B|A)$ as the **probability that event B occurs if the sample space is restricted to the outcomes associated with event A.**

EXAMPLE 6 FINDING CONDITIONAL PROBABILITY

A letter is randomly selected from the letters of the English alphabet. Find the probability of selecting a vowel, given that the outcome is a letter that precedes h.

SOLUTION We are looking for

$$P(\text{vowel}|\text{letter precedes h}).$$

This is the probability of a vowel if the sample space is restricted to the set of letters that precede h. Thus, the sample space is given by

$$S = \{a, b, c, d, e, f, g\}.$$

There are seven possible outcomes in the sample space. We can select a vowel from this set in one of two ways: a or e. Therefore, the probability of selecting a vowel, given that the outcome is a letter that precedes h, is $\frac{2}{7}$.

$$P(\text{vowel}|\text{letter precedes h}) = \frac{2}{7}$$

CHECK POINT 6 You are dealt one card from a 52-card deck. Find the probability of getting a heart, given that the card you were dealt is a red card.

EXAMPLE 7	CONDITIONAL PROBABILITIES WITH REAL-WORLD DATA

When women turn 40, their gynecologists typically remind them that it is time to undergo mammography screening for breast cancer. The data in Table 8.7 are based on 100,000 U.S. women, ages 40 to 50, who participated in mammography screening.

TABLE 8.7 MAMMOGRAPHY SCREENING ON 100,000 U.S. WOMEN, AGES 40 TO 50

	Breast Cancer	No Breast Cancer	Total
Positive Mammogram	720	6944	7664
Negative Mammogram	80	92,256	92,336
Total	800	99,200	100,000

Source: Gerd Gigerenzer, *Calculated Risks.* Simon and Schuster, 2002

Assuming that these numbers are representative of all U.S. women ages 40 to 50, find the probability that a woman in this age range

a. has a positive mammogram, given that she does not have breast cancer.

b. does not have breast cancer, given that she has a positive mammogram.

SOLUTION

a. We begin with the probability that a U.S. woman aged 40 to 50 has a positive mammogram, given that she does not have breast cancer:

$$P(\text{positive mammogram} \mid \text{no breast cancer}).$$

This is the probability of a positive mammogram if the data are restricted to women without breast cancer:

	No Breast Cancer
Positive Mammogram	6944
Negative Mammogram	92,256
Total	99,200

Within the restricted data, there are 6944 women with positive mammograms and 6944 + 92,256, or 99,200 women without breast cancer. Thus,

$$P(\text{positive mammogram} \mid \text{no breast cancer}) = \frac{6944}{99,200} = 0.07.$$

Among women without breast cancer, the probability of a positive mammogram is 0.07.

b. Now, we find the probability that a U.S. woman aged 40 to 50 does not have breast cancer, given that she has a positive mammogram:

$$P(\text{no breast cancer} \mid \text{positive mammogram}).$$

This is the probability of not having breast cancer if the data are restricted to women with positive mammograms:

	Breast Cancer	No Breast Cancer	Total
Positive Mammogram	720	6944	7664

Within the restricted data, there are 6944 women without breast cancer and 720 + 6944, or 7664 women with positive mammograms. Thus,

$$P(\text{no breast cancer} \mid \text{positive mammogram}) = \frac{6944}{7664} \approx 0.906.$$

Among women with positive mammograms, the probability of not having breast cancer is $\frac{6944}{7664}$, or approximately 0.906.

STUDY TIP

Example 7 shows that the probability of a positive mammogram among women without breast cancer, 0.07, is not the same as the probability of not having breast cancer among women with positive mammograms, approximately 0.9. In general, the conditional probability of B, given A, is not the same as the conditional probability of A, given B:

$$P(B \mid A) \neq P(A \mid B).$$

Use the data in Table 8.7 at the top of the previous page to find the probability that a U.S. woman aged 40 to 50

a. has a positive mammogram, given that she has breast cancer.

b. has breast cancer, given that she has a positive mammogram.

Express probabilities as decimals and, if necessary, round to three decimal places.

⋯⋯⋯●

We have seen that $P(B|A)$ is the probability that event B occurs if the sample space is restricted to event A. Thus,

$$P(B|A) = \frac{\text{number of outcomes of } B \text{ that are in the restricted sample space } A}{\text{number of outcomes in the restricted sample space } A}.$$

This can be stated in terms of the following formula:

A FORMULA FOR CONDITIONAL PROBABILITY

$$P(B|A) = \frac{n(B \cap A)}{n(A)} = \frac{\text{number of outcomes common to } B \text{ and } A}{\text{number of outcomes in } A}$$

EXERCISE SET 8.7 ●●●●●●

• Practice and Application Exercises

Exercises 1–26 involve probabilities with independent events.

Use the spinner shown to solve Exercises 1–10. It is equally probable that the pointer will land on any one of the six regions. If the pointer lands on a borderline, spin again. If the pointer is spun twice, find the probability it will land on

1. green and then red.

2. yellow and then green.

3. yellow and then yellow.

4. red and then red.

5. a color other than red each time.

6. a color other than green each time.

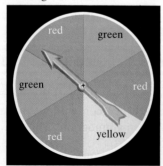

If the pointer is spun three times, find the probability it will land on

7. green and then red and then yellow.

8. red and then red and then green.

9. red every time.

10. green every time.

In Exercises 11–14, a single die is rolled twice. Find the probability of rolling

11. a 2 the first time and a 3 the second time.

12. a 5 the first time and a 1 the second time.

13. an even number the first time and a number greater than 2 the second time.

14. an odd number the first time and a number less than 3 the second time.

In Exercises 15–20, you draw one card from a 52-card deck. Then the card is replaced in the deck, the deck is shuffled, and you draw again. Find the probability of drawing

15. a picture card the first time and a heart the second time.

16. a jack the first time and a club the second time.

17. a king each time.

18. a 3 each time.

19. a red card each time.

20. a black card each time.

21. If you toss a fair coin six times, what is the probability of getting all heads?

22. If you toss a fair coin seven times, what is the probability of getting all tails?

In Exercises 23–24, a coin is tossed and a die is rolled. Find the probability of getting

23. a head and a number greater than 4.

24. a tail and a number less than 5.

25. The probability that South Florida will be hit by a major hurricane (category 4 or 5) in any single year is $\frac{1}{16}$.
(*Source:* National Hurricane Center)

   a. What is the probability that South Florida will be hit by a major hurricane two years in a row?

   b. What is the probability that South Florida will be hit by a major hurricane in three consecutive years?

   c. What is the probability that South Florida will not be hit by a major hurricane in the next ten years?

   d. What is the probability that South Florida will be hit by a major hurricane at least once in the next ten years?

26. The probability that a region prone to flooding will flood in any single year is $\frac{1}{10}$.

   a. What is the probability of a flood two years in a row?

   b. What is the probability of flooding in three consecutive years?

   c. What is the probability of no flooding for ten consecutive years?

   d. What is the probability of flooding at least once in the next ten years?

The graph shows that U.S. adults dependent on tobacco have a greater probability of suffering from some ailments than the general adult population. When making two or more selections from populations with large numbers, such as the U.S. adult population or the population dependent on tobacco, we assume that each selection is independent of every other selection. In Exercises 27–32, assume that the selections are independent events.

Probability That U.S. Adults Suffer from Various Ailments

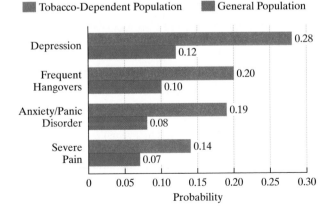

Source: MARS 2005 OTC/DTC

27. If two adults are randomly selected from the general population, what is the probability that they both suffer from depression?

28. If two adults are randomly selected from the population of cigarette smokers, what is the probability that they both suffer from depression?

29. If three adults are randomly selected from the population of cigarette smokers, what is the probability that they all suffer from frequent hangovers?

30. If three adults are randomly selected from the general population, what is the probability that they all suffer from frequent hangovers?

31. If three adults are randomly selected from the population of cigarette smokers, what is the probability, expressed as a decimal correct to four places, that at least one person suffers from anxiety/panic disorder?

32. If three adults are randomly selected from the population of cigarette smokers, what is the probability, expressed as a decimal correct to four places, that at least one person suffers from severe pain?

Exercises 33–48 involve probabilities with dependent events.

In Exercises 33–36, we return to our box of chocolates. There are 30 chocolates in the box, all identically shaped. Five are filled with coconut, 10 with caramel, and 15 are solid chocolate. You randomly select one piece, eat it, and then select a second piece. Find the probability of selecting

33. two solid chocolates in a row.

34. two caramel-filled chocolates in a row.

35. a coconut-filled chocolate followed by a caramel-filled chocolate.

36. a coconut-filled chocolate followed by a solid chocolate.

In Exercises 37–42, consider a political discussion group consisting of 5 Democrats, 6 Republicans, and 4 Independents. Suppose that two group members are randomly selected, in succession, to attend a political convention. Find the probability of selecting

37. two Democrats.

38. two Republicans.

39. an Independent and then a Republican.

40. an Independent and then a Democrat.

41. no Independents.

42. no Democrats.

In Exercises 43–48, an ice chest contains six cans of apple juice, eight cans of grape juice, four cans of orange juice, and two cans of mango juice. Suppose that you reach into the container and randomly select three cans in succession. Find the probability of selecting

43. three cans of apple juice.

44. three cans of grape juice.

45. a can of grape juice, then a can of orange juice, then a can of mango juice.

46. a can of apple juice, then a can of grape juice, then a can of orange juice.

47. no grape juice.

48. no apple juice.

In Exercises 49–56, the numbered disks shown are placed in a box and one disk is selected at random.

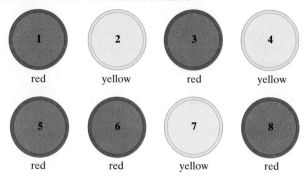

Find the probability of selecting

49. a 3, given that a red disk is selected.
50. a 7, given that a yellow disk is selected.
51. an even number, given that a yellow disk is selected.
52. an odd number, given that a red disk is selected.
53. a red disk, given that an odd number is selected.
54. a yellow disk, given that an odd number is selected.
55. a red disk, given that the number selected is at least 5.
56. a yellow disk, given that the number selected is at most 3.

The table shows the outcome of car accidents in Florida for a recent year by whether or not the driver wore a seat belt. Use the data to solve Exercises 57–60. Express probabilities as fractions and as decimals rounded to three places.

CAR ACCIDENTS IN FLORIDA

	Wore Seat Belt	No Seat Belt	Total
Driver Survived	412,368	162,527	574,895
Driver Died	510	1601	2111
Total	412,878	164,128	577,006

Source: Alan Agresti and Christine Franklin, *Statistics*, Prentice Hall, 2007

57. Find the probability of surviving a car accident, given that the driver wore a seat belt.
58. Find the probability of not surviving a car accident, given that the driver did not wear a seat belt.
59. Find the probability of wearing a seat belt, given that a driver survived a car accident.
60. Find the probability of not wearing a seat belt, given that a driver did not survive a car accident.

In Exercises 61–72, we return to the table showing the distribution, by marital status and gender, of the 212.5 million Americans ages 18 or older.

MARITAL STATUS OF THE U.S. POPULATION, AGES 18 OR OLDER, IN MILLIONS

	Never Married	Married	Widowed	Divorced	Total
Male	28.6	62.1	2.7	9.0	102.4
Female	23.3	62.8	11.3	12.7	110.1
Total	51.9	124.9	14.0	21.7	212.5

Source: U.S. Census Bureau

If one person is selected from the population described in the table at the bottom of the previous column, find the probability, expressed as a decimal rounded to three places, that the person

61. is not divorced.
62. is not widowed.
63. is widowed or divorced.
64. had never been married or is divorced.
65. is male or divorced.
66. is female or divorced.
67. is male, given that this person is divorced.
68. is female, given that this person is divorced.
69. is widowed, given that this person is a woman.
70. is divorced, given that this person is a man.
71. had never been married or is married, given that this person is a man.
72. had never been married or is married, given that this person is a woman.

• Writing in Mathematics

73. Explain how to find *and* probabilities with independent events. Give an example.
74. Explain how to find *and* probabilities with dependent events. Give an example.
75. What does $P(B|A)$ mean? Give an example.

In Exercises 76–80, write a probability problem involving the word "and" whose solution results in the probability fractions shown.

76. $\frac{1}{2} \cdot \frac{1}{2}$ 77. $\frac{1}{6} \cdot \frac{1}{6} \cdot \frac{1}{6}$ 78. $\frac{1}{2} \cdot \frac{1}{6}$

79. $\frac{13}{52} \cdot \frac{12}{51}$ 80. $\frac{1}{4} \cdot \frac{3}{5}$

• Critical Thinking Exercises

81. If the probability of being hospitalized during a year is 0.1, find the probability that no one in a family of five will be hospitalized in a year.
82. If a single die is rolled five times, what is the probability it lands on 2 on the first, third, and fourth rolls, but not on any of the other rolls?
83. Probabilities and Coincidence of Shared Birthdays
    a. If two people are selected at random, the probability that they do not have the same birthday (day and month) is $\frac{365}{365} \cdot \frac{364}{365}$. Explain why this is so. (Ignore leap years and assume 365 days in a year.)
    b. If three people are selected at random, find the probability that they all have different birthdays.
    c. If three people are selected at random, find the probability that at least two of them have the same birthday.
    d. If 20 people are selected at random, find the probability that at least 2 of them have the same birthday.
    e. How large a group is needed to give a 0.5 chance of at least two people having the same birthday?
84. Nine cards numbered from 1 through 9 are placed into a box and two cards are selected without replacement. Find the probability that both numbers selected are odd, given that their sum is even.

• Group Exercises

85. Do you live in an area prone to catastrophes, such as earthquakes, fires, tornados, hurricanes, or floods? If so, research the probability of this catastrophe occurring in a single year. Group members should then use this probability to write and solve a problem similar to Exercise 25 in this exercise set.

86. Group members should use the table for Exercises 61–72 to write and solve four probability problems different than those in the exercises. Two should involve *or* (one with events that are mutually exclusive and one with events that are not), one should involve *and*—that is, events in succession—and one should involve conditional probability.

SECTION 8.8 • EXPECTED VALUE

O B J E C T I V E S

1. Compute expected value.

2. Use expected value to solve applied problems.

3. Use expected value to determine the average payoff or loss in a game of chance.

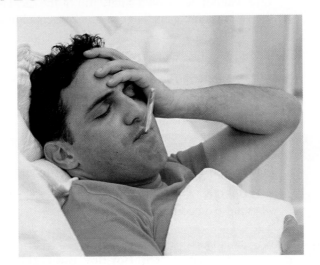

1 | Compute expected value.

Would you be willing to spend $50 a year for an insurance policy that pays $200,000 if you become too ill to continue your education? It is unlikely that this will occur. Insurance companies make money by compensating us for events that have a low probability. If one in every 5000 students needs to quit college due to serious illness, the probability of this event is $\frac{1}{5000}$. Multiplying the amount of the claim, $200,000, by its probability, $\frac{1}{5000}$, tells the insurance company what to expect on average for each policy:

$$\$200,000 \times \frac{1}{5000} = \$40.$$

Amount of the claim

Probability of paying the claim

Over the long run, the insurance company can expect to pay $40 for each policy it sells. By selling the policy for $50, the expected profit is $10 per policy. If 400,000 students choose to take out this insurance, the company can expect to make 400,000 × $10, or $4,000,000.

Expected value is a mathematical way to use probabilities to determine what to expect in various situations over the long run. Expected value is used to determine premiums on insurance policies, weigh the risks versus the benefits of alternatives in business ventures, and indicate to a player of any game of chance what will happen if the game is played repeatedly.

The standard way to find expected value is to multiply each possible outcome by its probability, and then add these products. We use the letter E to represent expected value.

EXAMPLE 1   COMPUTING EXPECTED VALUE

Find the expected value for the outcome of the roll of a fair die.

SOLUTION The outcomes are 1, 2, 3, 4, 5, and 6, each with a probability of $\frac{1}{6}$. The expected value, E, is computed by multiplying each outcome by its probability and then adding these products.

$$E = 1 \cdot \frac{1}{6} + 2 \cdot \frac{1}{6} + 3 \cdot \frac{1}{6} + 4 \cdot \frac{1}{6} + 5 \cdot \frac{1}{6} + 6 \cdot \frac{1}{6}$$

$$= \frac{1 + 2 + 3 + 4 + 5 + 6}{6} = \frac{21}{6} = 3.5$$

The expected value of the roll of a fair die is 3.5. This means that if the die is rolled repeatedly, there are an average of 3.5 dots per roll over the long run. This expected value cannot occur on a single roll of the die. However, it is a long-run average of the various outcomes that can occur when a fair die is rolled.

CHECK POINT 1 It is equally probable that a pointer will land on any one of four regions, numbered 1 through 4. Find the expected value for where the pointer will stop.

TABLE 8.8 OUTCOMES AND PROBABILITIES FOR THE NUMBER OF GIRLS IN A THREE-CHILD FAMILY

Outcome: Number of Girls	Probability
0	$\frac{1}{8}$
1	$\frac{3}{8}$
2	$\frac{3}{8}$
3	$\frac{1}{8}$

EXAMPLE 2   COMPUTING EXPECTED VALUE

Find the expected value for the number of girls for a family with three children.

SOLUTION A family with three children can have 0, 1, 2, or 3 girls. There are eight ways these outcomes can occur.

No girls   : Boy Boy Boy   *One way*
One girl   : Girl Boy Boy, Boy Girl Boy, Boy Boy Girl   *Three ways*
Two girls   : Girl Girl Boy, Girl Boy Girl, Boy Girl Girl   *Three ways*
Three girls : Girl Girl Girl   *One way*

Table 8.8 shows the probabilities for 0, 1, 2, and 3 girls.

The expected value, E, is computed by multiplying each outcome by its probability and then adding these products.

$$E = 0 \cdot \frac{1}{8} + 1 \cdot \frac{3}{8} + 2 \cdot \frac{3}{8} + 3 \cdot \frac{1}{8} = \frac{0 + 3 + 6 + 3}{8} = \frac{12}{8} = \frac{3}{2} = 1.5$$

The expected value is 1.5. This means that if we record the number of girls in many different three-child families, the average number of girls for all these families will be 1.5. In a three-child family, half the children are expected to be girls, so the expected value of 1.5 is consistent with this observation.

CHECK POINT 2 A fair coin is tossed four times in succession. Table 8.9 shows the probabilities for the different number of heads that can arise. Find the expected value for the number of heads.

TABLE 8.9

Number of Heads	Probability
0	$\frac{1}{16}$
1	$\frac{4}{16}$
2	$\frac{6}{16}$
3	$\frac{4}{16}$
4	$\frac{1}{16}$

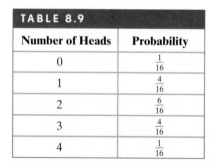

2 | Use expected value to solve applied problems.

Applications of Expected Value

Empirical probabilities can be determined in many situations by examining what has occurred in the past. For example, an insurance company can tally various claim amounts over many years. If 15% of these amounts are for a $2000 claim, then the probability of this claim amount is 0.15. By studying sales of similar houses in a particular area, a realtor can determine the probability that he or she will sell a listed house, another agent will sell the house, or the listed house will remain unsold. Once probabilities have been assigned to all possible outcomes, expected value can indicate what is expected to happen in the long run. These ideas are illustrated in Examples 3 and 4.

TABLE 8.10 PROBABILITIES FOR AUTO CLAIMS

Amount of Claim (to the nearest $2000)	Probability
$0	0.70
$2000	0.15
$4000	0.08
$6000	0.05
$8000	0.01
$10,000	0.01

EXAMPLE 3   DETERMINING AN INSURANCE PREMIUM

An automobile insurance company has determined the probabilities for various claim amounts for drivers ages 16 through 21, shown in Table 8.10.

a. Calculate the expected value and describe what this means in practical terms.

b. How much should the company charge as an average premium so that it does not lose or gain money on its claim costs?

SOLUTION

a. The expected value, E, is computed by multiplying each outcome by its probability, and then adding these products.

$$E = \$0(0.70) + \$2000(0.15) + \$4000(0.08) + \$6000(0.05)$$
$$+ \$8000(0.01) + \$10,000(0.01)$$
$$= \$0 + \$300 + \$320 + \$300 + \$80 + \$100$$
$$= \$1100$$

The expected value is $1100. This means that in the long run the average cost of a claim is $1100. The insurance company should expect to pay $1100 per car insured to people in the 16–21 age group.

b. At the very least, the amount that the company should charge as an average premium for each person in the 16–21 group is $1100. In this way, it will not lose or gain money on its claims costs. It's quite probable that the company will charge more, moving from break-even to profit.

CHECK POINT 3 Work Example 3 again if the probabilities for claims of $0 and $10,000 are reversed. Thus, the probability of a $0 claim is 0.01 and the probability of a $10,000 claim is 0.70.

THE REALTOR'S SUMMARY SHEET

My Cost:	$5000
My Possible Income:	
I sell house:	$30,000
Another agent sells house:	$15,000
House unsold after 4 months:	$0
The Probabilities:	
I sell house:	0.3
Another agent sells house:	0.2
House unsold after 4 months:	0.5
My Bottom Line:	
I take the listing only if I anticipate earning at least $6000.	

Business decisions are interpreted in terms of dollars and cents. In these situations, **expected value is calculated by multiplying the gain or loss for each possible outcome by its probability. The sum of these products is the expected value.**

EXAMPLE 4   EXPECTATION IN A BUSINESS DECISION

You are a realtor considering listing a $500,000 house. The cost of advertising and providing food for other realtors during open showings is anticipated to cost you $5000. The house is quite unusual, and you are given a four-month listing. If the house is unsold after four months, you lose the listing and receive nothing. You anticipate that the probability you sell your own listed house is 0.3, the probability that another agent sells your listing is 0.2, and the probability that the house is unsold after 4 months is 0.5. If you sell your own listed house, the commission is a hefty $30,000. If another realtor sells your listing, the commission is $15,000. The bottom line: You will not take the listing unless you anticipate earning at least $6000. Should you list the house?

SOLUTION Shown in the margin is a summary of the amounts of money and probabilities that will determine your decision. The expected value in this situation is the sum of each income possibility times its probability. The expected value represents the amount you can anticipate earning if you take the listing. If the expected value is not at least $6000, you should not list the house.

THE REALTOR'S SUMMARY
SHEET(repeated)

My Cost:	$5000
My Possible Income:	
I sell house:	$30,000
Another agent sells house:	$15,000
House unsold after 4 months:	$0
The Probabilities:	
I sell house:	0.3
Another agent sells house:	0.2
House unsold after 4 months:	0.5
My Bottom Line:	
I take the listing only if I anticipate earning at least $6000.	

The possible incomes listed in the margin, $30,000, $15,000, and $0, do not take into account your $5000 costs. Because of these costs, each amount needs to be reduced by $5000. Thus, you can gain $30,000 − $5000, or $25,000, or you can gain $15,000 − $5000, or $10,000. Because $0 − $5000 = −$5000, you can also lose $5000. Table 8.11 summarizes possible outcomes if you take the listing, and their respective probabilities.

TABLE 8.11 GAINS, LOSSES, AND PROBABILITIES FOR LISTING A $500,000 HOUSE		
Outcome	**Gain or Loss**	**Probability**
Sells house	$25,000	0.3
Another agent sells house	$10,000	0.2
House doesn't sell	−$5000	0.5

The expected value, E, is computed by multiplying each gain or loss in Table 8.11 by its probability, and then adding these results.

$$E = \$25{,}000(0.3) + \$10{,}000(0.2) + (-\$5000)(0.5)$$
$$= \$7500 + \$2000 + (-\$2500) = \$7000$$

You can expect to earn $7000 by listing the house. Because the expected value exceeds $6000, you should list the house.

○

CHECK POINT 4 The SAT is a multiple-choice test. Each question has five possible answers. The test taker must select one answer for each question or not answer the question. One point is awarded for each correct response and $\frac{1}{4}$ point is subtracted for each wrong answer. No points are added or subtracted for answers left blank. Table 8.12 summarizes the information for the outcomes of a random guess on an SAT question. Find the expected point value of a random guess. Is there anything to gain or lose on average by guessing? Explain your answer.

TABLE 8.12 GAINS AND LOSSES FOR GUESSING ON THE SAT		
Outcome	**Gain or Loss**	**Probability**
Guess correctly	1	$\frac{1}{5}$
Guess incorrectly	$-\frac{1}{4}$	$\frac{4}{5}$

3 | Use expected value to determine the average payoff or loss in a game of chance.

Expected Value and Games of Chance

Expected value can be interpreted as the average payoff in a contest or game when either is played a large number of times. **To find the expected value of a game, multiply the gain or loss for each possible outcome by its probability. Then add the products.**

EXAMPLE 5   EXPECTED VALUE AS AVERAGE PAYOFF

A game is played using one die. If the die is rolled and shows 1, 2, or 3, the player wins nothing. If the die shows 4 or 5, the player wins $3. If the die shows 6, the player wins $9. If there is a charge of $1 to play the game, what is the game's expected value? Describe what this means in practical terms.

SOLUTION Because there is a charge of $1 to play the game, a player who wins $9 gains $9 − $1, or $8. A player who wins $3 gains $3 − $1, or $2. If the player gets $0, there is a loss of $1 because $0 − $1 = −$1. The outcomes for the die, with their respective gains, losses, and probabilities, are summarized in Table 8.13.

TABLE 8.13 GAINS, LOSSES, AND PROBABILITIES IN A GAME OF CHANCE

Outcome	Gain or Loss	Probability
1, 2, or 3	−$1	$\frac{3}{6}$
4 or 5	$2	$\frac{2}{6}$
6	$8	$\frac{1}{6}$

Expected value, E, is computed by multiplying each gain or loss in Table 8.13 by its probability and then adding these results.

$$E = (-\$1)\left(\frac{3}{6}\right) + \$2\left(\frac{2}{6}\right) + \$8\left(\frac{1}{6}\right)$$

$$= \frac{-\$3 + \$4 + \$8}{6} = \frac{\$9}{6} = \$1.50$$

The expected value is $1.50. This means that in the long run, a player can expect to win an average of $1.50 for each game played. However, this does not mean that the player will win $1.50 on any single game. It does mean that if the game is played repeatedly, then, in the long run, the player should expect to win about $1.50 per play on the average. If 1000 games are played, one could expect to win $1500. However, if only three games are played, one's net winnings can range between −$3 and $24, even though the expected winnings are $1.50(3), or $4.50. ○

CHECK POINT 5 A charity is holding a raffle and sells 1000 raffle tickets for $2 each. One of the tickets will be selected to win a grand prize of $1000. Two other tickets will be selected to win consolation prizes of $50 each. Fill in the missing column in Table 8.14. Then find the expected value if you buy one raffle ticket. Describe what this means in practical terms. What can you expect to happen if you purchase five tickets?

TABLE 8.14 GAINS, LOSSES, AND PROBABILITIES IN A RAFFLE

Outcome	Gain or Loss	Probability
Win Grand Prize		$\frac{1}{1000}$
Win Consolation Prize		$\frac{2}{1000}$
Win Nothing		$\frac{997}{1000}$

Unlike the game in Example 5, games in gambling casinos are set up so that players will lose in the long run. These games have negative expected values. Such a game is roulette, French for "little wheel." We first saw the roulette wheel in Section 8.7. It is shown again in Figure 8.12. Recall that the wheel has 38 numbered slots (1 through 36, 0, and 00). In each play of the game, the dealer spins the wheel and a small ball in opposite directions. The ball is equally likely to come to rest in any one of the slots, which are colored black, red, or green. Gamblers can place a number of different bets in roulette. Example 6 illustrates one gambling option.

FIGURE 8.12 A U.S. roulette wheel

EXAMPLE 6   EXPECTED VALUE AND ROULETTE

One way to bet in roulette is to place $1 on a single number. If the ball lands on that number, you are awarded $35 and get to keep the $1 that you paid to play the game. If the ball lands on any one of the other 37 slots, you are awarded nothing and the $1 that you bet is collected. Find the expected value for playing roulette if you bet $1 on number 20. Describe what this means.

SOLUTION Table 8.15 contains the two outcomes of interest: the ball landing on your number, 20, and the ball landing elsewhere (in any one of the other 37 slots). The outcomes, their respective gains, losses, and probabilities, are summarized in the table.

TABLE 8.15 PLAYING ONE NUMBER WITH A 35 TO 1 PAYOFF IN ROULETTE

Outcome	Gain or Loss	Probability
Ball lands on 20	$35	$\frac{1}{38}$
Ball does not land on 20	−$1	$\frac{37}{38}$

Expected value, E, is computed by multiplying each gain or loss in Table 8.15 by its probability and then adding these results.

$$E = \$35\left(\frac{1}{38}\right) + (-\$1)\left(\frac{37}{38}\right) = \frac{\$35 - \$37}{38} = \frac{-\$2}{38} \approx -\$0.05$$

The expected value is approximately −$0.05. This means that in the long run, a player can expect to lose about 5¢ for each game played. If 2000 games are played, one could expect to lose $100.

CHECK POINT 6 In the game of one-spot keno, a card is purchased for $1. It allows a player to choose one number from 1 to 80. A dealer then chooses twenty numbers at random. If the player's number is among those chosen, the player is paid $3.20, but does not get to keep the $1 paid to play the game. Find the expected value of a $1 bet. Describe what this means.

EXERCISE SET 8.8 ●●●●●●

• Practice and Application Exercises

In Exercises 1–2, the numbers that each pointer can land on and their respective probabilities are shown. Compute the expected value for the number on which each pointer lands.

1.

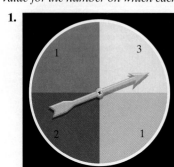

Outcome	Probability
1	$\frac{1}{2}$
2	$\frac{1}{4}$
3	$\frac{1}{4}$

2.

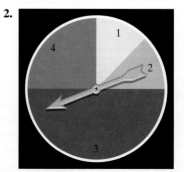

Outcome	Probability
1	$\frac{1}{8}$
2	$\frac{1}{8}$
3	$\frac{1}{2}$
4	$\frac{1}{4}$

The tables in Exercises 3–4 show claims and their probabilities for an insurance company.

   a. *Calculate the expected value and describe what this means in practical terms.*

b. *How much should the company charge as an average premium so that it breaks even on its claim costs?*

c. *How much should the company charge to make a profit of $50 per policy?*

3. PROBABILITIES FOR HOMEOWNERS' INSURANCE CLAIMS

Amount of Claim (to the nearest $50,000)	Probability
$0	0.65
$50,000	0.20
$100,000	0.10
$150,000	0.03
$200,000	0.01
$250,000	0.01

4. PROBABILITIES FOR MEDICAL INSURANCE CLAIMS

Amount of Claim (to the nearest $20,000)	Probability
$0	0.70
$20,000	0.20
$40,000	0.06
$60,000	0.02
$80,000	0.01
$100,000	0.01

5. An architect is considering bidding for the design of a new museum. The cost of drawing plans and submitting a model is $10,000. The probability of being awarded the bid is 0.1, and anticipated profits are $100,000, resulting in a possible gain of this amount minus the $10,000 cost for plans and a model. What is the expected value in this situation? Describe what this value means.

6. A construction company is planning to bid on a building contract. The bid costs the company $1500. The probability that the bid is accepted is $\frac{1}{5}$. If the bid is accepted, the company will make $40,000 minus the cost of the bid. Find the expected value in this situation. Describe what this value means.

7. It is estimated that there are 27 deaths for every 10 million people who use airplanes. A company that sells flight insurance provides $100,000 in case of death in a plane crash. A policy can be purchased for $1. Calculate the expected value and thereby determine how much the insurance company can make over the long run for each policy that it sells.

8. A 25-year-old can purchase a one-year life insurance policy for $10,000 at a cost of $100. Past history indicates that the probability of a person dying at age 25 is 0.002. Determine the company's expected gain per policy.

Exercises 9–10 are related to the SAT, described in Check Point 4 on page 666.

9. Suppose that you can eliminate one of the possible five answers. Modify the two probabilities shown in the final column in Table 8.12 on page 496 by finding the probabilities of guessing correctly and guessing incorrectly under these circumstances. What is the expected point value of a random guess? Is it advantageous to guess under these circumstances?

10. Suppose that you can eliminate two of the possible five answers. Modify the two probabilities shown in the final column in Table 8.12 on page 496 by finding the probabilities of guessing correctly and guessing incorrectly under these circumstances. What is the expected point value of a random guess? Is it advantageous to guess under these circumstances?

11. A store specializing in mountain bikes is to open in one of two malls. If the first mall is selected, the store anticipates a yearly profit of $300,000 if successful and a yearly loss of $100,000 otherwise. The probability of success is $\frac{1}{2}$. If the second mall is selected, it is estimated that the yearly profit will be $200,000 if successful; otherwise, the annual loss will be $60,000. The probability of success at the second mall is $\frac{3}{4}$. Which mall should be chosen in order to maximize the expected profit?

12. An oil company is considering two sites on which to drill, described as follows:

Site A: Profit if oil is found: $80 million
Loss if no oil is found: $10 million
Probability of finding oil: 0.2

Site B: Profit if oil is found: $120 million
Loss if no oil is found: $18 million
Probability of finding oil: 0.1

Which site has the larger expected profit? By how much?

13. In a product liability case, a company can settle out of court for a loss of $350,000, or go to trial, losing $700,000 if found guilty and nothing if found not guilty. Lawyers for the company estimate the probability of a not-guilty verdict to be 0.8.

a. Find the expected value of the amount the company can lose by taking the case to court.

b. Should the company settle out of court?

14. A service that repairs air conditioners sells maintenance agreements for $80 a year. The average cost for repairing an air conditioner is $350 and 1 in every 100 people who purchase maintenance agreements have air conditioners that require repair. Find the service's expected profit per maintenance agreement.

Exercises 15–19 involve computing expected values in games of chance.

15. A game is played using one die. If the die is rolled and shows 1, the player wins $5. If the die shows any number other than 1, the player wins nothing. If there is a charge of $1 to play the game, what is the game's expected value? What does this value mean?

16. A game is played using one die. If the die is rolled and shows 1, the player wins $1; if 2, the player wins $2; if 3, the player wins $3. If the die shows 4, 5, or 6, the player wins nothing. If there is a charge of $1.25 to play the game, what is the game's expected value? What does this value mean?

17. Another option in a roulette game (see Example 6 on page 498) is to bet $1 on red. (There are 18 red compartments, 18 black compartments, and 2 compartments that are neither red nor black.) If the ball lands on red, you get to keep the $1 that you paid to play the game and you are awarded $1. If the ball lands elsewhere, you are awarded nothing and the $1 that you bet is collected. Find the expected value for playing roulette if you bet $1 on red. Describe what this number means.

18. The spinner on a wheel of fortune can land with an equal chance on any one of ten regions. Three regions are red, four are blue, two are yellow, and one is green. A player wins $4 if the spinner stops on red and $2 if it stops on green. The player loses $2 if it stops on blue and $3 if it stops on yellow. What is the expected value? What does this mean if the game is played ten times?

19. For many years, organized crime ran a numbers game that is now run legally by many state governments. The player selects a three-digit number from 000 to 999. There are 1000 such numbers. A bet of $1 is placed on a number, say number 115. If the number is selected, the player wins $500. If any other number is selected, the player wins nothing. Find the expected value for this game and describe what this means.

• Writing in Mathematics

20. What does the expected value for the outcome of the roll of a fair die represent?

21. Explain how to find the expected value for the number of girls for a family with two children. What is the expected value?

22. How do insurance companies use expected value to determine what to charge for a policy?

23. Describe a situation in which a business can use expected value.

24. If the expected value of a game is negative, what does this mean? Also describe the meaning of a positive and a zero expected value.

25. The expected value for purchasing a ticket in a raffle is −$0.75. Describe what this means. Will a person who purchases a ticket lose $0.75?

• Critical Thinking Exercises

26. A popular state lottery is the 5/35 lottery, played in Arizona, Connecticut, Illinois, Iowa, Kentucky, Maine, Massachusetts, New Hampshire, South Dakota, and Vermont. In Arizona's version of the game, prizes are set: First prize is $50,000, second prize is $500, and third prize is $5. To win first prize, you must select all five of the winning numbers, numbered from 1 to 35. Second prize is awarded to players who select any four of the five winning numbers, and third prize is awarded to players who select any three of the winning numbers. The cost to purchase a lottery ticket is $1. Find the expected value of Arizona's "Fantasy Five" game, and describe what this means in terms of buying a lottery ticket over the long run.

27. Refer to the probabilities of dying at any given age on page 465 to solve this exercise. A 20-year-old woman wants to purchase a $200,000 one-year life insurance policy. What should the insurance company charge the woman for the policy if it wants an expected profit of $60?

• Group Exercise

28. This activity is a group research project intended for people interested in games of chance at casinos. The research should culminate in a seminar on games of chance and their expected values. The seminar is intended to last about 30 minutes and should result in an interesting and informative presentation made to the entire class.

Each member of the group should research a game available at a typical casino. Describe the game to the class and compute its expected value. After each member has done this, so that class members now have an idea of those games with the greatest and smallest house advantages, a final group member might want to research and present ways for currently treating people whose addiction to these games has caused their lives to swirl out of control.

●●●●●● CHAPTER SUMMARY, REVIEW, AND TEST

● S U M M A R Y	DEFINITIONS AND CONCEPTS	EXAMPLES

8.1 The Fundamental Counting Principle

The number of ways in which a series of successive things can occur is found by multiplying the number of ways in which each thing can occur.	Ex. 1, p. 439; Ex. 2, p. 439; Ex. 3, p. 440; Ex. 4, p. 440; Ex. 5, p. 441; Ex. 6, p. 441

8.2 Permutations

a. A permutation from a group of items occurs when no item is used more than once and the order of arrangement makes a difference. The Fundamental Counting Principle can be used to determine the number of permutations possible.	Ex. 1, p. 444; Ex. 2, p. 445

b. Factorial Notation

Ex. 3, p. 446

$$n! = n(n-1)(n-2)\cdots(3)(2)(1) \text{ and } 0! = 1$$

c. Permutations Formula

Ex. 4, p. 447;
Ex. 5, p. 448

The number of permutations possible if r items are taken from n items is $_nP_r = \dfrac{n!}{(n-r)!}$.

d. Permutations of Duplicate Items

Ex. 6, p. 449

The number of permutations of n items, where p items are identical, q items are identical, r items are identical, and so on, is

$$\frac{n!}{p!\,q!\,r!\ldots}.$$

8.3 Combinations

a. A combination from a group of items occurs when no item is used more than once and the order of items makes no difference.

Ex. 1, p. 451

b. Combinations Formula

Ex. 2, p. 453;
Ex. 3, p. 453;
Ex. 4, p. 454

The number of combinations possible if r items are taken from n items is $_nC_r = \dfrac{n!}{(n-r)!\,r!}$.

8.4 Fundamentals of Probability

a. Theoretical probability applies to experiments in which the set of all equally likely outcomes, called the sample space, is known. An event is any subset of the sample space.

b. The theoretical probability of event E with sample space S is

Ex. 1, p. 458;
Ex. 2, p. 460;
Ex. 3, p. 460

$$P(E) = \frac{\text{number of outcomes in } E}{\text{total number of possible outcomes}} = \frac{n(E)}{n(S)}.$$

c. Empirical probability applies to situations in which we observe the frequency of the occurrence of an event.

d. The empirical probability of event E is

Ex. 4, p. 461

$$P(E) = \frac{\text{observed number of times } E \text{ occurs}}{\text{total number of observed occurrences}}.$$

8.5 Probability with the Fundamental Counting Principle, Permutations, and Combinations

a. Probability of a permutation

Ex. 1, p. 466

$$= \frac{\text{the number of ways the permutation can occur}}{\text{total number of possible permutations}}.$$

b. Probability of a combination

Ex. 2, p. 467;
Ex. 3, p. 468

$$= \frac{\text{the number of ways the combination can occur}}{\text{total number of possible combinations}}.$$

8.6 Events Involving *Not* and *Or*; Odds

a. Complement Rules of Probability

Ex. 1, p. 472;
Ex. 2, p. 472

$$P(\text{not } E) = 1 - P(E) \quad \text{and} \quad P(E) = 1 - P(\text{not } E)$$

b. If it is impossible for events A and B to occur simultaneously, the events are mutually exclusive.

c. If A and B are mutually exclusive events, then $P(A \text{ or } B) = P(A) + P(B)$.

Ex. 3, p. 474;
Ex. 6(b), p. 476

d. If A and B are not mutually exclusive events, then

$$P(A \text{ or } B) = P(A) + P(B) - P(A \text{ and } B).$$

Ex. 4, p. 475;
Ex. 5, p. 475;
Ex. 6(a), p. 476

e. Probability to Odds

1. Odds in favor of $E = \dfrac{P(E)}{P(\text{not } E)}$ **2.** Odds against $E = \dfrac{P(\text{not } E)}{P(E)}$

Ex. 7, p. 477;
Ex. 8, p. 478

f. Odds to Probability

If odds in favor of E are a to b, then $P(E) = \dfrac{a}{a + b}$.

Ex. 9. p. 479

8.7 Events Involving *And*; Conditional Probability

a. Two events are independent if the occurrence of either of them has no effect on the probability of the other.

b. If A and B are independent events,

$$P(A \text{ and } B) = P(A) \cdot P(B).$$

Ex. 1, p. 484

c. The probability of a succession of independent events is the product of each of their probabilities.

Ex. 2, p. 484;
Ex. 3, p. 485

d. Two events are dependent if the occurrence of one of them has an effect on the probability of the other.

e. If A and B are dependent events,

$$P(A \text{ and } B) = P(A) \cdot P(B \text{ given that } A \text{ has occurred}).$$

Ex. 4, p. 487

f. The multiplication rule for dependent events can be extended to cover three or more dependent events. In the case of three such events,

$$P(A \text{ and } B \text{ and } C)$$
$$= P(A) \cdot P(B \text{ given } A \text{ occurred}) \cdot P(C \text{ given } A \text{ and } B \text{ occurred}).$$

Ex. 5, p. 487

g. The conditional probability of B, given A, written $P(B|A)$, is the probability of B if the sample space is restricted to A.

$$P(B|A) = \frac{n(B \cap A)}{n(A)} = \frac{\text{number of outcomes common to } B \text{ and } A}{\text{number of outcomes in } A}$$

Ex. 6, p. 488;
Ex. 7, p. 489

8.8 Expected Value

a. Expected value, E, is found by multiplying every possible outcome by its probability and then adding these products.

Ex. 1, p. 494;
Ex. 2, p. 494;
Ex. 3, p. 495

b. In situations involving business decisions, expected value is calculated by multiplying the gain or loss for each possible outcome by its probability. The sum of these products is the expected value.

Ex. 4, p. 495

c. In a game of chance, expected value is the average payoff when the game is played a large number of times. To find the expected value of a game, multiply the gain or loss for each possible outcome by its probability. Then add the products.

Ex. 5, p. 496;
Ex. 6, p. 498

REVIEW EXERCISES

8.1

1. A restaurant offers 20 appetizers and 40 main courses. In how many ways can a person order a two-course meal?

2. A popular brand of pen comes in red, green, blue, or black ink. The writing tip can be chosen from extra bold, bold, regular, fine, or micro. How many different choices of pens do you have with this brand?

3. In how many ways can first and second prize be awarded in a contest with 100 people, assuming that each prize is awarded to a different person?

4. You are answering three multiple-choice questions. Each question has five answer choices, with one correct answer per question. If you select one of these five choices for each question and leave nothing blank, in how many ways can you answer the questions?

5. A stock can go up, go down, or stay unchanged. How many possibilities are there if you own five stocks?

6. A person can purchase a condominium with a choice of five kinds of carpeting, with or without a pool, with or without a porch, and with one, two, or three bedrooms. How many different options are there for the condominium?

8.2

7. Six acts are scheduled to perform in a variety show. How many different ways are there to schedule their appearances?

8. In how many ways can five airplanes line up for departure on a runway?

9. You need to arrange seven of your favorite books along a small shelf. Although you are not arranging the books by height, the tallest of the books is to be placed at the left end and the shortest of the books at the right end. How many different ways can you arrange the books?

In Exercises 10–13, evaluate each factorial expression.

10. $\dfrac{16!}{14!}$

11. $\dfrac{800!}{799!}$

12. $5! - 3!$

13. $\dfrac{11!}{(11-3)!}$

In Exercises 14–15, use the formula for $_nP_r$ to evaluate each expression.

14. $_{10}P_6$

15. $_{100}P_2$

Use the formula for $_nP_r$ to solve Exercises 16–17.

16. A club with 15 members is to choose four officers—president, vice-president, secretary, and treasurer. In how many ways can these offices be filled?

17. Suppose you are asked to list, in order of preference, the five favorite CDs you purchased in the past 12 months. If you bought 20 CDs over this time period, in how many ways can the five favorite be ranked?

Use the formula for the number of permutations with duplicate items to solve Exercises 18–19.

18. In how many distinct ways can the letters of the word TORONTO be arranged?

19. In how many ways can the digits in the number 335,557 be arranged?

8.3

In Exercises 20–22, does the problem involve permutations or combinations? Explain your answer. (It is not necessary to solve the problem.)

20. How many different 4-card hands can be dealt from a 52-card deck?

21. How many different ways can a director select from 20 male actors to cast the roles of Mark, Roger, Angel, and Collins in the musical *Rent*?

22. How many different ways can a director select 4 actors from a group of 20 actors to attend a workshop on performing in rock musicals?

In Exercises 23–24, use the formula for $_nC_r$ to evaluate each expression.

23. $_{11}C_7$

24. $_{14}C_5$

Use the formula for $_nC_r$ to solve Exercises 25–28.

25. An election ballot asks voters to select four city commissioners from a group of ten candidates. In how many ways can this be done?

26. How many different 5-card hands can be dealt from a deck that has only hearts (13 different cards)?

27. From the 20 CDs that you've bought during the past year, you plan to take 3 with you on vacation. How many different sets of three CDs can you take?

28. A political discussion group consists of 12 Republicans and 8 Democrats. In how many ways can 5 Republicans and 4 Democrats be selected to attend a conference on politics and social issues?

8.4

In Exercises 29–32, a die is rolled. Find the probability of rolling

29. a 6.

30. a number less than 5.

31. a number less than 7.

32. a number greater than 6.

In Exercises 33–37, you are dealt one card from a 52-card deck. Find the probability of being dealt

33. a 5.

34. a picture card.

35. a card greater than 4 and less than 8.

36. a 4 of diamonds.

37. a red ace.

In Exercises 38–40, suppose that you reach into a bag and randomly select one piece of candy from 15 chocolates, 10 caramels, and 5 peppermints. Find the probability of selecting

38. a chocolate.

39. a caramel.

40. a peppermint.

41. Tay-Sachs disease occurs in 1 of every 3600 births among Jews from central and eastern Europe, and in 1 in 600,000 births in other populations. The disease causes abnormal accumulation of certain fat compounds in the spinal cord and brain, resulting in paralysis, blindness, and mental impairment. Death generally occurs before the age of five. If we use *t* to represent a Tay-Sachs gene and *T* a healthy gene, the table below shows the four possibilities for the children of one healthy, *TT*, parent, and one parent who carries the disease, *Tt*, but is not sick.

    a. Find the probability that a child of these parents will be a carrier without the disease.

    b. Find the probability that a child of these parents will have the disease.

		Second Parent	
		T	*t*
First	*T*	*TT*	*Tt*
Parent	*T*	*TT*	*Tt*

The table shows the employment status of the U.S. civilian labor force in 2004, by gender. Use the data in the table, expressed in millions, to solve Exercises 42–44.

EMPLOYMENT STATUS OF THE U.S. LABOR FORCE, IN MILLIONS, IN 2004

	Employed	**Unemployed**	**Total**
Male	74.5	33.2	107.7
Female	64.7	51.0	115.7
Total	139.2	84.2	223.4

Source: U.S. Bureau of Labor Statistics

Find the probability, expressed as a decimal rounded to three places, that a randomly selected person from the civilian labor force represented in the table

42. is employed.

43. is female.

44. is an unemployed male.

8.5

45. If cities A, B, C, and D are visited in random order, each city visited once, find the probability that city D will be visited first, city B second, city A third, and city C last.

In Exercises 46–49, suppose that six singers are being lined up to perform at a charity. Call the singers A, B, C, D, E, and F. The order of performance is determined by writing each singer's name on one of six cards, placing the cards in a hat, and then drawing one card at a time. The order in which the cards are drawn determines the order in which the singers perform. Find the probability that

46. singer C will perform last.

47. singer B will perform first and singer A will perform last.

48. the singers will perform in the following order: F, E, A, D, C, B.

49. the performance will begin with singer A or C.

50. A lottery game is set up so that each player chooses five different numbers from 1 to 20. If the five numbers match the five numbers drawn in the lottery, the player wins (or shares) the top cash prize. What is the probability of winning the prize

    a. with one lottery ticket?

    b. with 100 different lottery tickets?

51. A committee of four people is to be selected from six Democrats and four Republicans. Find the probability that

    a. all are Democrats.

    b. two are Democrats and two are Republicans.

52. If you are dealt 3 cards from a shuffled deck of red cards (26 different cards), find the probability of getting exactly 2 picture cards.

8.6

In Exercises 53–57, a die is rolled. Find the probability of

53. not rolling a 5.

54. not rolling a number less than 4.

55. rolling a 3 or a 5.

56. rolling a number less than 3 or greater than 4.

57. rolling a number less than 5 or greater than 2.

In Exercises 58–63, you draw one card from a 52-card deck. Find the probability of

58. not drawing a picture card.

59. not drawing a diamond.

60. drawing an ace or a king.

61. drawing a black 6 or a red 7.

62. drawing a queen or a red card.

63. drawing a club or a picture card.

In Exercises 64–69, it is equally probable that the pointer on the spinner shown will land on any one of the six regions, numbered 1 through 6, and colored as shown. If the pointer lands on a borderline, spin again. Find the probability of

64. not stopping on 4.

65. not stopping on yellow.

66. not stopping on red.

67. stopping on red or yellow.

68. stopping on red or an even number.

69. stopping on red or a number greater than 3.

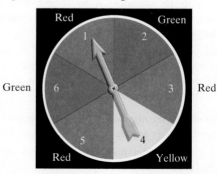

Use this information to solve Exercises 70–71. At a workshop on police work and the African-American community, there are 50 African-American male police officers, 20 African-American female police officers, 90 white male police officers, and 40 white female police officers. If one police officer is selected at random from the people at the workshop, find the probability that the selected person is

70. African American or male.

71. female or white.

Suppose that a survey of 350 college students is taken. Each student is asked the type of college attended (public or private) and the family's income level (low, middle, high). Use the data in the table to solve Exercises 72–75. Express probabilities as simplified fractions.

	Public	Private	Total
Low	120	20	140
Middle	110	50	160
High	22	28	50
Total	252	98	350

Find the probability that a randomly selected student in the survey

72. attends a public college.

73. is not from a high-income family.

74. is from a middle-income or a high-income family.

75. attends a private college or is from a high-income family.

76. One card is randomly selected from a deck of 52 cards. Find the odds in favor and the odds against getting a queen.

77. The winner of a raffle will receive a two-year scholarship to any college of the winner's choice. If 2000 raffle tickets were sold and you purchased 20 tickets, what are the odds against your winning the scholarship?

78. The odds in favor of a candidate winning an election are given at 3 to 1. What is the probability that this candidate will win the election?

8.7

Use the spinner shown to solve Exercises 79–83. It is equally likely that the pointer will land on any one of the six regions, numbered 1 through 6, and colored as shown. If the pointer lands on a borderline, spin again. If the pointer is spun twice, find the probability it will land on

79. yellow and then red.

80. 1 and then 3.

81. yellow both times.

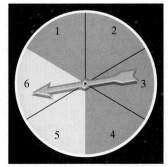

If the pointer is spun three times, find the probability it will land on

82. yellow and then 4 and then an odd number.

83. red every time.

84. What is the probability of a family having five boys born in a row?

85. The probability of a flood in any given year in a region prone to flooding is 0.2.

    a. What is the probability of a flood two years in a row?

    b. What is the probability of a flood for three consecutive years?

    c. What is the probability of no flooding for four consecutive years?

    d. What is the probability of a flood at least once in the next four years?

In Exercises 86–87, two students are selected from a group of four psychology majors, three business majors, and two music majors. The two students are to meet with the campus cafeteria manager to voice the group's concerns about food prices and quality. One student is randomly selected and leaves for the cafeteria manager's office. Then, a second student is selected. Find the probability of selecting

86. a music major and then a psychology major.

87. two business majors.

88. A final visit to the box of chocolates: It's now grown to a box of 50, of which 30 are solid chocolate, 15 are filled with jelly, and 5 are filled with cherries. The story is still the same: They all look alike. You select a piece, eat it, select a second piece, eat it, and help yourself to a final sugar rush. Find the probability of selecting a solid chocolate followed by two cherry-filled chocolates.

89. A single die is tossed. Find the probability that the tossed die shows 5, given that the outcome is an odd number.

90. A letter is randomly selected from the letters of the English alphabet. Find the probability of selecting a vowel, given that the outcome is a letter that precedes k.

91. The numbers shown below are each written on a colored chip. The chips are placed into a bag and one chip is selected at random. Find the probability of selecting

    a. an odd number, given that a red chip is selected.

    b. a yellow chip, given that the number selected is at least 3.

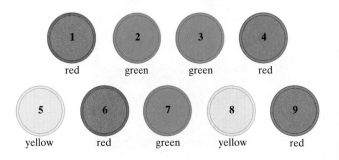

The data in the table are based on 145 Americans tested for tuberculosis. Use the data to solve Exercises 92–99. Express probabilities as simplified fractions.

	TB	No TB
Positive Screening Test	9	11
Negative Screening Test	1	124

Source: Deborah J. Bennett, *Randomness*, Harvard University Press, 1998

8.4 and 8.6–8.7

The table shows the distribution, by age and gender, of the 30,242 deaths in the United States involving firearms in 2002.

DEATHS IN THE UNITED STATES INVOLVING FIREARMS, 2002

	Under Age 5	Ages 5–14	Ages 15–19	Ages 20–24	Ages 25–44	Ages 45–64	Ages 65–74	Age ≥75	Total
Male	42	242	2209	3887	9850	5875	1768	2225	26,098
Female	29	106	265	419	1736	1165	225	199	4144
Total	71	348	2474	4306	11,586	7040	1993	2424	30,242

Source: National Safety Council

In Exercises 100–106, use the data in the table to find the probability, expressed as a fraction and as a decimal rounded to three places, that a firearm death in the United States

100. involved a male.

101. involved a person in the 25–44 age range.

102. involved a person less than 75 years old.

103. involved a person in the 20–24 age range or in the 25–44 age range.

104. involved a female or a person younger than 5.

105. involved a person in the 20–24 age range, given that this person was a male.

106. involved a male, given that this person was at least 75.

8.8

107. The numbers that the pointer can land on and their respective probabilities are shown below and in the next column.

Find the probability that a randomly selected person from this group

92. does not have TB.

93. tests positive.

94. does not have TB or tests positive.

95. does not have TB, given a positive test.

96. has a positive test, given no TB.

97. has TB, given a negative test.

Suppose that two people are randomly selected, in succession, from this group. Find the probability of selecting

98. two people with TB.

99. two people with positive screening tests.

Outcome	Probability
1	$\frac{1}{4}$
2	$\frac{1}{8}$
3	$\frac{1}{8}$
4	$\frac{1}{4}$
5	$\frac{1}{4}$

Compute the expected value for the number on which the pointer lands.

108. The table shows claims and their probabilities for an insurance company.

LIFE INSURANCE FOR AN AIRLINE FLIGHT

Amount of Claim	Probability
$0	0.9999995
$1,000,000	0.0000005

a. Calculate the expected value and describe what this value means.

b. How much should the company charge to make a profit of $9.50 per policy?

109. A construction company is planning to bid on a building contract. The bid costs the company $3000. The probability that the bid is accepted is $\frac{1}{4}$. If the bid is accepted, the company will make $30,000 minus the cost of the bid. Find the expected value in this situation. Describe what this value means.

110. A game is played using a fair coin that is tossed twice. The sample space is $\{HH, HT, TH, TT\}$. If exactly one head occurs, the player wins $5, and if exactly two tails occur, the player also wins $5. For any other outcome, the player receives nothing. There is a $4 charge to play the game. What is the expected value? What does this value mean?

•••••• CHAPTER 8 TEST

1. A person can purchase a particular model of a new car with a choice of ten colors, with or without automatic transmission, with or without four-wheel drive, with or without air conditioning, and with two, three, or four radio-CD speakers. How many different options are there for this model of the car?

2. Four acts are scheduled to perform in a variety show. How many different ways are there to schedule their appearances?

3. In how many ways can seven airplanes line up for a departure on a runway if the plane with the greatest number of passengers must depart first?

4. A human resource manager has 11 applicants to fill three different positions. Assuming that all applicants are equally qualified for any of the three positions, in how many ways can this be done?

5. From the ten books that you've recently bought but not read, you plan to take four with you on vacation. How many different sets of four books can you take?

6. In how many distinct ways can the letters of the word ATLANTA be arranged?

In Exercises 7–9, one student is selected at random from a group of 12 freshmen, 16 sophomores, 20 juniors, and 2 seniors. Find the probability that the person selected is

7. a freshman.   8. not a sophomore.

9. a junior or a senior.

10. If you are dealt one card from a 52-card deck, find the probability of being dealt a card greater than 4 and less than 10.

11. Seven movies (A, B, C, D, E, F, and G) are being scheduled for showing. The order of showing is determined by random selection. Find the probability that film C will be shown first, film A next-to-last, and film E last.

12. A lottery game is set up so that each player chooses six different numbers from 1 to 15. If the six numbers match the six numbers drawn in the lottery, the player wins (or shares) the top cash prize. What is the probability of winning the prize with 50 different lottery tickets?

In Exercises 13–14, it is equally probable that the pointer on the spinner shown will land on any one of the eight colored regions. If the pointer lands on a borderline, spin again.

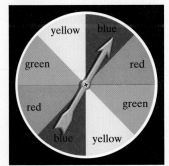

13. If the spinner is spun once, find the probability that the pointer will land on red or blue.

14. If the spinner is spun twice, find the probability that the pointer lands on red on the first spin and blue on the second spin.

15. A region is prone to flooding once every 20 years. The probability of flooding in any one year is $\frac{1}{20}$. What is the probability of flooding for three consecutive years?

16. One card is randomly selected from a deck of 52 cards. Find the probability of selecting a black card or a picture card.

17. A group of students consists of 10 male freshmen, 15 female freshmen, 20 male sophomores, and 5 female sophomores. If one person is randomly selected from the group, find the probability of selecting a freshman or a female.

18. A box contains five red balls, six green balls, and nine yellow balls. Suppose you select one ball at random from the box and do not replace it. Then you randomly select a second ball. Find the probability that both balls selected are red.

19. A quiz consisting of four multiple-choice questions has four available options (a, b, c, or d) for each question. If a person guesses at every question, what is the probability of answering *all* questions correctly?

20. A group is comprised of 20 men and 15 women. If one person is randomly selected from the group, find the odds against the person being a man.

21. The odds against a candidate winning an election are given at 1 to 4.
    a. What are the odds in favor of the candidate winning?
    b. What is the probability that the candidate will win the election?

A class is collecting data on eye color and gender. They organize the data they collected into the table shown. Numbers in the table represent the number of students from the class that belong to each of the categories. Use the data to solve Exercises 22–26. Express probabilities as simplified fractions.

	Brown	Blue	Green
Male	22	18	10
Female	18	20	12

Find the probability that a randomly selected student from this class

22. does not have brown eyes.

23. has brown eyes or blue eyes.

24. is female or has green eyes.

25. is male, given the student has blue eyes.

26. If two people are randomly selected, in succession, from the students in this class, find the probability that they both have green eyes.

27. An architect is considering bidding for the design of a new theater. The cost of drawing plans and submitting a model is $15,000. The probability of being awarded the bid is 0.2, and anticipated profits are $80,000, resulting in a possible gain of this amount minus the $15,000 cost for plans and models. What is the expected value if the architect decides to bid for the design? Describe what this value means.

28. A game is played by selecting one bill at random from a bag that contains ten $1 bills, five $2 bills, three $5 bills, one $10 bill, and one $100 bill. The player gets to keep the selected bill. There is a $20 charge to play the game. What is the expected value? What does this value mean?

CHAPTER 9

Statistics

I n a 1996 study, researchers found that employees described as plain had salaries below the median level and those described as attractive had salaries above the median level.

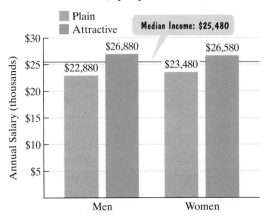

Annual Salaries of American Men and Women, by Physical Attractiveness

Source: Jeff Biddle and Daniel Hamermesh, CompPsych Survey

Statisticians collect numerical data from subgroups of populations to find out everything imaginable about the population as a whole, including whom they favor in an election, what they watch on TV, how much money they make, what worries them, and even how being attractive pays off. Comedians and statisticians joke that 62.38% of all statistics are made up on the spot. Because statisticians both record and influence our behavior, it is important to distinguish between good and bad methods for collecting, presenting, and interpreting data. In this chapter, you will gain an understanding of where data come from and how these numbers are used to make decisions.

SECTION 9.1 • SAMPLING, FREQUENCY DISTRIBUTIONS, AND GRAPHS

*M*A*S*H* took place in the early 1950s, during the Korean War. By the final episode, the show had lasted four times as long as the Korean War.

At the end of the twentieth century, there were 94 million households in the United States with television sets. The television program viewed by the greatest percentage of such households in that century was the final episode of *M*A*S*H*. Over 50 million American households watched this program.

Numerical information, such as the information about the top three TV shows of the twentieth century, shown in Table 9.1, is called **data**. The word **statistics** is often used when referring to data. However, statistics has a second meaning: Statistics is also a method for collecting, organizing, analyzing, and interpreting data, as well as drawing conclusions based on the data. This methodology divides statistics into two main areas. **Descriptive statistics** is concerned with collecting, organizing, summarizing, and presenting data. **Inferential statistics** has to do with making generalizations about and drawing conclusions from the data collected.

Program	**Total Households**	**Viewing Percentage**
1. *M*A*S*H* Feb. 28, 1983	50,150,000	60.2%
2. *Dallas* Nov. 21, 1980	41,470,000	53.3%
3. *Roots Part 8* Jan. 30, 1977	36,380,000	51.1%

TABLE 9.1 TV PROGRAMS WITH THE GREATEST U.S. AUDIENCE VIEWING PERCENTAGE OF THE TWENTIETH CENTURY

Source: Nielsen Media Research

1 | Describe the population whose properties are to be analyzed.

Populations and Samples

Consider the set of all American TV households. Such a set is called the *population*. In general, a **population** is the set containing all the people or objects whose properties are to be described and analyzed by the data collector.

The population of American TV households is huge. At the time of the *M*A*S*H* conclusion, there were nearly 84 million such households. Did over 50 million American TV households really watch the final episode of *M*A*S*H*? A friendly phone call to each household ("So, how are you? What's new? Watch any good television last night? If so, what?") is, of course, absurd. A **sample**, which is a subset or subgroup of the population, is needed. In this case, it would be appropriate to have a sample of a few thousand TV households to draw conclusions about the population of all TV households.

A Sampling Fiasco

Cover of the *Literary Digest*, October 31, 1936. General Research Division, The New York Public Library, Astor, Lenox and Tilden Foundations. The New York Public Library/Art Resource, NY

In 1936, the *Literary Digest* mailed out over ten million ballots to voters throughout the country. The results poured in, and the magazine predicted a landslide victory for Republican Alf Landon over Democrat Franklin Roosevelt. However, the prediction of the *Literary Digest* was wrong. Why? The mailing lists the editors used included people from their own subscriber list, directories of automobile owners, and telephone books. As a result, its sample was anything but random. It excluded most of the poor, who were unlikely to subscribe to the *Literary Digest*, or to own a car or telephone in the heart of the Depression. Prosperous people in 1936 were more likely to be Republican than the poor. Thus, although the sample was massive, it included a higher percentage of affluent individuals than the population as a whole did. A victim of both the Depression and the 1936 sampling fiasco, the *Literary Digest* folded in 1937.

EXAMPLE 1   POPULATIONS AND SAMPLES

A group of hotel owners in a large city decide to conduct a survey among citizens of the city to discover their opinions about casino gambling.

a. Describe the population.

b. One of the hotel owners suggests obtaining a sample by surveying all the people at six of the largest nightclubs in the city on a Saturday night. Each person will be asked to express his or her opinion on casino gambling. Does this seem like a good idea?

SOLUTION

a. The population is the set containing all the citizens of the city.

b. Questioning people at six of the city's largest nightclubs is a terrible idea. The nightclub subset is probably more likely to have a positive attitude toward casino gambling than the population of all the city's citizens.

CHECK POINT 1 A city government wants to conduct a survey among the city's homeless to discover their opinions about required residence in city shelters from midnight until 6 A.M.

a. Describe the population.

b. A city commissioner suggests obtaining a sample by surveying all the homeless people at the city's largest shelter on a Sunday night. Does this seem like a good idea? Explain your answer.

Random Sampling

There is a way to use a small sample to make generalizations about a large population: Guarantee that every member of the population has an equal chance to be selected for the sample. Surveying people at six of the city's largest nightclubs does not provide this guarantee. Unless it can be established that all citizens of the city frequent these clubs, which seems unlikely, this sampling scheme does not permit each citizen an equal chance of selection.

> **RANDOM SAMPLES**
>
> A **random sample** is a sample obtained in such a way that every element in the population has an equal chance of being selected for the sample.

Suppose that you are elated with the quality of one of your courses. Although it's an auditorium section with 120 students, you feel that the professor is lecturing right to you. During a wonderful lecture, you look around the auditorium to see if any of the other students are sharing your enthusiasm. Based on body language, it's hard to tell. You really want to know the opinion of the population of 120 students taking this course. You think about asking students to grade the course on an A to F scale, anticipating a unanimous A. You cannot survey everyone. Eureka! Suddenly you have an idea on how to take a sample. Place cards numbered from 1 through 120, one number per card, in a box. Because the course has assigned seating by number, each numbered card corresponds to a student in the class. Reach in and randomly select six cards. Each card, and therefore each student, has an equal chance of being selected. Then use the opinions about the course from the six randomly selected students to generalize about the course opinion for the entire 120-student population.

Your idea is precisely how random samples are obtained. In random sampling, each element in the population must be identified and assigned a number. The numbers are generally assigned in order. The way to sample from the larger numbered population is to generate random numbers using a computer or calculator.

Each numbered element from the population that corresponds to one of the generated random numbers is selected for the sample.

Call-in polls on radio and television are not reliable because those polled do not represent the larger population. A person who calls in is likely to have feelings about an issue that are consistent with the politics of the show's host. For a poll to be accurate, the sample must be chosen randomly from the larger population. The A. C. Nielsen Company uses a random sample of approximately 5000 TV households to measure the percentage of households tuned in to a television program.

2 Select an appropriate sampling technique.

The United States Census

A census is a survey that attempts to include the entire population. The U.S. Constitution requires a census of the American population every ten years. The 2000 census form was mailed to all households in the country. A census "long form" that asks many more questions than the basic census form is sent to a random sample of one-sixth of all households.

Although the census generates volumes of statistics, its main purpose is to give the government block-by-block population figures to create election districts with equal populations needs. The U.S. census is not foolproof. The 1990 census missed 1.6% of the American population, including an estimated 4.4% of the African American population, largely in inner cities.

3 Organize and present data.

EXAMPLE 2 SELECTING AN APPROPRIATE SAMPLING TECHNIQUE

We return to the hotel owners in the large city who are interested in how the city's citizens feel about casino gambling. Which of the following would be the most appropriate way to select a random sample?

a. Randomly survey people who live in the oceanfront condominiums in the city.

b. Survey the first 200 people whose names appear in the city's telephone directory.

c. Randomly select neighborhoods of the city and then randomly survey people within the selected neighborhoods.

SOLUTION Keep in mind that the population is the set containing all the city's citizens. A random sample must give each citizen an equal chance of being selected.

a. Randomly selecting people who live in the city's oceanfront condominiums is not a good idea. Many hotels lie along the oceanfront, and the oceanfront property owners might object to the traffic and noise as a result of casino gambling. Furthermore, this sample does not give each citizen of the city an equal chance of being selected.

b. If the hotel owners survey the first 200 names in the city's telephone directory, all citizens do not have an equal chance of selection. For example, individuals whose last name begins with a letter toward the end of the alphabet have no chance of being selected.

c. Randomly selecting neighborhoods of the city and then randomly surveying people within the selected neighborhoods is an appropriate technique. Using this method, each citizen has an equal chance of being selected.

In summary, given the three options, the sampling technique in part (c) is the most appropriate.

Surveys and polls involve data from a sample of some population. Regardless of the sampling technique used, the sample should exhibit characteristics typical of those possessed by the target population. This type of sample is called a **representative sample**.

CHECK POINT 2 Explain why the sampling technique described in Check Point 1(b) on page 511 is not a random sample. Then describe an appropriate way to select a random sample of the city's homeless.

Frequency Distributions

After data have been collected from a sample of the population, the next task facing the statistician is to present the data in a condensed and manageable form. In this way, the data can be more easily interpreted.

Suppose, for example, that researchers are interested in determining the age at which adolescent males show the greatest rate of physical growth. A random sample of 35 ten-year-old boys is measured for height and then remeasured each year until they reach 18. The age of maximum yearly growth for each subject is as follows:

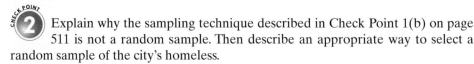

12, 14, 13, 14, 16, 14, 14, 17, 13, 10, 13, 18, 12, 15, 14, 15, 15, 14, 14, 13, 15, 16, 15, 12, 13, 16, 11, 15, 12, 13, 12, 11, 13, 14, 14.

A piece of data is called a **data item**. This list of data has 35 data items. Some of the data items are identical. Two of the data items are 11 and 11. Thus, we can say that the **data value** 11 occurs twice. Similarly, because five of the data items are 12, 12, 12, 12, and 12, the data value 12 occurs five times.

Collected data can be presented using a **frequency distribution**. Such a distribution consists of two columns. The data values are listed in one column. Numerical data are generally listed from smallest to largest. The adjacent column is labeled **frequency** and indicates the number of times each value occurs.

TABLE 9.2 A FREQUENCY DISTRIBUTION FOR A BOY'S AGE OF MAXIMUM YEARLY GROWTH

Age of Maximum Growth	Number of Boys (Frequency)
10	1
11	2
12	5
13	7
14	9
15	6
16	3
17	1
18	1
Total:	$n = 35$

35 is the sum of the frequencies.

EXAMPLE 3   CONSTRUCTING A FREQUENCY DISTRIBUTION

Construct a frequency distribution for the data of the age of maximum yearly growth for 35 boys:

12, 14, 13, 14, 16, 14, 14, 17, 13, 10, 13, 18, 12, 15, 14, 15, 15, 14, 14, 13, 15, 16, 15, 12, 13, 16, 11, 15, 12, 13, 12, 11, 13, 14, 14.

SOLUTION It is difficult to determine trends in the data above in its current format. Perhaps we can make sense of the data by organizing it into a frequency distribution. Let us create two columns. One lists all possible data values, from smallest (10) to largest (18). The other column indicates the number of times the value occurs in the sample. The frequency distribution is shown in Table 9.2.

The frequency distribution indicates that one subject had maximum growth at age 10, two at age 11, five at age 12, seven at age 13, and so on. The maximum growth for most of the subjects occurred between the ages of 12 and 15. Nine boys experienced maximum growth at age 14, more than at any other age within the sample. The sum of the frequencies, 35, is equal to the original number of data items.

The trend shown by the frequency distribution in Table 9.2 indicates that the number of boys who attain their maximum yearly growth at a given age increases until age 14 and decreases after that. This trend is not evident in the data in its original format.

 3 Construct a frequency distribution for the data showing final course grades for students in a precalculus course, listed alphabetically by student name in a grade book:

F, A, B, B, C, C, B, C, A, A, C, C, D, C, B, D, C, C, B, C.

A frequency distribution that lists all possible data items can be quite cumbersome when there are many such items. For example, consider the following data items. These are statistics test scores for a class of 40 students.

82	47	75	64	57	82	63	93
76	68	84	54	88	77	79	80
94	92	94	80	94	66	81	67
75	73	66	87	76	45	43	56
57	74	50	78	71	84	59	76

It's difficult to determine how well the group did when the grades are displayed like this. Because there are so many data items, one way to organize these data so that the results are more meaningful is to arrange the grades into groups, or **classes**, based on something that interests us. Many grading systems assign an A to grades in the 90–100 class, B to grades in the 80–89 class, C to grades in the 70–79 class, and so on. These classes provide one way to organize the data.

Looking at the 40 statistics test scores, we see that they range from a low of 43 to a high of 94. We can use classes that run from 40 through 49, 50 through 59, 60 through 69, and so on up to 90 through 99, to organize the scores. In Example 4, we go through the data and tally each item into the appropriate class. This method for organizing data is called a **grouped frequency distribution**.

| EXAMPLE 4 | CONSTRUCTING A GROUPED FREQUENCY DISTRIBUTION |

Use the classes 40–49, 50–59, 60–69, 70–79, 80–89, and 90–99 to construct a grouped frequency distribution for the 40 test scores on the previous page.

SOLUTION We use the 40 given scores and tally the number of scores in each class.

Test Scores (Class)	Tally	Number of Students (Frequency)
40–49	|||	3
50–59	|||||		6
60–69	|||||		6
70–79	||||| |||||		11
80–89	||||| ||||	9
90–99	|||||	5

The second score in the list, 47, is shown as the first tally in this row.

The first score in the list, 82, is shown as the first tally in this row.

TABLE 9.3	
Class	Frequency
40–49	3
50–59	6
60–69	6
70–79	11
80–89	9
90–99	5
Total:	$n = 40$

40, the sum of the frequencies, is the number of data items.

Omitting the tally column results in the grouped frequency distribution in Table 9.3. The distribution shows that the greatest frequency of students scored in the 70–79 class. The number of students decreases in classes that contain successively lower and higher scores. The sum of the frequencies, 40, is equal to the original number of data items.

The leftmost number in each class of a grouped frequency distribution is called the **lower class limit**. For example, in Table 9.3, the lower limit of the first class is 40 and the lower limit of the third class is 60. The rightmost number in each class is called the **upper class limit**. In Table 9.3, 49 and 69 are the upper limits for the first and third classes, respectively. Notice that if we take the difference between any two consecutive lower class limits, we get the same number:

$$50 - 40 = 10, \ 60 - 50 = 10, \ 70 - 60 = 10, \ 80 - 70 = 10, \ 90 - 80 = 10.$$

The number 10 is called the **class width**.

When setting up class limits, each class, with the possible exception of the first or last, should have the same width. Because each data item must fall into exactly one class, it is sometimes helpful to vary the width of the first or last class to allow for items that fall far above or below most of the data.

Use the classes in Table 9.3 to construct a grouped frequency distribution for the following 37 exam scores:

73	58	68	75	94	79	96	79
87	83	89	52	99	97	89	58
95	77	75	81	75	73	73	62
69	76	77	71	50	57	41	98
77	71	69	90	75.			

TABLE 9.2 (repeated) A FREQUENCY DISTRIBUTION FOR A BOY'S AGE OF MAXIMUM YEARLY GROWTH

Age of Maximum Growth	Number of Boys (Frequency)
10	1
11	2
12	5
13	7
14	9
15	6
16	3
17	1
18	1
Total:	$n = 35$

Histograms and Frequency Polygons

Take a second look at the frequency distribution for the age of a boy's maximum yearly growth, repeated in Table 9.2. A bar graph with bars that touch can be used to visually display the data. Such a graph is called a **histogram**. Figure 9.1 illustrates a histogram that was constructed using the frequency distribution in Table 9.2. A series of rectangles whose heights represent the frequencies are placed next to each other. For example, the height of the bar for the data value 10, shown in Figure 9.1, is 1. This corresponds to the frequency for 10 given in Table 9.2. The higher the bar, the more frequent the age. The break along the horizontal axis, symbolized by ⌁, eliminates listing the ages 1 through 9.

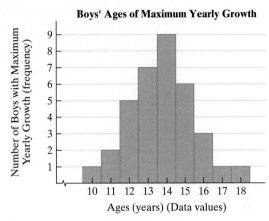

FIGURE 9.1 A histogram for a boy's age of maximum yearly growth

A line graph called a **frequency polygon** can also be used to visually convey the information shown in Figure 9.1. The axes are labeled just like those in a histogram. Thus, the horizontal axis shows data values and the vertical axis shows frequencies. Once a histogram has been constructed, it's fairly easy to draw a frequency polygon. Figure 9.2 shows a histogram with a dot at the top of each rectangle at its midpoint. Connect each of these midpoints with a straight line. To complete the frequency polygon at both ends, the lines should be drawn down to touch the horizontal axis. The completed frequency polygon is shown in Figure 9.3.

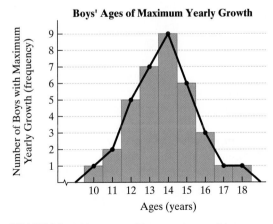

FIGURE 9.2 A histogram with a superimposed frequency polygon

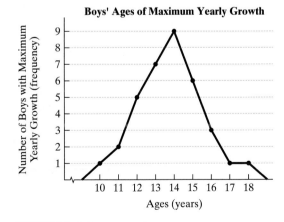

FIGURE 9.3 A frequency polygon

Stem-and-Leaf Plots

A unique way of displaying data uses a tool called a **stem-and-leaf plot**. Example 5 illustrates how we sort the data, revealing the same visual impression created by a histogram.

EXAMPLE 5 CONSTRUCTING A STEM-AND-LEAF PLOT

Use the data showing statistics test scores for 40 students to construct a stem-and-leaf plot:

82	47	75	64	57	82	63	93
76	68	84	54	88	77	79	80
94	92	94	80	94	66	81	67
75	73	66	87	76	45	43	56
57	74	50	78	71	84	59	76.

SOLUTION The plot is constructed by separating each data item into two parts. The first part is the *stem*. The **stem** consists of the tens digit. For example, the stem for the score of 82 is 8. The second part is the *leaf*. The **leaf** consists of the units digit for a given value. For the score of 82, the leaf is 2. The possible stems for the 40 scores are 4, 5, 6, 7, 8, and 9, entered in the left column of the plot.

Begin by entering each data item in the first row:

82 47 75 64 57 82 63 93.

Entering 82:

Stems	Leaves
4	
5	
6	
7	
8	2
9	

Adding 47:

Stems	Leaves
4	7
5	
6	
7	
8	2
9	

Adding 75:

Stems	Leaves
4	7
5	
6	
7	5
8	2
9	

Adding 64:

Stems	Leaves
4	7
5	
6	4
7	5
8	2
9	

Adding 57:

Stems	Leaves
4	7
5	7
6	4
7	5
8	2
9	

Adding 82:

Stems	Leaves
4	7
5	7
6	4
7	5
8	2 2
9	

Adding 63:

Stems	Leaves
4	7
5	7
6	4 3
7	5
8	2 2
9	

Adding 93:

Stems	Leaves
4	7
5	7
6	4 3
7	5
8	2 2
9	3

We continue in this manner and enter all the data items. Figure 9.4 shows the completed stem-and-leaf plot. If you turn the page so that the left margin is on the bottom and facing you, the visual impression created by the enclosed leaves is the same as that created by a histogram. An advantage over the histogram is that the stem-and-leaf plot preserves exact data items. The enclosed leaves extend farthest to the right when the stem is 7. This shows that the greatest frequency of students scored in the 70s. ○

Stems	Leaves
4	7 5 3
5	7 4 6 7 0 9
6	4 3 8 6 7 6
7	5 6 7 9 5 3 6 4 8 1 6
8	2 2 4 8 0 0 1 7 4
9	3 4 2 4 4

Tens digit → Stems Units digit → Leaves

FIGURE 9.4 A stem-and-leaf plot displaying 40 test scores

5 Construct a stem-and-leaf plot for the data in Check Point 4 on page 514.

Construct a stem-and-leaf plot for the data in Check Point 4 on page 514.

4 Identify deceptions in visual displays of data.

Deceptions in Visual Displays of Data

Benjamin Disraeli, Queen Victoria's prime minister, stated that there are "lies, damned lies, and statistics." The problem is not that statistics lie, but rather that liars use statistics. Graphs can be used to distort the underlying data, making it difficult for the viewer to learn the truth. One potential source of misunderstanding is the scale on the vertical axis used to draw the graph. This scale is important because it lets a researcher "inflate" or "deflate" a trend. For example, both graphs in Figure 9.5 present identical data for the percentage of people in the United States living below the poverty level from 2000 through 2004. The graph on the left stretches the scale on the vertical axis to create an overall impression of a poverty rate increasing rapidly over time. The graph on the right compresses the scale on the vertical axis to create an impression of a poverty rate that is slowly increasing, and beginning to level off, over time.

Percentage of People in the United States Living below the Poverty Level, 2000-2004

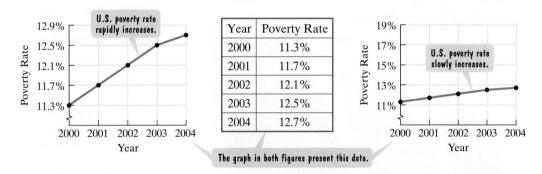

Year	Poverty Rate
2000	11.3%
2001	11.7%
2002	12.1%
2003	12.5%
2004	12.7%

FIGURE 9.5
Source: U.S. Census Bureau

THINGS TO WATCH FOR IN VISUAL DISPLAYS OF DATA

1. Is there a title that explains what is being displayed?

2. Are numbers lined up with tick marks on the vertical axis that clearly indicate the scale? Has the scale been varied to create a more or less dramatic impression than shown by the actual data?

3. Do too many design and cosmetic effects draw attention from or distort the data?

4. Has the wrong impression been created about how the data are changing because equally spaced time intervals are not used on the horizontal axis?

5. Are bar sizes scaled proportionately in terms of the data they represent?

6. Is there a source that indicates where the data in the display came from? Do the data come from an entire population or a sample? Was a random sample used and, if so, are there possible differences between what is displayed in the graph and what is occurring in the entire population? (We'll discuss these *margins of error* in Section 9.4.) Who is presenting the visual display, and does that person have a special case to make for or against the trend shown by the graph?

Table 9.4 on the next page contains two examples of misleading visual displays.

TABLE 9.4 EXAMPLES OF MISLEADING VISUAL DISPLAYS

Graphic Display	Presentation Problems
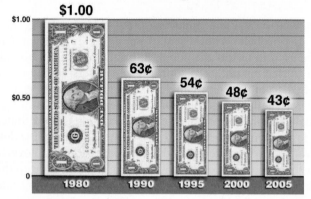 **Purchasing Power of the Diminishing Dollar** 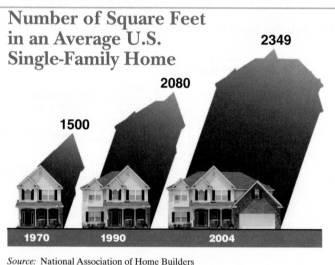 *Source:* Bureau of Labor Statistics	Although the length of each dollar bill is proportional to its spending power, the visual display varies both the length *and width* of the bills to show the diminishing power of the dollar over time. Because our eyes focus on the *areas* of the dollar-shaped bars, this creates the impression that the purchasing power of the dollar diminished even more than it really did. If the area of the dollar were drawn to reflect its purchasing power, the 2005 dollar would be approximately twice as large as the one shown in the graphic display.
Number of Square Feet in an Average U.S. Single-Family Home 2349 2080 1500 1970 1990 2004 *Source:* National Association of Home Builders	Cosmetic effects of homes with equal heights, but different frontal additions and shadow lengths, make it impossible to tell if they proportionately depict the given areas. Time intervals on the horizontal axis are not uniform in size, making it appear that dwelling swelling has been linear from 1970 through 2004. The data indicate that this is not the case. There was a greater increase in area from 1970 through 1980, averaging 29 square feet per year, than from 1990 through 2004, averaging approximately 19.2 square feet per year.

BLITZER BONUS

Creating an Inaccurate Picture by Leaving Something Out

On Monday, October 19, 1987, the Dow Jones Industrial Average plunged 508 points, losing 22.6% of its value. The graph shown on the left, which appeared in a major newspaper following "Black Monday" (as it was instantly dubbed), creates the impression that the Dow average had been "bullish" from 1972 through 1987, increasing throughout this period. The graph creates this inaccurate picture by leaving something out. The graph on the right illustrates that the stock market rose and fell sharply over these years. The impressively smooth curve on the left was obtained by plotting only three of the data points. By ignoring most of the data, increases and decreases are not accounted for and the actual behavior of the market over the 15 years leading to "Black Monday" is inaccurately conveyed.

The Dow Jones Industrial Average: 1972–1987

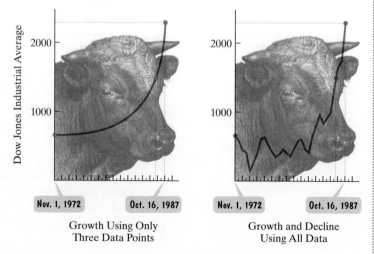

Growth Using Only Three Data Points

Growth and Decline Using All Data

Source: A. K. Dewdney, *200% of Nothing*, John Wiley and Sons, 1993

EXERCISE SET 9.1 ●●●●●●

• Practice and Application Exercises

1. "The Man Poll" of 1014 randomly selected American men ages 18 and older was taken by *Newsweek* June 2–4, 2003. The data shown below are from the poll.

IN GENERAL, HOW WOULD YOU DESCRIBE YOUR HEALTH?

	Age		
	18–34	**35–55**	**≥56**
Excellent	23%	19%	15%
Very good	37	39	32
Good	28	28	28
Fair	10	10	16
Poor	2	4	8
Don't know	0	0	1

a. Describe the population and the sample of this poll.

b. For each man, what variable is measured? Are the data quantitative (numerical) or qualitative (nonnumerical categories)?

2. The *American Association of Nurse Anesthetists Journal* (Feb. 2000) published the results of a study on the use of herbal medicines before surgery. Of 500 surgical patients who were randomly selected for the study, 51% used herbal or alternative medicines prior to surgery.

a. Describe the population and the sample of this study.

b. Is the sample representative of the population? Explain your answer.

c. For each patient, what variable is measured? Are the data quantitative (numerical) or qualitative (nonnumerical categories)?

3. The government of a large city needs to determine whether the city's residents will support the construction of a new jail. The government decides to conduct a survey of a sample of the city's residents. Which one of the following procedures would be most appropriate for obtaining a sample of the city's residents?

a. Survey a random sample of the employees and inmates at the old jail.

b. Survey every fifth person who walks into City Hall on a given day.

c. Survey a random sample of persons within each geographic region of the city.

d. Survey the first 200 people listed in the city's telephone directory.

4. The city council of a large city needs to know whether its residents will support the building of three new schools. The council decides to conduct a survey of a sample of the city's residents. Which procedure would be most appropriate for obtaining a sample of the city's residents?

a. Survey a random sample of teachers who live in the city.

b. Survey 100 individuals who are randomly selected from a list of all people living in the state in which the city in question is located.

c. Survey a random sample of persons within each neighborhood of the city.

d. Survey every tenth person who enters City Hall on a randomly selected day.

A questionnaire was given to students in an introductory statistics class during the first week of the course. One question asked, "How stressed have you been in the last $2\frac{1}{2}$ weeks, on a scale of 0 to 10, with 0 being not at all stressed and 10 being as stressed as possible?" The students' responses are shown in the frequency distribution. Use this frequency distribution to solve Exercises 5–8.

Stress Rating	Frequency
0	2
1	1
2	3
3	12
4	16
5	18
6	13
7	31
8	26
9	15
10	14

Source: Journal of Personality and Social Psychology, 69, 1102–1112

5. Which stress rating describes the greatest number of students? How many students responded with this rating?

6. Which stress rating describes the least number of students? How many responded with this rating?

7. How many students were involved in this study?

8. How many students had a stress rating of 8 or more?

9. A random sample of 30 college students is selected. Each student is asked how much time he or she spent on homework during the previous week. The following times (in hours) are obtained:

16, 24, 18, 21, 18, 16, 18, 17, 15, 21, 19, 17, 17, 16, 19, 18, 15, 15, 20, 17, 15, 17, 24, 19, 16, 20, 16, 19, 18, 17.

Construct a frequency distribution for the data.

10. A random sample of 30 male college students is selected. Each student is asked his height (to the nearest inch). The heights are as follows:

72, 70, 68, 72, 71, 71, 71, 69, 73, 71, 73, 75, 66, 67, 75, 74, 73, 71, 72, 67, 72, 68, 67, 71, 73, 71, 72, 70, 73, 70.

Construct a frequency distribution for the data.

A college professor had students keep a diary of their social interactions for a week. Excluding family and work situations, the number of social interactions of ten minutes or longer over the week is shown in the following grouped frequency distribution. Use this information to solve Exercises 11–18.

Number of Social Interactions	Frequency
0–4	12
5–9	16
10–14	16
15–19	16
20–24	10
25–29	11
30–34	4
35–39	3
40–44	3
45–49	3

Source: Society for Personality and Social Psychology

11. Identify the lower class limit for each class.

12. Identify the upper class limit for each class.

13. What is the class width?

14. How many students were involved in this study?

15. How many students had at least 30 social interactions for the week?

16. How many students had at most 14 social interactions for the week?

17. Among the classes with the greatest frequency, which class has the least number of social interactions?

18. Among the classes with the smallest frequency, which class has the least number of social interactions?

19. As of 2007, the following are the ages, in chronological order, at which U.S. presidents were inaugurated:

57, 61, 57, 57, 58, 57, 61, 54, 68, 51, 49, 64, 50, 48, 65, 52, 56, 46, 54, 49, 50, 47, 55, 55, 54, 42, 51, 56, 55, 51, 54, 51, 60, 62, 43, 55, 56, 61, 52, 69, 64, 46, 54.

Source: Time Almanac

Construct a grouped frequency distribution for the data. Use 41–45 for the first class and use the same width for each subsequent class.

20. The IQ scores of 70 students enrolled in a liberal arts course at a college are as follows:

102, 100, 103, 86, 120, 117, 111, 101, 93, 97, 99, 95, 95, 104, 104, 105, 106, 109, 109, 89, 94, 95, 99, 99, 103, 104, 105, 109, 110, 114, 124, 123, 118, 117, 116, 110, 114, 114, 96, 99, 103, 103, 104, 107, 107, 110, 111, 112, 113, 117, 115, 116, 100, 104, 102, 94, 93, 93, 96, 96, 111, 116, 107, 109, 105, 106, 97, 106, 107, 108.

Construct a grouped frequency distribution for the data. Use 85–89 for the first class and use the same width for each subsequent class.

21. Construct a histogram and a frequency polygon for the data involving stress ratings in Exercises 5–8.

22. Construct a histogram and a frequency polygon for the data in Exercise 9.

23. Construct a histogram and a frequency polygon for the data in Exercise 10.

24. The histogram shows the distribution of starting salaries (rounded to the nearest thousand dollars) for college graduates based on a random sample of recent graduates.

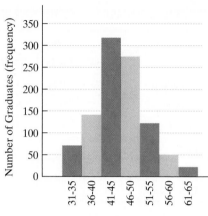

Starting Salaries of Recent College Graduates

Which one of the following is true according to the graph?

a. The graph is based on a sample of approximately 500 recent college graduates.

b. More college graduates had starting salaries in the $51,000–$55,000 range than in the $36,000–$40,000 range.

c. If the sample is truly representative, then for a group of 400 college graduates, we can expect about 28 of them to have starting salaries in the $31,000–$35,000 range.

d. The percentage of starting salaries falling above those shown by any rectangular bar is equal to the percentage of starting salaries falling below that bar.

25. The frequency polygon shows a distribution of IQ scores. Which one of the following is true based upon the graph?

a. The graph is based on a sample of approximately 50 people.

b. More people had an IQ score of 100 than any other IQ score, and as the deviation from 100 increases or decreases, the scores fall off in a symmetrical manner.

c. More people had an IQ score of 110 than a score of 90.

d. The percentage of scores above any IQ score is equal to the percentage of scores below that score.

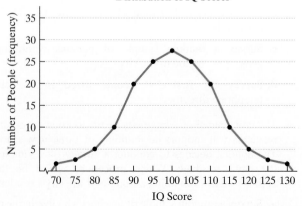

Distribution of IQ Scores

26. Construct a stem-and-leaf plot for the data in Exercise 19 showing the ages at which U.S. presidents were inaugurated.

27. A random sample of 40 college professors is selected from all professors at a university. The following list gives their ages:

63, 48, 42, 42, 38, 59, 41, 44, 45, 28, 54, 62, 51, 44, 63, 66, 59, 46, 51, 28, 37, 66, 42, 40, 30, 31, 48, 32, 29, 42, 63, 37, 36, 47, 25, 34, 49, 30, 35, 50.

Construct a stem-and-leaf plot for the data. What does the shape of the display reveal about the ages of the professors?

28. In "Ages of Oscar-Winning Best Actors and Actresses" (*Mathematics Teacher* magazine) by Richard Brown and Gretchen Davis, the stem-and-leaf plots shown compare the ages of actors and actresses for 30 winners of the Oscar at the time they won the award.

Actors	Stems	Actresses
	2	146667
98753221	3	00113344455778
88776543322100	4	11129
6651	5	
210	6	011
6	7	4
	8	0

a. What is the age of the youngest actor to win an Oscar?

b. What is the age difference between the oldest and the youngest actress to win an Oscar?

c. What is the oldest age shared by two actors to win an Oscar?

d. What differences do you observe between the two stem-and-leaf plots? What explanations can you offer for these differences?

In Exercises 29–33, describe what is misleading in each visual display of data.

29.

World Population, in Billions

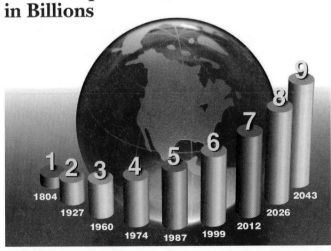

Source: U.S. Census Bureau

30.

Book Title Output in the United States

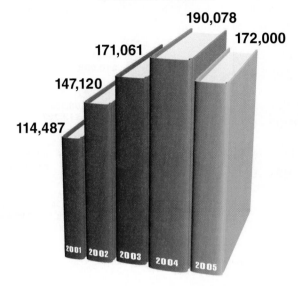

Source: R. R. Bowker

31.

Percentage of the World's Computers in Use, by Country

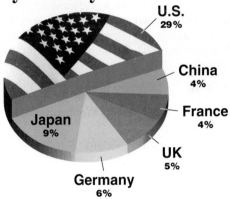

Source: Computer Industry Almanac

32.

Enrollment at the University of Georgia

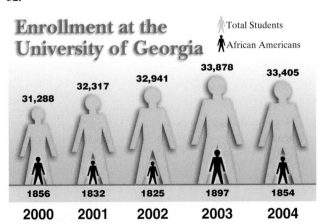

Source: University of Georgia Office of Institutional Research

33.

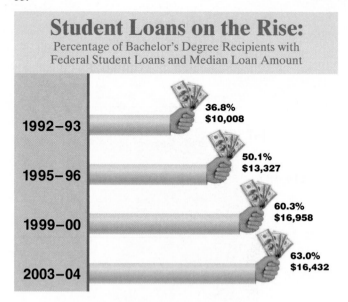

Student Loans on the Rise:
Percentage of Bachelor's Degree Recipients with
Federal Student Loans and Median Loan Amount

1992–93 36.8% $10,008

1995–96 50.1% $13,327

1999–00 60.3% $16,958

2003–04 63.0% $16,432

Source: American Council on Education

• Writing in Mathematics

34. What is a population? What is a sample?

35. Describe what is meant by a random sample.

36. Suppose you are interested in whether or not the students at your college would favor a grading system in which students may receive final grades of A+, A, A−, B+, B, B−, C+, C, C−, and so on. Describe how you might obtain a random sample of 100 students from the entire student population.

37. For Exercise 36, would questioning every fifth student as he or she is leaving the campus library until 100 students are interviewed be a good way to obtain a random sample? Explain your answer.

38. What is a frequency distribution?

39. What is a histogram?

40. What is a frequency polygon?

41. Describe how to construct a frequency polygon from a histogram.

42. Describe how to construct a stem-and-leaf plot from a set of data.

43. Describe two ways that graphs can be misleading.

• Critical Thinking Exercises

44. Construct a grouped frequency distribution for the following data, showing the length, in miles, of the 25 longest rivers in the United States. Use five classes that have the same width.

2540	2340	1980	1900	1900
1460	1450	1420	1310	1290
1280	1240	1040	990	926
906	886	862	800	774
743	724	692	659	649

Source: U.S. Department of the Interior

45. Use two line graphs drawn in the same coordinate system that show a better way to portray the enrollment information for 2000 through 2004 in Exercise 32.

• Group Exercises

46. The classic book on distortion using statistics is *How to Lie with Statistics* by Darrell Huff. This activity is designed for five people. Each person should select two chapters from Huff's book and then present to the class the common methods of statistical manipulation and distortion that Huff discusses.

47. Each group member should find one example of a graph that presents data with integrity and one example of a graph that is misleading. Use newspapers, magazines, the Internet, books, and so forth. Once graphs have been collected, each member should share his or her graphs with the entire group. Be sure to explain why one graph depicts data in a forthright manner and how the other graph misleads the viewer.

SECTION 9.2 • MEASURES OF CENTRAL TENDENCY

OBJECTIVES

1. Determine the mean for a data set.
2. Determine the median for a data set.
3. Determine the mode for a data set.
4. Determine the midrange for a data set.

© NAS. Reprinted with permission of North America Syndicate.

According to researchers, "Robert," the average American guy, is 31 years old, 5 feet 10 inches, 172 pounds, works 6.1 hours daily, and sleeps 7.7 hours. These numbers represent what is "average" or "typical" of American men. In statistics, such values are known as **measures of central tendency** because they are generally located toward the center of a distribution. Four such measures are discussed in this section:

the mean, the median, the mode, and the midrange. Each measure of central tendency is calculated in a different way. Thus, it is better to use a specific term (mean, median, mode, or midrange) than to use the generic descriptive term "average."

The Mean

By far the most commonly used measure of central tendency is the *mean*. The **mean** is obtained by adding all the data items and then dividing the sum by the number of items. The Greek letter sigma, Σ, called a **symbol of summation**, is used to indicate the sum of data items. The notation Σx, read "the sum of x," means to add all the data items in a given data set. We can use this symbol to give a formula for calculating the mean.

THE MEAN

The **mean** is the sum of the data items divided by the number of items.

$$\text{Mean} = \frac{\Sigma x}{n},$$

where Σx represents the sum of all the data items and n represents the number of items.

EXAMPLE 1   CALCULATING THE MEAN

Table 9.5 shows the ten youngest male singers in the United States to have a number 1 single. Find the mean age of these male singers at the time of their number 1 single.

TABLE 9.5 YOUNGEST U.S. MALE SINGERS TO HAVE A NUMBER 1 SINGLE

Artist/Year	Title	Age
Stevie Wonder, 1963	"Fingertips"	13
Donny Osmond, 1971	"Go Away Little Girl"	13
Michael Jackson, 1972	"Ben"	14
Laurie London, 1958	"He's Got the Whole World in His Hands"	14
Paul Anka, 1957	"Diana"	16
Brian Hyland, 1960	"Itsy Bitsy Teenie Weenie Yellow Polkadot Bikini"	16
Shaun Cassidy, 1977	"Da Doo Ron Ron"	17
Bobby Vee, 1961	"Take Good Care of My Baby"	18
Usher, 1998	"Nice & Slow"	19
Andy Gibb, 1977	"I Just Want to Be Your Everything"	19

Source: Russell Ash, *The Top 10 of Everything*

SOLUTION We find the mean by adding the ages and dividing this sum by 10, the number of data items.

$$\text{Mean} = \frac{\Sigma x}{n} = \frac{13 + 13 + 14 + 14 + 16 + 16 + 17 + 18 + 19 + 19}{10} = \frac{159}{10} = 15.9$$

The mean age of the ten youngest singers to have a number 1 single is 15.9.

One and only one mean can be calculated for any group of numerical data. The mean may or may not be one of the actual data items. In Example 1, the mean was 15.9, although no data item is 15.9.

Find the mean for each group of data items:

a. 10, 20, 30, 40, 50   **b.** 3, 10, 10, 10, 117.

The Mean American Millionaire

According to a study involving a random sample of 1300 of America's 2,270,000 million-aires, the average millionaire lives in a $300,000 home in an upper-middle-class neighbor-hood, is 54 years old, drives a four-year-old American car, and had an SAT score of 1190.

Source: Stanley, *The Millionaire Next Door*

---

1 | Determine the mean for a data set.

In Example 1, some of the data items were identical. We can use multiplication when computing the mean for these identical items:

$$\text{Mean} = \frac{13 + 13 + 14 + 14 + 16 + 16 + 17 + 18 + 19 + 19}{10}$$

$$= \frac{13 \cdot 2 + 14 \cdot 2 + 16 \cdot 2 + 17 \cdot 1 + 18 \cdot 1 + 19 \cdot 2}{10}$$

The data values 13, 14, 16, and 19 each have a frequency of 2.

When many data values occur more than once and a frequency distribution is used to organize the data, we can use the following formula to calculate the mean:

> **CALCULATING THE MEAN FOR A FREQUENCY DISTRIBUTION**
>
> $$\text{Mean} = \frac{\Sigma xf}{n},$$
>
> where
>
> x represents a data value.
>
> f represents the frequency of that data value.
>
> Σxf represents the sum of all the products obtained by multiplying each data value by its frequency.
>
> n represents the *total frequency* of the distribution.

TABLE 9.6 STUDENTS' STRESS-LEVEL RATINGS

Stress Rating x	Frequency f
0	2
1	1
2	3
3	12
4	16
5	18
6	13
7	31
8	26
9	15
10	14

Source: Journal of Personality and Social Psychology, 69, 1102–1112

EXAMPLE 2 CALCULATING THE MEAN FOR A FREQUENCY DISTRIBUTION

In the previous exercise set, we mentioned a questionnaire given to students in an introductory statistics class during the first week of the course. One question asked, "How stressed have you been in the last $2\frac{1}{2}$ weeks, on a scale of 0 to 10, with 0 being not at all stressed and 10 being as stressed as possible?" Table 9.6 shows the students' responses. Use this frequency distribution to find the mean of the stress-level ratings.

SOLUTION We use the formula

$$\text{Mean} = \frac{\Sigma xf}{n}.$$

First, we must find xf, obtained by multiplying each data value, x, by its frequency, f. Then, we need to find the sum of these products, Σxf. We can use the frequency distribution to organize these computations. Add a third column in which each data value is multiplied by its frequency. This column, shown on the right, is headed xf. Then, find the sum of the values, Σxf, in this column.

x	f	xf
0	2	$0 \cdot 2 = 0$
1	1	$1 \cdot 1 = 1$
2	3	$2 \cdot 3 = 6$
3	12	$3 \cdot 12 = 36$
4	16	$4 \cdot 16 = 64$
5	18	$5 \cdot 18 = 90$
6	13	$6 \cdot 13 = 78$
7	31	$7 \cdot 31 = 217$
8	26	$8 \cdot 26 = 208$
9	15	$9 \cdot 15 = 135$
10	14	$10 \cdot 14 = 140$

Totals: $n = 151$ $\quad \Sigma xf = 975$

Σxf is the sum of the numbers in the third column.

This value, the sum of the numbers in the second column, is the total frequency of the distribution.

Now, substitute these values into the formula for the mean. Remember that n is the *total frequency* of the distribution, or 151.

$$\text{Mean} = \frac{\Sigma x f}{n} = \frac{975}{151} \approx 6.46$$

The mean of the 0 to 10 stress-level ratings is approximately 6.46. Notice that the mean is greater than 5, the middle of the 0 to 10 scale.

Find the mean for the data items in the frequency distribution. (In order to save space, we've written the frequency distribution horizontally.)

Score, x	30	33	40	50
Frequency, f	3	4	4	1

2 | Determine the median for a data set.

The Median

The *median* age in the United States is 35.3. The oldest state by median age is Florida (38.7) and the youngest state is Utah (27.1). To find these values, researchers begin with appropriate random samples. The data items—that is, the ages—are arranged from youngest to oldest. The median age is the data item in the middle of each set of ranked, or ordered, data.

> **THE MEDIAN**
> To find the **median** of a group of data items,
>
> **1.** Arrange the data items in order, from smallest to largest.
> **2.** If the number of data items is odd, the median is the data item in the middle of the list.
> **3.** If the number of data items is even, the median is the mean of the two middle data items.

EXAMPLE 3   FINDING THE MEDIAN

Find the median for each of the following groups of data:

a. 84, 90, 98, 95, 88
b. 68, 74, 7, 13, 15, 25, 28, 59, 34, 47.

SOLUTION

a. Arrange the data items in order, from smallest to largest. The number of data items in the list, five, is odd. Thus, the median is the middle number.

84, 88, 90, 95, 98

Middle data item

The median is 90. Notice that two data items lie above 90 and two data items lie below 90.

b. Arrange the data items in order, from smallest to largest. The number of data items in the list, ten, is even. Thus, the median is the mean of the two middle data items.

7, 13, 15, 25, 28, 34, 47, 59, 68, 74

Middle data items
are 28 and 34.

$$\text{Median} = \frac{28 + 34}{2} = \frac{62}{2} = 31$$

The median is 31. Five data items lie above 31 and five data items lie below 31.

$$7 \quad 13 \quad 15 \quad 25 \quad 28 \quad | \quad 34 \quad 47 \quad 59 \quad 68 \quad 74$$

Five data items lie below 31.   Five data items lie above 31.

Median is 31.

 Find the median for each of the following groups of data:

a. 28, 42, 40, 25, 35

b. 72, 61, 85, 93, 79, 87.

If a relatively long list of data items is arranged in order, it may be difficult to identify the item or items in the middle. In cases like this, the median can be found by determining its position in the list of items.

> **POSITION OF THE MEDIAN**
>
> If n data items are arranged in order, from smallest to largest, the median is the value in the
>
> $$\frac{n+1}{2}$$
>
> position.

EXAMPLE 4   FINDING THE MEDIAN USING THE POSITION FORMULA

Listed below are the points scored per season by the 13 top point scorers in the National Football League. Find the median points scored per season for the top 13 scorers.

$$144, 144, 145, 145, 145, 146, 147, 149, 150, 155, 161, 164, 176$$

SOLUTION The data items are arranged from smallest to largest. There are 13 data items, so $n = 13$. The median is the value in the

$$\frac{n+1}{2} \text{ position} = \frac{13+1}{2} \text{ position} = \frac{14}{2} \text{ position} = \text{seventh position.}$$

We find the median by selecting the data item in the seventh position.

Position 3   Position 4   Position 7

$$144, \quad 144, \quad 145, \quad 145, \quad 145, \quad 146, \quad 147, \quad 149, \quad 150, \quad 155, \quad 161, \quad 164, \quad 176$$

Position 1   Position 2   Position 5   Position 6

The median is 147. Notice that six data items lie above 147 and six data items lie below it. The median points scored per season for the top 13 scorers in the National Football League is 147.

 Find the median for the following group of data items:

$$1, 2, 2, 2, 3, 3, 3, 3, 3, 5, 6, 7, 7, 10, 11, 13, 19, 24, 26.$$

TABLE 9.7 NUMBER OF HOME RUNS BY BASEBALL TEAMS IN THE NATIONAL LEAGUE, 2005

Team	Home Runs
Washington Nationals	117
Florida Marlins	128
San Francisco Giants	128
San Diego Padres	130
Pittsburgh Pirates	139
Los Angeles Dodgers	149
Colorado Rockies	150
Houston Astros	161
Philadelphia Phillies	167
St. Louis Cardinals	170
Milwaukee Brewers	175
New York Mets	175
Atlanta Braves	184
Arizona Diamondbacks	191
Chicago Cubs	194
Cincinnati Reds	222

Source: The World Almanac

EXAMPLE 5   FINDING THE MEDIAN USING THE POSITION FORMULA

Table 9.7 gives the number of home runs for the 16 baseball teams in the National League in 2005. Find the median number of home runs for these teams.

SOLUTION The data items are arranged from smallest to largest. There are 16 data items, so $n = 16$. The median is the value in the

$$\frac{n+1}{2} \text{ position} = \frac{16+1}{2} \text{ position} = \frac{17}{2} \text{ position} = 8.5 \text{ position}.$$

This means that the median is the mean of the data items in positions 8 and 9.

117, 128, 128, 130, 139, 149, 150, 161, 167, 170, 175, 175, 184, 191, 194, 222

$$\text{Median} = \frac{161+167}{2} = \frac{328}{2} = 164$$

The median number of home runs for the teams in the National League in 2005 was 164.

CHECK POINT 5 Listed below are the number of home runs for each of the 14 baseball teams in the American League in 2005. Find the median number of home runs for these teams.

126, 130, 134, 136, 147, 155, 157, 168, 189, 199, 200, 207, 229, 260

When individual data items are listed from smallest to largest, you can find the median by identifying the item or items in the middle or by using the $\frac{n+1}{2}$ formula for its position. However, the formula for the position of the median is useful when data items are organized in a frequency distribution.

EXAMPLE 6   FINDING THE MEDIAN FOR A FREQUENCY DISTRIBUTION

The frequency distribution for the stress-level ratings of 151 students is repeated below using a horizontal format. Find the median stress-level rating.

Stress rating / Number of college students

x	0	1	2	3	4	5	6	7	8	9	10
f	2	1	3	12	16	18	13	31	26	15	14

Total: $n = 151$

SOLUTION There are 151 data items, so $n = 151$. The median is the value in the

$$\frac{n+1}{2} \text{ position} = \frac{151+1}{2} \text{ position} = \frac{152}{2} \text{ position} = 76\text{th position}.$$

We find the median by selecting the data item in the 76th position. The frequency distribution indicates that the data items begin with

$$0, 0, 1, 2, 2, 2, \ldots.$$

We can write the data items all out and then select the median, the 76th data item. A more efficient way to proceed is to count down the frequency column in the distribution until we identify the 76th data item:

x	f
0	2
1	1
2	3
3	12
4	16
5	18
6	13
7	31
8	26
9	15
10	14

We count down the frequency column.

1, 2

3

4, 5, 6

7, 8, 9, 10, 11, 12, 13, 14, 15, 16, 17, 18

19, 20, 21, 22, 23, 24, 25, 26, 27, 28, 29, 30, 31, 32, 33, 34

35, 36, 37, 38, 39, 40, 41, 42, 43, 44, 45, 46, 47, 48, 49, 50, 51, 52,
53, 54, 55, 56, 57, 58, 59, 60, 61, 62, 63, 64, 65

66, 67, 68, 69, 70, 71, 72, 73, 74, 75, 76

Stop counting. We've reached the 76th data item.

The 76th data item is 7. The median stress-level rating is 7.

CHECK POINT 6 Find the median for the following frequency distribution.

Age at presidential inauguration

x	42	43	46	51	52	54	55	56	60	61	64	69
f	1	1	1	3	1	2	2	2	1	2	1	1

Number of U.S. presidents assuming office in the 20th century with the given age

Statisticians generally use the median, rather than the mean, when reporting income. Why? Our next example will help to answer this question.

EXAMPLE 7   COMPARING THE MEDIAN AND THE MEAN

Five employees in the assembly section of a television manufacturing company earn salaries of $19,700, $20,400, $21,500, $22,600, and $23,000 annually. The section manager has an annual salary of $95,000.

a. Find the median annual salary for the six people.

b. Find the mean annual salary for the six people.

SOLUTION

a. To compute the median, first arrange the salaries in order:

$19,700, $20,400, $21,500, $22,600, $23,000, $95,000.

Because the list contains an even number of data items, six, the median is the mean of the two middle items.

$$\text{Median} = \frac{\$21,500 + \$22,600}{2} = \frac{\$44,100}{2} = \$22,050$$

The median annual salary is $22,050.

b. We find the mean annual salary by adding the six annual salaries and dividing by 6.

$$\text{Mean} = \frac{\$19,700 + \$20,400 + \$21,500 + \$22,600 + \$23,000 + \$95,000}{6}$$

$$= \frac{\$202,200}{6} = \$33,700$$

The mean annual salary is $33,700.

In Example 7, the median annual salary is $22,050 and the mean annual salary is $33,700. Why such a big difference between these two measures of central tendency? The relatively high annual salary of the section manager, $95,000, pulls the mean salary to a value considerably higher than the median salary. When one or more data items are much greater than the other items, these extreme values can greatly influence the mean. In cases like this, the median is often more representative of the data.

This is why the median, rather than the mean, is used to summarize the incomes, by gender and race, shown in Figure 9.6. Because no one can earn less than $0, the distribution of income must come to an end at $0 for each of these eight groups. By contrast, there is no upper limit on income on the high side. In the United States, the wealthiest 5% of the population earn about 21% of the total income. The relatively few people with very high annual incomes tend to pull the mean income to a value considerably greater than the median income. Reporting mean incomes in Figure 9.6 would inflate the numbers shown, making them nonrepresentative of the millions of workers in each of the eight groups.

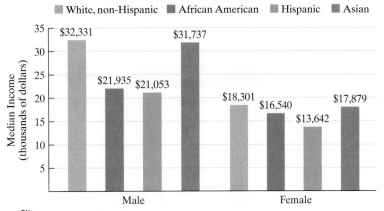

U.S. Median Income in 2003, by Gender and Race

FIGURE 9.6
Source: U.S. Census Bureau

The ten countries in Table 9.8 accounted for 75% of the nearly $900 billion spent in 2003 on defense worldwide.

TABLE 9.8 TOP TEN MILITARY SPENDERS, 2003			
Country	**National Expenditure (billions of dollars)**	**Dollars Spent per Resident**	**Percentage of Global Military Spending**
United States	$417.4	$1419	47%
Japan	$ 46.9	$ 367	5%
UK	$ 37.1	$ 627	4%
France	$ 35.0	$ 583	4%
China	$ 32.8	$ 25	4%
Germany	$ 27.2	$ 329	3%
Italy	$ 20.8	$ 362	2%
Iran	$ 19.2	$ 279	2%
Saudi Arabia	$ 19.1	$ 789	2%
South Korea	$ 13.9	$ 292	2%

Source: SIPRI, "The Major Spenders in 2003"

a. Find the mean national expenditure on defense, in billions of dollars, for the ten countries.

b. Find the median national expenditure on defense, in billions of dollars, for the ten countries.

c. Describe why one of the measures of central tendency is so much greater than the other.

3 | Determine the mode for a data set.

The Mode

Let's take one final look at the frequency distribution for the stress-level ratings of 151 college students.

Stress rating											
x	0	1	2	3	4	5	6	7	8	9	10
f	2	1	3	12	16	18	13	31	26	15	14

Number of college students

7 is the stress rating with the greatest frequency.

The data value that occurs most often in this distribution is 7, the stress rating for 31 of the 151 students. We call 7 the *mode* of this distribution.

> ### THE MODE
> The **mode** is the data value that occurs most often in a data set. If no data items are repeated, then the data set has no mode. If more than one data value has the highest frequency, then each of these data values is a mode.

EXAMPLE 8   FINDING THE MODE

Find the mode for the following group of data:

$$7, 2, 4, 7, 8, 10.$$

SOLUTION The number 7 occurs more often than any other. Therefore, 7 is the mode.

 Find the mode for the following group of data:

$$8, 6, 2, 4, 6, 8, 10, 8.$$

Be aware that a data set might not have a mode. For example, no data item in 2, 1, 4, 5, 3 is repeated, so this data group has no mode. By contrast, 3, 3, 4, 5, 6, 6 has two data values with the highest frequency, namely 3 and 6. Each of these data values is a mode and the data set is said to be **bimodal**.

4 | Determine the midrange for a data set.

The Midrange

Table 9.9 shows the ten hottest cities in the United States. Because temperature is constantly changing, you might wonder how the mean temperatures shown in the table are obtained.

First, we need to find a representative daily temperature. This is obtained by adding the lowest and highest temperatures for the day and then dividing this sum by 2. Next, we take the representative daily temperatures for all 365 days, add them, and divide the sum by 365. These are the mean temperatures that appear in Table 9.9.

Representative daily temperature,

$$\frac{\text{lowest daily temperature} + \text{highest daily temperature}}{2},$$

is an example of a measure of central tendency called the *midrange*.

> ### THE MIDRANGE
> The **midrange** is found by adding the lowest and highest data values and dividing the sum by 2.
>
> $$\text{Midrange} = \frac{\text{lowest data value} + \text{highest data value}}{2}$$

TABLE 9.9 TEN HOTTEST U.S. CITIES

City	Mean Temperature
Key West, FL	77.8°
Miami, FL	75.9°
West Palm Beach, FL	74.7°
Fort Myers, FL	74.4°
Yuma, AZ	74.2°
Brownsville, TX	73.8°
Phoenix, AZ	72.6°
Vero Beach, FL	72.4°
Orlando, FL	72.3°
Tampa, FL	72.3°

Source: National Oceanic and Atmospheric Administration

EXAMPLE 9   FINDING THE MIDRANGE

One criticism of major league baseball is that the discrepancy between team payrolls hampers fair competition. In 2006, the New York Yankees had the greatest payroll, a record $194,663,100 (median salary: $2,925,000). The Florida Marlins were the worst paid team, with a payroll of $14,998,500 (median salary: $327,000). Find the midrange for the annual payroll of major league baseball teams in 2006. (*Source*: usatoday.com)

SOLUTION

$$\text{Midrange} = \frac{\text{lowest annual payroll} + \text{highest annual payroll}}{2}$$

$$= \frac{\$14,998,500 + \$194,663,100}{2} = \frac{\$209,661,600}{2} = \$104,830,800$$

The midrange for the annual payroll of major league baseball teams in 2006 was $104,830,800.

We can find the mean annual payroll of the 30 professional baseball teams in 2006 by adding up the payrolls of all 30 teams and then dividing the sum by 30. It is much faster to calculate the midrange, which is often used as an estimate for the mean.

CHECK POINT 9   The best paid state governor is in New York, earning $179,000 annually. The worst paid is the governor of Maine, earning $70,000 annually. Find the midrange for annual salaries of U.S. governors.

EXAMPLE 10   FINDING THE FOUR MEASURES OF CENTRAL TENDENCY

Suppose your six exam grades in a course are

$$52, 69, 75, 86, 86, \text{ and } 92.$$

Compute your final course grade (90–100 = A, 80–89 = B, 70–79 = C, 60–69 = D, below 60 = F) using the

a. mean.   **b.** median.   **c.** mode.   **d.** midrange.

SOLUTION

a. The mean is the sum of the data items divided by the number of items, 6.

$$\text{Mean} = \frac{52 + 69 + 75 + 86 + 86 + 92}{6} = \frac{460}{6} \approx 76.67$$

Using the mean, your final course grade is C.

b. The six data items, 52, 69, 75, 86, 86, and 92, are arranged in order. Because the number of data items is even, the median is the mean of the two middle items.

$$\text{Median} = \frac{75 + 86}{2} = \frac{161}{2} = 80.5$$

Using the median, your final course grade is B.

c. The mode is the data value that occurs most frequently. Because 86 occurs most often, the mode is 86. Using the mode, your final course grade is B.

d. The midrange is the mean of the lowest and highest data values.

$$\text{Midrange} = \frac{52 + 92}{2} = \frac{144}{2} = 72$$

Using the midrange, your final course grade is C.

Consumer Reports magazine gave the following data for the number of calories in a meat hot dog for each of 17 brands:

173, 191, 182, 190, 172, 147, 146, 138, 175, 136, 179, 153, 107, 195, 135, 140, 138.

Find the mean, median, mode, and midrange for the number of calories in a meat hot dog for the 17 brands. If necessary, round answers to the nearest tenth of a calorie.

EXERCISE SET 9.2 ●●●●●●

• Practice Exercises

In Exercises 1–8, find the mean for each group of data items.

1. 7, 4, 3, 2, 8, 5, 1, 3

2. 11, 6, 4, 0, 2, 1, 12, 0, 0

3. 91, 95, 99, 97, 93, 95

4. 100, 100, 90, 30, 70, 100

5. 100, 40, 70, 40, 60

6. 1, 3, 5, 10, 8, 5, 6, 8

7. 1.6, 3.8, 5.0, 2.7, 4.2, 4.2, 3.2, 4.7, 3.6, 2.5, 2.5

8. 1.4, 2.1, 1.6, 3.0, 1.4, 2.2, 1.4, 9.0, 9.0, 1.8

In Exercises 9–12, find the mean for the data items in the given frequency distribution.

9.

Score x	Frequency f
1	1
2	3
3	4
4	4
5	6
6	5
7	3
8	2

10.

Score x	Frequency f
1	2
2	4
3	5
4	7
5	6
6	4
7	3

11.

Score x	Frequency f
1	1
2	1
3	2
4	5
5	7
6	9
7	8
8	6
9	4
10	3

12.

Score x	Frequency f
1	3
2	4
3	6
4	8
5	9
6	7
7	5
8	2
9	1
10	1

In Exercises 13–20, find the median for each group of data items.

13. 7, 4, 3, 2, 8, 5, 1, 3

14. 11, 6, 4, 0, 2, 1, 12, 0, 0

15. 91, 95, 99, 97, 93, 95

16. 100, 100, 90, 30, 70, 100

17. 100, 40, 70, 40, 60

18. 1, 3, 5, 10, 8, 5, 6, 8

19. 1.6, 3.8, 5.0, 2.7, 4.2, 4.2, 3.2, 4.7, 3.6, 2.5, 2.5

20. 1.4, 2.1, 1.6, 3.0, 1.4, 2.2, 1.4, 9.0, 9.0, 1.8

Find the median for the data items in the frequency distribution in

21. Exercise 9.

22. Exercise 10.

23. Exercise 11.

24. Exercise 12.

In Exercises 25–32, find the mode for each group of data items. If there is no mode, so state.

25. 7, 4, 3, 2, 8, 5, 1, 3

26. 11, 6, 4, 0, 2, 1, 12, 0, 0

27. 91, 95, 99, 97, 93, 95

28. 100, 100, 90, 30, 70, 100

29. 100, 40, 70, 40, 60

30. 1, 3, 5, 10, 8, 5, 6, 8

31. 1.6, 3.8, 5.0, 2.7, 4.2, 4.2, 3.2, 4.7, 3.6, 2.5, 2.5

32. 1.4, 2.1, 1.6, 3.0, 1.4, 2.2, 1.4, 9.0, 9.0, 1.8

Find the mode for the data items in the frequency distribution in

33. Exercise 9.

34. Exercise 10.

35. Exercise 11.

36. Exercise 12.

In Exercises 37–44, find the midrange for each group of data items.

37. 7, 4, 3, 2, 8, 5, 1, 3

38. 11, 6, 4, 0, 2, 1, 12, 0, 0

39. 91, 95, 99, 97, 93, 95

40. 100, 100, 90, 30, 70, 100

41. 100, 40, 70, 40, 60

42. 1, 3, 5, 10, 8, 5, 6, 8

43. 1.6, 3.8, 5.0, 2.7, 4.2, 4.2, 3.2, 4.7, 3.6, 2.5, 2.5

44. 1.4, 2.1, 1.6, 3.0, 1.4, 2.2, 1.4, 9.0, 9.0, 1.8

Find the midrange for the data items in the frequency distribution in

45. Exercise 9.

46. Exercise 10.

47. Exercise 11.

48. Exercise 12.

• Practice Plus

In Exercises 49–54, use each display of data items to find the mean, median, mode, and midrange.

49.

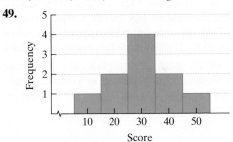

50.

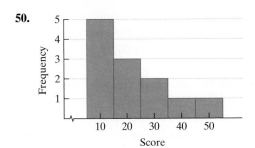

51.

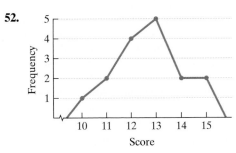

52.

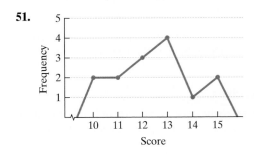

53.

Stems	Leaves		
2	1	4	5
3	0	1	1	3
4	2	5	

54.

Stems	Leaves		
2	8		
3	2	4	4	9
4	0	1	5	7

• Application Exercises

Exercises 55–59 present data on a variety of topics. For each data set described in boldface, find the

   a. *mean.*

   b. *median.*

   c. *mode (or state that there is no mode).*

   d. *midrange.*

55. Ages of the Justices of the United States Supreme Court in 2007

Roberts (52), Stevens (87), Scalia (71), Kennedy (71), Souter (68), Thomas (59), Ginsburg (74), Breyer (69), Alito (56)

56. Number of Reported Violent Attacks against the Homeless in the United States for Various Years from 1995 through 2005

$$60, 63, 52, 36, 70, 105, 86$$

Source: National Coalition for the Homeless

57. Number of Home Runs Hit by Each of the 12 Batters for the New York Yankees in 2005

$$0, 4, 8, 12, 14, 17, 19, 19, 23, 32, 34, 48$$

Source: The World Almanac

58. Number of Home Runs Hit by Each of the Ten Batters for the Florida Marlins in 2005

$$2, 3, 4, 5, 6, 8, 9, 16, 33, 33$$

Source: The World Almanac

59. Number of Social Interactions of College Students In Exercise Set 9.1, we presented a grouped frequency distribution showing the number of social interactions of ten minutes or longer over a one-week period for a group of college students. (These interactions excluded family and work situations.) Use the frequency distribution shown to solve this exercise. (This distribution was obtained by replacing the classes in the grouped frequency distribution previously shown with the midpoints of the classes.)

Social interactions in a week →

Number of college students →

x	2	7	12	17	22	27	32	37	42	47
f	12	16	16	16	10	11	4	3	3	3

The weights (to the nearest five pounds) of 40 randomly selected male college students are organized in a histogram with a superimposed frequency polygon. Use the graph to answer Exercises 60–63.

60. Find the mean weight.   **61.** Find the median weight.

62. Find the modal weight.   **63.** Find the midrange weight.

Weights of 40 Male College Students

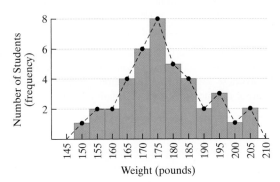

64. An advertisement for a speed-reading course claimed that the "average" reading speed for people completing the course was 1000 words per minute. Shown below are the actual data for the reading speeds per minute for a sample of 24 people who completed the course.

1000	900	800	1000	900	850
650	1000	1050	800	1000	850
700	750	800	850	900	950
600	1100	950	700	750	650

a. Find the mean, median, mode, and midrange. (If you prefer, first organize the data in a frequency distribution.)

b. Which measure of central tendency was given in the advertisement?

c. Which measure of central tendency is the best indicator of the "average" reading speed in this situation? Explain your answer.

65. In one common system for finding a grade-point average, or GPA,

$$A = 4, B = 3, C = 2, D = 1, F = 0.$$

The GPA is calculated by multiplying the number of credit hours for a course and the number assigned to each grade, and then adding these products. Then divide this sum by the total number of credit hours. Because each course grade is weighted according to the number of credits of the course, GPA is called a *weighted mean*. Calculate the GPA for this transcript:

Sociology: 3 cr. A; Biology: 3.5 cr. C; Music: 1 cr. B; Math: 4 cr. B; English: 3 cr. C.

• Writing in Mathematics

66. What is the mean and how is it obtained?

67. What is the median and how is it obtained?

68. What is the mode and how is it obtained?

69. What is the midrange and how is it obtained?

70. The "average" income in the United States can be given by the mean or the median.

a. Which measure would be used in anti-U.S. propaganda? Explain your answer.

b. Which measure would be used in pro-U.S. propaganda? Explain your answer.

71. In a class of 40 students, 21 have examination scores of 77%. Which measure or measures of central tendency can you immediately determine? Explain your answer.

72. You read an article that states, "Of the 411 players in the National Basketball Association, only 138 make more than the average salary of $3.12 million." Is $3.12 million the mean or the median salary? Explain your answer.

73. A student's parents promise to pay for next semester's tuition if an A average is earned in chemistry. With examination grades of 97%, 97%, 75%, 70%, and 55%, the student reports that an A average has been earned. Which measure of central tendency is the student reporting as the average? How is this student misrepresenting the course performance with statistics?

74. According to the National Oceanic and Atmospheric Administration, the coldest city in the United States is International Falls, Minnesota, with a mean Fahrenheit temperature of 36.8°. Explain how this mean is obtained.

75. Using Table 9.8 on page 529, explain why the mean amount spent on defense per resident is so much greater than the median amount spent on defense per resident for the ten countries.

• Critical Thinking Exercises

76. Give an example of a set of six examination grades (from 0 to 100) with each of the following characteristics:

a. The mean and the median have the same value, but the mode has a different value.

b. The mean and the mode have the same value, but the median has a different value.

c. The mean is greater than the median.

d. The mode is greater than the mean.

e. The mean, median, and mode have the same value.

f. The mean and mode have values of 72.

77. On an examination given to 30 students, no student scored below the mean. Describe how this occurred.

• Group Exercises

78. Select a characteristic, such as shoe size or height, for which each member of the group can provide a number. Choose a characteristic of genuine interest to the group. For this characteristic, organize the data collected into a frequency distribution and a graph. Compute the mean, median, mode, and midrange. Discuss any differences among these values. What happens if the group is divided (men and women, or people under a certain age and people over a certain age) and these measures of central tendency are computed for each of the subgroups? Attempt to use measures of central tendency to discover something interesting about the entire group or the subgroups.

79. A recent book on spotting bad statistics and learning to think critically about these influential numbers is *Damn Lies and Statistics* by Joel Best (University of California Press, 2001). This activity is designed for six people. Each person should select one chapter from Best's book. The group report should include examples of the use, misuse, and abuse of statistical information. Explain exactly how and why bad statistics emerge, spread, and come to shape policy debates. What specific ways does Best recommend to detect bad statistics?

SECTION 9.3 • MEASURES OF DISPERSION

OBJECTIVES

1. Determine the range for a data set.
2. Determine the standard deviation for a data set.

When you think of Houston, Texas and Honolulu, Hawaii, do balmy temperatures come to mind? Both cities have a mean temperature of 75°. However, the mean temperature does not tell the whole story. The temperature in Houston differs seasonally from a low of about 40° in January to a high of close to 100° in July and August. By contrast, Honolulu's temperature varies less throughout the year, usually ranging between 60° and 90°.

Measures of dispersion are used to describe the spread of data items in a data set. Two of the most common measures of dispersion, the *range* and the *standard deviation*, are discussed in this section.

1 | Determine the range for a data set.

The Range

A quick but rough measure of dispersion is the **range**, the difference between the highest and lowest data values in a data set. For example, if Houston's hottest annual temperature is 103° and its coldest annual temperature is 33°, the range in temperature is

$$103° - 33°, \text{ or } 70°.$$

If Honolulu's hottest day is 89° and its coldest day 61°, the range in temperature is

$$89° - 61°, \text{ or } 28°.$$

> THE RANGE
>
> The **range**, the difference between the highest and lowest data values in a data set, indicates the total spread of the data.
>
> Range = highest data value − lowest data value

EXAMPLE 1   COMPUTING THE RANGE

Figure 9.7 shows the number of workers, in millions, for the five countries with the largest labor forces. Find the range of workers, in millions, for these five countries.

SOLUTION

$$\text{Range} = \text{highest data value} - \text{lowest data value}$$
$$= 778 - 82 = 696$$

The range is 696 million workers.

Countries with the Most Workers

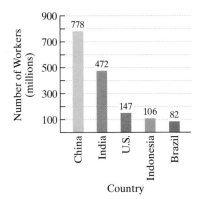

FIGURE 9.7
Source: Central Intelligence Agency

 Find the range for the following group of data items:

4, 2, 11, 7.

The Standard Deviation

A second measure of dispersion, and one that is dependent on *all* of the data items, is called the **standard deviation**. The standard deviation is found by determining how much each data item differs from the mean.

In order to compute the standard deviation, it is necessary to find by how much each data item deviates from the mean. First compute the mean. Then subtract the mean from each data item. Example 2 shows how this is done. In Example 3, we will use this skill to actually find the standard deviation.

EXAMPLE 2   PREPARING TO FIND THE STANDARD DEVIATION; FINDING DEVIATIONS FROM THE MEAN

Find the deviations from the mean for the five data items 778, 472, 147, 106, and 82, shown in Figure 9.7.

SOLUTION   First, calculate the mean.

$$\text{Mean} = \frac{\Sigma x}{n} = \frac{778 + 472 + 147 + 106 + 82}{5} = \frac{1585}{5} = 317$$

The mean for the five countries with the largest labor forces is 317 million workers. Now, let's find by how much each of the five data items in Figure 9.7 differs from 317, the mean. For China, with 778 million workers, the computation is shown as follows:

$$\text{Deviation from mean} = \text{data item} - \text{mean}$$
$$= 778 - 317 = 461.$$

This indicates that the labor force in China exceeds the mean by 461 million workers.

The computation for the United States, with 147 million workers, is given by

$$\text{Deviation from mean} = \text{data item} - \text{mean}$$
$$= 147 - 317 = -170.$$

This indicates that the labor force in the United States is 170 million workers below the mean.

The deviations from the mean for each of the five given data items are shown in Table 9.10.

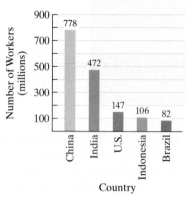

Countries with the Most Workers

FIGURE 9.7 (repeated)
Source: Central Intelligence Agency

TABLE 9.10 DEVIATIONS FROM THE MEAN

Data item	Deviation: data item − mean
778	778 − 317 = 461
472	472 − 317 = 155
147	147 − 317 = −170
106	106 − 317 = −211
82	82 − 317 = −235

CHECK POINT 2 Compute the mean for the following group of data items:

$$2, 4, 7, 11.$$

Then find the deviations from the mean for the four data items. Organize your work in table form just like Table 9.10. Keep track of these computations. You will be using them in Check Point 3.

The sum of the deviations for a set of data is always zero. For the deviations shown in Table 9.10,

$$461 + 155 + (-170) + (-211) + (-235) = 616 + (-616) = 0.$$

This shows that we cannot find a measure of dispersion by finding the mean of the deviations, because this value is always zero. However, a kind of average of the deviations from the mean, called the **standard deviation**, can be computed. We do so by squaring each deviation and later introducing a square root in the computation. Here are the details on how to find the standard deviation for a set of data:

2   Determine the standard deviation for a data set.

> ### COMPUTING THE STANDARD DEVIATION FOR A DATA SET
>
> **1.** Find the mean of the data items.
>
> **2.** Find the deviation of each data item from the mean:
>
> $$\text{data item} - \text{mean}.$$
>
> **3.** Square each deviation:
>
> $$(\text{data item} - \text{mean})^2.$$
>
> **4.** Sum the squared deviations:
>
> $$\Sigma(\text{data item} - \text{mean})^2.$$
>
> **5.** Divide the sum in step 4 by $n - 1$, where n represents the number of data items:
>
> $$\frac{\Sigma(\text{data item} - \text{mean})^2}{n - 1}.$$
>
> **6.** Take the square root of the quotient in step 5. This value is the standard deviation for the data set.
>
> $$\text{Standard deviation} = \sqrt{\frac{\Sigma(\text{data item} - \text{mean})^2}{n - 1}}$$

The computation of the standard deviation can be organized using a table with three columns:

Data item	Deviation: Data item − mean	(Deviation)^2: (Data item − mean)^2

In Example 2, we worked out the first two columns of such a table. Let's continue working with the data for the countries with the most workers and compute the standard deviation.

EXAMPLE 3   COMPUTING THE STANDARD DEVIATION

Figure 9.7, showing the number of workers, in millions, for the five countries with the largest labor forces, appears in the margin on page 536. Find the standard deviation, in millions, for these five countries.

SOLUTION

Step 1. Find the mean. From our work in Example 2, the mean is 317.

Step 2. Find the deviation of each data item from the mean: data item − mean. This, too, was done in Example 2 for each of the five data items.

Step 3. Square each deviation: (data item − mean)^2. We square each of the numbers in the (data item − mean) column, shown in Table 9.11. Notice that squaring the difference always results in a positive number.

TABLE 9.11 COMPUTING THE STANDARD DEVIATION

Data item	Deviation: data item − mean	(Deviation)^2: (data item − mean)^2
778	$778 - 317 = 461$	$461^2 = 461 \cdot 461 = 212{,}521$
472	$472 - 317 = 155$	$155^2 = 155 \cdot 155 = 24{,}025$
147	$147 - 317 = -170$	$(-170)^2 = (-170)(-170) = 28{,}900$
106	$106 - 317 = -211$	$(-211)^2 = (-211)(-211) = 44{,}521$
82	$82 - 317 = -235$	$(-235)^2 = (-235)(-235) = 55{,}225$
Totals:	0	365,192

The sum of the deviations for a set of data is always zero.

Adding the five numbers in the third column gives the sum of the squared deviations:

$$\Sigma(\text{data item} - \text{mean})^2.$$

TECHNOLOGY

Almost all scientific and graphing calculators compute the standard deviation of a set of data. Using the data items in Example 3,

778, 472, 147, 106, 82,

the keystrokes for obtaining the standard deviation on many scientific calculators are as follows:

778 $\boxed{\Sigma+}$ 472 $\boxed{\Sigma+}$ 147 $\boxed{\Sigma+}$

106 $\boxed{\Sigma+}$ 82 $\boxed{\Sigma+}$ $\boxed{\text{2nd}}$ $\boxed{\sigma n - 1}$.

Graphing calculators require that you specify if data items are from an entire population or a sample of the population.

Step 4. Sum the squared deviations: $\Sigma(\textbf{data item} - \textbf{mean})^2$. This step is shown in Table 9.11 on the previous page. The squares in the third column were added, resulting in a sum of 365,192.

Step 5. Divide the sum in step 4 by $n - 1$, where n represents the number of data items. The number of data items is 5 so we divide by 4.

$$\frac{\Sigma(\text{data item} - \text{mean})^2}{n - 1} = \frac{365,192}{5 - 1} = \frac{365,192}{4} = 91,298$$

Step 6. The standard deviation is the square root of the quotient in step 5.

$$\text{Standard deviation} = \sqrt{\frac{\Sigma(\text{data item} - \text{mean})^2}{n - 1}} = \sqrt{91,298} \approx 302.16$$

The standard deviation for the five countries with the largest labor forces is approximately 302.16 million workers.

Find the standard deviation for the group of data items in Check Point 2 on page 536. Round to two decimal places.

Example 4 illustrates that as the spread of data items increases, the standard deviation gets larger.

EXAMPLE 4　COMPUTING THE STANDARD DEVIATION

Find the standard deviation of the data items in each of the samples shown below.

Sample A	Sample B
17, 18, 19, 20, 21, 22, 23	5, 10, 15, 20, 25, 30, 35

SOLUTION Begin by finding the mean for each sample.

Sample A:

$$\text{Mean} = \frac{17 + 18 + 19 + 20 + 21 + 22 + 23}{7} = \frac{140}{7} = 20$$

Sample B:

$$\text{Mean} = \frac{5 + 10 + 15 + 20 + 25 + 30 + 35}{7} = \frac{140}{7} = 20$$

Although both samples have the same mean, the data items in sample B are more spread out. Thus, we would expect sample B to have the greater standard deviation. The computation of the standard deviation requires that we find $\Sigma(\text{data item} - \text{mean})^2$, shown in Table 9.12.

TABLE 9.12 COMPUTING STANDARD DEVIATIONS FOR TWO SAMPLES

Sample A			Sample B		
Data item	Deviation: data item − mean	(Deviation)²: (data item − mean)²	Data item	Deviation: data item − mean	(Deviation)²: (data item − mean)²
17	$17 - 20 = -3$	$(-3)^2 = 9$	5	$5 - 20 = -15$	$(-15)^2 = 225$
18	$18 - 20 = -2$	$(-2)^2 = 4$	10	$10 - 20 = -10$	$(-10)^2 = 100$
19	$19 - 20 = -1$	$(-1)^2 = 1$	15	$15 - 20 = -5$	$(-5)^2 = 25$
20	$20 - 20 = 0$	$0^2 = 0$	20	$20 - 20 = 0$	$0^2 = 0$
21	$21 - 20 = 1$	$1^2 = 1$	25	$25 - 20 = 5$	$5^2 = 25$
22	$22 - 20 = 2$	$2^2 = 4$	30	$30 - 20 = 10$	$10^2 = 100$
23	$23 - 20 = 3$	$3^2 = 9$	35	$35 - 20 = 15$	$15^2 = 225$
Totals:		$\Sigma(\text{data item} - \text{mean})^2 = 28$			$\Sigma(\text{data item} - \text{mean})^2 = 700$

Each sample contains seven data items, so we compute the standard deviation by dividing the sums in Table 9.12, 28 and 700, by 7 − 1, or 6. Then we take the square root of each quotient.

$$\text{Standard deviation} = \sqrt{\frac{\Sigma(\text{data item} - \text{mean})^2}{n - 1}}$$

Sample A: Sample B:

$$\text{Standard deviation} = \sqrt{\frac{28}{6}} \approx 2.16 \qquad \text{Standard deviation} = \sqrt{\frac{700}{6}} \approx 10.80$$

Sample A has a standard deviation of approximately 2.16 and sample B has a standard deviation of approximately 10.80. The scores in sample B are more spread out than those in sample A.

Find the standard deviation of the data items in each of the samples shown below. Round to two decimal places.

Sample A: 73, 75, 77, 79, 81, 83

Sample B: 40, 44, 92, 94, 98, 100

Figure 9.8 illustrates four sets of data items organized in histograms. From left to right, the data items are

Figure 9.8(a): 4, 4, 4, 4, 4, 4, 4

Figure 9.8(b): 3, 3, 4, 4, 4, 5, 5

Figure 9.8(c): 3, 3, 3, 4, 5, 5, 5

Figure 9.8(d): 1, 1, 1, 4, 7, 7, 7.

Each data set has a mean of 4. However, as the spread of data items increases, the standard deviation gets larger. Observe that when all the data items are the same, the standard deviation is 0.

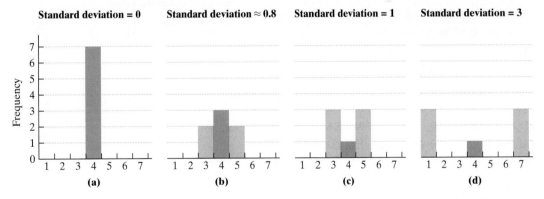

FIGURE 9.8 The standard deviation gets larger with increased dispersion among data items. In each case, the mean is 4.

EXAMPLE 5   INTERPRETING STANDARD DEVIATION

Two fifth-grade classes have nearly identical mean scores on an aptitude test, but one class has a standard deviation three times that of the other. All other factors being equal, which class is easier to teach, and why?

SOLUTION The class with the smaller standard deviation is easier to teach because there is less variation among student aptitudes. Course work can be aimed at the average student without too much concern that the work will be too easy for some or too difficult for others. By contrast, the class with greater dispersion poses a greater challenge. By teaching to the average student, the students whose scores are significantly above the mean will be bored; students whose scores are significantly below the mean will be confused.

 Shown below are the means and standard deviations of the yearly returns on two investments from 1926 through 2004.

Investment	Mean Yearly Interest	Standard Deviation
Small-Company Stocks	17.5%	33.3%
Large-Company Stocks	12.4%	20.4%

Source: Summary Statistics of Annual Total Returns 1926 to 2004 Yearbook, Ibbotson Associates, Chicago

a. Use the means to determine which investment provided the greater yearly return.

b. Use the standard deviations to determine which investment had the greater risk. Explain your answer.

EXERCISE SET 9.3 ●●●●●●

• Practice Exercises

In Exercises 1–6, find the range for each group of data items.

1. 1, 2, 3, 4, 5
2. 16, 17, 18, 19, 20
3. 7, 9, 9, 15
4. 11, 13, 14, 15, 17
5. 3, 3, 4, 4, 5, 5
6. 3, 3, 3, 4, 5, 5, 5

In Exercises 7–10, a group of data items and their mean are given.
   a. Find the deviation from the mean for each of the data items.
   b. Find the sum of the deviations in part (a).

7. 3, 5, 7, 12, 18, 27; Mean = 12
8. 84, 88, 90, 95, 98; Mean = 91
9. 29, 38, 48, 49, 53, 77; Mean = 49
10. 60, 60, 62, 65, 65, 65, 66, 67, 70, 70; Mean = 65

In Exercises 11–16, find a. the mean; b. the deviation from the mean for each data item; and c. the sum of the deviations in part (b).

11. 85, 95, 90, 85, 100
12. 94, 62, 88, 85, 91
13. 146, 153, 155, 160, 161
14. 150, 132, 144, 122
15. 2.25, 3.50, 2.75, 3.10, 1.90
16. 0.35, 0.37, 0.41, 0.39, 0.43

In Exercises 17–26, find the standard deviation for each group of data items. Round answers to two decimal places.

17. 1, 2, 3, 4, 5
18. 16, 17, 18, 19, 20
19. 7, 9, 9, 15
20. 11, 13, 14, 15, 17
21. 3, 3, 4, 4, 5, 5
22. 3, 3, 3, 4, 5, 5, 5
23. 1, 1, 1, 4, 7, 7, 7
24. 6, 6, 6, 6, 7, 7, 7, 4, 8, 3
25. 9, 5, 9, 5, 9, 5, 9, 5
26. 6, 10, 6, 10, 6, 10, 6, 10

In Exercises 27–28, compute the mean, range, and standard deviation for the data items in each of the three samples. Then describe one way in which the samples are alike and one way in which they are different.

27. Sample A: 6, 8, 10, 12, 14, 16, 18
    Sample B: 6, 7, 8, 12, 16, 17, 18
    Sample C: 6, 6, 6, 12, 18, 18, 18

28. Sample A: 8, 10, 12, 14, 16, 18, 20
    Sample B: 8, 9, 10, 14, 18, 19, 20
    Sample C: 8, 8, 8, 14, 20, 20, 20

• Practice Plus

In Exercises 29–36, use each display of data items to find the standard deviation. Where necessary, round answers to two decimal places.

29.
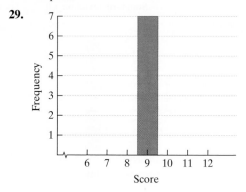

30.
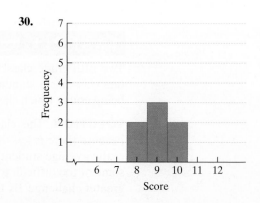

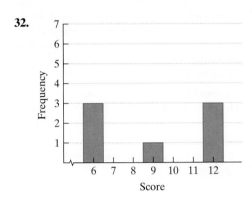

31.

32.

33.

Stems	Leaves
0	5
1	0 5
2	0 5

34.

Stems	Leaves
0	4 8
1	2 6
2	0

35.

Stems	Leaves
1	8 9 9 8 7 8
2	0 1 0 2

36.

Stems	Leaves
1	3 5 3 8 3 4
2	3 0 0 4

• Application Exercises

37. The data sets give the ages of Oscar winners from 1999 through 2005 at the time of the award.

Year	Best Actor	Age
1999	Kevin Spacey	40
2000	Russell Crowe	36
2001	Denzel Washington	47
2002	Adrien Brody	29
2003	Sean Penn	43
2004	Jamie Foxx	37
2005	Philip Seymour Hoffman	38

Year	Best Actress	Age
1999	Hilary Swank	25
2000	Julia Roberts	33
2001	Halle Berry	35
2002	Nicole Kidman	35
2003	Charlize Theron	28
2004	Hilary Swank	30
2005	Reese Witherspoon	29

Source: www.oscars.org

a. Without calculating, which data set has the greater mean age? Explain your answer.

b. Verify your conjecture from part (a) by calculating the mean age for each data set. Round answers to two decimal places.

c. Without calculating, which data set has the greater standard deviation? Explain your answer.

d. Verify your conjecture from part (c) by calculating the standard deviation for each data set. Round answers to two decimal places.

38. The data sets give the ages of the first six U.S. presidents and the last six U.S. presidents (through G. W. Bush).

AGE OF FIRST SIX U.S. PRESIDENTS AT INAUGURATION

President	Age
Washington	57
J. Adams	61
Jefferson	57
Madison	57
Monroe	58
J. Q. Adams	57

AGE OF LAST SIX U.S. PRESIDENTS AT INAUGURATION

President	Age
Ford	61
Carter	52
Reagan	69
G. H. W. Bush	64
Clinton	46
G. W. Bush	54

Source: Time Almanac

a. Without calculating, which set has the greater standard deviation? Explain your answer.

b. Verify your conjecture from part (b) by calculating the standard deviation for each data set. Round answers to two decimal places.

• Writing in Mathematics

39. Describe how to find the range of a data set.

40. Describe why the range might not be the best measure of dispersion.

41. Describe how the standard deviation is computed.

42. Describe what the standard deviation reveals about a data set.

43. If a set of test scores has a standard deviation of zero, what does this mean about the scores?

44. Two classes took a statistics test. Both classes had a mean score of 73. The scores of class A had a standard deviation of 5 and those of class B had a standard deviation of 10. Discuss the difference between the two classes' performance on the test.

45. A sample of cereals indicates a mean potassium content per serving of 93 milligrams and a standard deviation of 2 milligrams. Write a description of what this means for a person who knows nothing about statistics.

46. Over a one-month period, stock A had a mean daily closing price of 124.7 and a standard deviation of 12.5. By contrast, stock B had a mean daily closing price of 78.2 and a standard deviation of 6.1. Which stock was more volatile? Explain your answer.

• **Critical Thinking Exercises**

47. Which one of the following is true?

   a. If the same number is added to each data item in a set of data, the standard deviation does not change.

   b. If each number in a data set is multiplied by 4, the standard deviation is doubled.

   c. It is possible for a set of scores to have a negative standard deviation.

   d. Data sets with different means cannot have the same standard deviation.

48. Describe a situation in which a relatively large standard deviation is desirable.

49. If a set of test scores has a large range but a small standard deviation, describe what this means about students' performance on the test.

50. Use the data 1, 2, 3, 5, 6, 7. Without actually computing the standard deviation, which of the following best approximates the standard deviation?

   a. 2   **b.** 6   **c.** 10   **d.** 20

51. Use the data 0, 1, 3, 4, 4, 6. Add 2 to each of the numbers. How does this affect the mean? How does this affect the standard deviation?

• **Group Exercises**

52. As a follow-up to Group Exercise 78 on page 534, the group should reassemble and compute the standard deviation for each data set whose mean you previously determined. Does the standard deviation tell you anything new or interesting about the entire group or subgroups that you did not discover during the previous group activity?

53. Group members should consult a current almanac or the Internet and select intriguing data. The group's function is to use statistics to tell a story. Once "intriguing" data are identified, as a group

   a. Summarize the data. Use words, frequency distributions, and graphic displays.

   b. Compute measures of central tendency and dispersion, using these statistics to discuss the data.

SECTION 9.4 • THE NORMAL DISTRIBUTION

OBJECTIVES

1. Recognize characteristics of normal distributions.

2. Understand the 68–95–99.7 Rule.

3. Find scores at a specified standard deviation from the mean.

4. Use the 68–95–99.7 Rule.

5. Convert a data item to a z-score.

6. Understand percentiles and quartiles.

7. Solve applied problems involving normal distributions.

8. Use and interpret margins of error.

9. Recognize distributions that are not normal.

Mean Adult Heights

5'2" 5'7"   5'5" 5'10"   5'7" 6'0"

1900   2000   2050

Source: National Center for Health Statistics

Our heights are on the rise! In one million B.C., the mean height for men was 4 feet 6 inches. The mean height for women was 4 feet 2 inches. Because of improved diets and medical care, the mean height for men is now 5 feet 10 inches and for women it is 5 feet 5 inches. Mean adult heights are expected to plateau by 2050.

Suppose that a researcher selects a random sample of 100 adult men, measures their heights, and constructs a histogram. The graph is shown in Figure 9.9 at the top of the next page. Figure 9.9 illustrates what happens as the sample size increases. In Figure 9.9(c), if you were to fold the graph down the middle, the left side would fit the right side. As we move out from the middle, the heights of the bars are the same to the left and right. Such a histogram is called **symmetric**. As the sample size increases, so does the graph's symmetry. If it were possible to measure

1   Recognize characteristics of normal distributions.

the heights of all adult males, the entire population, the histogram would approach what is called the **normal distribution**, shown in Figure 9.9(d). This distribution is also called the **bell curve** or the **Gaussian distribution**, named for the German mathematician Carl Friedrich Gauss (1777–1855).

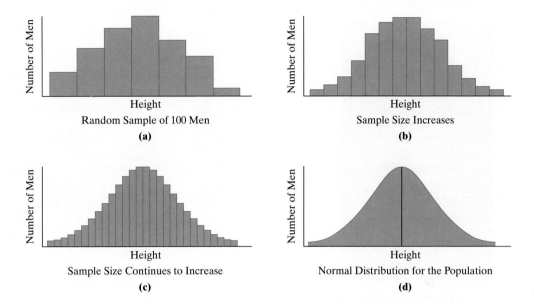

FIGURE 9.9 Heights of adult males

Figure 9.9(d) illustrates that the normal distribution is bell shaped and symmetric about a vertical line through its center. Furthermore, **the mean, median, and mode** of a normal distribution **are all equal** and located at the center of the distribution.

The shape of the normal distribution depends on the mean and the standard deviation. Figure 9.10 illustrates three normal distributions with the same mean, but different standard deviations. As the standard deviation increases, the distribution becomes more dispersed, or spread out, but retains its symmetric bell shape.

FIGURE 9.10

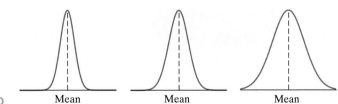

The normal distribution provides a wonderful model for all kinds of phenomena because many sets of data items closely resemble this population distribution. Examples include heights and weights of adult males, intelligence quotients, SAT scores, prices paid for a new car model, and life spans of light bulbs. In these distributions, the data items tend to cluster around the mean. The more an item differs from the mean, the less likely it is to occur.

The normal distribution is used to make predictions about an entire population using data from a sample. In this section, we focus on the characteristics and applications of the normal distribution.

2   Understand the 68–95–99.7 Rule.

The Standard Deviation and z-Scores in Normal Distributions

The standard deviation plays a crucial role in the normal distribution, summarized by the **68–95–99.7 Rule**. This rule is illustrated in Figure 9.11 on the next page.

These ancient steps each take on the shape of a normal distribution when the picture is viewed upside down. The center of each step is more worn than the outer edges. The greatest number of people have walked in the center, making this the mean, median, and mode for where people have walked.

THE 68-95-99.7 RULE FOR THE NORMAL DISTRIBUTION

1. Approximately 68% of the data items fall within 1 standard deviation of the mean (in both directions).
2. Approximately 95% of the data items fall within 2 standard deviations of the mean.
3. Approximately 99.7% of the data items fall within 3 standard deviations of the mean.

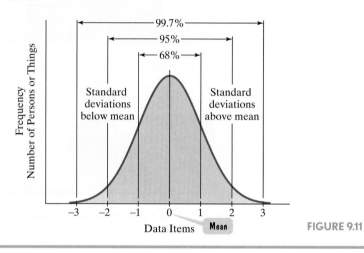

FIGURE 9.11

Figure 9.11 illustrates that a very small percentage of the data in a normal distribution lies more than 3 standard deviations above or below the mean. As we move from the mean, the curve falls rapidly, and then more and more gradually, toward the horizontal axis. The tails of the curve approach, but never touch, the horizontal axis, although they are quite close to the axis at 3 standard deviations from the mean. The range of the normal distribution is infinite. No matter how far out from the mean we move, there is always the probability (although very small) of a data item occurring even farther out.

3 Find scores at a specified standard deviation from the mean.

EXAMPLE 1 | FINDING SCORES AT A SPECIFIED STANDARD DEVIATION FROM THE MEAN

Male adult heights in North America are approximately normally distributed with a mean of 70 inches and a standard deviation of 4 inches. Find the height that is

a. 2 standard deviations above the mean.

b. 3 standard deviations below the mean.

SOLUTION

a. First, let us find the height that is 2 standard deviations above the mean.

$$\text{Height} = \text{mean} + 2 \cdot \text{standard deviation}$$
$$= 70 + 2 \cdot 4 = 70 + 8 = 78$$

A height of 78 inches is 2 standard deviations above the mean.

b. Next, let us find the height that is 3 standard deviations below the mean.

$$\text{Height} = \text{mean} - 3 \cdot \text{standard deviation}$$
$$= 70 - 3 \cdot 4 = 70 - 12 = 58$$

A height of 58 inches is 3 standard deviations below the mean.

The distribution of male adult heights in North America is illustrated as a normal distribution in Figure 9.12.

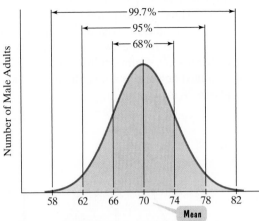

Normal Distribution of Male Adult Heights

Male Adult Heights in North America   **FIGURE 9.12**

1 Female adult heights in North America are approximately normally distributed with a mean of 65 inches and a standard deviation of 3.5 inches. Find the height that is

a. 3 standard deviations above the mean.

b. 2 standard deviations below the mean.

4 | Use the 68–95–99.7 Rule.

EXAMPLE 2   USING THE 68-95-99.7 RULE

Use the distribution of male adult heights in Figure 9.12 to find the percentage of men in North America with heights

a. between 66 inches and 74 inches.   **b.** between 70 inches and 74 inches.

c. above 78 inches.

SOLUTION

a. The 68–95–99.7 Rule states that approximately 68% of the data items fall within 1 standard deviation, 4, of the mean, 70.

$$\text{mean} - 1 \cdot \text{standard deviation} = 70 - 1 \cdot 4 = 70 - 4 = 66$$
$$\text{mean} + 1 \cdot \text{standard deviation} = 70 + 1 \cdot 4 = 70 + 4 = 74$$

Figure 9.12 shows that 68% of male adults have heights between 66 inches and 74 inches.

b. The percentage of men with heights between 70 inches and 74 inches is not given directly in Figure 9.12 or Figure 9.13. Because of the distribution's symmetry, the percentage with heights between 66 inches and 70 inches is the same as the percentage with heights between 70 and 74 inches. Figure 9.13 indicates that 68% have heights between 66 inches and 74 inches. Thus, half of 68%, or 34%, of men have heights between 70 inches and 74 inches.

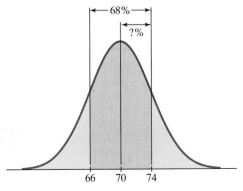

FIGURE 9.13 What percentage have heights between 70 inches and 74 inches?

c. The percentage of men with heights above 78 inches is not given directly in Figure 9.12 or Figure 9.14. A height of 78 inches is 2 standard deviations, $2 \cdot 4$, or 8 inches, above the mean, 70 inches. The 68–95–99.7 Rule states that approximately 95% of the data items fall within 2 standard deviations of the mean. Thus, approximately $100\% - 95\%$, or 5%, of the data items are farther than 2 standard deviations from the mean. The 5% of the data items are represented by the two shaded green regions in Figure 9.14. Because of the distribution's symmetry, half of 5%, or 2.5%, of the data items are more than 2 standard deviations above the mean. This means that 2.5% of men have heights above 78 inches.

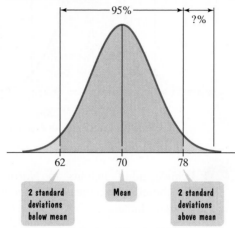

FIGURE 9.14 What percentage have heights above 78 inches?

  Use the distribution of male adult heights in North America in Figure 9.12 on page 545 to find the percentage of men with heights

a. between 62 inches and 78 inches.

b. between 70 inches and 78 inches.

c. above 74 inches.

Because the normal distribution of male adult heights in North America has a mean of 70 inches and a standard deviation of 4 inches, a height of 78 inches lies 2 standard deviations above the mean. In a normal distribution, a **z-score** describes how many standard deviations a particular data item lies above or below the mean. Thus, the z-score for the data item 78 is 2.

The following formula can be used to express a data item in a normal distribution as a z-score:

5 | Convert a data item to a z-score.

> **COMPUTING z-SCORES**
>
> A z-score describes how many standard deviations a data item in a normal distribution lies above or below the mean. The z-score can be obtained using
>
> $$z\text{-score} = \frac{\text{data item} - \text{mean}}{\text{standard deviation}}.$$
>
> Data items above the mean have positive z-scores. Data items below the mean have negative z-scores. The z-score for the mean is 0.

EXAMPLE 3   COMPUTING z-SCORES

The mean weight of newborn infants is 7 pounds and the standard deviation is 0.8 pound. The weights of newborn infants are normally distributed. Find the z-score for a weight of

a. 9 pounds.   **b.** 7 pounds.   **c.** 6 pounds.

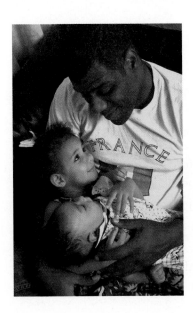

SOLUTION We compute the z-score for each weight by using the z-score formula. The mean is 7 and the standard deviation is 0.8.

a. The z-score for a weight of 9 pounds, written z_9, is

$$z_9 = \frac{\text{data item } - \text{ mean}}{\text{standard deviation}} = \frac{9 - 7}{0.8} = \frac{2}{0.8} = 2.5.$$

The z-score of a data item greater than the mean is always positive. A 9-pound infant is a chubby little tyke, with a weight that is 2.5 standard deviations above the mean.

b. The z-score for a weight of 7 pounds is

$$z_7 = \frac{\text{data item } - \text{ mean}}{\text{standard deviation}} = \frac{7 - 7}{0.8} = \frac{0}{0.8} = 0.$$

The z-score for the mean is always 0. A 7-pound infant is right at the mean, deviating 0 pounds above or below it.

c. The z-score for a weight of 6 pounds is

$$z_6 = \frac{\text{data item } - \text{ mean}}{\text{standard deviation}} = \frac{6 - 7}{0.8} = \frac{-1}{0.8} = -1.25.$$

The z-score of a data item less than the mean is always negative. A 6-pound infant's weight is 1.25 standard deviations below the mean.

Figure 9.15 shows the normal distribution of weights of newborn infants. The horizontal axis is labeled in terms of weights and z-scores.

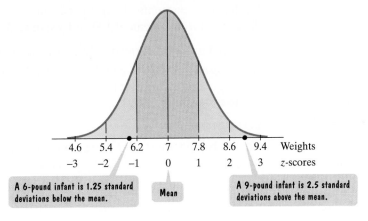

FIGURE 9.15 Infants' weights are normally distributed.

CHECK POINT 3 The length of horse pregnancies from conception to birth is normally distributed with a mean of 336 days and a standard deviation of 3 days. Find the z-score for a horse pregnancy of

a. 342 days.   b. 336 days.   c. 333 days.

In Example 4, we consider two normally distributed sets of test scores, in which a higher score generally indicates a better result. To compare scores on two different tests in relation to the mean on each test, we can use z-scores. The better score is the item with the greater z-score.

EXAMPLE 4   USING AND INTERPRETING z-SCORES

A student scores 70 on an arithmetic test and 66 on a vocabulary test. The scores for both tests are normally distributed. The arithmetic test has a mean of 60 and a standard deviation of 20. The vocabulary test has a mean of 60 and a standard deviation of 2. On which test did the student have the better score?

SOLUTION   To answer the question, we need to find the student's z-score on each test, using

$$z = \frac{\text{data item} - \text{mean}}{\text{standard deviation}}.$$

The arithmetic test has a mean of 60 and a standard deviation of 20.

$$z\text{-score for } 70 = z_{70} = \frac{70 - 60}{20} = \frac{10}{20} = 0.5$$

The vocabulary test has a mean of 60 and a standard deviation of 2.

$$z\text{-score for } 66 = z_{66} = \frac{66 - 60}{2} = \frac{6}{2} = 3$$

The arithmetic score, 70, is half a standard deviation above the mean, whereas the vocabulary score, 66, is 3 standard deviations above the mean. The student did much better than the mean on the vocabulary test.

○

CHECK POINT 4   The SAT (Scholastic Aptitude Test) has a mean of 500 and a standard deviation of 100. The ACT (American College Test) has a mean of 18 and a standard deviation of 6. Both tests measure the same kind of ability, with scores that are normally distributed. Suppose that you score 550 on the SAT and 24 on the ACT. On which test did you have the better score?

EXAMPLE 5   UNDERSTANDING z-SCORES

Intelligence quotients (IQs) on the Stanford-Binet intelligence test are normally distributed with a mean of 100 and a standard deviation of 16.

a. What is the IQ corresponding to a z-score of −1.5?

b. Mensa is a group of people with high IQs whose members have z-scores of 2.05 or greater on the Stanford-Binet intelligence test. What is the IQ corresponding to a z-score of 2.05?

SOLUTION

a. We begin with the IQ corresponding to a z-score of −1.5. The negative sign in −1.5 tells us that the IQ is $1\frac{1}{2}$ standard deviations below the mean.

$$\text{IQ} = \text{mean} - 1.5 \cdot \text{standard deviation}$$
$$= 100 - 1.5(16) = 100 - 24 = 76$$

The IQ corresponding to a z-score of −1.5 is 76.

b. Next, we find the IQ corresponding to a z-score of 2.05. The positive sign implied in 2.05 tells us that the IQ is 2.05 standard deviations above the mean.

$$\text{IQ} = \text{mean} + 2.05 \cdot \text{standard deviation}$$
$$= 100 + 2.05(16) = 100 + 32.8 = 132.8$$

The IQ corresponding to a z-score of 2.05 is 132.8. (An IQ score of at least 133 is required to join Mensa.)

○

CHECK POINT 5   Use the information in Example 5 to find the IQ corresponding to a z-score of

a. −2.25.   **b.** 1.75.

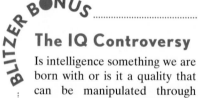

BLITZER BONUS

The IQ Controversy

Is intelligence something we are born with or is it a quality that can be manipulated through education? Can it be measured accurately and is IQ the way to measure it? There are no clear answers to these questions.

In a study by Carolyn Bird (*Pygmalion in the Classroom*), a group of third-grade teachers was told that they had classes of students with IQs well above the mean. These classes made incredible progress throughout the year. In reality, these were not gifted kids, but, rather, a random sample of all third-graders. It was the teachers' expectations, and not the IQs of the students, that resulted in increased performance.

<table>
<tr><td>**6**</td><td>Understand percentiles and quartiles.</td></tr>
</table>

Percentiles and Quartiles

A z-score measures a data item's position in a normal distribution. Another measure of a data item's position is its **percentile**. Percentiles are often associated with scores on standardized tests. If a score is in the 45th percentile, this means that 45% of the scores are less than this score. If a score is in the 95th percentile, this indicates that 95% of the scores are less than this score.

> ### PERCENTILES
> If n% of the items in a distribution are less than a particular data item, we say that the data item is in the **nth percentile** of the distribution.

EXAMPLE 6   INTERPRETING PERCENTILE

The cutoff IQ score for Mensa membership, 132.8, is in the 98th percentile. What does this mean?

SOLUTION Because 132.8 is in the 98th percentile, this means that 98% of IQ scores fall below 132.8.

 A student scored in the 75th percentile on the SAT. What does this mean?

Three commonly encountered percentiles are the *quartiles*. **Quartiles** divide data sets into four equal parts. The 25th percentile is the **first quartile**: 25% of the data fall below the first quartile. The 50th percentile is the **second quartile**: 50% of the data fall below the second quartile, so the second quartile is equivalent to the median. The 75th percentile is the **third quartile**: 75% of the data fall below the third quartile. Figure 9.16 illustrates the concept of quartiles for the normal distribution.

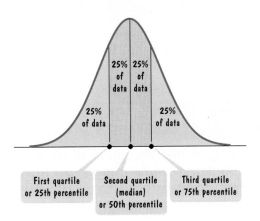

FIGURE 9.16 Quartiles

<table>
<tr><td>**7**</td><td>Solve applied problems involving normal distributions.</td></tr>
</table>

Problem Solving Using z-Scores and Percentiles

Table 9.13 on the next page gives a percentile interpretation for z-scores. For example, the portion of the table in the margin indicates that the corresponding percentile for a data item with a z-score of 2 is 97.72. A student with this score on a test whose results are normally distributed outperformed 97.72% of those who took the test.

In a normal distribution, the mean, median, and mode all have a corresponding z-score of 0. Table 9.13 shows that the percentile for a z-score of 0 is 50.00. Thus, 50% of the data items in a normal distribution are less than the mean, median, and mode. Consequently, 50% of the data items are greater than or equal to the mean, median, and mode.

Two entries from Table 9.13. The complete table is on the next page.

z-Score	Percentile
2.0	97.72
0.0	50.00

Table 9.13 can be used to find the percentage of data items that are less than any data item in a normal distribution. Begin by converting the data item to a z-score. Then, use the table to find the percentile for this z-score. This percentile is the percentage of data items that are less than the data item in question.

TABLE 9.13 z-SCORES AND PERCENTILES

z-Score	Percentile	z-Score	Percentile	z-Score	Percentile	z-Score	Percentile
−4.0	0.003	−1.0	15.87	0.0	50.00	1.1	86.43
−3.5	0.02	−0.95	17.11	0.05	51.99	1.2	88.49
−3.0	0.13	−0.90	18.41	0.10	53.98	1.3	90.32
−2.9	0.19	−0.85	19.77	0.15	55.96	1.4	91.92
−2.8	0.26	−0.80	21.19	0.20	57.93	1.5	93.32
−2.7	0.35	−0.75	22.66	0.25	59.87	1.6	94.52
−2.6	0.47	−0.70	24.20	0.30	61.79	1.7	95.54
−2.5	0.62	−0.65	25.78	0.35	63.68	1.8	96.41
−2.4	0.82	−0.60	27.43	0.40	65.54	1.9	97.13
−2.3	1.07	−0.55	29.12	0.45	67.36	2.0	97.72
−2.2	1.39	−0.50	30.85	0.50	69.15	2.1	98.21
−2.1	1.79	−0.45	32.64	0.55	70.88	2.2	98.61
−2.0	2.28	−0.40	34.46	0.60	72.57	2.3	98.93
−1.9	2.87	−0.35	36.32	0.65	74.22	2.4	99.18
−1.8	3.59	−0.30	38.21	0.70	75.80	2.5	99.38
−1.7	4.46	−0.25	40.13	0.75	77.34	2.6	99.53
−1.6	5.48	−0.20	42.07	0.80	78.81	2.7	99.65
−1.5	6.68	−0.15	44.04	0.85	80.23	2.8	99.74
−1.4	8.08	−0.10	46.02	0.90	81.59	2.9	99.81
−1.3	9.68	−0.05	48.01	0.95	82.89	3.0	99.87
−1.2	11.51	0.0	50.00	1.0	84.13	3.5	99.98
−1.1	13.57					4.0	99.997

EXAMPLE 7   FINDING THE PERCENTAGE OF DATA ITEMS LESS THAN A GIVEN DATA ITEM

According to the Department of Health and Education, cholesterol levels are normally distributed. For men between 18 and 24 years, the mean is 178.1 (measured in milligrams per 100 milliliters) and the standard deviation is 40.7. What percentage of men in this age range have a cholesterol level less than 239.15?

SOLUTION If you are familiar with your own cholesterol level, you probably recognize that a level of 239.15 is fairly high for a young man. Because of this, we would expect most young men to have a level less than 239.15. Let's see if this is so. Table 9.13 requires that we use z-scores. We compute the z-score for a 239.15 cholesterol level by using the z-score formula.

$$z_{239.15} = \frac{\text{data item} - \text{mean}}{\text{standard deviation}} = \frac{239.15 - 178.1}{40.7} = \frac{61.05}{40.7} = 1.5$$

A man between 18 and 24 with a 239.15 cholesterol level is 1.5 standard deviations above the mean, illustrated in Figure 9.17(a). The question mark indicates that we must find the percentage of men with a cholesterol level less than $z = 1.5$, the z-score for a 239.15 cholesterol level. Table 9.13 gives this percentage as a percentile.

Find 1.5 in the *z*-score column in the right portion of the table. The percentile given to the right of 1.5 is 93.32. Thus, 93.32% of men between 18 and 24 have a cholesterol level less than 239.15, shown in Figure 9.17(b).

A PORTION OF TABLE 9.13

z-Score	Percentile
1.4	91.92
1.5	93.32
1.6	94.52

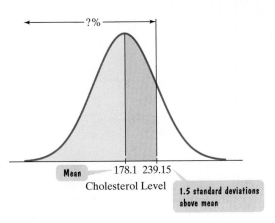

FIGURE 9.17(a)

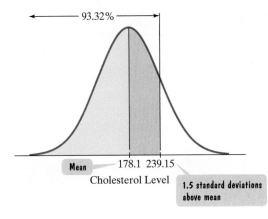

FIGURE 9.17(b)

CHECK POINT 7   The distribution of monthly charges for cellphone plans in the United States is approximately normal with a mean of $62 and a standard deviation of $18. What percentage of plans have charges that are less than $83.60?

The normal distribution accounts for all data items, meaning 100% of the scores. This means that Table 9.13 can also be used to find the percentage of data items that are greater than any data item in a normal distribution. Use the percentile in the table to determine the percentage of data items less than the data item in question. Then subtract this percentage from 100% to find the percentage of data items greater than the item in question. In using this technique, we will treat the phrases "greater than" and "greater than or equal to" as equivalent.

EXAMPLE 8   FINDING THE PERCENTAGE OF DATA ITEMS GREATER THAN A GIVEN DATA ITEM

Lengths of pregnancies of women are normally distributed with a mean of 266 days and a standard deviation of 16 days. What percentage of children are born from pregnancies lasting more than 274 days?

SOLUTION   Table 9.13 requires that we use *z*-scores. We compute the *z*-score for a 274-day pregnancy by using the *z*-score formula.

$$z_{274} = \frac{\text{data item} - \text{mean}}{\text{standard deviation}} = \frac{274 - 266}{16} = \frac{8}{16} = 0.5$$

A 274-day pregnancy is 0.5 standard deviation above the mean. Table 9.13 gives the percentile corresponding to 0.50 as 69.15. This means that 69.15% of pregnancies last less than 274 days, illustrated in Figure 9.18. We must find the number of pregnancies lasting more than 274 days by subtracting 69.15% from 100%.

$$100\% - 69.15\% = 30.85\%$$

Thus, 30.85% of children are born from pregnancies lasting more than 274 days.

A Portion of Table 9.13

z-Score	Percentile
0.45	67.36
0.50	69.15
0.55	70.88

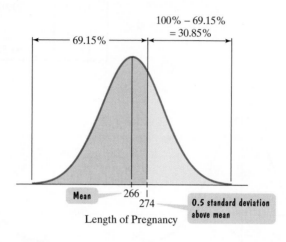

FIGURE 9.18

CHECK POINT 8 Female adult heights in North America are approximately normally distributed with a mean of 65 inches and a standard deviation of 3.5 inches. What percentage of North American women have heights that exceed 69.9 inches?

We have seen how Table 9.13 is used to find the percentage of data items that are less than or greater than any given item. The table can also be used to find the percentage of data items *between* two given items. Because the percentile for each item is the percentage of data items less than the given item, the percentage of data between the two given items is found by subtracting the lesser percent from the greater percent. This is illustrated in Figure 9.19.

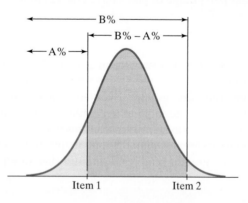

FIGURE 9.19 The percentile for data item 1 is A. The percentile for data item 2 is B. The percentage of data items between item 1 and item 2 is B% − A%.

FINDING THE PERCENTAGE OF DATA ITEMS BETWEEN TWO GIVEN ITEMS IN A NORMAL DISTRIBUTION

1. Convert each given data item to a *z*-score:

$$z = \frac{\text{data item} - \text{mean}}{\text{standard deviation}}.$$

2. Use Table 9.13 to find the percentile corresponding to each *z*-score in step 1.

3. Subtract the lesser percentile from the greater percentile and attach a % sign.

EXAMPLE 9	FINDING THE PERCENTAGE OF DATA ITEMS BETWEEN TWO GIVEN DATA ITEMS

The amount of time that self-employed Americans work each week is normally distributed with a mean of 44.6 hours and a standard deviation of 14.4 hours. What percentage of self-employed individuals in the United States work between 37.4 and 80.6 hours per week?

SOLUTION

Step 1. Convert each given data item to a z-score.

$$z_{37.4} = \frac{\text{data item} - \text{mean}}{\text{standard deviation}} = \frac{37.4 - 44.6}{14.4} = \frac{-7.2}{14.4} = -0.5$$

$$z_{80.6} = \frac{\text{data item} - \text{mean}}{\text{standard deviation}} = \frac{80.6 - 44.6}{14.4} = \frac{36}{14.4} = 2.5$$

A Portion of Table 9.13

z-Score	Percentile
−0.55	29.12
−0.50	30.85
−0.45	32.64

A Portion of Table 9.13

z-Score	Percentile
2.4	99.18
2.5	99.38
2.6	99.53

Step 2. Use Table 9.13 to find the percentile corresponding to these z-scores. The percentile given to the right of −0.50 is 30.85. This means that 30.85% of self-employed Americans work less than 37.4 hours per week.

Table 9.13 also gives the percentile corresponding to $z = 2.5$. Find 2.5 in the z-score column in the far-right portion of the table. The percentile given to the right of 2.5 is 99.38. This means that 99.38% of self-employed Americans work less than 80.6 hours per week.

Step 3. Subtract the lesser percentile from the greater percentile and attach a % sign. Subtracting percentiles, we obtain

$$99.38 - 30.85 = 68.53.$$

Thus, 68.53% of self-employed Americans work between 37.4 and 80.6 hours per week. The solution is illustrated in Figure 9.20.

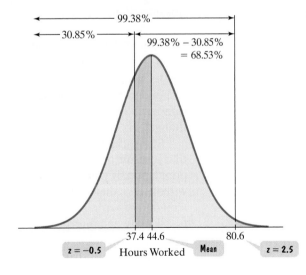

FIGURE 9.20

CHECK POINT **9** The distribution for the life of refrigerators is approximately normal with a mean of 14 years and a standard deviation of 2.5 years. What percentage of refrigerators have lives between 11 years and 18 years?

Our work in Examples 7 through 9 is summarized as follows:

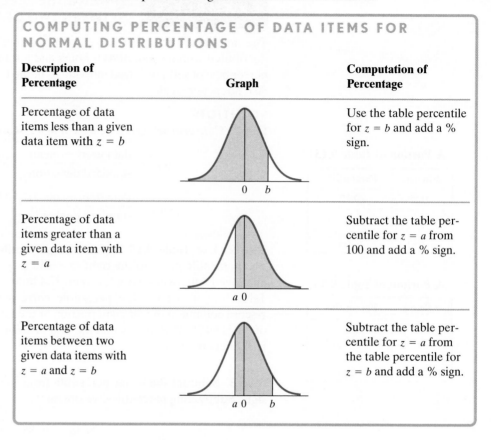

COMPUTING PERCENTAGE OF DATA ITEMS FOR NORMAL DISTRIBUTIONS

Description of Percentage	Graph	Computation of Percentage
Percentage of data items less than a given data item with $z = b$		Use the table percentile for $z = b$ and add a % sign.
Percentage of data items greater than a given data item with $z = a$		Subtract the table percentile for $z = a$ from 100 and add a % sign.
Percentage of data items between two given data items with $z = a$ and $z = b$		Subtract the table percentile for $z = a$ from the table percentile for $z = b$ and add a % sign.

8 | Use and interpret margins of error.

Polls and Margins of Error

When you were between the ages of 6 and 14, how would you have responded to this question:

What is bad about being a kid?

In a random sample of 1172 children ages 6 through 14, 17% of the children responded, "Getting bossed around." The problem is that this is a single random sample. Do 17% of kids in the entire population of children ages 6 through 14 think that getting bossed around is a bad thing?

Statisticians use properties of the normal distribution to estimate the probability that a result obtained from a single sample reflects what is truly happening in the population. If you look at the results of a poll like the one shown in the margin, you will observe that a *margin of error* is reported. Surveys and opinion polls often give a margin of error. Let's use our understanding of the normal distribution to see how to calculate and interpret margins of error.

Suppose that $p\%$ of the population of children ages 6 through 14 hold the opinion that getting bossed around is a bad thing about being a kid. Instead of taking only one random sample of 1172 children, we repeat the process of selecting a random sample of 1172 children hundreds of times. Then, we calculate the percentage of children for each sample who think being bossed around is bad. With random sampling, we expect to find the percentage in many of the samples close to $p\%$, with relatively few samples having percentages far from $p\%$. Figure 9.21 on the next page shows that the percentages of children from the hundreds of samples can be modeled by a normal distribution. The mean of this distribution is the actual population percent, $p\%$, and is the most frequent result from the samples.

What Is Bad about Being a Kid?

Kids Say	
Getting bossed around	17%
School, homework	15%
Can't do everything I want	11%
Chores	9%
Being grounded	9%

Source: Penn, Schoen, and Berland using 1172 interviews with children ages 6 to 14 from May 14 to June 1, 1999, Margin of error: ±2.9%

Note the margin of error.

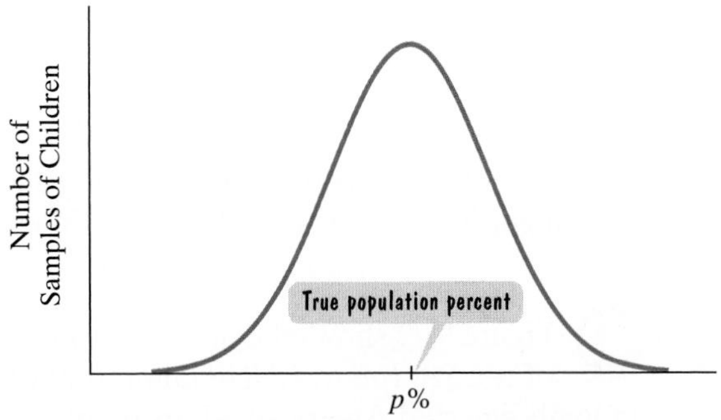

Percentage of Children Who Feel
Being Bossed Around Is Bad

FIGURE 9.21 Percentage of children who feel being bossed around is bad

Mathematicians have shown that the standard deviation of a normal distribution of samples like the one in Figure 9.21 is approximately $\dfrac{1}{2\sqrt{n}}$, where n is the sample size. Using the 68–95–99.7 Rule, approximately 95% of the samples have a percentage within 2 standard deviations of the true population percentage, $p\%$:

$$2 \text{ standard deviations} = 2 \cdot \frac{1}{2\sqrt{n}} = \frac{1}{\sqrt{n}}.$$

If we use a single random sample of size n, there is a 95% probability that the percent obtained will lie within two standard deviations, or $\dfrac{1}{\sqrt{n}}$, of the true population percent. We can be 95% confident that the true population percent lies between

$$\text{the sample percent} - \frac{1}{\sqrt{n}}$$

and

$$\text{the sample percent} + \frac{1}{\sqrt{n}}.$$

We call $\pm\dfrac{1}{\sqrt{n}}$ the **margin of error**.

> **MARGIN OF ERROR IN A SURVEY**
>
> If a statistic is obtained from a random sample of size n, there is a 95% probability that it lies within $\dfrac{1}{\sqrt{n}}$ of the true population statistic, where $\pm\dfrac{1}{\sqrt{n}}$ is called the **margin of error**.

EXAMPLE 10   USING AND INTERPRETING MARGIN OF ERROR

In a random sample of 1172 children ages 6 through 14, 17% of the children said getting bossed around is a bad thing about being a kid.

a. Verify the margin of error that was given for this survey.

b. Write a statement about the percentage of children in the population who feel that getting bossed around is a bad thing about being a kid.

SOLUTION

a. The sample size is $n = 1172$. The margin of error is

$$\pm\frac{1}{\sqrt{n}} = \pm\frac{1}{\sqrt{1172}} \approx \pm0.029 = \pm2.9\%.$$

b. There is a 95% probability that the true population percentage lies between

$$\text{the sample percent} - \frac{1}{\sqrt{n}} = 17\% - 2.9\% = 14.1\%$$

WHAT IS BAD ABOUT BEING A KID?

Kids Say	
Getting bossed around	17%
School, homework	15%
Can't do everything I want	11%
Chores	9%
Being grounded	9%

Source: Penn, Schoen, and Berland using 1172 interviews with children ages 6 to 14 from May 14 to June 1, 1999, Margin of error: ±2.9%

9 | Recognize distributions that are not normal.

FIGURE 9.23 Histogram of the ages of females interviewed by Kinsey and his associates

and

$$\text{the sample percent} + \frac{1}{\sqrt{n}} = 17\% + 2.9\% = 19.9\%.$$

We can be 95% confident that between 14.1% and 19.9% of all children feel that getting bossed around is a bad thing about being a kid.

CHECK POINT 10 Figure 9.22 shows the question and results of a *USA Today,* CNN/Gallup poll of 485 randomly selected American adults on physician-assisted suicide.

a. Find the margin of error for this survey. Round to the nearest tenth of a percent.

b. Write a statement about the percentage of American adults in the population who support physician-assisted suicide.

c. Based on your answer to part (b), explain how the title given with the circle graph in Figure 9.22 is misleading.

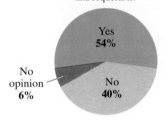

Majority Supports Assisted Suicide

Should a doctor be allowed to help a terminally ill patient end his or her life with an overdose of medication if the patient is mentally competent and requests it?

FIGURE 9.22
Source: USA Today, CNN/Gallup Poll

Other Kinds of Distributions

The histogram in Figure 9.23 represents the frequencies of the ages of women interviewed by Kinsey and his colleagues in their study of female sexual behavior. This distribution is not symmetric. The greatest frequency of women interviewed was in the 16–20 age range. The bars get shorter and shorter after this. The shorter bars fall on the right, indicating that relatively few older women were included in Kinsey's interviews.

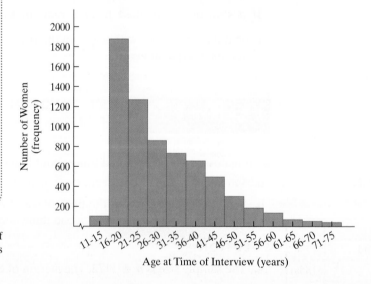

Although the normal distribution is the most important of all distributions in terms of analyzing data, not all data can be approximated by this symmetric distribution with its mean, median, and mode all having the same value.

In our discussion of measures of central tendency, we mentioned that the median, rather than the mean, is used to summarize income. Figure 9.24 at the top of the next page illustrates the population distribution of weekly earnings in the

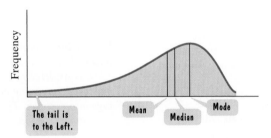

FIGURE 9.24 Skewed to the right

United States. There is no upper limit on weekly earnings. The relatively few people with very high weekly incomes tend to pull the mean income to a value greater than the median. The most frequent income, the mode, occurs toward the low end of the data items. The mean, median, and mode do not have the same value, and a normal distribution is not an appropriate model for describing weekly earnings in the United States.

The distribution in Figure 9.24 is called a *skewed distribution*. A distribution of data is **skewed** if a large number of data items are piled up at one end or the other, with a "tail" at the opposite end. In the distribution of weekly earnings in Figure 9.24, the tail is to the right. Such a distribution is said to be **skewed to the right**.

By contrast to the distribution of weekly earnings, the distribution in Figure 9.25 has more data items at the high end of the scale than at the low end. The tail of this distribution is to the left. The distribution is said to be **skewed to the left**. In many colleges, an example of a distribution skewed to the left is based on the student ratings of faculty teaching performance. Most professors are given rather high ratings, while only a few are rated terrible. These low ratings pull the value of the mean lower than the median.

FIGURE 9.25 Skewed to the left

E X E R C I S E   S E T   9 . 4 ●●●●●●

• Practice and Application Exercises

The scores on a test are normally distributed with a mean of 100 and a standard deviation of 20. In Exercises 1–10, find the score that is

1. 1 standard deviation above the mean.

2. 2 standard deviations above the mean.

3. 3 standard deviations above the mean.

4. $1\frac{1}{2}$ standard deviations above the mean.

5. $2\frac{1}{2}$ standard deviations above the mean.

6. 1 standard deviation below the mean.

7. 2 standard deviations below the mean.

8. 3 standard deviations below the mean.

9. one-half a standard deviation below the mean.

10. $2\frac{1}{2}$ standard deviations below the mean.

Not everyone pays the same price for the same model of a car. The figure illustrates a normal distribution for the prices paid for a particular model of a new car. The mean is $17,000 and the standard deviation is $500.

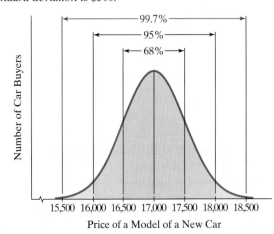

In Exercises 11–22, use the 68–95–99.7 Rule, illustrated in the figure at the bottom of the previous page, to find the percentage of buyers who paid

11. between $16,500 and $17,500.

12. between $16,000 and $18,000.

13. between $17,000 and $17,500.

14. between $17,000 and $18,000.

15. between $16,000 and $17,000.

16. between $16,500 and $17,000.

17. between $15,500 and $17,000.

18. between $17,000 and $18,500.

19. more than $17,500.

20. more than $18,000.

21. less than $16,000.

22. less than $16,500.

Intelligence quotients (IQs) on the Stanford-Binet intelligence test are normally distributed with a mean of 100 and a standard deviation of 16. In Exercises 23–32, use the 68–95–99.7 Rule to find the percentage of people with IQs

23. between 68 and 132.   **24.** between 84 and 116.

25. between 68 and 100.   **26.** between 84 and 100.

27. above 116.   **28.** above 132.

29. below 68.   **30.** below 84.

31. above 148.   **32.** below 52.

A set of data items is normally distributed with a mean of 60 and a standard deviation of 8. In Exercises 33–48, convert each data item to a z-score.

33. 68   **34.** 76   **35.** 84   **36.** 92

37. 64   **38.** 72   **39.** 74   **40.** 78

41. 60   **42.** 100   **43.** 52   **44.** 44

45. 48   **46.** 40   **47.** 34   **48.** 30

Yearly returns on large-company stocks are normally distributed with mean yearly interest at 12.4% and a standard deviation of 20.4%. In Exercises 49–56, find the z-score for an investment that

49. earns 43% annually.   **50.** earns 48.1% annually.

51. earns 58.3% annually.   **52.** earns 78.7% annually.

53. loses 13.1% annually.   **54.** loses 2.9% annually.

55. loses 18.2% annually.   **56.** loses 38.6% annually.

Intelligence quotients on the Stanford-Binet intelligence test are normally distributed with a mean of 100 and a standard deviation of 16. Intelligence quotients on the Wechsler intelligence test are normally distributed with a mean of 100 and a standard deviation of 15. Use this information to solve Exercises 57–58.

57. Use z-scores to determine which person has the higher IQ: an individual who scores 128 on the Stanford-Binet or an individual who scores 127 on the Wechsler.

58. Use z-scores to determine which person has the higher IQ: an individual who scores 150 on the Stanford-Binet or an individual who scores 148 on the Wechsler.

A set of data items is normally distributed with a mean of 400 and a standard deviation of 50. In Exercises 59–66, find the data item in this distribution that corresponds to the given z-score.

59. $z = 2$ **60.** $z = 3$

61. $z = 1.5$ **62.** $z = 2.5$

63. $z = -3$ **64.** $z = -2$

65. $z = -2.5$ **66.** $z = -1.5$

Use Table 9.13 on page 550 to solve Exercises 67–82.

*In Exercises 67–74, find the percentage of data items in a normal distribution that lie **a.** below and **b.** above the given z-score.*

67. $z = 0.6$ **68.** $z = 0.8$

69. $z = 1.2$ **70.** $z = 1.4$

71. $z = -0.7$ **72.** $z = -0.4$

73. $z = -1.2$ **74.** $z = -1.8$

In Exercises 75–82, find the percentage of data items in a normal distribution that lie between

75. $z = 0.2$ and $z = 1.4$.   **76.** $z = 0.3$ and $z = 2.1$.

77. $z = 1$ and $z = 3$.   **78.** $z = 2$ and $z = 3$.

79. $z = -1.5$ and $z = 1.5$.   **80.** $z = -1.2$ and $z = 1.2$.

81. $z = -2$ and $z = -0.5$.   **82.** $z = -2.2$ and $z = -0.3$.

Systolic blood pressure readings are normally distributed with a mean of 121 and a standard deviation of 15. (A reading above 140 is considered to be high blood pressure.) In Exercises 83–92, begin by converting any given blood pressure reading or readings into z-scores. Then use Table 9.13 on page 550 to find the percentage of people with blood pressure readings

83. below 142.   **84.** below 148.

85. above 130.   **86.** above 133.

87. above 103.   **88.** above 100.

89. between 142 and 154.   **90.** between 145 and 157.

91. between 112 and 130.   **92.** between 109 and 133.

The weights for 12-month-old baby boys are normally distributed with a mean of 22.5 pounds and a standard deviation of 2.2 pounds. In Exercises 93–96, use Table 9.13 on page 550 to find the percentage of 12-month-old baby boys who weigh

93. more than 25.8 pounds.

94. more than 23.6 pounds.

95. between 19.2 and 21.4 pounds.

96. between 18.1 and 19.2 pounds.

97. Using a random sample of 2272 American adults with children, a Harris survey asked respondents to name their dream job for their child or children. The top five responses and the percentage of parents who named each of these jobs are shown in the bar graph at the top of the next page.

What is Your Dream Job for Your Child/Children? Top Responses

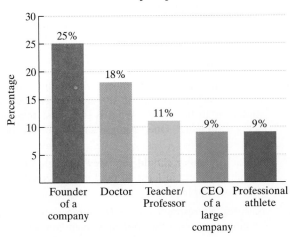

a. Find the margin of error, to the nearest tenth of a percent, for this survey.

b. Write a statement about the percentage of parents in the population who consider a doctor as the dream job for their child.

98. Using a random sample of 2297 American adults, an NBC *Today Show* poll asked respondents if they got enough sleep at night. The responses are shown in the circle graph.

Do You Get Enough Sleep at Night?

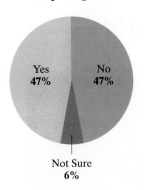

a. Find the margin of error, to the nearest tenth of a percent, for this survey.

b. Write a statement about the percentage of American adults in the population who do not get enough sleep at night.

99. Using a random sample of 4000 TV households, Nielsen Media Research found that 60.2% watched the final episode of *M*A*S*H*.

a. Find the margin of error in this percent.

b. Write a statement about the percentage of TV households in the population who tuned into the final episode of *M*A*S*H*.

100. Using a random sample of 4000 TV households, Nielsen Media Research found that 51.1% watched *Roots, Part 8*.

a. Find the margin of error in this percent.

b. Write a statement about the percentage of TV households in the population who tuned into *Roots, Part 8*.

101. In 1997, Nielsen Media Research increased its random sample to 5000 TV households. By how much, to the nearest tenth of a percent, did this improve the margin of error over that in Exercises 99 and 100?

102. If Nielsen Media Research were to increase its random sample from 5000 to 10,000 TV households, by how much, to the nearest tenth of a percent, would this improve the margin of error?

103. The histogram shows murder rates per 100,000 residents and the number of U.S. states that had these rates in 2003.

U.S. Murder Rates per 100,000 Residents, by State and Washington, D.C.

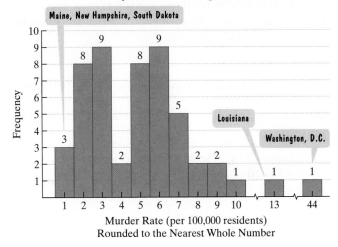

Source: FBI, *Crime in the United States*

a. Is the shape of this distribution best classified as normal, skewed to the right, or skewed to the left?

b. Calculate the mean murder rate per 100,000 residents for the 50 states and Washington, D.C.

c. Find the median murder rate per 100,000 residents for the 50 states and Washington, D.C.

d. Are the mean and median murder rates consistent with the shape of the distribution that you described in part (a)? Explain your answer.

e. The standard deviation for the data is approximately 6.1. If the distribution were roughly normal, what would be the z-score, rounded to one decimal place, for Washington, D.C.? Does this seem unusually high? Explain your answer.

• Writing in Mathematics

104. What is a symmetric histogram?

105. Describe the normal distribution and discuss some of its properties.

106. Describe the 68–95–99.7 Rule.

107. Describe how to determine the z-score for a data item in a normal distribution.

108. What does a z-score measure?

109. Give an example of both a commonly occurring and an infrequently occurring z-score. Explain how you arrived at these examples.

110. Describe when a z-score is negative.

111. If you score in the 83rd percentile, what does this mean?

112. If your weight is in the third quartile, what does this mean?

113. Explain how to find the percentage of data items between the first quartile and the third quartile.

114. Two students have scores with the same percentile, but for different administrations of the SAT. Does this mean that the students have the same score on the SAT? Explain your answer.

115. Give an example of a phenomenon that is normally distributed. Explain why. (Try to be creative and not use one of the distributions discussed in this section.) Estimate what the mean and the standard deviation might be and describe how you determined these estimates.

116. Give an example of a phenomenon that is not normally distributed and explain why.

• Critical Thinking Exercises

117. Find two z-scores so that 40% of the data in the distribution lies between them. (More than one answer is possible.)

118. A woman insists that she will never marry a man as short or shorter than she, knowing that only one man in 400 falls into this category. Assuming a mean height of 69 inches for men with a standard deviation of 2.5 inches (and a normal distribution), approximately how tall is the woman?

119. The placement test for a college has scores that are normally distributed with a mean of 500 and a standard deviation of 100. If the college accepts only the top 10% of examinees, what is the cutoff score on the test for admission?

• Group Exercise

120. For this activity, group members will conduct interviews with a random sample of students on campus. Each student is to be asked. "What is the worst thing about being a student?" One response should be recorded for each student.

    a. Each member should interview enough students so that there are at least 50 randomly selected students in the sample.

    b. After all responses have been recorded, the group should organize the four most common answers. For each answer, compute the percentage of students in the sample who felt that this is the worst thing about being a student.

    c. Find the margin of error for your survey.

    d. For each of the four most common answers, write a statement about the percentage of all students on your campus who feel that this is the worst thing about being a student.

SECTION 9.5 • SCATTER PLOTS, CORRELATION, AND REGRESSION LINES

OBJECTIVES

1. Make a scatter plot for a table of data items.

2. Interpret information given in a scatter plot.

3. Compute the correlation coefficient.

4. Write the equation of the regression line.

5. Use a sample's correlation coefficient to determine whether there is a correlation in the population.

Surprised by the number of people smoking cigarettes in movies and television shows made in the 1940s and 1950s? At that time, there was little awareness of the relationship between tobacco use and numerous diseases. Cigarette smoking was seen as a healthy way to relax and help digest a hearty meal. Then, in 1964, an equation changed everything. To understand the mathematics behind this turning point in public health, we need to explore situations involving data collected on two variables.

    Up to this point in the chapter, we have studied situations in which data sets involve a single variable, such as heights, weights, cholesterol levels, and lengths of pregnancies. By contrast, the 1964 study involved data collected on two variables from 11 countries—annual cigarette consumption for each adult male and deaths per million males from lung cancer. In this section, we consider situations in which there are two data items for each randomly selected person or thing. Our interest is in determining whether or not there is a relationship between the two variables and, if so, the strength of that relationship.

Scatter Plots and Correlation

Is there a relationship between education and prejudice? With increased education, does a person's level of prejudice tend to decrease? Notice that we are interested in two quantities—years of education and level of prejudice. For each person in our sample, we will record the number of years of school completed and the score on a test measuring prejudice. Higher scores on this 1-to-10 test indicate greater prejudice. Using x to represent years of education and y to represent scores on a test measuring prejudice, Table 9.14 shows these two quantities for a random sample of ten people.

TABLE 9.14 RECORDING TWO QUANTITIES IN A SAMPLE OF TEN PEOPLE										
Respondent	A	B	C	D	E	F	G	H	I	J
Years of education (x)	12	5	14	13	8	10	16	11	12	4
Score on prejudice test (y)	1	7	2	3	5	4	1	2	3	10

When two data items are collected for every person or object in a sample, the data items can be visually displayed using a *scatter plot*. A **scatter plot** is a collection of data points, one data point per person or object. We can make a scatter plot of the data in Table 9.14 by drawing a horizontal axis to represent years of education and a vertical axis to represent scores on a test measuring prejudice. We then represent each of the ten respondents with a single point on the graph. For example, the dot for respondent A is located to represent 12 years of education on the horizontal axis and 1 on the prejudice test on the vertical axis. Plotting each of the ten pieces of data in a rectangular coordinate system results in the scatter plot shown in Figure 9.26.

A scatter plot like the one in Figure 9.26 can be used to determine whether two quantities are related. If there is a clear relationship, the quantities are said to be **correlated**. The scatter plot shows a downward trend among the data points, although there are a few exceptions. People with increased education tend to have a lower score on the test measuring prejudice. **Correlation** is used to determine if there is a relationship between two variables and, if so, the strength and direction of that relationship.

Correlation and Causal Connections

Correlations can often be seen when data items are displayed on a scatter plot. Although the scatter plot in Figure 9.26 indicates a correlation between education and prejudice, we cannot conclude that increased education causes a person's level of prejudice to decrease. There are at least three possible explanations:

1. The correlation between increased education and decreased prejudice is simply a coincidence.
2. Education usually involves classrooms with a variety of different kinds of people. Increased exposure to diversity in the classroom setting, which accompanies increased levels of education, might be an underlying cause for decreased prejudice.
3. Education, the process of acquiring knowledge, requires people to look at new ideas and see things in different ways. Thus, education causes one to be more tolerant and less prejudiced.

Establishing that one thing causes another is extremely difficult, even if there is a strong correlation between these things. For example, as the air temperature increases, there is an increase in the number of people stung by jellyfish at the beach. This does not mean that an increase in air temperature causes more people to be stung. It might mean that because it is hotter, more people go into the water. With an increased number of swimmers, more people are likely to be stung. In short, correlation is not necessarily causation.

---

1 | Make a scatter plot for a table of data items.

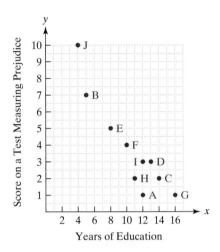

FIGURE 9.26 A scatter plot for education-prejudice data

STUDY TIP

The numbered list on the right represents three possibilities. Perhaps you can provide a better explanation about decreasing prejudice with increased education.

Regression Lines and Correlation Coefficients

Figure 9.27 shows the scatter plot for the education-prejudice data. Also shown is a straight line that seems to approximately "fit" the data points. Most of the data points lie either near or on this line. A line that best fits the data points in a scatter plot is called a **regression line**. The regression line is the particular line in which the spread of the data points around it is as small as possible.

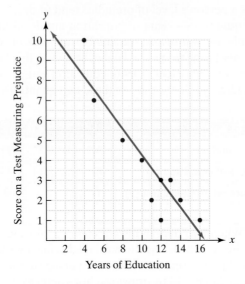

FIGURE 9.27 A scatter plot with a regression line

2 | Interpret information given in a scatter plot.

A measure that is used to describe the strength and direction of a relationship between variables whose data points lie on or near a line is called the **correlation coefficient**, designated by r. Figure 9.28 shows scatter plots and correlation coefficients. Variables are **positively correlated** if they tend to increase or decrease together, as in Figure 9.28 (a), (b), and (c). By contrast, variables are **negatively correlated** if one variable tends to decrease while the other increases, as in Figure 9.28 (e), (f), and (g). Figure 9.28 illustrates that a correlation coefficient, r, is a number between -1 and 1, inclusive. Figure 9.28(a) shows a value of 1. This indicates a **perfect positive correlation** in which all points in the scatter plot lie precisely on the regression line that rises from left to right. Figure 9.28(g) shows a value of -1. This indicates a **perfect negative correlation** in which all points in the scatter plot lie precisely on the regression line that falls from left to right.

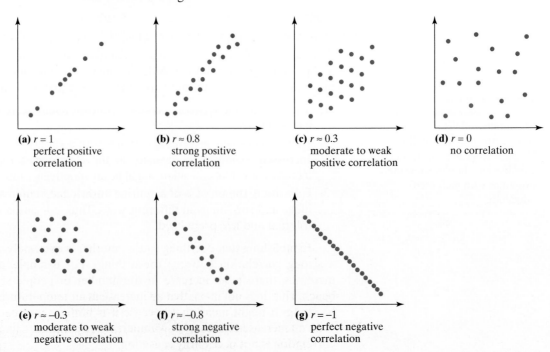

FIGURE 9.28 Scatter plots and correlation coefficients

(a) $r = 1$
perfect positive correlation

(b) $r \approx 0.8$
strong positive correlation

(c) $r \approx 0.3$
moderate to weak positive correlation

(d) $r = 0$
no correlation

(e) $r \approx -0.3$
moderate to weak negative correlation

(f) $r \approx -0.8$
strong negative correlation

(g) $r = -1$
perfect negative correlation

BLITZER BONUS

Beneficial Uses of Correlation Coefficients

- A Florida study showed a high positive correlation between the number of powerboats and the number of manatee deaths. Many of these deaths were seen to be caused by boats' propellers gashing into the manatees' bodies. Based on this study, Florida set up coastal sanctuaries where powerboats are prohibited so that these large gentle mammals that float just below the water's surface could thrive.

- In 1986, researchers studied how psychiatric patients readjusted to their community after their release from a mental hospital. A moderate positive correlation ($r = 0.38$) was found between patients' attractiveness and their postdischarge social adjustment. The better-looking patients were better off. The researchers suggested that physical attractiveness plays a role in patients' readjustment to community living because good-looking people tend to be treated better by others than homely people are.

Take another look at Figure 9.28. If r is between 0 and 1, as in (b) and (c), the two variables are positively correlated, but not perfectly. Although all the data points will not lie on the regression line, as in (a), an increase in one variable tends to be accompanied by an increase in the other.

Negative correlations are also illustrated in Figure 9.28. If r is between 0 and -1, as in (e) and (f), the two variables are negatively correlated, but not perfectly. Although all the data points will not lie on the regression line, as in (g), an increase in one variable tends to be accompanied by a decrease in the other.

EXAMPLE 1   INTERPRETING A CORRELATION COEFFICIENT

In a 1971 study involving 232 subjects, researchers found a relationship between the subjects' level of stress and how often they became ill. The correlation coefficient in this study was 0.32. Does this indicate a strong relationship between stress and illness?

SOLUTION The correlation coefficient $r = 0.32$ means that as stress increases, frequency of illness also tends to increase. However, 0.32 is only a moderate correlation, illustrated in Figure 9.28(c). There is not, based on this study, a strong relationship between stress and illness. In this study, the relationship is somewhat weak.

○

CHECK POINT 1 In a 1996 study involving obesity in mothers and daughters, researchers found a relationship between a high body-mass index for the girls and their mothers. (Body-mass index is a measure of weight relative to height. People with a high body-mass index are overweight or obese.) The correlation coefficient in this study was 0.51. Does this indicate a weak relationship between the body-mass index of daughters and the body-mass index of their mothers?

How to Obtain the Correlation Coefficient and the Equation of the Regression Line

The easiest way to find the correlation coefficient and the equation of the regression line is to use a graphing or statistical calculator. Graphing calculators have statistical menus that enable you to enter the x and y data items for the variables. Based on this information, you can instruct the calculator to display a scatter plot, the equation of the regression line, and the correlation coefficient.

We can also compute the correlation coefficient and the equation of the regression line by hand using formulas. First, we compute the correlation coefficient.

3 Compute the correlation coefficient.

COMPUTING THE CORRELATION COEFFICIENT BY HAND

The following formula is used to calculate the correlation coefficient, r:

$$r = \frac{n(\Sigma xy) - (\Sigma x)(\Sigma y)}{\sqrt{n(\Sigma x^2) - (\Sigma x)^2}\sqrt{n(\Sigma y^2) - (\Sigma y)^2}}.$$

In the formula,

$$n = \text{the number of data points, } (x, y)$$
$$\Sigma x = \text{the sum of the } x\text{-values}$$
$$\Sigma y = \text{the sum of the } y\text{-values}$$
$$\Sigma xy = \text{the sum of the product of } x \text{ and } y \text{ in each pair}$$
$$\Sigma x^2 = \text{the sum of the squares of the } x\text{-values}$$
$$\Sigma y^2 = \text{the sum of the squares of the } y\text{-values}$$
$$(\Sigma x)^2 = \text{the square of the sum of the } x\text{-values}$$
$$(\Sigma y)^2 = \text{the square of the sum of the } y\text{-values}$$

When computing the correlation coefficient by hand, organize your work in five columns:

x	y	xy	x^2	y^2

Find the sum of the numbers in each column. Then, substitute these values into the formula for r. Example 2 illustrates computing the correlation coefficient for the education-prejudice test data.

EXAMPLE 2   COMPUTING THE CORRELATION COEFFICIENT

Shown below are the data involving the number of years of school, x, completed by ten randomly selected people and their scores on a test measuring prejudice, y. Recall that higher scores on the measure of prejudice (1 to 10) indicate greater levels of prejudice. Determine the correlation coefficient between years of education and scores on a prejudice test.

Respondent	A	B	C	D	E	F	G	H	I	J
Years of education (x)	12	5	14	13	8	10	16	11	12	4
Score on prejudice test (y)	1	7	2	3	5	4	1	2	3	10

SOLUTION As suggested, organize the work in five columns.

x	y	xy	x^2	y^2
12	1	12	144	1
5	7	35	25	49
14	2	28	196	4
13	3	39	169	9
8	5	40	64	25
10	4	40	100	16
16	1	16	256	1
11	2	22	121	4
12	3	36	144	9
4	10	40	16	100
$\Sigma x = 105$	$\Sigma y = 38$	$\Sigma xy = 308$	$\Sigma x^2 = 1235$	$\Sigma y^2 = 218$

Add all values in the x-column.   Add all values in the y-column.   Add all values in the xy-column.   Add all values in the x²-column.   Add all values in the y²-column.

We use these five sums to calculate the correlation coefficient.

Another value in the formula for r that we have not yet determined is n, the number of data points (x, y). Because there are ten items in the x-column and ten items in the y-column, the number of data points (x, y) is ten. Thus, $n = 10$.

In order to calculate r, we also need to find the square of the sum of the x-values and the y-values:

$$(\Sigma x)^2 = (105)^2 = 11{,}025 \quad \text{and} \quad (\Sigma y)^2 = (38)^2 = 1444.$$

We are ready to determine the value for r.

$$r = \frac{n(\Sigma xy) - (\Sigma x)(\Sigma y)}{\sqrt{n(\Sigma x^2) - (\Sigma x)^2}\sqrt{n(\Sigma y^2) - (\Sigma y)^2}}$$

$$= \frac{10(308) - 105(38)}{\sqrt{10(1235) - 11{,}025}\sqrt{10(218) - 1444}}$$

$$= \frac{-910}{\sqrt{1325}\sqrt{736}}$$

$$\approx -0.92$$

TECHNOLOGY

GRAPHING CALCULATORS, SCATTER PLOTS, AND REGRESSION LINES

You can use a graphing calculator to display a scatter plot and the regression line. After entering the x and y data items for years of education and scores on a prejudice test, the calculator shows the scatter plot of the data and the regression line.

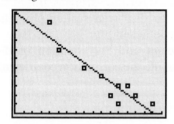

Also displayed below is the regression line's equation and the correlation coefficient, r. The slope shown below is approximately -0.69. The negative slope reinforces the fact that there is a negative correlation between the variables in Example 2.

```
LinReg
 y=ax+b
 a=-.6867924528
 b=11.01132075
 r=-.9214983162

■
```

The value for *r*, approximately −0.92, is fairly close to −1 and indicates a strong negative correlation. This means that the more education a person has, the less prejudiced that person is (based on scores on the test measuring levels of prejudice).

CHECK POINT 2 Is there a relationship between alcohol from moderate wine consumption and heart disease death rate? The table gives data from 19 developed countries. Using a calculator, determine the correlation coefficient between these variables. Round to two decimal places.

France → ... ← U.S.

Country	A	B	C	D	E	F	G	H	I	J	K	L	M	N	O	P	Q	R	S
Liters of alcohol from drinking wine, per person per year (*x*)	2.5	3.9	2.9	2.4	2.9	0.8	9.1	0.8	0.7	7.9	1.8	1.9	0.8	6.5	1.6	5.8	1.3	1.2	2.7
Deaths from heart disease, per 100,000 people per year (*y*)	211	167	131	191	220	297	71	211	300	107	167	266	227	86	207	115	285	199	172

Source: New York Times, December 28, 1994

Once we have determined that two variables are related, we can use the equation of the regression line to determine the exact relationship. Here is the formula for writing the equation of the line that best fits the data:

4 | Write the equation of the regression line.

WRITING THE EQUATION OF THE REGRESSION LINE BY HAND

The equation of the regression line is

$$y = mx + b,$$

where

$$m = \frac{n(\Sigma xy) - (\Sigma x)(\Sigma y)}{n(\Sigma x^2) - (\Sigma x)^2} \quad \text{and} \quad b = \frac{\Sigma y - m(\Sigma x)}{n}.$$

EXAMPLE 3   WRITING THE EQUATION OF THE REGRESSION LINE

a. Shown, again, in Figure 9.27 is the scatter plot and the regression line for the data in Example 2. Use the data to find the equation of the regression line that relates years of education and scores on a prejudice test.

b. Approximately what score on the test can be anticipated by a person with nine years of education?

SOLUTION

a. We use the sums obtained in Example 2. We begin by computing *m*.

$$m = \frac{n(\Sigma xy) - (\Sigma x)(\Sigma y)}{n(\Sigma x^2) - (\Sigma x)^2} = \frac{10(308) - 105(38)}{10(1235) - (105)^2} = \frac{-910}{1325} \approx -0.69$$

With a negative correlation coefficient, it makes sense that the slope of the regression line is negative. This line falls from left to right, indicating a negative correlation.

Now, we find the *y*-intercept, *b*.

$$b = \frac{\Sigma y - m(\Sigma x)}{n} = \frac{38 - (-0.69)(105)}{10} = \frac{110.45}{10} \approx 11.05$$

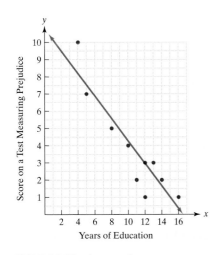

FIGURE 9.27   (repeated)

Using $m \approx -0.69$ and $b \approx 11.05$, the equation of the regression line, $y = mx + b$, is

$$y = -0.69x + 11.05,$$

where x represents the number of years of education and y represents the score on the prejudice test.

b. To anticipate the score on the prejudice test for a person with nine years of education, substitute 9 for x in the regression line's equation.

$$y = -0.69x + 11.05$$
$$y = -0.69(9) + 11.05 = 4.84$$

A person with nine years of education is anticipated to have a score close to 5 on the prejudice test.

5 Use a sample's correlation coefficient to determine whether there is a correlation in the population.

CHECK POINT 3 Use the data in Check Point 2 on page 565 to find the equation of the regression line. Use the equation to predict the heart disease death rate in a country where adults average 10 liters of alcohol per person per year.

The Level of Significance of r

In Example 2, we found a strong negative correlation between education and prejudice, computing the correlation coefficient, r, to be -0.92. However, the sample size ($n = 10$) was relatively small. With such a small sample, can we truly conclude that a correlation exists in the population? Or could it be that education and prejudice are not related? Perhaps the results we obtained were simply due to sampling error and chance.

Mathematicians have identified values to determine whether r, the correlation coefficient for a sample, can be attributed to a relationship between variables in the population. These values are shown in the second and third columns of Table 9.15. They depend on the sample size, n, listed in the left column. If $|r|$, the absolute value of the correlation coefficient computed for the sample, is greater than the value given in the table, a correlation exists between the variables in the population. The column headed $\alpha = 0.05$ denotes a **significance level of 5%**, meaning that there is a 0.05 probability that, when the statistician says the variables are correlated, they are actually not related in the population. The column on the right, headed $\alpha = 0.01$, denotes a **significance level of 1%**, meaning that there is a 0.01 probability that, when the statistician says the variables are correlated, they are actually not related in the population. Values in the $\alpha = 0.01$ column are greater than those in the $\alpha = 0.05$ column. Because of the possibility of sampling error, there is always a probability that when we say the variables are related, there is actually not a correlation in the population from which the sample was randomly selected.

TABLE 9.15 VALUES FOR DETERMINING CORRELATIONS IN A POPULATION

n	$\alpha = 0.05$	$\alpha = 0.01$
4	0.950	0.990
5	0.878	0.959
6	0.811	0.917
7	0.754	0.875
8	0.707	0.834
9	0.666	0.798
10	0.632	0.765
11	0.602	0.735
12	0.576	0.708
13	0.553	0.684
14	0.532	0.661
15	0.514	0.641
16	0.497	0.623
17	0.482	0.606
18	0.468	0.590
19	0.456	0.575
20	0.444	0.561
22	0.423	0.537
27	0.381	0.487
32	0.349	0.449
37	0.325	0.418
42	0.304	0.393
47	0.288	0.372
52	0.273	0.354
62	0.250	0.325
72	0.232	0.302
82	0.217	0.283
92	0.205	0.267
102	0.195	0.254

The larger the sample size, n, the smaller is the value of r needed for a correlation in the population.

EXAMPLE 4 DETERMINING A CORRELATION IN THE POPULATION

In Example 2, we computed $r = -0.92$ for $n = 10$. Can we conclude that there is a negative correlation between education and prejudice in the population?

SOLUTION Begin by taking the absolute value of the calculated correlation coefficient.

$$|r| = |-0.92| = 0.92$$

Now, look to the right of $n = 10$ in Table 9.15. Because 0.92 is greater than both of these values (0.632 and 0.765), we may conclude that a correlation does exist between education and prejudice in the population. (There is a probability of at most 0.01 that the variables are not really correlated in the population and our results could be attributed to chance.)

CHECK POINT
4 If you worked Check Point 2 correctly, you should have found that $r \approx -0.84$ for $n = 19$. Can you conclude that there is a negative correlation between moderate wine consumption and heart disease death rate?

BLITZER BONUS

Cigarettes and Lung Cancer

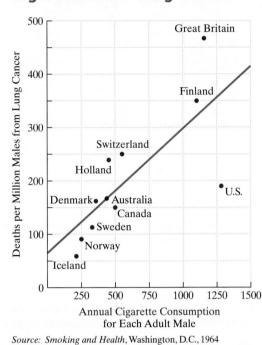

Source: *Smoking and Health*, Washington, D.C., 1964

This scatter plot shows a relationship between cigarette consumption among males and deaths due to lung cancer per million males. The data are from 11 countries and date back to a 1964 report by the U.S. Surgeon General. The scatter plot can be modeled by a line whose slope indicates an increasing death rate from lung cancer with increased cigarette consumption. At that time, the tobacco industry argued that in spite of this regression line, tobacco use is not the cause of cancer. Recent data do, indeed, show a causal effect between tobacco use and numerous diseases.

EXERCISE SET 9.5 ●●●●●●

• Practice and Application Exercises

In Exercises 1–8, make a scatter plot for the given data. Use the scatter plot to describe whether or not the variables appear to be related.

1.

x	1	6	4	3	7	2
y	2	5	3	3	4	1

2.

x	2	1	6	3	4
y	4	5	10	8	9

3.

x	8	6	1	5	4	10	3
y	2	4	10	5	6	2	9

4.

x	4	5	2	1
y	1	3	5	4

5.

Respondent	A	B	C	D	E	F	G
Years of education of parent (x)	13	9	7	12	12	10	11
Years of education of child (y)	13	11	7	16	17	8	17

6.

Respondent	A	B	C	D	E
IQ (x)	110	115	120	125	135
Annual income(y) (in thousands of dollars)	30	32	36	40	44

7. The data show the number of registered automatic weapons, in thousands, and the murder rate, in murders per 100,000, for eight randomly selected states.

Automatic weapons, x	11.6	8.3	6.9	3.6	2.6	2.5	2.4	0.6
Murder rate, y	13.1	10.6	11.5	10.1	5.3	6.6	3.6	4.4

Source: FBI and Bureau of Alcohol, Tobacco, and Firearms

8. The data show the number of employed and unemployed male workers, 20 years and older, in thousands, for six selected years in the United States.

Year	1995	1996	1997	1998	1999	2000
Employed, x	64,085	64,897	66,524	67,134	67,761	68,580
Unemployed, y	3239	3147	2826	2580	2433	2350

Source: Bureau of Labor Statistics

The scatter plot in the figure shows the relationship between the percentage of married women of child-bearing age using contraceptives and births per woman in selected countries. Use the scatter plot to determine whether each of the statements in Exercises 9–18 is true or false.

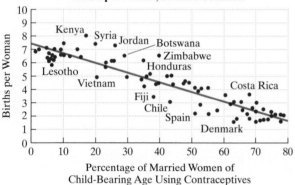

Contraceptive Prevalence and Average Number of Births per Woman, Selected Countries

Source: Population Reference Bureau

9. There is a strong positive correlation between contraceptive use and births per woman.

10. There is no correlation between contraceptive use and births per woman.

11. There is a strong negative correlation between contraceptive use and births per woman.

12. There is a causal relationship between contraceptive use and births per woman.

13. With approximately 43% of women of child-bearing age using contraceptives, there are 3 births per woman in Chile.

14. With 20% of women of child-bearing age using contraceptives, there are 6 births per woman in Vietnam.

15. No two countries have a different number of births per woman with the same percentage of married women using contraceptives.

16. The country with the greatest number of births per woman also has the smallest percentage of women using contraceptives.

17. Most of the data points do not lie on the regression line.

18. The number of selected countries shown in the scatter plot is approximately 20.

Just as money doesn't buy happiness for individuals, the two don't necessarily go together for countries either. However, the scatter plot does show a relationship between a country's annual per capita income and the percentage of people in that country who call themselves "happy." Use the scatter plot to determine whether each of the statements in Exercises 19–26 is true or false.

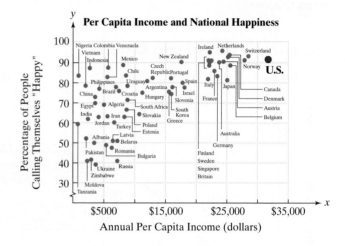

Source: Richard Layard, *Happiness: Lessons from a New Science*, Penguin, 2005

19. There is no correlation between per capita income and the percentage of people who call themselves "happy."

20. There is an almost-perfect positive correlation between per capita income and the percentage of people who call themselves "happy."

21. There is a positive correlation between per capita income and the percentage of people who call themselves "happy."

22. As per capita income decreases, the percentage of people who call themselves "happy" also tends to decrease.

23. The country with the lowest per capita income has the least percentage of people who call themselves "happy."

24. The country with the highest per capita income has the greatest percentage of people who call themselves "happy."

25. A reasonable estimate of the correlation coefficient for the data is 0.8.

26. A reasonable estimate of the correlation coefficient for the data is -0.3.

Use the scatter plots shown, labeled (a)–(f), to solve Exercises 27–30.

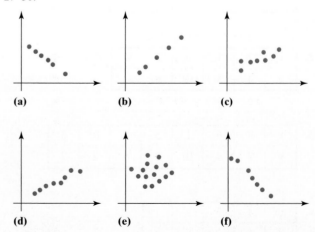

27. Which scatter plot indicates a perfect negative correlation?

28. Which scatter plot indicates a perfect positive correlation?

29. In which scatter plot is $r = 0.9$?

30. In which scatter plot is $r = 0.01$?

Compute r, the correlation coefficient, rounded to the nearest thousandth, for the data in

31. Exercise 1.

32. Exercise 2.

33. Exercise 3.

34. Exercise 4.

35. Use the data in Exercise 5 to solve this exercise.
   a. Determine the correlation coefficient between years of education of parent and child.
   b. Find the equation of the regression line for years of education of parent and child.
   c. Approximately how many years of education can we predict for a child with a parent who has 16 years of education?

36. Use the data in Exercise 6 to solve this exercise.
   a. Determine the correlation coefficient between IQ and income.
   b. Find the equation of the regression line for IQ and income.
   c. Approximately what annual income can be anticipated by a person whose IQ is 123?

37. Use the data in Exercise 7 to solve this exercise.
   a. Determine the correlation coefficient between the number of automatic weapons and the murder rate.
   b. Find the equation of the regression line.
   c. Approximately what murder rate can we anticipate in a state that has 14 thousand registered weapons?

38. Use the data in Exercise 8 to solve this exercise.
   a. Determine the correlation coefficient between the number of employed males and the number of unemployed males.
   b. Find the equation of the regression line.
   c. Approximately how many unemployed males can we anticipate for a year in which there are 70,000 thousand employed males?

In Exercises 39–45, the correlation coefficient, r, is given for a sample of n data points. Use the $\alpha = 0.05$ column in Table 9.15 on page 566 to determine whether or not we may conclude that a correlation does exist in the population. (Using the $\alpha = 0.05$ column, there is a probability of 0.05 that the variables are not really correlated in the population and our results could be attributed to chance. Ignore this possibility when concluding whether or not there is a correlation in the population.)

39. $n = 20, r = 0.5$

40. $n = 27, r = 0.4$

41. $n = 12, r = 0.5$

42. $n = 22, r = 0.04$

43. $n = 72, r = -0.351$

44. $n = 37, r = -0.37$

45. $n = 20, r = -0.37$

46. In the 1964 study on cigarette consumption and deaths due to lung cancer (see the Blitzer Bonus on page 737), $n = 11$ and $r = 0.73$. What can you conclude using the $\alpha = 0.05$ column in Table 9.15?

• Writing in Mathematics

47. What is a scatter plot?

48. How does a scatter plot indicate that two variables are correlated?

49. Give an example of two variables with a strong positive correlation and explain why this is so.

50. Give an example of two variables with a strong negative correlation and explain why this is so.

51. What is meant by a regression line?

52. When all points in a scatter plot fall on the regression line, what is the value of the correlation coefficient? Describe what this means.

For the pairs of quantities in Exercises 53–56, describe whether a scatter plot will show a positive correlation, a negative correlation, or no correlation. If there is a correlation, is it strong, moderate, or weak? Explain your answers.

53. Height and weight

54. Number of days absent and grade in a course

55. Height and grade in a course

56. Hours of television watched and grade in a course

57. Explain how to use the correlation coefficient for a sample to determine if there is a correlation in the population.

• Critical Thinking Exercises

58. Which one of the following is true?
   a. A scatter plot need not define y as a function of x.
   b. The correlation coefficient and the slope of the regression line for the same set of data can have opposite signs.
   c. When all points in a scatter plot fall on the regression line, the value of the correlation coefficient is 0.
   d. If the same number is subtracted from each x-item, but the y-item stays the same, the correlation coefficient for these new data points decreases.

59. Give an example of two variables with a strong correlation, where each variable is not the cause of the other.

• Technology Exercise

60. Use the linear regression feature of a graphing calculator to verify your work in any two exercises from Exercises 35–38, parts (a) and (b).

• Group Exercises

61. The group should select two variables related to people on your campus that it believes have a strong positive or negative correlation. Once these variables have been determined,
   a. Collect at least 30 ordered pairs of data (x, y) from a sample of people on your campus.
   b. Draw a scatter plot for the data collected.
   c. Does the scatter plot indicate a positive correlation, a negative correlation, or no relationship between the variables?
   d. Calculate r. Does the value of r reinforce the impression conveyed by the scatter plot?
   e. Find the equation of the regression line.
   f. Use the regression line's equation to make a prediction about a y-value given an x-value.
   g. Are the results of this project consistent with the group's original belief about the correlation between the variables, or are there some surprises in the data collected?

62. What is the opinion of students on your campus about …? Group members should begin by deciding on some aspect of college life around which student opinion can be polled. The poll should consist of the question, "What is your opinion of …?" Be sure to provide options such as excellent, good, average, poor, horrible, or a 1-to-10 scale, or possibly grades of A, B, C, D, F. Use a random sample of students on your campus and conduct the opinion survey. After collecting the data, present and interpret it using as many of the skills and techniques learned in this chapter as possible.

●●●●●● CHAPTER SUMMARY, REVIEW, AND TEST

● SUMMARY   DEFINITIONS AND CONCEPTS   EXAMPLES

9.1 Sampling, Frequency Distributions, and Graphs

a. A population is the set containing all objects whose properties are to be described and analyzed. A sample is a subset of the population.   Ex. 1, p. 511

b. Random samples are obtained in such a way that each member of the population has an equal chance of being selected.   Ex. 2, p. 512

c. Data can be organized and presented in frequency distributions, grouped frequency distributions, histograms, frequency polygons, and stem-and-leaf plots.   Ex. 3, p. 513; Ex. 4, p. 514; Figures 9.2 and 9.3, p. 515; Ex. 5, p. 516

d. The box on page 517 lists some things to watch for in visual displays of data.   Table 9.4, p. 518

9.2 Measures of Central Tendency

a. The mean is the sum of the data items divided by the number of items. Mean $= \dfrac{\Sigma x}{n}$.   Ex. 1, p. 523

b. The mean of a frequency distribution is computed using

$$\text{Mean} = \frac{\Sigma xf}{n},$$

where x is each data value, f is its frequency, and n is the total frequency of the distribution.   Ex. 2, p. 524

c. The median of ranked data is the item in the middle or the mean of the two middlemost items. The median is the value in the $\frac{n+1}{2}$ position in the list of ranked data.   Ex. 3, p. 525; Ex. 4, p. 526; Ex. 5, p. 527; Ex. 6, p. 527

d. When one or more data items are much greater than or much less than the other items, these extreme values greatly influence the mean, often making the median more representative of the data.   Ex. 7, p. 528

e. The mode of a data set is the value that occurs most often. If there is no such value, there is no mode. If more than one data value has the highest frequency, then each of these data values is a mode.   Ex. 8, p. 530

f. The midrange is computed using

$$\frac{\text{lowest data value + highest data value}}{2}.$$ Ex. 9, p. 531; Ex. 10, p. 531

9.3 Measures of Dispersion

a. Range = highest data value − lowest data value   Ex. 1, p. 535

b. Standard deviation $= \sqrt{\dfrac{\Sigma(\text{data item} - \text{mean})^2}{n - 1}}$

Ex. 2, p. 536;
Ex. 3, p. 537;
Ex. 4, p. 538

c. As the spread of data items increases, the standard deviation gets larger.

Ex. 5, p. 539

9.4 The Normal Distribution

a. The normal distribution is a theoretical distribution for the entire population. The distribution is bell shaped and symmetric about a vertical line through its center, where the mean, median, and mode are located.

b. The 68–95–99.7 Rule

Approximately 68% of the data items fall within 1 standard deviation of the mean,

95% of the data items fall within 2 standard deviations of the mean, and

99.7% of the data items fall within 3 standard deviations of the mean.

Ex. 1, p. 544;
Ex. 2, p. 545

c. A z-score describes how many standard deviations a data item in a normal distribution lies above or below the mean.

$$z\text{-score} = \frac{\text{data item} - \text{mean}}{\text{standard deviation}}$$

Ex. 3, p. 546;
Ex. 4, p. 548;
Ex. 5, p. 548

d. If $n\%$ of the items in a distribution are less than a particular data item, that data item is in the nth percentile of the distribution. The 25th percentile is the first quartile, the 50th percentile, or the median, is the second quartile, and the 75th percentile is the third quartile.

Ex. 6, p. 549;
Figure 9.16, p. 549

e. A table showing z-scores and their percentiles can be used to find the percentage of data items less than or greater than a given data item in a normal distribution, as well as the percentage of data items between two given items. See the boxed summary on computing percentage of data items on page 554.

Ex. 7, p. 550;
Ex. 8, p. 551;
Ex. 9, p. 553

f. If a statistic is obtained from a random sample of size n, there is a 95% probability that it lies within $\dfrac{1}{\sqrt{n}}$ of the true population statistic. $\pm\dfrac{1}{\sqrt{n}}$ is called the margin of error.

Ex. 10, p. 555

g. A distribution of data is skewed if a large number of data items are piled up at one end or the other, with a "tail" at the opposite end.

Figure 9.24, p. 557;
Figure 9.25, p. 557

9.5 Scatter Plots, Correlation, and Regression Lines

a. A plot of data points is called a scatter plot. If the points lie approximately along a line, the line that best fits the data is called a regression line.

b. A correlation coefficient, r, measures the strength and direction of a possible relationship between variables. If $r = 1$, there is a perfect positive correlation, and if $r = -1$, there is a perfect negative correlation. If $r = 0$, there is no relationship between the variables. Table 9.15 on page 566 indicates whether r denotes a correlation in the population.

Ex. 1, p. 563;
Ex. 4, p. 566

c. The formula for computing the correlation coefficient, r, is given in the box on page 563. The equation of the regression line is given in the box on page 565.

Ex. 2, p. 564;
Ex. 3, p. 565

REVIEW EXERCISES

9.1

A survey of 1511 randomly selected American women ages 25 through 60 was taken by CyberPulse Advisory Panel. The data below are from the poll. Use this information to solve Exercises 1–2.

How Often Do You Entertain Guests for Dinner?

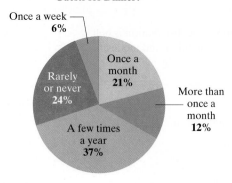

1. Describe the population and the sample of this poll.
2. For each woman polled, what variable is measured?
3. The government of a large city wants to know if its citizens will support a three-year tax increase to provide additional support to the city's community college system. The government decides to conduct a survey of the city's residents before placing a tax increase initiative on the ballot. Which one of the following is most appropriate for obtaining a sample of the city's residents?
   a. Survey a random sample of persons within each geographic region of the city.
   b. Survey a random sample of community college professors living in the city.
   c. Survey every tenth person who walks into the city's government center on two randomly selected days of the week.
   d. Survey a random sample of persons within each geographic region of the state in which the city is located.

A random sample of ten college students is selected and each student is asked how much time he or she spent on homework during the previous weekend. The following times, in hours, are obtained:

8, 10, 9, 7, 9, 8, 7, 6, 8, 7.

Use these data items to solve Exercises 4–6.

4. Construct a frequency distribution for the data.
5. Construct a histogram for the data.
6. Construct a frequency polygon for the data.

The 50 grades on a physiology test are shown. Use the data to solve Exercises 7–8.

44	24	54	81	18
34	39	63	67	60
72	36	91	47	75
57	74	87	49	86
59	14	26	41	90
13	29	13	31	68
63	35	29	70	22
95	17	50	42	27
73	11	42	31	69
56	40	31	45	51

7. Construct a grouped frequency distribution for the data. Use 0–39 for the first class, 40–49 for the second class, and make each subsequent class width the same as the second class.
8. Construct a stem-and-leaf plot for the data.
9. Describe what is misleading about the size of the barrels in the following visual display.

Average Daily Price per Barrel of Oil

Source: U.S. Department of Energy

9.2

In Exercises 10–11, find the mean for each group of data items.

10. 84, 90, 95, 89, 98
11. 33, 27, 9, 10, 6, 7, 11, 23, 27
9. Find the mean for the data items in the given frequency distribution.

Score x	Frequency f
1	2
2	4
3	3
4	1

In Exercises 13–14, find the median for each group of data items.

13. 33, 27, 9, 10, 6, 7, 11, 23, 27
14. 28, 16, 22, 28, 34
15. Find the median for the data items in the frequency distribution in Exercise 9.

In Exercises 16–17, find the mode for each group of data items. If there is no mode, so state.

16. 33, 27, 9, 10, 6, 7, 11, 23, 27
17. 582, 585, 583, 585, 587, 587, 589
18. Find the mode for the data items in the frequency distribution in Exercise 9.

In Exercises 19–20, find the midrange for each group of data items.

19. 84, 90, 95, 88, 98
20. 33, 27, 9, 10, 6, 7, 11, 23, 27
21. Find the midrange for the data items in the frequency distribution in Exercise 9.

22. Researchers at Emory University studied national health-care data from 14,000 Americans in 1987 and 2002. Explain how the research team obtained the mean annual health-care costs shown in the bar graph.

Mean Annual Health-Care Costs

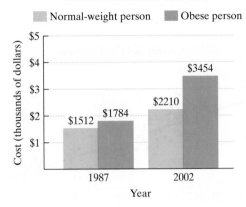

Source: Kenneth Thorpe, Emory University

23. A student took seven tests in a course, scoring between 90% and 95% on three of the tests, between 80% and 89% on three of the tests, and below 40% on one of the tests. In this distribution, is the mean or the median more representative of the student's overall performance in the course? Explain your answer.

24. The data items below are the ages of U.S. presidents at the time of their first inauguration.

57 61 57 57 58 57 61 54 68 51 49 64 50 48
65 52 56 46 54 49 51 47 55 55 54 42 51 56
55 51 54 51 60 62 43 55 56 61 52 69   64 46 54

    a. Organize the data in a frequency distribution.

    b. Use the frequency distribution to find the mean age, median age, modal age, and midrange age of the presidents when they were inaugurated.

9.3

In Exercises 25–26, find the range for each group of data items.

25. 28, 34, 16, 22, 28

26. 312, 783, 219, 312, 426, 219

27. The mean for the data items 29, 9, 8, 22, 46, 51, 48, 42, 53, 42 is 35. Find **a.** the deviation from the mean for each data item and **b.** the sum of the deviations in part (a).

28. Use the data items 36, 26, 24, 90, and 74 to find **a.** the mean, **b.** the deviation from the mean for each data item, and **c.** the sum of the deviations in part (b).

In Exercises 29–30, find the standard deviation for each group of data items.

29. 3, 3, 5, 8, 10, 13

30. 20, 27, 23, 26, 28, 32, 33, 35

31. A test measuring anxiety levels is administered to a sample of ten college students with the following results. (High scores indicate high anxiety.)

            10, 30, 37, 40, 43, 44, 45, 69, 86, 86

    Find the mean, range, and standard deviation for the data.

32. Compute the mean and the standard deviation for each of the following data sets. Then, write a brief description of similarities and differences between the two sets based on each of your computations.

    Set A: 80, 80, 80, 80   Set B: 70, 70, 90, 90

33. Describe how you would determine

    a. which of the two groups, men or women, at your college has a higher mean grade point average.

    b. which of the groups is more consistently close to its mean grade point average.

9.4

The scores on a test are normally distributed with a mean of 70 and a standard deviation of 8. In Exercises 34–36, find the score that is

34. 2 standard deviations above the mean.

35. $3\frac{1}{2}$ standard deviations above the mean.

36. $1\frac{1}{4}$ standard deviations below the mean.

The ages of people living in a retirement community are normally distributed with a mean age of 68 years and a standard deviation of 4 years. In Exercises 37–43, use the 68–95–99.7 Rule to find the percentage of people in the community whose ages

37. are between 64 and 72.   **38.** are between 60 and 76.

39. are between 68 and 72.   **40.** are between 56 and 80.

41. exceed 72.   **42.** are less than 72.

43. exceed 76.

A set of data items is normally distributed with a mean of 50 and a standard deviation of 5. In Exercises 44–48, convert each data item to a z-score.

44. 50   **45.** 60   **46.** 58

47. 35   **48.** 44

49. A student scores 60 on a vocabulary test and 80 on a grammar test. The data items for both tests are normally distributed. The vocabulary test has a mean of 50 and a standard deviation of 5. The grammar test has a mean of 72 and a standard deviation of 6. On which test did the student have the better score? Explain why this is so.

The number of miles that a particular brand of car tires lasts is normally distributed with a mean of 32,000 miles and a standard deviation of 4000 miles. In Exercises 50–52, find the data item in this distribution that corresponds to the given z-score.

50. $z = 1.5$ **51.** $z = 2.25$ **52.** $z = -2.5$

The mean cholesterol level for all men in the United States is 200 and the standard deviation is 15. In Exercises 53–56, use Table 9.13 on page 550 to find the percentage of U.S. men whose cholesterol level

53. is less than 221.   **54.** is greater than 173.

55. is between 173 and 221.   **56.** is between 164 and 182.

Use the percentiles for the weights of adult men over 40 to solve Exercises 57–59.

Weight	Percentile
235	86
227	third quartile
180	second quartile
173	first quartile

Find the percentage of men over 40 who weigh

57. less than 227 pounds.   **58.** more than 235 pounds.

59. between 227 and 235 pounds.

60. Using a random sample of 2041 executives of American companies, a Korn/Ferry survey asked respondents if their career was related to the area of their college degree. The poll indicated that 85% of the executives responded "yes" and 15% said "no."

  a. Find the margin of error, to the nearest tenth of a percent, for this survey.

  b. Write a statement about the percentage of American executives in the population whose career is not related to their college degree.

61. The histogram indicates the frequencies of the number of syllables per word for 100 randomly selected words in Japanese.

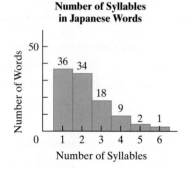

Number of Syllables in Japanese Words

  a. Is the shape of this distribution best classified as normal, skewed to the right, or skewed to the left?

  b. Find the mean, median, and mode for the number of syllables in the sample of Japanese words.

  c. Are the measures of central tendency from part (b) consistent with the shape of the distribution that you described in part (a)? Explain your answer.

9.5

In Exercises 62–63, make a scatter plot for the given data. Use the scatter plot to describe whether or not the variables appear to be related.

62.

x	1	3	4	6	8	9
y	1	2	3	3	5	5

63.

Country	Canada	U.S.	Mexico	Brazil	Costa Rica
Life expectancy in years, x	79	76	72	64	76
Infant deaths per 1000 births, y	5.6	6.4	25.9	40.0	13.1

Denmark	China	Egypt	Pakistan	Bangladesh	Australia	Japan	Russia
76	70	62	59	57	80	80	65
6.8	45.5	69.3	93.5	97.7	5.3	4.1	23.3

Source: U.S. Bureau of the Census International Database

The scatter plot in the figure shows the relationship between the percentage of adult females in a country who are literate and the mortality of children under five. Also shown is the regression line. Use this information to determine whether each of the statements in Exercises 64–70 is true or false.

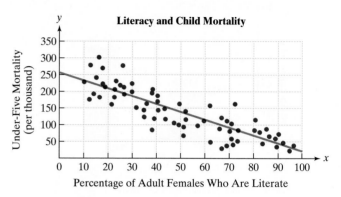

Source: United Nations

64. There is a perfect negative correlation between the percentage of adult females who are literate and under-five mortality.

65. As the percentage of adult females who are literate increases, under-five mortality tends to decrease.

66. The country with the least percentage of adult females who are literate has the greatest under-five mortality.

67. No two countries have the same percentage of adult females who are literate but different under-five mortalities.

68. There are more than 20 countries in this sample.

69. There is no correlation between the percentage of adult females who are literate and under-five mortality.

70. The country with the greatest percentage of adult females who are literate has an under-five mortality rate that is less than 50 children per thousand.

71. Which one of the following scatter plots indicates a correlation coefficient of approximately −0.9?

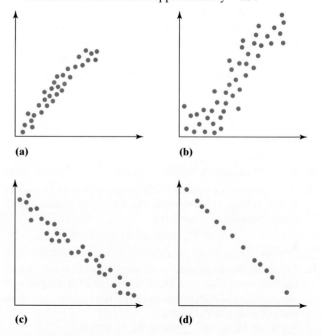

(a)

(b)

(c)

(d)

72. Use the data in Exercise 62 to solve the exercise.

   a. Compute r, the correlation coefficient, rounded to the nearest thousandth.

   b. Find the equation of the regression line.

73. The graph, based on Nielsen Media Research 2005 data taken from random samples of Americans at various ages, indicates that as we get older, we watch more television.

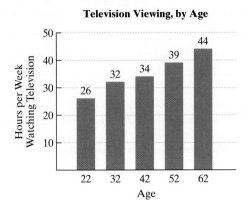

Television Viewing, by Age

Source: Nielsen Media Research

   a. Let x represent one's age and let y represent hours per week watching television. Calculate the correlation coefficient.

   b. Using Table 9.15 on page 566 and the $\alpha = 0.05$ column, determine whether there is a correlation between age and time spent watching television in the American population.

• • • • • • • CHAPTER 9 TEST

1. Politicians in the Florida Keys need to know if the residents of Key Largo think the amount of money charged for water is reasonable. The politicians decide to conduct a survey of a sample of Key Largo's residents. Which procedure would be most appropriate for a sample of Key Largo's residents?

   a. Survey all water customers who pay their water bills at Key Largo City Hall on the third day of the month.

   b. Survey a random sample of executives who work for the water company in Key Largo.

   c. Survey 5000 individuals who are randomly selected from a list of all people living in Georgia and Florida.

   d. Survey a random sample of persons within each neighborhood of Key Largo.

Use these scores on a ten-point quiz to solve Exercises 2–4.

$$8, 5, 3, 6, 5, 10, 6, 9, 4, 5, 7, 9, 7, 4, 8, 8$$

2. Construct a frequency distribution for the data.

3. Construct a histogram for the data.

4. Construct a frequency polygon for the data.

Use the 30 test scores listed below to solve Exercises 5–6.

79	51	67	50	78
62	89	83	73	80
88	48	60	71	79
89	63	55	93	71
41	81	46	50	61
59	50	90	75	61

5. Construct a grouped frequency distribution for the data. Use 40–49 for the first class and use the same width for each subsequent class.

6. Construct a stem-and-leaf display for the data.

7. The graph shows the percentage of students in the United States through grade 12 who were home-schooled in 1999 and 2003. What impression does the roofline in the visual display imply about what occurred in 2000 through 2002? How might this be misleading?

Source: National Center for Education Statistics

Use the six data items listed below to solve Exercises 8–11.

$$3, 6, 2, 1, 7, 3$$

8. Find the mean.   **9.** Find the median.

10. Find the midrange.   **11.** Find the standard deviation.

Use the frequency distribution shown to solve Exercises 12–14.

Score x	Frequency f
1	3
2	5
3	2
4	2

12. Find the mean.

13. Find the median.

14. Find the mode.

15. The annual salaries of four salespeople and the owner of a bookstore are

$$\$17{,}500, \ \$19{,}000, \ \$22{,}000, \ \$27{,}500, \ \$98{,}500.$$

Is the mean or the median more representative of the five annual salaries? Briefly explain your answer.

According to the American Freshman, *the number of hours that college freshmen spend studying each week is normally distributed with a mean of 7 hours and a standard deviation of 5.3 hours. In Exercises 16–17, use the 68–95–99.7 Rule to find the percentage of college freshmen who study*

16. between 7 and 12.3 hours each week.

17. more than 17.6 hours each week.

18. IQ scores are normally distributed in the population. Who has a higher IQ: a student with a 120 IQ on a scale where 100 is the mean and 10 is the standard deviation, or a professor with a 128 IQ on a scale where 100 is the mean and 15 is the standard deviation? Briefly explain your answer.

19. Use the z-scores and the corresponding percentiles shown below to solve this exercise. Test scores are normally distributed with a mean of 74 and a standard deviation of 10. What percentage of the scores are above 88?

z-Score	Percentile
1.1	86.43
1.2	88.49
1.3	90.32
1.4	91.92
1.5	93.32

20. Use the percentiles in the table shown below to find the percentage of scores between 630 and 690.

Score	Percentile
780	99
750	87
720	72
690	49
660	26
630	8
600	1

21. Using a random sample of 100 students from a campus of approximately 12,000 students, 60% of the students in the sample said they were very satisfied with their professors.

  a. Find the margin of error in this percent.

  b. Write a statement about the percentage of the entire population of students from this campus who are very satisfied with their professors.

22. Make a scatter plot for the given data. Use the scatter plot to describe whether or not the variables appear to be related.

x	1	4	3	5	2
y	5	2	2	1	4

The scatter plot shows the number of minutes each of 16 people exercise per week and the number of headaches per month each person experiences. Use the scatter plot to determine whether each of the statements in Exercises 23–25 is true or false.

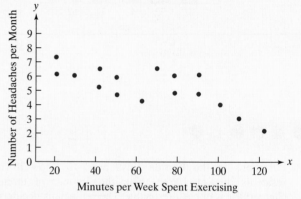

23. An increase in the number of minutes devoted to exercise causes a decrease in headaches.

24. There is a perfect negative correlation between time spent exercising and number of headaches.

25. The person who exercised most per week had the least number of headaches per month.

26. Is the relationship between the price of gas and the number of people visiting our national parks a positive correlation, a negative correlation, or is there no correlation? Explain your answer.

10

Number Representation and Calculation

A dorable on the outside and clever on the inside, it's not hard to imagine friendly robots as our home-helping buddies. Built-in microchips with extraordinary powers based on ancient numeration systems enable your robot to recognize you, engage in (meaningful?) conversation, and perform household chores. If you find the idea of a friendship with a sophisticated machine a bit unsettling, consider a robot dog or cat. Scientists have designed these critters to blend computer technology with the cuddly appeal of animals. They move, play, and sleep like real pets, and can even be programmed to sing and dance. Without an understanding of how we represent numbers, none of this technology could exist.

••••••

Connections between binary numeration systems and computer technology are discussed in "Letters and Words in Base Two" on page 587, "Music in Base Two" on page 589, and "Base Two, Logic, and Computers" on page 596.

SECTION 10.1 • OUR HINDU-ARABIC SYSTEM AND EARLY POSITIONAL SYSTEMS

OBJECTIVES

1. Evaluate an exponential expression.
2. Write a Hindu-Arabic numeral in expanded form.
3. Express a number's expanded form as a Hindu-Arabic numeral.
4. Understand and use the Babylonian numeration system.
5. Understand and use the Mayan numeration system.

FIGURE 10.1

All of us have an intuitive understanding of *more* and *less*. As humanity evolved, this sense of more and less was used to develop a system of counting. A tribe needed to know how many sheep it had, and whether the flock was increasing or decreasing in number. The earliest way of keeping count probably involved some tally method, using one vertical mark on a cave wall for each sheep. Later, a variety of vocal sounds developed as a tally for the number of things in a group. Finally, written symbols, or numerals, were used to represent numbers.

A **number** is an abstract idea that addresses the question, "How many?" A **numeral** is a symbol used to represent a number. Different symbols may be used to represent the same number. Numerals used to represent how many buffalo are shown in Figure 10.1 include

|||| ||||	IX	9.
Tally method	Roman numeral	Hindu-Arabic numeral

We take numerals and the numbers that they represent for granted and use them every day. A **system of numeration** consists of a set of basic numerals and rules for combining them to represent numbers. It took humanity thousands of years to invent numeration systems that made computation a reasonable task. Today we use a system of writing numerals that was invented in India and brought to Europe by the Arabs. Our numerals are therefore called **Hindu-Arabic numerals**.

Like literature or music, a numeration system has a profound effect on the culture that created it. Computers, which affect our everyday lives, are based on an understanding of our Hindu-Arabic system of numeration. In this section, we study the characteristics of our numeration system. We also take a brief journey through history to look at two numeration systems that pointed the way toward an amazing cultural creation, our Hindu-Arabic system.

1 | Evaluate an exponential expression.

Exponential Notation

An understanding of *exponents* is important in understanding the characteristics of our numeration system.

> **EXPONENTIAL NOTATION**
> If n is a natural number (1, 2, 3, and so on),
>
>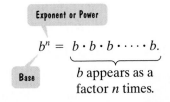
>
> $$b^n = \underbrace{b \cdot b \cdot b \cdots b.}_{b \text{ appears as a factor } n \text{ times.}}$$
>
> b^n is read "the nth power of b" or "b to the nth power." Thus, the nth power of b is defined as the product of n factors of b. The expression b^n is called an **exponential expression**. Furthermore, $b^1 = b$.

EXAMPLE 1   UNDERSTANDING EXPONENTIAL NOTATION

Evaluate the following:

a. 10^2 **b.** 10^3 **c.** 10^4 **d.** 2^6 **e.** 1^7 **f.** 7^1.

SOLUTION

a.

b. $10^3 = 10 \times 10 \times 10 = 1000$

c. $10^4 = 10 \times 10 \times 10 \times 10 = 10,000$

d. $2^6 = 2 \times 2 \times 2 \times 2 \times 2 \times 2 = 64$

e. $1^7 = 1 \times 1 \times 1 \times 1 \times 1 \times 1 \times 1 = 1$

f. $7^1 = 7$

 Evaluate the following:

a. 7^2 **b.** 5^3 **c.** 1^4 **d.** 10^5 **e.** 10^6 **f.** 18^1.

---

2 | Write a Hindu-Arabic numeral in expanded form.

Our Hindu-Arabic Numeration System

An important characteristic of our Hindu-Arabic system is that we can write the numeral for any number, large or small, using only ten symbols. The ten symbols that we use are

$$0, 1, 2, 3, 4, 5, 6, 7, 8, \text{ and } 9.$$

These symbols are called **digits**, from the Latin word for fingers.

With the use of exponents, Hindu-Arabic numerals can be written in **expanded form** in which the value of the digit in each position is made clear. In a Hindu-Arabic numeral, the place value of the first digit on the right is 1. The place value of the second digit from the right is 10. The place value of the third digit from the right is 100, or 10^2. For example, we can write 663 in expanded form by thinking of 663 as six 100s plus six 10s plus three 1s. This means that 663 in expanded form is

$$663 = (6 \times 100) + (6 \times 10) + (3 \times 1)$$
$$= (6 \times 10^2) + (6 \times 10^1) + (3 \times 1).$$

Because the value of a digit varies according to the position it occupies in a numeral, the Hindu-Arabic numeration system is called a **positional-value**, or **place-value**, system. The positional values in the system are based on powers of ten and are

$$\ldots, 10^5, 10^4, 10^3, 10^2, 10^1, 1.$$

Tally Sticks

This notched reindeer antler dates from 15,000 B.C. Humans learned how to keep track of numbers by tallying notches on bones with the same intelligence that led them to preserve and use fire, and at around the same time. Using tally sticks, early people grasped the idea that nine buffalo and nine sheep had something in common: the abstract idea of *nine*. As the human mind conceived of numbers separately from the things they represented, systems of numeration developed.

3 | Express a number's expanded form as a Hindu-Arabic numeral.

EXAMPLE 2 WRITING HINDU-ARABIC NUMERALS IN EXPANDED FORM

Write each of the following in expanded form:

a. 3407 **b.** 53,525.

SOLUTION

a. $3407 = (3 \times 10^3) + (4 \times 10^2) + (0 \times 10^1) + (7 \times 1)$

or $= (3 \times 1000) + (4 \times 100) + (0 \times 10) + (7 \times 1)$

Because $0 \times 10^1 = 0$, this term could be left out, but the expanded form is clearer when it is included.

b. $53,525 = (5 \times 10^4) + (3 \times 10^3) + (5 \times 10^2) + (2 \times 10^1) + (5 \times 1)$

or $= (5 \times 10,000) + (3 \times 1000) + (5 \times 100) + (2 \times 10) + (5 \times 1)$

 Write each of the following in expanded form:

a. 4026 **b.** 24,232.

EXAMPLE 3 EXPRESSING A NUMBER'S EXPANDED FORM AS A HINDU-ARABIC NUMERAL

Express each expanded form as a Hindu-Arabic numeral:

a. $(7 \times 10^3) + (5 \times 10^1) + (4 \times 1)$

b. $(6 \times 10^5) + (8 \times 10^1)$.

SOLUTION For clarification, we begin by showing all powers of ten, starting with the highest exponent given. Any power of ten that is left out is expressed as 0 times that power of ten.

a. $(7 \times 10^3) + (5 \times 10^1) + (4 \times 1)$

$= (7 \times 10^3) + (0 \times 10^2) + (5 \times 10^1) + (4 \times 1)$

$= 7054$

b. $(6 \times 10^5) + (8 \times 10^1)$

$= (6 \times 10^5) + (0 \times 10^4) + (0 \times 10^3) + (0 \times 10^2) + (8 \times 10^1) + (0 \times 1)$

$= 600,080$

 Express each expanded form as a Hindu-Arabic numeral:

a. $(6 \times 10^3) + (7 \times 10^1) + (3 \times 1)$

b. $(8 \times 10^4) + (9 \times 10^2)$.

Examples 2 and 3 show how there would be no Hindu-Arabic system without an understanding of zero and the invention of a symbol to represent nothingness. The system must have a symbol for zero to serve as a placeholder in case one or more powers of ten are not needed. The concept of zero was a new and radical invention, one that changed our ability to think about the world.

Early Positional Systems

Our Hindu-Arabic system developed over many centuries. Its digits can be found carved on ancient Hindu pillars over 2200 years old. In 1202, the Italian mathematician Leonardo Fibonacci (1170–1250) introduced the system to Europe, writing of its special characteristic: "With the nine Hindu digits and the Arab symbol 0, any number can be written." The Hindu-Arabic system came into widespread use only when printing was invented in the fifteenth century.

The Hindu-Arabic system uses powers of ten. However, positional systems can use powers of any number, not just 10. Think about our system of time, based on powers of 60:

Jasper Johns, *"Zero"*. © Jasper Johns/ Licensed by VAGA, New York, NY.

$$1 \text{ minute} = 60 \text{ seconds}$$
$$1 \text{ hour} = 60 \text{ minutes} = 60 \times 60 \text{ seconds} = 60^2 \text{ seconds.}$$

What is significant in a positional system is position and the powers that positions convey. The first early positional system that we will discuss uses powers of 60, just like those used for units of time.

The Babylonian Numeration System

4 | Understand and use the Babylonian numeration system.

The city of Babylon, 55 miles south of present-day Baghdad, was the center of Babylonian civilization that lasted for about 1400 years between 2000 B.C. and 600 B.C. The Babylonians used wet clay as a writing surface. Their clay tablets were heated and dried to give a permanent record of their work, which we are able to decipher and read today. Table 10.1 gives the numerals of this civilization's numeration system.

The place values in the Babylonian system use powers of 60. The place values are

TABLE 10.1 BABYLONIAN NUMERALS		
Babylonian numerals	∨	＜
Hindu-Arabic numerals	1	10

$$\ldots, \quad 60^3, \quad 60^2, \quad 60^1, \quad 1.$$

$60^3 = 60 \times 60 \times 60 = 216{,}000$ $60^2 = 60 \times 60 = 3600$

The Babylonians left a space to distinguish the various place values in a numeral from one another. For example,

∨   ＜   ∨∨

means

$$\downarrow \qquad \downarrow \qquad \downarrow$$
$$(1 \times 60^2) + (10 \times 60^1) + (1 + 1) \times 1$$
$$= (1 \times 3600) + (10 \times 60) + (2 \times 1)$$
$$= 3600 + 600 + 2 = 4202.$$

EXAMPLE 4   CONVERTING FROM A BABYLONIAN NUMERAL TO A HINDU-ARABIC NUMERAL

Write

∨∨   ＜∨   ＜＜∨∨

as a Hindu-Arabic numeral.

SOLUTION From left to right, the place values are 60^2, 60^1, and 1. Represent the numeral in each place as a familiar Hindu-Arabic numeral using Table 10.1.

Multiply each Hindu-Arabic numeral by its respective place value. Then find the sum of these products.

$$\mathsf{v\,v} \qquad\qquad \mathsf{<\,v} \qquad\qquad\qquad \mathsf{<\,<\,v\,v}$$

means

$$\downarrow \qquad\qquad\qquad \downarrow \qquad\qquad\qquad \downarrow$$

$$(1 + 1) \times 60^2 + (10 + 1) \times 60^1 + (10 + 10 + 1 + 1) \times 1$$

$$= (2 \times 60^2) + (11 \times 60^1) + (22 \times 1)$$

$$= (2 \times 3600) + (11 \times 60) + (22 \times 1)$$

$$= 7200 + 660 + 22 = 7882.$$

This sum indicates that the given Babylonian numeral is 7882 when written as a Hindu-Arabic numeral.

A major disadvantage of the Babylonian system is that it did not contain a symbol for zero. Some Babylonian tablets have a larger gap between the numerals or the insertion of the symbol $\lessgtr$ to indicate a missing place value, but this led to some ambiguity and confusion.

CHECK POINT 4 Write

$$\mathsf{v\,v\,v \quad <\,< \quad <\,<\,<\,v}$$

as a Hindu-Arabic numeral.

5 | Understand and use the Mayan numeration system.

The Mayan Numeration System

The Maya, a tribe of Central American Indians, lived on the Yucatan Peninsula. At its peak, between 300 and 1000 A.D., their civilization covered an area including parts of Mexico, all of Belize and Guatemala, and part of Honduras. They were famous for their magnificent architecture, their astronomical and mathematical knowledge, and their excellence in the arts. Their numeration system was the first to have a symbol for zero. Table 10.2 gives the Mayan numerals.

TABLE 10.2 MAYAN NUMERALS

0	1	2	3	4	5	6	7	8	9
⬯	•	••	•••	••••	—	•̲	••̲	•••̲	••••̲

10	11	12	13	14	15	16	17	18	19
═	•̳	••̳	•••̳	••••̳	≡	•̳̳	••̳̳	•••̳̳	••••̳̳

The place values in the Mayan system are

$$..., \quad 18 \times 20^3, \quad 18 \times 20^2, \quad 18 \times 20, \quad 20, \quad 1$$

$18 \times 20 \times 20 \times 20 = 144{,}000$ $18 \times 20 \times 20 = 7200$ $18 \times 20 = 360$

Notice that instead of giving the third position a place value of 20^2, the Mayans used 18×20. This was probably done so that their calendar year of 360 days would be a basic part of the numeration system.

Numerals in the Mayan system are expressed vertically. The place value at the bottom of the column is 1.

EXAMPLE 5   USING THE MAYAN NUMERATION SYSTEM

Write

as a Hindu-Arabic numeral.

SOLUTION The given Mayan numeral has four places. From top to bottom, the place values are 7200, 360, 20, and 1. Represent the numeral in each row as a familiar Hindu-Arabic numeral using Table 10.2. Multiply each Hindu-Arabic numeral by its respective place value. Then find the sum of these products.

Mayan numeral		Hindu-Arabic numeral		Place value		
⦁⦁⦁⦁	=	14	×	7200	=	100,800
⬯	=	0	×	360	=	0
⦁⦁	=	7	×	20	=	140
⦁⦁	=	12	×	1	=	12
						100,952

The sum on the right indicates that the given Mayan numeral is 100,952 when written as a Hindu-Arabic numeral.

CHECK POINT 5 Write

as a Hindu-Arabic numeral.

EXERCISE SET 10.1 ●●●●●●

• Practice Exercises

In Exercises 1–8, evaluate the expression.

1. 5^2 **2.** 6^2 **3.** 2^3 **4.** 4^3

5. 3^4 **6.** 2^4 **7.** 10^5 **8.** 10^6

In Exercises 9–22, write each Hindu-Arabic numeral in expanded form.

9. 36   **10.** 65   **11.** 249   **12.** 698

13. 703   **14.** 902   **15.** 4856   **16.** 5749

17. 3070   **18.** 9007   **19.** 34,569   **20.** 67,943

21. 230,007,004   **22.** 909,006,070

In Exercises 23–32, express each expanded form as a Hindu-Arabic numeral.

23. $(7 \times 10^1) + (3 \times 1)$

24. $(9 \times 10^1) + (4 \times 1)$

25. $(3 \times 10^2) + (8 \times 10^1) + (5 \times 1)$

26. $(7 \times 10^2) + (5 \times 10^1) + (3 \times 1)$

27. $(5 \times 10^5) + (2 \times 10^4) + (8 \times 10^3) + (7 \times 10^2)$
$+ (4 \times 10^1) + (3 \times 1)$

28. $(7 \times 10^6) + (4 \times 10^5) + (2 \times 10^4) + (3 \times 10^3)$
$\qquad\qquad\qquad + (1 \times 10^2) + (9 \times 10^1) + (6 \times 1)$

29. $(7 \times 10^3) + (0 \times 10^2) + (0 \times 10^1) + (2 \times 1)$

30. $(9 \times 10^4) + (0 \times 10^3) + (0 \times 10^2) + (4 \times 10^1)$
$\qquad\qquad\qquad\qquad\qquad + (5 \times 1)$

31. $(6 \times 10^8) + (2 \times 10^3) + (7 \times 1)$

32. $(3 \times 10^8) + (5 \times 10^4) + (4 \times 1)$

In Exercises 33–40, use Table 10.1 on page 581 to write each Babylonian numeral as a Hindu-Arabic numeral.

33. ⟨⟨∨∨∨
34. ⟨⟨⟨∨∨
35. ⟨⟨∨ ∨∨
36. ⟨⟨ ⟨∨∨
37. ∨∨∨ ⟨∨∨ ∨∨∨
38. ∨∨ ⟨∨ ⟨⟨∨∨
39. ⟨∨ ⟨∨ ⟨∨ ⟨∨
40. ⟨⟨ ⟨⟨ ⟨∨∨ ⟨∨∨

In Exercises 41–50, use Table 10.2 on page 582 to write each Mayan numeral as a Hindu-Arabic numeral.

41. ⁙⁙
42. ⁙⁖
43. ⁙⁙ / ⊙
44. ⁙⁖ / ⊙ / • / —
45. ⁙ / ⁙ / ⁙
46. • / • / •
47. •• / ⊙ / ⊙ / ⊙
48. ⁙ / — / ⊙
49. — / = / ⊙ / =
50. — / ⊙ / ⁙ / =

• Practice Plus

In Exercises 51–54, express the result of each addition as a Hindu-Arabic numeral in expanded form.

51. ∨ ⟨⟨ ⟨⟨∨ + ⟨∨ ⟨⟨⟨ ∨∨∨∨

52. ⟨∨ ⟨ ⟨∨∨∨ + ∨∨∨ ⟨⟨ ∨∨

53. • / • / • + — / ⊙ / ⁙

54. •• / — / •• + • / = / ⊙

If n is a natural number, then $10^{-n} = \dfrac{1}{10^n}$. Negative powers of 10 can be used to write the decimal part of Hindu-Arabic numerals in expanded form. For example,

$0.8302 = (8 \times 10^{-1}) + (3 \times 10^{-2}) + (0 \times 10^{-3}) + (2 \times 10^{-4})$

$\quad = \left(8 \times \dfrac{1}{10^1}\right) + \left(3 \times \dfrac{1}{10^2}\right) + \left(0 \times \dfrac{1}{10^3}\right) + \left(2 \times \dfrac{1}{10^4}\right)$

$\quad = \left(8 \times \dfrac{1}{10}\right) + \left(3 \times \dfrac{1}{100}\right) + \left(0 \times \dfrac{1}{1000}\right) + \left(2 \times \dfrac{1}{10,000}\right).$

In Exercises 55–62, express each expanded form as a Hindu-Arabic numeral.

55. $(4 \times 10^{-1}) + (7 \times 10^{-2}) + (5 \times 10^{-3}) + (9 \times 10^{-4})$

56. $(6 \times 10^{-1}) + (8 \times 10^{-2}) + (1 \times 10^{-3}) + (2 \times 10^{-4})$

57. $(7 \times 10^{-1}) + (2 \times 10^{-4}) + (3 \times 10^{-6})$

58. $(8 \times 10^{-1}) + (3 \times 10^{-4}) + (7 \times 10^{-6})$

59. $(5 \times 10^3) + (3 \times 10^{-2})$

60. $(7 \times 10^4) + (5 \times 10^{-3})$

61. $(3 \times 10^4) + (7 \times 10^2) + (5 \times 10^{-2}) + (8 \times 10^{-3})$
$\qquad\qquad\qquad\qquad\qquad + (9 \times 10^{-5})$

62. $(7 \times 10^5) + (3 \times 10^2) + (2 \times 10^{-1}) + (2 \times 10^{-3})$
$\qquad\qquad\qquad\qquad\qquad + (1 \times 10^{-5})$

• Application Exercises

The Chinese "rod system" of numeration is a base ten positional system. The digits for 1 through 9 are shown as follows:

The vertical digits in the second row are used for place values of 1, 10^2, 10^4, and all even powers of 10. The horizontal digits in the third row are used for place values of 10^1, 10^3, 10^5, 10^7, and all odd powers of 10. A blank space is used for the digit zero. In Exercises 63–66, write each Chinese "rod system" numeral as a Hindu-Arabic numeral.

63. ≣ 𝍡 ☰ ⏽⏽⏽⏽
64. ≣ 𝍡 ═ ⏽⏽⏽⏽⏽
65. ≣ ≣ 𝍡
66. ⏶ 𝍦 ⏽⏽

67. Humans have debated for decades about what messages should be sent to the stars to grab the attention of extraterrestrials and demonstrate our mathematical prowess. In the 1970s, Soviet scientists suggested we send the exponential message

$$10^2 + 11^2 + 12^2 = 13^2 + 14^2.$$

The Soviets called this equation "mind-catching." Evaluate the exponential expressions and verify that the sums on the two sides are equal. What is the significance of this sum?

• Writing in Mathematics

68. Describe the difference between a number and a numeral.

69. Explain how to evaluate 7^3.

70. What is the base in our Hindu-Arabic numeration system? What are the digits in the system?

71. Why is a symbol for zero needed in a positional system?

72. Explain how to write a Hindu-Arabic numeral in expanded form.

73. Describe one way that the Babylonian system is similar to the Hindu-Arabic system and one way that it is different from the Hindu-Arabic system.

74. Describe one way that the Mayan system is similar to the Hindu-Arabic system and one way that it is different from the Hindu-Arabic system.

75. **Research activity** Write a report on the history of the Hindu-Arabic system of numeration. Useful references include history of mathematics books, encyclopedias, and the World Wide Web.

• Critical Thinking Exercises

76. Write ∨ ＜∨∨ ＜∨ as a Mayan numeral.

77. Write •• as a Babylonian numeral.
         ••
         ••

78. Use Babylonian numerals to write the numeral that precedes and the numeral that follows:

$$\text{＜∨ ＜＜＜＜＜ ∨∨∨∨∨∨∨∨∨.}$$

• Group Exercise

79. Your group task is to create an original positional numeration system that is different from the three systems discussed in this section.

    a. Construct a table showing your numerals and the corresponding Hindu-Arabic numerals.

    b. Explain how to represent numbers in your system, and express a three-digit and a four-digit Hindu-Arabic numeral in your system.

SECTION 10.2 • NUMBER BASES IN POSITIONAL SYSTEMS

OBJECTIVES

1. Change numerals in bases other than ten to base ten.
2. Change base ten numerals to numerals in other bases.

You are being drawn deeper into cyberspace, spending more time online each week. With constantly improving high-resolution images, cyberspace is reshaping your life by nourishing shared enthusiasms. The people who built your computer talk of "incredible bandwidth" that will give you the visual experience, in high-definition 3-D format, of being in the same room with a person who is actually in another city.

Because of our ten fingers and ten toes, the base ten Hindu-Arabic system seems to be an obvious choice. However, it is not base ten that computers use to process information and communicate with one another. Your experiences in cyberspace are sustained with a binary, or base two, system. In this section, we study numeration systems with bases other than ten. An understanding of such systems will help you to appreciate the nature of a positional system. You will also attain a better understanding of the computations you have used all of your life. You will even get to see how the world looks from a computer's point of view.

1 | Change numerals in bases other than ten to base ten.

Changing Numerals in Bases Other Than Ten to Base Ten

The base of a positional numeration system refers to the number of individual digit symbols that can be used in that system as well as to the number whose powers define the place values. For example, the digit symbols in a base five system are 0, 1, 2, 3, and 10. The place values in a base five system are powers of 5:

$$\ldots, 5^4, 5^3, 5^2, 5^1, 1$$
$$= \ldots, 5 \times 5 \times 5 \times 5, 5 \times 5 \times 5, 5 \times 5, 5, 1$$
$$= \ldots, 625, 125, 25, 5, 1.$$

When a numeral appears without a subscript, it is assumed that the base is ten. Bases other than ten are indicated with a spelled-out subscript, as in the numeral

$$122_{\text{five}}.$$

This numeral is read "one two two base five." Do not read it as "one hundred twenty two" because that terminology implies a base ten numeral, naming 122 in base ten.

We can convert 122_{five} to a base ten numeral by following the same procedure used in Section 10.1 to change the Babylonian and Mayan numerals to base ten Hindu-Arabic numerals. In the case of 122_{five}, the numeral has three places. From left to right, the place values are 5^2, 5^1, and 1. Multiply each digit in the numeral by its respective place value. Then add these products.

$$
\begin{aligned}
122_{\text{five}} &= (1 \times 5^2) + (2 \times 5^1) + (2 \times 1) \\
&= (1 \times 25) + (2 \times 5) + (2 \times 1) \\
&= 25 + 10 + 2 \\
&= 37
\end{aligned}
$$

Thus,

$$122_{\text{five}} = 37.$$

In base five, we do not need a digit symbol for 5 because

$$10_{\text{five}} = (1 \times 5^1) + (0 \times 1) = 5.$$

Likewise, the base ten numeral 6 is represented as 11_{five}, the base ten numeral 7 as 12_{five}, and so on. Table 10.3 shows base ten numerals from 0 through 20 and their base five equivalents.

In any base, the digit symbols begin at 0 and go up to one less than the base. In base b, the digit symbols begin at 0 and go up to $b - 1$. The place values in a base b system are powers of b:

$$\dots, b^4, b^3, b^2, b, 1.$$

Table 10.4 shows the digit symbols and place values in various bases.

TABLE 10.3

Base Ten	Base Five
0	0
1	1
2	2
3	3
4	4
5	10
6	11
7	12
8	13
9	14
10	20
11	21
12	22
13	23
14	24
15	30
16	31
17	32
18	33
19	34
20	40

TABLE 10.4 DIGIT SYMBOLS AND PLACE VALUES IN VARIOUS BASES

Base	Digit Symbols	Place Values
two	$0, 1$	$\dots, 2^4, 2^3, 2^2, 2^1, 1$
three	$0, 1, 2$	$\dots, 3^4, 3^3, 3^2, 3^1, 1$
four	$0, 1, 2, 3$	$\dots, 4^4, 4^3, 4^2, 4^1, 1$
five	$0, 1, 2, 3, 4$	$\dots, 5^4, 5^3, 5^2, 5^1, 1$
six	$0, 1, 2, 3, 4, 5$	$\dots, 6^4, 6^3, 6^2, 6^1, 1$
seven	$0, 1, 2, 3, 4, 5, 6$	$\dots, 7^4, 7^3, 7^2, 7^1, 1$
eight	$0, 1, 2, 3, 4, 5, 6, 7$	$\dots, 8^4, 8^3, 8^2, 8^1, 1$
nine	$0, 1, 2, 3, 4, 5, 6, 7, 8$	$\dots, 9^4, 9^3, 9^2, 9^1, 1$
ten	$0, 1, 2, 3, 4, 5, 6, 7, 8, 9$	$\dots, 10^4, 10^3, 10^2, 10^1, 1$

We have seen that in base five, 10_{five} represents one group of 5 and no groups of 1. Thus, $10_{\text{five}} = 5$. Similarly, in base six, 10_{six} represents one group of 6 and no groups of 1. Thus, $10_{\text{six}} = 6$. In general $10_{\text{base } b}$ represents one group of b and no groups of 1. This means that $10_{\text{base } b} = b$.

Here is the procedure for changing a numeral in a base other than ten to base ten:

> ### CHANGING TO BASE TEN
> To change a numeral in a base other than ten to a base ten numeral,
> 1. Find the place value for each digit in the numeral.
> 2. Multiply each digit in the numeral by its respective place value.
> 3. Find the sum of the products in step 2.

TECHNOLOGY

You can use a calculator to convert to base ten. For example, to convert 4726_{eight} to base ten, press the following keys:

MANY SCIENTIFIC CALCULATORS

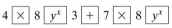

$4 \times 8 \boxed{y^x} 3 + 7 \times 8 \boxed{y^x}$
$2 + 2 \times 8 + 6 \boxed{=}$

MANY GRAPHING CALCULATORS

$4 \times 8 \boxed{\wedge} 3 + 7 \times 8 \boxed{\wedge} 2$
$+ 2 \times 8 + 6 \boxed{\text{ENTER}}$.

BLITZER BONUS

Letters and Words in Base Two

Wilhelm Leibniz (1646–1716)

Letters are converted into base two numbers for computer processing. A through Z are assigned 65 through 90, with each number expressed in base two. Thus, the binary code for A(65) is 1000001. Similarly, a through z are assigned 97 through 122 in base two.

The German mathematician Wilhelm Leibniz was the first modern thinker to promote the base two system. He never imagined that one day the base two system would enable computers to process information and communicate with one another.

EXAMPLE 1   CONVERTING TO BASE TEN

Convert 4726_{eight} to base ten.

SOLUTION The given base eight numeral has four places. From left to right, the place values are

$$8^3, 8^2, 8^1, \text{ and } 1.$$

Multiply each digit in the numeral by its respective place value. Then find the sum of these products.

Place value: 8^3	Place value: 8^2	Place value: 8^1	Place value: 1
4	7	2	6_{eight}

$$
\begin{aligned}
4726_{\text{eight}} &= (4 \times 8^3) + (7 \times 8^2) + (2 \times 8^1) + (6 \times 1) \\
&= (4 \times 8 \times 8 \times 8) + (7 \times 8 \times 8) + (2 \times 8) + (6 \times 1) \\
&= 2048 + 448 + 16 + 6 \\
&= 2518
\end{aligned}
$$

 Convert 3422_{five} to base ten.

EXAMPLE 2   CONVERTING TO BASE TEN

Convert 100101_{two} to base ten.

SOLUTION Multiply each digit in the numeral by its respective place value. Then find the sum of these products.

Place value: 2^5	Place value: 2^4	Place value: 2^3	Place value: 2^2	Place value: 2^1	Place value: 1
1	0	0	1	0	1_{two}

$$
\begin{aligned}
100101_{\text{two}} &= (1 \times 2^5) + (0 \times 2^4) + (0 \times 2^3) + (1 \times 2^2) + (0 \times 2^1) + (1 \times 1) \\
&= (1 \times 32) + (0 \times 16) + (0 \times 8) + (1 \times 4) + (0 \times 2) + (1 \times 1) \\
&= 32 + 0 + 0 + 4 + 0 + 1 \\
&= 37
\end{aligned}
$$

 Convert 110011_{two} to base ten.

The word *digital* in computer technology refers to a method of encoding numbers, letters, visual images, and sounds using a **binary**, or base two, **system** of 0s and 1s. Because computers use electrical signals that are groups of on–off pulses of electricity, the digits in base two are convenient. In binary code, 1 indicates the passage of an electrical pulse ("on") and 0 indicates its interruption ("off"). For example, the number 37 (100101_{two}) becomes the binary code on–off–off–on–off–on. Microchips in a computer store and process these binary signals.

In addition to base two, computer applications often involve base eight, called an **octal system**, and base sixteen, called a **hexadecimal system**. Base sixteen presents a problem because digit symbols are needed from 0 up to one less than the base. This means that we need more digit symbols than the ten (0, 1, 2, 3, 4, 5, 6, 7, 8, and 9) used in our base ten system. Computer programmers use the letters A, B, C, D, E, and F as base sixteen digit symbols for the numbers ten through fifteen, respectively.

Additional digit symbols in base sixteen:

A = 10   B = 11
C = 12   D = 13
E = 14   F = 15

EXAMPLE 3   CONVERTING TO BASE TEN

Convert $EC7_{sixteen}$ to base ten.

SOLUTION From left to right, the place values are

$$16^2, 16^1, \text{ and } 1.$$

The digit symbol E represents 14 and the digit symbol C represents 12. Although this numeral looks a bit strange, follow the usual procedure: Multiply each digit in the numeral by its respective place value. Then find the sum of these products.

Place value: 16^2	Place value: 16^1	Place value: 1
E	C	$7_{sixteen}$
E = 14	C = 12	

$$
\begin{aligned}
EC7_{sixteen} &= (14 \times 16^2) + (12 \times 16^1) + (7 \times 1) \\
&= (14 \times 16 \times 16) + (12 \times 16) + (7 \times 1) \\
&= 3584 + 192 + 7 \\
&= 3783
\end{aligned}
$$

 CHECK POINT 3 Convert $AD4_{sixteen}$ to base ten.

---

2 | Change base ten numerals to numerals in other bases.

Changing Base Ten Numerals to Numerals in Other Bases

To convert a base ten numeral to a numeral in a base other than ten, we need to find how many groups of each place value are contained in the base ten numeral. When the base ten numeral consists of one or two digits, we can do this mentally. For example, suppose that we want to convert the base ten numeral 6 to a base four numeral. The place values in base four are

$$\ldots, 4^3, 4^2, 4, 1.$$

The place values that are less than 6 are 4 and 1. We can express 6 as one group of four and two ones:

$$6_{ten} = (1 \times 4) + (2 \times 1) = 12_{four}.$$

EXAMPLE 4   A MENTAL CONVERSION FROM BASE TEN TO BASE FIVE

Convert the base ten numeral 8 to a base five numeral.

SOLUTION The place values in base five are

$$\ldots, 5^3, 5^2, 5, 1.$$

The place values that are less than 8 are 5 and 1. We can express 8 as one group of five and three ones:

$$8_{ten} = (1 \times 5) + (3 \times 1) = 13_{five}.$$

 CHECK POINT 4 Convert the base ten numeral 6 to a base five numeral.

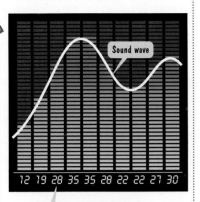
If a conversion cannot be performed mentally, you can use divisions to determine how many groups of each place value are contained in a base ten numeral.

EXAMPLE 5   USING DIVISIONS TO CONVERT FROM BASE TEN TO BASE EIGHT

Convert the base ten numeral 299 to a base eight numeral.

SOLUTION The place values in base eight are

$$\ldots, 8^3, 8^2, 8^1, 1, \quad \text{or} \quad \ldots, 512, 64, 8, 1.$$

The place values that are less than 299 are 64, 8, and 1. We can use divisions to show how many groups of each of these place values are contained in 299. Divide 299 by 64. Divide the remainder by 8.

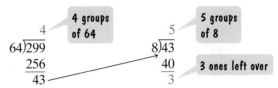

These divisions show that 299 can be expressed as 4 groups of 64, 5 groups of 8, and 3 ones:

$$\begin{aligned}
299 &= (4 \times 64) + (5 \times 8) + (3 \times 1) \\
&= (4 \times 8^2) + (5 \times 8^1) + (3 \times 1) \\
&= 453_{\text{eight}}.
\end{aligned}$$

CHECK POINT 5 Convert the base ten numeral 365 to a base seven numeral.

EXAMPLE 6   USING DIVISIONS TO CONVERT FROM BASE TEN TO BASE SIX

Convert the base ten numeral 3444 to a base six numeral.

SOLUTION The place values in base six are

$$\ldots, 6^5, 6^4, 6^3, 6^2, 6^1, 1, \quad \text{or} \quad \ldots, 7776, 1296, 216, 36, 6, 1.$$

We use the powers of 6 that are less than 3444 and perform successive divisions by these powers.

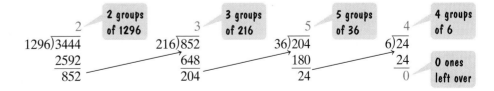

Using these four quotients and the final remainder, we can immediately write the answer.

$$3444 = 23540_{\text{six}}$$

CHECK POINT 6 Convert the base ten numeral 2763 to a base five numeral.

EXERCISE SET 10.2 ●●●●●●

• Practice Exercises

In Exercises 1–18, convert the numeral to a numeral in base ten.

1. 43_{five} **2.** 34_{five} **3.** 52_{eight}

4. 67_{eight} **5.** 132_{four} **6.** 321_{four}

7. 1011_{two} **8.** 1101_{two} **9.** 2035_{six}

10. 2073_{nine} **11.** 70355_{eight} **12.** 41502_{six}

13. 2096_{sixteen} **14.** 3104_{fifteen} **15.** 110101_{two}

16. 101101_{two} **17.** $\text{ACE5}_{\text{sixteen}}$ **18.** $\text{EDF7}_{\text{sixteen}}$

In Exercises 19–28, mentally convert each base ten numeral to a numeral in the given base.

19. 7 to base five   **20.** 9 to base five

21. 11 to base seven   **22.** 12 to base seven

23. 2 to base two   **24.** 3 to base two

25. 13 to base four   **26.** 19 to base four

27. 37 to base six   **28.** 25 to base six

In Exercises 29–40, use divisions to convert each base ten numeral to a numeral in the given base.

29. 87 to base five   **30.** 85 to base seven

31. 108 to base four   **32.** 199 to base four

33. 19 to base two   **34.** 23 to base two

35. 138 to base three   **36.** 129 to base three

37. 386 to base six   **38.** 428 to base nine

39. 1599 to base seven   **40.** 1346 to base eight

• Practice Plus

In Exercises 41–44, use Table 10.1 on page 581 to write each Hindu-Arabic numeral as a Babylonian numeral.

41. 3052   **42.** 6704   **43.** 23,546   **44.** 41,265

In Exercises 45–48, use Table 10.2 on page 582 to write each Hindu-Arabic numeral as a Mayan numeral.

45. 9307   **46.** 8703   **47.** 28,704   **48.** 34,847

49. Convert 34_{five} to base seven.

50. Convert 46_{eight} to base five.

51. Convert 110010011_{two} to base eight.

52. Convert 101110001_{two} to base eight.

• Application Exercises

Read the Blitzer Bonus on page 587. Then use the information in the essay to solve Exercises 53–60.

In Exercises 53–56, write the binary representation for each letter.

53. F   **54.** Y   **55.** m   **56.** p

In Exercises 57–58, break each binary sequence into groups of seven digits and write the word represented by the sequence.

57. 101000010000011001100

58. 100110010101011000011001011

In Exercises 59–60, write a sequence of binary digits that represents each word.

59. Mom   **60.** Dad

• Writing in Mathematics

61. Explain how to determine the place values for a four-digit numeral in base six.

62. Describe how to change a numeral in a base other than ten to a base ten numeral.

63. Describe how to change a base ten numeral to a numeral in another base.

• Critical Thinking Exercises

In Exercises 64–65, write in the indicated base the counting numbers that precede and follow the number expressed by the given numeral.

64. 888_{nine}

65. $\text{EC5}_{\text{sixteen}}$

66. Arrange from smallest to largest:

$$11111011_{\text{two}}, 3A6_{\text{twelve}}, 673_{\text{eight}}.$$

• Group Exercises

The following topics are appropriate for either individual or group research projects. A report should be given to the class on the researched topic. Useful references include history of mathematics books, books whose purpose is to excite the reader about mathematics, encyclopedias, and the World Wide Web.

67. Societies that Use Numeration Systems with Bases Other Than Ten

68. The Use of Fingers to Represent Numbers

69. Applications of Bases Other Than Ten

70. Binary, Octal, Hexadecimal Bases and Computers

71. Babylonian and Mayan Civilizations and Their Contributions

SECTION 10.3 • COMPUTATION IN POSITIONAL SYSTEMS

People have always looked for ways to make calculations faster and easier. The Hindu-Arabic system of numeration made computation simpler and less mysterious. More people were able to perform computation with ease, leading to the widespread use of the system.

All computations in bases other than ten are performed exactly like those in base ten. However, when a computation is equal to or exceeds the given base, use the mental conversions discussed in the previous section to convert from the base ten numeral to a numeral in the desired base.

$\boxed{1}$ Add in bases other than ten.

The 4^1, or fours' column   **The ones' column**

$$33_{\text{four}}$$
$$+\ 13_{\text{four}}$$

Addition

EXAMPLE 1   ADDITION IN BASE FOUR

Add:

$$33_{\text{four}}$$
$$+\ 13_{\text{four}}.$$

SOLUTION We will begin by adding the numbers in the right-hand column. In base four, the digit symbols are 0, 1, 2, and 3. If a sum in this, or any, column exceeds 3, we will have to convert this base ten number to base four. We begin by adding the numbers in the right-hand, or ones', column:

$$3_{\text{four}} + 3_{\text{four}} = 6.$$

6 is not a digit symbol in base four. However, we can express 6 as one group of four and two ones left over:

$$3_{\text{four}} + 3_{\text{four}} = 6_{\text{ten}} = (1 \times 4) + (2 \times 1) = 12_{\text{four}}.$$

Now we record the sum of the right-hand column, 12_{four}:

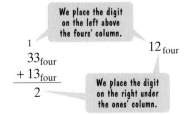

We place the digit on the left above the fours' column.

$$\begin{array}{r} 1 \\ 33_{\text{four}} \\ +\ 13_{\text{four}} \\ \hline 2 \end{array} \qquad 12_{\text{four}}$$

We place the digit on the right under the ones' column.

Next, we add the three digits in the fours' column:

$$1_{\text{four}} + 3_{\text{four}} + 1_{\text{four}} = 5.$$

5 is not a digit symbol in base four. However, we can express 5 as one group of four and one left over:

$$1_{\text{four}} + 3_{\text{four}} + 1_{\text{four}} = 5_{\text{ten}} = (1 \times 4) + (1 \times 1) = 11_{\text{four}}.$$

Record the 11_{four}.

$$
\begin{array}{r}
1 \\
33_{\text{four}} \\
+\ 13_{\text{four}} \\
\hline
112_{\text{four}}
\end{array}
$$

This is the desired sum.

You can check the sum by converting $33_{\text{four}}, 13_{\text{four}},$ and 112_{four} to base ten: $33_{\text{four}} = 15, 13_{\text{four}} = 7,$ and $112_{\text{four}} = 22.$ Because $15 + 7 = 22,$ our work is correct.

CHECK POINT **1** Add:

$$
\begin{array}{r}
32_{\text{five}} \\
+\ 44_{\text{five}}
\end{array}.
$$

EXAMPLE 2   ADDITION IN BASE TWO

Add:

$$
\begin{array}{r}
111_{\text{two}} \\
+\ 101_{\text{two}}
\end{array}.
$$

SOLUTION We begin by adding the numbers in the right-hand, or ones', column:

$$1_{\text{two}} + 1_{\text{two}} = 2.$$

2 is not a digit symbol in base two. We can express 2 as one group of 2 and zero ones left over:

$$1_{\text{two}} + 1_{\text{two}} = 2_{\text{ten}} = (1 \times 2) + (0 \times 1) = 10_{\text{two}}.$$

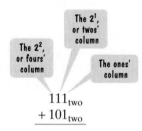

The 2^2, or fours' column

The 2^1, or twos' column

The ones' column

$$
\begin{array}{r}
111_{\text{two}} \\
+\ 101_{\text{two}}
\end{array}
$$

Now we record the sum of the right-hand column, 10_{two}:

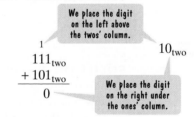

We place the digit on the left above the twos' column.

$$
\begin{array}{r}
1 \\
111_{\text{two}} \\
+\ 101_{\text{two}} \\
\hline
0
\end{array}
\qquad 10_{\text{two}}
$$

We place the digit on the right under the ones' column.

Next, we add the three digits in the twos' column:

$$1_{\text{two}} + 1_{\text{two}} + 0_{\text{two}} = 2_{\text{ten}} = (1 \times 2) + (0 \times 1) = 10_{\text{two}}.$$

Now we record the sum of the middle column, 10_{two}:

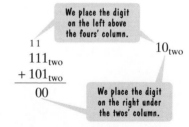

We place the digit on the left above the fours' column.

$$
\begin{array}{r}
1\ 1 \\
111_{\text{two}} \\
+\ 101_{\text{two}} \\
\hline
00
\end{array}
\qquad 10_{\text{two}}
$$

We place the digit on the right under the twos' column.

Finally, we add the three digits in the fours' column:

$$1_{\text{two}} + 1_{\text{two}} + 1_{\text{two}} = 3.$$

3 is not a digit symbol in base two. We can express 3 as one group of 2 and one 1 left over:

$$1_{\text{two}} + 1_{\text{two}} + 1_{\text{two}} = 3_{\text{ten}} = (1 \times 2) + (1 \times 1) = 11_{\text{two}}.$$

Record the 11_{two}.

$$
\begin{array}{r}
\overset{1\,1}{111_{two}} \\
+\ 101_{two} \\
\hline
1100_{two}
\end{array}
$$

This is the desired sum.

You can check the sum by converting to base ten: $111_{two} = 7$, $101_{two} = 5$, and $1100_{two} = 12$. Because $7 + 5 = 12$, our work is correct.

CHECK POINT 2 Add:

$$
\begin{array}{r}
111_{two} \\
+\ 111_{two}.
\end{array}
$$

Subtraction

To subtract in bases other than ten, we line up the digits with the same place values and subtract column by column, beginning with the column on the right. If "borrowing" is necessary to perform the subtraction, borrow the amount of the base. For example, when we borrow in base ten subtraction, we borrow 10s. Likewise, we borrow 2s in base two, 3s in base three, 4s in base four, and so on.

EXAMPLE 3   SUBTRACTION IN BASE FOUR

Subtract:

$$
\begin{array}{r}
31_{four} \\
-\ 12_{four}.
\end{array}
$$

SOLUTION We start by performing subtraction in the right column, $1_{four} - 2_{four}$. Because 2_{four} is greater than 1_{four}, we need to borrow from the preceding column. We are working in base four, so we borrow one group of 4. This gives a sum of $4 + 1$, or 5, in base ten. Now we subtract 2 from 5, obtaining a difference of 3:

We borrow one group of 4. Now there are 2 groups of 4 for this place value, not 3.

$$
\begin{array}{r}
\overset{2\,5}{\cancel{3}1_{four}} \\
-\ 12_{four} \\
\hline
3_{four}
\end{array}
$$

We add the borrowed group of 4 to 1 in base ten: $1 + 4 = 5$.

Now we perform the subtraction in the second column from the right:

We subtract 1 from 2.

$$
\begin{array}{r}
\overset{2\,5}{\cancel{3}1_{four}} \\
-\ 12_{four} \\
\hline
13_{four}
\end{array}
$$

This is the desired difference.

You can check the difference by converting to base ten: $31_{four} = 13$, $12_{four} = 6$, and $13_{four} = 7$. Because $13 - 6 = 7$, our work is correct.

CHECK POINT 3 Subtract:

$$
\begin{array}{r}
41_{five} \\
-\ 23_{five}.
\end{array}
$$

---

2 Subtract in bases other than ten.

3 | Multiply in bases other than ten.

EXAMPLE 4 SUBTRACTION IN BASE FIVE

Subtract:

$$3431_{five} - 1242_{five}.$$

SOLUTION

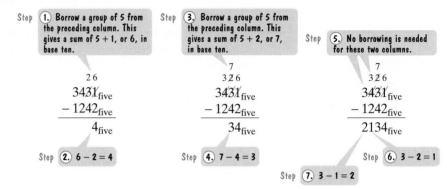

Step ① Borrow a group of 5 from the preceding column. This gives a sum of 5 + 1, or 6, in base ten.

Step ② 6 − 2 = 4

Step ③ Borrow a group of 5 from the preceding column. This gives a sum of 5 + 2, or 7, in base ten.

Step ④ 7 − 4 = 3

Step ⑤ No borrowing is needed for these two columns.

Step ⑥ 3 − 2 = 1

Step ⑦ 3 − 1 = 2

Thus, $3431_{five} - 1242_{five} = 2134_{five}$.

CHECK POINT 4 Subtract: $5144_{seven} - 3236_{seven}$.

Multiplication

EXAMPLE 5 MULTIPLICATION IN BASE SIX

Multiply:

$$\begin{array}{r} 34_{six} \\ \times\ 2_{six} \end{array}.$$

SOLUTION We multiply just as we do in base ten. That is, first we will multiply the digit 2 by the digit 4 directly above it. Then we will multiply the digit 2 by the digit 3 in the left column. Keep in mind that only the digit symbols 0, 1, 2, 3, 4, and 5 are permitted in base six. We begin with

$$2_{six} \times 4_{six} = 8_{ten} = (1 \times 6) + (2 \times 1) = 12_{six}.$$

Record the 2 and carry the 1:

$$\begin{array}{r} \overset{1}{34}_{six} \\ \times\ 2_{six} \\ \hline 2_{six} \end{array}.$$

Our next computation involves both multiplication and addition:

$$(2_{six} \times 3_{six}) + 1_{six} = 6 + 1 = 7_{ten} = (1 \times 6) + (1 \times 1) = 11_{six}.$$

Record the 11_{six}.

$$\begin{array}{r} 34_{six} \\ \times\ 2_{six} \\ \hline 112_{six} \end{array}$$

This is the desired product.

Let's check the product by converting to base ten: $34_{six} = 22$, $2_{six} = 2$, and $112_{six} = 44$. Because $22 \times 2 = 44$, our work is correct.

CHECK POINT 5 Multiply:

$$\begin{array}{r} 45_{seven} \\ \times\ 3_{seven} \end{array}.$$

4   Divide in bases other than ten.

Division

The answer in a division problem is called a **quotient**. A multiplication table showing products in the same base as the division problem is helpful.

EXAMPLE 6   DIVISION IN BASE FOUR

Use Table 10.5, showing products in base four, to perform the following division:

$$3_{four}\overline{)222_{four}}.$$

SOLUTION We can use the same method to divide in base four that we use in base ten. Begin by dividing 22_{four} by 3_{four}. Use Table 10.5 to find in the vertical column headed by 3 the largest product that is less than or equal to 22_{four}. This product is 21_{four}. Because $3_{four} \times 3_{four} = 21_{four}$, the first number in the quotient is 3_{four}.

TABLE 10.5 MULTIPLICATION: BASE FOUR

×	0	1	2	3
0	0	0	0	0
1	0	1	2	3
2	0	2	10	12
3	0	3	12	21

Divisor → $3_{four}\overline{)222_{four}}$ ← Dividend, with quotient 3, First digit in the quotient

Now multiply $3_{four} \times 3_{four}$ and write the product, 21_{four}, under the first two digits of the dividend.

$$\begin{array}{r} 3 \\ 3_{four}\overline{)222_{four}} \\ 21 \end{array}$$

Subtract: $22_{four} - 21_{four} = 1_{four}$.

$$\begin{array}{r} 3 \\ 3_{four}\overline{)222_{four}} \\ \underline{21} \\ 1 \end{array}$$

Bring down the next digit in the dividend, 2_{four}.

$$\begin{array}{r} 3 \\ 3_{four}\overline{)222_{four}} \\ \underline{21} \\ 12 \end{array}$$

We now return to Table 10.5. Find in the vertical column headed by 3 the largest product that is less than or equal to 12_{four}. Because $3_{four} \times 2_{four} = 12_{four}$, the next numeral in the quotient is 2_{four}. We use this information to finish the division.

This is the desired quotient.

$$\begin{array}{r} 32_{four} \\ 3_{four}\overline{)222_{four}} \\ \underline{21} \\ 12 \\ \underline{12} \\ 0 \end{array}$$

Let's check the quotient by converting to base ten: $3_{four} = 3$, $222_{four} = 42$, and $32_{four} = 14$. Because $3\overline{)42}^{\,14}$, our work is correct.

○

CHECK POINT 6   Use Table 10.5, showing products in base four, to perform the following division:

$$2_{four}\overline{)112_{four}}.$$

BLITZER BONUS

Base Two, Logic, and Computers

Smaller than a fingernail, a computer's microchip operates like a tiny electronic brain. The microchip in Figure 10.2 is magnified almost 1200 times, revealing transistors with connecting tracks positioned above them. These tiny transistors switch on and off to control electronic signals, processing thousands of pieces of information per second. Since 1971, the number of transistors that can fit onto a single chip has increased from over 2000 to a staggering 500 million.

We have seen that communication inside a computer takes the form of sequences of on–off electric pulses that digitally represent numbers, words, sounds, and visual images. These binary streams are manipulated when they pass through the microchip's gates, shown in Figure 10.3. The **not gate** takes a digital sequence and changes all the 0s to 1s and all the 1s to 0s.

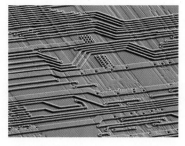

FIGURE 10.2

The *and* and *or gates* take two input sequences and produce one output sequence. The **and gate** outputs a 1 if both sequences have a 1; otherwise, it outputs a 0.

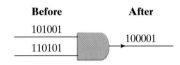

The **or gate** outputs a 1 if either sequence has a 1; otherwise, it outputs a 0.

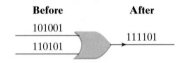

These gates are at the computational heart of a computer. They should remind you of negation, conjunction, and disjunction in logic, except that T is now 1 and F is now 0. Without the merging of base two and logic, computers as we know them would not exist.

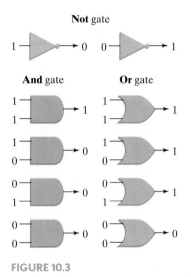

FIGURE 10.3

EXERCISE SET 10.3 ●●●●●●

• Practice Exercises

In Exercises 1–12, add in the indicated base.

1. 23_{four}
$+ 13_{four}$

2. 31_{four}
$+ 22_{four}$

3. 11_{two}
$+ 11_{two}$

4. 101_{two}
$+ \ 11_{two}$

5. 342_{five}
$+ 413_{five}$

6. 323_{five}
$+ 421_{five}$

7. 645_{seven}
$+ 324_{seven}$

8. 632_{seven}
$+ 564_{seven}$

9. 6784_{nine}
$+ 7865_{nine}$

10. 1021_{three}
$+ 2011_{three}$

11. 14632_{seven}
$+ \ 5604_{seven}$

12. $53B_{sixteen}$
$+ 694_{sixteen}$

In Exercises 13–24, subtract in the indicated base.

13. 32_{four}
$- 13_{four}$

14. 21_{four}
$- 12_{four}$

15. 23_{five}
$- 14_{five}$

16. 32_{seven}
$- 16_{seven}$

17. 475_{eight}
$- 267_{eight}$

18. 712_{nine}
$- 483_{nine}$

19. 563_{seven}
$- 164_{seven}$

20. 462_{eight}
$- 177_{eight}$

21. 1001_{two}
$- \ 111_{two}$

22. 1000_{two}
$- \ 101_{two}$

23. 1200_{three}
$- 1012_{three}$

24. $4C6_{sixteen}$
$- 198_{sixteen}$

In Exercises 25–34, multiply in the indicated base.

25. 25_{six}
$\times \ 4_{six}$

26. 34_{five}
$\times \ 3_{five}$

27. 11_{two}
$\times \ 1_{two}$

28. 21_{four}
$\times \ 3_{four}$

29. 543_{seven}
$\times \ 5_{seven}$

30. 243_{nine}
$\times \ 6_{nine}$

31. 623_{eight}
$\times \ 4_{eight}$

32. 543_{six}
$\times \ 5_{six}$

33. 21_{four}
$\times 12_{four}$

34. 32_{four}
$\times 23_{four}$

In Exercises 35–38, use the multiplication tables shown below to divide in the indicated base.

MULTIPLICATION: BASE FOUR

×	0	1	2	3
0	0	0	0	0
1	0	1	2	3
2	0	2	10	12
3	0	3	12	21

MULTIPLICATION: BASE FIVE

×	0	1	2	3	4
0	0	0	0	0	0
1	0	1	2	3	4
2	0	2	4	11	13
3	0	3	11	14	22
4	0	4	13	22	31

35. $2_{\text{four}}\overline{)100_{\text{four}}}$

36. $2_{\text{four}}\overline{)321_{\text{four}}}$

37. $3_{\text{five}}\overline{)224_{\text{five}}}$

38. $4_{\text{five}}\overline{)134_{\text{five}}}$

• Practice Plus

In Exercises 39–46, perform the indicated operations.

39. $10110_{\text{two}} + 10100_{\text{two}} + 11100_{\text{two}}$

40. $11100_{\text{two}} + 11111_{\text{two}} + 10111_{\text{two}}$

41. $11111_{\text{two}} + 10110_{\text{two}} - 101_{\text{two}}$

42. $10111_{\text{two}} + 11110_{\text{two}} - 111_{\text{two}}$

43. $1011_{\text{two}} \times 101_{\text{two}}$

44. $1101_{\text{two}} \times 110_{\text{two}}$

45. $D3_{\text{sixteen}} \times 8A_{\text{sixteen}}$

46. $B5_{\text{sixteen}} \times 2C_{\text{sixteen}}$

• Application Exercises

Read the Blitzer Bonus on page 596. Then use the information in the essay to solve Exercises 47–52. Each exercise shows the binary sequences 10011 and 11001 about to be manipulated by passing through a microchip's series of gates. Provide the result(s) of these computer manipulations, designated by   ?   *in each diagram.*

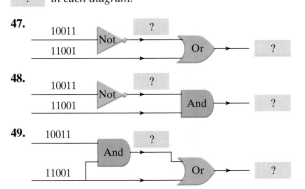

47.

48.

49.

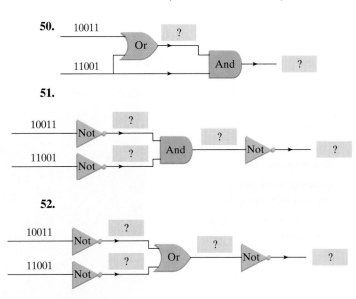

50.

51.

52.

53. Use the equivalence $p \rightarrow q \equiv \sim p \vee q$ to select the circuit in Exercises 47–52 that illustrates a conditional gate.

• Writing in Mathematics

54. Describe how to add two numbers in a base other than ten. How do you express and record the sum of numbers in a column if that sum exceeds the base?

55. Describe how to subtract two numbers in a base other than ten. How do you subtract a larger number from a smaller number in the same column?

56. Describe two difficulties that youngsters encounter when learning to add, subtract, multiply, and divide using Hindu-Arabic numerals. Base your answer on difficulties that are encountered when performing these computations in bases other than ten.

• Critical Thinking Exercises

57. Divide: $31_{\text{seven}}\overline{)2426_{\text{seven}}}$.

58. Use the Mayan numerals in Table 10.2 on page 582 to solve this exercise. Add $\overset{\bullet}{\underline{\quad}}$ and $\ominus$ without converting to Hindu-Arabic numerals.

• Group Exercises

59. Group members should research various methods that societies have used to perform computations. Include finger multiplication, the galley method (sometimes called the Gelosia method), Egyptian duplation, subtraction by complements, Napier's bones, and other methods of interest in your presentation to the entire class.

60. Organize a debate. One side represents people who favor performing computations by hand, using the methods and procedures discussed in this section, but applied to base ten numerals. The other side represents people who favor the use of calculators for performing all computations. Include the merits of each approach in the debate.

SECTION 10.4 • LOOKING BACK AT EARLY NUMERATION SYSTEMS

OBJECTIVES

1. Understand and use the Egyptian system.
2. Understand and use the Roman system.
3. Understand and use the traditional Chinese system.
4. Understand and use the Ionic Greek system.

Super Bowl XXV, played on January 27, 1991, resulted in the closest score of all time: NY Giants: 20; Buffalo: 19. If you are intrigued by sports facts and figures, you are probably aware that major sports events, such as the Super Bowl, are named using Roman numerals. Perhaps you have seen the use of Roman numerals in dating movies and television shows, or on clocks and watches.

In this section, we embark on a brief journey through time and numbers. Our Hindu-Arabic numeration system, the focus of this chapter, is successful because it expresses numbers with just ten symbols and makes computation with these numbers relatively easy. By these standards, the early numeration systems discussed in this section, such as Roman numerals, are unsuccessful. By looking briefly at these systems, you will see that our system is outstanding when compared with other historical systems.

1 | Understand and use the Egyptian system.

The Egyptian Numeration System

Like most great civilizations, ancient Egypt had several numeration systems. The oldest is hieroglyphic notation, which developed around 3400 B.C. Table 10.6 lists the Egyptian hieroglyphic numerals with the equivalent Hindu-Arabic numerals. Notice that the numerals are powers of ten. Their numeral for 1,000,000, or 10^6, looks like someone who just won the lottery!

STUDY TIP

It is not necessary to memorize the symbols for the four numeration systems discussed in this section. Focus your attention on understanding the idea behind each system and how these ideas have been incorporated into our Hindu-Arabic system.

TABLE 10.6 EGYPTIAN HIEROGLYPHIC NUMERALS		
Hindu-Arabic Numeral	**Egyptian Numeral**	**Description**
1			Staff
10	∩	Heel bone
100	◉	Spiral
1000	⚯	Lotus blossom
10,000	⌐	Pointing finger
100,000	⌒	Tadpole
1,000,000	⚚	Astonished person

It takes far more space to represent most numbers in the Egyptian system than in our system. This is because a number is expressed by repeating each numeral the required number of times. However, no numeral, except perhaps the astonished person, should be repeated more than nine times. If we were to use the Egyptian system to represent 764, we would need to write

100 100 100 100 100 100 100 10 10 10 10 10 10 10 1 1 1 1

and then represent each of these symbols with the appropriate hieroglyphic numeral from Table 10.6. Thus, 764 as an Egyptian numeral is

$$\text{⦿⦿⦿⦿⦿⦿⦿}\cap\cap\cap\cap\cap\cap\cap||||.$$

The ancient Egyptian system is an example of an **additive system**, one in which the number represented is the sum of the values of the numerals.

EXAMPLE 1 USING THE EGYPTIAN NUMERATION SYSTEM

Write the following numeral as a Hindu-Arabic numeral:

$$\text{⚱}\, \text{ℓℓℓ}\cap\cap\cap||||.$$

SOLUTION Using Table 10.6, find the value of each of the Egyptian numerals. Then add them.

$$1{,}000{,}000 + 10{,}000 + 10{,}000 + 10 + 10 + 10 + 1 + 1 + 1 + 1 = 1{,}020{,}034$$

○

CHECK POINT 1 Write the following numeral as a Hindu-Arabic numeral:

$$\text{ℐ ℐ ℐ}\,\text{⦿⦿}\cap\cap||.$$

EXAMPLE 2 USING THE EGYPTIAN NUMERATION SYSTEM

Write 1752 as an Egyptian numeral.

SOLUTION First break down the Hindu-Arabic numeral into quantities that match the Egyptian numerals:

$$1752 = 1000 + 700 + 50 + 2$$
$$= 1000 + 100 + 100 + 100 + 100 + 100 + 100 + 100$$
$$+ 10 + 10 + 10 + 10 + 10 + 1 + 1.$$

Now, use Table 10.6 to find the Egyptian symbol that matches each quantity. For example, the lotus blossom, ⚱, matches 1000. Write each of these symbols and leave out the addition signs. Thus, the number 1752 can be expressed as

$$\text{⚱}\,\text{⦿⦿⦿⦿⦿⦿⦿}\cap\cap\cap\cap\cap||.$$

○

CHECK POINT 2 Write 2563 as an Egyptian numeral.

2 | Understand and use the Roman system.

The Roman Numeration System

The Roman numeration system was developed between 500 B.C. and 100 A.D. It evolved as a result of tax collecting and commerce in the vast Roman Empire. The Roman numerals shown in Table 10.7 were used throughout Europe until the eighteenth century. They are still commonly used in outlining, on clocks, for certain copyright dates, and in numbering some pages in books. Roman numerals are selected letters from the Roman alphabet.

TABLE 10.7 ROMAN NUMERALS							
Roman numeral	I	V	X	L	C	D	M
Hindu-Arabic numeral	1	5	10	50	100	500	1000

If the symbols in Table 10.7 decrease in value from left to right, then add their values to obtain the value of the Roman numeral as a whole. For example, CX = 100 + 10 = 110. On the other hand, if symbols increase in value from left to right, then subtract the value of the symbol on the left from the symbol on the right. For example, IV means 5 − 1 = 4 and IX means 10 − 1 = 9.

Only the Roman numerals representing 1, 10, 100, 1000, . . . , can be subtracted. Furthermore, they can be subtracted only from their next two greater Roman numerals.

Roman numeral (values that can be subtracted are shown in red)	I	V	X	L	C	D	M
Hindu-Arabic numeral	1	5	10	50	100	500	1000

I can be subtracted only from V and X.   X can be subtracted only from L and C.   C can be subtracted only from D and M.

EXAMPLE 3   USING ROMAN NUMERALS

Write CLXVII as a Hindu-Arabic numeral.

SOLUTION Because the numerals decrease in value from left to right, we add their values to find the value of the Roman numeral as a whole.

$$CLXVII = 100 + 50 + 10 + 5 + 1 + 1 = 167$$

 Write MCCCLXI as a Hindu-Arabic numeral.

EXAMPLE 4   USING ROMAN NUMERALS

Write MCMXCVI as a Hindu-Arabic numeral.

SOLUTION

$$
\begin{array}{ccccccc}
M & & CM & & XC & V & I \\
\downarrow & & \downarrow & & \downarrow & \downarrow & \downarrow
\end{array}
$$
$$= 1000 + (1000 - 100) + (100 - 10) + 5 + 1$$
$$= 1000 + 900 + 90 + 5 + 1 = 1996$$

 Write MCDXLVII as a Hindu-Arabic numeral.

Have you ever noticed that clock faces with Roman numerals frequently show the number 4 as IIII instead of IV? One possible reason is that IIII provides aesthetic balance when visually paired with VIII on the other side. A more intriguing reason (although not necessarily true) is that the Romans did not want to offend the god Jupiter (spelled IVPITER) by daring to place the first two letters of his name on the face of a clock.

Because Roman numerals involve subtraction as well as addition, it takes far less space to represent most numbers than in the Egyptian system. It is never necessary to repeat any symbol more than three consecutive times. For example, we write 46 as a Roman numeral using

$$\text{XLVI} \quad \text{rather than} \quad \text{XXXXVI.}$$

> XL = 50 − 10 = 40

EXAMPLE 5   USING ROMAN NUMERALS

Write 249 as a Roman numeral.

SOLUTION

$$
\begin{aligned}
249 &= \quad 200 \quad + \quad 40 \quad + \quad 9 \\
&= 100 + 100 + (50 - 10) + (10 - 1) \\
&= \quad\;\; C \quad\;\;\; C \qquad\;\; XL \qquad\quad IX
\end{aligned}
$$

Thus, 249 = CCXLIX.

CHECK POINT 5   Write 399 as a Roman numeral.

The Roman numeration system uses bars above numerals or groups of numerals to show that the numbers are to be multiplied by 1000. For example,

$$\overline{\text{L}} = 50 \times 1000 = 50{,}000 \quad \text{and} \quad \overline{\text{CM}} = 900 \times 1000 = 900{,}000.$$

Placing bars over Roman numerals reduces the number of symbols needed to represent large numbers.

3 Understand and use the traditional Chinese system.

The Traditional Chinese Numeration System

The numerals used in the traditional Chinese numeration system are given in Table 10.8. At least two things are missing—a symbol for zero and a surprised lottery winner!

TABLE 10.8 TRADITIONAL CHINESE NUMERALS												
Traditional Chinese numerals	一	二	三	四	五	六	七	八	九	十	百	千
Hindu-Arabic numerals	1	2	3	4	5	6	7	8	9	10	100	1000

3
1000
2
100
6
10
4

Representing 3264 vertically is the first step in expressing it as a Chinese numeral.

So, how are numbers represented with this set of symbols? Chinese numerals are written vertically. Using our digits, the number 3264 is expressed as shown in the margin.

The next step is to replace each of these seven symbols with a traditional Chinese numeral from Table 10.8. Our next example illustrates this procedure.

Writing 3264 as a Chinese numeral

EXAMPLE 6 USING THE TRADITIONAL CHINESE NUMERATION SYSTEM

Write 3264 as a Chinese numeral.

SOLUTION First, break down the Hindu-Arabic numeral into quantities that match the Chinese numerals. Represent each quantity vertically. Then, use Table 10.8 on the previous page to find the Chinese symbol that matches each quantity. This procedure, with the resulting Chinese numeral, is shown in the margin.

The Chinese system does not need a numeral for zero because it is not positional. For example, we write 8006, using zeros as placeholders, to indicate that two powers of ten, namely 10^2, or 100, and 10^1, or 10, are not needed. The Chinese leave this out, writing

$$
\begin{array}{cc}
8 & 八 \\
1000 & 千 \\
6 \ , \ \text{or} & 六 .
\end{array}
$$

CHECK POINT 6 Write 2693 as a Chinese numeral.

4 | Understand and use the Ionic Greek system.

The Ionic Greek Numeration System

The ancient Greeks, masters of art, architecture, theater, literature, philosophy, geometry, and logic, were not masters when it came to representing numbers. The Ionic Greek numeration system, which can be traced back as far as 450 B.C., used letters of their alphabet for numerals. Table 10.9 shows the many symbols (too many symbols!) used to represent numbers.

TABLE 10.9	IONIC GREEK NUMERALS							
1	α	alpha	10	ι	iota	100	ρ	rho
2	β	beta	20	κ	kappa	200	σ	sigma
3	γ	gamma	30	λ	lambda	300	τ	tau
4	δ	delta	40	μ	mu	400	υ	upsilon
5	ϵ	epsilon	50	ν	nu	500	ϕ	phi
6	ι	vau	60	ξ	xi	600	χ	chi
7	ζ	zeta	70	o	omicron	700	ψ	psi
8	η	eta	80	π	pi	800	ω	omega
9	θ	theta	90	Q	koph	900	⊤⊤	sampi

To represent a number from 1 to 999, the appropriate symbols are written next to one another. For example, the number $21 = 20 + 1$. When 21 is expressed as a Greek numeral, the plus sign is left out:

$$21 = \kappa\alpha.$$

Similarly, the number 823 written as a Greek numeral is $\omega\kappa\gamma$.

EXAMPLE 7 USING THE IONIC GREEK NUMERATION SYSTEM

Write $\psi\lambda\delta$ as a Hindu-Arabic numeral.

SOLUTION $\psi = 700$, $\lambda = 30$, and $\delta = 4$. Adding these numbers gives 734.

CHECK POINT 7 Write $\omega\pi\epsilon$ as a Hindu-Arabic numeral.

One of the many unsuccessful features of the Greek numeration system is that new symbols have to be added to represent higher numbers. It is like an alphabet that gets bigger each time a new word is used and has to be written.

EXERCISE SET 10.4 ●●●●●●

• Practice Exercises

Use Table 10.6 on page 598 to solve Exercises 1–12.

In Exercises 1–6, write each Egyptian numeral as a Hindu-Arabic numeral.

1. ꙮꙮꙮ∩∩||

2. (figures) ꙮꙮ ∩|||||

3. (figures) ꙮꙮꙮꙮ ∩||||

4. ꙮꙮ ∩|||

5. ꙮ∩∩∩||

6. (figures) ꙮꙮꙮ||

In Exercises 7–12, write each Hindu-Arabic numeral as an Egyptian numeral.

7. 423   **8.** 825   **9.** 1846
10. 1425   **11.** 23,547 **12.** 2,346,031

Use Table 10.7 on page 600 to solve Exercises 13–36.

In Exercises 13–28, write each Roman numeral as a Hindu-Arabic numeral.

13. XI   **14.** CL   **15.** XVI
16. LVII   **17.** XL   **18.** CM
19. LIX   **20.** XLIV   **21.** CXLVI
22. CLXI   **23.** MDCXXI   **24.** MMCDXLV
25. MMDCLXXVII **26.** MDCXXVI   **27.** $\overline{\text{IX}}$CDLXVI
28. $\overline{\text{V}}$MCCXI

In Exercises 29–36, write each Hindu-Arabic numeral as a Roman numeral.

29. 43   **30.** 96   **31.** 129   **32.** 469
33. 1896   **34.** 4578   **35.** 6892   **36.** 5847

Use Table 10.8 on page 601 to solve Exercises 37–48.

In Exercises 37–42, write each traditional Chinese numeral as a Hindu-Arabic numeral.

37. 八十八 **38.** 七百五 **39.** 五百二十七 **40.** 三千八十一 **41.** 二千七百七十六 **42.** 八千二百三十六

In Exercises 43–48, write each Hindu-Arabic numeral as a traditional Chinese numeral.

43. 43   **44.** 269   **45.** 583
46. 2965   **47.** 4870   **48.** 7605

Use Table 10.9 on page 602 to solve Exercises 49–56.

In Exercises 49–52, write each Ionic Greek numeral as a Hindu-Arabic numeral.

49. $\iota\beta$ **50.** $\phi\epsilon$ **51.** $\sigma\lambda\delta$ **52.** $\psi o\theta$

In Exercises 53–56, write each Hindu-Arabic numeral as an Ionic Greek numeral.

53. 43   **54.** 257   **55.** 483   **56.** 895

• Practice Plus

57. Write (figures) ꙮꙮꙮ∩∩|||| as a Roman numeral and as a traditional Chinese numeral.

58. Write (figures) ꙮꙮꙮꙮ∩|||| as a Roman numeral and as a traditional Chinese numeral.

59. Write MDCCXLI as an Egyptian numeral and as a traditional Chinese numeral.

60. Write MMCCXLV as an Egyptian numeral and as a traditional Chinese numeral.

In Exercises 61–64, write each numeral as a numeral in base five.

61. ꙮꙮꙮꙮ|||| **62.** ꙮꙮꙮ∩∩∩||

63. CXCII   **64.** CMLXXIV

In Exercises 65–66, perform each subtraction without converting to Hindu-Arabic numerals.

65.
ꙮꙮ ∩∩∩ |
− ꙮ ∩∩∩ |||
————————

66.
ꙮꙮ ∩∩ ||
− ꙮ ∩∩ |||
————————

• Application Exercises

67. Look at the back of a U.S. one dollar bill. What date is written in Roman numerals along the base of the pyramid with an eye? What is this date's significance?

68. A construction crew demolishing a very old building was surprised to find the numeral MCMLXXXIX inscribed on the cornerstone. Explain why they were surprised.

The Braille numeration system is a base ten positional system that uses raised dots in 2-by-3 cells as digit symbols.

Braille Digit Symbols   Other Symbols

0 1 2 3 4 5 6 7 8 9

Comma
Written before all numbers

In Exercises 69–70, use the digit symbols at the bottom of the previous page to express each Braille numeral as a Hindu-Arabic numeral and as a Roman numeral.

69.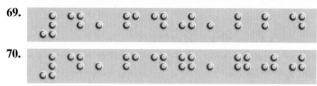

70.

• Writing in Mathematics

71. Describe how a number is represented in the Egyptian numeration system.

72. If you are interpreting a Roman numeral, when do you add values and when do you subtract them? Give an example to illustrate each case.

73. Describe how a number is represented in the traditional Chinese numeration system.

74. Describe one disadvantage of the Ionic Greek numeration system.

75. If you could use only one system of numeration described in this section, which would you prefer? Discuss the reasons for your choice.

• Critical Thinking Exercises

76. Arrange these three numerals from smallest to largest.

CCCCXLIX

77. Use Egyptian numerals to write the numeral that precedes and the numeral that follows

𓍢𓍢𓉔𓉔𓉔𓉔𓉔𓉔𓉔𓉔𓉔𓉔𓉔𓉔||||||||.

78. After reading this section, a student had a numeration nightmare about selling flowers in a time-warped international market. She started out with 200 flowers, selling XLVI of them to a Roman,

𓉔𓉔𓉔||

to an Egyptian,

=
+

to a traditional Chinese family, and the remainder to a Greek. How many flowers were sold to the Greek? Express the answer in the Ionic Greek numeration system.

• Group Exercises

Take a moment to read the introduction to the group exercises on page 590. Exercises 79–83 list some additional topics for individual or group research projects.

79. A Time Line Showing Significant Developments in Numeration Systems

80. Animals and Number Sense

81. The Hebrew Numeration System (or any system not discussed in this chapter)

82. The Rhind Papyrus and What We Learned from It

83. Computation in an Early Numeration System

●●●●●● CHAPTER SUMMARY, REVIEW, AND TEST

● S U M M A R Y   DEFINITIONS AND CONCEPTS   EXAMPLES

10.1 Our Hindu-Arabic System and Early Positional Systems

a. In a positional-value, or place-value, numeration system, the value of each symbol, called a digit, varies according to the position it occupies in the number.

b. The Hindu-Arabic numeration system is a base ten system with the digits 0, 1, 2, 3, 4, 5, 6, 7, 8, and 9. The place values in the system are

$$\ldots, 10^5, 10^4, 10^3, 10^2, 10^1, 1.$$

Ex. 2, p. 580;
Ex. 3, p. 580

c. The Babylonian numeration system is a base 60 system, with place values given by

$$\ldots, \quad 60^3, \quad 60^2, \quad 60^1, \quad 1.$$
$$\text{or} \quad \text{or} \quad \text{or}$$
$$216{,}000 \quad 3600 \quad 60$$

Babylonian numerals are given in Table 10.1 on page 581.

Ex. 4, p. 581

d. The Mayan numeration system has place values given by

$$\ldots, \quad 18 \times 20^3, \quad 18 \times 20^2, \quad 18 \times 20, \quad 20, \quad 1.$$
$$\text{or} \quad \text{or} \quad \text{or}$$
$$144{,}000 \quad 7200 \quad 360$$

Mayan numerals are given in Table 10.2 on page 582.

Ex. 5, p. 583

10.2 Number Bases in Positional Systems

a. The base of a positional numeration system refers to the number of individual digit symbols used in the system as well as to the powers of the numbers used in place values. In base b, there are b digit symbols (from 0 through $b - 1$ inclusive) with place values given by

$$\ldots, b^4, b^3, b^2, b^1, 1.$$

b. To change a numeral in a base other than ten to a base ten numeral,

    1. Multiply each digit in the numeral by its respective place value.

    2. Find the sum of the products in step 1.

Ex. 1, p. 587;
Ex. 2, p. 587;
Ex. 3, p. 588

c. To change a base ten numeral to a base b numeral, use mental conversions or repeated divisions by powers of b to find how many groups of each place value are contained in the base ten numeral.

Ex. 4, p. 588;
Ex. 5, p. 589;
Ex. 6, p. 589

10.3 Computation in Positional Systems

a. Computations in bases other than ten are performed using the same procedures as in ordinary base ten arithmetic. When a computation is equal to or exceeds the given base, use mental conversions to convert from the base ten numeral to a numeral in the desired base.

Ex. 1, p. 591;
Ex. 2, p. 592;
Ex. 3, p. 593;
Ex. 4, p. 594;
Ex. 5, p. 594

b. To divide in bases other than ten, it is convenient to use a multiplication table for products in the required base.

Ex. 6, p. 595

10.4 Looking Back at Early Numeration Systems

a. A successful numeration system expresses numbers with relatively few symbols and makes computation with these numbers fairly easy.

b. By the standard in (a), the Egyptian system (Table 10.6 on page 598), the Roman system (Table 10.7 on page 600), the Chinese system (Table 10.8 on page 601), and the Greek system (Table 10.9 on page 602) are all unsuccessful. Unlike our Hindu-Arabic system, these systems are not positional and contain no symbol for zero.

Ex. 1, p. 599;
Ex. 2, p. 599;
Ex. 3, p. 600;
Ex. 4, p. 600;
Ex. 5, p. 601;
Ex. 6, p. 602;
Ex. 7, p. 602

REVIEW EXERCISES

10.1

In Exercises 1–2, evaluate the expression.

1. 11^2 **2.** 7^3

In Exercises 3–5, write each Hindu-Arabic numeral in expanded form.

3. 472   **4.** 8076   **5.** 70,329

In Exercises 6–7, express each expanded form as a Hindu-Arabic numeral.

6. $(7 \times 10^5) + (0 \times 10^4) + (6 \times 10^3) + (9 \times 10^2)$
$$+ (5 \times 10^1) + (3 \times 1)$$

7. $(7 \times 10^8) + (4 \times 10^7) + (3 \times 10^2) + (6 \times 1)$

Use Table 10.1 on page 581 to write each Babylonian numeral in Exercises 8–9 as a Hindu-Arabic numeral.

8. < ˅   < ˅ ˅ ˅   **9.** ˅ ˅   <<   <<<

Use Table 10.2 on page 582 to write each Mayan numeral in Exercises 10–11 as a Hindu-Arabic numeral.

10.

11.

12. Describe how a positional system is used to represent a number.

10.2

In Exercises 13–18, convert the numeral to a numeral in base ten.

13. 34_{five} **14.** 110_{two} **15.** 643_{seven}

16. 1084_{nine} **17.** $\text{FD3}_{\text{sixteen}}$ **18.** 202202_{three}

In Exercises 19–24, convert each base ten numeral to a numeral in the given base.

19. 89 to base five   **20.** 21 to base two

21. 473 to base three   **22.** 7093 to base seven

23. 9348 to base six   **24.** 554 to base twelve

10.3

In Exercises 25–28, add in the indicated base.

25. $\begin{array}{r} 46_{\text{seven}} \\ +53_{\text{seven}} \end{array}$ **26.** $\begin{array}{r} 574_{\text{eight}} \\ +605_{\text{eight}} \end{array}$ **27.** $\begin{array}{r} 11011_{\text{two}} \\ +10101_{\text{two}} \end{array}$ **28.** $\begin{array}{r} 43\text{C}_{\text{sixteen}} \\ +694_{\text{sixteen}} \end{array}$

In Exercises 29–32, subtract in the indicated base.

29. $\begin{array}{r} 34_{\text{six}} \\ -25_{\text{six}} \end{array}$ **30.** $\begin{array}{r} 624_{\text{seven}} \\ -246_{\text{seven}} \end{array}$ **31.** $\begin{array}{r} 1001_{\text{two}} \\ -110_{\text{two}} \end{array}$ **32.** $\begin{array}{r} 4121_{\text{five}} \\ -1312_{\text{five}} \end{array}$

In Exercises 33–35, multiply in the indicated base.

33. 32_{four}
$\times\ 3_{\text{four}}$

34. 43_{seven}
$\times\ 6_{\text{seven}}$

35. 123_{five}
$\times\ 4_{\text{five}}$

In Exercises 36–37, divide in the indicated base. Use the multiplication tables on page 215.

36. $2_{\text{four}}\overline{)332_{\text{four}}}$

37. $4_{\text{five}}\overline{)103_{\text{five}}}$

10.4

Use Table 10.6 on page 598 to solve Exercises 38–41.

In Exercises 38–39, write each Egyptian numeral as a Hindu-Arabic numeral.

38.

39.

In Exercises 40–41, write each Hindu-Arabic numeral as an Egyptian numeral.

40. 2486

41. 34,573

In Exercises 42–43, assume a system that represents numbers exactly like the Egyptian system, but with different symbols. In particular, A = 1, B = 10, C = 100, and D = 1000.

42. Write DDCCCBAAAA as a Hindu-Arabic numeral.

43. Write 5492 as a numeral in terms of A, B, C, and D.

44. Describe how the Egyptian system or the system in Exercises 42–43 is used to represent a number. Discuss one disadvantage of such a system when compared to our Hindu-Arabic system.

Use Table 10.7 on page 600 to solve Exercises 45–49.

In Exercises 45–47, write each Roman numeral as a Hindu-Arabic numeral.

45. CLXIII

46. MXXXIV

47. MCMXC

In Exercises 48–49, write each Hindu-Arabic numeral as a Roman numeral.

48. 49

49. 2965

50. Explain when to subtract the value of symbols when interpreting a Roman numeral. Give an example.

Use Table 10.8 on page 601 to solve Exercises 51–54.

In Exercises 51–52, write each traditional Chinese numeral as a Hindu-Arabic numeral.

51. 五
百
五
十
四

52. 八
千
二
百
五
十
三

In Exercises 53–54, write each Hindu-Arabic numeral as a traditional Chinese numeral.

53. 274

54. 3587

In Exercises 55–58, assume a system that represents numbers exactly like the traditional Chinese system, but with different symbols. The symbols are shown as follows:

Numerals in the System	A	B	C	D	E	F	G	H	I	X	Y	Z
Hindu-Arabic Numerals	1	2	3	4	5	6	7	8	9	10	100	1000

Express each numeral in Exercises 55–56 as a Hindu-Arabic numeral.

55. C
Y
F
X
E

56. D
Z
E
Y
B
X

Express each Hindu-Arabic numeral in Exercises 57–58 as a numeral in the system used for Exercises 55–56.

57. 793

58. 6854

59. Describe how the Chinese system or the system in Exercises 55–58 is used to represent a number. Discuss one disadvantage of such a system when compared to our Hindu-Arabic system.

Use Table 10.9 on page 602 to solve Exercises 60–63.

In Exercises 60–61, write each Ionic Greek numeral as a Hindu-Arabic numeral.

60. $\chi\nu\gamma$

61. $\chi o\eta$

In Exercises 62–63, write each Hindu-Arabic numeral as an Ionic Greek numeral.

62. 453

63. 902

In Exercises 64–68, assume a system that represents numbers exactly like the Greek Ionic system, but with different symbols. The symbols are shown as follows:

Decimal	1	2	3	4	5	6	7	8	9
Ones	A	B	C	D	E	F	G	H	I
Tens	J	K	L	M	N	O	P	Q	R
Hundreds	S	T	U	V	W	X	Y	Z	a
Thousands	b	c	d	e	f	g	h	i	j
Ten thousands	k	l	m	n	o	p	q	r	s

In Exercises 64–66, express each numeral as a Hindu-Arabic numeral.

64. UNG

65. mhZRD

66. rXJH

In Exercises 67–68, express each Hindu-Arabic numeral as a numeral in the system used for Exercises 64–66.

67. 597

68. 25,483

69. Discuss one disadvantage of the Greek Ionic system or the system described in Exercises 64–68 when compared to our Hindu-Arabic system.

●●●●●● CHAPTER 10 TEST

1. Evaluate 9^3.

2. Write 567 in expanded form.

3. Write 63,028 in expanded form.

4. Express as a Hindu-Arabic numeral:

$$(7 \times 10^3) + (4 \times 10^2) + (9 \times 10^1) + (3 \times 1).$$

5. Express as a Hindu-Arabic numeral:

$$(4 \times 10^5) + (2 \times 10^2) + (6 \times 1).$$

6. What is the difference between a number and a numeral?

7. Explain why a symbol for zero is needed in a positional system.

8. Place values in the Babylonian system are

$$\ldots, 60^3, 60^2, 60^1, 1.$$

Use the numerals shown to write the following Babylonian numeral as a Hindu-Arabic numeral:

<< <∨∨ <∨.

Babylonian	∨	<
Hindu-Arabic	1	10

9. Place values in the Mayan system are

$$\ldots, 18 \times 20^3, 18 \times 20^2, 18 \times 20, 20, 1.$$

Use the numerals shown to write the following Mayan numeral as a Hindu-Arabic numeral:

••••
•
⬯ .

Mayan	⬯	•	••	•••	••••	—	⎯•⎯
Hindu-Arabic	0	1	2	3	4	5	6

In Exercises 10–12, convert the numeral to a numeral in base ten.

10. 423_{five} 11. 267_{nine} 12. 110101_{two}

In Exercises 13–15, convert each base ten numeral to a numeral in the given base.

13. 77 to base three   14. 56 to base two

15. 1844 to base five

In Exercises 16–18, perform the indicated operation.

16. $\begin{array}{r} 234_{\text{five}} \\ + 423_{\text{five}} \end{array}$ 17. $\begin{array}{r} 562_{\text{seven}} \\ - 145_{\text{seven}} \end{array}$ 18. $\begin{array}{r} 54_{\text{six}} \\ \times \ \ 3_{\text{six}} \end{array}$

19. Use the multiplication table shown to perform this division: $3_{\text{five}} \overline{)1213_{\text{five}}}$.

A MULTIPLICATION TABLE FOR BASE FIVE

×	0	1	2	3	4
0	0	0	0	0	0
1	0	1	2	3	4
2	0	2	4	11	13
3	0	3	11	14	22
4	0	4	13	22	31

Use the symbols in the tables shown below to solve Exercises 20–23.

Hindu-Arabic Numeral	Egyptian Numeral
1	|
10	∩
100	⟡
1000	⚇
10,000	⸾
100,000	⸜
1,000,000	⚲

Hindu-Arabic Numeral	Roman Numeral
1	I
5	V
10	X
50	L
100	C
500	D
1000	M

20. Write the following numeral as a Hindu-Arabic numeral:

⸾⸾ ⟡⟡⟡ |||.

21. Write 32,634 as an Egyptian numeral.

22. Write the Roman numeral MCMXCIV as a Hindu-Arabic numeral.

23. Express 459 as a Roman numeral.

24. Describe one difference between how a number is represented in the Egyptian system and the Roman system.

Dosage Calculations

This unit pulls together all the math skills reviewed and practiced previously in this text. Your task will be to determine the individual dose a client will receive.

In order to calculate an individual dose, one must know three important pieces of information: the desired dose, the dosage strength, and the medications' unit of measure. These are given in each dosage calculation.

Term	Symbol	Meaning	Example
dosage ordered or desired dose	D	the amount of medication that the physician has ordered for the client	Give 500 milligrams Give grains/v Give 1.2 milliliters
dosage strength or supply on hand	H	the amount of drug in a specific unit of measure	250 milligrams grains/v
unit of measure or quantity of unit	Q	the unit of measure for the specific dosage strength or supply on hand	_____ per 2 mL _____ per capsule _____ per tablet

We can see how these are used in the medication order:
The physician ordered Zithromax 500 milligrams once a day for his client.

The nurse looks at her medication label:

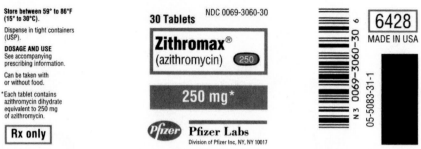

Used with permission from Pfizer, Inc.

The drug label reads Zithromax 250 milligrams per tablet.

The three essential pieces of information are

D = 500 milligrams

H = 250 milligrams

Q = 1 tablet

When using the dosage formula provided in this chapter, you must ensure that the medication information is in the correct place. This is true with any math formula. This formula can be used for most medication orders and is useful to memorize:

$$\frac{\text{desired or dosage ordered}}{\text{supply on hand}} \times \text{quantity} = \text{unknown dosage}$$

The formula is abbreviated as

$$\frac{\text{D}}{\text{H}} \times \text{Q} = x$$

Rule 1: The dosage ordered/desired and the have/supply must be in the same unit of measure.

Rule 2: The quantity and the unknown dosage will be in the same unit of measure.

Use the formula

$$\frac{\text{dosage(D)}}{\text{supply on hand(H)}} \times \text{quantity(Q)} = \text{medication given}$$

The dosage is the amount of the medication that the doctor orders. The supply on hand is the available form of the drug. In other words, milligrams, grams, caplets, tablets, and so on. This is what the pharmacy or the medication cabinet has on hand. The quantity is the amount of medication per tablet, milliliter, milligram, and so on.

It is important that the dosage and the supply on hand are in the same unit of measure. Thus, if the doctor's order is in milligrams, and you only have the medication in grams, you will convert the order to grams to match the supply that you have on hand.

You can apply this formula in two steps:

Example   The doctor orders 250 milligrams. The supply in the medicine cabinet is in 125 milligrams tablets.

To solve with dosage calculation formula:

$$\frac{D}{H} \times Q = x \qquad \begin{matrix} \text{Order} = 250 \text{ milligrams} \\ \text{Have} = 125 \text{ milligrams} \end{matrix} \qquad \text{quantity} = \left\{ \begin{matrix} \text{solid form of} \\ \text{medication, and} \\ Q \text{ is 1, so } Q \text{ can be} \\ \text{eliminated as a math} \\ \text{step in this problem.} \end{matrix} \right.$$

   a. Put the information into the format

$$\frac{D}{H} \times Q = x \quad \frac{250 \text{ milligrams}}{125 \text{ milligrams}} \times 1 \text{ tablet} = X$$

   b. Calculate. Remember that the horizontal line indicates division, so divide 250 by 125.

The result will be 2 tablets.

Example   The doctor orders 60 milligrams of liquid cough syrup. The liquid cough syrup has a label that reads 100 milligrams in 5 milliliters.

   a. Put the information into the format

$$\frac{D}{H} \times Q = x \rightarrow \frac{60 \text{ milliliters}}{100 \text{ milliliters}} \times 5 \text{ milliliters} = \underline{\hspace{1cm}} \text{ milliliters}$$

   b. Multiply and divide.

$$\frac{60 \times 5}{100} = \frac{300}{100} =$$

   c. Reduce to solve.

$$\frac{300}{100} = 3 \text{ milliliters}$$

The answer is 3 milliliters.

Example   The doctor orders Zithromax 500 milligrams. The supply in the medicine cabinet is Zithromax 250 milligrams per tablet.

> Notice that the desired dose and the strength of the dosage supplied are in the same unit of measure. Thus, no conversion is needed.

a. Put the information into the format

$$\frac{D}{H} \times Q = x \rightarrow \frac{500 \text{ milligrams}}{250 \text{ milligrams}} \times 1 \text{ tablet} = \underline{\qquad} \text{ tablets}$$

b. Multiply and divide.

$$\frac{500 \text{ milligrams}}{250 \text{ milligrams}} = 2 \text{ tablets}$$

The doctor orders Zithromax 500 milligrams. The supply in the medicine cabinet is Zithromax 250 milligrams per tablet.

> Notice that the desired dose and the strength of the dosage supplied are in the same unit of measure. Thus, no conversion is needed.

To solve with dimensional analysis

a. Place the unit of measure of the unknown on one side of the equation.

$$? \text{ tablets} =$$

b. The first factor is the unit of measure over the dosage strength.

$$? \text{ tablets} = \frac{1 \text{ tablet}}{250 \text{ milligrams}}$$

c. Multiply the first factor by the second, which is the dosage ordered over the number 1.

$$? \text{ tablets} = \frac{1 \text{ tablet}}{250 \text{ milligrams}} \times \frac{500 \text{ milligrams}}{1}$$

d. Cancel like units and multiply and divide.

$$? \text{ tablets} = \frac{1 \text{ tablet} \times 500}{250 \times 1} \quad \frac{500}{250} = 2 \text{ tablets}$$

The final answer is 2 tablets.

Example The doctor orders 60 milligrams of liquid cough syrup. The liquid cough syrup has a label that reads 100 milligrams in 5 milliliters.

a. Place the unit of measure of the unknown on one side of the equation

$$? \text{ milliliters} =$$

The first factor is the unit of measure over the dosage strength

$$? \text{ milliliters} = \frac{5 \text{ milliliters}}{100 \text{ milligrams}}$$

b. Multiply the first factor by the second, which is the dosage ordered over the number 1.

$$? \text{ milliliters} = \frac{5 \text{ milliliters}}{100 \text{ milligrams}} \times \frac{60 \text{ milligrams}}{1}$$

c. Cancel like units and multiply and divide.

$$? \text{ milliliters} = \frac{5}{100} \times \frac{60}{1} = \frac{300}{100} = 3 \text{ milliliters}$$

The final answer is 3 milliliters.

Practice   Choose a method of calculating dosage and complete the following dosage calculations:

1. Order: 30 milligrams
   Have: 10 milligrams per tablet
   Give: _____

2. Order: 1 milligram
   Have: 5 milligrams per milliliter
   Give: _____

3. Order: 1500 milligrams
   Have: 500 milligrams per tablet
   Give: _____

4. Order: 15 milligrams
   Have: 7.5 milligrams per tablet
   Give: _____

5. Order: 10 milligrams
   Have: 20 milligrams per milliliter
   Give: _____

6. Order: 0.25 gram
   Have: 50 milligrams in 2 milliliters
   Give: _____

7. Order: 1.5 milligrams
   Have: 3.0 milligrams per milliliter
   Give: _____

8. Order: 0.1 gram
   Have: 25 milligrams in 2 milliliters
   Give: _____

9. Order: 0.15 gram
   Have: 25 milligrams per tablet
   Give: _____

10. Order: 10 milligrams
   Have: 2.5 milligrams per capsule
   Give: _____

Now that the formula is familiar to you, the next step is to apply the metric and apothecary conversions you learned in this unit.

Convert the unit of measure of the "order" and "have" to the same unit of measure. One guideline is that it is often easier to convert the order to the have measure unit. This also helps in being able to compute the answer. Once the units are identifiable, it is easy to make the conversion. To review conversions among systems, reread Unit 13.

Practice

1. Order: 1 gram
   Have: 50 milligrams in 2 milliliters
   Give: _____

2. Order: 0.5 gram
   Have: 200 milligrams per tablet
   Give: _____

3. Order: 0.15 gram
   Have: 300 milligrams per caplet
   Give: _____

4. Order: grains x
   Have: 180 milligrams per milliliter
   Give: _____

5. Order: 0.06 gram
   Have: 15 milligrams per tablet
   Give: _____

6. Order: 1.5 gram
   Have: 125 milligrams per 2 milliliters
   Give: _____

7. Order: 1.5 grams
   Have: 1000 milligrams per tablet
   Give: _____

8. Order: grains iss
   Have: 30 milligrams per tablet
   Give: _____

9. Order: 1.5 gram
   Have: 750 milligrams per tablet
   Give: _____

10. Order: grain $\frac{1}{8}$
    Have: 7.5 milligrams per tablet
    Give: _____

More Dosage Calculation Practice

1. Order: 25 milligrams/orally
   Have: 10 milligrams scored tablets
   Give: _____

2. Order: 125 milligrams
   Have: 100 milligrams in 4 milliliters
   Give: _____

3. Order: grains iss
   Have: 50 milligrams per caplet
   Give: _____

4. Order: 75 milligrams
   Have: 25 milligrams in 2 milliliters
   Give: _____

5. Order: 25 milligrams/orally
   Have: 10 milligrams caplet
   Give: _____

6. Order: 300 milligrams
   Have: grains v in each tablet
   Give: _____

7. Order: 12.5 milliliters orally after meals
   Have: 25 milliliters
   Give: _____

8. Order: 0.25 milliliter by mouth
   Have: 0.125 milliliter
   Give: _____

9. Order: 120 milligrams by mouth
   Have: grain ss per tablet
   Give: _____

10. Order: 1500 milligrams
    Have: 500 milligrams per caplet
    Give: _____

Practice Using Drug Labels

Use the medication labels to complete these calculations. The drug label will supply the dosage strength and the unit.

1. The physician orders Glucotrol XL 10 milligrams once a day.

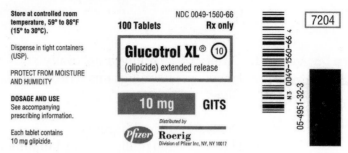

Used with permission from Pfizer, Inc.

Give: _____

2. The client has a medication order for Cozaar 50 milligrams once a day without food.

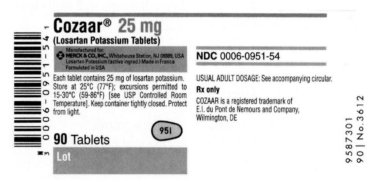

The labels for the products Prinivil, Fosamax, Singulair, Cozaar, Pepcid, Hyzaar, and Zocor are reproduced with the permission of Merck & Co., Inc., copyright owner.

Give: _____

3. The order is for Feldene 20 milligrams per day.

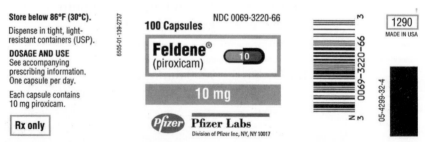

Used with permission from Pfizer, Inc.

Give: _____

4. The physician writes an order for Zoloft 25 milligrams per day.

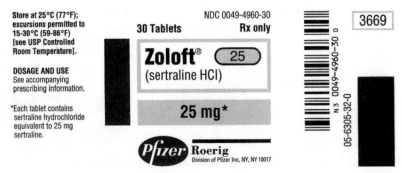

Used with permission from Pfizer, Inc.

Give: _____

5. Dr. Ballard writes an order for Procardia XL 60 milligrams once daily.

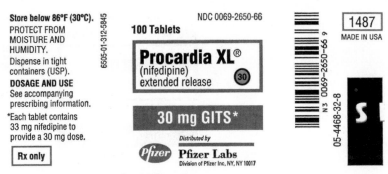

Used with permission from Pfizer, Inc.

Give: _____

6. The nurse receives a new order for Cardura XL 16 milligrams to control blood pressure.

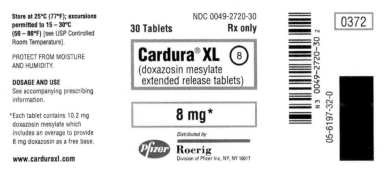

Used with permission from Pfizer, Inc.

Give: _____

7. The physician has written an order for Dilantin 100 milligrams chewable tablets.

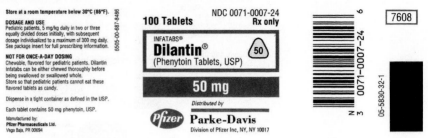

Used with permission from Pfizer, Inc.

Give: _____

8. The client has a medication order for Neurontin (oral solution) 500 milligrams per dose three times a day.

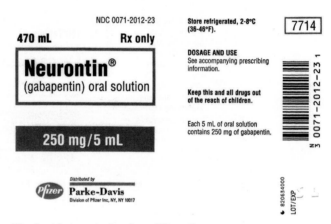

Used with permission from Pfizer, Inc.

Each dose give: _____

9. The nurse is asked to give the client Norvasc 10 milligrams per day.

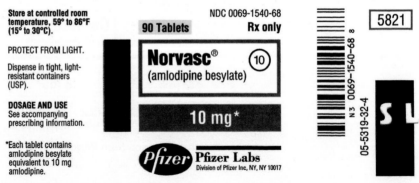

Used with permission from Pfizer, Inc.

Give: _____

10. The physician writes an order for Plendil 7.5 milligrams once a day in the morning.

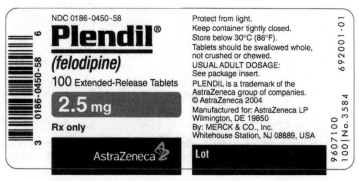

Used with permission from AstraZeneca Pharmaceuticals LP

Give: _____

DOSAGE CALCULATION SELF-TEST

1. The doctor's order is for 20 milligrams. You have 10 milligrams in 5 milliliters. Give _____.

2. Order: 250 milligrams of a drug by mouth. You have scored tables in 100 milligrams dosages. Give _____.

3. Order: pain medication 0.6 gram orally every 4 hours. In the supply are tablets labeled grains v of the pain medication. Give _____.

4. Order: 1.25 milligrams. Have 0.25 milligrams in 5 milliliters. Give _____.

5. Order: Nexium 40 milligrams delayed-release capsules once a day.

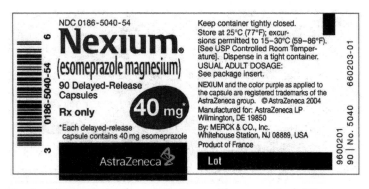

Used with permission from AstraZeneca Pharmaceuticals LP

Give: _____

6. Order: Zocor 80 milligrams per day divided in 3 doses of 20 milligrams, 20 milligrams, and an evening dose of 40 milligrams.

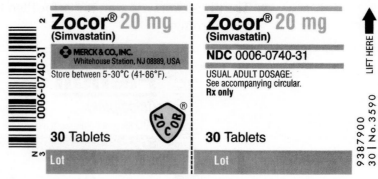

The labels for the products Prinivil, Fosamax, Singulair, Cozaar, Pepcid, Hyzaar, and Zocor are reproduced with the permission of Merck & Co., Inc., copyright owner.

Calculate for the evening dose only. Give: _____

7. Order: Prinivil 15 milligrams once daily.

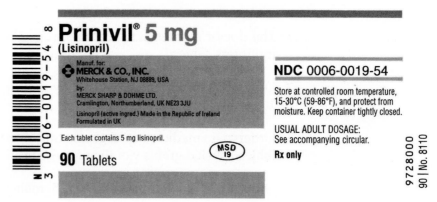

The labels for the products Prinivil, Fosamax, Singulair, Cozaar, Pepcid, Hyzaar, and Zocor are reproduced with the permission of Merck & Co., Inc., copyright owner.

Give: _____

8. The physician orders Cardura 1 milligrams once daily at bedtime.

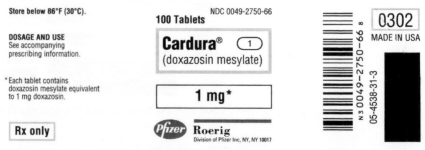

Used with permission from Pfizer, Inc.

Give: _____

9. The doctor orders 200 milligrams of a drug by mouth every 4 hours. The vial contains 125 milligrams in 5 milliliter. Give _____ milliliters.

10. Order: grains iii
    Have: 60 milligram tablets
    Give: _____

11. Order: 50 milligrams orally
    Have: 12.5 milligrams in each 5 milliliters
    Give: _____

12. Order: grain $\dfrac{1}{150}$
    Have: 200 micrograms per tablet
    Give: _____

13. Order: grains v orally
    Have: 0.15 grains per tablet
    Give: _____

14. Dr. Brown orders 0.2 grams of zidovudine in tablets every 4 hours for an HIV patient. The pharmacy carries this medication in 100 milligram tablets. How many tablets will the patient receive? _____

15. The nurse has 15 milligram tablets in her medicine cabinet. Dr. Smith orders 30 milligrams of phenobarbital. She will give _____.

Using Excel®

Microsoft Excel is a program that can be used to perform a multitude of tasks, including making spreadsheets and graphs. In this appendix, we will present a brief introduction to Excel. Many publications are available that offer detailed and complete explanations on using Excel. We will give instructions for a PC. The screens and instructions for a Mac are a little different.

Figure B.1 shows an Excel screen. Depending on the version of Excel you are using, the Excel screen on your computer may be a little different.

In Excel, columns are referred to with letters and rows are referred to with numbers. The highlighted, or active cell, in Fig. B.1 is A1. When entering information in Excel, you can enter **labels**, used to identify information, **values** (or numbers), or **formulas** (calculations written in a special notation). When you enter a formula in a cell, Excel displays the result of the formula in the active cell, not the formula itself, after you press the Enter key. Formulas always begin with an equal (=) sign. After you enter a label, a value, or a formula in a cell, you press the Enter key to enter the information. Do not be concerned if, when listing labels, the labels overflow into a second cell. After you finish inserting all the labels, you can extend the column width by placing the mouse pointer on the line between the two columns at the top of the column and then double clicking the mouse button. The column widths will then automatically adjust in size.

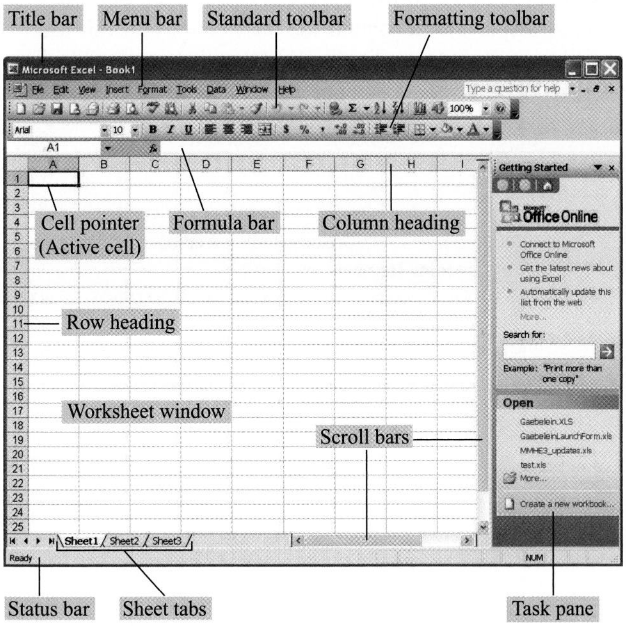

Consider the Excel spreadsheet in Fig. B.2 on page 624. Labels, shaded in orange, are given across row 1 and down column A. Values, shaded in green, are given in cells B2 through D2 and B3 through D3. Calculations from formulas, shaded in yellow, are given in cells E2 and E3.

Title bar   Menu bar   Standard toolbar   Formatting toolbar

Cell pointer (Active cell)   Formula bar   Column heading

Row heading

Worksheet window

Scroll bars

Status bar   Sheet tabs   Task pane

Figure B.1

In Fig. B.2, we are using Excel to calculate simple interest on a loan, using the simple interest formula, as will be explained shortly. Under column A, we list the dates on which the loans were made.

	A	B	C	D	E
1	**Date**	**Principal**	**Rate**	**Time**	**Interest**
2	**May 22, 2006**	$ 2,000.00	0.06	1	$ 120.00
3	**June 5, 2007**	$ 5,000.00	0.05	3	$ 750.00

Sheet1 / Sheet2 / Sheet3 /

Ready

Figure B.2

To get the dollar signs in column B, highlight column B by placing the mouse pointer on the B at the top of column B and then click on the $ in the formatting toolbar. Repeat the process to get the dollar signs in column E. After you insert the labels and values, we use the formula

$$\text{Interest} = \text{principal} \times \text{rate} \times \text{time}$$

to determine the simple interest in column E. To use an Excel formula to calculate the interest for May 22, 2006, move the cursor to cell E2 and then click the mouse to activate that cell. Type in the formula =B2*C2*D2. After you press the Enter key, the answer, $120, is displayed. To obtain the answer for cell E3, use =B3*C3*D3. Notice that * is used to indicate multiplication and that there are no blank spaces in the formula.

Now consider the spreadsheet in Fig. B.3, which shows a budget.

	A	B	C	D
1		**Budgeted**	**Actual**	**Difference**
2	**Income Items**			
3	Sales income	$ 35,600.00	$ 39,200.00	$ 3,600.00
4	CD interest	$ 1,620.00	$ 1,490.00	$ (130.00)
5	Other income	$ 5,080.00	$ 6,580.00	$ 1,500.00
6	*Total Income*	$ 42,300.00	$ 47,270.00	
7				
8	**Expense Items**			
9	Rent	$ 10,230.00	$ 10,150.00	$ (80.00)
10	Food	$ 8,573.00	$ 8,450.00	$ (123.00)
11	Clothing	$ 2,510.00	$ 2,370.00	$ (140.00)
12	Medical	$ 1,080.00	$ 960.00	$ (120.00)
13	Entertainment	$ 1,280.00	$ 1,280.00	$ –
14	Insurance	$ 1,200.00	$ 1,420.00	$ 220.00
15	Other	$ 6,110.00	$ 7,190.00	$ 1,080.00
16	*Total Expenses*	$ 30,983.00	$ 31,820.00	
17				
18	**Net Income**	$ 11,317.00	$ 15,450.00	

Sheet1 / Sheet2 / Sheet3 /

Ready

Figure B.3

To obtain the spreadsheet in Fig. B.3, do the following. First input the labels in cells B1, C1, and D1 and also under column A. Then input the values in cells B3 through B5, B9 through B15, C3 through C5, and C9 through C15. Next we can determine the difference between the actual amounts and budgeted amounts, column D, by subtracting the values in column B from the values in column C. Begin by activating cell D3. Then type =C3-B3 and press the Enter key. At this point, the difference, $39,200 − $35,600, or $3600, fills in cell D3. If we wanted to determine the amount to go in cell D4, we could type in =C4-B4 and continue this process for all amounts in column D. Excel, however, has a number of procedures that can be used to copy formulas from one cell to another cell that needs a similar formula. Copying can save time when building a spreadsheet with multiple columns or rows that need similar formulas. When copying formulas, Excel automatically rewrites the cell reference so that the formula refers to the appropriate cells. You can see the formula for a particular cell at any time by activating that cell and looking in the formula bar near the top of the screen. You can copy formulas using the **Copy** and **Paste** commands in the Edit menu. To copy a formula from one cell to another, click on the cell containing the formula you wish to copy, click on the Edit menu, and then click on Copy. Click on the cell where you want the copied formula to go. Then click on the Edit menu and click Paste. This method will copy the formula to the new cell, and the cell reference used in the formula will automatically change to the appropriate cells for the new calculation.

A quick way to copy a formula to one or more adjacent cells is with the *fill handle*. To copy this way, position the mouse pointer on the selection's *fill handle* (a tiny square in the bottom right-hand corner of the cell selected). The mouse pointer turns into a black cross. Press and hold the mouse button while you drag the cross down the column, or to the right across the row, until you reach the desired cell. A gray or black border stretches over the cells you pass, highlighting the desired cells. When you release the mouse button, the formula is copied to all the cells that were highlighted.

You can complete cells D4 and D5 using the fill handle. Then, in cell D9, we enter the formula =C9-B9. We then use the fill handle to complete cells D10 through D15.

To obtain the sum of the budgeted income, cell B6, we can use the auto sum button on the standard toolbar or we can enter a formula. To determine the sum of the values in cells B3, B4, and B5, we can enter the formula =SUM(B3:B5) in cell B6. After you press enter, the sum $42,300 is displayed. Then you can obtain the sum of cells C3 through C5, which will go in cell C6, by using =SUM(C3:C5) or by using the fill handle as explained earlier. We obtain the sum of the total budgeted expenses, B16, and total actual expenses, C16, in a similar manner. For example, in cell B16, we use the formula =SUM(B9:B15) to obtain the sum of columns B9 through B15.

Finally, to obtain the budgeted net income, cell B18, we subtract the total budgeted expenses from the total budgeted income. Thus, in cell B18 we use the formula =B6-B16. Similarly, in cell C18 we use =C6-C16.

The preceding explanation should give you a basic idea of how Excel works. Note that when you change a value in a cell in the spreadsheet, the corresponding formulas that use that value automatically recalculate the answer and display the resulting answer.

TIMELY TIP

In Microsoft Excel formulas, use

* for multiplication
/ for division
^ for exponents

Suppose that cell B3 of a spreadsheet has a value of 5. If in cell B4 you had the formula $=B3\wedge2$, you would get an answer of 25 in cell B4 after pressing the Enter key. Suppose that you wanted to find the square root of the number 16, which is in cell D7 of a spreadsheet. In cell D8, you could use the formula $=D7\wedge(1/2)$ or $=D7\wedge0.5$. After the Enter key is pressed, the answer 4 is displayed in cell D8.

If you find you left something out and wish to add another row or column to your spreadsheet, place the cursor where you want to add the new row or column. Then go to the Insert menu and select either Row or Column. If you want to delete either a row or column, highlight that row or column and then go to the Edit menu and click on Delete.

If you want to find the sum of the numbers in consecutive cells and another number in a non-consecutive cell, you can use a comma in the formula. For example, $=SUM(C5:C10, C:13)$ adds the numbers in cells C5 through C10 and the number in cell C13.

If items such as dates are automatically converted to a format different than what you want, use the Format menu and select Cells. Here you will see many formats that can be adjusted. To change the format of dates, for example, select the Format menu, then select Cells, select Numbers, and then select Dates.

The only way to get to understand Excel is to work and experiment with it. When doing so, you may want to go to the Insert menu and select Function. Here you can select from many different types of functions in many different areas of mathematics and business.

Approaches to Problem Solving

UNIT AC1

The Problem-Solving Power of Units: We explore the powerful technique of working with units, both to solve problems and to check answers.

UNIT AC2

Standardized Units: More Problem-Solving Power: We review standardized units of both the U.S. customary and the metric systems and investigate units for problems involving temperature, energy, density, and concentration.

In your past mathematics classes, it might have seemed that mathematics problems involved only numbers and symbols. But the mathematical problems that you encounter in other classes, jobs, and daily life are almost always posed in words. In this appendix, we will begin to consider *quantitative* problem solving, in which the problems involve words *and* numbers or equations.

AC1

The Problem-Solving Power of Units

Just as critical thinking can be approached in many different ways, there's no single best approach to solving quantitative problems. However, people have spent lifetimes coming up with strategies and guidelines that can help. The overall goal of this chapter is to help you learn some of these strategies and guidelines.

We will begin by looking at how the units of a problem can be useful in figuring out what the problem is about, as well as for solving the problem and checking its answer.

You Can't Add Apples and Oranges

It may be a cliché, but mathematically it is true that you can't add apples and oranges. The reason is that we can add or subtract only quantities of the same type. For example, we can add 5 apples and 3 apples to get 8 apples. But apples and oranges are different things, so if we try to add 5 apples and 3 oranges, all we can say is that we have 5 apples and 3 oranges.

More generally, numbers in real problems usually represent a quantity of *something*, which we can describe by its **units.** If we count the number of apples in a basket, the result has units of *apples.* If we measure the length of a room, the result may have units of *feet.* If we ask how fast a car is traveling, the answer may have units of *miles per hour.*

Technical Note

When abbreviating units, we do not distinguish between singular and plural. For example, we use *mi* for both mile and miles.

> **DEFINITION**
>
> The **units** of a quantity describe what is being measured or counted.

We can add or subtract numbers only when they have the same units. However, we can multiply and divide quantities with the same or different units, much as we multiply and divide numbers. A few examples should clarify the idea:

- If you drove 100 miles in two hours, your average speed was the distance traveled (100 mi) divided by the time it took (2 hr):

$$\frac{100 \text{ mi}}{2 \text{ hr}} = \frac{50 \text{ mi}}{1 \text{ hr}} = 50 \frac{\text{mi}}{\text{hr}}$$

We read this answer as "50 miles per hour." Note that the word *per* means "divided by" (or "for every").

- To find the *area* of a room, we multiply its length by its width (Figure AC.1). If the room is 12 feet long and 10 feet wide, its area is

$$12 \text{ ft} \times 10 \text{ ft} = 120 \text{ (ft} \times \text{ft)} = 120 \text{ ft}^2$$

We read this area as "120 square feet," remembering that the word *square* implies something raised to the second power. Note that we multiply the num-

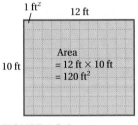

FIGURE AC.1 Each small square is one foot on a side and therefore has an area of 1 square foot. The floor of the room contains a total of 120 of these squares, so its total area is 120 square feet.

bers (12 × 10 = 120) separately from the units (ft × ft = ft²) but keep track of both.

- To find the *volume* of a box, we multiply its width, depth, and height (Figure AC.2). If the box is 6 inches wide, 4 inches deep, and 10 inches long, its volume is

$$6 \text{ in.} \times 4 \text{ in.} \times 10 \text{ in.} = 240 \text{ (in.} \times \text{in.} \times \text{in.)} = 240 \text{ in.}^3$$

We read this volume as "240 cubic inches," remembering that the word *cubic* implies something raised to the third power. (The abbreviation "in." includes a period.)

- To find the energy used by a light bulb, we multiply its power rating (in watts or kilowatts) by the length of time it is turned on. If a movie set uses a 0.5-kilowatt light bulb for 6 hours, its energy usage is

$$0.5 \text{ kilowatt} \times 6 \text{ hr} = 3 \text{ kilowatt} \times \text{hr}$$

We read this answer as "3 kilowatt-hours," where the hyphen between the units implies multiplication. (See Unit AC2 for further discussion of energy units.)

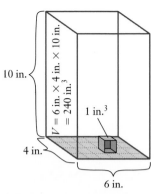

FIGURE AC.2 Each small cube is one inch on a side and therefore has a volume of 1 cubic inch. The box contains 240 of these cubes, so its volume is 240 cubic inches.

READING UNITS

Operation	Key word or symbol	Example
Division	*per*	Read miles ÷ hours as "miles per hour."
Raising to second power	*square*	Read ft × ft, or ft², as "square feet" or "feet squared."
Raising to third power	*cube* or *cubic*	Read ft × ft × ft, or ft³, as "cubic feet" or "feet cubed."
Multiplication	hyphen	Read kilowatts × hours as "kilowatt-hours."

✱EXAMPLE 1 *Identifying Units*

Identify the units of the answer for each of the following cases.

  a. The price you paid for gasoline, found by dividing its total cost in dollars by the number of gallons of gas that you bought.
  b. The area of a circle, found with the formula πr^2, where r is the radius of the circle measured in centimeters. (Note that π is a pure number and has no units.)
  c. A volume found by multiplying an area measured in acres by a depth measured in feet.

SOLUTION

  a. The price of the gasoline has units of dollars divided by gallons, which we write as $/gal and read as "dollars per gallon."

b. The area of the circle has units of centimeters to the second power, which we write as cm^2 and read as "square centimeters."

c. In this case, the volume has units of acres × feet, which we read as "acre-feet." This unit of volume is commonly used by hydrologists (water engineers) in the United States. Now try Exercises 29–36.

....

Time out to think

Look for numbers in a newspaper or magazine. For at least five cases, identify the units of the numbers.

A Brief Review

Working with Fractions

We can express a fraction in three basic ways: as a *common fraction* such as $\frac{1}{2}$; as a fraction in *decimal form* such as 0.5; and as a *percentage* such as 50%. Here, we review the first two forms.

Common Fractions

Common fractions have the form a/b, where a and b can be any numbers as long as b is not zero. The number on top is called the **numerator** and the number on the bottom is called the **denominator**. A fraction represents division:

$$\begin{array}{c}\text{numerator} \to \\ \text{denominator} \to\end{array} \frac{a}{b} \qquad \text{means} \qquad a \div b$$

We can write an integer as a fraction with a denominator of 1. For example:

$$3 = \frac{3}{1} \qquad \text{or} \qquad -4 = \frac{-4}{1}$$

Adding and Subtracting Fractions

If two fractions have a common (same) denominator, we can add or subtract them by adding or subtracting their numerators. For example:

$$\frac{1}{5} + \frac{2}{5} = \frac{1+2}{5} = \frac{3}{5} \qquad \text{or} \qquad \frac{7}{9} - \frac{2}{9} = \frac{7-2}{9} = \frac{5}{9}$$

Otherwise, we must write the fractions with a common denominator before adding or subtracting. For example,

we can add $\frac{1}{2} + \frac{1}{3}$ by writing them with a common denominator of 6 as $\frac{3}{6}$ and $\frac{2}{6}$, respectively:

$$\frac{1}{2} + \frac{1}{3} = \frac{3}{6} + \frac{2}{6} = \frac{3+2}{6} = \frac{5}{6}$$

Multiplying Fractions

To multiply fractions, we multiply the numerators and denominators separately. For example:

$$\frac{1}{3} \times \frac{2}{5} = \frac{1 \times 2}{3 \times 5} = \frac{2}{15}$$

Sometimes we can simplify fractions at the same time we multiply them by *canceling* terms that occur in both the numerator and the denominator. For example:

$$\frac{3}{4} \times \frac{5}{3} = \frac{\cancel{3} \times 5}{4 \times \cancel{3}} = \frac{5}{4}$$

Reciprocals and Division

Two numbers are **reciprocals** if their product is 1. For example:

$$2 \text{ and } \frac{1}{2} \text{ are reciprocals because } 2 \times \frac{1}{2} = 1$$

$$\frac{4}{3} \text{ and } \frac{3}{4} \text{ are reciprocals because } \frac{4}{3} \times \frac{3}{4} = 1$$

We find the reciprocal of any fraction by inverting it (interchanging the numerator and the denominator). For an integer like 2, we think of it as $\frac{2}{1}$ to find that its reciprocal is $\frac{1}{2}$. In general:

Unit Conversions

Many everyday problems involve nothing more than converting one set of units to another. For example, you might want to convert a distance from kilometers to miles or a recipe measure from quarts to cups.

The basic "trick" of unit conversions is to devise an appropriate way of multiplying by 1. For example, the following are all different ways of writing 1.

$$1 = \frac{1}{1} = \frac{8}{8} = \frac{\frac{1}{4}}{\frac{1}{4}} = \frac{1 \text{ kilogram}}{1 \text{ kilogram}} = \frac{1 \text{ week}}{7 \text{ days}} = \frac{12 \text{ inches}}{1 \text{ foot}}$$

The last expression shows the necessity of stating units: $12 \div 1$ is *not* 1, but 12 in. $\div$ 1 ft *is* 1 because 12 inches and 1 foot are equal.

- The reciprocal of a is $\frac{1}{a}$ $(a \neq 0)$.

- The reciprocal of $\frac{a}{b}$ is $\frac{b}{a}$ $(a \neq 0, b \neq 0)$.

To divide fractions, we replace the division with multiplication by the reciprocal. This process is sometimes called *invert and multiply*, as shown in the following examples:

$$10 \div \frac{1}{2} = 10 \times \underbrace{\frac{2}{1}}_{} = 20$$
$$\underbrace{\qquad\qquad}_{\text{invert}}$$
and multiply

$$\frac{3}{4} \div \frac{2}{5} = \frac{3}{4} \times \underbrace{\frac{5}{2}}_{} = \frac{15}{8}$$
$$\underbrace{\qquad\qquad}_{\text{invert}}$$
and multiply

Rules Summary

Addition/subtraction (common denominator required):

$$\frac{a}{c} + \frac{b}{c} = \frac{a+b}{c} \quad \text{or} \quad \frac{a}{c} - \frac{b}{c} = \frac{a-b}{c}$$

Multiplication:

$$\frac{a}{b} \times \frac{c}{d} = \frac{a \times c}{b \times d}$$

Division (invert and multiply):

$$\frac{a}{b} \div \frac{c}{d} = \frac{a}{b} \times \frac{d}{c}$$

Decimal Form

For a fraction in decimal form, each digit corresponds to a certain place value, which is always a power of 10 (such as 10, 100, 1000, . . .). The following example shows values for the decimal places in the number 3.141.

3	.	1	4	1
ones		tenths	hundredths	thousandths
(1)		$(0.1 = \frac{1}{10})$	$(0.01 = \frac{1}{100})$	$(0.001 = \frac{1}{1000})$

Converting to Common Form

Converting a fraction from decimal to common form requires only recognizing the value of the last digit in the decimal. For example:

$$0.4 = \frac{4}{10} \qquad 3.15 = \frac{315}{100} \qquad 0.097 = \frac{97}{1000}$$

Converting to Decimal Form

To convert a common fraction into decimal form, we carry out the division implied by the fraction. For example:

$$\frac{1}{4} = 1 \div 4 = 0.25$$

Many common fractions cannot be written *exactly* in decimal form, but instead have an endless repeating pattern of digits. For example, the decimal form of $\frac{1}{3}$ contains an endless string of 3s:

$$\frac{1}{3} = 0.3333333\ldots$$

Mathematically, we represent the repeating digits by putting a bar over them. For example, the bar in $0.\overline{3}$ means that the 3 repeats indefinitely. In practice, we usually round repeating decimals to one or a few digits. For example, we might round the decimal form of $\frac{1}{3}$ to 0.33.

Now try Exercises 23–28.

Conversion Factors

The statement 12 in. = 1 ft is an example of a **conversion factor.** We can write this conversion factor in three equivalent ways (the latter two forms come from dividing on both sides of the first equation):

$$12 \text{ in.} = 1 \text{ ft} \quad \text{or} \quad \frac{12 \text{ in.}}{1 \text{ ft}} = 1 \quad \text{or} \quad \frac{1 \text{ ft}}{12 \text{ in.}} = 1$$

The key to unit conversions is to use the correct form of the conversion factor for the problem at hand.

✳EXAMPLE 2 *Feet to Inches*

Convert a distance of 7 feet into inches.

SOLUTION   We begin with *feet* and want to end up with *inches.* We therefore need the conversion factor between *inches* and *feet* in a form that has *feet* in the denominator, so that *feet* will cancel:

$$7 \text{ ft} = 7 \text{ ft} \times \underbrace{\frac{12 \text{ in.}}{1 \text{ ft}}}_{1} = 84 \text{ in.}$$

Note that we really just multiplied 7 feet by 1 in a form that allowed us to change the units. Seven feet is the same as 84 inches.   Now try Exercises 37–38. ◀

✳EXAMPLE 3 *Inches to Feet*

Convert a length of 102 inches to feet.

SOLUTION   This time we use the conversion factor in the form with *inches* in the denominator, so that *inches* will cancel:

$$102 \text{ in.} = 102 \text{ in.} \times \underbrace{\frac{1 \text{ ft}}{12 \text{ in.}}}_{1} = 8.5 \text{ ft}$$

Thus, 102 inches is equivalent to 8.5 feet.   Now try Exercises 39–40. ◀

✳EXAMPLE 4 *Using a Chain of Conversions*

How many seconds are there in one day?

SOLUTION   Most of us don't immediately know the answer to this question, but we do know that 1 day = 24 hr, 1 hr = 60 min, and 1 min = 60 s. We can answer the question by setting up a *chain* of unit conversions in which we start with *day* and end up with *seconds:*

$$1 \text{ day} \times \frac{24 \text{ hr}}{1 \text{ day}} \times \frac{60 \text{ min}}{1 \text{ hr}} \times \frac{60 \text{ s}}{1 \text{ min}} = 86,400 \text{ s}$$

By using the conversion factors needed to cancel the appropriate units, we are left with the answer in *seconds.* There are 86,400 seconds in one day.   Now try Exercises 41–48. ◀

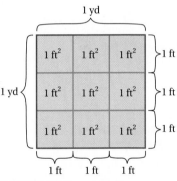

FOXTROT © 1995 by Bill Amend. Reprinted with permission of UNIVERSAL PRESS SYNDI-CATE. All rights reserved.

Conversions with Units Raised to Powers

We must take special care when converting units raised to powers. For example, suppose we want to know the number of square feet in a square yard. We may not know the conversion factor between square yards (yd^2) and square feet (ft^2), but we know that 1 yd = 3 ft. Therefore, we can replace 1 yard by 3 feet when we write out 1 square yard:

$$1 \text{ yd}^2 = 1 \text{ yd} \times 1 \text{ yd} = 3 \text{ ft} \times 3 \text{ ft} = 9 \text{ ft}^2$$

That is, 1 square yard is the same as 9 square feet. We can also find this conversion factor by squaring both sides of the yards-to-feet conversion:

$$1 \text{ yd} = 3 \text{ ft} \xrightarrow[\text{both sides}]{\text{square}} (1 \text{ yd})^2 = (3 \text{ ft})^2 \xrightarrow[\text{each term}]{\text{square}} 1 \text{ yd}^2 = 9 \text{ ft}^2$$

Figure AC.3 confirms that, indeed, 9 square feet fit exactly into 1 square yard. As usual, we can write the conversion factor in three equivalent forms:

$$1 \text{ yd}^2 = 9 \text{ ft}^2 \quad \text{or} \quad \frac{1 \text{ yd}^2}{9 \text{ ft}^2} = 1 \quad \text{or} \quad \frac{9 \text{ ft}^2}{1 \text{ yd}^2} = 1$$

FIGURE AC.3 Notice that 1 square yard contains 9 square feet.

✳EXAMPLE 5 *Carpeting a Room*

You want to carpet a room that measures 10 feet by 12 feet, making an area of 120 square feet. But carpet is usually sold by the square yard rather than by the square foot. How many square yards of carpet do you need?

SOLUTION   We need to convert the room's area from units of *square feet* to *square yards*, so we use the conversion factor in the form that has square feet (ft^2) in the denominator:

$$120 \text{ ft}^2 \times \frac{1 \text{ yd}^2}{9 \text{ ft}^2} = \frac{120}{9} \text{ yd}^2 \approx 13.3 \text{ yd}^2$$

(The symbol ≈ means "approximately equal to.") Note that we rounded the answer to the nearest 0.1 square yard. Most stores will not sell fractions of a square yard, so you will need to buy 14 square yards of carpet.   Now try Exercises 49–52. ◂

❈ EXAMPLE 6 *Cubic Units: Purchasing Garden Soil*

You are preparing a vegetable garden that is 40 feet long and 16 feet wide, and you need enough soil to fill it to a depth of 1 foot. The landscape supply store sells soil by the cubic yard. How much soil should you order?

SOLUTION To find the volume of soil that you need, we multiply the garden's length (40 feet), width (16 feet), and depth (1 foot):

$$40 \text{ ft} \times 16 \text{ ft} \times 1 \text{ ft} = 640 \text{ ft}^3$$

Because soil is sold by the cubic yard, we need to convert this volume from units of *cubic feet* to *cubic yards*. We know that 1 yd = 3 ft, so we find the cubic conversion factor by cubing both sides of this equation:

$$1 \text{ yd} = 3 \text{ ft} \xrightarrow{\text{cube both sides}} (1 \text{ yd})^3 = (3 \text{ ft})^3 \xrightarrow{\text{cube each term}} 1 \text{ yd}^3 = 27 \text{ ft}^3$$

In the last step, we recognized that $3^3 = 3 \times 3 \times 3 = 27$. As usual, we can write this conversion factor in three equivalent forms:

$$1 \text{ yd}^3 = 27 \text{ ft}^3 \quad \text{or} \quad \frac{1 \text{ yd}^3}{27 \text{ ft}^3} = 1 \quad \text{or} \quad \frac{27 \text{ ft}^3}{1 \text{ yd}^3} = 1$$

To convert the soil volume from cubic feet to cubic yards, we use the conversion factor in the form that has cubic feet (ft^3) in the denominator:

$$640 \text{ ft}^3 \times \frac{1 \text{ yd}^3}{27 \text{ ft}^3} = \frac{640}{27} \text{ yd}^3 \approx 23.7 \text{ yd}^3$$

You will need to order about 24 cubic yards of soil for your garden.

Now try Exercises 53–56. ◀

Currency Conversions

Different countries use different money, or **currency**. If you travel internationally, you'll need to change money from one currency to another. Converting between currencies is a unit conversion problem in which the conversion factors are the exchange rates.

Table AC.1 shows a typical table of currency exchange rates. The *Dollars per Foreign* column gives the conversion factor in the form useful for converting from

By the Way

Currency exchange rates change nearly every day. Sometimes, especially when markets are volatile, currency rates change hour by hour or even minute by minute. You can find exchange rates listed on the Web.

TABLE AC.1 Sample Currency Exchange Rates (June 2006)

Currency	Dollars per Foreign	Foreign per Dollar
British pound	1.858	0.5382
Canadian dollar	0.8996	1.112
European euro	1.272	0.7862
Japanese yen	0.008965	111.5
Mexican peso	0.09136	10.95

foreign currency into U.S. dollars. For example, the row for Mexico shows 0.09136 in this column, which means

$$1 \text{ peso} = \$0.09136$$

The *Foreign per Dollar* column gives the conversion factor in the form useful for converting U.S. dollars into foreign currency. In this case,

$$\$1 = 10.95 \text{ pesos}$$

Time out to think
Find the reciprocals of the numbers in the *Dollars per Foreign* column of Table AC.1. Are your results the numbers in the *Foreign per Dollar* column? Explain.

HISTORICAL NOTE

The euro came into being as a new currency for 11 countries of the European Union in January 1999. These countries immediately tied their currency values to the euro but, to ease the transition, decided to keep their national currencies in circulation for three additional years. Euro bills and coins were put in circulation in January 2002.

❋EXAMPLE 7 *Price Conversion*

At a French department store, the price for a pair of jeans is 45 euros. What is the price in U.S. dollars? Use the exchange rates in Table AC.1.

SOLUTION   From the *Dollars per Foreign* column in Table AC.1, we see that

$$1 \text{ euro} = \$1.272$$

As usual, we can write this conversion factor in two other equivalent forms:

$$\frac{1 \text{ euro}}{\$1.272} = 1 \qquad \text{or} \qquad \frac{\$1.272}{1 \text{ euro}} = 1$$

We use the latter form to convert the price from euros to dollars:

$$45 \text{ euro} \times \frac{\$1.272}{1 \text{ euro}} \approx \$57.24$$

The price of 45 euros is equivalent to $57.24.   **Now try Exercises 57–60.** ◀

❋EXAMPLE 8 *Buying Currency*

You are on holiday in Mexico and need cash. How many pesos can you buy with $100? Use the exchange rates in Table AC.1 and assume the transaction does not involve any fees.

SOLUTION   From the *Foreign per Dollar* column in Table AC.1, we see that

$$\$1 = 10.95 \text{ pesos}$$

Two other equivalent forms of this conversion are

$$\frac{10.95 \text{ peso}}{\$1} = 1 \qquad \text{or} \qquad \frac{\$1}{10.95 \text{ peso}} = 1$$

The first form allows us to convert dollars to pesos:

$$\$100 \times \frac{10.95 \text{ peso}}{\$1} = 1095 \text{ peso}$$

Your $100 will buy 1095 pesos.   **Now try Exercises 61–64.** ◀

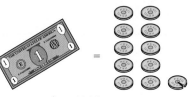

$1 = 10.95 pesos

1 peso = $0.09136

Practical Matters

Changing Money in Foreign Countries

It costs money to change currency, so you should always look for the best deal. Two factors affect the cost of changing currency: (1) the exchange rate and (2) fees for the exchange.

Published exchange rates are usually "wholesale" rates available only to banks. Most money changers—including airport change stations, hotels, and exchange booths on streets—make money by giving you a rate that is not as good as the wholesale rate. For example, if the wholesale rate is 10.9 pesos to the dollar, a money changer might give you only 10.3 pesos per dollar.

Fees can also affect the cost of changing currency. Many money changers (especially in hotels, stores, and street booths) charge a fee every time you make an exchange. Here are a few general hints for changing currency:

- Before you travel, get a small amount of your destination's currency from your local bank. That way, if you need cash upon arrival, you won't be forced to accept a poor exchange rate or high fees.

- Once you get to your destination, banks usually offer better exchange rates than other money changers. The best deal may be your ATM card, which generally gets bank exchange rates with the added convenience of ATM machines (at least in countries where ATM machines are common). But be sure you're aware of any fees: Before your trip, find out whether your bank charges a fee for foreign ATM transactions. Any fee charged by the ATM owner will usually (but not always) be stated during your transaction.

- Consider using a credit card for purchases and hotel and restaurant bills. Credit cards generally offer good exchange rates and, unlike cash, can be replaced if lost or stolen. But be sure to check whether your credit card company adds any fees for foreign purchases. And avoid using your credit card to get cash unless it is an emergency, because most credit cards charge high fees and interest for cash advances.

Time out to think

Find the current value of the Mexican peso in dollars. How does it compare to the value listed in Table AC.1? If it is significantly different, suggest some possible economic reasons for the change in the peso's value.

Problem Solving with Units

We have covered basic ideas of units and conversions, so we are ready to apply them to problem solving. In some cases, units can help us decide how to solve a problem. In all cases, units offer a useful way of checking answers. The following box summarizes how we work with units. As you study, notice how these ideas are applied in the examples throughout this chapter and the rest of this book.

WORKING WITH UNITS

Step 1: Identify the units involved in the problem. Use the units to help you decide how to approach the problem and what units to expect in the answer.

Step 2: Perform any operations (such as multiplication or division) on both the numbers and their associated units. Remember:

- You cannot add or subtract numbers with different units (such as apples and oranges), but you can combine different units through multiplication, division, or raising to powers.
- To make your work with units easier, replace division with multiplication by the reciprocal. For example,

$$\text{instead of dividing by } 60 \,\frac{\text{s}}{\text{min}}, \text{ multiply by } \frac{1 \text{ min}}{60 \text{ s}}.$$

Step 3: When you complete your calculations, make sure that your answer has the units you expected. If it doesn't, then you've done something wrong.

✳EXAMPLE 9 *Distance, Time, and Speed*

A car is traveling 25 miles every half-hour. How fast is it going?

SOLUTION   The "how fast" suggests that the final answer should be a speed. In this case, since the problem involves units of miles and hours, we should expect a speed in *miles per hour.* Knowing that these units mean miles *divided by* hours helps us realize that we should divide the distance traveled by the time it takes:

$$25 \text{ mi} \div \frac{1}{2} \text{ hr} = 25 \text{ mi} \times \frac{2}{1 \text{ hr}} = 50 \,\frac{\text{mi}}{\text{hr}}$$

Note that we replaced the division with multiplication by the reciprocal: Be sure you understand why the reciprocal of $\frac{1}{2}$ hr is $\frac{2}{1 \text{ hr}}$. The car is traveling at a speed of 50 miles per hour.

Now try Exercises 65–68. ◀

✳EXAMPLE 10 *Buying Farm Land*

You are buying 30 acres of farm land at a cost of $12,000 per acre. What is the total cost?

SOLUTION   The question asks about total cost, so the answer should be in *dollars.* We multiply the acreage by the cost per acre:

$$30 \text{ acres} \times \frac{\$12,000}{1 \text{ acre}} = \$360,000$$

Note how the unit *acre* "cancels" to leave the answer in units of dollars, as we expected. The land will cost $360,000.   Now try Exercises 69–78. ◀

Using Units to Check Answers

Checking answers is one of the most important reasons for clearly showing all units. If the answer does not come out with the expected units, then something has gone wrong. Of course, you should always check your method and your calculations as well as your units. An answer with the correct units could still contain other errors.

By the Way

You can use your familiarity with *miles per hour* to find the important general relationship among distance, time, and speed. Simply remember that miles are a distance and hours are a time, so a speed like miles per hour must be a distance (such as miles) divided by a time (such as hours):

$$\text{speed} = \frac{\text{distance}}{\text{time}}$$

By the Way

An *acre* is a unit of area originally defined as the amount of land a pair of oxen could plow in a day. Today it is defined as 43,560 square feet. One square mile is 640 acres.

✳EXAMPLE 11 *Exam Check*

You are a grader for a math course. An exam question reads: "Eli purchased 5 pounds of apples at a price of 50 cents per pound. How much did he pay for the apples?" On the paper you are grading, a student has written: "$50 \div 5 = 10$. He paid 10 cents." Write a note to the student explaining what went wrong.

SOLUTION Dear student—First, notice that your answer does not make sense. If one pound of apples costs 50¢, how could five pounds cost only 10¢? You could have prevented your error by keeping track of the units. In the exam question, the number 50 has units of *cents per pound* and the number 5 has units of *pounds*. Thus, your calculation of "$50 \div 5 = 10$" means

$$50 \frac{\text{¢}}{\text{lb}} \div 5 \text{ lb} = 50 \frac{\text{¢}}{\text{lb}} \times \frac{1}{5 \text{ lb}} = 10 \frac{\text{¢}}{\text{lb}^2}$$

(As usual, we replaced the division with multiplication by the reciprocal.) Your calculation gives units of "cents per square pound," so it cannot be correct for a question that asks for a simple price. The correct calculation multiplies the price per pound by the weight in pounds:

$$50 \frac{\text{¢}}{\text{lb}} \times 5 \text{ lb} = 250\text{¢} = \$2.50$$

The units now work out as they should: The 5 pounds of apples cost $2.50.

Now try Exercises 79–82. ◀

Using Units to Help You Solve Problems

As we've seen, knowing the units to expect in the answer can help determine how to solve a problem. The following two examples illustrate how powerful this idea can be. The first shows how units can help us get "unstuck" on an everyday sort of problem, while the second shows how units can help us come up with a strategy for a more complex problem—in this case, a problem relevant to the issue of global warming.

✳EXAMPLE 12 *Gas Mileage*

After a long day of driving, your destination is only 90 miles away. You know that your car gets 25 miles per gallon. How much gas do you need in your tank if you are to reach your destination without stopping? If you have a 12-gallon tank and the fuel gauge shows it is one-quarter full, will you make it? Show how units can help answer this question.

SOLUTION The question asks "how much gas," so we are looking for an answer with units of *gallons*. We have two other pieces of information available: the distance of 90 *miles* and the car's gas mileage of 25 *miles per gallon*. Thus, we are looking for a way to combine these two pieces of information to get an answer in gallons. We can do it by dividing the distance by the mileage:

$$90 \text{ mi} \div \frac{25 \text{ mi}}{1 \text{ gal}} = 90 \text{ mi} \times \frac{1 \text{ gal}}{25 \text{ mi}} = 3.6 \text{ gal}$$

You'll need 3.6 gallons of gas to drive the 90 miles. One-quarter of a 12-gallon tank is only 3 gallons, so you'd better stop for gas.   Now try Exercises 83–86.

✳EXAMPLE 13 *Melting of the Ice Caps*

Measurements of polar ice show that, if all Earth's polar ice melted, about 25 million cubic kilometers of water would be added to the oceans—most of it coming from Antarctica. How much would sea level rise as a result? Useful data: The total surface area of the Earth's oceans is about 340 million square kilometers.

SOLUTION   Because the question asks how much sea level would rise, we are looking for an answer with units of height, such as kilometers or meters. We are given two pieces of information that seem relevant: a volume of water in *cubic kilometers* and a surface area for the oceans in *square kilometers*. If we divide these two numbers, we get a result with units of kilometers:

$$\frac{25 \text{ million km}^3}{340 \text{ million km}^2} \approx 0.074 \text{ km} = 74 \text{ m}$$

Of course, the fact that this result has the expected units doesn't necessarily make it right. We must also ask whether it makes sense. In this case, it does. Dividing a volume by an area does indeed give a depth (because units of km^3 divided by units of km^2 give units of km), and the depth we've found represents the rise in sea level as long as the melting does not appreciably change the surface area of the oceans. (Because most continents have coastal hills or mountains that are higher than the expected sea level rise, ocean water would not spread very far inland. Thus, the ocean surface area would increase only slightly.) Perhaps the greatest surprise is the size of the answer: Complete polar melting would cause sea level to rise by some 74 meters, which is more than 240 feet. Thus, if this ever occurs, future archaeologists will have to be extreme deep sea divers to visit the ruins of modern coastal cities.   Now try Exercise 87.

By the Way

The Antarctic ice sheet contains more than 90% of the Earth's ice. This ice sheet covers an area of 13 million square kilometers, with an average depth of 2 kilometers (1.2 mi). In some places, the ice is more than 4.5 kilometers (2.8 mi) thick.

Time out to think

Although it would probably take thousands of years for the ice caps to melt fully, some melting may already be occurring due to global warming. Suppose that 1% of the ice melts during the next 100 years, raising sea level by about 2.4 feet. How do you think such a sea level rise would affect human civilization? Explain.

EXERCISES AC

QUICK QUIZ

Choose the best answer to each of the following questions. Explain your reasoning with one or more complete sentences.

1. What does the word *per* mean?

   a. divided by   b. multiplied by   c. in addition to

2. Which of the following represents 4 square miles?

   a. a line of small squares that is 4 miles long

   b. a square 2 miles on a side

   c. a square 4 miles on a side

3. If you multiply an area in square feet by a height in feet, the result will have units of

a. feet.   b. feet^2.   c. feet^3.

4. There are 1760 yards in a mile. Therefore, one cubic mile represents

a. 1760 square yards.   b. 1760^3 yards^3.

c. 1760 yard-miles.

5. The fact that 1 liter = 1.06 quarts can be written as the conversion factor

a. 1.06 quarts/liter.   b. 1.06 liters/quart.

c. 1 quart/1.06 liters.

6. Which of the following units describes the gas mileage of your car?

a. gallons per mile   b. kilometers per liter

c. dollars per gallon

7. If the current exchange rate is \$1.20 per euro, then

a. \$1 is worth more than 1 euro.

b. 1 euro is worth more than \$1.

c. 1 euro is equal to \$0.80.

8. One square foot is equivalent to

a. 12 square inches.   b. 120 square inches.

c. 144 square inches.

9. You are given two pieces of information: (1) the volume of a lake in cubic feet and (2) the average depth of the lake in feet. You are asked to find the surface area of the lake in square feet. You should

a. multiply the volume by the depth.

b. divide the volume by the depth.

c. divide the depth by the volume.

10. You are given two pieces of information: (1) the price of gasoline in dollars per gallon and (2) the gas mileage of a car in miles per gallon. You are asked to find the cost of driving this car in dollars per mile. You should

a. divide the price of gas by the car's gas mileage.

b. multiply the price of gas by the car's gas mileage.

c. divide the car's gas mileage by the price of gas.

REVIEW QUESTIONS

11. What are units? Describe how to read units that involve division, multiplication, squares, and cubes.

12. Explain why a unit conversion really involves just multiplying by 1.

13. Describe the three forms in which we can write any conversion factor. Given the conversion in one form, such as 1 lb = 16 oz, how do you find the other two forms?

14. Explain in words or with a picture why there are 9 square feet in 1 square yard and 27 cubic feet in 1 cubic yard. Then describe generally how to find conversion factors involving squares or cubes.

15. Describe how to read and use the currency data in Table 2.1.

16. Briefly describe how units can help you check your answers and solve problems. Give examples.

DOES IT MAKE SENSE?

Decide whether each of the following statements makes sense (or is clearly true) or does not make sense (or is clearly false). Explain your reasoning.

17. I drove at a speed of 35 miles for the entire trip.

18. Our house has a floor area of 1500 square feet.

19. I have a box with a volume of two square feet.

20. I needed five acres of water to fill the swimming pool.

21. I figured out how long the airplane will take to reach Beijing by dividing the airplane's speed by the distance to Beijing.

22. I figured out how long the airplane will take to reach Beijing by dividing the distance to Beijing by the airplane's speed.

BASIC SKILLS & CONCEPTS

Working with Fractions. Exercises 23–28 use skills covered in the Brief Review on pp. 630–631.

23. Evaluate the following expressions.

a. $\frac{3}{4} \times \frac{1}{2}$ b. $\frac{2}{3} \times \frac{3}{5}$ c. $\frac{1}{2} + \frac{3}{2}$ d. $\frac{2}{3} + \frac{1}{6}$

e. $\frac{2}{3} \times \frac{1}{4}$ f. $\frac{1}{4} + \frac{3}{8}$ g. $\frac{5}{8} - \frac{1}{4}$ h. $\frac{3}{2} \times \frac{2}{3}$

24. Evaluate the following expressions.

a. $\frac{1}{3} + \frac{1}{5}$ b. $\frac{10}{3} \times \frac{3}{7}$ c. $\frac{3}{4} - \frac{1}{8}$ d. $\frac{1}{2} + \frac{2}{3} + \frac{3}{4}$

e. $\frac{6}{5} + \frac{4}{15}$ f. $\frac{3}{5} \times \frac{2}{7}$ g. $\frac{1}{3} + \frac{13}{6}$ h. $\frac{3}{5} \times \frac{10}{3} \times \frac{3}{2}$

25. Write each of the following as a common fraction.

a. 3.5   b. 0.3   c. 0.05   d. 4.1

e. 2.15   f. 0.35   g. 0.98   h. 4.01

26. Write each of the following as a common fraction.

   a. 2.75   b. 0.45   c. 0.005   d. 1.16

   e. 6.5   f. 4.123   g. 0.0003   h. 0.034

27. Convert the following fractions to decimal form; round to the nearest thousandth if necessary.

   a. $\dfrac{1}{4}$ b. $\dfrac{3}{8}$ c. $\dfrac{2}{3}$ d. $\dfrac{3}{5}$

   e. $\dfrac{13}{2}$ f. $\dfrac{23}{6}$ g. $\dfrac{103}{50}$ h. $\dfrac{42}{26}$

28. Convert the following fractions to decimal form; round to the nearest thousandth if necessary.

   a. $\dfrac{1}{5}$ b. $\dfrac{4}{9}$ c. $\dfrac{4}{11}$ d. $\dfrac{12}{7}$

   e. $\dfrac{28}{9}$ f. $\dfrac{56}{11}$ g. $\dfrac{102}{49}$ h. $\dfrac{15}{4}$

Identifying Units. In Exercises 29–36, identify the units you would expect for the given quantity. State the units both in words (e.g., dollars per gallon) and mathematically (e.g., $/gal).

29. The price of apple juice, found by dividing its cost in dollars by its volume in ounces.

30. A speed, found by dividing a distance measured in kilometers by a time measured in seconds.

31. The cost of a piece of carpet, found by dividing its price in dollars by its area in square yards.

32. The flow rate of a river in which 5000 cubic feet of water flow past a particular location every second.

33. The price of eggplants in Italy, found by dividing their cost in euros by their weight in kilograms.

34. The price of fabric, found by dividing its cost in dollars by its area in square feet.

35. The gas mileage of a car, found by dividing the distance in miles that it travels by the amount of gas in gallons that it uses.

36. The density of a rock, found by dividing its weight in grams by its volume in cubic centimeters.

Unit Conversions. In Exercises 37–46, carry out the indicated unit conversion.

37. Convert 3.5 miles to units of feet.

38. Convert 10 feet to units of inches.

39. Convert 3.5 hours to units of minutes.

40. Convert 6 hours to units of seconds.

41. Convert 3 pounds to units of ounces.

42. Convert 4 acres to units of square feet.

43. Convert 2 weeks to units of minutes.

44. Convert 60 miles per hour to units of miles per minute.

45. Convert 35 gallons to units of quarts.

46. Convert 12 years to units of hours (ignoring leap years).

47. Area and Volume Calculations. Clearly show the use of units in the following exercises.

   a. A reservoir has a rectangular base measuring 120 feet by 40 feet and is 9 feet deep. Find the area of the base and the amount of water the reservoir holds when it is full.

   b. A soccer field is a rectangle measuring 110 yards by 55 yards. Find the area of the field and the volume of snow on the field after a 3-foot snowfall.

   c. A large building has a square base 120 feet on a side and is 330 feet high. Find the area of the base and the volume of the building.

48. Area and Volume Calculations. Clearly show the use of units in the following exercises.

   a. A warehouse is 40 yards long and 25 yards wide and piled with cartons to a height of 3 yards. What is the area of the warehouse floor? What is the total volume of the cartons? (Assume there is no space between cartons.)

   b. The bed of a pickup truck is 3.5 feet deep, 12 feet long, and 5 feet wide. What is the area of the bed's floor? What is the volume of the bed?

   c. A can has a circular base with an area of 6 square inches and is 4 inches tall. What is its total volume?

Conversions with Units Raised to Powers. Use the appropriate rules to answer Exercises 49–56.

49. Find a conversion factor between square feet and square inches. Write it in three forms.

50. Find a conversion factor between cubic feet and cubic inches. Write it in three forms.

51. Given that 1 meter = 100 centimeters, find a conversion factor between square meters and square centimeters. Write it in three forms.

52. Find the area in square yards of a rectangular room that measures 16 feet by 22 feet.

53. A box-shaped water tank measures 12 feet by 8 feet by 4 feet. Find its volume in cubic yards.

54. How many cubic inches are there in 4.5 cubic feet?

55. An air conditioning system can circulate 320 cubic feet of air per minute. How many cubic yards of air can it circulate per minute?

56. A hot tub pump circulates 4 cubic feet of water per minute. How many cubic inches of water does it circulate each minute?

Currency Conversions. Answer the questions in Exercises 57–64 using the exchange rates in Table AC.1.

57. Which is worth more: 1 Mexican peso or $1 U.S.? Explain.

58. Which is worth more: 1 euro or $1 Canadian? Explain.

59. You return from a trip with 2500 Mexican pesos. How much are your pesos worth in U.S. dollars?

60. How many euros can you buy with $120 U.S.?

61. How many U.S. dollars can you buy with 12,000 yen?

62. Bottled water costs 0.75 euro per liter in Paris. What is the price in units of U.S. dollars per quart? (1 quart = 0.9464 liter)

63. Gasoline sells for 11 pesos per liter in Mexico. What is the price in units of U.S. dollars per gallon? (1 gallon = 3.785 liters)

64. Cantaloupes sell for 1.80 euros per kilogram in Belgium. What is the price in units of U.S. dollars per pound? (1 kilogram = 2.205 pounds)

Working with Units. Use units to help you answer the questions in Exercises 65–78.

65. A car travels 13 miles in 15 minutes. How fast is it going in miles per hour?

66. An airplane travels 95 miles in 10 minutes. How fast is it going in miles per hour?

67. The film *Shrek 2* grossed $436 million. If tickets cost $8 each, approximately how many people saw the film?

68. During your softball season you had 54 hits in 152 at-bats. What was your batting average in hits per at-bats?

69. You buy 4.7 pounds of apples priced at $1.29 per pound. How much do you pay?

70. You buy 2.8 kilograms of cherries priced at $3.50 per kilogram. How much do you pay?

71. In 2003, there were approximately 555,000 deaths in the United States due to cancer. Find the mortality rate in units of deaths per 100,000 people, assuming a U.S. population of 300 million.

72. In 2003, there were approximately 695,000 deaths in the United States due to heart disease. Find the mortality rate in units of deaths per 100,000 people, assuming a U.S. population of 300 million.

73. There are approximately 3 million births in the United States each year. Find the birth rate in births per minute.

74. Montana has approximately 148,000 public school students and spends a total of $371 million on public education. What is the expenditure per pupil?

75. You take a trip in which you drive 1200 miles in 24 hours. What is your average speed for the entire trip?

76. You work 40 hours per week and are paid $13.50 per hour. If you work all 52 weeks in a year, how much will you earn?

77. If you sleep an average of 7 hours each night, how many hours do you sleep in a year?

78. A human heart beats about 60 times per minute. If an average human being lives to the age of 75, how many times does the average heart beat in a lifetime?

What Went Wrong? Exercises 79–82 include an exam question and a solution given by a student. State whether each solution is right or wrong. If it is wrong, write a note to the student explaining why the answer is wrong and how to solve the problem correctly.

79. *Exam Question:* A candy store sells chocolate for $7.70 per pound. The piece you want to buy weighs 0.11 pound. How much will it cost, to the nearest cent? (Neglect sales tax.)

Student Solution: 0.11 ÷ 7.70 = 0.014. It will cost 1.4¢.

80. *Exam Question:* You ride your bike up a steep mountain road at 5 miles per hour. How far do you go in 3 hours?

Student Solution: 5 ÷ 3 = 1.7. I rode 1.7 miles.

81. *Exam Question:* You can buy a 50-pound bag of flour for $11 or you can buy a 1-pound bag for $0.39. Compare the per pound cost for the large and small bags.

Student Solution: The large bag price is 50 ÷ $11 = $4.55 per pound, which is much more than the 39¢ per pound price of the small bag.

82. *Exam Question:* The average person needs 1500 Calories a day. A can of Coke contains 140 Calories. How many Cokes would you need to drink to fill your daily caloric needs? (Note: This diet may not meet other nutritional needs!)

Student Solution: 1500 × 140 = 210,000. You would need to drink 210,000 Cokes to meet your daily caloric needs.

Gas Mileage. Exercises 83–86 involve practical gas mileage calculations.

83. Suppose you drive a car with an average gas mileage of 28 miles per gallon. If you plan to take a 2500-mile cross-country trip, how many gallons of gasoline should you expect to use?

84. Suppose you drive a car with an average gas mileage of 35 miles per gallon. If you plan to take a 2500-mile cross-country trip, how much should you budget (in dollars) for gasoline if the price of gasoline averages $3.25 per gallon?

85. Gas mileage actually varies slightly with the driving speed of a car (as well as with highway vs. city driving). Suppose your car averages 38 miles per gallon on the highway if your average speed is 55 miles per hour and averages 32 miles per gallon on the highway if your average speed is 70 miles per hour.

    a. What is the driving time for a 2000-mile trip if you drive at an average speed of 55 miles per hour? What is the driving time at 70 miles per hour?

    b. Assume a gasoline price of $3.25 per gallon. What is the gasoline cost for a 2000-mile trip if you drive at an average speed of 55 miles per hour? What is the gasoline cost at 70 miles per hour?

86. Suppose your car averages 32 miles per gallon on the highway if your average speed is 60 miles per hour and averages 25 miles per gallon on the highway if your average speed is 75 miles per hour.

    a. What is the driving time for a 1500-mile trip if you drive at an average speed of 60 miles per hour? What is the driving time at 75 miles per hour?

    b. Assume a gasoline price of $3.25 per gallon. What is the gasoline cost for a 1500-mile trip if you drive at an average speed of 60 miles per hour? What is the gasoline cost at 75 miles per hour?

87. **Filling a Pool.** A swimming pool is 75 feet long and 54 feet wide. It is only partially filled with water, so the water surface is 6 inches below where it is supposed to be. How much water would it take, in cubic feet, to raise the water level by 6 inches?

88. **Practical Carpet Problem.** Suppose you want to install carpet in a room that measures 18 feet by 22 feet. The carpet you want costs $28.50 per square yard and comes only in rolls that are 12 feet wide (and at least 100 feet long). If you allow only one seam (where two pieces of carpet meet), what is the most efficient way to lay the carpet and how much will the carpet cost?

FURTHER APPLICATIONS

89. **House Footprint.** A local zoning ordinance says that a house's "footprint" (area of its ground floor) cannot occupy more than $\frac{1}{4}$ of the lot it is built on. Suppose you own a $\frac{1}{4}$-acre lot. What is the maximum allowed footprint for your house, in square feet (1 acre = 43,560 ft^2)?

90. **Full of Hot Air.** The average person breathes 6 times per minute (at rest), inhaling and exhaling half a liter of air each time. How much "hot air" (the air is warmed by the body), in liters, does the average person exhale each day?

91. **E-Books.** Computer memory is measured in units of bytes, where one byte is enough memory to store one character (a letter in the alphabet or a number). How many typical pages of text can be stored on a 2-gigabyte hard drive (a gigabyte is one billion bytes)? Assume 2000 bytes per page.

92. **Dog Years.** Sometimes the age of dogs is described in a unit called "dog years." A commonly used conversion is that 1 real year equals 7 dog years.

    a. If your dog is 15 real years old, what is her age in dog years?

    b. People often refer to the third year in the life of a human child as the "terrible twos" stage. If dogs have a terrible twos stage in their third dog year, how old are they, in real time, during this stage?

    c. Based on what you know about dogs, do you think the common conversion of 1 real year to 7 dog years seems reasonable? Explain.

93. **Shower vs. Bath.** Assume that when you take a bath, you fill to the halfway point a tub (assumed to be a box) that measures 6 feet by 3 feet by 2.5 feet. When you take a shower, you use a shower head with a flow rate of 1.75 gallons per minute, and you typically spend 10 minutes in the shower. There are 7.5 gallons in one cubic foot.

    a. Do you use more water taking a shower or taking a bath?

    b. How long would you need to shower to use as much water as you use taking a bath?

    c. Assuming your shower is in a bath tub, propose a non-mathematical way to compare, in one experiment, the amounts of water you use taking a shower and a bath.

94. **Hurricane Katrina.** Experts estimate that when the levees around New Orleans broke in the aftermath of Hurricane Katrina, water flowed into the city at a peak rate of 9 billion gallons per day. There are 7.5 gallons in one cubic foot.

    a. Find the flow rate in units of cubic feet per second (cfs).

Compare this flow rate to the average flow rate of the Colorado River in the Grand Canyon: 30,000 cfs.

b. Assume that the flooded part of the city had an area of 6 square miles. Estimate how much (in feet) the water level rose in one day at the given flow rate.

95. **Glen Canyon Flood.** The Department of the Interior released a "spike flood" from the Glen Canyon Dam on the Colorado River. Its purpose was to restore the river and the habitats along its banks, particularly in the Grand Canyon. The reservoir behind the dam contains about 1.2 trillion (1,200,000,000,000) cubic feet of water. The release from the dam lasted a week at a rate of 25,800 cubic feet of water per second. About how much water was released during the 1-week flood? What percentage of the total water in the reservoir was released during the flood?

96. **Home Project.** Assume you are building a simple shed and doing some landscaping. The shed will be the shape of a box that is 10 feet long, 10 feet wide, and 8 feet tall. The area you are landscaping is 75 feet long and 40 feet wide. For each of the following questions, find the price of the needed item at a local store.

a. How much would it cost to plant the entire landscaping area with grass seed? (Hint: Grass seed is usually rated by how many square feet can be covered by each pound of seed.)

b. Suppose you decide to cover the landscaping area with sod (i.e., rolls of pre-grown grass). How much will the sod cost?

c. You decide that before any planting, you need to add 8 inches of high-quality top soil to the entire landscape area. How much will the soil cost?

d. How much will it cost to paint the exterior walls of the shed? (Hint: Paint cans generally tell you how much area can be covered with the paint they contain.)

WEB PROJECTS

Find useful links for Web Projects on the text Web site: **www.aw.com/bennett-briggs**

97. **South American Adventure.** Suppose you are planning an extended trip through many countries in South America. Use one of the many currency exchange sites on the Web to get all the exchange rates you'll need. Make a brief table showing each currency you'll need and the value of each currency in dollars.

98. **Polar Ice Melting.** Starting with a search on "glaciers" or "glaciology" (the study of glaciers), use the Web to learn more about polar ice melting. Focus on one aspect of the issue, such as whether global warming is causing melting, or the environmental impacts of melting, or the geological history of ice ages. Write a one-page summary of what you learn.

IN THE NEWS

99. **Are the Units Clear?** Find a news story that involves numerical data. Are all the numbers in the story given with meaningful units, or is the meaning of some of the units unclear? Briefly summarize how well (or not well) the article uses units.

100. **Units on the Highway.** Next time you are on the highway, look for three signs that use numbers (such as speed limits or distances to nearest exits). Are the units of the numbers given? If not, how are you expected to know the units? In cases where the units are not given, do you think the units would be obvious to everyone? Why or why not?

101. **False Advertising?** A Goodyear tire commercial began by stating that the Goodyear Aquatread tire can "channel away" 1 gallon of water per second. The announcer then said: "One gallon per second—that's 396 gallons per mile." What's wrong with this statement? What point do you think the advertisement was trying to make? Can you find other examples of advertisements that misstate units?

UNIT AC2 Standardized Units: More Problem-Solving Power

Working with units can be a powerful problem-solving technique—but only if the units are clear and meaningful. When units (such as feet, miles, or kilograms) are *standardized*, everyone agrees on their meaning. Having a good understanding of standardized units will allow you to study a broader range of problems.

Standardized Unit Systems: U.S. and Metric

Today, only one system of standardized units enjoys wide international use: the international metric system, also known as SI (from the French *Système International d'Unités*). However, the United States still uses an ancient measurement system sometimes called the English system, but more formally known as the *U.S. customary system* (USCS). Let's briefly review each system.

The U.S. Customary System

The roots of U.S. customary units reach back to ancient Middle Eastern civilizations, including the Egyptians, Sumerians, Babylonians, and Hebrews. Units of length were based on individual body measurements. For example, the *foot* was once the length of the foot of whoever was doing the measuring, and our word *inch* comes from the Latin *uncia*, meaning "thumb-width." There are 12 inches in one foot because the Romans discovered that most adult feet are about 12 thumb-widths long. The Romans paced out longer distances. Our word *mile* comes from the Latin *milia passum*, meaning "one thousand paces."

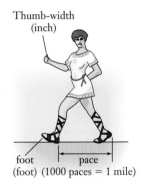

Thumb-width (inch)

foot pace
(foot) (1000 paces = 1 mile)

....

Time out to think

How many of *your* thumb-widths fit along your bare foot? Were the Romans correct in believing there are 12 thumb-widths in a foot?

As you might imagine, lengths that vary from person to person can lead to difficulties. For example, if you are buying 10 feet of rope, is it the length of your foot or the seller's foot that should be used to measure the rope? Many cultures therefore standardized units according to body measures of one particular person, such as a king. But such measures still changed every time one king was replaced by another. The first permanent standardization began when English King Henry I (1100–1135) set

TABLE AC.2   USCS Lengths (common abbreviations in parentheses)

1 inch (in.)	= 2.54 centimeters	1 furlong	= 40 rods = $\frac{1}{8}$ mile
1 foot (ft)	= 12 inches	1 mile (mi)	= 1760 yards = 5280 feet
1 yard (yd)	= 3 feet	1 nautical mile	= 1.852 km ≈ 6076.1 feet
1 rod	= 5.5 yards	1 land league	= 3 miles
1 fathom	= 6 feet	1 marine league	= 3 nautical miles

HISTORICAL NOTE

The *avoirdupois* measures were standardized by London merchants around the year 1300. The term *avoirdupois* comes from the French for "goods of weight." The *troy* system was probably named for the town of Troyes, France, and was established in the 15th century. The apothecary system was developed by medieval pharmacists (*apothecary* is a synonym for *pharmacy*).

TABLE AC.3   USCS Weights (common abbreviations in parentheses)

Avoirdupois Measures		Troy Measures		Apothecary Measures	
1 grain	= 0.0648 gram	1 grain	= 0.0648 gram	1 grain	= 0.0648 gram
1 ounce (oz)	= 437.5 grains	1 carat = 0.2 gram	= 3.086 grains	1 scruple	= 20 grains
1 pound (lb)	= 16 ounces	1 pennyweight	= 24 grains	1 dram	= 3 scruples
1 ton	= 2000 pounds	1 troy ounce	= 480 grains	1 apoth. ounce	= 8 drams
1 long ton	= 2240 pounds	1 troy pound	= 12 troy ounces	1 apoth. pound	= 12 ounces

the *yard* as the measurement from the tip of *his* nose to the tip of *his* thumb on *his* outstretched arm. A few centuries later, the English brought their units to the American colonies, and they have since undergone further modification and standardization. Today, all lengths in the U.S. customary system are based on the inch, which is defined by law to be exactly 2.54 centimeters. Table AC.2 summarizes units of length in the U.S. customary system.

For measuring weight, the U.S. customary system actually has three distinct sets of units. Traditionally, jewelers used *troy* measures of weight, pharmacists used *apothecary* measures of weight, and most other commerce was conducted with *avoirdupois* measures of weight. Table AC.3 summarizes all three systems, but only the avoirdupois measures are commonly used today. The basic unit of weight in all three sets is the *grain*, an ancient unit originally based on the weight of a typical grain of wheat.

The basic U.S. customary unit of volume is the cubic inch (in.^{3}), but from here the system becomes complicated, because units with the same name represent different volumes depending on whether we're working with dry or liquid materials. For example, a *dry* pint is 33.60 cubic inches, while a *liquid* pint is only 28.88 cubic inches (Figure AC.4). Thus, a container that holds one pint of water is too small for one pint of flour. (If you travel, it can be even more complicated, because British customary measures differ from U.S. measures. For example, a British pint of beer is about 20% larger than a U.S. pint of beer.) Table AC.4 summarizes USCS measures of volume.

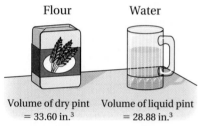

Flour   Water

Volume of dry pint   Volume of liquid pint
= 33.60 in.^{3} = 28.88 in.^{3}

FIGURE AC.4 In the U.S. customary system, a dry pint (such as a pint of flour) contains a greater volume than a liquid pint (such as a pint of water).

TABLE AC.4   USCS Volumes (common abbreviations in parentheses)

Liquid Measures		Dry Measures	
1 tablespoon (tbsp or T)	= 3 teaspoons (tsp or t)	1 in.^{3}	≈ 16.387 cm^3
1 fluid ounce (fl oz)	= 2 tablespoons = 1.805 in.^{3}	1 ft^3	= 1728 in.^{3} = 7.48 gallons
1 cup (c)	= 8 fluid ounces	1 yd^3	= 27 ft^3
1 pint (pt)	= 16 fluid ounces = 28.88 in.^{3}	1 dry pint (pt)	= 33.60 in.^{3}
1 quart (qt)	= 2 pints = 57.75 in.^{3}	1 dry quart (qt)	= 2 dry pints = 67.2 in.^{3}
1 gallon (gal)	= 4 quarts	1 peck	= 8 dry quarts
1 barrel of petroleum	= 42 gallons	1 bushel	= 4 pecks
1 barrel of liquid	= 31 gallons	1 cord	= 128 ft^3

Practical Matters

Gems and Gold Jewelry

If you've ever bought jewelry, you've probably seen labels stating *karats* or *carats*. But you may be surprised to know that these are not just alternative spellings of the same word. A *carat* is a unit of weight defined to be exactly 0.2 gram (see Table AC.3). A *karat* is a measure of the purity of gold: 24-karat gold is 100% pure, 18-karat gold is 75% pure, 14-karat gold is 58% pure (because $\frac{14}{24} \approx 0.58$), and so on.

If you are buying gold jewelry, look for a label stating both its purity in karats and its weight (usually given in grams); the amount of gold you are actually buying depends on both. For example:

- Ten grams of 18-karat gold actually contain 7.5 grams of pure gold, since 18-karat gold is 75% pure.
- Ten grams of 14-karat gold actually contain 5.8 grams of pure gold, since 14-karat gold is 58% pure.

Although a higher karat value is purer, it comes with an important practical tradeoff. Gold is a soft metal, and the metals (usually silver and copper) mixed into lower-karat gold give it added strength. Thus, for example, a 14-karat gold ring is stronger and more durable than an 18-karat gold ring.

You'll deal with carats rather than karats if you are buying gems such as diamonds or emeralds. Because 1 carat is 0.2 gram, the number of carats tells you the precise weight of the gem. However, several factors besides weight are important to the price, such as the gem's shape and color.

If you are gem shopping, you'll need to make trade-offs among weight, color, and clarity (and sometimes other factors as well) to stay within your budget. For example, if you are looking for a round diamond, $10,000 might buy either a 1-carat diamond with good color and clarity or a 2-carat diamond with poorer color and clarity. Given the cost of most gems, you should spend some time doing price comparisons before buying.

✳EXAMPLE 1 *The Kentucky Derby*

In the Kentucky Derby, horses race a distance of 10 furlongs. How many miles is the race?

SOLUTION   From Table AC.2, 1 furlong $= \frac{1}{8}$ mi, which is the same as 0.125 mile. We can write this conversion factor in two other equivalent forms:

$$\frac{1 \text{ furlong}}{0.125 \text{ mi}} = 1 \qquad \text{or} \qquad \frac{0.125 \text{ mi}}{1 \text{ furlong}} = 1$$

The second form allows us to convert furlongs to miles:

$$10 \text{ furlong} \times \frac{0.125 \text{ mi}}{1 \text{ furlong}} = 1.25 \text{ mi}$$

The Kentucky Derby is a race of 1.25 miles.   Now try Exercises 45–48. ◀

✳EXAMPLE 2 *20,000 Leagues Under the Sea*

In Jules Verne's novel *20,000 Leagues Under the Sea*, does the title refer to an ocean depth? How do you know?

SOLUTION From Table AC.2, 1 marine league = 3 nautical miles. Thus, 20,000 leagues is

$$20{,}000 \text{ leagues} \times \frac{3 \text{ naut. mi}}{1 \text{ league}} = 60{,}000 \text{ naut. mi}$$

Because the oceans are at most a few miles deep, 20,000 leagues cannot possibly refer to an ocean depth. The book's title refers to the distance traveled by submarine under the sea.   Now try Exercises 49–52. ◀

The International Metric System

The international metric system was invented in France late in the 18th century and is now used throughout the world. The metric system was designed for two primary reasons: (1) to replace many customary units with just a few basic units and (2) to simplify conversions through use of a decimal (base 10) system. Similar ideas had already been applied to currency. For example, in 1785, the United States replaced the customary currencies of the individual states with a national currency, the dollar (devised by Thomas Jefferson). Like the metric system, the dollar is based on a decimal relationship (because 100¢ = $1).

The basic units of length, mass, time, and volume in the metric system are

- the **meter** for length, abbreviated m
- the **kilogram** for mass, abbreviated kg
- the **second** for time, abbreviated s
- the **liter** for volume, abbreviated L

These basic units can be combined with a prefix that indicates multiplication by a power of 10. For example, *kilo* means 1000 so a kilometer is 1000 meters, and *micro* means *one-millionth* so a microgram is a millionth of a gram. Table AC.5 lists common metric prefixes.

HISTORICAL NOTE

In 1790, Thomas Jefferson (then Secretary of State) proposed adoption of the metric system to Congress. Had Congress agreed, the United States would have been the *first* country to adopt the metric system—ahead of France, which adopted it in 1795.

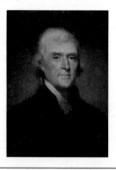

TABLE AC.5 Metric Prefixes

SMALL VALUES			LARGE VALUES		
Prefix	Abbrev.	Value	Prefix	Abbrev.	Value
deci	d	10^{-1} (one-tenth)	deca	da	10^{1} (ten)
centi	c	10^{-2} (one-hundredth)	hecto	h	10^{2} (hundred)
milli	m	10^{-3} (one-thousandth)	kilo	k	10^{3} (thousand)
micro	μ	10^{-6} (one-millionth)	mega	M	10^{6} (million)
nano	N	10^{-9} (one-billionth)	giga	G	10^{9} (billion)
pico	P	10^{-12} (one-trillionth)	tera	T	10^{12} (trillion)

Note: The abbreviation for micro, μ, is the Greek letter mu.

Time out to think

People often say that expensive things cost "megabucks." What does this statement mean literally? Can you think of other cases where metric prefixes have entered popular language?

A Brief Review

Powers of 10

Powers of 10 indicate how many times to multiply 10 by itself. For example:

$$10^2 = 10 \times 10 = 100$$
$$10^6 = 10 \times 10 \times 10 \times 10 \times 10 \times 10 = 1{,}000{,}000$$

Negative powers indicate reciprocals of corresponding positive powers. For example:

$$10^{-2} = \frac{1}{10^2} = \frac{1}{100} = 0.01$$
$$10^{-6} = \frac{1}{10^6} = \frac{1}{1{,}000{,}000} = 0.000001$$

Thus, powers of 10 follow two basic rules:

1. A positive exponent tells how many 0s follow the 1. For example, 10^0 is a 1 followed by no 0s; 10^8 is a 1 followed by eight 0s.

2. A negative exponent tells how many places are to the right of the decimal point, including the 1. For example, $10^{-1} = 0.1$ has one place to the right of the decimal point; $10^{-6} = 0.000001$ has six places to the right of the decimal point.

Multiplying and Dividing Powers of 10

Multiplying powers of 10 simply requires adding exponents. For example:

$$10^4 \times 10^7 = \underbrace{10{,}000}_{10^4} \times \underbrace{10{,}000{,}000}_{10^7}$$
$$= \underbrace{100{,}000{,}000{,}000}_{=\,10^{4+7}\,=\,10^{11}}$$

$$10^5 \times 10^{-3} = \underbrace{100{,}000}_{10^5} \times \underbrace{0.001}_{10^{-3}}$$
$$= \underbrace{100}_{=\,10^{5+(-3)}\,=\,10^2}$$

$$10^{-8} \times 10^{-5} = \underbrace{0.00000001}_{10^{-8}} \times \underbrace{0.00001}_{10^{-5}}$$
$$= \underbrace{0.0000000000001}_{=\,10^{-8+(-5)}\,=\,10^{-13}}$$

Dividing powers of 10 requires subtracting exponents. For example:

$$\frac{10^5}{10^3} = \underbrace{100{,}000}_{10^5} \div \underbrace{1000}_{10^3} = \underbrace{100}_{=\,10^{5-3}\,=\,10^2}$$

$$\frac{10^3}{10^7} = \underbrace{1000}_{10^3} \div \underbrace{10{,}000{,}000}_{10^7} = \underbrace{0.0001}_{=\,10^{3-7}\,=\,10^{-4}}$$

$$\frac{10^{-4}}{10^{-6}} = \underbrace{0.0001}_{10^{-4}} \div \underbrace{0.000001}_{10^{-6}} = \underbrace{100}_{=\,10^{-4-(-6)}\,=\,10^2}$$

Powers of Powers of 10

We can use the multiplication and division rules to raise powers of 10 to other powers. For example:

$$(10^4)^3 = 10^4 \times 10^4 \times 10^4 = 10^{4+4+4} = 10^{12}$$

Note that we get the same result by simply multiplying the two powers:

$$(10^4)^3 = 10^{4 \times 3} = 10^{12}$$

Adding and Subtracting Powers of 10

There is no shortcut for adding or subtracting powers of 10, as there is for multiplication or division. The values must be written in longhand notation. For example:

$$10^6 + 10^2 = 1{,}000{,}000 + 100$$
$$= 1{,}000{,}100$$
$$10^8 + 10^{-3} = 100{,}000{,}000 + 0.001$$
$$= 100{,}000{,}000.001$$
$$10^7 - 10^3 = 10{,}000{,}000 - 1000$$
$$= 9{,}999{,}000$$

Summary

We summarize our findings as follows, using n and m to represent any numbers:

- To *multiply* powers of 10, *add* exponents:

$$10^n \times 10^m = 10^{n+m}$$

- To *divide* powers of 10, *subtract* exponents:

$$\frac{10^n}{10^m} = 10^{n-m}$$

- To *raise* powers of 10 to other powers, multiply exponents:

$$(10^n)^m = 10^{n \times m}$$

Now try Exercises 29–44. ◄

HISTORICAL NOTE

People around the world use the same base 10 (decimal) counting system. This may seem natural because we have 10 fingers, but various ancient cultures used base 2, base 3, base 5, base 20, and other bases. Vestiges of other bases remain in our language. For example, we have 60 seconds in a minute and 60 minutes in an hour because the ancient Babylonians used base 60. Similarly, a dozen is 12 and a gross is 12 × 12 = 144, presumably because base 12 was once common in northern Europe.

By the Way

Technically, pounds are a unit of *weight* and kilograms are a unit of *mass,* so the given conversions between pounds and kilograms are valid only on Earth. That is, on Earth, a 50-kilogram astronaut weighs about 110 pounds. In Earth orbit, the astronaut still has a mass of 50 kilograms, but has a weight of zero (weightless).

✳EXAMPLE 3 *Using Metric Prefixes*

a. Convert 2759 centimeters to meters.
b. How many nanoseconds are in a microsecond?

SOLUTION

a. Table AC.5 shows that *centi* means 10^{-2}, so 1 cm = 10^{-2} m or, equivalently, 1 m = 100 cm. Thus, 2759 centimeters is the same as

$$2759 \text{ cm} \times \frac{1 \text{ m}}{100 \text{ cm}} = 27.59 \text{ m}$$

b. We compare the quantities by dividing the longer time (microsecond) by the shorter time (nanosecond):

$$\frac{1 \text{ } \mu s}{1 \text{ ns}} = \frac{10^{-6} \text{ s}}{10^{-9} \text{ s}} = 10^{-6-(-9)} = 10^{-6+9} = 10^{3}$$

A microsecond is 10^3, or 1000, times as long as a nanosecond, so there are 1000 nanoseconds in a microsecond.   Now try Exercises 53–58. ◄

Metric–USCS Conversions

We carry out conversions between metric and USCS units like any other unit conversions. Table AC.6 lists a few handy conversion factors. It's useful to memorize approximate conversions, particularly if you plan to travel internationally or if you work with metric units in sports or business. For example, if you remember that a kilometer is about 0.6 mile, you will know that a 10-kilometer road race is about 6 miles. Similarly, if you remember that a meter is about 10% longer than a yard, you'll know that a 100-meter race is about the same as a 110-yard race.

TABLE AC.6 USCS–Metric Conversions	
USCS to Metric	**Metric to USCS**
1 in. = 2.540 cm	1 cm = 0.3937 in.
1 ft = 0.3048 m	1 m = 3.28 ft
1 yd = 0.9144 m	1 m = 1.094 yd
1 mi = 1.6093 km	1 km = 0.6214 mi
1 lb = 0.4536 kg	1 kg = 2.205 lb
1 fl oz = 29.574 mL	1 mL = 0.03381 fl oz
1 qt = 0.9464 L	1 L = 1.057 qt
1 gal = 3.785 L	1 L = 0.2642 gal

✳EXAMPLE 4 *Gas Price per Liter*

At a gas station in Mexico, the price of gasoline is 8.0 pesos per liter. What is the price in dollars per gallon? Use the currency exchange rate in Table AC.1.

SOLUTION   We use a chain of conversions to convert from pesos to dollars and then from liters to gallons. From Table AC.1, the currency conversion is $0.09136 per peso. From Table AC.6, there are 3.785 liters per gallon.

$$\frac{8.0 \text{ peso}}{1 \text{ L}} \times \frac{\$0.09136}{1 \text{ peso}} \times \frac{3.785 \text{ L}}{1 \text{ gal}} \approx \frac{\$2.77}{1 \text{ gal}}$$

The price of the gasoline is about $2.77 per gallon.   Now try Exercises 59–63. ◀◼

✳EXAMPLE 5 *Square Kilometers to Square Miles*

How many square kilometers are in one square mile?

SOLUTION   We square both sides of the conversion factor, 1 mi = 1.6093 km.

$$(1 \text{ mi})^2 = (1.6093 \text{ km})^2 \quad \Rightarrow \quad 1 \text{ mi}^2 = 2.5898 \text{ km}^2$$

One square mile is 2.5898 square kilometers.   Now try Exercises 64–68. ◀◼

Temperature Units: Fahrenheit, Celsius, and Kelvin

Three temperature scales are commonly used today (Figure AC.5). The **Fahrenheit** scale is used in the United States. It is defined so that water freezes at 32°F and boils at 212°F. Internationally, temperature is usually measured on the **Celsius** scale, which places the freezing point of water at 0°C and the boiling point at 100°C. In science, temperature is usually measured on the **Kelvin** scale, which is the same as the Celsius scale except for its zero point. A temperature of 0 K is the coldest possible temperature, known as **absolute zero.** It is approximately −273.15°C or −459.67°F. The following box summarizes conversions among the three scales.

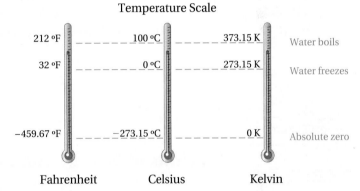

Temperature Scale

212 °F	100 °C	373.15 K	Water boils
32 °F	0 °C	273.15 K	Water freezes
−459.67 °F	−273.15 °C	0 K	Absolute zero

Fahrenheit   Celsius   Kelvin

FIGURE AC.5

TEMPERATURE CONVERSIONS

The conversions are given both in words and with formulas in which C, F, and K are Celsius, Fahrenheit, and Kelvin temperatures, respectively.

To Convert from	Conversion in Words	Conversion Formula
Celsius to Fahrenheit	Multiply by 1.8 (or $\frac{9}{5}$). Then add 32.	$F = 1.8C + 32$
Fahrenheit to Celsius	Subtract 32. Then divide by 1.8 (or multiply by $\frac{5}{9}$).	$C = \dfrac{F - 32}{1.8}$
Celsius to Kelvin	Add 273.15.	$K = C + 273.15$
Kelvin to Celsius	Subtract 273.15.	$C = K - 273.15$

Where do these conversion formulas come from? It's easy to see their origin by studying Figure AC.5. For conversions between Kelvin and Celsius, note that the scales are the same except for the 273.15° difference in their zero points. Thus, we simply add 273.15 to a Celsius temperature to get a Kelvin temperature. For conversions between Celsius and Fahrenheit, look at the differences in temperature between the freezing and boiling points of water. The Celsius scale has 100°C between these points, while the Fahrenheit scale has 212°F − 32°F = 180°F between them. Thus, each Celsius degree represents $\frac{180}{100}$ = 1.8 Fahrenheit degrees, which explains the factor of 1.8 (or $\frac{9}{5}$) in the conversions. The 32 appears in the Celsius–Fahrenheit conversions to account for the difference in their zero points.

✳EXAMPLE 6 *Human Body Temperature*

Average human body temperature is 98.6°F. What is it in Celsius and Kelvin?

SOLUTION We convert from Fahrenheit to Celsius by subtracting 32 and then dividing by 1.8:

$$C = \frac{F - 32}{1.8} = \frac{98.6 - 32}{1.8} = \frac{66.6}{1.8} = 37.0$$

We find the Kelvin equivalent by adding 273.15 to the Celsius temperature:

$$K = C + 273.15 = 37 + 273.15 = 310.15 \text{ K}$$

Human body temperature is 37°C or 310.15 K. Now try Exercises 69–72. ◄

Time out to think

The local weather report says that tomorrow's temperature will be 59°, but does not specify whether it is in Celsius or Fahrenheit. Can you tell which it is? How?

Units of Energy and Power

We pay energy bills to power companies, we use energy from gasoline to run our cars, and we argue about whether nuclear energy is a sensible alternative to fossil fuels. But what *is* energy?

Broadly speaking, energy is what makes matter move or heat up. We need energy from food to keep our hearts beating, to maintain our body temperatures, and to walk or run. A car needs energy to move the pistons in its engine, which turn the wheels. A light bulb needs energy to generate the heat that makes its filament glow.

For Americans, the most familiar energy unit is the food *Calorie* (uppercase C) used to measure the energy our bodies can draw from food. A typical adult uses about 2500 Calories of energy each day. The international metric unit of energy is the **joule.** Outside the United States, most foods and beverages are labeled with their energy content in joules (or kilojoules) rather than Calories. One Calorie is equivalent to 4184 joules.

The words *energy* and *power* are often used together, but they are not quite the same. Power is the *rate* at which energy is used, which means it has units of energy divided by time. The most common unit of power is the **watt,** defined as 1 joule per second.

ENERGY AND POWER

Energy is what makes matter move or heat up. The international metric unit of energy is the **joule.**

Power is the *rate* at which energy is used. The international metric unit of energy is the **watt,** defined as

$$1 \text{ watt} = 1 \frac{\text{joule}}{\text{s}}$$

✳EXAMPLE 7 *Pedal Power*

You are riding an exercise bicycle at a fitness center. The readout states that you are using 500 Calories per hour. Are you generating enough power to light a 100-watt bulb (1 Calorie = 4184 joules)?

SOLUTION   We use a chain of conversions to go from Calories per hour to joules per second:

$$\frac{500 \text{ Cal}}{1 \text{ hr}} \times \frac{4184 \text{ joule}}{1 \text{ Cal}} \times \frac{1 \text{ hr}}{60 \text{ min}} \times \frac{1 \text{ min}}{60 \text{ s}} \approx 581 \frac{\text{joule}}{\text{s}}$$

Your pedaling generates energy at a rate of 581 joules per second, which is a power of 581 watts—enough to light five (almost six) 100-watt bulbs.

Now try Exercises 73–74. ◀

Electric Utility Bills

If you check an electric utility bill, you'll probably find that it refers to electric usage in units of **kilowatt-hours.** The hyphen in this unit tells us that it means 1 kilowatt × 1 hour, which is equivalent to 1000 watts × 1 hour. Replacing 1000 watts with 1000 joule/s, we find

$$1 \text{ kilowatt-hour} = \frac{1000 \text{ joule}}{1 \text{ s}} \times 1 \text{ hr} \times \frac{60 \text{ min}}{1 \text{ hr}} \times \frac{60 \text{ s}}{1 \text{ min}} = 3{,}600{,}000 \text{ joule}$$

DEFINITION

A **kilowatt-hour** is a unit of energy:

1 kilowatt-hour = 3.6 million joules

By the Way

If you purchase a gas appliance, such as a gas stove or a kerosene heater, its energy requirements may be labeled in *British thermal units,* or BTUs. One BTU is equivalent to 1055 joules.

✳EXAMPLE 8 *Operating Cost of a Light Bulb*

Your utility company charges 8¢ per kilowatt-hour of electricity. How much does it cost to keep a 100-watt light bulb on for a week?

SOLUTION   One watt is one joule per second, so a 100-watt light bulb consumes energy at a rate of 100 joules per second. The energy used by the bulb in a week is 100 joule/s × 1 week. Using a chain of conversions to convert a week to seconds, we have

$$\frac{100 \text{ joule}}{1 \text{ s}} \times 1 \text{ week} \times \frac{7 \text{ day}}{1 \text{ week}} \times \frac{24 \text{ hr}}{1 \text{ day}} \times \frac{60 \text{ min}}{1 \text{ hr}} \times \frac{60 \text{ s}}{1 \text{ min}} = 60{,}480{,}000 \text{ joule}$$

Next, we convert this result to kilowatt-hours, remembering that 1 kilowatt-hour is 3,600,000 joules:

$$60{,}480{,}000 \text{ joule} \times \frac{1 \text{ kilowatt-hour}}{3{,}600{,}000 \text{ joule}} = 16.8 \text{ kilowatt-hour}$$

The light bulb uses 16.8 kilowatt-hours of energy in a week. At a price of 8¢ per kilowatt-hour, the total cost is

$$16.8 \text{ kilowatt-hr} \times 8 \frac{¢}{\text{kilowatt-hr}} = 134.4¢ \approx \$1.34$$

The electricity to keep the 100-watt light bulb on all week costs about $1.34 (assuming a price of 8¢ per kilowatt-hour).   Now try Exercises 75–76. ◀

Time out to think

Check a utility bill (yours or a friend's). Is the electricity usage metered in units of kilowatt-hours (often abbreviated kWh)? If not, what units are used? If so, what is the price per kilowatt-hour?

Practical Matters

Save Money and Save the Earth

You can save both money and energy by replacing standard (incandescent) light bulbs with more efficient bulbs, such as compact fluorescent bulbs. The compact fluorescent bulbs save energy because virtually all the energy they use goes into making light, whereas most of the energy used by standard bulbs goes into heat (that's why standard bulbs get so hot when they are turned on). As a result, a compact fluorescent bulb needs much less energy to generate the same light as a standard bulb. For example, a typical 25-watt compact fluorescent produces the same light as a 100-watt standard bulb.

To see how much you can save, consider a 100-watt light bulb that is left on all the time. At an energy cost of 8¢ per kilowatt-hour, this light bulb costs $1.34 to operate for a week (see Example 8), which translates into about $70 per year. Replacing the 100-watt bulb with a 25-watt compact fluorescent means your annual energy cost will be only one-fourth (25%) as much, or $17.50. Thus, the light bulb replacement saves some $52.50 per year in energy costs while providing just as much light. This savings more than makes up for the fact that compact fluorescent bulbs are more expensive than standard bulbs. (Compact fluorescent bulbs also last typically ten times longer than standard bulbs.)

Of course, you probably don't (or shouldn't) leave 100-watt light bulbs on all the time, so your savings for a single light bulb will be less than calculated above. Nevertheless, your savings may still be quite substantial. And, while you save money by switching to more efficient bulbs, you also reduce total energy usage, which helps protect the environment.

Units of Density and Concentration

You'll encounter many other standardized units in everyday life. In most cases, these units will be variations on units with which you are already familiar. Thus, you should be able to make sense of units from their context. Units that describe various types of density or concentration are particularly common.

Density describes compactness or crowding. Here are a few of the many ways that the idea of density is used:

- *Material density* is given in units of mass per unit volume, such as grams per cubic centimeter (g/cm^3). A useful reference is the density of water—about 1 g/cm^3. Objects with densities less than 1 g/cm^3 float in water, while higher-density objects sink.

- *Population density* is given by the number of people per unit area. For example, if 750 people live in a square region that is 1 mile on a side, the population density of the area is 750 people/mi^2.

- *Information density* is often used to describe how much memory can be stored by digital media. For example, each square inch on the surface of a DVD holds about 100 megabytes of information, so we say that a DVD has an information density of 100 MB/in^2.

....

Time out to think

Use the concept of density to explain why you float better in a swimming pool when your lungs are filled with air than when you fully exhale.

Concentration describes the amount of one substance mixed with another. Here are two of the many ways that the idea of concentration is used:

- The *concentration of an air pollutant* is often measured by the number of molecules of the pollutant per million molecules of air. For example, if there are 12 molecules of carbon monoxide in each 1 million molecules of air, we state the carbon monoxide concentration as 12 parts per million (ppm). (The U.S. Environmental Protection Agency says that air is unhealthy if the carbon monoxide concentration is above 9 ppm.)

- **Blood alcohol content** (BAC) describes the concentration of alcohol in a person's body. It is usually measured in units of grams of alcohol per 100 milliliters of blood. For example, in most states a person is considered legally intoxicated if his or her blood alcohol content is at or above 0.08 gram of alcohol per 100 milliliters of blood (written as 0.08 g/100 mL).

✳EXAMPLE 9 *New York City*

Manhattan Island has a population of about 1.5 million people living in an area of about 57 square kilometers. What is its population density? If there were no high-rise apartments, how much space would be available per person?

SOLUTION   We divide the population by the area to find that

$$\text{population density} = \frac{1,500,000 \text{ people}}{57 \text{ km}^2} \approx 26,000 \frac{\text{people}}{\text{km}^2}$$

HISTORICAL NOTE

A king once asked the famed Greek scientist Archimedes (c. 287–212 B.C.E.) to test whether a crown was made of pure gold, as claimed by its goldsmith, or a mixture of silver and gold. Archimedes was at first unsure how to do it, but had a sudden insight while taking a bath one day. Knowing that silver is less dense than gold, he realized he could compare the rise in water level for the crown and for an equal weight of pure gold. Thrilled at this insight, he ran naked through the streets shouting "Eureka!" (meaning "I have found it"). For the goldsmith, the news wasn't so great: The crown was partly silver, so the king had him executed.

Manhattan's population density is about 26,000 people per square kilometer. If there were no high rises, each resident would have 1/26,000 square kilometer of land. This number is easier to interpret if we convert from square kilometers to square meters:

$$\frac{1 \text{ km}^2}{26,000 \text{ people}} \times \left(\frac{1000 \text{ m}}{1 \text{ km}}\right)^2 = \frac{1 \text{ km}^2}{26,000 \text{ people}} \times \frac{1,000,000 \text{ m}^2}{1 \text{ km}^2} \approx 38 \frac{\text{m}^2}{\text{person}}$$

Without high rises, each person would have only 38 square meters, equivalent to a room about 6 meters, or 20 feet, on a side—and this does not include any space for roads, schools, or other common properties. Clearly, Manhattan Island could not fit so many residents without high rises.   Now try Exercises 77–82.

✷EXAMPLE 10 *Blood Alcohol Content*

An average-sized man has about 5 liters (5000 milliliters) of blood, and an average 12-ounce can of beer contains about 15 grams of alcohol (assuming the beer is about 6% alcohol by volume). If all the alcohol were immediately absorbed into the bloodstream, what blood alcohol content would we find in an average-sized man who quickly drank a single can of beer?

SOLUTION   If the alcohol were absorbed immediately, the man's 5000 milliliters of blood would contain the entire 15 grams of alcohol from the beer. We express this concentration as

$$\frac{15 \text{ g alcohol}}{5000 \text{ mL blood}}$$

We can convert this concentration to the standard units for blood alcohol (g/100 mL) in two steps. First, we first carry out the division to find the concentration in grams per milliliter:

$$\frac{15 \text{ g}}{5000 \text{ mL}} = 0.003 \frac{\text{g}}{\text{mL}}$$

Now, we multiply both the top and the bottom of the fraction by 100 to find the concentration in grams per 100 milliliters:

$$0.003 \frac{\text{g}}{\text{mL}} \times \frac{100}{100} = 0.3 \frac{\text{g}}{100 \text{ mL}}$$

By the Way

According to the American Medical Association, brain function is impaired when the blood alcohol content reaches 0.04 g/100 mL of blood—which is half the legal limit of 0.08 g/100 mL. A blood alcohol content at or above 0.4 g/100 mL usually leads to coma and sometimes leads to death.

The man's blood alcohol concentration would be 0.3 gram per 100 milliliters of blood—almost four times the legal limit of 0.08 g/100 mL! In reality, the man's blood alcohol content won't get this high from a single beer because it takes some time for the alcohol to be absorbed into the bloodstream and because metabolic processes gradually eliminate the absorbed alcohol. (For a typical adult, alcohol is absorbed into the bloodstream over a period of between 30 minutes and a couple of hours, depending on how much food the person has eaten. It is eliminated from the bloodstream at a rate of about 10 to 15 grams per hour.) Nevertheless, a single beer is certainly enough to cause impaired brain function—making it unsafe to drive—and this example points out how quickly and easily a person can become dangerously intoxicated.   Now try Exercises 83–84.

Time out to think

Many college students have lost their lives by rapidly consuming several "shots" of strong alcoholic drinks. Explain why such rapid consumption of alcohol can lead to death, even when the total amount of alcohol consumed may not sound like a lot.

EXERCISES AC2

QUICK QUIZ

Choose the best answer to each of the following questions. Explain your reasoning with one or more complete sentences.

1. One kilometer is
   a. 10 meters.   b. 100 meters.   c. 1000 meters.

2. A megaton is
   a. 100 tons.   b. 1000 tons.   c. 1 million tons.

3. A millimeter is approximately the size of
   a. the ball point in a pen.   b. a golf ball.
   c. a basketball.

4. You are buying apples while traveling in Europe. The price is most likely to be quoted in
   a. euros per kilogram.   b. euros per milliliter.
   c. euros per kilometer.

5. A liter is approximately equivalent to
   a. a mile.   b. a pound.   c. a quart.

6. A temperature of 105°C is
   a. typical of Phoenix in the summer.
   b. typical of Antarctica in the winter.
   c. boiling hot.

7. Which of the following is *not* a unit of energy?
   a. joules   b. watts   c. kilowatt-hours

8. You want to know how much total energy is required to operate a 100-watt light bulb. Do you need any more information?
   a. No.
   b. Yes; you need to know the temperature of the light bulb when it is on.
   c. Yes; you need to know how long the light bulb is on.

9. New Mexico has a population density of about 12 people per square mile and an area of about 120,000 square miles. To find its actual population, you should

   a. multiply the population density by the area.
   b. divide the population density by the area.
   c. divide the area by the population density.

10. The concentration of carbon dioxide in Earth's atmosphere might be stated in
    a. grams per meter.   b. parts per million.
    c. joules per watt.

REVIEW QUESTIONS

11. Briefly describe the origin and use of common units in the U.S. customary system.

12. Briefly describe the origin and use of metric units.

13. What are the basic metric units of length, mass, time, and volume? How are the metric prefixes used?

14. Using examples, show how to convert among the Fahrenheit, Celsius, and Kelvin temperature scales.

15. What is *energy?* List at least three common units of energy. Under what circumstances do the different units tend to be used?

16. What is the difference between *energy* and *power?* What are the standard units for power?

17. What do we mean by *density?* What do we mean by *concentration?* Describe common units of density and concentration, including blood alcohol content, with examples.

DOES IT MAKE SENSE?

Decide whether each of the following statements makes sense (or is clearly true) or does not make sense (or is clearly false). Explain your reasoning. Hint: Be sure to consider whether the units are appropriate to the statement, as well as whether the stated amount makes any sense. For example, a statement that someone is 15 feet tall uses the units (feet) appropriately, but does not make sense because no one is that tall.

18. I drank 2 liters of water today.

19. I know a professional bicyclist who weighs 300 kilograms.

20. Today I drove along the interstate at 100 kilometers per hour.

21. I know someone who can run 35 liters per second.

22. A guy on our track team can high-jump 7 meters.

23. My friend ran 10,000 meters in less than an hour.

24. The book I sent you weighs 3 milligrams.

25. My car's gas tank holds 12 meters of gasoline.

26. My daily food intake gives me about 10 million joules of energy.

27. Our utility company charges 10¢ per watt for the electricity we use.

28. The beach ball we played with had a density of 10 grams per cubic centimeter.

BASIC SKILLS & CONCEPTS

Powers of 10. Do Exercises 29–44 using skills covered in the Brief Review on p. 649.

29. $10^4 \times 10^7$

30. $10^5 \times 10^{-3}$

31. $\dfrac{10^6}{10^2}$

32. $\dfrac{10^8}{10^{-4}}$

33. $10^{-2} \times 10^{-6}$

34. $\dfrac{10^{-6}}{10^{-8}}$

35. $10^{12} \times 10^{23}$

36. $\dfrac{10^{-4}}{10^5}$

37. $\dfrac{10^{25}}{10^{15}}$

38. $10^1 + 10^0$

39. $10^2 + 10^{-1}$

40. $10^2 - 10^1$

41. $\dfrac{10^{12}}{10^{-4}}$

42. $10^{23} \times 10^{-23}$

43. $10^4 + 10^2$

44. $\dfrac{10^{15}}{10^{-5}}$

USCS Units. Exercises 45–52 involve conversions within the U.S. customary system. Your solution should clearly show the use of conversion factors.

45. What is your height in inches?

46. What is your weight in ounces (avoirdupois)? in tons?

47. One cubic foot holds 7.48 gallons of water, and one gallon of water weighs 8.33 pounds. How much does a cubic foot of water weigh in pounds? in ounces (avoirdupois)?

48. A boat is moving at 30 knots (nautical miles per hour). What is its speed in miles per hour?

49. How many liquid pints does a 2-gallon container hold? How many cubic inches does it hold?

50. Most soda cans contain 12 fluid ounces. How many cubic inches do they contain?

51. How many cubic feet do 100,000 bushels of corn occupy?

52. A small city produces 500,000 cubic feet of garbage per week. If all of this garbage were stacked neatly (in a nice vertical pile) on a 100-yard by 60-yard football field, how high would the pile be (in feet)?

Metric Prefixes. For each pair of units in Exercises 53–58, state how much larger or smaller the first unit is than the second. For example, 1 kilometer is 1000 time larger than 1 meter.

53. centimeter, kilometer

54. milliliter, liter

55. liter, milliliter

56. micrometer, centimeter

57. square meter, square kilometer

58. cubic centimeter, cubic meter

USCS–Metric Conversions. Convert each measurement in Exercises 59–68 to the units specified.

59. 8 meters to feet

60. 125 centimeters to yards

61. 10 pounds to kilograms

62. 84 quarts to liters

63. 45 liters to gallons

64. 10 square miles to square kilometers

65. 5 cubic centimeters to cubic inches

66. 8550 square feet to square meters

67. 10 kilograms per cubic meter to pounds per cubic foot

68. 25 miles per hour to meters per second

Celsius-Fahrenheit Conversions. In Exercises 69–70, convert Celsius temperatures into Fahrenheit or Fahrenheit temperatures into Celsius.

69. a. 45°F   b. 20°C   c. −15°C   d. −30°C
    e. 70°F

70. a. −8°C   b. 15°F   c. 15°C   d. 75°F
    e. 20°F

Celsius-Kelvin Conversions. In Exercises 71–72, convert Celsius temperatures into Kelvin or Kelvin temperatures into Celsius.

71. a. 50 K   b. 240 K   c. 10°C

72. a. −40°C   b. 400 K   c. 125°C

73. Basketball Power. You burn 1000 Calories while playing basketball for an hour. What is your average power during the game, in watts? Is it enough to keep a 100-watt light bulb shining? Explain.

74. Aerobics Power. You burn 300 Calories while doing an aerobics class for 45 minutes. What is your average power during the class, in watts? Is it enough to keep a 100-watt light bulb shining? Explain.

Electric Bills. For the electric bills described in Exercises 75–76, do the following:

a. Determine your total electrical energy use, in joules.

b. Determine your average power use, in watts.

c. Assuming the power company generated the energy by burning oil, calculate the amount of oil needed to provide the energy shown on your bill. Give your answer in both liters and gallons. (Hint: Burning 1 liter of oil releases 12 million joules of energy.)

75. Your electric bill states that you used 1000 kilowatt-hours of energy in June.

76. Your electric bill states that you used 970 kilowatt-hours of energy in September.

Densities. In Exercises 77–82, give the densities in appropriate units (population data from 2000 census).

77. A 40-gram pebble has a volume of 10 cubic centimeters. What is its density? Will it sink or float in water?

78. A jug has a volume of 8 liters (which is 8000 cubic centimeters) and a mass of 6 kilograms. What is its density? Will it sink or float in water?

79. The land area of the United States is about 3.5 million square miles, and the population is about 300 million people. What is the average population density?

80. Which has the greater population density: Hawaii, with a population of 1.3 million and an area of 6425 square miles, or Arizona, with a population of 5.2 million and an area of 113,609 square miles?

81. New Jersey and Wyoming have areas of 7419 and 97,105 square miles, respectively, and populations of 8.4 million and 490,000, respectively. Calculate and compare their average population densities.

82. A new computer hard drive holds 250 gigabytes of information on a surface area of 40 square centimeters. Calculate the information density on the disk.

83. Blood Alcohol Content: Wine. A typical glass of wine contains about 20 grams of alcohol. Consider a 110-pound woman, with approximately 4 liters (4000 milliliters) of blood, who drinks two glasses of wine.

a. If all the alcohol were immediately absorbed into her bloodstream, what would her blood alcohol content be? Explain why it is fortunate that, in reality, the alcohol is not absorbed immediately.

b. Again assume that all the alcohol is absorbed immediately, but now assume that her body eliminates the alcohol (through metabolism) at a rate of 10 grams per hour. What is her blood alcohol content 3 hours after drinking the wine? Is it safe for her to drive at this time? Explain.

84. Blood Alcohol Content: Hard Liquor. Eight ounces of a hard liquor (such as whiskey) typically contain about 70 grams of alcohol. Consider a 200-pound man, with approximately 6 liters (6000 milliliters) of blood, who quickly drinks 8 ounces of hard liquor.

a. If all the alcohol were immediately absorbed into his bloodstream, what would his blood alcohol content be? Explain why it is fortunate that, in reality, the alcohol is not absorbed immediately.

b. Again assume that all the alcohol is absorbed immediately, but now assume that his body eliminates the alcohol (through metabolism) at a rate of 15 grams per hour. What is his blood alcohol content 4 hours after drinking the liquor? Is it safe for him to drive at this time? Explain.

FURTHER APPLICATIONS

85. The Metric Mile. In track and field, the 1500-meter race is sometimes called the *metric mile*.

a. Compare the metric mile to a USCS mile. Complete the sentence: The metric mile is _____% of the USCS mile.

b. Look up the current men's and women's world records for the mile. If you assume that the runners maintain the same pace for the metric mile, what should their times be for the metric mile? Compare your predicted records at this pace to the actual current world records for the metric mile.

86. Metric Tools. Many tools come in both USCS and metric standards. In a precision socket set, the smallest USCS subdivision is $\frac{1}{16}$ inch; the smallest metric subdivision is 0.5 millimeter. Are the tools interchangeable? Explain.

87. Tallest Mountain? Mauna Kea, the highest mountain on the island of Hawaii, rises 13,796 feet above sea level. It extends an additional 18,200 feet from sea level to its base on the ocean floor. How tall is Mauna Kea from its base to its peak, in feet, miles, and kilometers? Compare its total extent to the height of Mt. Everest above sea level (29,035 ft). Would it be fair to call Mauna Kea the highest mountain in the world? Why or why not?

88. **The Cullinan Diamond and the Star of Africa.** The largest single rough diamond ever found, the Cullinan diamond, weighed 3106 carats. It was used to cut the world's largest diamond gem, the Star of Africa (530.2 carats), which is part of the British crown jewels collection. How much did the Cullinan diamond weigh in milligrams? in (avoirdupois) pounds? How much does the Star of Africa weigh in milligrams? in (avoirdupois) pounds?

Gems and Gold. Exercises 89–92 use karats and carats (see the Practical Matters box).

89. You find a nugget that is 25% gold. What is its purity in karats?

90. You purchase a 14-karat gold chain that weighs 15 grams. How much gold have you purchased (in grams)? Bonus: At the current price of gold, how much is the gold in the chain worth?

91. How much does a 2.5-carat diamond weigh in grams?

92. Is it possible to have jewelry made of 30-karat gold? Why or why not?

93. **Refrigerator Cost.** Your refrigerator uses an average power of 350 watts, and your utility company charges 10¢ per kilowatt-hour of energy (including taxes and fees). How much does it cost to run your refrigerator for a year? Explain.

94. **Hair Dryer Cost.** You have an 1800-watt hair dryer that you use for an average of 10 minutes per day. Your utility company charges 11¢ per kilowatt-hour of energy (including taxes and fees). How much does it cost to run the hair dryer each day? each year?

95. **Compact Fluorescent Light Bulbs.** You replace a 100-watt standard light bulb with a 25-watt compact fluorescent bulb that supplies the same light. Over a 10,000-hour life (typical for a compact fluorescent bulb), how much energy, in kilowatt-hours, do you save? If electricity costs 10¢ per kilowatt-hour, how much money do you save?

96. **Human Wattage.** Suppose you require 2500 food Calories per day (which is about average).

   a. What is your average power, in watts? Compare your answer to the wattage of some familiar appliance.

   b. How much energy, in joules, do you require from food in a year? Counting all forms of energy (such as gasoline, electricity, and energy for heating), the average U.S. citizen consumes about 400 billion joules of energy each year. Compare this value to the energy needed from food alone.

97. **Coal Power Plant.** A new coal-burning power plant can generate 1.5 gigawatts (billion watts) of power. Burning 1 kilogram of coal yields about 450 kilowatt-hours of energy. How much energy, in kilowatt-hours, can the plant generate each month? How much coal, in kilograms, is needed by this power plant each month? If a typical home uses 1000 kilowatt-hours per month, how many homes can this power plant supply with energy?

98. **Nuclear Power Plant.** Operating at full capacity, the Fort St. Vrain Nuclear Power Station in Colorado can generate 740 megawatts of power (with all four units operating). Nuclear fission of 1 kilogram of uranium (in the form of uranium-235) releases 16 million kilowatt-hours of energy. How much energy, in kilowatt-hours, can the plant generate each month? How much uranium, in kilograms, is needed by this power plant each month? If a typical home uses 1000 kilowatt-hours per month, how many homes can this power plant supply with energy?

Solar Energy. Use the following facts in Exercises 99–100: Solar (photovoltaic) cells convert sunlight directly into electricity. If solar cells were 100% efficient, they would generate about 1000 watts of power per square meter of surface area when exposed to direct sunlight. With lower efficiency, they generate proportionally less power. For example, 10% efficient cells generate 100 watts of power in direct sunlight.

99. Suppose a 1-square-meter panel of solar cells has an efficiency of 20% and receives the equivalent of 6 hours of direct sunlight per day. How much energy, in joules, can it produce each day? What average power, in watts, does the panel produce?

100. Suppose you want to supply 1 kilowatt of power to a house (the average household power requirement) by putting solar panels on its roof. For the solar cells described in Exercise 99, how many square meters of solar panels would you need? Assume that you can make use of the average power from the solar cells (by, for example, storing the energy in batteries until it is needed).

101. **Wind Power: One Turbine.** Modern wind energy "farms" use large wind turbines to generate electricity from the wind. At a typical installation, a single modern turbine can produce an average power of about 200 kilowatts. (This average takes wind variations into account.) How much energy, in kilowatt-hours, can such a turbine

generate in a year? Given that the average household uses about 10,000 kilowatt-hours of energy each year, how many households can be powered by a single wind turbine?

102. **California Wind Power.** California currently has wind farms capable of generating a total of about 4300 megawatts (4.3 gigawatts) of power (about 1.5% of the state's total electricity).

    a. How much energy, in kilowatt-hours, can these wind farms generate each year? Given that the average household uses about 10,000 kilowatt-hours of energy each year, how many households can be powered by these wind farms?

    b. One of the great advantages of wind power is that it does not produce the carbon dioxide emissions that contribute to global warming. On average, energy produced from fossil fuels generates about 1.5 pounds of carbon dioxide for every kilowatt-hour of energy. Suppose California did not have its wind farms and the energy were instead produced from fossil fuels. How much more carbon dioxide would be entering the atmosphere each year?

Currency Conversions. Find today's currency conversion rates, and use them to answer Exercises 103–108. Be sure to state clearly the currency conversion you use.

103. You see oranges in an Italian market priced at 0.8 euro per kilogram. What is the price in dollars per pound?

104. Gasoline at a German gas station costs 5.80 euros per liter. What is the price in dollars per gallon?

105. A French car manufacturer claims that its newest economy model has gas "mileage" of 20 kilometers per liter. What is the gas mileage in miles per gallon?

106. A supermarket in Mexico sells milk for 7.0 pesos per liter. What is the price in dollars per quart?

107. A fine ale in an English pub sells for 3.75 pounds (currency) per liter. What is the price in dollars per ounce?

108. A piece of land in the Belgian countryside with an area of 0.1 square kilometer is priced at 9000 euros. What is the price in dollars per acre?

109. **Project: Personal Energy Audit.** Do a thorough electrical energy audit of your home, apartment, or dormitory. That is, determine the energy used in a typical month by each of your electrical appliances, and your total energy usage per month for electricity. Based on the cost of electricity in your area, calculate the average monthly cost for your electricity. After studying your findings, propose at least three energy conservation strategies that you would consider implementing to save money and energy. Discuss the pros and cons of each strategy.

WEB PROJECTS

Find useful links for Web Projects on the text Web site: **www.aw.com/bennett-briggs**

110. **Metric History.** Research some aspect of the history of the metric system, such as how it came to be adopted around the world or how various units have been scientifically defined. Write a short report on your findings.

111. **Energy Issues.** The question of how we will continue to meet our energy needs is one of the most important issues of our time. Research one aspect of this issue using information available at the Web site for the U.S. Energy Information Administration. Write a short report on your findings.

112. **Pollution Progress.** Investigate the average concentrations of various pollutants in a major city of your choice. Find the EPA standards for each pollutant, and find some of the hazards associated with exposure to each pollutant. Track how the levels of pollution in this city have changed over the past 20 years. Based on your findings, do you think it is likely that pollution in this city will get better or worse over the next decade? Summarize your findings and your conclusions in a one- or two-page report.

113. **Alcohol Poisoning.** Research some aspect of the dangers of alcohol, such as drunk driving or alcohol poisoning (in which a person dies from drinking too much too fast). Find statistics related to this issue, especially data that relate the blood alcohol content to dangers. Summarize your findings in a short report about how society might combat the danger.

114. **Wind Power.** Learn more about both the currently installed wind power and the future potential for wind

power in your state. Overall, do you expect wind power to be important in the future in your state? Why or why not?

IN THE NEWS

115. Everyday Metric. Describe three ways that you use metric units in your everyday life.

116. Should the United States Go Metric? Discuss the pros and cons of having the United States switch fully to the metric system. Do you think it will ever happen?

117. Energy. Look for a news article concerning energy or power. What units are used to describe energy or power? Summarize the article and explain the meaning of the units.

118. Density and Concentration. Look for a news article that uses units of density or concentration in any context. Summarize the article and explain the meaning of the units.

119. Utility Bill. Analyze a utility bill. Explain all the units shown, and determine the relative costs of different energy uses. What changes would you recommend if the recipient of the bill wanted to lower energy costs?

120. Pollution Problems. What (if any) pollutants are of concern in the area where you live? What units are used to describe their concentrations? At what concentrations are the pollutants considered dangerous? Suggest ways that these pollution problems might be addressed.

Answers to Selected Exercises

CHAPTER 1

Section 1.1

1. a) $1, 2, 3, 4, 5, \ldots$ **b)** Counting numbers   **3.** Inductive reasoning is the process of reasoning to a general conclusion through observation of specific cases.   **5.** A counterexample is a specific case that satisfies the conditions of the conjecture but shows the conjecture is false.   **7.** Inductive reasoning   **9.** Inductive reasoning, a general conclusion is obtained from observation of specific cases.   **11.** $5 \times 7 = 35$ **13.** 1   5   10   10   5   1

15.   **17.**   **19.** 25, 30, 35   **21.** $-1, 1, -1$ **23.** $\dfrac{1}{16}, \dfrac{1}{64}, \dfrac{1}{256}$ **25.** 36, 49, 64   **27.** 34, 55, 89   **29.** Y

31. a) 36, 49, 64   **b)** square 6, 7, 8, 9 and 10   **c)** No, 72 is between 8^2 and 9^2, so it is not a square number.   **33.** Blue: 1, 5, 7, 10, 12   Purple: 2, 4, 6, 9, 11   Yellow: 3, 8   **35. a)** $\approx \$6$ billion   **b)** We are using specific cases to make a prediction.

37.   **39. a)** You should obtain the original number.   **b)** You should obtain the original number.
c) The result is the original number.   **d)** $n, 8n, 8n + 16, \dfrac{8n + 16}{8} = n + 2, n + 2 - 2 = n$

41. a) 5   **b)** You should obtain the number 5.   **c)** The result is always the number 5.
d) $n, n + 1, \dfrac{n + (n + 1) + 9}{2} = \dfrac{2n + 10}{2} = n + 5, n + 5 - n = 5$ **43.** $3 + 5 = 8$, which is not an odd number.
45. $(3 + 2)/2 = 5/2$, which is not an even number.   **47.** $1 - 2 = -1$, which is not a counting number.
49. a) The sum of the measures of the interior angles should be $180°$.   **b)** Yes, the sum of the measures of the interior angles should be $180°$.   **c)** The sum of the measures of the interior angles of a triangle is $180°$.   **51.** 129, the numbers in positions are found as follows: $\begin{matrix} a & b \\ c & a + b + c \end{matrix}$ **53.** (c)

Section 1.2

Answers in this section will vary depending on how you round your numbers. All answers are approximate.

1. 2210   **3.** 1,200,000,000   **5.** 8000   **7.** 900   **9.** 200   **11.** 1,200,000,000   **13.** \$240   **15.** \$32.80
17. 180 miles   **19.** 13,200 lb   **21.** \$3.90   **23.** 16   **25.** \$37   **27.** \$120   **29.** \$41   **31.** ≈ 20 mi
33. a) 100   **b)** 50   **c)** 125   **35. a)** 5 million   **b)** 98 million   **c)** 65 million   **d)** 280 million
37. a) 85%   **b)** 15%   **c)** 59,500,000 acres   **d)** No, since we are not given the area of each state.
39. 25   **41.** ≈ 160 bananas   **43.** $150°$ **45.** 10%   **47.** 9 square units   **49.** 150 feet   **51.–59.** Answers will vary.
61. There are 336 dimples on a regulation golf ball.

Section 1.3

1. 76.5 mi   **3.** 19.36 ft   **5.** \$29,026   **7. a)** \$196,800   **b)** \$26,600   **c)** \$220,320   **9.** \$12.50   **11.** \$70
13. \$71,989.20   **15. a)** ≈ 122 **b)** Answers will vary. A close approximation can be obtained by multiplying the U.S. sizes by 2.54.   **17. a)** 9.2 min   **b)** 62 min   **c)** 40 min   **d)** 47 min   **19. a)** \$1.5 trillion   **b)** \$22,000   **21.** \$82.08
23. a) \$74.40   **b)** \$264   **c)** \$64   **25. a)** $3,153,600 \text{ cm}^3$ **b)** ≈ 1.4 days   **27. a)** \$75   **b)** \$15   **c)** Long term by \$3   **29. a)** Divide the Total Emissions by the Emissions per Capita.   **b)** ≈ 298.6 million   **c)** ≈ 1307.6 million or 1.3076 billion   **31.** \$990, less than initial investment   **33. a)** 48 rolls   **b)** \$198 if she purchases four 10 packs and two 4 packs
35. a) Water/milk: 3 cups; salt: $\frac{3}{8}$ tsp; Cream of Wheat: 9 tbsp (or $\frac{9}{16}$ cup)
   b) Water/milk: $2\frac{7}{8}$ cups; salt: $\frac{3}{8}$ tsp; Cream of Wheat: $\frac{5}{8}$ cup (or 10 tbsp)
   c) Water/milk: $2\frac{3}{4}$ cups; salt: $\frac{3}{8}$ tsp; Cream of Wheat: $\frac{9}{16}$ cup (or 9 tbsp)
   d) Differences exist in water/milk because the amount for 4 servings is not twice that for 2 servings. Differences also exist in Cream of Wheat because $\frac{1}{2}$ cup is not twice 3 tbsp.
37. 144 square inches   **39.** The area is 4 times as large.   **41.** 66 ft   **43.** at -1 **45.** \$60,000   **47. a)** 30   **b)** 140
49.   **51.** | 8 | 6 | 16 |
| --- | --- | --- |
| 18 | 10 | 2 |
| 4 | 14 | 12 |
   53. The sum of the four corners is 4 times the number in the center.

55. Multiply the center number by 9.   **57.** 6 ways   **59.**

	7	
3	1	4
5	8	6
	2	

Other answers are possible, but 1 and 8 must appear in the center.

61.

1	2	3	4	5
2	3	4	5	1
3	4	5	1	2
4	5	1	2	3
5	1	2	3	4

Other answers are possible.   **63.** Mary is the skier.   **65.** 714 square units   **67.** $120

Chapter 1 Review Exercises

1. 31, 36, 41   **2.** 25, 36, 49   **3.** $-48, 96, -192$ **4.** 25, 32, 40   **5.** 10, 4, -3 **6.** $\dfrac{3}{8}, \dfrac{3}{16}, \dfrac{3}{32}$

7. ⊙▭⊙   **8.** △ ○ ▫   **9.** (c)

10. a) The final number is twice the original number.   **b)** The final number is twice the original number.
c) The final number is twice the original number.
d) $n, 10n, 10n + 5, \dfrac{10n + 5}{5} = 2n + 1, 2n + 1 - 1 = 2n$

11. This process will always result in an answer of 3.   **12.** $1^2 + 2^2 = 5$

Answers to Exercises 13–25 will vary depending on how you round your numbers. All answers are approximate.

13. 420,000,000   **14.** 2000   **15.** 200   **16.** Answers will vary.   **17.** $300   **18.** $36   **19.** 3 mph   **20.** $14.00
21. 2 mi   **22.** 0.15 million   **23.** 0.8 million   **24.** 13 square units   **25.** Length $\approx$ 22 ft; height $\approx$ 8 ft
26. $7.50   **27.** $1.16   **28.** Berkman's is cheaper by $20.00.   **29.** $32,996   **30. a)** 288 lb   **b)** 12,500 ft^2
31. $311   **32.** 7.05 mg   **33.** $882   **34.** 6 hr 45 min   **35.** July 26, 11:00 A.M.

36. a) 6.45 cm^2 **b)** 16.39 cm^3 **c)** 1 cm $\approx$ 0.39 in.   **37.** 201   **38.**

21	7	8	18
10	16	15	13
14	12	11	17
9	19	20	6

39.

23	25	15
13	21	29
27	17	19

40. 59 min 59 sec   **41.** 6   **42.** $25 Room
$ 3 Men
$ 2 Clerk
$30   **43.** 140 lb

44. Yes; 3 quarters and 4 dimes, or 1 half dollar, 1 quarter and 4 dimes, or 1 quarter and 9 dimes. Other answers are possible.

45. 216 cm^3

46. Place six coins in each pan with one coin off to the side. If it balances, the heavier coin is the one on the side. If the pan does not balance, take the six coins on the heavier side and split them into two groups of three. Select the three heavier coins and weigh two coins. If the pan balances, it is the third coin. If the pan does not balance, you can identify the heavier coin.

47. 125,250   **48.** 16 blue   **49.** 90

50. The fifth figure will be an octagon with sides of equal length. Inside the octagon will be a seven sided figure with each side of equal length. The figure will have one antenna.   **51.** 61

52. Some possible answers are shown. Others are possible.

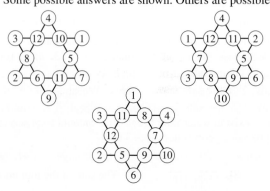

53. a) 2 **b)** 6 **c)** 24 **d)** 120 **e)** $n(n-1)(n-2)\ldots 1$, (or $n!$), where $n =$ the number of people in line

Chapter 3 Test

1. 19, 23, 27 **2.** $\frac{1}{16}, \frac{1}{32}, \frac{1}{64}$ **3. a)** The result is the original number plus 1. **b)** The result is the original number plus 1.

c) The result will always be the original number plus 1. **d)** $n, 5n, 5n + 10, \dfrac{5n + 10}{5} = n + 2, n + 2 - 1 = n + 1$

The answers for Exercises 4–6 are approximate.

4. 12,000 **5.** 2,100,000 **6.** 9 square units **7. a)** ≈ 23.03 **b)** He is in the at risk range.

8. 36 min **9.** 32 cans **10.** $7\frac{1}{2}$ min **11.** ≈ 39.5 in. by 29.6 in. (The actual dimensions are 100.5 cm by 76.5 cm.)

12. $49.00 **13.**

40	15	20
5	25	45
30	35	10

14. Less time if she had driven at 45 mph for the entire trip

15. $2 \cdot 6 \cdot 8 \cdot 9 \cdot 13$; 11 does not divide 11,232. **16.** 243 jelly beans **17. a)** $11.97 **b)** $11.81

c) Save 16 cents by using the 25% off coupon. **18.** 24

CHAPTER 2

Section 2.1

Check Point Exercises

1. b **2.** $2^3 \cdot 3 \cdot 5$ **3.** 75 **4.** 96 **5.** 90 **6.** 5:00 P.M.

Exercise Set 2.1

1. a. yes **b.** no **c.** yes **d.** no **e.** no **f.** yes **g.** no **h.** no **i.** no **3. a.** yes **b.** yes **c.** yes **d.** no **e.** yes
f. yes **g.** no **h.** no **i.** yes **5. a.** yes **b.** no **c.** yes **d.** no **e.** no **f.** no **g.** no **h.** no **i.** no **7. a.** yes
b. yes **c.** yes **d.** no **e.** yes **f.** yes **g.** yes **h.** no **i.** yes **9. a.** yes **b.** yes **c.** yes **d.** yes **e.** yes **f.** yes
g. yes **h.** yes **i.** yes **11.** true; $5 + 9 + 5 + 8 = 27$ which is divisible by 3. **13.** true; the last two digits of 10,612 form the number 12 and
12 is divisible by 4. **15.** false **17.** true; 104,538 is an even number so it is divisible by 2. $1 + 0 + 4 + 5 + 3 + 8 = 21$ which is divisible by 3 so it
is divisible by 3. Any number divisible by 2 and 3 is divisible by 6. **19.** true; the last three digits of 20,104 form the number 104 and 104 is divisible
by 8. **21.** false **23.** true; $5 + 1 + 7 + 8 + 7 + 2 = 30$ which is divisible by 3 so it is divisible by 3. The last two digits of 517,872 form the
number 72 and 72 is divisible by 4 so it is divisible by 4. Any number divisible by 3 and 4 is divisible by 12. **25.** $3 \cdot 5^2$ **27.** $2^3 \cdot 7$
29. $3 \cdot 5 \cdot 7$ **31.** $2^2 \cdot 5^3$ **33.** $3 \cdot 13 \cdot 17$ **35.** $3 \cdot 5 \cdot 59$ **37.** $2^5 \cdot 3^2 \cdot 5$ **39.** $2^2 \cdot 499$ **41.** $3 \cdot 5^2 \cdot 7^2$ **43.** $2^3 \cdot 3 \cdot 5^2 \cdot 11 \cdot 13$
45. 14 **47.** 2 **49.** 12 **51.** 24 **53.** 38 **55.** 15 **57.** 168 **59.** 336 **61.** 540 **63.** 360 **65.** 3420 **67.** 4560 **69.** 8
71. 6 **73.** 2, 6 **75.** perfect **77.** not perfect **79.** not an emirp **81.** emirp **83.** not a Germain prime **85.** not a Germain prime
87. 648; 648; Answers will vary. An example is: The product of the greatest common divisor and least common multiple of two numbers equals the
product of the two numbers. **89.** The numbers are the prime numbers between 1 and 97. **91.** 12 **93.** 10 **95.** July 1 **97.** 90 min or $1\frac{1}{2}$ hr
111. GCD: $2^{14} \cdot 3^{25} \cdot 5^{30}$; LCM: $2^{17} \cdot 3^{37} \cdot 5^{31}$ **113.** 2:20 A.M. on the third day **115.** yes **117.** yes

Section 2.2

Check Point Exercises

1.

(a)   (b)   (c)

$-5\,-4\,-3\,-2\,-1\ \ 0\ \ 1\ \ 2\ \ 3\ \ 4\ \ 5$

2. a. $>$ **b.** $<$ **c.** $<$ **d.** $<$ **3. a.** 8 **b.** 6 **4. a.** 37 **b.** -4 **c.** -24

5. $15 billion **6. a.** 25 **b.** -25 **c.** -64 **d.** 81 **7.** 36 **8.** 82

Exercise Set 2.2

1. $-5\,-4\,-3\,-2\,-1\ \ 0\ \ 1\ \ 2\ \ 3\ \ 4\ \ 5$ **3.** $-5\,-4\,-3\,-2\,-1\ \ 0\ \ 1\ \ 2\ \ 3\ \ 4\ \ 5$ **5.** $<$ **7.** $<$ **9.** $>$ **11.** $<$ **13.** 14
15. 14 **17.** 300,000 **19.** -12 **21.** 4 **23.** -3 **25.** -5 **27.** -18 **29.** 0 **31.** 5 **33.** -7 **35.** 14 **37.** 11 **39.** -9
41. -28 **43.** -54 **45.** 21 **47.** -12 **49.** 13 **51.** 0 **53.** 25 **55.** 25 **57.** 64 **59.** -125 **61.** 625 **63.** -81
65. 81 **67.** -3 **69.** -7 **71.** 30 **73.** 0 **75.** undefined **77.** -20 **79.** -31 **81.** 25 **83.** 13 **85.** 13 **87.** 33
89. 32 **91.** -24 **93.** 0 **95.** -32 **97.** 45 **99.** 14 **101.** -36 **103.** 88 **105.** $-10 - (-2)^3$; -2 **107.** $[2(7-10)]^2$; 36
109. $389 billion **111.** $25 billion **113.** 19,757 ft **115.** $-$158 billion; deficit **117.** $554 billion **119.** 7°F **121.** -2°F
133. $(8-2) \cdot 3 - 4 = 14$ **135.** -36

Section 2.3

Check Point Exercises

1. $\frac{4}{5}$ **2.** $\frac{21}{8}$ **3.** $1\frac{2}{3}$ **4. a.** 0.375 **b.** $0.\overline{45}$ **5. a.** $\frac{9}{10}$ **b.** $\frac{43}{50}$ **c.** $\frac{53}{1000}$ **6.** $\frac{2}{9}$ **7.** $\frac{79}{99}$ **8. a.** $\frac{8}{33}$ **b.** $\frac{3}{2}$ or $1\frac{1}{2}$

c. $\frac{51}{10}$ or $5\frac{1}{10}$ **9. a.** $\frac{36}{55}$ **b.** $-\frac{4}{3}$ or $-1\frac{1}{3}$ **c.** $\frac{3}{2}$ or $1\frac{1}{2}$ **10. a.** $\frac{2}{3}$ **b.** $\frac{3}{2}$ or $1\frac{1}{2}$ **c.** $-\frac{9}{4}$ or $-2\frac{1}{4}$ **11.** $\frac{19}{20}$ **12.** $-\frac{17}{60}$ **13.** $\frac{5}{12}$

14. $2\frac{4}{5}$ eggs; 3 eggs

Exercise Set 2.3

1. $\frac{2}{3}$ **3.** $\frac{5}{6}$ **5.** $\frac{4}{7}$ **7.** $\frac{5}{9}$ **9.** $\frac{9}{10}$ **11.** $\frac{14}{19}$ **13.** $\frac{19}{8}$ **15.** $-\frac{38}{5}$ **17.** $\frac{199}{16}$ **19.** $4\frac{3}{5}$ **21.** $-8\frac{4}{9}$ **23.** $35\frac{11}{20}$ **25.** 0.75

27. 0.35   **29.** 0.875   **31.** $0.\overline{81}$ **33.** $3.\overline{142857}$ **35.** $0.\overline{285714}$ **37.** $\frac{3}{10}$ **39.** $\frac{2}{5}$ **41.** $\frac{39}{100}$ **43.** $\frac{41}{50}$ **45.** $\frac{29}{40}$ **47.** $\frac{5399}{10,000}$

49. $\frac{7}{9}$ **51.** 1   **53.** $\frac{4}{11}$ **55.** $\frac{257}{999}$ **57.** $\frac{21}{88}$ **59.** $-\frac{7}{120}$ **61.** $\frac{3}{2}$ **63.** 6   **65.** $\frac{10}{3}$ **67.** $-\frac{14}{15}$ **69.** 6   **71.** $\frac{5}{11}$ **73.** $\frac{2}{3}$

75. $\frac{2}{3}$ **77.** $\frac{7}{10}$ **79.** $\frac{9}{10}$ **81.** $\frac{53}{120}$ **83.** $\frac{1}{2}$ **85.** $\frac{7}{12}$ **87.** $-\frac{71}{150}$ **89.** $1\frac{5}{12}$ **91.** $\frac{4}{15}$ **93.** $\frac{7}{24}$ **95.** $\frac{7}{12}$ **97.** $-\frac{3}{4}$

99. Both are equal to $\frac{169}{36}$.   **101.** $-\frac{9}{40}$ **103.** $-1\frac{1}{36}$ **105.** $-19\frac{3}{4}$ **107.** $\frac{1}{2^2 \cdot 3}$ **109.** $-\frac{289}{2^4 \cdot 5^4 \cdot 7}$ **111.** $0.\overline{54}; 0.58\overline{3}; <$

113. $-0.8\overline{3}; -0.\overline{8}; >$ **115.** $\frac{86}{192}; \frac{43}{96}$ **117.** $\frac{1}{3}$ cup butter, $\frac{5}{2} = 2.5$ ounces unsweetened chocolate, $\frac{3}{4}$ cup sugar, 1 teaspoon vanilla, 1 egg,

$\frac{1}{2}$ cup flour   **119.** $\frac{5}{6}$ cup butter, $\frac{25}{4} = 6.25$ ounces unsweetened chocolate, $\frac{15}{8} = 1\frac{7}{8}$ cups sugar, $\frac{5}{2} = 2\frac{1}{2}$ teaspoons vanilla, $\frac{5}{2} = 2\frac{1}{2}$ eggs,

$\frac{5}{4} = 1\frac{1}{4}$ cups flour   **121.** 24 brownies   **123.** $3\frac{2}{3}$ c   **125.** $\frac{4}{5}$ yr   **127.** $-\frac{9}{10}$ yr   **129.** $\frac{1}{3}$ of the business   **131.** $1\frac{3}{20}$ mi; $\frac{7}{20}$ mi   **133.** $\frac{1}{10}$

147.

say does that   Star-span-gled Ban-ner   yet   wave O'er the

149. a. 0.24625   **b.** 1.45248   **c.** 0.00112

Section 2.4

Check Point Exercises

1. a. $2\sqrt{3}$ **b.** $2\sqrt{15}$ **c.** cannot be simplified   **2. a.** $\sqrt{30}$ **b.** 10   **c.** $2\sqrt{3}$ **3. a.** 4   **b.** $2\sqrt{2}$ **4. a.** $18\sqrt{3}$ **b.** $-5\sqrt{13}$

c. $8\sqrt{10}$ **5. a.** $3\sqrt{3}$ **b.** $-13\sqrt{2}$ **6. a.** $\frac{5\sqrt{10}}{2}$ **b.** $\frac{\sqrt{14}}{7}$ **c.** $\frac{5\sqrt{2}}{6}$

Exercise Set 2.4

1. 3   **3.** 5   **5.** 8   **7.** 11   **9.** 13   **11. a.** 13.2   **b.** 13.15   **c.** 13.153   **13. a.** 133.3   **b.** 133.27 **c.** 133.270   **15. a.** 1.8

b. 1.77   **c.** 1.772   **17.** $2\sqrt{5}$ **19.** $4\sqrt{5}$ **21.** $5\sqrt{10}$ **23.** $14\sqrt{7}$ **25.** $\sqrt{42}$ **27.** 6   **29.** $3\sqrt{2}$ **31.** $2\sqrt{13}$ **33.** 3

35. $3\sqrt{5}$ **37.** $-4\sqrt{3}$ **39.** $13\sqrt{3}$ **41.** $-2\sqrt{13}$ **43.** $2\sqrt{5}$ **45.** $7\sqrt{2}$ **47.** $3\sqrt{5}$ **49.** $2\sqrt{2}$ **51.** $34\sqrt{2}$ **53.** $-\frac{3}{2}\sqrt{3}$

55. $11\sqrt{3}$ **57.** $\frac{5\sqrt{3}}{3}$ **59.** $3\sqrt{7}$ **61.** $\frac{2\sqrt{30}}{5}$ **63.** $\frac{5\sqrt{3}}{2}$ **65.** $\frac{\sqrt{10}}{5}$ **67.** $20\sqrt{2} - 5\sqrt{3}$ **69.** $-7\sqrt{7}$ **71.** $\frac{43\sqrt{2}}{35}$ **73.** $\frac{5\sqrt{6}}{6}$

75. $6\sqrt{3}$ miles; 10.4 miles   **77.** 70 mph; He was speeding.   **79. a.** 41 in.   **b.** 40.6 in.; quite well   **81. a.** 36 cm   **b.** 44.7 cm

c. 46.9 cm   **d.** The model describes healthy children.   **83.** $0.6R_f$; 60 weeks   **93.** $<$ **95.** $>$ **97.** -7 and -6

99. Answers will vary.; An example is $(3 + \sqrt{2}) - (1 + \sqrt{2}) = 2$.

Section 2.5

Check Point Exercises

1. a. $\sqrt{9}$ **b.** $0, \sqrt{9}$ **c.** $-9, 0, \sqrt{9}$ **d.** $-9, -1.3, 0, 0.\overline{3}, \sqrt{9}$ **e.** $\frac{\pi}{2}, \sqrt{10}$ **f.** $-9, -1.3, 0, 0.\overline{3}, \frac{\pi}{2}, \sqrt{9}, \sqrt{10}$

2. a. associative property of multiplication   **b.** commutative property of addition   **c.** distributive property of multiplication over addition
d. commutative property of multiplication   **3. a.** yes   **b.** no

Exercise Set 2.5

1. a. $\sqrt{100}$ **b.** $0, \sqrt{100}$ **c.** $-9, 0, \sqrt{100}$ **d.** $-9, -\frac{4}{5}, 0, 0.25, 9.2, \sqrt{100}$ **e.** $\sqrt{3}$ **f.** $-9, -\frac{4}{5}, 0, 0.25, \sqrt{3}, 9.2, \sqrt{100}$

3. a. $\sqrt{64}$ **b.** $0, \sqrt{64}$ **c.** $-11, 0, \sqrt{64}$ **d.** $-11, -\frac{5}{6}, 0, 0.75, \sqrt{64}$ **e.** $\sqrt{5}, \pi$ **f.** $-11, -\frac{5}{6}, 0, 0.75, \sqrt{5}, \pi, \sqrt{64}$

5. 0   **7.** Answers will vary; an example is: $\frac{1}{2}$.   **9.** Answers will vary; an example is: 1.   **11.** Answers will vary; an example is: $\sqrt{2}$.

13. 4   **15.** 6   **17.** 4; 3   **19.** 7   **21.** $30 + 5\sqrt{2}$ **23.** $3\sqrt{7} + \sqrt{14}$ **25.** $5\sqrt{3} + 3$ **27.** $2\sqrt{3} + 6$

29. commutative property of addition   **31.** associative property of addition   **33.** commutative property of addition

35. distributive property of multiplication over addition   **37.** associative property of multiplication   **39.** Answers will vary; an example is: $1 - 2 = -1$.   **41.** Answers will vary; an example is: $4 \div 8 = \frac{1}{2}$.   **43.** Answers will vary; an example is: $\sqrt{2} \cdot \sqrt{2} = 2$.   **45.** true   **47.** false
49. distributive property; commutative property of addition; associative property of addition; distributive property; commutative property of addition
51. vampire   **53.** vampire   **55.** narcissistic   **57.** narcissistic   **59. a.** distributive property   **b.** approximately 108 mg; Answers will vary.
69. c

Section 2.6

Check Point Exercises

1. a. 1   **b.** 1   **c.** 1   **d.** -1 **2. a.** $\frac{1}{81}$ **b.** $\frac{1}{216}$ **c.** $\frac{1}{12}$ **3. a.** 7,400,000,000   **b.** 0.000003017   **4. a.** 7.41×10^9
b. 9.2×10^{-8} **5.** $\$5.19 \times 10^{11}$ **6.** 520,000   **7.** 0.0000023   **8. a.** 1.872×10^4 **b.** 18,720   **9.** $2500

Exercise Set 2.6

1. $2^5 = 32$ **3.** $4^3 = 64$ **5.** $2^6 = 64$ **7.** $1^{20} = 1$ **9.** $4^2 = 16$ **11.** $2^4 = 16$ **13.** 1   **15.** 1   **17.** -1 **19.** $\frac{1}{4}$ **21.** $\frac{1}{64}$
23. $\frac{1}{32}$ **25.** $3^2 = 9$ **27.** $3^{-2} = \frac{1}{9}$ **29.** $2^{-4} = \frac{1}{16}$ **31.** 270   **33.** 912,000   **35.** 80,000,000   **37.** 100,000   **39.** 0.79
41. 0.0215   **43.** 0.000786   **45.** 0.00000318   **47.** 3.7×10^2 **49.** 3.6×10^3 **51.** 3.2×10^4 **53.** 2.2×10^8 **55.** 2.7×10^{-2}
57. 3.7×10^{-3} **59.** 2.93×10^{-6} **61.** 8.2×10^7 **63.** 4.1×10^5 **65.** 2.1×10^{-6} **67.** 600,000   **69.** 60,000   **71.** 0.123
73. 30,000   **75.** 3,000,000   **77.** 0.03   **79.** 0.0021   **81.** $(8.2 \times 10^7)(3.0 \times 10^9) = 2.46 \times 10^{17}$ **83.** $(5.0 \times 10^{-4})(6.0 \times 10^6) = 3 \times 10^3$
85. $\frac{9.5 \times 10^6}{5 \times 10^2} = 1.9 \times 10^4$ **87.** $\frac{8 \times 10^{-5}}{2 \times 10^2} = 4 \times 10^{-7}$ **89.** $\frac{4.8 \times 10^{11}}{1.2 \times 10^{-4}} = 4 \times 10^{15}$ **91.** $\frac{11}{18}$ **93.** $\frac{99}{25} = 3\frac{24}{25}$ **95.** 2.5×10^{-3}
97. 8×10^{-5} **99.** $\$4.65 \times 10^{10}$ **101.** $\$1 \times 10^8$ **103.** approximately 67 hot dogs per person   **105.** $2.5 \times 10^2 = 250$ chickens

107. a. $\$1.0813 \times 10^4$; \$10,813   **b.** \$901   **109.** Medicare; \$3242   **111.** 1.06×10^{-18} gram   **113.** 3.1536×10^7 **125.** d   **127.** $\frac{1}{4}$

Section 2.7

Check Point Exercises

1. 100, 120, 140, 160, 180, and 200   **2.** 8, 5, 2, -1, -4, and -7 **3.** -34 **4. a.** $a_n = 1.16n + 10.84$ **b.** 68.8 million
5. $12, -6, 3, -\frac{3}{2}, \frac{3}{4}$, and $-\frac{3}{8}$ **6.** 3645   **7.** $a_n = 3(2)^{n-1}$; 384

Exercise Set 2.7

1. 8, 10, 12, 14, 16, and 18   **3.** 200, 220, 240, 260, 280, and 300   **5.** $-7, -3, 1, 5, 9$, and 13   **7.** $-400, -100, 200, 500, 800$, and 1100
9. $7, 4, 1, -2, -5$, and -8 **11.** $200, 140, 80, 20, -40$, and -100 **13.** $\frac{5}{2}, 3, \frac{7}{2}, 4, \frac{9}{2}$, and 5   **15.** $\frac{3}{2}, \frac{7}{4}, 2, \frac{9}{4}, \frac{5}{2}$, and $\frac{11}{4}$
17. 4.25, 4.55, 4.85, 5.15, 5.45, and 5.75   **19.** 4.5, 3.75, 3, 2.25, 1.5, and 0.75   **21.** 33   **23.** 252   **25.** 67   **27.** 955   **29.** 82   **31.** -142
33. -43 **35.** -248 **37.** $\frac{23}{2}$ **39.** 1.75   **41.** $a_n = 1 + (n-1)4$; 77   **43.** $a_n = 7 + (n-1)(-4)$; -69 **45.** $a_n = 9 + (n-1)2$; 47
47. $a_n = -20 + (n-1)(-4)$; -96 **49.** 4, 8, 16, 32, 64, and 128   **51.** 1000, 1000, 1000, 1000, 1000, and 1000   **53.** $3, -6, 12, -24, 48$, and -96
55. $10, -40, 160, -640, 2560$, and $-10,240$ **57.** $2000, -2000, 2000, -2000, 2000$, and -2000 **59.** $-2, 6, -18, 54, -162$, and 486
61. $-6, 30, -150, 750, -3750$, and 18,750   **63.** $\frac{1}{4}, \frac{1}{2}, 1, 2, 4$, and 8   **65.** $\frac{1}{4}, \frac{1}{8}, \frac{1}{16}, \frac{1}{32}, \frac{1}{64}$, and $\frac{1}{128}$ **67.** $-\frac{1}{16}, \frac{1}{4}, -1, 4, -16$, and 64
69. 2, 0.2, 0.02, 0.002, 0.0002, and 0.00002   **71.** 256   **73.** $2,324,522,934 \approx 2.32 \times 10^9$ **75.** 50   **77.** 320   **79.** -2 **81.** 486
83. $\frac{3}{64}$ **85.** $-\frac{2}{27}$ **87.** $\approx -1.82 \times 10^{-9}$ **89.** 0.1   **91.** $a_n = 3(4)^{n-1}$; 12,288   **93.** $a_n = 18\left(\frac{1}{3}\right)^{n-1}$; $\frac{2}{81}$ **95.** $a_n = 1.5(-2)^{n-1}$; 96
97. $a_n = 0.0004(-10)^{n-1}$; 400   **99.** arithmetic; 18 and 22   **101.** geometric; 405 and 1215   **103.** arithmetic; 13 and 18
105. geometric; $\frac{3}{16}$ and $\frac{3}{32}$ **107.** arithmetic; $\frac{5}{2}$ and 3   **109.** geometric; 7 and -7 **111.** arithmetic; -49 and -63
113. geometric; $25\sqrt{5}$ and 125   **115.** arithmetic; 310   **117.** geometric; 59,048   **119.** geometric; -1023 **121.** arithmetic; 80   **123.** 5050
125. a. $a_n = 23.08 + 0.12n$ **b.** 27.88 years old   **127.** Company A; \$1400   **129.** \$16,384   **131.** \$3,795,957
133. a. 1.013, 1.013, 1.013, 1.013, 1.013, 1.013, 1.013; the population is increasing geometrically with $r \approx 1.013$.   **b.** $a_n = 29.76(1.013)^{n-1}$
c. ≈ 33.86; very well   **143.** d

Chapter 2 Review Exercises

1. 2: yes; 3: yes; 4: yes; 5: no; 6: yes; 8: yes; 9: no; 10: no; 12: yes   **2.** 2: yes; 3: yes; 4: no; 5: yes; 6: yes; 8: no; 9: yes; 10: yes; 12: no   **3.** $3 \cdot 5 \cdot 47$
4. $2^6 \cdot 3 \cdot 5$ **5.** $3 \cdot 5^2 \cdot 7 \cdot 13$ **6.** GCD: 6; LCM: 240   **7.** GCD: 6; LCM: 900   **8.** GCD: 2; LCM: 27,432   **9.** 12   **10.** 11:48 A.M.
11. $<$ **12.** $>$ **13.** 860   **14.** 53   **15.** 0   **16.** -3 **17.** -11 **18.** -15 **19.** 1   **20.** 99   **21.** -15 **22.** 9   **23.** -4
24. -16 **25.** -16 **26.** 10   **27.** -2 **28.** 17   **29.** \$658 billion   **30.** $\frac{8}{15}$ **31.** $\frac{6}{25}$ **32.** $\frac{11}{12}$ **33.** $\frac{64}{11}$ **34.** $-\frac{23}{7}$ **35.** $5\frac{2}{5}$

36. $-1\frac{8}{9}$ **37.** 0.8   **38.** $0.\overline{428571}$ **39.** 0.625   **40.** 0.5625   **41.** $\frac{3}{5}$ **42.** $\frac{17}{25}$ **43.** $\frac{147}{250}$ **44.** $\frac{21}{2500}$ **45.** $\frac{5}{9}$ **46.** $\frac{34}{99}$

47. $\frac{113}{999}$ **48.** $\frac{21}{50}$ **49.** $\frac{35}{6}$ **50.** $\frac{8}{3}$ **51.** $-\frac{1}{4}$ **52.** $\frac{2}{3}$ **53.** $\frac{43}{36}$ **54.** $\frac{37}{60}$ **55.** $\frac{11}{15}$ **56.** $\frac{5}{16}$ **57.** $\frac{15}{112}$ **58.** $\frac{27}{40}$

59. $11\frac{1}{4}$ or about 11 pounds   **60.** $\frac{5}{12}$ of the tank   **61.** $2\sqrt{7}$ **62.** $6\sqrt{2}$ **63.** $5\sqrt{6}$ **64.** $10\sqrt{3}$ **65.** $4\sqrt{3}$ **66.** $5\sqrt{2}$

67. $2\sqrt{3}$ **68.** 3   **69.** $5\sqrt{5}$ **70.** $-6\sqrt{11}$ **71.** $7\sqrt{2}$ **72.** $-17\sqrt{3}$ **73.** $12\sqrt{2}$ **74.** $6\sqrt{5}$ **75.** $\frac{\sqrt{6}}{3}$

76. $8\sqrt{3} \approx 13.9$ feet per second   **77. a.** $\sqrt{81}$ **b.** $0, \sqrt{81}$ **c.** $-17, 0, \sqrt{81}$ **d.** $-17, -\frac{9}{13}, 0, 0.75, \sqrt{81}$ **e.** $\sqrt{2}, \pi$

f. $-17, -\frac{9}{13}, 0, 0.75, \sqrt{2}, \pi, \sqrt{81}$ **78.** Answers will vary; an example is: 0.   **79.** Answers will vary; an example is: $\frac{1}{2}$.

80. Answers will vary; an example is: $\sqrt{2}$.   **81.** commutative property of addition   **82.** associative property of multiplication

83. distributive property of multiplication over addition   **84.** commutative property of multiplication   **85.** commutative property of multiplication

86. commutative property of addition   **87.** Answers will vary; an example is: $2 \div 6 = \frac{1}{3}$.   **88.** Answers will vary; an example is: $0 - 2 = -2$.

89. 216   **90.** 64   **91.** 16   **92.** 729   **93.** 25   **94.** 1   **95.** 1   **96.** $\frac{1}{216}$ **97.** $\frac{1}{16}$ **98.** $\frac{1}{49}$ **99.** 27   **100.** 460

101. 37,400   **102.** 0.00255   **103.** 0.0000745   **104.** 7.52×10^3 **105.** 3.59×10^6 **106.** 7.25×10^{-3} **107.** 4.09×10^{-7}

108. 4.2×10^{13} **109.** 9.7×10^{-5} **110.** 390   **111.** 1,150,000   **112.** 0.023   **113.** 40   **114.** $(6.0 \times 10^4)(5.4 \times 10^5) = 3.24 \times 10^{10}$

115. $(9.1 \times 10^4)(4 \times 10^{-4}) = 3.64 \times 10^1$ **116.** $\frac{8.4 \times 10^6}{4 \times 10^3} = 2.1 \times 10^3$ **117.** $\frac{3 \times 10^{-6}}{6 \times 10^{-8}} = 5 \times 10^1$ **118.** 1000 yr   **119.** $\$4.5 \times 10^{10}$

120. 1.3×10^{10} people   **121.** 7, 11, 15, 19, 23, and 27   **122.** $-4, -9, -14, -19, -24,$ and -29 **123.** $\frac{3}{2}, 1, \frac{1}{2}, 0, -\frac{1}{2},$ and -1 **124.** 20

125. -30 **126.** -38 **127.** $a_n = -7 + (n-1)4; 69$ **128.** $a_n = 200 + (n-1)(-20); -180$ **129.** 3, 6, 12, 24, 48, and 96

130. $\frac{1}{2}, \frac{1}{4}, \frac{1}{8}, \frac{1}{16}, \frac{1}{32},$ and $\frac{1}{64}$ **131.** $16, -8, 4, -2, 1,$ and $-\frac{1}{2}$ **132.** 54   **133.** $\frac{1}{2}$ **134.** -48 **135.** $a_n = 1(2)^{n-1}; 128$

136. $a_n = 100\left(\frac{1}{10}\right)^{n-1}; \frac{1}{100,000}$ **137.** arithmetic; 24 and 29   **138.** geometric; 162 and 486   **139.** geometric; $\frac{1}{256}$ and $\frac{1}{1024}$

140. arithmetic; -28 and -35 **141. a.** $a_n = 32.04 - 0.54n$ **b.** 22.32%   **c.** potatoes: $a_n = 19.27 - 0.27n$; 14.41%; salads: $a_n = 13.99 - 0.29n$;

8.77%; bread: $a_n = 10.06 - 0.26n$; 5.38%   **142. a.** $\frac{5.9}{4.2} \approx 1.4; \frac{8.3}{5.9} \approx 1.4; \frac{11.6}{8.3} \approx 1.4; \frac{16.2}{11.6} \approx 1.4; \frac{22.7}{16.2} \approx 1.4$ **b.** $4.2(1.4)^{n-1}$ **c.** 62.0 million

Chapter 2 Test

1. 2, 3, 4, 6, 8, 9, and 12   **2.** $2^2 \cdot 3^2 \cdot 7$ **3.** GCD: 24; LCM: 144   **4.** 1   **5.** -4 **6.** -32 **7.** $0.58\overline{3}$ **8.** $\frac{64}{99}$ **9.** $\frac{1}{5}$ **10.** $\frac{37}{60}$

11. $-\frac{19}{2}$ **12.** $\frac{7}{12}$ **13.** $5\sqrt{2}$ **14.** $9\sqrt{2}$ **15.** $3\sqrt{2}$ **16.** $-7, -\frac{4}{5}, 0, 0.25, \sqrt{4},$ and $\frac{22}{7}$ **17.** commutative property of addition

18. distributive property of multiplication over addition   **19.** 243   **20.** 64   **21.** $\frac{1}{64}$ **22.** 7500   **23.** $\frac{4.9 \times 10^4}{7 \times 10^{-3}} = 7 \times 10^6$

24. \$7267   **25.** $1, -4, -9, -14, -19,$ and -24 **26.** 22   **27.** $16, 8, 4, 2, 1,$ and $\frac{1}{2}$ **28.** 320

CHAPTER 3

Section 3.1

Check Point Exercises

1. 608   **2.** -2 **3.** -94 **4.** Model 3   **5.** $3x - 21$ **6.** $38x^2 + 23x$ **7.** $2x + 36$

Exercise Set 6.1

1. 27   **3.** 23   **5.** 29   **7.** -2 **9.** 140   **11.** 217   **13.** 176   **15.** 30   **17.** 44   **19.** 22   **21.** 27   **23.** -12 **25.** 69
27. -33 **29.** -8 **31.** 10°C   **33.** 60 ft   **35.** $17x$ **37.** $-3x^2$ **39.** $3x + 15$ **41.** $8x - 12$ **43.** $15x + 16$ **45.** $27x - 10$
47. $29y - 29$ **49.** $8y - 12$ **51.** $16y - 25$ **53.** $12x^2 + 11$ **55.** $-2x^2 - 9$ **57.** $x - (x + 4); -4$ **59.** $6(-5x); -30x$
61. $5x - 2x; 3x$ **63.** $8x - (3x + 6); 5x - 6$ **65.** 313; very well   **67.** 1348   **69.** Model 1   **71.** very well   **73. a.** \$32,000
b. \$32,616; reasonably well   **c.** \$32,597; reasonably well   **75.** Model 1   **83.** d   **85. a.** \$50.50, \$5.50, and \$1.00 per clock, respectively
b. no; Answers will vary.

Section 3.2

Check Point Exercises

1. $\{6\}$ **2.** $\{-2\}$ **3.** $\{2\}$ **4.** $\{5\}$ **5.** $\{-2\}$ **6.** 3.7; shown as the point (3.7, 10)   **7.** $w = \frac{P - 2l}{2}$ **8.** $m = \frac{T - D}{p}$ **9.** $\varnothing$

10. $\{x \mid x$ is a real number$\}$

Exercise Set 3.2

1. {10} **3.** {−17} **5.** {12} **7.** {9} **9.** {−3} **11.** $\left\{-\frac{1}{4}\right\}$ **13.** {3} **15.** {11} **17.** {−17} **19.** {11} **21.** $\left\{\frac{7}{5}\right\}$

23. $\left\{\frac{25}{3}\right\}$ **25.** {8} **27.** {−3} **29.** {2} **31.** {−4} **33.** $\left\{-\frac{1}{5}\right\}$ **35.** {−4} **37.** {5} **39.** {6} **41.** $\left\{-\frac{7}{2}\right\}$ **43.** {1}

45. {24} **47.** {20} **49.** {5} **51.** $L = \frac{A}{W}$ **53.** $b = \frac{2A}{h}$ **55.** $P = \frac{I}{rt}$ **57.** $m = \frac{E}{c^2}$ **59.** $m = \frac{y - b}{x}$ **61.** $a = 2A - b$

63. $r = \frac{S - P}{Pt}$ **65.** $x = \frac{C - By}{A}$ **67.** $n = \frac{a_n - a_1}{d} + 1$ or $n = \frac{a_n - a_1 + d}{d}$ **69.** ∅ **71.** {$x \mid x$ is a real number} **73.** $\left\{\frac{2}{3}\right\}$

75. {$x \mid x$ is a real number} **77.** ∅ **79.** {0} **81.** ∅ **83.** {0} **85.** 2 **87.** 161 **89.** {−2} **91.** ∅ **93.** {10} **95.** {−2}

97. 2013 **99.** 120 chirps per minute **101.** 409.2 ft **103.** 2011 **105.** 2014 **107.** 2022 **117.** c

Section 3.3

Check Point Exercises

1. 12 **2.** 2011 **3.** basketball: 1.6 million; bicycle riding: 1.3 million; football: 1 million **4.** 300 min

Exercise Set 6.3

1. 6 **3.** 19 and 45 **5.** 2050 **7.** 2008 **9.** 2025; 9,900,000 **11.** births: 375 thousand; deaths: 146 thousand **13.** race: 3844; sexual orientation: 1239 **15.** after 5 months; $165 **17.** 30 times **19.** $600 of merchandise; $580 **21.** 11 hr **23.** $1350 **29.** 5 ft 7 in. **31.** uncle: 60 yr old; woman: 20 yr old **33.** $4000 for the mother; $8000 for the boy; $2000 for the girl

Section 3.4

Check Point Exercises

1. a. {15} **b.** {140} **2.** $1500 **3.** 720 deer **4.** 66 gal **5.** 556 ft **6.** ≈ 4.36 lb per in^2

Exercise Set 3.4

1. {14} **3.** {27} **5.** $\left\{-\frac{9}{4}\right\}$ **7.** {−15} **9.** $\left\{\frac{7}{2}\right\}$ **11.** {10} **13.** 156 **15.** 30 **17.** $x = \frac{ab}{c}$ **19.** $x = \frac{(a + b)d}{c}$ **21.** $x = \frac{ab}{c}$

23. $1115.38 **25.** ≈ 20,489 fur seal pups **27.** $950 **29.** 31 lb **31.** 154.1 in. or ≈ 12.8 ft **33.** ≈ 607 lb **35.** 120 ft **37.** 0.88°C

39. 6.4 lb **41.** 112 decibels **49.** The front sprocket can be replaced by a 100-tooth sprocket, or the rear sprocket can be replaced with a 12-tooth sprocket. **51.** The destructive power is 4 times as strong.

Section 3.5

Check Point Exercises

1. a.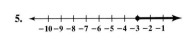

b.

c.

2. {$x \mid x \le 4$};

3. a. {$x \mid x < 8$};

b. {$x \mid x > -3$};

4. {$x \mid x < -6$};

5. {$x \mid x \ge 1$};

6. {$x \mid -1 \le x < 4$};

7. at least 83%

Exercise Set 3.5

1.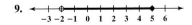

3.

5.

7.

9.

11.

13. {$x \mid x > 5$};

15. {$x \mid x \le 5$};

17. {$x \mid x < 3$};

19. $\{x \mid x < 5\}$;

21. $\{x \mid x \geq -5\}$;

23. $\{x \mid x > 5\}$;

25. $\{x \mid x < 5\}$;

27. $\{x \mid x < 8\}$;

29. $\{x \mid x > -6\}$;

31. $\{x \mid x > -5\}$;

33. $\{x \mid x \leq 5\}$;

35. $\{x \mid x \leq 3\}$;

37. $\{x \mid x < 16\}$;

39. $\{x \mid x > -3\}$;

41. $\{x \mid x \geq -2\}$;

43. $\{x \mid x > -4\}$;

45. $\{x \mid x \geq 4\}$;

47. $\left\{x \mid x > \dfrac{11}{3}\right\}$;

49. $\{x \mid x > 2\}$;

51. $\{x \mid x < 3\}$;

53. $\left\{x \mid x > \dfrac{5}{3}\right\}$;

55. $\{x \mid x \geq -10\}$;

57. $\{x \mid x < -6\}$;

59. $\{x \mid 3 < x < 5\}$;

61. $\{x \mid -1 \leq x < 3\}$;

63. $\{x \mid -5 < x \leq -2\}$;

65. $\{x \mid 3 \leq x < 6\}$;

67. $x > \dfrac{C - By}{A}$ **69.** $x < \dfrac{C - By}{A}$ **71.** $\{x \mid x + 5 \geq 2x\}$ **73.** $\{x \mid 2(4 + x) \leq 36\}$ **75.** $\left\{x \mid \dfrac{3x}{5} + 4 \leq 34\right\}$ **77.** $\{x \mid 0 < x < 4\}$

79. intimacy $\geq$ passion or passion $\leq$ intimacy   **81.** commitment $>$ passion or passion $<$ commitment   **83.** 9; after 3 years
85. more than 28 years; years after 2012   **87. a.** 88; no   **b.** at least 68   **89.** at most 1280 mi   **91.** at most 29 bags   **93.** between 80 and
110 minutes, inclusive   **99.** more than 1200 packages

Section 3.6

Check Point Exercises

1. $x^2 + 11x + 30$ **2.** $28x^2 - x - 15$ **3.** $(x + 2)(x + 3)$ **4.** $(x + 5)(x - 2)$ **5.** $(5x - 4)(x - 2)$ **6.** $(3y - 1)(2y + 7)$

7. $\{-6, 3\}$ **8.** $\{-2, 8\}$ **9.** $\left\{-4, \dfrac{1}{2}\right\}$ **10.** $\left\{-\dfrac{1}{2}, \dfrac{1}{4}\right\}$ **11.** $\left\{\dfrac{3 + \sqrt{7}}{2}, \dfrac{3 - \sqrt{7}}{2}\right\}$ **12.** approximately 26 years old

Exercise Set 3.6

1. $x^2 + 8x + 15$ **3.** $x^2 - 2x - 15$ **5.** $2x^2 + 3x - 2$ **7.** $12x^2 - 43x + 35$ **9.** $(x + 2)(x + 3)$ **11.** $(x - 5)(x + 3)$
13. $(x - 5)(x - 3)$ **15.** $(x - 12)(x + 3)$ **17.** prime   **19.** $(x + 1)(x + 16)$ **21.** $(2x + 1)(x + 3)$ **23.** $(2x - 5)(x - 6)$
25. $(3x + 2)(x - 1)$ **27.** $(3x - 28)(x + 1)$ **29.** $(3x - 4)(2x - 1)$ **31.** $(2x + 3)(2x + 5)$ **33.** $\{-3, 8\}$ **35.** $\left\{-\dfrac{5}{4}, 2\right\}$
37. $\{-5, -3\}$ **39.** $\{-3, 5\}$ **41.** $\{-3, 7\}$ **43.** $\{-8, -1\}$ **45.** $\{6\}$ **47.** $\left\{-\dfrac{1}{2}, 4\right\}$ **49.** $\left\{-2, \dfrac{9}{5}\right\}$ **51.** $\left\{-\dfrac{7}{2}, -\dfrac{1}{3}\right\}$ **53.** $\{-5, -3\}$
55. $\left\{\dfrac{-5 + \sqrt{13}}{2}, \dfrac{-5 - \sqrt{13}}{2}\right\}$ **57.** $\{-2 + \sqrt{10}, -2 - \sqrt{10}\}$ **59.** $\{-2 + \sqrt{11}, -2 - \sqrt{11}\}$ **61.** $\{-3, 6\}$ **63.** $\left\{-\dfrac{2}{3}, \dfrac{3}{2}\right\}$
65. $\{1 + \sqrt{11}, 1 - \sqrt{11}\}$ **67.** $\left\{\dfrac{1 + \sqrt{57}}{2}, \dfrac{1 - \sqrt{57}}{2}\right\}$ **69.** $\left\{\dfrac{-3 + \sqrt{3}}{6}, \dfrac{-3 - \sqrt{3}}{6}\right\}$ **71.** $\left\{\dfrac{3}{2}\right\}$ **73.** $\left\{-\dfrac{2}{3}, 4\right\}$ **75.** $\{-3, 1\}$
77. $\left\{1, -\dfrac{5}{2}\right\}$ **79.** $\{\pm \sqrt{6}\}$ **81.** $1 + \sqrt{7}$ **83.** 9 teams   **85.** exactly   **87.** 2014   **89.** 33-yr-olds and 58-yr-olds; The formula models
the trend in the data quite well.   **97.** 8 and 16   **99.** $(x^n + 9)(x^n + 11)$

Chapter 3 Review Exercises

1. 33   **2.** 15   **3.** −48   **4.** 805 million; fairly well, but slight overestimation   **5.** $17x - 15$ **6.** $5y - 13$ **7.** $14x^2 + x$ **8.** $\{6\}$

9. $\{2\}$ **10.** $\{12\}$ **11.** $\left\{-\dfrac{13}{3}\right\}$ **12.** $\{2\}$ **13.** $\varnothing$ **14.** $\{x \mid x \text{ is a real number}\}$ **15.** $x = \dfrac{By + C}{A}$ **16.** $h = \dfrac{2A}{b}$

17. $B = 2A - C$ **18.** $g = \dfrac{s - vt}{t^2}$ **19.** 2012   **20.** $7x - 1 = 5x + 9; 5$ **21.** Chicken Caesar: 495; Express Taco: 620; Chicken: 590

22. 2013   **23.** 500 min   **24.** United States: 20.5 million barrels per day; China: 6.5 million barrels per day   **25.** $\{5\}$

26. $\{-65\}$ **27.** $\left\{\dfrac{2}{5}\right\}$ **28.** $\{3\}$ **29.** 324 teachers   **30.** 287 trout   **31.** $154   **32.** 1600 ft   **33.** 5 hr

34. $\{x \mid x < 4\}$;   **35.** $\{x \mid x > -8\}$;   **36.** $\{x \mid x \geq -3\}$;

37. $\{x \mid x > 6\}$;   **38.** $\{x \mid x \geq 4\}$;   **39.** $\{x \mid x \leq 2\}$;

40. $\left\{x \mid -\dfrac{3}{4} < x \leq 1\right\}$;

41. at least 64   **42.** $x^2 + 4x - 45$ **43.** $12x^2 - 13x - 14$ **44.** $(x - 4)(x + 3)$

45. $(x - 5)(x - 3)$ **46.** prime   **47.** $(3x - 2)(x - 5)$ **48.** $(2x - 5)(3x + 2)$ **49.** prime

50. $\{-7, 2\}$ **51.** $\{-4, 8\}$ **52.** $\left\{-8, \dfrac{1}{2}\right\}$ **53.** $\{-5, -2\}$ **54.** $\{1, 3\}$

55. $\left\{\dfrac{5 + \sqrt{41}}{2}, \dfrac{5 - \sqrt{41}}{2}\right\}$ **56.** $\left\{-3, \dfrac{1}{2}\right\}$ **57.** $\left\{\dfrac{3 + 2\sqrt{6}}{3}, \dfrac{3 - 2\sqrt{6}}{3}\right\}$ **58.** 2012

Chapter 3 Test

1. −44   **2.** $14x - 4$ **3.** 616 convictions   **4.** $\{-5\}$ **5.** $\{2\}$ **6.** $\varnothing$ **7.** $\{-15\}$ **8.** $y = \dfrac{Ax + A}{B}$ **9.** 2008   **10.** 63.8

11. fitness trainer: $50,950; teacher: $28,080   **12.** 5 years   **13.** 20 prints; $3.80   **14.** $\left\{\dfrac{15}{2}\right\}$ **15.** $\{3\}$ **16.** 6000 tule elk

17. 137.5 lb per in^2 **18.** 4 hours

19. $\{x \mid x \leq -3\}$;   **20.** $\{x \mid x > 7\}$;   **21.** $\left\{x \mid -2 \leq x < \dfrac{5}{2}\right\}$;

22. at least 92   **23.** $6x^2 - 7x - 20$ **24.** $(2x - 5)(x - 2)$ **25.** $\{-9, 4\}$ **26.** $\left\{\dfrac{-2 + \sqrt{2}}{2}, \dfrac{-2 - \sqrt{2}}{2}\right\}$ **27.** 2018   **28.** 2018

29. quite well

CHAPTER 4

Section 4.1

Check Point Exercises

1. 12.5%   **2.** 2.3%   **3. a.** 0.67   **b.** 2.5   **4. a.** $75.60   **b.** $1335.60   **5. a.** $133   **b.** $247   **6.** $4365   **7. a.** $66\dfrac{2}{3}\%$ **b.** 40%
8. 35%   **9.** 20%   **10. a.** $1152   **b.** 4% decrease

Exercise Set 8.1

1. 40%   **3.** 25%   **5.** 37.5%   **7.** 2.5%   **9.** 11.25%   **11.** 59%   **13.** 38.44%   **15.** 287%   **17.** 1487%   **19.** 10,000%
21. 0.72   **23.** 0.436   **25.** 1.3   **27.** 0.02   **29.** 0.005   **31.** 0.00625   **33.** 0.625   **35.** 6   **37.** 7.2   **39.** 5   **41.** 170   **43.** 20%
45. 12%   **47. a.** $1008   **b.** $17,808   **49. a.** $103.20   **b.** $756.80   **51.** $4815   **53.** $2442.50   **55.** $7030   **57.** $15,220
59. a. $1530   **b.** $1405   **c.** 14.7%   **61.** 56.1%   **63.** 50%   **65.** 15%   **67.** no; 2% decrease   **77.** $2588.93

Section 4.2

Check Point Exercises

1. $150   **2.** $336   **3.** $2091   **4.** 18%   **5.** $3846.16   **6. a.** $1200   **b.** $3800   **c.** 15.8%

Exercise Set 4.2

1. $240   **3.** $10.80   **5.** $318.75   **7.** $426.25   **9.** $3420   **11.** $38,350   **13.** $9390   **15.** 7.5%   **17.** 9%   **19.** 31.3%
21. $5172.42   **23.** $8917.20   **25.** $4509.59   **27. a.** $93.33   **b.** $1906.67   **c.** 7.3%   **29. a.** $1560   **b.** $10,440   **c.** 7.5%
31. $r = \dfrac{A - P}{Pt}$ **33.** $P = \dfrac{A}{1 + rt}$ **35. a.** $247.50   **b.** $4247.50   **37.** 21.4%   **39.** $2654.87   **45. a.** $A = 275t + 5000$
b. Answers will vary; an example is: The rate of change of the future value per year is $275.

Section 4.3

Check Point Exercises

1. a. $1216.65   **b.** $216.65   **2. a.** $6253.23   **b.** $2053.23   **3. a.** $14,859.47   **b.** $14,918.25   **4.** $6189.55   **5. a.** $6628.28
b. 10.5%   **6.** $\approx$ 8.24%

Exercise Set 8.3

1. a. $10,816   **b.** $816   **3. a.** $3655.21   **b.** $655.21   **5. a.** $12,795.12   **b.** $3295.12   **7. a.** $5149.12   **b.** $649.12
9. a. $1855.10   **b.** $355.10   **11. a.** $49,189.33   **b.** $29,189.33   **13. a.** $13,116.51   **b.** $13,140.67   **c.** $13,157.04   **d.** $13,165.31
15. 7% compounded monthly   **17.** $8374.84   **19.** $7528.59   **21. a.** $10,457.65   **b.** 4.6%   **23.** 6.1%   **25.** 6.2%   **27.** 6.2%
29. 8.3%; 8.25%; 8% compounded monthly   **31.** 5.6%; 5.5%; 5.5% compounded semiannually   **33.** 22.5 yr   **35.** 4.3 yr   **37.** 8.3 yr
39. a. $\approx$ $4,117,800,000   **b.** $\approx$ $4,277,900,000   **41.** $65,728.51   **43.** $21,679.39   **51.** $8544.49

Section 4.4

Check Point Exercises

1. a. $6620   **b.** $620   **2. a.** $777,170   **b.** $657,170   **3. a.** $333,946   **b.** $291,946   **4. a.** $187   **b.** deposits: $40,392; interest:
$59,608   **5. a.** high: $63.38; low: $42.37   **b.** $2160   **c.** 1.5%; This is much lower than a bank account paying 3.5%.   **d.** 7,203,200 shares
e. high: $49.94; low: $48.33   **f.** $49.50   **g.** The closing price is up $0.03 from the previous day's closing price.   **h.** $\approx$ $1.34

Exercise Set 4.4

1. a. $66,132   **b.** $26,132   **3. a.** $702,528   **b.** $542,528   **5. a.** $50,226   **b.** $32,226   **7. a.** $9076   **b.** $4076   **9. a.** $28,850
b. $4850   **11. a.** $4530   **b.** deposits: $81,540; interest: $58,460   **13. a.** $1323   **b.** deposits: $158,760; interest: $41,240   **15. a.** $356
b. deposits: $170,880; interest: $829,120   **17. a.** $920   **b.** deposits: $18,400; interest: $1600   **19. a.** high: $73.25; low: $45.44   **b.** $840
c. 2.2%; Answers will vary.   **d.** 591,500 shares   **e.** high: $56.38; low: $54.38   **f.** $55.50   **g.** $1.25 increase   **h.** $\approx$ $3.26   **21. a.** $30,000

b. $30,000   **23. a.** $287   **b.** with: $6254; without: $7115   **c.** with: 12.5%; without: 14.2%   **25.** $P = \dfrac{Ar}{(1 + r)^t - 1}$; the deposit at the end of

each year that yields A dollars after t years with interest rate r compounded annually   **27. a.** $11,617   **b.** $1617   **29. a.** $87,052

b. $63,052   **31. a.** $693,031   **b.** $293,031   **33. a.** $401   **b.** deposits: $3208; interest: $292   **35.** $641; $3,653,860

Section 4.5

Check Point Exercises

1. a. $13,720   **b.** $19,180   **c.** $5180   **2.** $\approx$ 13.5%   **3. a.** $\approx$ $2057.85   **b.** $9597.15   **4. a.** $\approx$ $1885.18   **b.** $9769.82
5. a. $59.52   **b.** $4849.52   **c.** $135   **6.** unpaid balance method: $113.40; previous balance method: $122.40; average daily balance
method: $115.43

Exercise Set 8.5

1. a. $22,000   **b.** $29,600   **c.** $2600   **3. a.** $1000   **b.** $1420   **c.** $320   **5.** 12.5%   **7.** 14.5%   **9.** 13.0%   **11. a.** $17,000
b. $22,133   **c.** $4633   **d.** 10.0%   **13. a.** $1805.73   **b.** $11,534.62   **c.** $1686.11   **d.** $11,654.24   **15. a.** $11.05   **b.** $1013.05
c. $\approx$ $28   **17. a.** $4.96   **b.** $618.61   **c.** $61.86   **19. a.** $7.50   **b.** $45   **c.** $13.75   **31.** b   **33.** Answers will vary.
35. a. 31 days; $376.26   **b.** $4.89   **c.** $471.04

Section 4.6

Check Point Exercises

1. a. $1627   **b.** $117,360   **c.** $148,860
2.

Payment Number	Interest Payment	Principal Payment	Balance of Loan
1	$1166.67	$383.33	$199,616.67
2	$1164.43	$385.57	$199,231.10

3. a. payment: $367; interest: $2616   **b.** payment: $278; interest: $5016   **c.** Monthly payments are less with the longer-term loan, but there
is more interest with this loan.

Exercise Set 4.6

1. a. $44,000   **b.** $176,000   **c.** $5280   **d.** $1171   **e.** $245,560   **3.** $60,120   **5.** 20-year at 7.5%; $106,440   **7.** Mortgage A; $11,300
9. a. $210   **b.** $840   **11. a.** $137; lower monthly payment   **b.** $732; less interest   **13.** monthly payment: $386; total interest: $432;
$176 more each month; $408 less interest

15. a. monthly payment: $244.13; total interest: $1718.24
b.

Payment Number	Interest	Principal	Loan Balance
1	$66.67	$177.46	$9822.54
2	$65.48	$178.65	$9643.89
3	$64.29	$179.84	$9464.05

17. a. monthly payment: $347.13; total interest: $43,311.20

b.

Payment Number	Interest	Principal	Loan Balance
1	$283.33	$63.80	$39,936.20
2	$282.88	$64.25	$39,871.95
3	$282.43	$64.70	$39,807.25

c. $148.81 more each month; $23,798.40 less interest

27.

$$P\left(1 + \frac{r}{n}\right)^{nt} = \frac{PMT\left[\left(1 + \frac{r}{n}\right)^{nt} - 1\right]}{\frac{r}{n}}$$

$$P\left(\frac{r}{n}\right)\left(1 + \frac{r}{n}\right)^{nt} = PMT\left[\left(1 + \frac{r}{n}\right)^{nt} - 1\right]$$

$$\frac{P\left(\frac{r}{n}\right)\left(1 + \frac{r}{n}\right)^{nt}}{\left(1 + \frac{r}{n}\right)^{nt} - 1} = PMT$$

$$\frac{P\left(\frac{r}{n}\right)}{1 - \left(1 + \frac{r}{n}\right)^{-nt}} = PMT$$

Chapter 4 Review Exercises

1. 80% **2.** 12.5% **3.** 75% **4.** 72% **5.** 0.35% **6.** 475.6% **7.** 0.65 **8.** 0.997 **9.** 1.50 **10.** 0.03 **11.** 0.0065
12. 0.0025 **13.** 9.6 **14. a.** $1.44 **b.** $25.44 **15. a.** $297.50 **b.** $552.50 **16.** $3535 **17.** 12.5% increase **18.** 35% decrease
19. no; $9900; 1% decrease **20.** $180 **21.** $2520 **22.** $1200 **23.** $900 **24. a.** $122.50 **b.** $3622.50 **25.** $12,738 **26.** 7.5%
27. $13,389.12 **28.** $9287.93 **29.** 40% **30. a.** $94.50 **b.** $1705.50 **c.** 7.4% **31. a.** $8114.92 **b.** $1114.92 **32. a.** $38,490.80
b. $8490.80 **33. a.** $5556.46 **b.** $3056.46 **34.** 7% compounded monthly; $362 **35.** $16,653.64 **36.** $13,175.19 **37. a.** $2122.73
b. 6.1% **38.** 5.6%; Answers will vary; an example is: The same amount of money would earn 5.6% in a simple interest account for a year.
39. 6.25% compounded monthly **40. a.** $19,129 **b.** $8729 **41. a.** $91,361 **b.** $55,361 **42. a.** $1049 **b.** $20,980; $4020
43. high: $64.06; low: $26.13 **44.** $144 **45.** 0.3% **46.** 545,800 shares **47.** high: $61.25; low: $59.25 **48.** $61.00 **49.** $1.75 increase
50. $1.49 **52. a.** $16,000 **b.** $21,500 **c.** $5000 **d.** 11.5% **53. a.** $250.40 **b.** $4229.60 **54. a.** $213.11 **b.** $4336.89
55. Answers will vary. **56. a.** $16.50 **b.** $1756.50 **c.** $49 **57. a.** $28.80 **b.** $64.80 **c.** $34.61 **58. a.** $48,000 **b.** $192,000
c. $3840 **d.** $1277 **e.** $267,720 **59.** 20-year at 8%; $53,040; Answers will vary. **60. a.** option A: $769; option B: $699; Answers will vary.
b. Mortgage A: $20,900 **61. a.** monthly payment: $465; total interest: $1740 **b.** monthly payment: $305; total interest: $3300 **c.** Longer term
has lower monthly payment but greater total interest.

62. a. $464.89
b. $1845.36
c.

Payment Number	Interest	Principal	Loan Balance
1	$139.68	$325.21	$8986.79
2	$134.80	$330.09	$8656.70
3	$129.85	$335.04	$8321.66

Chapter 4 Test

1. a. $18 **b.** $102 **2.** $3430 **3.** 75% **4.** $72; $2472 **5.** 25% **6.** $6698.57 **7.** 4.58%; Answers will vary; an example is:
The same amount of money would earn 4.58% in a simple interest account for a year. **8. a.** $8297 **b.** $2297 **9. a.** $7067 **b.** $1067
c. Only part of the $6000 is invested for the entire five years.; Answers will vary. **10.** $2070 **11.** $704 per month; $1,162,080 interest
12. high: $25.75; low: $25.50 **13.** $2030 **14.** $386.25 **15.** $13,000 **16.** $21,000 **17.** $5000 **18.** 13.5% **19.** $819.67
20. $6680.33 **21.** $15.60 **22.** $1335.60 **23.** $37 **24.** $16.80 **25.** $12,000 **26.** $108,000 **27.** $2160 **28.** $830.52
29. $190,987.20

30. a. monthly payment: $230; total interest: $7600
b.

Payment Number	Interest	Principal	Loan Balance
1	$113.33	$116.67	$19,883.33
2	$112.67	$117.33	$19,766.00

CHAPTER 5

Section 5.1

1. The metric system   **3.** It is the standard of measurement accepted worldwide. There is only one basic unit of measurement for each quantity. It is based on the number 10, which makes many calculations easier than the U.S. customary system.
5. a) Answers will vary.   **b)** 0.002 146 km   **c)** 60 800 dm   **7.** Answers will vary.   **9. a)** 10,000 times   **b)** 10 000 cm
c) 0.0001 hm   **11.** Yard   **13.** 5   **15.** 22   **17.** (b)   **19.** (c)   **21.** (f)   **23. a)** 100   **b)** 0.001   **c)** 1000
d) 0.01   **e)** 10   **f)** 0.1   **25.** cg; $\frac{1}{100}$ g   **27.** dg; $\frac{1}{10}$ g   **29.** hg; 100 g   **31.** 3 000 000 g   **33.** 5000   **35.** 0.0085
37. 0.024 26   **39.** 0.024 35   **41.** 13 400   **43.** 325 hg   **45.** 895 000 mℓ **47.** 1.40 g   **49.** 4.0302 daℓ
51. 590 cm, 2.3 dam, 0.47 km   **53.** 1.4 kg, 1600 g, 16 300 dg   **55.** 203 000 mm, 2.6 km, 52.6 hm   **57.** Jim, 1 m $>$ 1 yd
59. The pump that removes 1 daℓ per minute   **61. a)** 346 cm   **b)** 3460 mm   **63. a)** 6.417 km/ℓ **b)** 6417 m/ℓ
65. a) 2160 mℓ **b)** 2.16 ℓ **c)** \$1.13 per liter   **67. a)** 108 m   **b)** 0.108 km   **c)** 108 000 mm   **69. a)** 11 120 km
b) 11 120 000 m   **71.** 1000   **73.** $1 \times 10^{24} =$ 1 000 000 000 000 000 000 000 000   **75.** $\approx$ 30 eggs   **77.** $\approx$ 4.1 cups
79. 7 dam   **81.** 6 mg   **83.** 2 daℓ **85.** gram   **87.** liter   **89.** meter   **91.** kilometer   **93.** degrees celsius

Section 5.2

1. Volume   **3.** Area   **5.** Volume   **7.** Volume   **9.** Area   **11.** Length   **13.–17.** Answers will vary.
19. A cubic decimeter   **21.** A cubic centimeter   **23.** Area   **25.** Centimeters   **27.** Centimeters or millimeters
29. Centimeters   **31.** Kilometers   **33.** Centimeters   **35.** Kilometers   **37.** (c)   **39.** (c)   **41.** (b)   **43.** (c)
45.–49. Answers will vary.   **51.** Centimeter, kilometer   **53.** Meter   **55.** Centimeter   **57.** Square centimeters
59. Square centimeters or square meters   **61.** Square meters or hectares   **63.** Square centimeters   **65.** Square meters
67. (a)   **69.** (b)   **71.** (a)   **73.** (c)   **75.–79.** Answers will vary.   **81.** Liters   **83.** Kiloliters   **85.** Cubic meters or
cubic centimeters   **87.** Liters   **89.** Cubic meters   **91.** (c)   **93.** (c)   **95.** (c)   **97.** (a)   **99. b)** 152 561 cm^3
101. $\approx$ 0.20 m^3 **103.** Longer side $\approx$ 4 cm, shorter side $\approx$ 2.2 cm, area $\approx$ 8.8 cm^2 **105.** $\approx$ 326.85 m^2
107. a) 3869 m^2 **b)** 369 m^2 **109. a)** 3151.2 m^2 **b)** 0.315 12 ha   **111.** \$304   **113. a)** 56 000 cm^3
b) 56 000 mℓ **c)** 56 ℓ **115.** 100 times larger   **117.** 1000 times larger   **119.** 100   **121.** 100   **123.** 0.000 001
125. 1 000 000   **127.** 218   **129.** 76   **131.** 60 kℓ **133.** Answers will vary.   **135.** 6700
137. a) 4,014,489,600 sq in.   **b)** Answers will vary.   **139. a)** Answers will vary. The average use is 5150.7 ℓ/day.
b) Answers will vary. The average use is 493.2 ℓ/day.

Section 5.3

1. Kilogram   **3.** 2   **5.** Answers will vary. One possible answer is 32°C.   **7.** Answers will vary.   **9.** Kilograms
11. Grams   **13.** Grams   **15.** Kilograms   **17.** Kilograms or metric tonnes   **19.** (b)   **21.** (b)   **23.** (b)
25.–27. Answers will vary.   **29.** (c)   **31.** (b)   **33.** (c)   **35.** (c)   **37.** (c)   **39.** 77°F   **41.** $\approx$ 33.3°C
43. $\approx$ −17.8°C   **45.** 98.6°F   **47.** $\approx$ −10.6°C   **49.** 32°F   **51.** $\approx$ −28.9°C   **53.** $\approx$ 73.9 by the formula
55. 71.6°F   **57.** 95.18°F   **59.** 64.04°F–74.30°F   **61.** \$20.25   **63.** 444 g   **65. a)** 2304 m^3 **b)** 2304 kℓ
c) 2304 t   **67.** Yes: 78°F is about 25.6°C.   **69.** 0.0042   **71.** 17 400 000 g   **73. a)** 1200 g   **b)** 1200 cm^3
75. a) 5.625 ft^3 **b)** $\approx$ 351.6 lb   **c)** $\approx$ 42.4 gal   **77. a)** −79.8°F   **b)** 36.5°F   **c)** 510 000 000°C

Section 5.4

1. Dimensional analysis is a procedure used to convert from one unit of measurement to a different unit of measurement.
3. $\dfrac{60 \text{ seconds}}{1 \text{ minute}}$ or $\dfrac{1 \text{ minute}}{60 \text{ seconds}}$ **5.** $\dfrac{1 \text{ lb}}{0.45 \text{ kg}}$ **7.** $\dfrac{3.8 \ \ell}{1 \text{ gal}}$ **9.** 157.48 cm   **11.** 1.26 m   **13.** 266.67 lb   **15.** 62.4 km
17. 1687.5 acres   **19.** 33.19 pints   **21.** 1.46 mi^2 **23.** 54 kg   **25.** 28 grams   **27.** 0.45 kilogram
29. 2.54 centimeters, 1.6 kilometers   **31.** 0.9 meter   **33.** $\approx$ 561.11 yd   **35.** $\approx$ 1146.67 ft   **37.** 37.5 mph
39. 43.2 m^2 **41.** 50 mph   **43.** 0.21 oz   **45.** 360 m^3 **47.** \$0.495 per pound   **49.** $\approx$ 9078.95 gal   **51.** 6 qt
53. a) −8460 cm   **b)** −84.6 m   **55. a)** 10.89 ft^2 **b)** 35.937 ft^3 **57.** 25.2 mg   **59.** 6840 mg, or 6.84 g
61. a) 25 mg   **b)** 900 mg   **63. a)** 289.2 m   **b)** 76 500 t   **c)** 44.8 kph   **65. a)** 0.9 € per pound
b) \$1.17 per pound   **67.** 1.0 cc, or b)   **69. a)** 4000 cc   **b)** $\approx$ 244.09 in.^{3} **71.** A kilogram   **73.** A liter
75. A decimeter   **77.** wonton   **79.** 1 kilohurtz   **81.** 1 megaphone   **83.** 2 kilomockingbird   **85.** 1 decoration

Chapter 5 Review Exercises

1. $\frac{1}{100}$ of base unit   **2.** 1000 $\times$ base unit   **3.** $\frac{1}{1000}$ of base unit   **4.** 100 $\times$ base unit   **5.** 10 $\times$ base unit
6. $\frac{1}{10}$ of base unit   **7.** 0.040 g   **8.** 320 cℓ **9.** 0.016 mm   **10.** 1 kg   **11.** 4620 ℓ **12.** 19 260 dg
13. 3000 mℓ, 14 630 cℓ, 2.67 kℓ **14.** 0.047 km, 47 000 cm, 4700 m   **15.** Centimeters   **16.** Grams   **17.** Degrees Celsius
18. Millimeters or centimeters   **19.** Square meters   **20.** Milliliters or cubic centimeters   **21.** Millimeters
22. Kilograms or tonnes   **23.** Kilometers   **24.** Meters or centimeters   **25. a)** Answers will vary.   **b)** Answers will vary.
26. a) Answers will vary.   **b)** Answers will vary.   **27.** (c)   **28.** (b)   **29.** (c)   **30.** (a)   **31.** (a)   **32.** (b)
33. 3.6 t   **34.** 4 300 000 g   **35.** 75.2°F   **36.** 20°C   **37.** $\approx$ −21.1°C   **38.** 102.2°F

39. $l = 4$ cm, $w = 1.6$ cm, $A = 6.4$ cm^2 **40.** $r = 1.5$ cm, $A \approx 7.07$ cm^2 **41. a)** 80 m^3 **b)** 80 000 kg
42. a) 899.79 cm^2 **b)** 0.089 979 m^2 **43. a)** 96 000 cm^3 **b)** 0.096 m^3 **c)** 96 000 mℓ **d)** 0.096 kℓ
44. 10,000 times larger **45.** ≈ 9.84 in. **46.** ≈ 233.33 lb **47.** 74.7 m **48.** ≈ 111.11 yd **49.** 72 kph
50. ≈ 63.16 qt **51.** 76 ℓ **52.** ≈ 78.95 yd^3 **53.** ≈ 12.77 in.^{2} **54.** 3.8 ℓ **55.** 11.4 m^3 **56.** 99.2 km
57. 0.9 ft **58.** 82.55 mm **59. a)** 1050 kg **b)** ≈ 2333.33 lb **60.** 32.4 m^2 **61. a)** 190 kℓ **b)** 190 000 kg
62. a) 104 kph **b)** 104 000 meters per hour **63. a)** 252 ℓ **b)** 252 kg **64.** \$1.58 per pound

Chapter 5 Test

1. 0.497 daℓ **2.** 2 730 000 cm **3.** 100 times greater **4.** 2.4 km **5.** (b) **6.** (a) **7.** (c) **8.** (c) **9.** (b)
10. 10,000 times greater **11.** 1,000,000,000 times greater **12.** 6300 g **13.** ≈ 28.13 mi **14.** ≈ -26.11°C
15. 68°F **16. a)** 300 000 g **b)** ≈ 666.67 lb **17. a)** 3200 m^3 **b)** 3 200 000 ℓ (or 3200 kℓ) **c)** 3 200 000 kg
18. \$245

CHAPTER 6

Section 6.1

1. a) Undefined terms, definitions, postulates (axioms), and theorems **b)** First, Euclid introduced undefined terms. Second, he introduced certain definitions. Third, he stated primitive propositions called postulates about the undefined terms and definitions. Fourth, he proved, using deductive reasoning, other propositions called theorems. **3.** Two lines that do not lie in the same plane and do not intersect are called skew lines. **5.** Two angles in the same plane are adjacent angles when they have a common vertex and a common side but no common interior points. **7.** Two angles, the sum of whose measure is 180°, are called supplementary angles.
9. An angle whose measure is greater than 90° but less than 180° is an obtuse angle. **11.** An angle whose measure is less than 90° is an acute angle. **13.** Ray, $\overrightarrow{BA}$ **15.** Half line, $\overset{\circ}{BA}$ **17.** Ray, $\overrightarrow{AB}$ **19.** Half open line segment, $\overset{\circ}{AB}$ **21.** $\overrightarrow{BG}$ **23.** $\overrightarrow{BD}$
25. $\{B, F\}$ **27.** $\{C\}$ **29.** $\angle CFG$ **31.** $\overleftrightarrow{BC}$ **33.** $\{B\}$ **35.** $\overrightarrow{BC}$ **37.** $\angle ABE$ **39.** $\overline{BF}$ **41.** $\overset{\circ}{AC}$
43. $\overset{\circ}{BE}$ **45.** Obtuse **47.** Straight **49.** Right **51.** None of these angles **53.** 64° **55.** $57\frac{1}{4}$° **57.** 25.3°
59. 91° **61.** 159.5° **63.** $136\frac{2}{7}$° **65.** (b) **67.** (f) **69.** (a) **71.** $m\angle 1 = 49°, m\angle 2 = 41°$ **73.** 134° and 46°
75. Angles 3, 4, and 7 each measure 125°; angles 1, 2, 5, and 6 each measure 55°. **77.** Angles 2, 4, and 5 each measure 120°; angles 1, 3, 6, and 7 each measure 60°. **79.** $m\angle 1 = 64°, m\angle 2 = 26°$ **81.** $m\angle 1 = 33°, m\angle 2 = 57°$
83. $m\angle 1 = 134°, m\angle 2 = 46°$ **85.** $m\angle 1 = 29°, m\angle 2 = 151°$ **87. a)** An infinite number **b)** An infinite number
89. An infinite number

For Exercises 91–97, each answer given is one of many possible answers.

91. Plane ABG and plane JCD **93.** $\overleftrightarrow{BG}$ and $\overleftrightarrow{DG}$ **95.** Plane $AGB \cap$ plane $ABC \cap$ plane $BCD = \{B\}$
97. $\overleftrightarrow{BC} \cap$ plane $ABG = \{B\}$ **99.** Always true. If any two lines are parallel to a third line, then they must be parallel to each other.
101. Sometimes true. Vertical angles are only complementary when each is equal to 45°. **103.** Sometimes true. Alternate interior angles are only complementary when each is equal to 45°. **105.** Answers will vary. **107.** No. Line l and line n may be parallel or skew. **109.** 360°

Section 6.2

1. A polygon is a closed figure in a plane determined by three or more straight line segments. **3.** The different types of triangles are acute, obtuse, right, isosceles, equilateral, and scalene. Descriptions will vary. **5.** If the corresponding sides of two similar figures are the same length, the figures are congruent figures. **7. a)** Triangle **b)** Regular **9. a)** Octagon **b)** Regular
11. a) Rhombus **b)** Not regular **13. a)** Octagon **b)** Not regular **15. a)** Isosceles **b)** Acute
17. a) Isosceles **b)** Right **19. a)** Scalene **b)** Acute **21. a)** Scalene **b)** Right **23.** Rectangle
25. Square **27.** Rhombus **29.** 17° **31.** 150° **33.** $m\angle 1 = 90°, m\angle 2 = 50°, m\angle 3 = 130°, m\angle 4 = 50°$,
$m\angle 5 = 50°, m\angle 6 = 40°, m\angle 7 = 90°, m\angle 8 = 130°, m\angle 9 = 140°, m\angle 10 = 40°, m\angle 11 = 140°, m\angle 12 = 40°$ **35.** 720°
37. 1080° **39.** 3240° **41. a)** 60° **b)** 120° **43. a)** 108° **b)** 72° **45. a)** 144° **b)** 36°
47. $x = 2, y = 1.6$ **49.** $x = 2\frac{2}{5}, y = 7\frac{1}{2}$ **51.** $x = 20, y = 21\frac{1}{4}$ **53.** 3 **55.** $3\frac{1}{3}$ **57.** 28 **59.** 30 **61.** 28°
63. 9 **65.** 10 **67.** 70° **69.** 55° **71.** 35° **73.** 70 ft **75. a)** ≈ 113.14 mi **b)** ≈ 75.43 mi
77. $D'E' = 4, E'F' = 5, D'F' = 3$ **79. a)** $m\angle HMF = m\angle TMB, m\angle HFM = m\angle TBM, m\angle MHF = m\angle MTB$ **b)** 44 ft

Section 6.3

Throughout this section, we used the $\boxed{\pi}$ key on a scientific calculator to determine answers in calculations involving π. If you use 3.14 for π, your answers may vary slightly.

1. a) Answers will vary. **b)** Answers will vary. **c)**

```
        6
  ┌──────────┐
2 │          │
  └──────────┘
```

The area of this rectangle is 12 square units. The perimeter of this rectangle is 16 units.

3. a) To determine the number of square feet, multiply the number of square yards by 9.   **b)** To determine the number of square yards, divide the number of square feet by 9.   **5.** 17.5 in.^{2} **7.** 17.5 cm^2 **9. a)** 210 ft^2 **b)** 62 ft   **11. a)** 6000 cm^2 **b)** 654 cm   **13. a)** 288 in.^{2} **b)** 74 in.   **15. a)** 50.27 m^2 **b)** 25.13 m   **17. a)** 132.73 ft^2 **b)** 40.84 ft **19. a)** 17 yd   **b)** 40 yd   **c)** 60 yd^2 **21. a)** 12 km   **b)** 30 km   **c)** 30 km^2 **23.** $\approx$ 21.46 m^2 **25.** 8 in.^{2} **27.** 90 yd^2 **29.** $\approx$ 65.73 in.^{2} **31.** $\approx$ 307.88 cm^2 **33.** 23 yd^2 **35.** 132.3 ft^2 **37.** 234,000 cm^2 **39.** 0.8625 m^2 **41. a)** $5973   **b)** $7623   **43.** $2890   **45.** $2908.80   **47.** $234.21   **49. a)** 288 ft   **b)** 4700 tiles **51.** 21 ft   **53.** $\approx$ 312 ft   **55. a)** $A = s^2$ **b)** $A = 4s^2$ **c)** Four times larger   **57.** 24 cm^2 **59.** Answers will vary.

Section 6.4

Throughout this section, we used the $\boxed{\pi}$ key on a scientific calculator to determine answers in calculations involving π. If you use 3.14 for π, your answers may vary slightly.

1. a) Volume is a measure of the capacity of a figure.   **b)** Surface area is the sum of the areas of the surfaces of a three-dimensional figure.   **3.** A polyhedron is a closed surface formed by the union of polygonal regions. A regular polyhedron is one whose faces are all regular polygons of the same size and shape.   **5.** Answers will vary.   **7. a)** 8 m^3 **b)** 28 m^2 **9. a)** 125 ft^3 **b)** 150 ft^2 **11. a)** 150.80 in.^{3} **b)** 175.93 in.^{2} **13. a)** 131.95 cm^3 **b)** 163.22 cm^2 **15. a)** 381.70 cm^3 **b)** 254.47 cm^2 **17.** 384 in.^{3} **19.** 524.33 cm^3 **21.** 324 mm^3 **23.** 392 ft^3 **25.** 284.46 cm^3 **27.** 24 ft^3 **29.** 243 ft^3 **31.** $\approx$ 5.67 yd^3 **33.** 3,700,000 cm^3 **35.** 7.5 m^3 **37.** Tubs $\approx$ 141.37 in.^{3}; boxes = 125 in.^{3} **39.** 40,840 mm^2 **41.** $\approx$ 2.50 qt   **43. a)** 120,000 cm^3 **b)** 120,000 mℓ **c)** 120 ℓ **45.** $\approx$ 283.04 in.^{3} **47. a)** $\approx$ 323.98 in.^{3} **b)** $\approx$ 0.19 ft^3 **49.** $\approx$ 14.14 in.^{3} **51.** Ten edges   **53.** Six vertices   **55.** Fourteen edges **57. a)** $\approx$ 5.11 $\times$ 10^8 km^2 **b)** $\approx$ 3.79 $\times$ 10^7 km^2 **c)** $\approx$ 13 times larger   **d)** $\approx$ 1.09 $\times$ 10^{12} km^3 **e)** $\approx$ 2.20 $\times$ 10^{10} km^3 **f)** $\approx$ 50 times larger   **59. a)–e)** Answers will vary.   **f)** If we double the length of each edge of a cube, the new volume will be eight times the original volume.   **61. a)** Answers will vary. **b)** $V_1 = a^3$; $V_2 = a^2b$; $V_3 = a^2b$; $V_4 = ab^2$; $V_5 = a^2b$; $V_6 = ab^2$; $V_7 = b^3$ **c)** ab^2

Section 6.5

1. The act of moving a geometric figure from some starting position to some ending position without altering its shape or size is called rigid motion. The four main rigid motions studied in this section are reflections, translations, rotations, and glide reflections.
3. A reflection is a rigid motion that moves a figure to a new position that is a mirror image of the figure in the starting position.
5. A rotation is a rigid motion performed by rotating a figure in the plane about a specific point.   **7.** A translation is a rigid motion that moves a figure by sliding it along a straight line segment in the plane.   **9.** A glide reflection is a rigid motion formed by performing a translation (or glide) followed by a reflection.   **11.** A geometric figure is said to have reflective symmetry if the positions of a figure before and after a reflection are identical (except for vertex labels).   **13.** A tessellation is a pattern consisting of the repeated use of the same geometric figures to entirely cover a plane, leaving no gaps.

This figure contains the answers for Exercises 15 and 16.

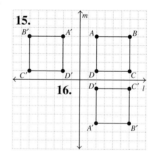

This figure contains the answers for Exercises 17 and 18.

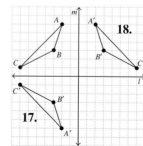

This figure contains the answers for Exercises 19 and 20.

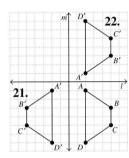

This figure contains the answers for Exercises 21 and 22.

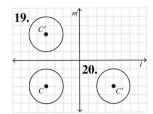

This figure contains the answers to Exercises 23 and 24.

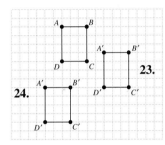

This figure contains the answers to Exercises 25 and 26.

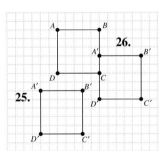

This figure contains the answers to Exercises 27 and 28.

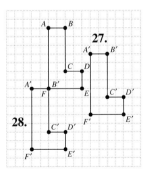

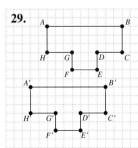

This figure contains the answers to Exercises 31 and 32.

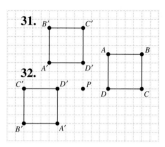

This figure contains the answers to Exercises 33 and 34.

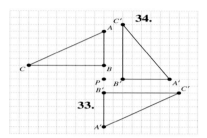

This figure contains the answers to Exercises 35 and 36.

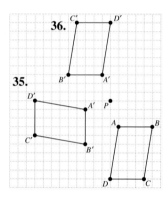

This figure contains the answers to Exercises 37 and 38.

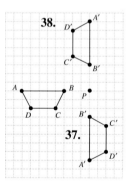

This figure contains the answers to Exercises 39 and 40.

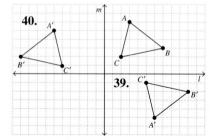

This figure contains the answers to Exercises 41 and 42.

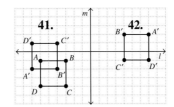

This figure contains the answers to Exercises 43 and 44.

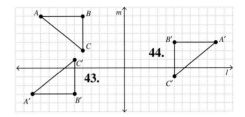

This figure contains the answers to Exercises 45 and 46.

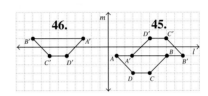

47. a) 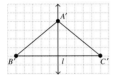 **b)** Yes **c)** Yes **49. a)** 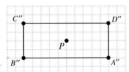 **b)** No **c)** No

51. a) 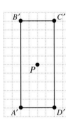 **b)** No **c)** No **d)** **e)** Yes **f)** Yes

53. a)–c) 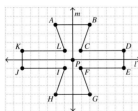 **d)** No. Any 90° rotation will result in the figure being in a different position than the starting position.

55. a) and b) 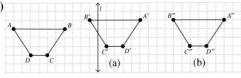 **c)** No. **d)** The order in which the translation and the reflection are performed is important. The figure obtained in part (a) is the glide reflection.

57. Answers will vary. **59. a)** Answers will vary. **b)** A regular pentagon cannot be used as a tessellating shape.

61. Although answers will vary depending on the font, the following capital letters have reflective symmetry about a vertical line drawn through the center of the letter: A, H, I, M, O, T, U, V, W, X, Y.

Section 6.6

1. Topology is sometimes referred to as "rubber sheet geometry" because it deals with bending and stretching of geometric figures. **3.** Take a strip of paper, give one end a half twist, and tape the ends together. **5.** Four **7.** A Jordan curve is a topological object that can be thought of as a circle twisted out of shape. **9.** The number of holes that go through the object determines the genus of an object. **11.–19.** Answers will vary. **21.** Outside **23.** Inside **25.** Outside **27.** Outside **29.** 1 **31.** 5 **33.** Larger than 5 **35.** 5 **37.** 0 **39.** Larger than 5 **41. a)–d)** Answers will vary. **43.** One **45.** Two **47. a)** No, it has an inside and an outside. **b)** Two **c)** Two **d)** Two strips, one inside the other **49.–51.** Answers will vary.

Section 6.7

1.–5. Answers will vary. **7. a)** *Euclidean:* Given a line and a point not on the line, one and only one line can be drawn parallel to the given line through the given point. **b)** *Elliptical:* Given a line and a point not on the line, no line can be drawn through the given point parallel to the given line. **c)** *Hyperbolic:* Given a line and a point not on the line, two or more lines can be drawn through the given point parallel to the given line. **9.** A plane **11.** A pseudosphere **13.** Spherical: elliptical geometry; flat: Euclidean geometry; saddle-shaped: hyperbolic geometry

15. **17.**

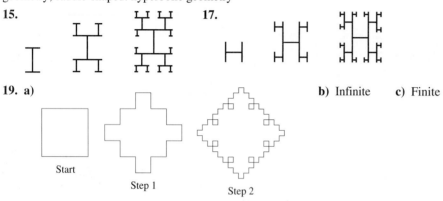

19. a) **b)** Infinite **c)** Finite

Start

Step 1

Step 2

Chapter 6 Review Exercises

In the Review Exercises and Chapter Test questions, we used the $\boxed{\pi}$ key on a scientific calculator to determine answers in calculations involving π. If you use 3.14 for π, your answers may vary slightly.

1. $\{B\}$ **2.** $\overline{AD}$ **3.** $\triangle BFC$ **4.** $\overleftrightarrow{BH}$ **5.** $\{F\}$ **6.** $\{\}$ **7.** $66.3°$ **8.** $55.3°$ **9.** 10.2 in. **10.** 2 in.
11. $58°$ **12.** $92°$ **13.** $m\angle 1 = 50°, m\angle 2 = 120°, m\angle 3 = 120°, m\angle 4 = 70°, m\angle 5 = 110°, m\angle 6 = 70°$
14. $540°$ **15. a)** 80 cm^2 **b)** 36 cm **16. a)** 13 in.^2 **b)** 19.4 in. **17. a)** 84 in.^2 **b)** 42 in. **18. a)** 6 km^2
b) 12 km **19. a)** 530.93 cm^2 **b)** 81.68 cm **20.** 41.20 in.^2 **21.** 35.43 cm^2 **22.** \$1176 **23. a)** 120 cm^3
b) 164 cm^2 **24. a)** 2035.75 in.^3 **b)** 904.78 in.^2 **25. a)** 603.19 mm^3 **b)** 435.20 mm^2 **26. a)** 268.08 ft^3
b) 201.06 ft^2 **27.** 432 m^3 **28.** 28 ft^3 **29.** 75.40 cm^3 **30.** 791.68 cm^3 **31. a)** $\approx 67.88 \text{ ft}^3$ **b)** 4610.7 lb; yes
c) ≈ 510.3 gal

This figure contains the answers for Exercises 32 and 33.

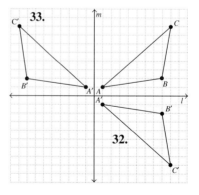

This figure contains the answers for Exercises 34 and 35.

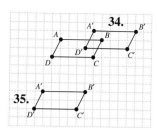

This figure contains the answers for Exercises 36–38.

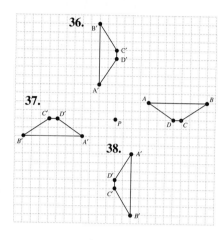

This figure contains the answers for Exercises 39 and 40.

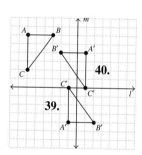

41. Yes **42.** No **43.** No **44.** Yes **45. a)–d)** Answers will vary. **46.** Answers will vary. **47.** Outside
48. Euclidean: Given a line and a point not on the line, one and only one line can be drawn parallel to the given line through the given point. Elliptical: Given a line and a point not on the line, no line can be drawn through the given point parallel to the given line. Hyperbolic: Given a line and a point not on the line, two or more lines can be drawn through the given point parallel to the given line.

49.

50.

Chapter 6 Test

1. $\overrightarrow{EF}$ **2.** $\triangle BCD$ **3.** $\{D\}$ **4.** $\overleftrightarrow{AC}$ **5.** 77.6° **6.** 128.3° **7.** 64° **8.** 1440° **9.** ≈ 2.69 cm

10. a) 12 in. **b)** 30 in. **c)** 30 in.^{2} **11. a)** 1436.76 cm^3 **b)** 615.75 cm^2 **12.** 59.43 m^3 **13.** 112 ft^3

14.

15.

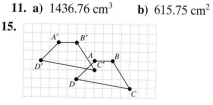

16.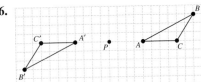

17.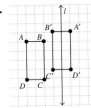

18. a) No   **b)** Yes

19. A surface with one side and one edge   **20. a)–b)** Answers will vary.   **21.** Euclidean: Given a line and a point not on the line, one and only one line can be drawn parallel to the given line through the given point. Elliptical: Given a line and a point not on the line, no line can be drawn through the given point parallel to the given line. Hyperbolic: Given a line and a point not on the line, two or more lines can be drawn through the given point parallel to the given line.

CHAPTER 7

Section 7.1

Check Point Exercises

1. L is the set of the first six letters of the alphabet.   **2.** $M = \{$April, August$\}$ **3.** $O = \{1, 3, 5, 7, 9\}$ **4. a.** not the empty set
b. empty set   **c.** not the empty set   **d.** not the empty set   **5. a.** true   **b.** true   **c.** false   **6. a.** $A = \{1, 2, 3\}$
b. $B = \{15, 16, 17, 18, \ldots\}$ **c.** $O = \{1, 3, 5, 7, \ldots\}$ **7. a.** $\{1, 2, 3, 4, \ldots, 199\}$ **b.** $\{51, 52, 53, 54, \ldots, 200\}$ **8. a.** $n(A) = 5$
b. $n(B) = 1$ **c.** $n(C) = 8$ **d.** $n(D) = 0$ **9.** Yes; each language in the table is paired with a distinct number of 15–24-year olds.
10. a. true   **b.** false

Exercise Set 2.1

1. well defined; set   **3.** not well defined; not a set   **5.** well defined; set   **7.** the set of planets in our solar system   **9.** the set of months
that begin with J   **11.** the set of natural numbers greater than 5   **13.** the set of natural numbers between 6 and 20, inclusive
15. $\{$winter, spring, summer, fall$\}$ **17.** $\{$September, October, November, December$\}$ **19.** $\{1, 2, 3\}$ **21.** $\{1, 3, 5, 7, 9, 11\}$
23. $\{1, 2, 3, 4, 5\}$ **25.** $\{6, 7, 8, 9, \ldots\}$ **27.** $\{7, 8, 9, 10\}$ **29.** $\{10, 11, 12, 13, \ldots, 79\}$ **31.** $\{2\}$ **33.** not the empty set
35. empty set   **37.** not the empty set   **39.** empty set   **41.** empty set   **43.** not the empty set   **45.** not the empty set   **47.** true
49. true   **51.** false   **53.** true   **55.** false   **57.** false   **59.** true   **61.** false   **63.** false   **65.** true   **67.** 5   **69.** 15   **71.** 0
73. 1   **75.** 4   **77.** 5   **79.** 0   **81. a.** not equivalent; Answers will vary.   **b.** not equal; Answers will vary.   **83. a.** equivalent; Answers will
vary.   **b.** not equal; Answers will vary.   **85. a.** equivalent; Answers will vary.   **b.** equal; Answers will vary.   **87. a.** equivalent; Answers will
vary.   **b.** not equal; Answers will vary.   **89. a.** equivalent; Answers will vary.   **b.** equal; Answers will vary.   **91.** infinite   **93.** finite
95. finite   **97.** $\{x \mid x \in \mathbf{N} \text{ and } x \geq 61\}$ **99.** $\{x \mid x \in \mathbf{N} \text{ and } 61 \leq x \leq 89\}$ **101.** Answers will vary; an example is: $\{0, 1, 2, 3\}$ and $\{1, 2, 3, 4\}$.
103. impossible; Answers will vary.   **105.** $\{$New Zealand, Australia, United States$\}$ **107.** $\{$Australia, United States, United Kingdom,
Switzerland, Ireland$\}$ **109.** $\{$United Kingdom, Switzerland, Ireland$\}$ **111.** $\varnothing$ or $\{ \}$ **113.** $\{12, 19\}$ **115.** $\{20, 21\}$
117. no one-to-one correspondence; not equivalent   **125.** a

Section 7.2

Check Point Exercises

1. a. $\not\subseteq$ **b.** $\subseteq$ **c.** $\subseteq$ **2. a.** $\subseteq, \subset$ **b.** $\subseteq, \subset$ **3.** yes   **4. a.** 16; 15   **b.** 64; 63   **5. a.** 8; the number of different combinations of the books that you can take on vacation   **b.** $\varnothing$, $\{The\ Da\ Vinci\ Code\}$, $\{The\ Lord\ of\ the\ Rings\}$, $\{America\ (The\ Book)\}$,
$\{The\ Da\ Vinci\ Code, The\ Lord\ of\ the\ Rings\}$, $\{The\ Da\ Vinci\ Code, America\ (The\ Book)\}$, $\{The\ Lord\ of\ the\ Rings, America\ (The\ Book)\}$,
$\{The\ Da\ Vinci\ Code, The\ Lord\ of\ the\ Rings, America\ (The\ Book)\}$ **c.** 7

Exercise Set 7.2

1. $\subseteq$ **3.** $\not\subseteq$ **5.** $\not\subseteq$ **7.** $\not\subseteq$ **9.** $\subseteq$ **11.** $\not\subseteq$ **13.** both   **15.** $\subseteq$ **17.** both   **19.** $\subseteq$ **21.** neither   **23.** true
25. false; Answers will vary.   **27.** true   **29.** false; Answers will vary.   **31.** true   **33.** false; Answers will vary.   **35.** true
37. $\varnothing$, $\{$border collie$\}$, $\{$poodle$\}$, $\{$border collie, poodle$\}$ **39.** $\varnothing$, $\{t\}$, $\{a\}$, $\{b\}$, $\{t, a\}$, $\{t, b\}$, $\{a, b\}$, $\{t, a, b\}$ **41.** $\varnothing$ and $\{0\}$ **43.** 16; 15
45. 64; 63   **47.** 128; 127   **49.** 8; 7   **51.** false; The set $\{1, 2, 3, \ldots, 1000\}$ has $2^{1000} - 1$ proper subsets.   **53.** true   **55.** false; $\varnothing \subseteq \{\varnothing, \{\varnothing\}\}$
57. true   **59.** true   **61.** true   **63.** false; The set of subsets of $\{a, e, i, o, u\}$ contains 32 elements.   **65.** false; $D \subseteq T$ **67.** true
69. false; If $x \in W$, then $x \in D$.   **71.** true   **73.** true   **75.** 32   **77.** 64   **79.** 256   **87.** b   **89.** 7

Section 7.3

Check Point Exercises

1. a. $\{1, 5, 6, 7, 9\}$ **b.** $\{1, 5, 6\}$ **c.** $\{7, 9\}$ **2. a.** $\{a, b, c, d\}$ **b.** $\{e\}$ **c.** $\{e, f, g\}$ **d.** $\{f, g\}$ **3.** $\{b, c, e\}$ **4. a.** $\{7, 10\}$
b. $\varnothing$ **c.** $\varnothing$ **5. a.** $\{1, 3, 5, 6, 7, 10, 11\}$ **b.** $\{1, 2, 3, 4, 5, 6, 7\}$ **c.** $\{1, 2, 3\}$ **6. a.** $\{a, d\}$ **b.** $\{a, d\}$ **7. a.** $\{5\}$
b. $\{2, 3, 7, 11, 13, 17, 19\}$ **c.** $\{2, 3, 5, 7, 11, 13\}$ **d.** $\{17, 19\}$ **e.** $\{5, 7, 11, 13, 17, 19\}$ **f.** $\{2, 3\}$ **8.** 385 students

Exercise Set 7.3

1. the set of all composers   **3.** the set of all brands of soft drinks   **5.** $\{c, d, e\}$ **7.** $\{b, c, d, e, f\}$ **9.** $\{6, 7, 8, 9, \ldots, 20\}$
11. $\{2, 4, 6, 8, \ldots, 20\}$ **13.** $\{21, 22, 23, 24, \ldots\}$ **15.** $\{1, 3, 5, 7, \ldots\}$ **17.** $\{1, 3\}$ **19.** $\{1, 2, 3, 5, 7\}$ **21.** $\{2, 4, 6\}$ **23.** $\{4, 6\}$

25. {1, 3, 5, 7} or A **27.** {1, 2, 4, 6, 7} **29.** {1, 2, 4, 6, 7} **31.** {4, 6} **33.** {1, 3, 5, 7} or A **35.** ∅ **37.** {1, 2, 3, 4, 5, 6, 7} or U
39. {1, 3, 5, 7} or A **41.** {g, h} **43.** {a, b, g, h} **45.** {b, c, d, e, f} or C **47.** {c, d, e, f} **49.** {a, g, h} or A **51.** {a, b, c, d, e, f, g, h}
or U **53.** {a, b, c, d, e, f, g, h} or U **55.** {c, d, e, f} **57.** {a, g, h} or A **59.** ∅ **61.** {a, b, c, d, e, f, g, h} or U **63.** {a, g, h} or A
65. {a, c, d, e, f, g, h} **67.** {1, 3, 4, 7} **69.** {1, 2, 3, 4, 5, 6, 7, 8, 9} **71.** {3, 7} **73.** {1, 4, 8, 9} **75.** {8, 9} **77.** {1, 4}
79. {△, two, four, six} **81.** {△, #, $, two, four, six} **83.** 6 **85.** 5 **87.** {#, $, two, four, six, 10, 01} **89.** {two, four, six} **91.** 4
93. 31 **95.** 27 **97.** {1, 2, 3, 4, 5, 6, 7, 8} or U **99.** {1, 3, 5, 7} or A **101.** {1, 7} **103.** {1, 3, 5, 6, 7, 8}
105. {23, 29, 31, 37, 41, 43, 53, 59, 61, 67, 71} **107.** 60 **109.** {Ashley, Mike, Josh} **111.** {Ashley, Mike, Josh, Emily, Hanna, Ethan}
113. {Ashley} **115.** {Jacob} **117.** I **119.** I **121.** IV **123.** I **125.** IV **127.** II **129.** III **131.** I
133. {spacial-temporal toys, sports equipment, toy cars and trucks} **135.** {dollhouses, spacial-temporal toys, sports equipment, toy cars and trucks}
137. ∅ **139.** 283 people **153.** d
155. 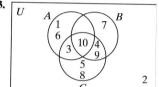 **157.**

Section 7.4

Check Point Exercises

1. a. {a, b, c, d, f} **b.** {a, b, c, d, f} **c.** {a, b, d}
2. a. {5, 6, 7, 8, 9} **b.** {1, 2, 5, 6, 7, 8, 9, 10, 12} **c.** {5, 6, 7} **d.** {3, 4, 6, 8, 11} **e.** {1, 2, 3, 5, 6, 7, 8, 9, 10, 11, 12}
3. 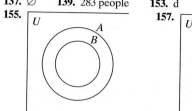 **4. a.** IV **b.** IV **c.** $(AB)' = A' \cap B'$ **5. a.** II, IV, and V **b.** II, IV, and V
c. $A \cap (BC) = (A \cap B)(A \cap C)$

Exercise Set 7.4

1. {1, 2, 3, 5, 7} **3.** {1, 2, 3, 5, 7} **5.** {2} **7.** {2} **9.** ∅ **11.** {4, 6} **13.** {a, b, g, h} **15.** {a, b, g, h} **17.** {b} **19.** {b}
21. ∅ **23.** {c, d, e, f} **25.** II, III, V, and VI **27.** I, II, IV, V, VI, and VII **29.** II and V **31.** I, IV, VII, and VIII **33.** {1, 2, 3, 4, 5, 6, 7, 8}
35. {1, 2, 3, 4, 5, 6, 7, 8, 9, 10, 11} **37.** {12, 13} **39.** {4, 5, 6} **41.** {6} **43.** {1, 2, 3, 4, 5, 7, 8, 9, 10, 11, 12, 13}
45. 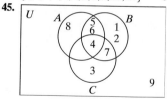 **47.**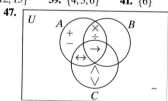

49. a. II **b.** II **c.** $A \cap B = B \cap A$ **51. a.** I, III, and IV **b.** IV **c.** no; Answers will vary. **53.** not equal **55.** not equal
57. equal **59. a.** II, IV, V, VI, and VII **b.** II, IV, V, VI, and VII **c.** $(A \cap B)C = (AC) \cap (BC)$ **61. a.** II, IV, and V
b. I, II, IV, V, and VI **c.** no; Answers will vary. **63.** not true **65.** true; theorem **67.** true; theorem **69. a.** {c, e, f}; {c, e, f}
b. {1, 3, 5, 7, 8}; {1, 3, 5, 7, 8} **c.** $A \cup (B' \cap C') = (A \cup B') \cap (A \cup C')$ **d.** theorem **71.** $(A \cap B)' \cap (A \cup B)$ **73.** $A' \cup B$
75. $(A \cap B) \cup C$ **77.** $A' \cap (B \cup C)$ **79.** {Ann, Jose, Al, Gavin, Amy, Ron, Grace} **81.** {Jose} **83.** {Lily, Emma}
85. {Lily, Emma, Ann, Jose, Lee, Maria, Fred, Ben, Sheila, Ellen, Gary} **87.** {Lily, Emma, Al, Gavin, Amy, Lee, Maria} **89.** {Al, Gavin, Amy}
91. The set of students who scored 90% or above on exam 1 and exam 3 but not on exam 2 **93.** II **95.** V **97.** I **99.** III **101.** V
103. VII **105.** 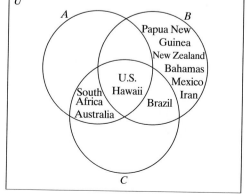 **109.** AB^+ **111.** no

Section 7.5

Check Point Exercises

1. a. 75   **b.** 90   **c.** 20   **d.** 145   **e.** 55   **f.** 70   **g.** 30   **h.** 175   **2. a.** 490 men   **b.** 510 men
3.   **4. a.** 63   **b.** 3   **c.** 136   **d.** 30   **e.** 228   **f.** 22

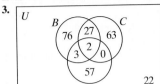

Exercise Set 7.5

1. 26   **3.** 17   **5.** 37   **7.** 7   **9.** I: 14; III: 22; IV: 5   **11.** 17   **13.** 6   **15.** 28   **17.** 9   **19.** 3   **21.** 19   **23.** 21   **25.** 34
27. I: 5; II: 1; III: 4; IV: 3; VI: 1; VII: 8; VIII: 6   **29.** I: 5; II: 10; III: 3; IV: 4; V: 7; VI: 1; VII: 6; VIII: 2   **31.** impossible; There are only 10 elements
in set A but there are 13 elements in set A that are also in sets B or C. A similar problem exists for set C.   **33.** 18   **35.** 9   **37.** 9

39. a–d.

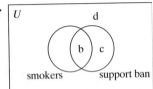

41. a–d.

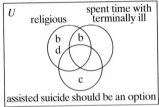

e. Answers will vary.

43.

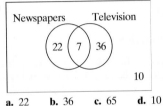

a. 22   **b.** 36   **c.** 65   **d.** 10

45.

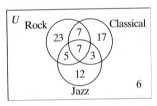

a. 23   **b.** 3   **c.** 32   **d.** 52
e. 22   **f.** 6
47. a. 1500   **b.** 1135   **c.** 56   **d.** 327   **e.** 526   **f.** 366   **g.** 1191   **51.** b   **53.** Under the
conditions given concerning enrollment in math, chemistry, and psychology courses, the total number of students is 100, not 90.

Chapter 7 Review Exercises

1. the set of days of the week beginning with the letter T   **2.** the set of natural numbers between 1 and 10, inclusive   **3.** $\{m, i, s\}$
4. $\{8, 9, 10, 11, 12\}$ **5.** $\{1, 2, 3, \dots, 30\}$ **6.** not empty   **7.** empty set   **8.** $\in$ **9.** $\notin$ **10.** 12   **11.** 15   **12.** $\neq$ **13.** $\neq$
14. equivalent   **15.** both   **16.** finite   **17.** infinite   **18.** $\subseteq$ **19.** $\not\subseteq$ **20.** $\subseteq$ **21.** $\subseteq$ **22.** both   **23.** false; Answers will vary.
24. false; Answers will vary.   **25.** true   **26.** false; Answers will vary.   **27.** true   **28.** false; It has $2^1 = 2$ subsets.   **29.** true
30. $\varnothing, \{1\}, \{5\}, \{1, 5\}; \{1, 5\}$ **31.** 32; 31   **32.** 8; 7   **33.** $\{1, 2, 4\}$ **34.** $\{1, 2, 3, 4, 6, 7, 8\}$ **35.** $\{5\}$ **36.** $\{6, 7, 8\}$ **37.** $\{6, 7, 8\}$
38. $\{4, 5, 6\}$ **39.** $\{2, 3, 6, 7\}$ **40.** $\{1, 4, 5, 6, 8, 9\}$ **41.** $\{4, 5\}$ **42.** $\{1, 2, 3, 6, 7, 8, 9\}$ **43.** $\{2, 3, 7\}$ **44.** $\{6\}$ **45.** $\{1, 2, 3, 4, 5, 6, 7, 8, 9\}$
46. 33   **47.** $\{1, 2, 3, 4, 5\}$ **48.** $\{1, 2, 3, 4, 5, 6, 7, 8\}$ or U **49.** $\{c, d, e, f, k, p, r\}$ **50.** $\{f, p\}$ **51.** $\{c, d, f, k, p, r\}$ **52.** $\{c, d, e\}$
53. $\{a, b, c, d, e, g, h, p, r\}$ **54.** $\{f\}$ **55.**

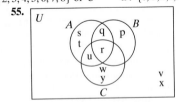

56. Use Figure 7.21 on page 414.

Set	Regions in the Venn Diagram
A	I, II
B	II, III
$A \cup B$	I, II, III
$(A \cup B)'$	IV

Set	Regions in the Venn Diagram
A'	III, IV
B'	I, IV
$A' \cap B'$	IV

Since $(A \cup B)'$ and $A' \cap B'$ represent the same region, $(A \cup B)' = A' \cap B'$.

57. Use Figure 7.22 on page 415.

Set	Regions in the Venn Diagram
A	I, II, IV, V
B	II, III, V, VI
C	IV, V, VI, VII
$B \cup C$	II, III, IV, V, VI, VII
$A \cap (B \cup C)$	II, IV, V

Set	Regions in the Venn Diagram
A	I, II, IV, V
B	II, III, V, VI
C	IV, V, VI, VII
$B \cap C$	V, VI
$A \cup (B \cap C)$	I, II, IV, V, VI

Since $A \cap (B \cup C)$ and $A \cup (B \cap C)$ do not represent the same regions, $A \cap (B \cup C) = A \cup (B \cap C)$ is false.

58. a. I   **b.** III   **c.** VIII   **d.** II   **e.** V

59. a–c.

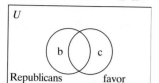

60. a. 250   **b.** 800   **c.** 200   **61. a.** 50   **b.** 26   **c.** 130   **d.** 46   **e.** 0

Chapter 7 Test

1. {18, 19, 20, 21, 22, 23, 24}   **2.** false; Answers will vary.   **3.** true   **4.** true   **5.** false; Answers will vary.   **6.** true
7. false; Answers will vary.   **8.** false; Answers will vary.   **9.** false; Answers will vary.   **10.** ∅, {6}, {9}, {6, 9}; {6, 9}   **11.** {a, b, c, d, e, f}
12. {a, b, c, d, f, g}   **13.** {b, c, d}   **14.** {a, e}   **15.** 5   **16.** {b, c, d, i, j, k}   **17.** {a}   **18.** {a, f, h}
19.

20. theorem   **21. a.** V   **b.** VII   **c.** IV   **d.** I   **e.** VI
22. a.

b. 263   **c.** 25   **d.** 62   **e.** 0   **f.** 147   **g.** 116

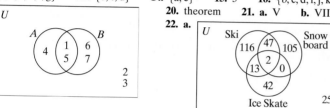

CHAPTER 8

Section 8.1

Check Point Exercises

1. 150   **2.** 40   **3.** 30   **4.** 160   **5.** 729   **6.** 90,000

Exercise Set 8.1

1. 80   **3.** 12   **5.** 6   **7.** 40   **9.** 144; Answers will vary.   **11.** 8   **13.** 96   **15.** 243   **17.** 144   **19.** 676,000
21. 2187   **27.** 720 hr

Section 8.2

Check Point Exercises

1. 2   **2.** 120   **3. a.** 504   **b.** 524,160   **c.** 100   **4.** 840   **5.** 15,120   **6.** 420

Exercise Set 8.2

1. 720   **3.** 120   **5.** 120   **7.** 362,880   **9.** 6   **11.** 4   **13.** 504   **15.** 570,024   **17.** 3,047,466,240   **19.** 600   **21.** 10,712
23. 5034   **25.** 24   **27.** 6   **29.** 42   **31.** 1716   **33.** 3024   **35.** 6720   **37.** 720   **39.** 1   **41.** 720   **43.** 8,648,640   **45.** 120
47. 15,120   **49.** 180   **51.** 831,600   **53.** 105   **55.** 280   **65.** 360   **67.** 14,400   **69.** $\dfrac{n(n-1)\cdots 3 \cdot 2 \cdot 1}{2} = n(n-1)\cdots 3$

Section 8.3

Check Point Exercises

1. a. combinations   **b.** permutations   **2.** 35   **3.** 1820   **4.** 23,049,600

Exercise Set 8.3

1. combinations   **3.** permutations   **5.** 6   **7.** 126   **9.** 330   **11.** 8   **13.** 1   **15.** 4060   **17.** 1   **19.** 7   **21.** 0   **23.** $\dfrac{3}{4}$
25. −9499   **27.** $\dfrac{3}{68}$ **29.** 20   **31.** 495   **33.** 24,310   **35.** 22,957,480   **37.** 360 ways   **39.** 1716 ways   **41.** 1140 ways

43. 840 passwords   **45.** 2730 cones   **47.** 735   **49.** 4,516,932,420   **51.** 720   **53.** 20   **55.** 24   **57.** 12   **63.** The 5/36 lottery is easier to win.; Answers will vary.   **65.** 570 sec or 9.5 min; 2340 sec or 39 min

Section 8.4

Check Point Exercises

1. a. $\frac{1}{6}$ **b.** $\frac{1}{2}$ **c.** 0   **d.** 1   **2. a.** $\frac{1}{13}$ **b.** $\frac{1}{2}$ **c.** $\frac{1}{26}$ **3.** $\frac{1}{2}$ **4. a.** 0.24   **b.** 0.48

Exercise Set 8.4

1. $\frac{1}{6}$ **3.** $\frac{1}{2}$ **5.** $\frac{1}{3}$ **7.** 1   **9.** 0   **11.** $\frac{1}{13}$ **13.** $\frac{1}{4}$ **15.** $\frac{3}{13}$ **17.** $\frac{1}{52}$ **19.** 0   **21.** $\frac{1}{4}$ **23.** $\frac{1}{2}$ **25.** $\frac{1}{2}$ **27.** $\frac{3}{8}$ **29.** $\frac{3}{8}$

31. $\frac{7}{8}$ **33.** 0   **35.** $\frac{1}{4}$ **37.** $\frac{1}{9}$ **39.** 0   **41.** $\frac{3}{10}$ **43.** $\frac{1}{5}$ **45.** $\frac{1}{2}$ **47.** 0   **49.** $\frac{1}{4}$ **51.** $\frac{1}{4}$ **53.** $\frac{1}{2}$ **55.** 0.43   **57.** 0.13

59. 0.03   **61.** 0.38   **63.** 0.78   **65.** 0.12   **75.** $\frac{3}{8} = 0.375$

Section 8.5

Check Point Exercises

1. $\frac{1}{60}$ **2.** $\frac{1}{13,983,816} \approx 0.0000000715$ **3. a.** $\frac{1}{6}$ **b.** $\frac{1}{2}$

Exercise Set 8.5

1. a. 120   **b.** 6   **c.** $\frac{1}{20}$ **3. a.** $\frac{1}{6}$ **b.** $\frac{1}{30}$ **c.** $\frac{1}{720}$ **d.** $\frac{1}{3}$ **5. a.** 84   **b.** 10   **c.** $\frac{5}{42}$ **7.** $\frac{1}{18,009,460} \approx 0.0000000555$;

$\frac{100}{18,009,460} \approx 0.00000555$ **9. a.** $\frac{1}{177,100} \approx 0.00000565$ **b.** $\frac{27,132}{177,100} \approx 0.153$ **11.** $\frac{3}{10} = 0.3$ **13. a.** 2,598,960   **b.** 1287

c. $\frac{1287}{2,598,960} \approx 0.000495$ **15.** $\frac{11}{1105} \approx 0.00995$ **17.** $\frac{36}{270,725} \approx 0.000133$ **23.** \$9,004,730   **25.** $\frac{1}{10}$

Section 8.6

Check Point Exercises

1. $\frac{3}{4}$ **2. a.** $\frac{160}{191}$ **b.** $\frac{182}{191}$ **3.** $\frac{1}{3}$ **4.** $\frac{27}{50}$ **5.** $\frac{3}{4}$ **6. a.** 0.99   **b.** 0.65   **7. a.** 2:50 or 1:25   **b.** 50:2 or 25:1   **8.** 199:1

9. 1:15; $\frac{1}{16}$

Exercise Set 8.6

1. $\frac{12}{13}$ **3.** $\frac{3}{4}$ **5.** $\frac{10}{13}$ **7.** $\frac{2,598,924}{2,598,960} \approx 0.999986$ **9.** $\frac{2,595,216}{2,598,960} \approx 0.998559$ **11. a.** 0.10   **b.** 0.90   **13.** $\frac{23}{28}$ **15.** $\frac{95}{112}$ **17.** $\frac{2}{13}$

19. $\frac{1}{13}$ **21.** $\frac{1}{26}$ **23.** $\frac{9}{22}$ **25.** $\frac{5}{6}$ **27.** $\frac{7}{13}$ **29.** $\frac{11}{26}$ **31.** $\frac{3}{4}$ **33.** $\frac{5}{8}$ **35.** $\frac{33}{40}$ **37.** $\frac{4}{5}$ **39.** $\frac{7}{10}$ **41.** $\frac{8}{11}$ **43.** $\frac{108}{187}$

45. $\frac{122}{187}$ **47.** 3:8; 8:3   **49.** $\frac{93}{143}$ **51.** $\frac{127}{143}$ **53.** $\frac{5}{13}$ **55.** 38:105; 105:38   **57.** 1:142; 142:1   **59.** 11:2; 2:11   **61.** 2:1   **63.** 1:2

65. a. 9:91   **b.** 91:9   **67.** 1:3   **69.** 1:1   **71.** 12:1   **73.** 25:1   **75.** 47:5   **77.** 49:1   **79.** 9:10   **81.** 14:5   **83.** 14:5   **85.** 9:10

87. $\frac{3}{7}$ **89.** $\frac{4}{25}$; 84   **91.** $\frac{1}{1000}$ **101.** 0.06

Section 8.7

Check Point Exercises

1. $\frac{1}{361} \approx 0.00277$ **2.** $\frac{1}{16}$ **3. a.** $\frac{625}{130,321} \approx 0.005$ **b.** $\frac{38,416}{130,321} \approx 0.295$ **c.** $\frac{91,905}{130,321} \approx 0.705$ **4.** $\frac{1}{221} \approx 0.00452$ **5.** $\frac{11}{850} \approx 0.0129$

6. $\frac{1}{2}$ **7. a.** $\frac{9}{10} = 0.9$ **b.** $\frac{45}{479} \approx 0.094$

Exercise Set 8.7

1. $\frac{1}{6}$ **3.** $\frac{1}{36}$ **5.** $\frac{1}{4}$ **7.** $\frac{1}{36}$ **9.** $\frac{1}{8}$ **11.** $\frac{1}{36}$ **13.** $\frac{1}{3}$ **15.** $\frac{3}{52}$ **17.** $\frac{1}{169}$ **19.** $\frac{1}{4}$ **21.** $\frac{1}{64}$ **23.** $\frac{1}{6}$ **25. a.** $\frac{1}{256} \approx 0.00391$

b. $\frac{1}{4096} \approx 0.000244$ **c.** ≈ 0.524 **d.** ≈ 0.476 **27.** 0.0144   **29.** 0.008   **31.** 0.4686   **33.** $\frac{7}{29}$ **35.** $\frac{5}{87}$ **37.** $\frac{2}{21}$ **39.** $\frac{4}{35}$

41. $\frac{11}{21}$ **43.** $\frac{1}{57}$ **45.** $\frac{8}{855}$ **47.** $\frac{11}{57}$ **49.** $\frac{1}{5}$ **51.** $\frac{2}{3}$ **53.** $\frac{3}{4}$ **55.** $\frac{3}{4}$ **57.** $\frac{412,368}{412,878} \approx 0.999$ **59.** $\frac{412,368}{574,895} \approx 0.717$ **61.** 0.898

63. 0.168   **65.** 0.542   **67.** 0.415   **69.** 0.103   **71.** 0.886   **81.** 0.59049   **83. a.** Answers will vary.   **b.** $\frac{365}{365} \cdot \frac{364}{365} \cdot \frac{363}{365} \approx 0.992$

c. ≈ 0.008 **d.** 0.411   **e.** 23 people

Section 8.8

Check Point Exercises

1. 2.5   **2.** 2   **3. a.** $8000; In the long run, the average cost of a claim is $8000.   **b.** $8000   **4.** 0; no; Answers will vary.
5. table entries: $998, $48, and $-$2 ; expected value: $-$0.90 ; In the long run, a person can expect to lose an average of $0.90 for each ticket purchased.; Answers will vary.   **6.** $-$0.20 ; In the long run, a person can expect to lose an average of $0.20 for each card purchased.

Exercise Set 8.8

1. 1.75   **3. a.** $29,000; In the long run, the average cost of a claim is $29,000.   **b.** $29,000   **c.** $29,050   **5.** $0; Answers will vary.   **7.** $0.73
9. $\frac{1}{16} = 0.0625$; yes   **11.** the second mall   **13. a.** $140,000   **b.** no   **15.** $\approx -$0.17 ; In the long run, a person can expect to lose an average of about $0.17 for each game played.   **17.** $\approx -$0.05 ; In the long run, a person can expect to lose an average of about $0.05 for each game played.   **19.** $-$0.50 ; In the long run, a person can expect to lose an average of $0.50 for each game played.   **27.** $160

Chapter 8 Review Exercises

1. 800   **2.** 20   **3.** 9900   **4.** 125   **5.** 243   **6.** 60   **7.** 720   **8.** 120   **9.** 120   **10.** 240   **11.** 800   **12.** 114   **13.** 990
14. 151,200   **15.** 9900   **16.** 32,760   **17.** 1,860,480   **18.** 420   **19.** 60   **20.** combinations   **21.** permutations   **22.** combinations
23. 330   **24.** 2002   **25.** 210   **26.** 1287   **27.** 1140   **28.** 55,440   **29.** $\frac{1}{6}$ **30.** $\frac{2}{3}$ **31.** 1   **32.** 0   **33.** $\frac{1}{13}$ **34.** $\frac{3}{13}$ **35.** $\frac{3}{13}$
36. $\frac{1}{52}$ **37.** $\frac{1}{26}$ **38.** $\frac{1}{2}$ **39.** $\frac{1}{3}$ **40.** $\frac{1}{6}$ **41. a.** $\frac{1}{2}$ **b.** 0   **42.** 0.623   **43.** 0.518   **44.** 0.149   **45.** $\frac{1}{24}$ **46.** $\frac{1}{6}$ **47.** $\frac{1}{30}$
48. $\frac{1}{720}$ **49.** $\frac{1}{3}$ **50. a.** $\frac{1}{15,504} \approx 0.0000645$ **b.** $\frac{100}{15,504} \approx 0.00645$ **51. a.** $\frac{1}{14}$ **b.** $\frac{3}{7}$ **52.** $\frac{3}{26}$ **53.** $\frac{5}{6}$ **54.** $\frac{1}{2}$ **55.** $\frac{1}{3}$
56. $\frac{2}{3}$ **57.** 1   **58.** $\frac{10}{13}$ **59.** $\frac{3}{4}$ **60.** $\frac{2}{13}$ **61.** $\frac{1}{13}$ **62.** $\frac{7}{13}$ **63.** $\frac{11}{26}$ **64.** $\frac{5}{6}$ **65.** $\frac{5}{6}$ **66.** $\frac{1}{2}$ **67.** $\frac{2}{3}$ **68.** 1   **69.** $\frac{5}{6}$
70. $\frac{4}{5}$ **71.** $\frac{3}{4}$ **72.** $\frac{18}{25}$ **73.** $\frac{6}{7}$ **74.** $\frac{3}{5}$ **75.** $\frac{12}{35}$ **76.** in favor: 1:12; against: 12:1   **77.** 99:1   **78.** $\frac{3}{4}$ **79.** $\frac{2}{9}$ **80.** $\frac{1}{36}$ **81.** $\frac{1}{9}$
82. $\frac{1}{36}$ **83.** $\frac{8}{27}$ **84.** $\frac{1}{32}$ **85. a.** 0.04   **b.** 0.008   **c.** 0.4096   **d.** 0.5904   **86.** $\frac{1}{9}$ **87.** $\frac{1}{12}$ **88.** $\frac{1}{196}$ **89.** $\frac{1}{3}$ **90.** $\frac{3}{10}$
91. a. $\frac{1}{2}$ **b.** $\frac{2}{7}$ **92.** $\frac{27}{29}$ **93.** $\frac{4}{29}$ **94.** $\frac{144}{145}$ **95.** $\frac{11}{20}$ **96.** $\frac{11}{135}$ **97.** $\frac{1}{125}$ **98.** $\frac{1}{232}$ **99.** $\frac{19}{1044}$ **100.** $\frac{26,098}{30,242} \approx 0.863$
101. $\frac{11,586}{30,242} \approx 0.383$ **102.** $\frac{27,818}{30,242} \approx 0.920$ **103.** $\frac{15,892}{30,242} \approx 0.525$ **104.** $\frac{4186}{30,242} \approx 0.138$ **105.** $\frac{3887}{26,098} \approx 0.149$ **106.** $\frac{2225}{2424} \approx 0.918$
107. 3.125   **108. a.** $0.50; In the long run, the average cost of a claim is $0.50.   **b.** $10.00   **109.** $4500; Answers will vary.
110. $-$0.25 ; In the long run, a person can expect to lose an average of $0.25 for each game played.

Chapter 8 Test

1. 240   **2.** 24   **3.** 720   **4.** 990   **5.** 210   **6.** 420   **7.** $\frac{6}{25}$ **8.** $\frac{17}{25}$ **9.** $\frac{11}{25}$ **10.** $\frac{5}{13}$ **11.** $\frac{1}{210}$ **12.** $\frac{10}{1001} \approx 0.00999$ **13.** $\frac{1}{2}$
14. $\frac{1}{16}$ **15.** $\frac{1}{8000} = 0.000125$ **16.** $\frac{8}{13}$ **17.** $\frac{3}{5}$ **18.** $\frac{1}{19}$ **19.** $\frac{1}{256}$ **20.** 3:4   **21. a.** 4:1   **b.** $\frac{4}{5}$ **22.** $\frac{3}{5}$ **23.** $\frac{39}{50}$ **24.** $\frac{3}{5}$
25. $\frac{9}{19}$ **26.** $\frac{7}{150}$ **27.** $1000; Answers will vary.   **28.** $-$12.75 ; In the long run, a person can expect to lose an average of $12.75 for each game played.

CHAPTER 9

Section 9.1

Check Point Exercises

1. a. the set containing all the city's homeless   **b.** no: People already in the shelters are probably less likely to be against mandatory residence in the shelters.   **2.** By selecting people from a shelter, homeless people who do not go to the shelters have no chance of being selected. An appropriate method would be to randomly select neighborhoods of the city and then randomly survey homeless people within the selected neighborhood.

3.

Grade	Frequency
A	3
B	5
C	9
D	2
F	1
	20

4.

Class	Frequency
40–49	1
50–59	5
60–69	4
70–79	15
80–89	5
90–99	7
	37

5.

Stem	Leaves
4	1
5	8 2 8 0 7
6	8 2 9 9
7	3 5 9 9 7 5 5 3 3 6 7 1 7 1 5
8	7 3 9 9 1
9	4 6 9 7 5 8 0

Exercise Set 9.1

1. a. population: all American men aged 18 or older; sample: those men actually polled   **b.** each man's impression of his own health; qualitative
3. c   **5.** 7; 31   **7.** 151

9.

Time Spent on Homework (in hours)	Number of Students
15	4
16	5
17	6
18	5
19	4
20	2
21	2
22	0
23	0
24	2
	30

11. 0, 5, 10, ..., 40, 45   **13.** 5   **15.** 13   **17.** the 5–9 class   **19.**

Age at Inauguration	Number of Presidents
41–45	2
46–50	8
51–55	15
56–60	9
61–65	7
66–70	2
	43

21. a.

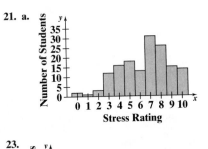

b.

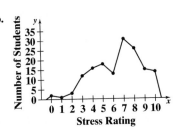

23.

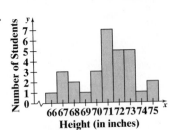

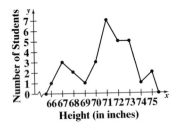

25. b   **27.**

Stem	Leaves
2	8 8 9 5
3	8 7 0 1 2 7 6 4 0 5
4	8 2 2 1 4 5 4 6 2 0 8 2 7 9
5	9 4 1 9 1 0
6	3 2 3 6 6 3

The greatest number of college professors are in their 40s.

29. Time intervals on the horizontal axis do not represent equal amounts of time.   **31.** Percentages do not add up to 100%.
33. It is not clear whether the lengths of the bars represent the percentage or the loan amount.

45.

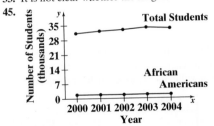

Section 9.2

Check Point Exercises

1. a. 30   **b.** 30   **2.** 36   **3. a.** 35   **b.** 82   **4.** 5   **5.** 162.5   **6.** 54.5   **7. a.** $66.94 billion   **b.** $30 billion
c. One data items is much greater than the other items.   **8.** 8   **9.** $124,500   **10.** mean: 158.6 cal; median: 153 cal; mode: 138 cal; midrange: 151 cal

Exercise Set 9.2

1. 4.125 **3.** 95 **5.** 62 **7.** ≈ 3.45 **9.** ≈ 4.71 **11.** ≈ 6.26 **13.** 3.5 **15.** 95 **17.** 60 **19.** 3.6 **21.** 5 **23.** 6
25. 3 **27.** 95 **29.** 40 **31.** 2.5, 4.2 (bimodal) **33.** 5 **35.** 6 **37.** 4.5 **39.** 95 **41.** 70 **43.** 3.3 **45.** 4.5 **47.** 5.5
49. mean: 30; median: 30; mode: 30; midrange: 30 **51.** mean: approximately 12.4; median: 12.5; mode: 13; midrange: 12.5
53. mean: approximately 31.3; median: 31; mode: 31; midrange: 33 **55. a.** 67.4 **b.** 69 **c.** 71 **d.** 69.5 **57. a.** approximately 19.2
b. 18 **c.** 19 **d.** 24 **59. a.** ≈ 17.27 **b.** 17 **c.** 7, 12, 17 **d.** 24.5 **61.** 175 lb **63.** 177.5 lb **65.** ≈ 2.76
77. All 30 students had the same grade.

Section 9.3

Check Point Exercises

1. 9 **2.** mean: 6;

Data item	Deviation
2	−4
4	−2
7	1
11	5

3. ≈ 3.92 **4.** sample A: 3.74; sample B: 28.06 **5. a.** stocks **b.** stocks; Answers will vary.

Exercise Set 9.3

1. 4 **3.** 8 **5.** 2

7. a.

Data item	Deviation
3	−9
5	−7
7	−5
12	0
18	6
27	15

b. 0

9. a.

Data item	Deviation
29	−20
38	−11
48	−1
49	0
53	4
77	28

b. 0

11. a. 91
b.

Data item	Deviation
85	−6
95	4
90	−1
85	−6
100	9

c. 0

13. a. 155
b.

Data item	Deviation
146	−9
153	−2
155	0
160	5
161	6

c. 0

15. a. 2.70
b.

Data item	Deviation
2.25	−0.45
3.50	0.80
2.75	0.05
3.10	0.40
1.90	−0.80

c. 0

17. ≈ 1.58 **19.** ≈ 3.46 **21.** ≈ 0.89 **23.** 3 **25.** ≈ 2.14
27. *Sample A*: mean: 12; range: 12; standard deviation: ≈ 4.32
Sample B: mean: 12; range: 12; standard deviation: ≈ 5.07
Sample C: mean: 12; range: 12; standard deviation: 6
The samples have the same mean and range, but different standard deviations.
29. 0 **31.** 1 **33.** 7.91 **35.** 1.55 **37. a.** Best Actor; Most of the ages for Best Actor are in the upper 30s and lower 40s while all of the ages
for Best Actress are in the upper 20s and lower 30s. **b.** Best Actor: 38.57; Best Actress: 30.71 **c.** Best Actor; There is greater spread in the ages
for Best Actor, since one age, 29, is much lower than the other ages. **d.** Best Actor: 5.68; Best Actress: 3.77 **47.** a **51.** The mean is increased
by 2.; The standard deviation is unaffected.

Section 9.4

Check Point Exercises

1. a. 75.5 in. **b.** 58 in. **2. a.** 95% **b.** 47.5% **c.** 16% **3. a.** 2 **b.** 0 **c.** −1 **4.** ACT **5. a.** 64 **b.** 128
6. 75% of the scores on the SAT are less than this student's score. **7.** 88.49% **8.** 8.08% **9.** 83.01% **10. a.** ±4.5%
b. We can be 95% confident that between 49.5% and 58.5% of American adults support physician-assisted suicide. **c.** The percentage of
American adults who support physician-assisted suicide may be less than 50%.

Exercise Set 9.4

1. 120 **3.** 160 **5.** 150 **7.** 60 **9.** 90 **11.** 68% **13.** 34% **15.** 47.5% **17.** 49.85% **19.** 16% **21.** 2.5% **23.** 95%
25. 47.5% **27.** 16% **29.** 2.5% **31.** 0.15% **33.** 1 **35.** 3 **37.** 0.5 **39.** 1.75 **41.** 0 **43.** −1 **45.** −1.5 **47.** −3.25
49. 1.5 **51.** 2.25 **53.** −1.25 **55.** −1.5 **57.** The person who scores 127 on the Wechsler has the higher IQ. **59.** 500 **61.** 475
63. 250 **65.** 275 **67. a.** 72.57% **b.** 27.43% **69. a.** 88.49% **b.** 11.51% **71. a.** 24.2% **b.** 75.8% **73. a.** 11.51%
b. 88.49% **75.** 33.99% **77.** 15.74% **79.** 86.64% **81.** 28.57% **83.** 91.92% **85.** 27.43% **87.** 88.49% **89.** 6.69%

91. 45.14%   **93.** 6.68%   **95.** 24.17%   **97. a.** ±2.1%   **b.** We can be 95% confident that between 15.9% and 20.1% of parents in the population consider a doctor as the dream job for their child.   **99. a.** ±1.6%   **b.** We can be 95% confident that between 58.6% and 61.8% of all TV households watched the final episode of "M*A*S*H".   **101.** 0.2%   **103. a.** skewed to the right   **b.** 5.6 murders per 100,000 residents **c.** 5 murders per 100,000 residents   **d.** yes; The mean is greater than the median which is consistent with a distribution skewed to the right. **e.** 6.3; yes; For a normal distribution, almost 100% of the z-scores are between -3 and 3.   **119.** 630

Section 9.5

Check Point Exercises

1. This indicates a moderate relationship.   **2.** -0.84 **3.** $y = -22.97x + 260.56$; 30.86 deaths per 100,000 people   **4.** yes

Exercise Set 12.5

1.

There appears to be a positive correlation.

3.
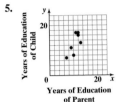
There appears to be a negative correlation.

5.
There appears to be a positive correlation.

7.
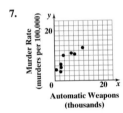
There appears to be a positive correlation.

9. false   **11.** true   **13.** true   **15.** false   **17.** true   **19.** false   **21.** true   **23.** false   **25.** false   **27.** a   **29.** d   **31.** 0.855 **33.** -0.954 **35. a.** 0.75   **b.** $y = 1.52x - 3.38$ **c.** 21 years   **37. a.** 0.885   **b.** $y = 0.85x + 4.05$ **c.** 16 murders per 100,000 people **39.** A correlation does exist.   **41.** A correlation does not exist.   **43.** A correlation does exist.   **45.** A correlation does not exist.

Chapter 9 Review Exercises

1. population: American women ages 25 through 60; sample: 1511 women randomly selected from the population   **2.** how often she entertains guests for dinner   **3.** a

4.

Time Spent on

Homework (in hours)	Number of Students
6	1
7	3
8	3
9	2
10	1
	10

5.
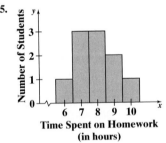

6.
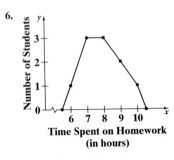

7.

Grades	Number of Students
0–39	19
40–49	8
50–59	6
60–69	6
70–79	5
80–89	3
90–100	3
	50

8.

Stem	Leaves
1	8 4 3 3 7 1
2	4 6 9 9 2 7
3	4 9 6 1 5 1 1
4	4 7 9 1 2 2 0 5
5	4 7 9 0 6 1
6	3 7 0 8 3 9
7	2 5 4 0 3
8	1 7 6
9	1 0 5

9. Sizes of barrels are not scaled proportionally in terms of the data they represent.   **10.** 91.2   **11.** 17   **12.** 2.3   **13.** 11   **14.** 28 **15.** 2   **16.** 27   **17.** 585, 587 (bimodal)   **18.** 2   **19.** 91   **20.** 19.5   **21.** 2.5

24. a.

Age at First Inauguration	Number of Presidents
42	1
43	1
44	0
45	0
46	2
47	1
48	1
49	2
50	1
51	5
52	2
53	0
54	5
55	4
56	3
57	4
58	1
59	0
60	1
61	3
62	1
63	0
64	2
65	1
66	0
67	0
68	1
69	1
	43

b. mean: $\approx$ 54.84 yr; median: 55 yr; mode: 51 yr, 54 yr (bimodal); midrange: 55.5 yr   **25.** 18   **26.** 564

27. a.

Data item	Deviation
29	–6
9	–26
8	–27
22	–13
46	11
51	16
48	13
42	7
53	18
42	7

b. 0

28. a. 50

b.

Data item	Deviation
36	–14
26	–24
24	–26
90	40
74	24

c. 0

29. $\approx$ 4.05   **30.** $\approx$ 5.13   **31.** mean: 49; range: 76; standard deviation: $\approx$ 24.32   **32.** Set A: mean: 80; standard deviation: 0; Set B: mean: 80; standard deviation: $\approx$ 11.55; Answers will vary.   **33.** Answers will vary.   **34.** 86   **35.** 98   **36.** 60   **37.** 68%   **38.** 95%   **39.** 34%   **40.** 99.7%   **41.** 16%   **42.** 84%   **43.** 2.5%   **44.** 0   **45.** 2   **46.** 1.6   **47.** −3   **48.** −1.2   **49.** vocabulary test   **50.** 38,000 miles   **51.** 41,000 miles   **52.** 22,000 miles   **53.** 91.92%   **54.** 96.41%   **55.** 88.33%   **56.** 10.69%   **57.** 75%   **58.** 14%   **59.** 11%   **60. a.** ±2.2%   **b.** We can be 95% confident that between 12.8% and 17.2% of executives of American companies have careers not related to their college degrees.   **61. a.** skewed to the right   **b.** mean: 2.1 syllables; median: 2 syllables; mode: 1 syllable   **c.** yes; The mean is greater than the median which is consistent with a distribution skewed to the right.

62.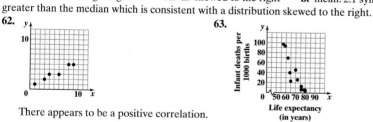

There appears to be a positive correlation.

63.

There appears to be a negative correlation.

64. false   **65.** true   **66.** false   **67.** false   **68.** true   **69.** false   **70.** true   **71.** c   **72. a.** 0.972   **b.** $y = 0.509x + 0.537$ **73. a.** 0.99   **b.** There is a correlation.

Chapter 9 Test

1. d   **2.**

Score	Frequency
3	1
4	2
5	3
6	2
7	2
8	3
9	2
10	1
	16

3.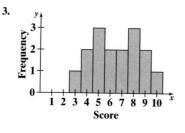

4.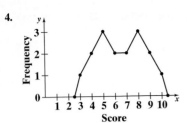

5.

Class	Frequency
40–49	3
50–59	6
60–69	6
70–79	7
80–89	6
90–99	2
	30

6.

Stem	Leaves
4	8 1 6
5	1 0 5 0 9 0
6	7 2 0 3 1 1
7	9 8 3 1 9 1 5
8	9 3 0 8 9 1
9	3 0

7. The roofline gives the impression that the percentage of home-schooled students grew at the same rate each year between the years shown which might not have happened.   **8.** $\approx$ 3.67   **9.** 3   **10.** 4   **11.** $\approx$ 2.34   **12.** 2.25   **13.** 2   **14.** 2   **15.** Answers will vary.
16. 34%   **17.** 2.5%   **18.** student   **19.** 8.08%   **20.** 41%
21. a. $\pm 10\%$ **b.** We can be 95% confident that between 50% and 70% of all students are very satisfied with their professors.
22.   ; There appears to be a strong negative correlation.
23. false   **24.** false   **25.** true   **26.** Answers will vary.

CHAPTER 10

Section 10.1

Check Point Exercises

1. a. 49   **b.** 125   **c.** 1   **d.** 100,000   **e.** 1,000,000   **f.** 18   **2. a.** $(4 \times 10^3) + (0 \times 10^2) + (2 \times 10^1) + (6 \times 1)$ or
$(4 \times 1000) + (0 \times 100) + (2 \times 10) + (6 \times 1)$ **b.** $(2 \times 10^4) + (4 \times 10^3) + (2 \times 10^2) + (3 \times 10^1) + (2 \times 1)$ or
$(2 \times 10,000) + (4 \times 1000) + (2 \times 100) + (3 \times 10) + (2 \times 1)$ **3. a.** 6073   **b.** 80,900   **4.** 12,031   **5.** 80,293

Exercise Set 10.1

1. 25   **3.** 8   **5.** 81   **7.** 100,000   **9.** $(3 \times 10^1) + (6 \times 1)$ **11.** $(2 \times 10^2) + (4 \times 10^1) + (9 \times 1)$ **13.** $(7 \times 10^2) + (0 \times 10^1) + (3 \times 1)$
15. $(4 \times 10^3) + (8 \times 10^2) + (5 \times 10^1) + (6 \times 1)$ **17.** $(3 \times 10^3) + (0 \times 10^2) + (7 \times 10^1) + (0 \times 1)$
19. $(3 \times 10^4) + (4 \times 10^3) + (5 \times 10^2) + (6 \times 10^1) + (9 \times 1)$
21. $(2 \times 10^8) + (3 \times 10^7) + (0 \times 10^6) + (0 \times 10^5) + (0 \times 10^4) + (7 \times 10^3) + (0 \times 10^2) + (0 \times 10^1) + (4 \times 1)$
23. 73   **25.** 385   **27.** 528,743   **29.** 7002   **31.** 600,002,007   **33.** 23   **35.** 1262   **37.** 11,523   **39.** 2,416,271   **41.** 14   **43.** 6846
45. 3048   **47.** 14,411   **49.** 75,610   **51.** $(4 \times 10^4) + (6 \times 10^3) + (2 \times 10^2) + (2 \times 10^1) + (5 \times 1)$
53. $(2 \times 10^3) + (2 \times 10^2) + (9 \times 10^1) + (9 \times 1)$ **55.** 0.4759   **57.** 0.700203   **59.** 5000.03   **61.** 30,700.05809   **63.** 9734   **65.** 8097
67. 365 is the number of days in a non-leap year.   **77.** $<<<<VVVV$ $<<VVVVVVV$

Section 10.2

Check Point Exercises

1. 487   **2.** 51   **3.** 2772   **4.** 11_{five} **5.** 1031_{seven} **6.** 42023_{five}

Exercise Set 10.2

1. 23   **3.** 42   **5.** 30   **7.** 11   **9.** 455   **11.** 28,909   **13.** 8342   **15.** 53   **17.** 44,261   **19.** 12_{five} **21.** 14_{seven} **23.** 10_{two}
25. 31_{four} **27.** 101_{six} **29.** 322_{five} **31.** 1230_{four} **33.** 10011_{two} **35.** 12010_{three} **37.** 1442_{six} **39.** 4443_{seven}
41. $<<<<<$ $<<<<<VV$ **43.** VVVVVV $<<<VV$ $<<VVVVVV$
45. **47.**

49. 25_{seven} **51.** 623_{eight} **53.** 1000110   **55.** 1101101   **57.** PAL   **59.** 100110111011111101101   **65.** $\text{EC4}_{\text{sixteen}}$; $\text{EC6}_{\text{sixteen}}$

Section 10.3

Check Point Exercises

1. 131_{five} **2.** 1110_{two} **3.** 13_{five} **4.** 1605_{seven} **5.** 201_{seven} **6.** 23_{four}

Exercise Set 10.3

1. 102_{four} **3.** 110_{two} **5.** 1310_{five} **7.** 1302_{seven} **9.** 15760_{nine} **11.** 23536_{seven} **13.** 13_{four} **15.** 4_{five} **17.** 206_{eight} **19.** 366_{seven} **21.** 10_{two} **23.** 111_{three} **25.** 152_{six} **27.** 11_{two} **29.** 4011_{seven} **31.** 3114_{eight} **33.** 312_{four} **35.** 20_{four} **37.** 41_{five} remainder of 1_{five} **39.** 1000110_{two} **41.** 110000_{two} **43.** 110111_{two} **45.** $71BE_{sixteen}$ **47.** 01100; 11101 **49.** 10001; 11001 **51.** 01100; 00110; 00100; 11011 **53.** The circuit in Exercise 47 **57.** 56_{seven}

Section 10.4

Check Point Exercises

1. 300,222 **2.** **3.** 1361 **4.** 1447 **5.** CCCXCIX **6.** **7.** 885

Exercise Set 10.4

1. 322 **3.** 300,423 **5.** 132 **7.** **9.**
11. **13.** 11 **15.** 16 **17.** 40 **19.** 59 **21.** 146 **23.** 1621 **25.** 2677 **27.** 9466 **29.** XLIII **31.** CXXIX **33.** MDCCCXCVI **35.** $\overline{\text{VI}}$DCCCXCII **37.** 88 **39.** 527 **41.** 2776 **43.** **45.** **47.** **49.** 12 **51.** 234 **53.** $\mu\gamma$ **55.** $\nu\pi\gamma$

57. MMCCCXXIV; **59. a.** **b.**

61. 3104_{five} **63.** 1232_{five} **65.** **67.** 1776; Declaration of Independence

69. 4,640,224; $\overline{\text{MMMM}}$DCXL CCXXIV **77.** Preceding:

Following:

Chapter 10 Review Exercises

1. 121 **2.** 343 **3.** $(4 \times 10^2) + (7 \times 10^1) + (2 \times 1)$ **4.** $(8 \times 10^3) + (0 \times 10^2) + (7 \times 10^1) + (6 \times 1)$
5. $(7 \times 10^4) + (0 \times 10^3) + (3 \times 10^2) + (2 \times 10^1) + (9 \times 1)$ **6.** 706,953 **7.** 740,000,306 **8.** 673 **9.** 8430 **10.** 2331
11. 65,536 **12.** Each position represents a particular value. The symbol in each position tells how many of that value are represented.
13. 19 **14.** 6 **15.** 325 **16.** 805 **17.** 4051 **18.** 560 **19.** 324_{five} **20.** 10101_{two} **21.** 122112_{three} **22.** 26452_{seven}
23. 111140_{six} **24.** $3A2_{twelve}$ **25.** 132_{seven} **26.** 1401_{eight} **27.** 110000_{two} **28.** $AD0_{sixteen}$ **29.** 5_{six} **30.** 345_{seven} **31.** 11_{two}
32. 2304_{five} **33.** 222_{four} **34.** 354_{seven} **35.** 1102_{five} **36.** 133_{four} **37.** 12_{five} **38.** 1246 **39.** 12,432
40. **41.** **42.** 2314
43. DDDDDCCCCBBBBBBBBBAA **44.** Answers will vary. **45.** 163 **46.** 1034 **47.** 1990 **48.** XLIX **49.** MMCMLXV
50. If symbols increase in value from left to right, subtract the value of the symbol on the left from the symbol on the right. Answers will vary.

51. 554   **52.** 8253   **53.** 二百七十四   **54.** 三千五百八十七   **55.** 365   **56.** 4520   **57.** G   **58.** F   **59.** Answers will vary.
Y Z
I H
X Y
C E
X
D

60. 653   **61.** 678   **62.** $\nu\nu\gamma$ **63.** $\prod\beta$ **64.** 357   **65.** 37,894   **66.** 80,618   **67.** WRG   **68.** lfVQC   **69.** Answers will vary.

Chapter 10 Test

1. 729   **2.** $(5 \times 10^2) + (6 \times 10^1) + (7 \times 1)$ **3.** $(6 \times 10^4) + (3 \times 10^3) + (0 \times 10^2) + (2 \times 10^1) + (8 \times 1)$ **4.** 7493   **5.** 400,206
6. A number represents "How many?" whereas a numeral is a symbol used to write a number.   **7.** A symbol for zero is needed for a place holder when there are no values for a position.   **8.** 72,731   **9.** 1560   **10.** 113   **11.** 223   **12.** 53   **13.** 2212_{three} **14.** 111000_{two}

15. 24334_{five} **16.** 1212_{five} **17.** 414_{seven} **18.** 250_{six} **19.** 221_{five} **20.** 20,303   **21.** $\mathcal{(((}$ 𝕏𝕏 𝟡𝟡𝟡𝟡𝟡𝟡𝟡 ∩∩∩|||
22. 1994   **23.** CDLIX   **24.** Answers will vary.

Photo Credits ● ● ● ● ● ●

Subject Index ●●●●●●

Index of Applications●●●●●